Solution Key

ALGEBRA
AND TRIGONOMETRY

Structure and Method   **Book 2**

Mary P. Dolciani
Robert H. Sorgenfrey
Richard G. Brown
Robert B. Kane

HOUGHTON MIFFLIN COMPANY · BOSTON

Atlanta   Dallas   Geneva, Ill.   Lawrenceville, N.J.   Palo Alto   Toronto

Printed in U.S.A.

ISBN: 0-395-35259-2

ABCDEFGHIJ-A-943210/898765

CONTENTS

Chapter   Page

1. Basic Concepts of Algebra 1
2. Inequalities and Proof 16
3. Linear Equations and Functions 36
4. Products and Factors of Polynomials 79
5. Rational Expressions 105
6. Irrational and Complex Numbers 142
7. Quadratic Equations and Functions 160
8. Variation and Polynomial Equations 190
9. Analytic Geometry 225
10. Exponential and Logarithmic Functions 262
11. Sequences and Series 284
12. Triangle Trigonometry 306
13. Trigonometric Graphs and Identities 344
14. Trigonometric Applications and Inverse Functions 376
15. Matrices and Determinants 416
16. Probability and Statistics 439

Appendix: Computation with Common Logarithms 455

Pages 4-5 · WRITTEN EXERCISES

A 1. 1

2. -5

3. -3

4. 0

5. 2

6. $-3\frac{1}{2}$

7. $-2\frac{1}{2}$

8. $1\frac{1}{3}$

9. $5 > 1$

10. $-2 < -1$

11. $-8 < 8$

12. $11 > 0$

13. $0 > -\frac{1}{2}$

14. $-3 < -\frac{8}{3}$

15.

$0 > -2$

16.

$5 > -5$

17.

$-\frac{3}{2} > -4$

18.

$-\frac{5}{3} < -\frac{2}{3}$

19. $|3| - |-2| = 3 - 2 = 1$

20. $-\left|-\frac{1}{5}\right| = -\left(\frac{1}{5}\right) = -\frac{1}{5}$

21. $3 \cdot |-2| = 3(2) = 6$

22. $|-2| \cdot |-0.25| = 2(0.25) = 0.5$

B 23. $-6, -1, 0, 4, 8$

24. $-20, -13, -4, 3, 9$

25. $-\frac{5}{2}, -2, -\frac{1}{2}, \frac{3}{2}, 3$

26. $-2, -\frac{4}{3}, -\frac{1}{3}, 0, \frac{2}{3}$

27. $-3, -2.6, -2.2, -1.8$

28. $-7.5, -7.35, -7.3, -7$

29. -1

30. 0

31. 3

32. -4.327

33. $2 + \sqrt{2}$

C 34. 0, 8

35. $-2, -10$

Page 5 · COMPUTER EXERCISES

1. Answers may vary. A sample program is given.

```
10 INPUT A, B
20 IF A < B THEN 50
30 PRINT A; " < "; B; " IS FALSE"
40 GOTO 60
50 PRINT A; " < "; B; " IS TRUE"
60 END
```

2. a. $-3 < 12$ IS TRUE   **b.** $-5 < -9$ IS FALSE   **c.** $0 < 6$ IS TRUE

     d. $7 < 7$ IS FALSE   **e.** $-10 < 4$ IS TRUE   **f.** $-8 < -8$ IS FALSE

3. Answers may vary. A sample program is given.

```
10 INPUT A,B
20 LET C = (A + B)/2
30 PRINT C
40 END
```

4. a. 5.5   **b.** 0   **c.** 1.565

     d. -5.16 **e.** 9.055   **f.** 1

Pages 10-11 · WRITTEN EXERCISES

A   **1.** $7 = 7$ **2.** $3 \neq \dfrac{1}{3}$ **3.** $36 \neq 4$

    4. $5 = 5$ **5.** $36 = 36$ **6.** $12 \neq 2$

    7. $6 \neq 10$ **8.** $20 = 20$

    9. $13 \neq 25$ **10.** $6 = 6$

11. a. 10 **b.** $10 - 7 - 3 = 0$ **c.** $10 - (7 - 3) = 10 - 4 = 6$

12. a. $30 + 2 = 32$ **b.** $3 \times 14 \div 2 = 42 \div 2 = 21$ **c.** $(30 + 4) \div 2 = 34 \div 2 = 17$

13. a. $9 - 1 + 4 = 8 + 4 = 12$ **b.** $9 - 3^2 = 9 - 9 = 0$ **c.** $10^2 = 100$

14. a. $36 - 3 + 3 = 36$ **b.** $(36 - 18) \div 6 + 3 = 18 \div 6 + 3 = 3 + 3 = 6$

     c. $(36 - 18) \div 9 = 18 \div 9 = 2$

15. $100 \div 25 + 3(9 - 8) = 4 + 3 = 7$ **16.** $42 \div 3 - 5 = 14 - 5 = 9$

17. $[64 - 5(10)] \div 7 = [64 - 50] \div 7 = 14 \div 7 = 2$

18. $2[3(9) + 42] = 2(27 + 42) = 2(69) = 138$

19. $5 \cdot 27 - 4 \cdot 9 + 9 + 2 = 135 - 36 + 11 = 110$

20. $1 \cdot 125 + 3 \cdot 25 - 45 - 8 = 125 + 75 - 53 = 147$

21. $5 \cdot 27 - 4(9 + 9 + 2) = 135 - 4(20) = 135 - 80 = 55$

22. $5^3 + 15^2 - (45 - 8) = 125 + 225 - 37 = 313$

23. $\dfrac{99 + 1}{49 + 1} + 1 - 3 = \dfrac{100}{50} - 2 = 2 - 2 = 0$

24. $\dfrac{36 - 4 \cdot 3}{8 \cdot 3} = \dfrac{36 - 12}{24} = \dfrac{24}{24} = 1$ **25.** $2 \cdot 4^3 + 5 \cdot 4^2 + 4 - 7 = 205$

26. $3^3 - 2 \cdot 3^2 - 3 + 1 = 7$ **27.** $(4 \cdot 5 - 3)^2 = 17^2 = 289$ **28.** $4 \cdot 5^2 - 7 \cdot 4 \cdot 3 - 4^2 = 0$

29. $\dfrac{4^4}{2(5 + 3)^2} = \dfrac{256}{128} = 2$ **30.** $\dfrac{5 \cdot 3^2 - 7 \cdot 3 - 4}{4 \cdot 5} = \dfrac{20}{20} = 1$

31. $\dfrac{7(5^2 - 4^2)}{5 + 3 + 1} = \dfrac{63}{9} = 7$

32. $\dfrac{2 \cdot 4 + 3(5 + 3)}{4(5^2 - 3^2)} = \dfrac{32}{64} = \dfrac{1}{2}$

33. $\dfrac{5 + 3}{4} + \dfrac{4 + 5}{3} = 2 + 3 = 5$

34. $\dfrac{4}{5 + 3} + \dfrac{3}{4 + 5} = \dfrac{1}{2} + \dfrac{1}{3} = \dfrac{5}{6}$

35. $\left(\dfrac{3 \cdot 4 + 3}{5}\right)^5 = 3^5 = 243$

36. $\dfrac{(4 + 5 + 3)^2}{4 \cdot 5 \cdot 3^2} = \dfrac{144}{180} = \dfrac{4}{5}$

B **37.** $(24 \div 3) - 2 \cdot (3 + 1) = 0$

38. $[72 \div (8 + 1)] - (3 + 5) = 0$

39. $(9 - 2) \cdot (4 + 3) - 2 = 47$

40. $[(8 + 7) \cdot 2 - 6] \div (5^2 - 1) = 1$

41. $(2^2 - 1)^3 \cdot (1 + 1) = 54$

42. $(5 - 2)^2 + 4 \cdot (7 - 3) = 25$

43. $\dfrac{5(5 - 3)^2 + 2 \cdot 4^2}{5 - 1 + 3(2 \cdot 4 - 5)} = \dfrac{52}{13} = 4$

44. $\dfrac{[7 + (7 - 2)^2]^2}{7^2 - 3 \cdot 7 \cdot 2 + (2 + 1)^2} = \dfrac{1024}{16} = 64$

45. $\dfrac{(2 \cdot 3^2 + 8^2)(13 \cdot 3 - 3 \cdot 8)^2}{5 \cdot 3^2 + 4 \cdot 3 \cdot 8 + 8^2} = \dfrac{18450}{205} = 90$

46. $\dfrac{(6^2 + 8^2)(6^2 - 8)^2}{(6 + 8)^2(3 \cdot 8^2 - 2 \cdot 6 \cdot 8 - 6^2)} = \dfrac{78400}{11760} = \dfrac{20}{3}$

47. a. $\dfrac{4(4 + 1)(2 \cdot 4 + 1)}{6} = \dfrac{4 \cdot 5 \cdot 9}{6} = 30;\ \dfrac{5(5 + 1)(2 \cdot 5 + 1)}{6} = \dfrac{5 \cdot 6 \cdot 11}{6} = 55;$

$\dfrac{6(6 + 1)(2 \cdot 6 + 1)}{6} = 91$

b. $1^2 + 2^2 + 3^2 + 4^2 = 1 + 4 + 9 + 16 = 30;\ 1^2 + 2^2 + 3^2 + 4^2 + 5^2 =$

$30 + 25 = 55;\ 1^2 + 2^2 + 3^2 + 4^2 + 5^2 + 6^2 = 55 + 36 = 91$

C **48-50.** Answers may vary. One example is given.

48. $3 \cdot 3 \cdot 3 - (3 + 3) = 21$

49. $2(2 + 2)^2 - 2 \cdot 2 \cdot 2 = 24$

50. $0 = 2^2 - (2 + 2);\ 1 = \dfrac{2^2 - 2}{2};\ 2 = 2 + \dfrac{2 - 2}{2};\ 3 = \dfrac{2^2 + 2}{2};\ 4 = \dfrac{2 + 2}{2} + 2;\ 5 = 2^2 + \dfrac{2}{2};$

$6 = 2 \cdot 2 \cdot 2 - 2$

Page 11 · CALCULATOR KEY-IN

Note: Answers to Exs. 7, 9, 10, and 12 may vary due to differences in number of digits displayed and rounding.

1. 45

2. 24

3. 15

4. 50

5. 4.25

6. 23.5

7. 3.9655172

8. 55

9. 0.777777778

10. 1.184927536

11. 22.7375

12. 0.557984496

Pages 16-18 · WRITTEN EXERCISES

A **1.** $[52 + 3y] + (-52) = [3y + 52] + (-52) = 3y + [52 + (-52)] = 3y + 0 = 3y$

2. $1 \cdot 0 = 0$

3. $\left[\left(\frac{1}{2}t\right)2\right]s^2 = \left[\left(t \cdot \frac{1}{2}\right)2\right]s^2 = \left[t\left(\frac{1}{2} \cdot 2\right)\right]s^2 = [t \cdot 1]s^2 = ts^2$

4. $\frac{5}{3} \cdot \frac{3}{5} + \frac{5}{3}z = 1 + \frac{5}{3}z$ $\qquad\qquad$ **5.** $-7.2 + 0 = -7.2$

6. $56\left[\left(\frac{1}{7}a\right)\left(\frac{1}{8}b\right)\right] = 56\left[\left[\left(\frac{1}{7}a\right)\frac{1}{8}\right]b\right] = 56\left[\left[\frac{1}{8}\left(\frac{1}{7}a\right)\right]b\right] = 56\left[\left[\left(\frac{1}{8} \cdot \frac{1}{7}\right)a\right]b\right]$

$\qquad = 56\left[\left(\frac{1}{56}a\right)b\right] = \left[56\left(\frac{1}{56}a\right)\right]b = \left[\left(56 \cdot \frac{1}{56}\right)a\right]b = (1 \cdot a)b = ab$

7. $3r + \frac{1}{3}r = \frac{10}{3}r$ $\qquad\qquad$ **8.** $1 \cdot r = r$

9. $\frac{1}{11}(11 \cdot 1) + (-1) = \left(\frac{1}{11} \cdot 11\right)1 + (-1) = 1 \cdot 1 + (-1) = 1 + (-1) = 0$

10. a. Comm. prop. for mult. $\qquad$ **b.** Assoc. prop. for mult.

11. a. Comm. prop. for add. $\qquad$ **b.** Assoc. prop. for add.
$\quad$ **c.** Prop. of opp. $\qquad\qquad\qquad$ **d.** Ident. prop. for add.

12. a. Dist. prop. of mult. with respect to add.
$\quad$ **b.** Comm. prop. for add. $\qquad\qquad$ **c.** Assoc. prop. for add.

13. a. Comm. prop. for add. $\qquad\qquad$ **b.** Assoc. prop. for add.
$\quad$ **c.** Assoc. prop. for add. $\qquad\qquad$ **d.** Prop. of opp.
$\quad$ **e.** Ident. prop. for add.

14. a. Dist. prop. of mult. with respect to add.
$\quad$ **b.** Assoc. prop. for mult. $\quad$ **c.** Prop. of recip. $\qquad$ **d.** Ident. prop. for mult.

15. a. Comm. prop. for add. $\quad$ **b.** Assoc. prop. for add. $\qquad$ **c.** Prop. of opp.
$\quad$ **d.** Ident. prop. for add. $\qquad\qquad\qquad$ **e.** Prop. of recip.

16. a. Assoc. prop. for add. $\qquad\qquad$ **b.** Ident. prop. for mult.
$\quad$ **c.** Dist. prop. of mult. with respect to add.
$\quad$ **d.** Ident. prop. for mult. $\qquad\qquad$ **e.** Dist. prop. of mult. with respect to add.

17. no $\qquad\qquad$ **18.** yes $\qquad\qquad\qquad$ **19.** yes

20. yes $\qquad\qquad$ **21.** yes $\qquad\qquad\qquad$ **22.** yes

B $\quad$ **23.** (2) Add. prop. of equality $\qquad\qquad$ (3) Assoc. prop. for add.
$\qquad$ (4) Prop. of opp. $\qquad$ (5) Ident. prop. for add. $\qquad$ (6) Mult. prop. of equality
$\qquad$ (7) Assoc. prop. for mult. $\qquad\qquad$ (8) Prop. of recip.
$\qquad$ (9) Ident. prop. for mult. $\qquad\qquad$ (10) Subst. prop.

$\quad$ **24.** (1) $\frac{1}{3}x + (-1) = 0$ (Given);

$\qquad$ (2) $\left[\frac{1}{3}x + (-1)\right] + 1 = 0 + 1$ (Add. prop. of equality);

(3) $\frac{1}{3}x + [(-1) + 1] = 0 + 1$ (Assoc. prop. for add.);

(4) $\frac{1}{3}x + 0 = 0 + 1$ (Prop. of opp.);   (5) $\frac{1}{3}x = 1$ (Ident. prop. for add.)

(6) $3\left(\frac{1}{3}x\right) = 3 \cdot 1$ (Mult. prop. of equality);

(7) $\left(3 \cdot \frac{1}{3}\right)x = 3 \cdot 1$ (Assoc. prop. for mult.);

(8) $1 \cdot x = 3 \cdot 1$ (Prop. of recip.);   (9) $x = 3$ (Ident. prop. for mult.)

25. a. closed   **b.** closed

26. a. not closed; for example, $1 + 2 = 3$ is not in the set
   b. not closed; $2 \cdot 2 = 4$ is not in the set

27. a. not closed; for example, $1 + 3 = 4$ is not in the set   **b.** closed

28. a. closed   **b.** closed

29. a. not closed; for example, $1 + \frac{1}{2} = \frac{3}{2}$ is not in the set   **b.** closed

30. a. closed   **b.** closed

31. a. closed   **b.** closed

32. a. not closed; for example, $\sqrt{2} + (-\sqrt{2}) = 0$ is not in the set
   b. not closed; for example, $(\sqrt{2})(\sqrt{2}) = 2$ is not in the set

33. a. closed   **b.** closed

34. a. not closed; for example, $\frac{1}{2} + \frac{1}{2} = 1$ is not in the set   **b.** closed

C 35. Answers may vary. Example: the negative integers

Pages 21-22 · WRITTEN EXERCISES

A 1. -85 **2.** 36 **3.** 36

4. -36 **5.** 0 **6.** -45.2

7. -3.05 **8.** 116 **9.** -0.43

10. 10 **11.** 0 **12.** -0.99

13. 10 **14.** -90 **15.** -4.3

16. -8.09 **17.** 0 **18.** -18

19. 11 **20.** -16 **21.** 47

22. 3 **23.** $5a - 20b$ **24.** $7x^2 - 3x + 2$

25. $3.6 - 3r + 6s$ **26.** $70x - 15y + 10z$ **27.** $2m^3 + m - \frac{1}{2}$

28. $6t^2 - 4 + 4 = 6t^2$

B **29.** 2   **30.** −8   **31.** 11

32. −5   **33.** −4   **34.** 12

35. −10   **36.** 0   **37.** −9

38. 10.1   **39.** −0.09   **40.** −24.54

41. $7 + (3 − 5) + (8 − 1) + (4 − 2) = 14$; 14 passengers

42. $42.78 − (−41.67) = 84.45$; 84.45°   **43.** $1609 − (−28) = 1637$; 1637 m

44. $−183.0 − (−218.4) = 35.4$; $−195.8 − (−209.9) = 14.1$; oxygen has the greater range by $35.4 − 14.1 = 21.3$°C

45. $7:52:39 + 0:00:56 + 0:12:18 = 8:05:53$; 5 minutes and 53 seconds after 8:00 A.M.

46. a. no; $5 − 3 = 2$; $3 − 5 = −2$ **b.** no; $(5 − 3) − 2 = 0$; $5 − (3 − 2) = 4$

C **47.** no   **48.** no   **49.** yes   **50.** no

Page 23 · READING ALGEBRA

1. Simplify, add, and subtract polynomials.

2. open sentence, solution, root, solving, solution set, equivalent equations, empty set, null set

3. A monomial is a numeral, a variable, or an indicated product of a numeral and one or more variables; equivalent equations are equations having the same solution set over a given domain. The definitions appear on pages 33 and 38 and in the glossary on pages 811 and 810.

4. Answers may vary; see list on page 38 of the text.

5. $7z^2 + 4z + 3$

6. You could find the definition in the glossary or use the index to find the definition in the text; page 9

7. The index lists references in Chapters 1, 4, and 8.

Page 27 · WRITTEN EXERCISES

A **1.** −960   **2.** 660   **3.** −8

4. 3   **5.** 0   **6.** 39

7. −9   **8.** 36   **9.** $27xyz$

10. $4st$ **11.** $−6mn$ **12.** $4abc$

13. −33   **14.** −460   **15.** 780

16. 16   **17.** $−2x^2 + x − 3$ **18.** $−20t + 12q$

19. $5r + 60$ **20.** $−3y^3 + 2y^2 − 4$

B　**21. a.** $5(-1)^3 - 7(-1)^2 + 4(-1) - 2 = -18$　**b.** $5 \cdot 2^3 - 7 \cdot 2^2 + 4 \cdot 2 - 2 = 18$

　　22. a. $2 \cdot 0^3 + 3 \cdot 0^2 - 0 + 9 = 9$　　　　**b.** $2(-3)^3 + 3(-3)^2 - (-3) + 9 = -15$

　　23. a. $(2 - 3)(3 + 3) = -6$　　　　　　**b.** $(2 - (-3))(3 + (-3)) = 0$

　　24. a. $(5 - 9)(9 - 5) = -16$　　　　　　**b.** $(-5 - 9)(9 - (-5)) = -196$

C　**25. a.** 5　　　　　**b.** 1, 3, or 6　　　　**c.** 8　　　　**d.** −2　　　　**e.** 3.5

Pages 27-28 · COMPUTER EXERCISES

1. Answers may vary. A sample program is given.

```
10 INPUT X
20 LET E = 5 * X ↑ 3 − 7 * X ↑ 2 + 3 * X + 2
30 PRINT E
40 END
```

2. **a.** 3　　　　　**b.** 380.585　　　　**c.** −127.375　　　　**d.** −212.28352

3. Answers may vary. For example, add line 5 and change line 20 as follows:

```
5 INPUT A, B, C, D
20 LET E = A * X ↑ 3 − B * X ↑ 2 + C * X + D
```

4. **a.** 5.897　　　　**b.** −186.542125　　　　**c.** 29.921848　　　　**d.** 392.66634

Pages 30-31 · WRITTEN EXERCISES

A　**1.** 8　　　　　　　　**2.** 0　　　　　　　**3.** $-\dfrac{1}{3}$

　　4. 24　　　　　　　**5.** 2　　　　　　　**6.** −8

　　7. −22　　　　　　**8.** 4　　　　　　　**9.** −1

　　10. $-\dfrac{21}{2}$　　　　　**11.** $-\dfrac{4}{5}$　　　　　**12.** −9

　　13. −45　　　　　　**14.** 56　　　　　　**15.** $4q^3 - q^2 + 2$

　　16. $-2d^2 + d + 1$　　　　**17.** $-3.75a^2 + 5.625ab + 1.875b^2$

　　18. $9r^3 + 2r - 1$

B　**19. a.** $\dfrac{[(-1)^2 - (-1) - 6]^2}{2(-1) + 1} = \dfrac{16}{-1} = -16$　　**b.** $\dfrac{[(-4)^2 - (-4) - 6]^2}{2(-4) + 1} = \dfrac{196}{-7} = -28$

　　20. a. $\dfrac{[1 - (-3)][(-3)^2 - 5]}{\frac{1}{3}(-3) - 7} = \dfrac{16}{-8} = -2$　　**b.** $\dfrac{[1 - (-9)][(-9)^2 - 5]}{\frac{1}{3}(-9) - 7} = \dfrac{760}{-10} = -76$

　　21. a. $\dfrac{\frac{1}{2} + 2}{\frac{1}{2} - 3} = \dfrac{5}{2}\left(-\dfrac{2}{5}\right) = -1$　　**b.** $\dfrac{-\frac{2}{3} + 2}{-\frac{2}{3} - 3} = \dfrac{4}{3}\left(-\dfrac{3}{11}\right) = -\dfrac{4}{11}$

22. a. $\dfrac{4 - (-5)}{[(-5) + 1][(-5) - 1]} = \dfrac{9}{24} = \dfrac{3}{8}$ **b.** $\dfrac{4 - \dfrac{3}{4}}{\left(\dfrac{3}{4} + 1\right)\left(\dfrac{3}{4} - 1\right)} = \dfrac{13}{4}\left(-\dfrac{16}{7}\right) = -\dfrac{52}{7}$

23-24. Answers may vary. One example is given.

23. $2 \div 1 = 2;\ 1 \div 2 = \dfrac{1}{2}$ **24.** $(12 \div 4) \div 3 = 1;\ 12 \div (4 \div 3) = 12 \cdot \dfrac{3}{4} = 9$

C   **25.** yes   **26.** no   **27.** yes

     28. yes   **29.** yes   **30.** no

Page 31 · CHALLENGE

Answers may vary. For example: $23 = 2^3 + 2^3 + 1^3 + 1^3 + 1^3 + 1^3 + 1^3 + 1^3 + 1^3$

Pages 36-37 · WRITTEN EXERCISES

A   **1.** $7x - 6 + 3x + 4 - 10x = -2$ **2.** $8 - y + 1 - 10 + 4y = 3y - 1$

     3. $2z - 6 + 5z + 9 - 4 = 7z - 1$ **4.** $6h + 3 - 8h - 3 + 5 = -2h + 5$

     5. $6r - 3 - r^2 + 4r - 5 = -r^2 + 10r - 8$

     6. $-2a^2 - 6 + 3a^2 - a + 1 = a^2 - a - 5$

     7. $8b^2 - 6b + 9 - 5b^2 - 6b + 3 = 3b^2 - 12b + 12$

     8. $-c^4 + 2c^2 - 12 - 3c^2 - 4c + 7 = -c^4 - c^2 - 4c - 5$

     9. $7x - 9 + x^3 + 8x^2 + 4 - 7x - 2x^2 = x^3 + 6x^2 - 5$

   10. $-8y^2 + 12 - 8 - 14y^2 = -22y^2 + 4$

   11. $3x - 3y - 4x - 12xy - 10y + xy = -x - 13y - 11xy$

   12. $15a - 5b + 15b - 5a - 8ab = 10a + 10b - 8ab$

   13. $7a - ab - ab - b = 7a - 2ab - b$ **14.** $3xy - 6x + 5y - xy = 2xy - 6x + 5y$

   15. $-rs - 5r + 12 - 6rs = -7rs - 5r + 12$

   16. $2tw - 9t - 4t - 14 = 2tw - 13t - 14$

   17. $6a - 8b + 2 - 4a - 2ab - \dfrac{1}{2}b = 2a - \dfrac{17}{2}b - 2ab + 2$

   18. $10w^2 - 5w + 15 + 21 - 12w = 10w^2 - 17w + 36$

B   **19.** $5r^3 + 7r^2 - 2 - 3r - 4r^3 - 8r^4 + 6r^2 + 2r - 10 = -8r^4 + r^3 + 13r^2 - r - 12$

   20. $-z^5 + 3z^3 + 7z - 12 + 9z^3 - 4z^2 - 7z + 12 = -z^5 + 12z^3 - 4z^2$

   21. $x^3 + 2x^2y + 3xy^2 + 4y^3 + 5xy^2 - 2y^3 + 6x^2y = x^3 + 8x^2y + 8xy^2 + 2y^3$

   22. $9f^2g - 7fg + 8fg^2 - 13fg^2 + f^2g^2 - 4f^2g - 5g^3 = -7fg - 5fg^2 + 5f^2g$
        $+ f^2g^2 - 5g^3$

23. $5(6r - 2 + 9 - 3r) + 4r - 18 = 5(3r + 7) + 4r - 18 = 15r + 35 + 4r - 18$
$= 19r + 17$

24. $11m - 3(-8m + 12 + 5m) + 6 = 11m - 3(-3m + 12) + 6 = 11m + 9m - 36 + 6$
$= 20m - 30$

25. $(x^3 + 2x^2 + x - 8) - (4x^4 - 3x^2 + 2x - 1) = x^3 + 2x^2 + x - 8 - 4x^4 + 3x^2 - 2x$
$+ 1 = -4x^4 + x^3 + 5x^2 - x - 7$

26. $(5x^3 - 7x^2 + 4) - (x^3 - 7x^2 + 5x - 6) = 5x^3 - 7x^2 + 4 - x^3 + 7x^2 - 5x + 6$
$= 6x^3 - 5x + 10$

27. $3x^3 - 2ax^2 + bx + 1 - cx^3 - 5x^2 + 7x - 9 = (3 - c)x^3 + (-2a - 5)x^2$
$+ (b + 7)x - 8; 3 - c = -1, c = 4; -2a - 5 = 1, a = -3; b + 7 = -2, b = -9;$
$-8 = 4d, d = -2$

28. $a + 8y^3 - 3by^2 - 9y^2 - 6 - 5cy^3 + dy = (8 - 5c)y^3 + (-3b - 9)y^2 + dy$
$+ (a - 6); 8 - 5c = 8, c = 0; -3b - 9 = 0, b = -3; d = 1; a - 6 = -4, a = 2$

Page 37 · HISTORICAL NOTE

1. $16\dfrac{5}{8}$ **2.** 75 jumps   **3.** A: $7\dfrac{2}{17}$ denars; B: $9\dfrac{14}{17}$ denars

Pages 41-42 · WRITTEN EXERCISES

A   **1.** $4x - 11 = 1; 4x = 12; x = 3$ **2.** $\dfrac{3}{2}m - 9 = 0; \dfrac{3}{2}m = 9; m = 6$

3. $13b = 20 + 3b; 10b = 20; b = 2$ **4.** $2p + 9 = p + 9; p = 0$

5. $6z + 3 = 3 - 5z; 11z = 0; z = 0$ **6.** $5 - 9y = 11 - 7y; -6 = 2y; y = -3$

7. $\dfrac{1}{8}a + 3 = 2; \dfrac{1}{8}a = -1; a = -8$ **8.** $5n = 2n - 42 - 3n; 6n = -42; n = -7$

9. $-7 + s = s + 2; -7 = 2;$ no solution   **10.** $-0.4k = -8; k = 20$

11. $3c + 7c = 9c - 3 + 3; c = 0$ **12.** $\dfrac{7}{8}t - 2 = -16; \dfrac{7}{8}t = -14; t = -16$

13. $37 + 8x = 28 - 4x; 12x = -9; x = -\dfrac{3}{4}$

14. $2h = 5h - 6 - 7h; 4h = -6; h = -\dfrac{3}{2}$

15. $12d - 27 = 12d - 30; -27 = -30;$ no solution

16. $10 - 5v = 7v - 26; -12v = -36; v = 3$

17. $-\dfrac{1}{4}w + \dfrac{3}{4} = 2; -\dfrac{1}{4}w = \dfrac{5}{4}; w = -5$

18. $0.6f + 0.3 = -6; 0.6f = -6.3; f = -10.5$

19. $4.8y - 1.6 + 2 = 5y; 0.4 = 0.2y; y = 2$

20. $6 + 4r = 2r + 3; 2r = -3; r = -\dfrac{3}{2}$ **21.** $2 - 7 + 3u = -47; 3u = -42; u = -14$

22. $\dfrac{3}{4}x + \dfrac{21}{4} - x = 50; -\dfrac{1}{4}x = \dfrac{179}{4}; x = -179$

23. $\dfrac{y}{4} - \dfrac{7y}{3} = 5; 12\left(\dfrac{y}{4} - \dfrac{7y}{3}\right) = 60; 3y - 28y = 60; -25y = 60; y = -\dfrac{12}{5}$

24. $7z - 66 + 12z = 10; 19z = 76; z = 4$

25. $(3 + 2)(1 - 2) = -5; 2(2) - 9 = -5;$ yes

26. $2(-1)^2 - (-1) + 4 = 7; -1 + 6 = 5;$ no

27. $1 - 4(-3) - 3(-3)^2 = -14; 1 - 13(-3) = 40;$ no

28. $\dfrac{6 - 12}{6 - 4} = -3; 6 - 3 = 3;$ no   **29.** $\dfrac{5(-4) + 2}{2(-4) - 1} = 2; \dfrac{-(-4)}{2} = 2;$ yes

30. $4\left(-\dfrac{1}{2}\right)^3 + \left(-\dfrac{1}{2}\right) = -1;$ no   **31.** $2x - 3y = 6; 2x = 3y + 6; x = \dfrac{3}{2}y + 3$

32. $A = \dfrac{1}{2}bh; 2A = bh; h = \dfrac{2A}{b}$ **33.** $E = \dfrac{mv^2}{2}; 2E = mv^2; m = \dfrac{2E}{v^2}$

34. $ax + b = 0; ax = -b; x = -\dfrac{b}{a}$ **35.** $y = mx + b; y - b = mx; x = \dfrac{y - b}{m}$

36. $I = Prt; r = \dfrac{I}{Pt}$

B **37.** $z + a = 3z - 3a; 4a = 2z; z = 2a$

38. $S = -\dfrac{1}{2}gt^2 + vt; S + \dfrac{1}{2}gt^2 = vt; v = \dfrac{S + \dfrac{1}{2}gt^2}{t} = \dfrac{S}{t} + \dfrac{1}{2}gt$

39. $C = \dfrac{5}{9}(F - 32); \dfrac{9}{5}C = F - 32; F = \dfrac{9}{5}C + 32$

40. $x(a + b) = a - b; xa + xb = a - b; xb + b = a - xa; b(x + 1) = a - xa;$
$b = \dfrac{a - xa}{x + 1}$

41. $107.9 = 83t; t = 1.3$

42. $120\pi = 2\pi \cdot 5h + 2\pi \cdot 5^2; 120\pi = 10\pi h + 50\pi; 10\pi h = 70\pi; h = 7$

43. $3 = \dfrac{27 + 9 + c + 14}{4}; 12 = 50 + c; c = -38$

44. $130 = E(2.5)^2; 130 = E(6.25); E = 20.8$

45. $277.50 = 250(1 + r \cdot 2); 1.11 = 1 + 2r; 0.11 = 2r; r = 0.055$

46. $-2 = \dfrac{1 - (-5)}{1 - x_1}; -2(1 - x_1) = 6; 1 - x_1 = -3; -x_1 = -4; x_1 = 4$

47. $28 = \dfrac{7}{2}[2(-5) + (7 - 1)d]; \; 8 = -10 + 6d; \; 6d = 18; \; d = 3$

48. $40 = \dfrac{1}{2}(0.2)v^2; \; 400 = v^2; \; v = 20$ **49.** $t - 3t^2 = 15 - 2t - 3t^2; \; 3t = 15; \; t = 5$

50. $x^2 + 3x = 5x + x^2 + 16; \; -2x = 16; \; x = -8$

51. $6s^2 - 8s - 30 = 6s^2 - 6; \; -8s = 24; \; s = -3$

52. $n^2 - \dfrac{1}{3}n = -7 + n^2; \; -\dfrac{1}{3}n = -7; \; n = 21$

C   **53.** $A = P(1 + rt); \; \dfrac{A}{P} = 1 + rt; \; \dfrac{A}{P} - 1 = rt; \; r = \dfrac{\dfrac{A}{P} - 1}{t} = \dfrac{A}{Pt} - \dfrac{1}{t}$ or $\dfrac{A - P}{Pt}$

54. $m = \dfrac{y_2 - y_1}{x_2 - x_1}; \; m(x_2 - x_1) = y_2 - y_1; \; x_2 - x_1 = \dfrac{y_2 - y_1}{m}; \; x_1 = x_2 - \dfrac{y_2 - y_1}{m}$

55. $S = \dfrac{n}{2}[2a + (n - 1)d]; \; \dfrac{2S}{n} = 2a + (n - 1)d; \; \dfrac{2S}{n} - 2a = (n - 1)d;$

     $d = \dfrac{\dfrac{2S}{n} - 2a}{n - 1} = \dfrac{2S}{n(n - 1)} - \dfrac{2a}{n - 1}$ or $\dfrac{2S - 2an}{n(n - 1)}$

56. $E = \dfrac{1}{2}mv^2; \; 2E = mv^2; \; v^2 = \dfrac{2E}{m}; \; v = \sqrt{\dfrac{2E}{m}} = \dfrac{\sqrt{2Em}}{m}$

Pages 46-47 · WRITTEN EXERCISES

A   **1.** $\dfrac{x}{20}$ h   **2.** $180 - 2(2x) = 180 - 4x; \; (180 - 4x)°$

3. $\dfrac{s}{10}$ h   **4.** $n + (n - 1) + (n - 2) + (n - 3) = 4n - 6$

5. $(4r + 1) - 3 = (4r - 2)$ years old

6. $180 - [s + (s + 8)] = 180 - (2s + 8) = 172 - 2s; \; (172 - 2s)°$

7. $(2m - 7) + m + m = 4m - 7; \; (4m - 7)$ cm

8. $(180 - z) - (90 - z) = 90; \; 90°$

9. $12[(0.49 - 0.25)c] = 12(0.24c) = 2.88c; \; 2.88c$ dollars

10. $\dfrac{s + (s + 2) + (s + 4) + (s + 6) + (s + 8)}{5} = \dfrac{5s + 20}{5} = s + 4$

11. $2\left(j - \dfrac{3}{4}j\right) = 2\left(\dfrac{1}{4}j\right) = \dfrac{1}{2}j$ km   **12.** $\dfrac{s}{2}$

13. $\dfrac{200 - y}{65}$ h   **14.** $1.5[s + (s - 80)] = 1.5(2s - 80) = (3s - 120)$ km

15. $2w + 2(w + 10) + w = 2w + 2w + 20 + w = (5w + 20)$ m

16. Six years ago, Diana was $d - 6$ years old and Rob was $\frac{1}{2}(d - 6) = \frac{1}{2}d - 3$ years old. Rob's age now is $\left(\frac{1}{2}d - 3\right) + 6 = \frac{1}{2}d + 3$.

17. $2r + 1(r + 20) = 2r + r + 20 = (3r + 20)$ km

18. $7.99v + 6.99(2v) = 7.99v + 13.98v = 21.97v$

B   **19-29.** Answers may vary; examples are given.

19. Let t = Tony's age now; $t + 4$ = Carlos's age now; $(t + 12) + [(t + 4) + 12]$ $= 4(t + 4)$

20. Let c = number of kilograms of cashews; $10 - c$ = number of kilograms of almonds; $7c + 9(10 - c) = 7.8(10)$

21. Let d = number of dimes; $2d$ = number of nickels; $2d - 3$ = number of quarters; $10d + 5(2d) + 25(2d - 3) = 205$

22. Let j = Jill's rate in km/h; $j + 4$ = Bill's rate in km/h; $2.5j + 2.5(j + 4) = 50$

23. Let d = denominator; $\dfrac{d - 3}{d} = \dfrac{3}{4}$

24. Let w = number of liters of water added; $0.80(5 + w) = 5$

25. Let b = measure of $\angle B$ in degrees; $b + 20$ = measure of $\angle A$; $2b$ = measure of $\angle D$; $4b$ = measure of $\angle C$; $b + (b + 20) + 2b + 4b = 360$

26. Let s = length of a side in centimeters; $s = \dfrac{1}{3}s + 20$

27. Let c = cost of child's ticket; $c + 2$ = cost of adult's ticket; $\dfrac{3c + 2(c + 2)}{5} = 3.30$

28. Let d = distance Megan drove in kilometers; $\dfrac{d}{64} = \dfrac{d}{60} - \dfrac{1}{3}$

C   **29.** Let n = number of hits Heidi has gotten so far; $\dfrac{n + 2}{25} = \dfrac{n}{20} + 0.02$

Pages 51-53 · PROBLEMS

A   **1.** Let n = first number; $7n$ = second number; $n + 7n = 136$; $8n = 136$; $n = 17$; $7n = 119$; 17 and 119

2. Let n = larger number; $n - 7$ = smaller number; $n + (n - 7) = 55$; $2n - 7 = 55$; $2n = 62$; $n = 31$; $n - 7 = 24$; 31 and 24

3. Let d = distance driven in kilometers; $206.36 = 125 + 0.18(d - 350)$; $81.36 = 0.18(d - 350)$; $452 = d - 350$; $d = 802$; 802 km

4. Let x = length of longest side in centimeters; $x + 3(x - 5) = 33$; $x + 3x - 15 = 33$; $4x = 48$; $x = 12$; 12 cm

5. Let h = number of hours it will take to travel 1440 km apart; $470h + 490h = 1440$; $960h = 1440$; $h = 1.5$; time after 1.5 hours of flight = 11:15 A.M.

6. Let s = speed of first plane in km/h; $s + 40$ = speed of second plane; $1.5s + 0.5(s + 40) = 1260$; $1.5s + 0.5s + 20 = 1260$; $2s = 1240$; $s = 620$; $s + 40 = 660$; the speed of the first plane is 620 km/h, the second, 660 km/h.

7. Let n = first integer; $n + 1$, $n + 2$, and $n + 3$ are the next three integers; $n + (n + 1) + (n + 2) + (n + 3) = -26$; $4n + 6 = -26$; $4n = -32$; $n = -8$; $n + 1 = -7$; $n + 2 = -6$; $n + 3 = -5$; the integers are -8, -7, -6, and -5.

8. Let n = first integer; $n + 2$ and $n + 4$ are the next two even integers; $n + (n + 2) + (n + 4) = 30$; $3n + 6 = 30$; $3n = 24$; $n = 8$; $n + 2 = 10$; $n + 4 = 12$; the integers are 8, 10, and 12.

9. Let d = original cost of shirt in dollars; $1.05(0.75)d = 8.19$; $0.7875d = 8.19$; $d = 10.4$; $10.40

10. Let x = measure of angle in degrees; $180 - x = 3(90 - x) + 6$; $180 - x = 270 - 3x + 6$; $2x = 96$; $x = 48$; $48°$

11. Let t = tens' digit; $t + 1$ = hundreds' digit; $3(t + 1)$ = ones' digit; $t + (t + 1) + 3(t + 1) = 14$; $t + t + 1 + 3t + 3 = 14$; $5t + 4 = 14$; $5t = 10$; $t = 2$; $t + 1 = 3$; $3(t + 1) = 9$; 329

12. Let d = distance traveled at 84 km/h in kilometers; $450 - d$ = distance traveled at 80 km/h. $\dfrac{d}{84} + \dfrac{450 - d}{80} = 5.5$; $20d + 9450 - 21d = 9240$; $-d = -210$; $d = 210$; 210 km

13. not enough information

14. Let n = first number; $n + 4$ and $n + 8$ are the others; $n + (n + 4) + (n + 8) = 48$; $3n + 12 = 48$; $3n = 36$; $n = 12$, $n + 4 = 16$; $n + 8 = 20$; 12, 16, and 20

15. Let d = expense for last week in dollars; $\dfrac{18 + 6 + 10 + d}{4} = 8$; $d + 34 = 32$; $d = -2$; not possible; no solution

16. Let n = first number; $n + 2$ and $n + 4$ are the others; $n + (n + 2) + (n + 4) = 17$; $3n + 6 = 17$; $3n = 11$; not possible; no solution

17. not enough information

18. Let r = rate of interest for $800 investment; $r + 0.04$ = rate of interest for second investment; $800r + 2000(r + 0.04) = 234$; $800r + 2000r + 80 = 234$; $2800r = 154$; $r = 0.055$; $r + 0.04 = 0.095$; rates are 5.5% and 9.5%; for this solution method, the info. about the difference in the incomes is not needed. Alternatively, the problem could be solved using that info., in which case the total would not be needed: $800r + 146 = 2000(r + 0.04)$; $800r + 146 = 2000r + 80$; $186 = 1200r$; $r = 0.055$ and so on, as above.

B **19.** Let t = time it took slower plane in hours; $t - \dfrac{1}{15}$ = time it took faster plane;

$720t = 750\left(t - \dfrac{1}{15}\right)$; $720t = 750t - 50$; $50 = 30t$; $t = \dfrac{5}{3}$; $720\left(\dfrac{5}{3}\right) = 1200$; 1200 km

20. Let n = number of liters of pure antifreeze to be added; $0.5(n + 8) = 0.4(8) + n$; $0.5n + 4 = 3.2 + n$; $0.8 = 0.5n$; $n = 1.6$; 1.6 L

21. Let c = original concentration in parts per million; $2c = 7(c - 55)$; $2c = 7c - 385$; $385 = 5c$; $c = 77$; 77 ppm

22. Let w = width of pool in meters; $1.5w$ = length of pool; $(w + 4)(1.5w + 4) = 112$; $1.5w^2 + 10w + 16 - 1.5w^2 = 112$; $10w + 16 = 112$; $10w = 96$; $w = 9.6$; $1.5w = 14.4$; the pool is 9.6 m by 14.4 m.

C **23.** Let w = number of votes for winner; $1427 - w$ = number of votes for loser; $w - 60 = (1427 - w) + 60 - 3$; $w - 60 = 1427 - w + 57$; $2w = 1544$; $w = 772$; the winner received 772 votes, the loser, 655.

24. Let u = units' digit; $u + 2$ = tens' digit; $2(10(u + 2) + u) + 3(10u + (u + 2)) = 321$; $2(10u + 20 + u) + 3(10u + u + 2) = 321$; $2(11u + 20) + 3(11u + 2) = 321$; $22u + 40 + 33u + 6 = 321$; $55u + 46 = 321$; $55u = 275$; $u = 5$; $u + 2 = 7$; 75

Page 54 · EXTRA

1. $\forall_x\ 2x = x + x$ **2.** $\exists_y\ y^2 = 17$ **3.** $\forall_x\ \forall_y\ x + y = y + x$

4. $\forall_r\ \exists!_x\ r + x = 0$ **5.** False; for example, let $a = -1$.

6. True   **7.** True

8. False; for example, let $a = 0$, $b = 2$, $c = 2$.

Pages 55-56 · CHAPTER REVIEW

1. d   **2.** a; $|-15| - |6 - 2| = 15 - 4 = 11$ **3.** b; $\dfrac{3 + 9 \cdot 5}{10 - 8} = \dfrac{48}{2} = 24$

4. a; $\dfrac{4^2 - 2 \cdot 3}{2} = \dfrac{16 - 6}{2} = 5$ **5.** c; $(x - y) + (-y) = x - 2y \neq x$ **6.** b   **7.** a

8. d; $(3m)(-1)(-7m) = 21m^2$ **9.** a; $\dfrac{-192 \div 8}{-4} = 6$

10. c; $3y^3 + y^2 + (-7 + 6)y + (2 + -5) = 3y^3 + y^2 - y - 3$

11. a; $8q^2 - 8\left(\dfrac{1}{2}\right) - q - (-4) = 8q^2 - 4 - q + 4 = 8q^2 - q$

12. d; $3(t - 4) + 1 = t + 9$; $3t - 12 + 1 = t + 9$; $2t = 20$; $t = 10$

13. a; $A = \dfrac{1}{2}ap$; $2A = ap$; $a = \dfrac{2A}{p}$

14. c; sides are y, $y - 2$, $y - 4$; perimeter is $y + (y - 2) + (y - 4) = 3y - 6$

15. c; $d = rt$; $12 = rt$; $r = \dfrac{12}{t}$

16. d; let t = time spent driving; in t hours the buses travel $45t$ and $30t$ miles, respectively; $45t + 30t = 375$; $75t = 375$; $t = 5$; therefore, they will be 375 miles apart at 1 P.M.

Page 57 · CHAPTER TEST

1. $-3\dfrac{1}{2} + 4\dfrac{1}{4} = -3\dfrac{2}{4} + 4\dfrac{1}{4} = \dfrac{3}{4}$

2. $-\dfrac{7}{3},\ -2,\ -1\dfrac{2}{3},\ -\dfrac{4}{3},\ \dfrac{1}{3}$

3. $5|-35| - 2|-17| = 5 \cdot 35 - 2 \cdot 17 = 175 - 34 = 141$

4. $144 \div 9 - 12 = 16 - 12 = 4$

5. $\dfrac{4^2 - 6}{4} + \dfrac{4 \cdot 3}{6} = \dfrac{10}{4} + \dfrac{12}{6} = 4\dfrac{1}{2}$

6. a. Comm. prop. for add.
b. Assoc. prop. for add.
c. Prop. of opp.
d. Ident. prop. for add.

7. $6yz^2$

8. $|-28| - |32| = 28 - 32 = -4$

9. $-9 - (-7) - 14 = -16$

10. 5

11. $-36yz$

12. $\dfrac{(-7)^2}{[(-126) \div (-3)](-6)} = \dfrac{49}{42(-6)} = -\dfrac{7}{36}$

13. $-2n^3 + 6n^2 - n + 7$

14. $-12t^2 + 18 - 12 - 27t^2 = -39t^2 + 6$

15. $4x^2y - 5xy + 10xy^2 + 2xy^2 + 3x^2y^2 + 5xy = 4x^2y + 3x^2y^2 + 12xy^2$

16. $\dfrac{5}{7}w - 15 = 5w + 30$; $5w - 105 = 35w + 210$; $-315 = 30w$; $w = -\dfrac{21}{2}$

17. $2q - 5q^2 = 12 - 6q - 5q^2$; $8q = 12$; $q = \dfrac{3}{2}$

18. $(2w - 1) - 2 = 2w - 3$

19. $\dfrac{p}{2} + 4$

20. Let r = rate of interest of \$400 investment; $r + 0.03$ = rate of interest of \$1200 investment; Solution 1: $400r + 84 = 1200(r + 0.03)$; $400r + 84 = 1200r + 36$; $48 = 800r$; $r = 0.06$; $r + 0.03 = 0.09$; Solution 2: $400r + 1200(r + 0.03) = 132$; $400r + 1200r + 36 = 132$; $1600r = 96$; $r = 0.06$; $r + 0.03 = 0.09$; the rates are 6% and 9%.

Page 62 · WRITTEN EXERCISES

A **1.** $r - 7 < -9$; $r < -2$; $\{r : r < -2\}$

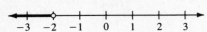

2. $v - 3 > 2$; $v > 5$; $\{v : v > 5\}$

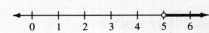

3. $3z > -18$; $z > -6$; $\{z : z > -6\}$

4. $-14 < -7s$; $2 > s$; $\{s : s < 2\}$

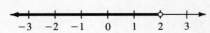

5. $-\dfrac{1}{4}k > 2$; $k < -8$; $\{k : k < -8\}$

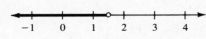

6. $0 < \dfrac{3}{5}a$; $0 < a$; $\{a : a > 0\}$

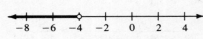

7. $8x - 9 < 2x$; $6x < 9$; $x < \dfrac{3}{2}$; $\left\{x : x < \dfrac{3}{2}\right\}$

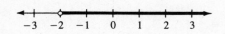

Ex. 7

Ex. 8

8. $13 + 2y < 5$; $2y < -8$; $y < -4$; $\{y : y < -4\}$

9. $\dfrac{1}{2}z + 3 > 2$; $\dfrac{1}{2}z > -1$; $z > -2$; $\{z : z > -2\}$

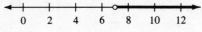

Ex. 9

Ex. 10

10. $\dfrac{4}{3}q - 7 > -19$; $\dfrac{4}{3}q > -12$; $q > -9$; $\{q : q > -9\}$

11. $26 - 3b < 2b - 9$; $-5b < -35$; $b > 7$; $\{b : b > 7\}$

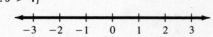

Ex. 11

Ex. 12

12. $2(c - 1) < c + c$; $2c - 2 < 2c$; $-2 < 0$; true for all real numbers.

13. $-(1 + 2.4w) > 5$; $1 + 2.4w < -5$; $2.4w < -6$; $w < -2.5$; $\{w : w < -2.5\}$

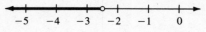

Ex. 13

Ex. 14

14. $3.9n + 6 < 3(n - 4)$; $1.3n + 2 < n - 4$; $0.3n < -6$; $n < -20$; $\{n : n < -20\}$

15. $4(6x - 5) > 3(8x + 1)$; $24x - 20 > 24x + 3$; $-20 > 3$; no solution; $\emptyset$

16. $7(2y - 7) > 4(y + 2) - 1$; $14y - 49 > 4y + 8 - 1$; $10y > 56$; $y > 5.6$; $\{y : y > 5.6\}$

Ex. 16

Ex. 17

17. $4 - 5(7 - 2t) < -2(t + 2)$; $4 - 35 + 10t < -2t - 4$; $12t < 27$; $t < 2\frac{1}{4}$; $\left\{t : t < 2\frac{1}{4}\right\}$

18. $7x - 5(9 + 2x) > 3(1 - x)$; $7x - 45 - 10x > 3 - 3x$; $-3x - 45 > 3 - 3x$; $-45 > 3$; no solution; $\emptyset$

19. $1 - (5 - 2m) > 7m + 4(m - 1)$; $1 - 5 + 2m > 7m + 4m - 4$; $2m - 4 > 11m - 4$; $-9m > 0$; $m < 0$; $\{m : m < 0\}$

Ex. 19

20. $2s + 5(s - 2) > 7(s + 1) - 17$; $2s + 5s - 10 > 7s + 7 - 17$; $7s - 10 > 7s - 10$; no solution; $\emptyset$

B **21.** $g - 3(2 - 4g) < 7 - (8g - 9 + g)$; $g - 6 + 12g < 7 - 8g + 9 - g$; $13g - 6 < -9g + 16$; $22g < 22$; $g < 1$; $\{g : g < 1\}$

22. $2(9d - 10) - \dfrac{6}{5}d > 8(3d - 1)$; $10(9d - 10) - 6d > 40(3d - 1)$; $90d - 100 - 6d > 120d - 40$; $84d - 100 > 120d - 40$; $-36d > 60$; $d < -\dfrac{5}{3}$; $\left\{d : d < -\dfrac{5}{3}\right\}$

23. $2(t + 2) - 7t > t - 3(2t + 1) - 1$; $2t + 4 - 7t > t - 6t - 3 - 1$; $-5t + 4 > -5t - 4$; $4 > -4$; true for all real numbers

24. $4[5x - (3x - 7)] < 2(4x - 5)$; $2(2x + 7) < 4x - 5$; $4x + 14 < 4x - 5$; $14 < -5$; no solution; $\emptyset$

25. True

26. False; for example, $-2 > -3$, but $(-2)^2 < (-3)^2$.

27. True

28. True

29. False; for example, $3 > 2$ and $2 > 0$, but $(3 - 2) < (2 - 0)$.

C **30.** True

31. False; for example, let $x = 1$; $1 + \dfrac{1}{1} = 2$.

32. True

33. True

34. False; for example, $\left(-\dfrac{1}{2}\right)^3 = -\dfrac{1}{8} > -\dfrac{1}{2}$, and $-\dfrac{1}{2} < 1$.

Page 63 · COMPUTER EXERCISES

1. 10 INPUT "A, B, C:"; A, B, C
   20 INPUT "LOWER LIMIT:"; L
   30 INPUT "UPPER LIMIT:"; U
   40 FOR X = L TO U
   50 IF A * X + B < C THEN 70
   60 GOTO 80
   70 PRINT X; ", ";
   80 NEXT X
   90 END

2. **a.** $\{1, 2, 3, 4, 5, 6\}$ **b.** $\{5, 6, 7\}$ **c.** $\emptyset$

3. Add the following lines:

   05 LET F = 0
   75 LET F = 1
   85 IF F = 1 THEN 90
   86 PRINT "NO SOLUTIONS"

4. **a.** no solutions   **b.** $\{-10, -9, -8, -7, -6, -5, -4, -3, -2, -1, 0, 1\}$

Page 66 · WRITTEN EXERCISES

A

1. $x - 5 \leq 1$; $x \leq 6$; $\{x : x \leq 6\}$

2. $y + 10 \geq 7$; $y \geq -3$; $\{y : y \geq -3\}$

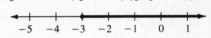

3. $-5 < z + 1 \leq 1$; $-6 < z \leq 0$; $\{z : -6 < z \leq 0\}$

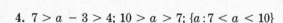

Ex. 3   **Ex. 4**

4. $7 > a - 3 > 4$; $10 > a > 7$; $\{a : 7 < a < 10\}$

5. $-3 > 2b - 9 > -7$; $6 > 2b > 2$; $3 > b > 1$; $\{b : 1 < b < 3\}$

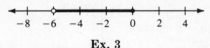

Ex. 5   **Ex. 6**

6. $-13 \leq 5c + 2 < 12$; $-15 \leq 5c < 10$; $-3 \leq c < 2$; $\{c : -3 \leq c < 2\}$

7. $r - 3 < 1$ or $\dfrac{1}{2}r \geq 3$; $r < 4$ or $r \geq 6$; $\{r : r < 4$ or $r \geq 6\}$

 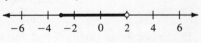

Ex. 7   **Ex. 8**

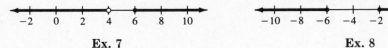

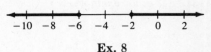

8. $-9s \leq 18$ or $s + 6 \leq 0$; $s \geq -2$ or $s \leq -6$; $\{s : s \leq -6$ or $s \geq -2\}$

9. $8 < 5 - 3w \leq 14$; $3 < -3w \leq 9$; $-1 > w \geq -3$; $\{w : -3 \leq w < -1\}$

Ex. 9

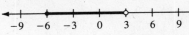

Ex. 10

10. $-9 > \frac{2}{3}j - 11 \geq -15$; $2 > \frac{2}{3}j \geq -4$; $3 > j \geq -6$; $\{j : -6 \leq j < 3\}$

11. $2 \geq \frac{1}{4}d + 1 \geq -1$; $1 \geq \frac{1}{4}d \geq -2$; $4 \geq d \geq -8$; $\{d : -8 \leq d \leq 4\}$

Ex. 11

Ex. 12

12. $-3 < -7 - 4x < 3$; $4 < -4x < 10$; $-1 > x > -2.5$; $\{x : -2.5 < x < -1\}$

13. $-1 < 5 - \frac{1}{3}h \leq -3$; $-6 < -\frac{1}{3}h \leq -8$; $18 > h \geq 24$; $24 \leq h < 18$; no solution; $\emptyset$

14. $3y - 4 \leq -1$ or $y - 1 \geq 0$; $3y \leq 3$ or $y \geq 1$; $y \leq 1$ or $y \geq 1$; true for all real numbers

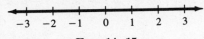

Exs. 14, 15

Ex. 17

15. $7q - 1 > q + 11$ or $-11q > -33$; $6q > 12$ or $q < 3$; $q > 2$ or $q < 3$; true for all real numbers

16. $5n - 1 > 0$ and $4n + 2 < 0$; $5n > 1$ and $4n < -2$; $n > \frac{1}{5}$ and $n < -\frac{1}{2}$; no solution; $\emptyset$

17. $x - 7 < 3x - 5 < x + 11$; $-7 < 2x - 5 < 11$; $-2 < 2x < 16$; $-1 < x < 8$; $\{x : -1 < x < 8\}$

18. $3y + 5 \geq 2y + 1 > y - 1$; $3y + 5 \geq 2y + 1$ and $2y + 1 > y - 1$; $y \geq -4$ and $y > -2$; $\{y : y > -2\}$

Ex. 18

Ex. 19

19. $-\frac{3}{4}m \geq m - 1$ or $-\frac{3}{4}m < m + 1$; $-\frac{7}{4}m \geq -1$ or $-\frac{7}{4}m < 1$; $m \leq \frac{4}{7}$ or $m > -\frac{4}{7}$; true for all real numbers

20. $3z + 7 \leq 4z$ and $3z + 7 > -4z$; $-z \leq -7$ and $7z > -7$; $z \geq 7$ and $z > -1$; $\{z : z \geq 7\}$

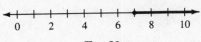

Ex. 20

21. $18 > -6(s - 7) \geq -9$; $-3 < s - 7 \leq 1.5$; $4 < s \leq 8.5$; $\{s : 4 < s \leq 8.5\}$

22. $-10 < 4(2 - t) \leq -2$; $-2.5 < 2 - t \leq -0.5$; $-4.5 < -t \leq -2.5$; $4.5 > t \geq 2.5$; $\{t : 2.5 \leq t < 4.5\}$

23. $-2 - 5z > 7$ and $-2 - 5z < -7$; $-5z > 9$ and $-5z < -5$; $z < -\dfrac{9}{5}$ and $z > 1$; no solution; $\emptyset$

24. $-1 - 5u < u + 11$ and $\dfrac{u}{5} - \dfrac{1}{2} \leq \dfrac{u}{4}$; $-6u < 12$ and $4u - 10 \leq 5u$; $u > -2$ and $-u \leq 10$; $u > -2$ and $u \geq -10$; $\{u : u > -2\}$

C 25. $-5 \leq 3 + 2k \leq 1$ or $0 \leq 3(k - 1) \leq 9$; $-8 \leq 2k \leq -2$ or $0 \leq k - 1 \leq 3$; $-4 \leq k \leq -1$ or $1 \leq k \leq 4$; $\{k : -4 \leq k \leq -1$ or $1 \leq k \leq 4\}$

26. $-6 < 2(g - 3) < 2$ or $4 < 3 - g < 9$; $-3 < g - 3 < 1$ or $1 < -g < 6$; $0 < g < 4$ or $-1 > g > -6$; $\{g : 0 < g < 4$ or $-6 < g < -1\}$

27. $-7 \leq 2k + 1 < 9$ and $(k - 1 \geq 2$ or $2 - k \geq 5)$; $-8 \leq 2k < 8$ and $(k \geq 3$ or $-k \geq 3)$; $-4 \leq k < 4$ and $(k \geq 3$ or $k \leq -3)$; $\{k : -4 \leq k \leq -3$ or $3 \leq k < 4\}$

28. $[3p - 1 < 8$ or $2(p - 1) < -6]$ and $-1 \leq 2p \leq 3$; $[3p < 9$ or $p - 1 < -3]$ and $-\dfrac{1}{2} \leq p \leq \dfrac{3}{2}$; $[p < 3$ or $p < -2]$ and $-\dfrac{1}{2} \leq p \leq \dfrac{3}{2}$; $p < 3$ and $-\dfrac{1}{2} \leq p \leq \dfrac{3}{2}$; $\left\{p : -\dfrac{1}{2} \leq p \leq \dfrac{3}{2}\right\}$

Pages 69-70 · PROBLEMS

A 1. Let w = width in centimeters; $2w + 3$ = length; $2w + 2(2w + 3) \leq 72$; $2w + 4w + 6 \leq 72$; $6w \leq 66$; $w \leq 11$; 11 cm

2. Let n = first odd integer; the next consecutive odd integers are $n + 2$ and $n + 4$; $54 < n + (n + 2) + (n + 4) < 63$; $54 < 3n + 6 < 63$; $48 < 3n < 57$; $16 < n < 19$; $n = 17$; $\{17, 19, 21\}$

3. Let n = number of each type of coin; $5n + 10n + 25n < 300$; $40n < 300$; $n < 7.5$; she has at most 7 of each.

4. Let b = length in centimeters of longer base; $\dfrac{1}{2}b$ = length of shorter base and $\dfrac{1}{2}b - 1$ = length of each leg; $2\left(\dfrac{1}{2}b - 1\right) + \dfrac{1}{2}b + b \geq 23$; $b - 2 + \dfrac{1}{2}b + b \geq 23$; $\dfrac{5}{2}b \geq 25$; $b \geq 10$; 10 cm

5. Let t = number of tables; $4t$ = number of chairs; $20t + 15(4t) \leq 8(60)$; $20t + 60t \leq 480$; $80t \leq 480$; $t \leq 6$; $4t \leq 24$; 6 tables, 24 chairs

6. Let n = number of sweaters; $0.3(22.50)n \geq 1000$; $6.75n \geq 1000$; $n \geq 148.\overline{148}$; at least 149

7. Let f = father's age; $\frac{1}{3}f - 5$ = boy's age; $f - \left(\frac{1}{3}f - 5\right) > 23$; $\frac{2}{3}f + 5 > 23$; $\frac{2}{3}f > 18$; $f > 27$; the father is over 27, the boy is over 4.

8. Let x = first score; $x + 6$ = second score; $80 \leq \dfrac{x + (x + 6) + 90}{3} \leq 89$; $240 \leq 2x + 96 \leq 267$; $144 \leq 2x \leq 171$; $72 \leq x \leq 85.5$; assuming only whole-number scores are given, her first score was between 72 and 85, inclusive.

B 9. Let x = time for each stop in hours; $\dfrac{30}{\frac{1}{4} + 3x} \geq 50$; $30 \geq 50\left(\frac{1}{4} + 3x\right)$; $30 \geq \dfrac{50}{4} + 150x$;

$120 \geq 50 + 600x$; $70 \geq 600x$; $x \leq \dfrac{7}{60}$; $\dfrac{7}{60}$ h = 7 min

10. Let r = rate in km/h; $\dfrac{20}{30} + \dfrac{30}{r} < 1.5$; $\dfrac{30}{r} < \dfrac{3}{2} - \dfrac{2}{3}$; $\dfrac{30}{r} < \dfrac{5}{6}$; $30 < \dfrac{5}{6}r$; $r > 36$; more than 36 km/h

11. Let r = Roger's age now; $2r$ = Melanie's age 8 years ago; $2r + 8$ = Melanie's age now; $r + 2r + 8 \leq 41$; $3r \leq 33$; $r \leq 11$; at most 11

12. Let n = number of liters of antifreeze to be added; $n + 5$ = number of liters produced; $0.6 \leq \dfrac{n}{n + 5} \leq 0.8$; $0.6n + 3 \leq n \leq 0.8n + 4$; $n \geq 0.6n + 3$ and $n \leq 0.8n + 4$; $0.4n \geq 3$ and $0.2n \leq 4$; $n \geq 7.5$ and $n \leq 20$; between 7.5 L and 20 L

C 13. Let w = width of painting in centimeters; $w + 4$ = length; framed painting is $w + 8$ by $w + 4$; $(w + 8)(w + 4) - w(w + 4) \geq 180$; $(w + 4)[(w + 8) - w] \geq 180$; $(w + 4)(8) \geq 180$; $8w + 32 \geq 180$; $8w \geq 148$; $w \geq 18.5$; $w + 4 \geq 22.5$; the painting is at least 22.5 cm long and 18.5 cm wide.

14. Let n = first positive integer; $n + 1$ and $n + 2$ are the next two; $12(n + 2) \geq n(n + 1) + 52$; $12n + 24 \geq n^2 + n + 52$; $-n^2 + 11n - 28 \geq 0$; $n^2 - 11n + 28 \leq 0$; $(n - 7)(n - 4) \leq 0$; either $(n - 7 \geq 0$ and $n - 4 \leq 0)$ or $(n - 7 \leq 0$ and $n - 4 \geq 0)$; either $(n \geq 7$ and $n \leq 4)$ (reject) or $(n \leq 7$ and $n \geq 4)$; $n = 4, 5, 6,$ or 7; $\{4, 5, 6\}$, $\{5, 6, 7\}$, $\{6, 7, 8\}$, $\{7, 8, 9\}$

Page 73 · WRITTEN EXERCISES

A 1.

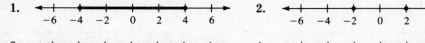

2.

3.

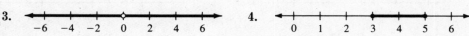

4.

5.

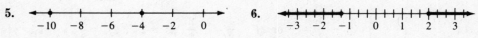

6.

7.

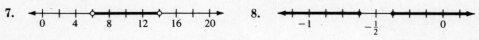

8.

9. $|4f + 18| = 0$; $4f + 18 = 0$; $4f = -18$; $f = -4\frac{1}{2}$; $\left\{-4\frac{1}{2}\right\}$

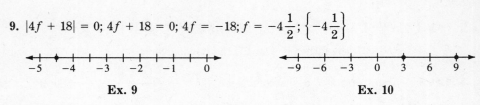

Ex. 9   Ex. 10

10. $\left|2 - \dfrac{g}{3}\right| = 1$; $2 - \dfrac{g}{3} = 1$ or $2 - \dfrac{g}{3} = -1$; $6 - g = 3$ or $6 - g = -3$; $-g = -3$ or
$-g = -9$; $g = 3$ or $g = 9$; $\{3, 9\}$

11. $|5n - 25| \geq 0$; $5n - 25 \geq 0$ or $5n - 25 \leq 0$; $5n \geq 25$ or $5n \leq 25$; $n \geq 5$ or $n \leq 5$; true
for all real numbers

Ex. 11   Ex. 12

12. $|2y + 3| > 11$; $2y + 3 > 11$ or $2y + 3 < -11$; $2y > 8$ or $2y < -14$; $y > 4$ or $y < -7$;
$\{y : y < -7$ or $y > 4\}$

13. $\left|k - \dfrac{7}{2}\right| \leq \dfrac{5}{2}$; $-\dfrac{5}{2} \leq k - \dfrac{7}{2} \leq \dfrac{5}{2}$; $1 \leq k \leq 6$; $\{k : 1 \leq k \leq 6\}$

Ex. 13   Ex. 14

14. $|3q - 9| \leq 0$; $3q - 9 = 0$; $3q = 9$; $q = 3$; $\{3\}$

15. $3 > \left|\dfrac{b - 1}{2}\right|$; $-3 < \dfrac{b - 1}{2} < 3$; $-6 < b - 1 < 6$; $-5 < b < 7$; $\{b : -5 < b < 7\}$

Ex. 15   Ex. 16

16. $1 < |3c + 4|$; $3c + 4 > 1$ or $3c + 4 < -1$; $3c > -3$ or $3c < -5$; $c > -1$ or $c < -\dfrac{5}{3}$;
$\left\{c : c < -\dfrac{5}{3}$ or $c > -1\right\}$

17. $2 = |4s + 5|$; $4s + 5 = 2$ or $4s + 5 = -2$; $4s = -3$ or $4s = -7$; $s = -\dfrac{3}{4}$ or $s = -\dfrac{7}{4}$;
$\left\{-\dfrac{3}{4}, -\dfrac{7}{4}\right\}$

Ex. 17   Ex. 18

18. $\left|2j - \dfrac{4}{3}\right| = \dfrac{2}{3}$; $2j - \dfrac{4}{3} = \dfrac{2}{3}$ or $2j - \dfrac{4}{3} = -\dfrac{2}{3}$; $2j = 2$ or $2j = \dfrac{2}{3}$; $j = 1$ or $j = \dfrac{1}{3}$;
$\left\{1, \dfrac{1}{3}\right\}$

19. $4 \le |2p - 5|$; $2p - 5 \ge 4$ or $2p - 5 \le -4$; $2p \ge 9$ or $2p \le 1$; $p \ge 4\frac{1}{2}$ or $p \le \frac{1}{2}$; $\left\{p : p \le \frac{1}{2} \text{ or } p \ge 4\frac{1}{2}\right\}$

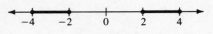

Ex. 19   Ex. 20

20. $1 > |2 - 0.8n|$; $-1 < 2 - 0.8n < 1$; $-3 < -0.8n < -1$; $1 < 0.8n < 3$; $1.25 < n < 3.75$; $\left\{n : \frac{5}{4} < n < \frac{15}{4}\right\}$

21. $|x + 7| - 1 = 5$; $|x + 7| = 6$; $x + 7 = 6$ or $x + 7 = -6$; $x = -1$ or $x = -13$; $\{-1, -13\}$

22. $|18 + 5y| + 2 = 2$; $|18 + 5y| = 0$; $18 + 5y = 0$; $5y = -18$; $y = -3\frac{3}{5}$; $\left\{-3\frac{3}{5}\right\}$

23. $9 - |3 - m| \le 1$; $-|3 - m| \le -8$; $|3 - m| \ge 8$; $3 - m \ge 8$ or $3 - m \le -8$; $-m \ge 5$ or $-m \le -11$; $m \le -5$ or $m \ge 11$; $\{m : m \le -5 \text{ or } m \ge 11\}$

24. $6 - |4 + t| \ge 5$; $-|4 + t| \ge -1$; $|4 + t| \le 1$; $-1 \le 4 + t \le 1$; $-5 \le t \le -3$; $\{t : -5 \le t \le -3\}$

25. $5|6z - 7| - 7 < 8$; $5|6z - 7| < 15$; $|6z - 7| < 3$; $-3 < 6z - 7 < 3$; $4 < 6z < 10$; $\frac{2}{3} < z < \frac{5}{3}$; $\left\{z : \frac{2}{3} < z < \frac{5}{3}\right\}$

26. $14 - 2|7v + 3| \le 23$; $-2|7v + 3| \le 9$; $|7v + 3| \ge -\frac{9}{2}$; true for all real numbers

27. $11 + \frac{1}{2}|0.4a - 1| > 13$; $\frac{1}{2}|0.4a - 1| > 2$; $|0.4a - 1| > 4$; $0.4a - 1 > 4$ or $0.4a - 1 < -4$; $0.4a > 5$ or $0.4a < -3$; $a > 12.5$ or $a < -7.5$; $\{a : a < -7.5$ or $a > 12.5\}$

28. $2\left|\frac{3b - 4}{5}\right| - 15 > 39$; $2\left|\frac{3b - 4}{5}\right| > 54$; $\left|\frac{3b - 4}{5}\right| > 27$; $\frac{3b - 4}{5} > 27$ or $\frac{3b - 4}{5} < -27$; $3b - 4 > 135$ or $3b - 4 < -135$; $3b > 139$ or $3b < -131$; $b > 46\frac{1}{3}$ or $b < -43\frac{2}{3}$; $\left\{b : b < -43\frac{2}{3} \text{ or } b > 46\frac{1}{3}\right\}$

29. $7 + 5|c| \le 1 - 3|c|$; $8|c| \le -6$; $|c| \le -\frac{3}{4}$; no solution; $\emptyset$

30. $\frac{1}{2}|d| + 5 \ge 2|d| - 13$; $-1\frac{1}{2}|d| \ge -18$; $|d| \le 12$; $-12 \le d \le 12$; $\{d : -12 \le d \le 12\}$

31. $2 \le |x| \le 4$; $|x| \ge 2$ and $|x| \le 4$; $x \ge 2$ or $x \le -2$ and $-4 \le x \le 4$; $\{x : -4 \le x \le -2$ or $2 \le x \le 4\}$

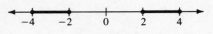

Ex. 31   Ex. 32

32. $3 \le |y + 2| < 4$; $|y + 2| \ge 3$ and $|y + 2| < 4$; $(y + 2 \ge 3$ or $y + 2 \le -3)$ and $(-4 < y + 2 < 4)$; $(y \ge 1$ or $y \le -5)$ and $(-6 < y < 2)$; $\{y : -6 < y \le -5$ or $1 \le y < 2\}$

33. $0 < |3 - t| < 5$; $|3 - t| > 0$ and $|3 - t| < 5$; $t \ne 3$ and $-5 < 3 - t < 5$; $t \ne 3$ and $-8 < -t < 2$; $t \ne 3$ and $-2 < t < 8$; $\{t : -2 < t < 3$ or $3 < t < 8\}$

   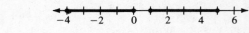

Ex. 33   **Ex. 34**

34. $1 \le |2r - 1| \le 9$; $|2r - 1| \ge 1$ and $|2r - 1| \le 9$; $(2r - 1 \ge 1$ or $2r - 1 \le -1)$ and $-9 \le 2r - 1 \le 9$; $(2r \ge 2$ or $2r \le 0)$ and $-8 \le 2r \le 10$; $(r \ge 1$ or $r \le 0)$ and $-4 \le r \le 5$; $\{r : -4 \le r \le 0$ or $1 \le r \le 5\}$

35. $|a| < |2a - 3|$; $-|2a - 3| < a < |2a - 3|$; (1) $a > -|2a - 3|$ and (2) $a < |2a - 3|$; (1) $|2a - 3| > -a$; $2a - 3 > -a$ or $2a - 3 < a$; $3a > 3$ or $a < 3$; $a > 1$ or $a < 3$; true for all real numbers; (2) $2a - 3 > a$ or $2a - 3 < -a$; $a > 3$ or $3a < 3$; $a > 3$ or $a < 1$; $\{a : a < 1$ or $a > 3\}$

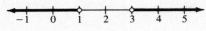   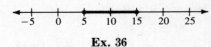

Ex. 35   **Ex. 36**

36. $|b| \ge |15 - 2b|$; $-|b| \le 15 - 2b \le |b|$; (1) $|b| \ge 2b - 15$ and (2) $|b| \ge 15 - 2b$; (1) $b \ge 2b - 15$ or $b \le 15 - 2b$; $b \le 15$ or $3b \le 15$; $b \le 15$ or $b \le 5$; $b \le 15$; (2) $b \ge 15 - 2b$ or $b \le 2b - 15$; $3b \ge 15$ or $b \ge 15$; $b \ge 5$ or $b \ge 15$; $b \ge 5$; $\{b : 5 \le b \le 15\}$

Page 73 · COMPUTER EXERCISES

1.
```
10   F = 0
20   PRINT "ENTER A, B, C AND D"
30   INPUT A, B, C, D
40   PRINT A; "<ABS(";C; "X + ";D;") < "; B
50   FOR X = -50 TO 50
60   LET T = ABS(C * X + D)
70   IF A < T AND T < B THEN 80
80   GOTO 100
90   PRINT "X = "; X
100   F = 1
110   NEXT X
120   IF F = 0 THEN PRINT "NO INTEGERS FOUND"
130   END
```

2. **a.** $x = -3, -2, -1, 0, 1, 2, 15, 16, 17, 18, 19$
    b. $x = -12, -11, -10, -9, -8, -7, -6, -5, -4, -3, -2$

Pages 76-77 · WRITTEN EXERCISES

A   1.
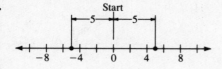

2.
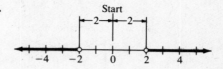

3.
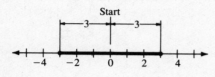

4.
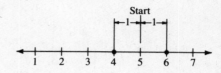

5.
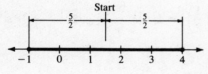

6.
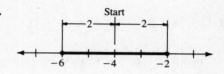

7.
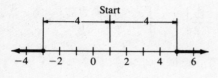

8.
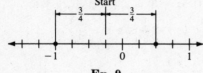

9. $|4a + 1| = 3$; $\left|4\left(a + \dfrac{1}{4}\right)\right| = 3$; $4\left|a + \dfrac{1}{4}\right| = 3$; $\left|a + \dfrac{1}{4}\right| = \dfrac{3}{4}$

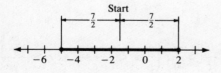

Ex. 9

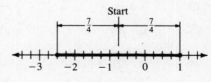

Ex. 10

10. $5 < |3y - 7|$; $5 < \left|3\left(y - \dfrac{7}{3}\right)\right|$; $5 < 3\left|y - \dfrac{7}{3}\right|$; $\dfrac{5}{3} < \left|y - \dfrac{7}{3}\right|$; $\left|y - \dfrac{7}{3}\right| > \dfrac{5}{3}$

11. $7 \ge |2n + 3|$; $7 \ge \left|2\left(n + \dfrac{3}{2}\right)\right|$; $7 \ge 2\left|n + \dfrac{3}{2}\right|$; $\dfrac{7}{2} \ge \left|n + \dfrac{3}{2}\right|$; $\left|n + \dfrac{3}{2}\right| \le \dfrac{7}{2}$

Ex. 11

Ex. 12

12. $|3 + 4q| \le 7$; $\left|4\left(\dfrac{3}{4} + q\right)\right| \le 7$; $4\left|\dfrac{3}{4} + q\right| \le 7$; $\left|\dfrac{3}{4} + q\right| \le \dfrac{7}{4}$

13. $\left|\dfrac{1}{2}(x - 2)\right| \geq 1;\ \dfrac{1}{2}|x - 2| \geq 1;\ |x - 2| \geq 2$

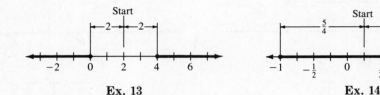

Ex. 13   Ex. 14

14. $\left|\dfrac{1}{4} - z\right| \leq \dfrac{5}{4};\ \left|z - \dfrac{1}{4}\right| \leq \dfrac{5}{4}$

B **15.** $|9 - 2x| = 7;\ \left|-2\left(x - \dfrac{9}{2}\right)\right| = 7;\ 2\left|x - \dfrac{9}{2}\right| = 7;\ \left|x - \dfrac{9}{2}\right| = \dfrac{7}{2};\ \{1, 8\}$

16. $|-3t - 9| > 4;\ |-3(t + 3)| > 4;\ 3|t + 3| > 4;\ |t + 3| > \dfrac{4}{3};\ \left\{t:t < -4\dfrac{1}{3} \text{ or } t > -1\dfrac{2}{3}\right\}$

17. $|2e - 1| + 1 \leq 3;\ |2e - 1| \leq 2;\ \left|2\left(e - \dfrac{1}{2}\right)\right| \leq 2;\ 2\left|e - \dfrac{1}{2}\right| \leq 2;\ \left|e - \dfrac{1}{2}\right| \leq 1;$
$\left\{e: -\dfrac{1}{2} \leq e \leq 1\dfrac{1}{2}\right\}$

18. $|r + 3| + 4 \leq 4;\ |r + 3| \leq 0;\ |r + 3| = 0;\ \{-3\}$

19. $3|0.1w + 2| - 8 > -5;\ 3|0.1w + 2| > 3;\ |0.1w + 2| > 1;\ |0.1(w + 20)| > 1;$
$0.1|w + 20| > 1;\ |w + 20| > 10;\ \{w:w < -30 \text{ or } w > -10\}$

20. $5 - 2|1.5z + 3| \geq 1;\ -2|1.5z + 3| \geq -4;\ |1.5z + 3| \leq 2;\ |1.5(z + 2)| \leq 2;$
$1.5|z + 2| \leq 2;\ \dfrac{3}{2}|z + 2| \leq 2;\ |z + 2| \leq \dfrac{4}{3};\ \left\{z: -3\dfrac{1}{3} \leq z \leq -\dfrac{2}{3}\right\}$

21. $\dfrac{1}{2}\left|\dfrac{5}{6} - \dfrac{n}{2}\right| - 1 > 0;\ \dfrac{1}{2}\left|\dfrac{5}{6} - \dfrac{n}{2}\right| > 1;\ \left|\dfrac{5}{6} - \dfrac{n}{2}\right| > 2;\ \left|-\dfrac{1}{2}\left(n - \dfrac{5}{3}\right)\right| > 2;$
$\dfrac{1}{2}\left|n - \dfrac{5}{3}\right| > 2;\ \left|n - \dfrac{5}{3}\right| > 4;\ \left\{n:n < -2\dfrac{1}{3} \text{ or } n > 5\dfrac{2}{3}\right\}$

22. $40|3 - 0.2c| = 4;\ |3 - 0.2c| = 0.1;\ |-0.2(c - 15)| = 0.1;\ 0.2|c - 15| = 0.1;$
$|c - 15| = 0.5;\ \{15.5, 14.5\}$

C **23.** $\{x:b - a \leq x \leq b + a\}$

24. $\{x:x \leq -b - a \text{ or } x \geq -b + a\}$

25. $\left|a\left(x + \dfrac{b}{a}\right)\right| > c;\ a\left|x + \dfrac{b}{a}\right| > c;\ \left|x + \dfrac{b}{a}\right| > \dfrac{c}{a};\ \left\{x:x < \dfrac{-b - c}{a} \text{ or } x > \dfrac{-b + c}{a}\right\}$

26. $|b - ax| < c;\ \left|-a\left(x - \dfrac{b}{a}\right)\right| < c;\ a\left|x - \dfrac{b}{a}\right| < c;\ \left|x - \dfrac{b}{a}\right| < \dfrac{c}{a};\ \dfrac{b}{a} - \dfrac{c}{a}x < \dfrac{b}{a} + \dfrac{c}{a}$
$\left\{x:\dfrac{b - c}{a} < x < \dfrac{b + c}{a}\right\}$

27. $|ax| + b > c$; $|ax| > c - b$; $a|x| > c - b$; $|x| > \dfrac{c - b}{a}$; $x < -\dfrac{c - b}{a}$ or $x > \dfrac{c - b}{a}$; $\left\{ x : x < \dfrac{b - c}{a} \text{ or } x > \dfrac{c - b}{a} \right\}$

28. $a|x + b| \leq c$; $|x + b| \leq \dfrac{c}{a}$; $\left\{ x : -b - \dfrac{c}{a} \leq x \leq -b + \dfrac{c}{a} \right\}$

Page 78 · COMPUTER KEY-IN

1. a. $-2 < x < \dfrac{11}{2}$ **b.** $-\dfrac{1}{3} < x < \dfrac{4}{3}$ **c.** $x < \dfrac{5}{2}$ or $x > \dfrac{13}{2}$ **d.** $x < 1$ or $x > \dfrac{17}{5}$

2. a. $-10 < x < 6$ **b.** $x < -\dfrac{11}{3}$ or $x > \dfrac{19}{3}$ **c.** $x < -\dfrac{51}{2}$ or $x > \dfrac{39}{2}$ **d.** $4 < x < 8$

Pages 83-84 · WRITTEN EXERCISES

A

1. (1) Given; (2) Add. prop. of equality; (3) Assoc. prop. of add.; (4) Prop. of opp.; (5) Ident. prop. for add.

2. (1) Given; (2) Add. prop. of equality; (3) Add. prop. of equality; (4) Trans. prop. of equality

3. (1) Given; (2) Add. prop. of equality; (3) Assoc. prop. of add.; (4) Prop. of opp.; (5) Ident. prop. for add.

4. (1) Given; (2) Prop. of recip.; (3) Assoc. prop. of mult.; (4) Prop. of recip.; (5) Ident. prop. for mult.; (6) Trans. prop. of equality

5. (1) Ident. prop. for mult.; (2) Dist. prop.; (3) Prop. of opp.; (4) Mult. prop. of 0; (5) Prop. of opp.; (6) Trans. prop. of equality; (7) Canc. rule for add.; (8) Comm. prop. of mult.

6. (1) Given; (2) Prop. of recip.; (3) Mult. prop. of equality; (4) Assoc. prop. of mult.; (5) Prop. of Recip.; (6) Ident. prop. for mult.; (7) Mult. prop. of 0

7. (1) Def. of subtr.; (2) Dist. prop.; (3) Mult. prop. of -1; (4) Assoc. prop. of mult.; (5) Comm. prop. of mult.; (6) Assoc. prop. of mult.; (7) Mult. prop. of -1; (8) Def. of subtr.; (9) Trans. prop. of equality; (10) Comm. prop. of mult.

8. (1) Given; (2) Def. of div.; (3) Dist. prop. for mult. with resp. to subtr.; (4) Def. of div.; (5) Trans. prop. of equality

B

9. (1) $a + c = b + c$ (Given); (2) $c + a = c + b$ (Comm. prop. for add.); (3) $a = b$ (Canc. rule for add.)

10. (1) $a = b$ and $c = d$ (Given); (2) $ac = bc$ and $bc = bd$ (Mult. prop. of equality); (3) $ac = bd$ (Trans. prop. of equality)

11. (1) $x = y$ (Given);   (2) $x \cdot x = y \cdot y$ (Ex. 10);

(3) $x^2 = y^2$ (Def. of square)

12. (1) a, b, and c are real numbers. (Given)

(2) $(a + b) + c = c + (a + b)$ (Comm. prop. of add.)

(3) $\qquad = (c + a) + b$ (Assoc. prop. of add.)

(4) $\qquad = b + (c + a)$ (Comm. prop. of add.)

(5) $\therefore (a + b) + c = b + (c + a)$ (Trans. prop. of equality)

13. (1) a and b are real numbers.   (Given)

(2) $(-a)(-b) = [(-1)a][(-1)b]$ (Mult. prop. of -1)

(3) $\qquad = [(-1)a][b(-1)]$ (Comm. prop. of mult.)

(4) $\qquad = [(-1)(ab)](-1)$ (Assoc. prop. of mult.)

(5) $\qquad = (-1)[(-1)(ab)]$ (Comm. prop. of mult.)

(6) $\qquad = [(-1)(-1)]ab$ (Assoc. prop. of mult.)

(7) $\qquad = [-(-1)]ab$ (Mult. prop. of -1)

(8) $\qquad = 1 \cdot ab$ $(-(-1) = 1)$

(9) $\qquad = ab$ (Ident. prop. for mult.)

(10) $\therefore (-a)(-b) = ab$ (Trans. prop. of equality)

C **14.** (1) a is a real number; $a \neq 0$ (Given)

(2) $-a \neq 0$ (If $-a = 0$, $0 = a + (-a) = a + 0 = a$)

(3) $\dfrac{1}{a}$ and $\dfrac{1}{-a}$ are real numbers.   (Prop. of recip.)

(4) $\dfrac{1}{-a}(-a) = 1$ (Prop. of recip.)

(5) $\left(-\dfrac{1}{a}\right)(-a) = \left(\dfrac{1}{a}\right)a$ (Ex. 13, above)

(6) $\qquad = 1$ (Prop. of recip.)

(7) $\dfrac{1}{-a}$ and $-\dfrac{1}{a}$ are reciprocals of $-a$ (Def. of recip.)

(8) $\dfrac{1}{-a} = -\dfrac{1}{a}$ (Recip. are unique)

15. (1) $ax + b = c$; $a \neq 0$ (Given)

(2) $\dfrac{1}{a}$ is a real number.   (Prop. of recip.)

(3) $ax = c + (-b)$ (Ex. 1)

(4) $\dfrac{1}{a}(ax) = \dfrac{1}{a}[c + (-b)]$ (Mult. prop. of equality)

(5) $\left(\dfrac{1}{a} \cdot a\right)x = \dfrac{1}{a}[c + (-b)]$ (Assoc. prop. of mult.)

(6) $1 \cdot x = \dfrac{1}{a}[c + (-b)]$ (Prop. of recip.)

(7) $x = \dfrac{1}{a}[c + (-b)]$ (Ident. prop. for mult.)

Pages 87-89 · WRITTEN EXERCISES

A **1.** (1) Given;   (2) Mult. prop. of order;   (3) Mult. prop. of −1

2. (1) Given;   (2) Mult. prop. of order;   (3) Mult. prop. of −1;   (4) Mult. prop. of 0

3. (1) Given;   (2) Add. prop. of order;   (3) Def. of subtr.

4. (1) Given;   (2) Mult. prop. of order;   (3) Comm. prop. for mult.;
(4) Mult. prop. of order; (5) Trans. prop. of order;   (6) Def. of square

5. (1) Given;   (2) Mult. prop. of order;   (3) Comm. prop. of mult.;
(4) Mult. prop. of order; (5) Trans. prop. of order;   (6) Def. of square

6. (1) Given;   (2) Mult. prop. of order;   (3) Given;
(4) Mult. prop. of order; (5) Comm. prop. of mult.;   (6) Trans. prop. of order

7. (1) Given;

(2) For every nonzero real number a, a and $\dfrac{1}{a}$ have the same sign;

(3) Mult. prop. of order;   (4) Def. of div.

8. (1) Given;

(2) For every nonzero real number a, a and $\dfrac{1}{a}$ have the same sign;

(3) Mult. prop. of order;   (4) Def. of div.

9. (1) $a > 0$ (Given);   (2) $(-1)a < (-1)0$ (Mult. prop. of order);
(3) $-a < (-1)0$ (Mult. prop. of −1);   (4) $-a < 0$ (Mult. prop. of 0)

10. (1) $a > 0$ and $b > 0$ (Given);   (2) $a \cdot b > 0 \cdot b$ (Mult. prop. of order);
(3) $ab > 0$ (Mult. prop. of 0)

11. (1) $a < 0$ and $b < 0$ (Given);   (2) $a \cdot b > 0 \cdot b$ (Mult. prop. of order);
(3) $ab > 0$ (Mult. prop. of 0)

B **12.** (1) $a > 0$ and $b < 0$ (Given);
(2) $|a| \cdot |b| = a(-b)$ ($|n| = n$ if $n \geq 0$; $|n| = -n$ if $n < 0$);
(3) $a(-b) = a[(-1)b]$ (Mult. prop. of −1);
(4) $a[(-1)b] = [a(-1)]b$ (Assoc. prop. of mult.);
(5) $[a(-1)]b = (-a)b$ (Mult. prop. of −1);
(6) $|a| \cdot |b| = (-a)b$ (Trans. prop. of equality);
(7) $a \cdot b < 0 \cdot b$ (Mult. prop. of order);
(8) $ab < 0$ (Mult. prop. of 0)
(9) $|ab| = -(ab)$ ($|n| = -n$ if $n < 0$);
(10) $-(ab) = (-1)ab$ (Mult. prop. of −1);
(11) $(-1)ab = [(-1)a]b$ (Assoc. prop. of mult.);
(12) $[(-1)a]b = (-a)b$ (Mult. prop. of −1);
(13) $|ab| = (-a)b$ and $|ab| = |a| \cdot |b|$ (Trans. prop. of equality)

13. (1) $a < 0$ and $b > 0$ (Given);

    (2) $|a| \cdot |b| = (-a)b$ $(|n| = n$ if $n \geq 0; |n| = -n$ if $n < 0)$

    (3) $a \cdot b < 0 \cdot b$ (Mult. prop. of order);

    (4) $ab < 0$ (Mult. prop. of 0);

    (5) $|ab| = -(ab)$ $(|n| = -n$ if $n < 0)$;

    (6) $-(ab) = (-1)(ab)$ (Mult. prop. of -1);

    (7) $(-1)(ab) = [(-1)a]b$ (Assoc. prop. of mult.);

    (8) $[(-1)a]b = (-a)b$ (Mult. prop. of -1);

    (9) $|ab| = (-a)b$ and $|ab| = |a| \cdot |b|$ (Trans. prop. of equality)

14. (1) $a < 1$ and $a > 0$ (Given);   (2) $a \cdot a < 1 \cdot a$ (Mult. prop. of order);

    (3) $a^2 < 1 \cdot a$ (Def. of square);   (4) $a^2 < a$ (Ident. prop. for mult.)

15. Assume temporarily that $\dfrac{1}{a} \leq 0$; then $a > 0$ and $\dfrac{1}{a} \leq 0$, so $a \cdot \dfrac{1}{a} \leq a \cdot 0$ by the Mult.

prop. of order; that is, $a \cdot \dfrac{1}{a} \leq 0$; this contradicts the fact that for any nonzero a,

$1 = a \cdot \dfrac{1}{a} > 0$. Then $\dfrac{1}{a} > 0$.

16. Assume temporarily that $\dfrac{1}{a} \geq 0$; then $a < 0$ and $\dfrac{1}{a} \geq 0$, so $a \cdot \dfrac{1}{a} \leq a \cdot 0$ by the Mult.

prop. of order; that is, $a \cdot \dfrac{1}{a} \leq 0$; this contradicts the fact that for every nonzero a,

$1 = a \cdot \dfrac{1}{a} > 0$. Then $\dfrac{1}{a} < 0$.

C **17.**   (1) $a < b$ (Given);

        (2) $a + a < b + a$ and $b + a < b + b$ (Add. prop. of order);

        (3) $a + a < a + b$ and $a + b < b + b$ (Comm. prop. for add.);

        (4) $2a < a + b$ and $a + b < 2b$ (Subst.);

        (5) $\dfrac{1}{2}(2a) < \dfrac{1}{2}(a + b)$ and $\dfrac{1}{2}(a + b) < \dfrac{1}{2}(2b)$ (Mult. prop. of order);

        (6) $\left(\dfrac{1}{2} \cdot 2\right)a < \dfrac{1}{2}(a + b)$ and $\dfrac{1}{2}(a + b) < \left(\dfrac{1}{2} \cdot 2\right)b$ (Assoc. prop. of mult.);

        (7) $1 \cdot a < \dfrac{1}{2}(a + b)$ and $\dfrac{1}{2}(a + b) < 1 \cdot b$ (Prop. of recip.);

        (8) $a < \dfrac{1}{2}(a + b)$ and $\dfrac{1}{2}(a + b) < b$ (Ident. prop. for mult.);

        (9) $a < \dfrac{1}{2}(a + b) < b$ (Trans. prop. of order);

      (10) $a < \dfrac{a + b}{2} < b$ (Def. of div.)

18. Assume temporarily that $a = 1$; since $a > 0$, $\dfrac{1}{a}$ is a real number and since $a = 1$,

$a \cdot \dfrac{1}{a} = 1 \cdot \dfrac{1}{a}$; $1 = \dfrac{1}{a}$; that is $a = \dfrac{1}{a}$; this contradicts the hypothesis that $a > \dfrac{1}{a}$ and

so $a \neq 1$. Next assume that $a < 1$; $a \cdot \dfrac{1}{a} < 1 \cdot \dfrac{1}{a}$; $a \cdot \dfrac{1}{a} < \dfrac{1}{a}$; $1 < \dfrac{1}{a}$; $a < 1 < \dfrac{1}{a}$; this

contradicts the hypothesis and so a is not less than 1; then by the comparison property
of order, $a > 1$.

Pages 91-92 · CHAPTER REVIEW

1. a; $-\dfrac{1}{2}a > -3$; $(-2)\left(-\dfrac{1}{2}a\right) < (-2)(-3)$; $a < 6$

2. b; $2(v + 3) < 5v - 6$; $2v + 6 < 5v - 6$; $12 < 3v$; $4 < v$; $v > 4$

3. b; $5 \geq \dfrac{n}{2} - 1 > -2$; $6 \geq \dfrac{n}{2} > -1$; $12 \geq n > -2$

4. c; $3 - t > 2$ or $t + 3 \geq 7$; $1 > t$ or $t \geq 4$; $t < 1$ or $t \geq 4$

5. c; let $x =$ number of quarters, then $10x =$ number of nickels; $25x + 5(10x) \leq 700$;

$75x \leq 700$; $x \leq 9\dfrac{1}{3}$; since x must be an integer, the greatest value of x is 9, and of $10x$

is 90; 90 nickels

6. d; $11 - \dfrac{g}{5} = 4$ or $11 - \dfrac{g}{5} = -4$; $-\dfrac{g}{5} = -7$ or $-\dfrac{g}{5} = -15$; $g = 35$ or $g = 75$

7. d; $|2p + 3| < 17$; $-17 < 2p + 3 < 17$; $-20 < 2p < 14$; $-10 < p < 7$

8. c; $3 - h > 19$ or $3 - h < -19$; $-h > 16$ or $-h < -22$; $h < -16$ or $h > 22$

9. c; $|2t - 8| > 2$; $|2(t - 4)| > 2$; $|2||t - 4| > 2$; $|t - 4| > 1$

10. c   11. a   12. a

13. d   14. a; if $c > 0$ then $\dfrac{1}{c} > 0$; $a\left(\dfrac{1}{c}\right) < b\left(\dfrac{1}{c}\right)$; $\dfrac{a}{c} < \dfrac{b}{c}$

Page 92 · CHAPTER TEST

1. $4x - 7 < 3x$; $x < 7$; $\{x : x < 7\}$

2. $2(3x - 1) > 3(x - 1)$; $6x - 2 > 3x - 3$; $3x > -1$; $x > -\dfrac{1}{3}$; $\left\{x : x > -\dfrac{1}{3}\right\}$

3. $-5 < 1 - w < 3$; $-6 < -w < 2$; $6 > w > -2$; $\{w : -2 < w < 6\}$

4. $3 \geq \dfrac{y}{6}$ or $y - 1 < \dfrac{1}{2}$; $18 \geq y$ or $y < \dfrac{3}{2}$; $\{y : y \leq 18\}$

5. Let $n =$ first even integer; $n + 2$ and $n + 4$ are the next two;

$n + (n + 2) + (n + 4) > 105$; $3n + 6 > 105$; $3n > 99$; $n > 33$; $n = 34$; $\{34, 36, 38\}$

6. $|3x - 30| = 3$; $3x - 30 = 3$ or $3x - 30 = -3$; $3x = 33$ or $3x = 27$; $x = 11$ or $x = 9$; $\{11, 9\}$

7. $3|x + 8| \geq 42$; $|x + 8| \geq 14$; $x + 8 \geq 14$ or $x + 8 \leq -14$; $x \geq 6$ or $x \leq -22$; $\{x : x \geq 6$ or $x \leq -22\}$

8. $|5x + 1| < 7$; $-7 < 5x + 1 < 7$; $-8 < 5x < 6$; $-\dfrac{8}{5} < x < \dfrac{6}{5}$; $\{x : -1.6 < x < 1.2\}$

9.   10.

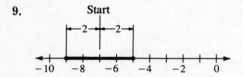

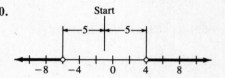

11. If an integer has exactly two factors, one and itself, then it is prime.

12. (1) Given;   (2) Add. prop. of equality;   (3) Assoc. prop. for add.;
    (4) Prop. of opp.;   (5) Ident. prop. for add.

13. Not true; for example, $-3 < -2$, but $(-3)^2 > (-2)^2$

14. Not true; for example, $-3 < -2$ and $0 < 1$, but $(-3)(0) > (-2)(1)$

15. True

Page 95 · EXTRA

1. Since q is false, $q \rightarrow r$ is true.

2. Since r is true, $\sim r$ is false; $\sim r \wedge p$ is false.

3. Since p is true, $p \vee \sim q$ is true.

4. Since p is true, $p \vee q$ is true; r is true; $r \wedge (p \vee q)$ is true.

5. Since p is true, $p \vee (q \wedge r)$ is true.

6. Since p is true, $p \vee r$ is true; q is false; $(p \vee r) \rightarrow q$ is false.

7. Since p is true, $\sim p$ is false; $\sim p \rightarrow (q \vee \sim r)$ is true.

8. Since q is false, $q \rightarrow r$ is true; r is true, $r \rightarrow (q \rightarrow r)$ is true.

9. Since p is true, $p \vee q$ is true; r is true; $r \wedge (p \vee q)$ is true; r and p are true, so $(r \wedge p)$ is true and $(r \wedge p) \vee (r \wedge q)$ is true; $[r \wedge (p \vee q)] \rightarrow [(r \wedge p) \vee (r \wedge q)]$ is true.

10.-12. $p \rightarrow q$ is false only when p is true and q is false.

10. q is false; p is true; $q \rightarrow p$ is true.

11. p is true; $\sim q$ is true; $p \wedge \sim q$ is true.

12. p is true; q is false; $p \vee q$ is true; $(p \vee q) \wedge p$ is true.

13.

p	q	$p \vee q$	$q \vee p$
T	T	T	T
T	F	T	T
F	T	T	T
F	F	F	F

logically equivalent

14.

q	$\sim q$	$q \vee \sim q$
T	F	T
F	T	T

not logically equivalent

15.

p	q	$p \vee q$	$(p \vee q) \rightarrow p$
T	T	T	T
T	F	T	T
F	T	T	F
F	F	F	T

not a tautology

16.

p	q	$\sim q$	$q \wedge \sim q$	$(q \wedge \sim q) \rightarrow p$
T	T	F	F	T
T	F	T	F	T
F	T	F	F	T
F	F	T	F	T

tautology

17.

p	q	r	$p \vee q$	$r \wedge (p \vee q)$	$r \wedge p$	$r \wedge q$	$(r \wedge p) \vee (r \wedge q)$
T	T	T	T	T	T	T	T
T	T	F	T	F	F	F	F
T	F	T	T	T	T	F	T
T	F	F	T	F	F	F	F
F	T	T	T	T	F	T	T
F	T	F	T	F	F	F	F
F	F	T	F	F	F	F	F
F	F	F	F	F	F	F	F

Recall that $p \leftrightarrow q$ is true whenever p and q have the same truth value. Since columns 5 and 8 are identical, $r \wedge (p \vee q)$ and $(r \wedge p) \vee (r \wedge q)$ always have the same truth value; then $r \wedge (p \vee q) \leftrightarrow (r \wedge p) \vee (r \wedge q)$ is always true, that is, is a tautology.

18.

p	q	r	$p \rightarrow q$	$q \rightarrow r$	$(p \rightarrow q) \wedge (q \rightarrow r)$	$p \rightarrow r$	$[(p \rightarrow q) \wedge (q \rightarrow r)] \rightarrow (p \rightarrow r)$
T	T	T	T	T	T	T	T
T	T	F	T	F	F	F	T
T	F	T	F	T	F	T	T
T	F	F	F	T	F	F	T
F	T	T	T	T	T	T	T
F	T	F	T	F	F	T	T
F	F	T	T	T	T	T	T
F	F	F	T	T	T	T	T

tautology

Page 96 · MIXED REVIEW

1. $-|-1| \cdot |-2| = -(1) \cdot (2) = -2$

2. $5(14 - 2^3) \div 3 + 2 = 5(14 - 8) \div 3 + 2 = 5(6) \div 3 + 2 = 30 \div 3 + 2 = 10 + 2 = 12$

3. $\dfrac{[7 - (5 - 1)]4^2}{9 \cdot 3 - 11} = \dfrac{(7 - 4)16}{27 - 11} = \dfrac{3 \cdot 16}{16} = 3$

4. $|3 - 7.1| - (-5) = |-4.1| + 5 = 4.1 + 5 = 9.1$

5. $(-8 + 1)(-9 - 3) = -7(-12) = 84$

6. $\dfrac{\left(-28 \div \dfrac{7}{4}\right) \div (-2)}{(-1 - 1)^2} = \dfrac{\left(-28 \cdot \dfrac{4}{7}\right) \div (-2)}{(-2)^2} = \dfrac{-16 \div (-2)}{4} = \dfrac{8}{4} = 2$

7. $-\dfrac{3}{4}(4t^4 - 16t^2 + 8) + \dfrac{5}{6}(6 - 54t + 18t^2 - 12t^3) = -3t^4 + 12t^2 - 6 + 5 - 45t$
$+ 15t^2 - 10t^3 = -3t^4 - 10t^3 + 27t^2 - 45t - 1$

8. (1) Given;   (2) Add. prop. of equality;   (3) Assoc. prop. for add.;
     (4) Prop. of opp.;   (5) Ident. prop. for add.

9. $5(-3)^3 + 2(-3)^2 - 38 = 5(-27) + 2(9) - 38 = -135 + 18 - 38 = -155$

10. $A = P + Prt;\ Prt = A - P;\ t = \dfrac{A - P}{Pr}$

11. Let t = time spent driving; for first leg of trip, $t_1 = \dfrac{d}{60}$; for return, $t_2 = \dfrac{d}{45}$;

$t = t_1 + t_2 = \dfrac{d}{60} + \dfrac{d}{45} = \dfrac{7d}{180}$

12. Let n = number of kilograms of peanuts; $10 - n$ = number of kilograms of raisins; $5.5n + 4(10 - n) = 4.9(10)$; $5.5n + 40 - 4n = 49$; $1.5n = 9$; $n = 6$; 6 kg

13. Let g = Grace's age now; $g + 5$ = brother's age now; $g + 6 \geq \dfrac{3}{4}[(g + 5) + 6]$;

$g + 6 \geq \dfrac{3}{4}(g + 11)$; $\dfrac{4}{3}g + 8 \geq g + 11$; $\dfrac{1}{3}g \geq 3$; $g \geq 9$; Grace is at least 9.

14. Let n and $5n$ be the integers; $n + 5n \leq 75$; $6n \leq 75$; $n \leq 12.5$; the greatest integer less than or equal to 12.5 is 12; $5(12) = 60$; 12 and 60

15. $-2(7x - 3) > 3(4 - 5x)$; $-14x + 6 > 12 - 15x$; $x > 6$; $\{x : x > 6\}$

16. $\left| z + \dfrac{3}{4} \right| \geq \dfrac{5}{4}$; $z + \dfrac{3}{4} \geq \dfrac{5}{4}$ or $z + \dfrac{3}{4} \leq -\dfrac{5}{4}$; $z \geq \dfrac{1}{2}$ or $z \leq -2$; $\left\{ z : z \leq -2 \text{ or } z \geq \dfrac{1}{2} \right\}$

17. $1 \geq 1 - \dfrac{1}{3}k > -1$; $0 \geq -\dfrac{1}{3}k > -2$; $0 \leq k < 6$; $\{k : 0 \leq k < 6\}$

18. $9|3m + 2| - 11 < -2$; $9|3m + 2| < 9$; $|3m + 2| < 1$; $-1 < 3m + 2 < 1$;

$-3 < 3m < -1$; $-1 < m < -\dfrac{1}{3}$; $\left\{ m : -1 < m < -\dfrac{1}{3} \right\}$

19. $7(r - 3) < 4r - 27$ or $-\dfrac{5}{4}r + \dfrac{1}{2} < 3$; $7r - 21 < 4r - 27$ or $-\dfrac{5}{4}r < \dfrac{5}{2}$; $3r < -6$ or

$r > -2$; $r < -2$ or $r > -2$; $\{r : r \neq -2\}$

Page 97 · PREPARING FOR COLLEGE ENTRANCE EXAMS

1. C **2.** D **3.** C

4. D **5.** C **6.** D

7. A

Page 102 · WRITTEN EXERCISES

A 1. $x + 2y = 6$; $2y = -x + 6$; $y = -\dfrac{1}{2}x + 3$; $y = -\dfrac{1}{2}(4) + 3 = 1$;

$y = -\dfrac{1}{2}(0) + 3 = 3$; $y = -\dfrac{1}{2}(-2) + 3 = 4$; $(4, 1)$; $(0, 3)$; $(-2, 4)$

2. $3x - y = 5$; $-y = -3x + 5$; $y = 3x - 5$; $y = 3(0) - 5 = -5$; $y = 3(3) - 5 = 4$;

$y = 3(-5) - 5 = -20$; $(0, -5)$; $(3, 4)$; $(-5, -20)$

3. $5x - 2y = 7$; $-2y = -5x + 7$; $y = \dfrac{-5x + 7}{-2} = \dfrac{5x - 7}{2}$; $y = \dfrac{5(1) - 7}{2} = -1$;

$y = \dfrac{5(3) - 7}{2} = 4$; $y = \dfrac{5(-3) - 7}{2} = -11$; $(1, -1)$; $(3, 4)$; $(-3, -11)$

4. $7x + 2y = 1$; $2y = -7x + 1$; $y = \dfrac{-7x + 1}{2}$; $y = \dfrac{-7(3) + 1}{2} = -10$;

$y = \dfrac{-7(-1) + 1}{2} = 4$; $y = \dfrac{-7(-3) + 1}{2} = 11$; $(3, -10)$; $(-1, 4)$; $(-3, 11)$

5. $2x - 3y = 7$; $-3y = -2x + 7$; $y = \dfrac{-2x + 7}{-3} = \dfrac{2x - 7}{3}$; $y = \dfrac{2(-1) - 7}{3} = -3$;

$y = \dfrac{2(2) - 7}{3} = -1$; $y = \dfrac{2\left(\dfrac{1}{2}\right) - 7}{3} = -2$; $(-1, -3)$; $(2, -1)$; $\left(\dfrac{1}{2}, -2\right)$

6. $3x + 5y = 11$; $5y = -3x + 11$; $y = \dfrac{-3x + 11}{5}$; $y = \dfrac{-3(2) + 11}{5} = 1$;

$y = \dfrac{-3(3) + 11}{5} = \dfrac{2}{5}$; $y = \dfrac{-3\left(\dfrac{1}{3}\right) + 11}{5} = 2$; $(2, 1)$; $\left(3, \dfrac{2}{5}\right)$; $\left(\dfrac{1}{3}, 2\right)$

7. $x + 5y = 7$; $x = -5y + 7$; $x = -5(1) + 7 = 2$; $x = -5(2) + 7 = -3$;

$x = -5(3) + 7 = -8$; $(2, 1)$; $(-3, 2)$; $(-8, 3)$

8. $x - 7y = -3$; $x = 7y - 3$; $x = 7(1) - 3 = 4$; $x = 7(2) - 3 = 11$; $x = 7(3) - 3 = 18$;

$(4, 1)$; $(11, 2)$; $(18, 3)$

9. $2x + 2y = -3$; $2y = -2x - 3$; $y = \dfrac{-2x - 3}{2}$; $y = \dfrac{-2\left(\dfrac{1}{2}\right) - 3}{2} = -2$;

$\dfrac{1}{2} = \dfrac{-2x - 3}{2}$; $1 = -2x - 3$; $-2x = 4$; $x = -2$; $y = \dfrac{-2\left(-\dfrac{1}{2}\right) - 3}{2} = -1$; $\left(\dfrac{1}{2}, -2\right)$;

$\left(-2, \dfrac{1}{2}\right)$; $\left(-\dfrac{1}{2}, -1\right)$

10. $3x - 3y = 2$; $-3y = -3x + 2$; $3y = 3x - 2$; $y = \dfrac{3x - 2}{3}$; $y = \dfrac{3\left(-\dfrac{1}{3}\right) - 2}{3} = -1$;

$\dfrac{1}{3} = \dfrac{3x - 2}{3}$; $3x - 2 = 1$; $3x = 3$; $x = 1$; $y = \dfrac{3\left(\dfrac{2}{3}\right) - 2}{3} = 0$; $\left(-\dfrac{1}{3}, -1\right)$; $\left(1, \dfrac{1}{3}\right)$;

$\left(\dfrac{2}{3}, 0\right)$

11. $5x - 7y = 20$; $5x = 7y + 20$; $x = \dfrac{7y + 20}{5}$; $x = \dfrac{7(0) + 20}{5} = 4$; $0 = \dfrac{7y + 20}{5}$;

$7y + 20 = 0$; $7y = -20$; $y = -\dfrac{20}{7}$; $x = \dfrac{7(5) + 20}{5} = 11$; $(4, 0)$; $\left(0, -\dfrac{20}{7}\right)$; $(11, 5)$

12. $7x + 4y = 16$; $4y = -7x + 16$; $y = \dfrac{-7x + 16}{4}$; $y = \dfrac{-7(0) + 16}{4} = 4$; $0 = \dfrac{-7x + 16}{4}$;

$-7x + 16 = 0$; $-7x = -16$; $x = \dfrac{16}{7}$; $y = \dfrac{-7(-4) + 16}{4} = 11$; $(0, 4)$; $\left(\dfrac{16}{7}, 0\right)$; $(-4, 11)$

13. $x + 2y = k$; $3 + 2(1) = k$; $k = 5$ 14. $2x - 3y = k$; $2(1) - 3(-2) = k$; $k = 8$

15. $kx - 3y = 7$; $2k - 3(3) = 7$; $2k - 9 = 7$; $2k = 16$; $k = 8$

16. $4x + ky = 5$; $4(-1) + 3k = 5$; $-4 + 3k = 5$; $3k = 9$; $k = 3$

17. $2x + ky = k$; $2(3) + 2k = k$; $6 + 2k = k$; $k = -6$

18. $kx - 3y = k$; $3k - 3(-2) = k$; $3k + 6 = k$; $2k = -6$; $k = -3$

19.

x	$y = -x + 5$
0	5
1	4
2	3
3	2
4	1
5	0

If $x > 5$, $y < 0$;

$\{(0, 5), (1, 4), (2, 3), (3, 2), (4, 1), (5, 0)\}$

20.

x	$y = -2x + 8$
0	8
1	6
2	4
3	2
4	0

If $x > 4$, $y < 0$;

$\{(0, 8), (1, 6), (2, 4), (3, 2), (4, 0)\}$

21.

x	$y = \dfrac{-x + 21}{5}$
1	4
6	3
11	2
16	1
21	0

If $x > 21$, $y < 0$;

$\{(1, 4), (6, 3), (11, 2), (16, 1), (21, 0)\}$

22.

x	$y = \dfrac{-x + 14}{4}$
2	3
6	2
10	1
14	0

If $x > 14$, $y < 0$;

$\{(2, 3), (6, 2), (10, 1), (14, 0)\}$

B 23.

x	$y = \dfrac{-2x + 18}{3}$
0	6
3	4
6	2
9	0

If $x > 9$, $y < 0$;
$\{(0, 6), (3, 4), (6, 2), (9, 0)\}$

24.

x	$y = \dfrac{-5x + 30}{2}$
0	15
2	10
4	5
6	0

If $x > 6$, $y < 0$;
$\{(0, 15), (2, 10), (4, 5), (6, 0)\}$

25.

x	$-x + 4$	$y \le -x + 4$
1	3	1, 2, 3
2	2	1, 2
3	1	1

If $x > 3$, $y \le 0$;
$\{(1, 1), (1, 2), (1, 3), (2, 1), (2, 2), (3, 1)\}$

26.

x	$\dfrac{-x + 6}{2}$	$y < \dfrac{-x + 6}{2}$
1	$\dfrac{5}{2}$	1, 2
2	2	1
3	$\dfrac{3}{2}$	1

If $x > 3$, $y \le 0$;
$\{(1, 1), (1, 2), (2, 1), (3, 1)\}$

27.

x	$\dfrac{-2x + 12}{3}$	$y < \dfrac{-2x + 12}{3}$
1	$\dfrac{10}{3}$	1, 2, 3
2	$\dfrac{8}{3}$	1, 2
3	2	1
4	$\dfrac{4}{3}$	1

If $x > 4$, $y \le 0$;
$\{(1, 1), (1, 2), (1, 3), (2, 1), (2, 2), (3, 1), (4, 1)\}$

28.

x	$\dfrac{-3x + 8}{2}$	$y \le \dfrac{-3x + 8}{2}$
1	$\dfrac{5}{2}$	1, 2
2	1	1

If $x > 2$, $y < 0$;
$\{(1, 1), (1, 2), (2, 1)\}$

29.

x	$y = \dfrac{-x^2 + 8}{2}$
2	2

If $x > 2$, $y < 0$; $\{(2, 2)\}$

30.

x	$y = \dfrac{-x^2 + 11}{2}$
1	5
3	1

If $x > 3$, $y < 0$; $\{(1, 5), (3, 1)\}$

31.

x	$\dfrac{-x^2 + 8}{2}$	$y \leq \dfrac{-x^2 + 8}{2}$
1	$\dfrac{7}{2}$	1, 2, 3
2	2	1, 2

If $x > 2$, $y < 0$;
$\{(1, 1), (1, 2), (1, 3), (2, 1), (2, 2)\}$

32.

x	$\dfrac{-x^2 + 11}{2}$	$y < \dfrac{-x^2 + 11}{2}$
1	5	1, 2, 3, 4
2	$\dfrac{7}{2}$	1, 2, 3

If $x > 2$, $y \leq 0$;
$\{(1, 1), (1, 2), (1, 3), (1, 4), (2, 1), (2, 2), (2, 3)\}$

33.

x	$\dfrac{-x + 14}{3}$	$y^2 < \dfrac{-x + 14}{3}$	x	$\dfrac{-x + 14}{3}$	$y^2 < \dfrac{-x + 14}{3}$
1	$\dfrac{13}{3}$	1, 2	6	$\dfrac{8}{3}$	1
2	4	1	7	$\dfrac{7}{3}$	1
3	$\dfrac{11}{3}$	1	8	2	1
4	$\dfrac{10}{3}$	1	9	$\dfrac{5}{3}$	1
5	3	1	10	$\dfrac{4}{3}$	1

If $x > 10$, $y \leq 0$; $\{(1, 1), (1, 2), (2, 1), (3, 1), (4, 1), (5, 1), (6, 1), (7, 1), (8, 1), (9, 1), (10, 1)\}$

C 34. Let t = tens' digit and u = units' digit; original number = $10t + u$; number with digits interchanged = $10u + t$; $10t + u - (10u + t) = 9t - 9u = 9(t - u)$; since t and u are integers, $t - u$ is an integer and $10t + u - (10u + t) = 9(t - u)$ is an integral multiple of 9.

Page 103 · PROBLEMS

A **1.** **a.** Let n = number of nickels; d = number of dimes.

 b. $5n + 10d = 35$

 c. $10d = 35 - 5n$; $d = \dfrac{35 - 5n}{10}$; if $n = 1$, $d = \dfrac{35 - 5}{10} = 3$; if $n = 3$,

$d = \dfrac{35 - 15}{10} = 2$; if $n = 5$, $d = \dfrac{35 - 25}{10} = 1$; if $n = 7$, $d = \dfrac{35 - 35}{10} = 0$; if $n > 7$,

$d < 0$; 1 nickel and 3 dimes, 3 nickels and 2 dimes, 5 nickels and 1 dime, or 7 nickels and 0 dimes.

2. **a.** Let f = number of \$5 bills, t = number of \$20 bills.

 b. $5f + 20t = 65$

 c. $20t = -5f + 65$; $t = \dfrac{-5f + 65}{20}$; if $f = 1$, $t = \dfrac{-5 + 65}{20} = 3$; if $f = 5$,

$t = \dfrac{-25 + 65}{20} = 2$; if $f = 9$, $t = \dfrac{-45 + 65}{20} = 1$; if $f = 13$, $t = \dfrac{-65 + 65}{20} = 0$; if

$f > 13$, $t < 0$; she should use 1 \$5 bill and 3 \$20 bills, 5 \$5 bills and 2 \$20 bills, 9 \$5 bills and 1 \$20 bill, or 13 \$5 bills and 0 \$20 bills.

3. **a.** Let f = number of 15¢ stamps and t = number of 20¢ stamps.

 b. $15f + 20t = 195$

 c. $20t = 195 - 15f$; $t = \dfrac{195 - 15f}{20}$; if $f = 1$, $t = \dfrac{195 - 15}{20} = 9$; if $f = 5$,

$t = \dfrac{195 - 75}{20} = 6$; if $f = 9$, $t = \dfrac{195 - 135}{20} = 3$; if $f = 13$, $t = \dfrac{195 - 195}{20} = 0$; if

$f > 13$, $t < 0$; she can use 1 15¢ stamp and 9 20¢ stamps, 5 15¢ stamps and 6 20¢ stamps, 9 15¢ stamps and 3 20¢ stamps, or 13 15¢ stamps and 0 20¢ stamps.

4. **a.** Let d = number of dimes; q = number of quarters.

 b. $10d + 25q = 215$

 c. $25q = 215 - 10d$; $q = \dfrac{215 - 10d}{25}$; if $d = 4$, $q = \dfrac{215 - 40}{25} = 7$; if $d = 9$,

$q = \dfrac{215 - 90}{25} = 5$; if $d = 14$, $q = \dfrac{215 - 140}{25} = 3$; if $d = 19$, $q = \dfrac{215 - 190}{25} = 1$; he

can have 4 dimes and 7 quarters, 9 dimes and 5 quarters, 14 dimes and 3 quarters, or 19 dimes and 1 quarter.

5. **a.** Let x = length in meters of three sides; y = length in meters of fourth side.

 b. $3x + y = 20$; $y = -3x + 20$; also, since $3x > y$, $6x > 3x + y = 20$, and $x > 3\dfrac{2}{3}$;

if $x = 4$, $y = -12 + 20 = 8$; if $x = 5$, $y = -15 + 20 = 5$; if $x = 6$,

$y = -18 + 20 = 2$; the sides are of length 4 m, 4 m, 4 m, and 8 m; 5 m each; or 6 m, 6 m, 6 m, and 2 m.

B **6.** **a.** Let n = number of nickels and q = number of quarters; $p = 2n$ = number of pennies and $d = q + 2$ = number of dimes.

 b. $5n + 25q + 2n + 10(q + 2) = 195$

c. $7n + 35q = 175;\ n + 5q = 25;\ 5q = 25 - n;\ q = \dfrac{25 - n}{5};$ if $n = 5,$

$q = \dfrac{25 - 5}{5} = 4,\ p = 2 \cdot 5 = 10,$ and $d = 4 + 2 = 6;$ if $n = 10,\ q = \dfrac{25 - 10}{5} = 3,$

$p = 2 \cdot 10 = 20,$ and $d = 3 + 2 = 5;$ if $n = 15,\ q = \dfrac{25 - 15}{5} = 2,\ p = 2 \cdot 15 = 30,$

and $d = 2 + 2 = 4;$ if $n = 20,\ q = \dfrac{25 - 20}{5} = 1,\ p = 2 \cdot 20 = 40,$ and

$d = 1 + 2 = 3;$ if $n = 25,\ q = 0,\ p = 50,\ d = 2.$ The box contains 5 nickels, 4 quarters, 10 pennies and 6 dimes; 10 nickels, 3 quarters, 20 pennies, and 5 dimes; 15 nickels, 2 quarters, 30 pennies, and 4 dimes; 20 nickels, 1 quarter, 40 pennies, and 3 dimes; or 25 nickels, 0 quarters, 50 pennies, and 2 dimes.

7. a. Let $x =$ length in centimeters of congruent sides, $y =$ length in centimeters of third side.

b. $2x + y = 15$

c. $y = -2x + 15;$ also $2x > y,$ so $4x > 2x + y = 15,$ and $x > 3\dfrac{3}{4};$ if $x = 4,$

$y = -8 + 15 = 7;$ if $x = 5,\ y = -10 + 15 = 5,$ if $x = 6,\ y = -12 + 15 = 3;$ if $x = 7,\ y = -14 + 15 = 1;$ the sides are of length 4 cm, 4 cm, and 7 cm; 5 cm each; 6 cm, 6 cm, and 3 cm; or 7 cm, 7 cm, and 1 cm.

8. Let $N = 10t + u;$ then $K = 10u + t;\ 10t + u - (10u + t) = 45;\ 9t - 9u = 45;$ $t - u = 5;\ t = u + 5;$ if $u = 0,\ t = 5;$ if $u = 1,\ t = 1 + 5 = 6;$ if $u = 2,\ t = 2 + 5 = 7;$ if $u = 3,\ t = 3 + 5 = 8;$ if $u = 4,\ t = 4 + 5 = 9;\ N = 50, 61, 72, 83,$ or $94.$

9. Let $N = 10t + u;$ then $K = 10u + t;\ \dfrac{10t + u + 10u + t + 20}{3} = 25;\ 11t + 11u +$

$20 = 75;\ 11t + 11u = 55;\ t + u = 5;\ u = -t + 5;$ if $t = 1,\ u = -1 + 5 = 4;$ if $t = 2,$ $u = -2 + 5 = 3;$ if $t = 3,\ u = -3 + 5 = 2;$ if $t = 4,\ u = -4 + 5 = 1;$ if $t = 5,\ u = 0;$ $N = 14, 23, 32, 41,$ or $50.$

C **10.** Let $N = 10t + u;$ then $K = 10u + t;\ 10t + u + 2(10u + t) < 50;\ 10t + u + 20u +$

$2t < 50;\ 12t + 21u < 50;\ 21u < -12t + 50;\ u < \dfrac{-12t + 50}{21};$ if $t = 1,$

$\dfrac{-12t + 50}{21} = \dfrac{38}{51}$ and $u = 1;$ if $t = 2,\ \dfrac{-12t + 50}{21} = \dfrac{26}{21}$ and $u = 1;$ if $t = 3,\ u = 0;$ if $t = 4,\ u = 0;$ if $t > 4,\ u < 0;\ N = 11, 21, 30,$ or $40.$

11. Let $N = 10t + u;$ then $K = 10u + t;\ 10t + u - (10u + t) > 50;\ 10t + u - 10u -$

$t > 50;\ 9t - 9u > 50;\ 9t > 9u + 50;\ t > \dfrac{9u + 50}{9};$ if $u = 0,\ t > \dfrac{50}{9},\ t = 6, 7, 8, 9;$

if $u = 1,\ \dfrac{9u + 50}{9} = \dfrac{59}{9}$ and $t = 7, 8,$ or $9;$ if $u = 2,\ \dfrac{9u + 50}{9} = \dfrac{68}{9},$ and $t = 8$ or $9;$

if $u = 3,\ \dfrac{9u + 50}{9} = \dfrac{77}{9},$ and $t = 9;\ N = 60, 70, 80, 90, 71, 81, 91, 82, 92,$ or $93.$

12. Let x = number present at first meeting and y = number present at second; $2x$ = number present at third; $\dfrac{2x + x + y}{3} = 8$; $3x + y = 24$; $y = -3x + 24$; also, $y \leq 12$ and $2x \leq 12$ so $x \leq 6$; if $0 < x < 3$, $y > 12$; if $x = 4$, $y = -12 + 24 = 12$; if $x = 5$, $y = -15 + 24 = 9$; if $x = 6$, $y = -18 + 24 = 6$; the number present at meetings 1, 2, and 3 were 4, 12, and 8; 5, 9, and 10; or 6, 6, and 12.

13. Let x, y, and $24 - (x + y)$ be the lengths in centimeters of the first, second, and third pieces, respectively, with each length being an even integer; $x < y$ and $y < 24 - (x + y)$; $y < 24 - x - y$; $2y < 24 - x$; $2x < 2y < 24 - x$; $3x < 2y + x < 24$; then $x < 8$ and $y < \dfrac{-x + 24}{2}$, y and even integer; if $x = 2$, $\dfrac{-x + 24}{2} = 11$, and $y = 4, 6, 8$, or 10; if $x = 4$, $\dfrac{-x + 24}{2} = 10$, and $y = 6$ or 8; if $x = 6$, $\dfrac{-x + 24}{2} = 9$, and $y = 8$; the following ordered triples represent the possible lengths in centimeters of the first, second, and third pieces, respectively: $(2, 4, 18)$, $(2, 6, 16)$, $(2, 8, 14)$, $(2, 10, 12)$, $(4, 6, 14)$, $(4, 8, 12)$, $(6, 8, 10)$.

Page 108 · WRITTEN EXERCISES

A   1.

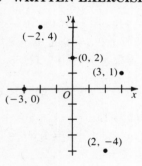

2.

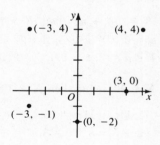

3.

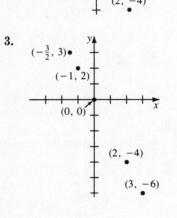

4.

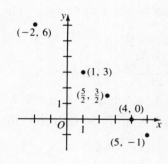

5.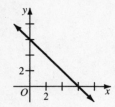

6.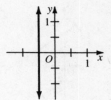

7.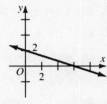

8.

9.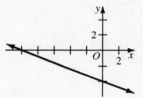

10.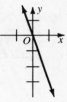

11.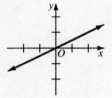

12.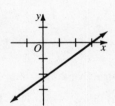

13.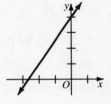

14.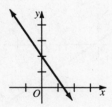

15.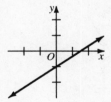

16.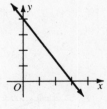

17.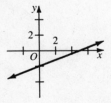

18.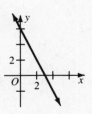

19.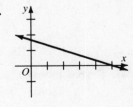

20.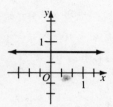

21.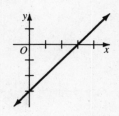

22.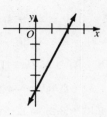

B **23.** 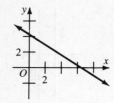   **24.**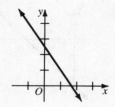

25. $5x + ky = 4; 5(2) + (-2k) = 4; 10 - 2k = 4; -2k = -6; k = 3$

26. $kx + 3y = k + 1; 2k + 3(-3) = k + 1; 2k - 9 = k + 1; k = 10$

27. $kx + (k - 1)y = 5; 2k + (k - 1) = 5; 3k - 1 = 5; 3k = 6; k = 2$

28. $3x + 2y = k; 3(-1) + 2k = k; -3 + 2k = k; k = 3$

29. Graphs intersect and $(3, 2); 2(3) + 3(2) = 12; 2(3) - 2 = 4.$

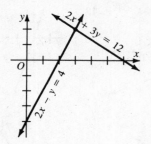

Ex. 29

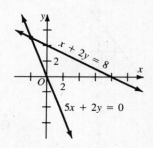

Ex. 30

30. Graphs intersect and $(-2, 5); -2 + 2(5) = 8; 5(-2) + 2(5) = 0.$

31. Graphs intersect at $(-3, -1); 5(-3) - 3(-1) + 12 = 0; -3 + 3(-1) + 6 = 0.$

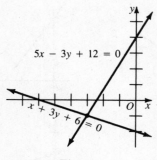

Ex. 31

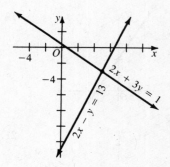

Ex. 32

32. Graphs intersect at $(5, -3); 2(5) - (-3) = 13; 2(5) + 3(-3) = 1.$

C 33. 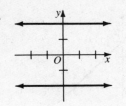   34. 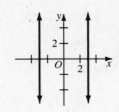   35.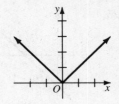

36. 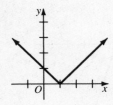   37. 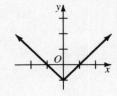   38.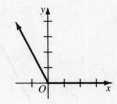

Pages 113-114 · WRITTEN EXERCISES

A 1. $\dfrac{9-3}{5-2}=2$ 2. $\dfrac{4-1}{0-3}=-1$ 3. $\dfrac{2-5}{3-(-1)}=-\dfrac{3}{4}$

4. $\dfrac{1-(-1)}{-3-3}=-\dfrac{1}{3}$ 5. vertical   6. $\dfrac{-4-(-2)}{-3-(-1)}=1$

7. $\dfrac{\dfrac{3}{2}-\dfrac{1}{2}}{1-3}=-\dfrac{1}{2}$ 8. $\dfrac{0-\left(-\dfrac{1}{2}\right)}{-2-0}=-\dfrac{1}{4}$ 9. vertical

10. $\dfrac{-3-1}{3-(-5)}=-\dfrac{1}{2}$ 11. $\dfrac{m-0}{1-0}=m$ 12. $\dfrac{d-b}{c-a}$ or $\dfrac{b-d}{a-c}$

13. $-\dfrac{A}{B}=-\dfrac{1}{1}=-1$ 14. $-\dfrac{A}{B}=-\dfrac{1}{-1}=1$ 15. $-\dfrac{A}{B}=-\dfrac{2}{-3}=\dfrac{2}{3}$

16. $5x+2y=-6$; $-\dfrac{A}{B}=-\dfrac{5}{2}$ 17. $6x+2y=3$; $-\dfrac{A}{B}=-\dfrac{6}{2}=-3$

18. $-\dfrac{A}{B}=-\dfrac{5}{5}=-1$ 19. $x-2y=4$; $-\dfrac{A}{B}=-\dfrac{1}{-2}=\dfrac{1}{2}$

20. $x=3-3y$; $x+3y=3$; $-\dfrac{A}{B}=-\dfrac{1}{3}$ 21. $2x+3y=6$; $-\dfrac{A}{B}=-\dfrac{2}{3}$

22. $x-3y=6$; $-\dfrac{A}{B}=-\dfrac{1}{-3}=\dfrac{1}{3}$ 23. $6x+ay=6a$; $-\dfrac{A}{B}=-\dfrac{6}{a}$

24. $x-ky=a$; $-\dfrac{A}{B}=-\dfrac{1}{-k}=\dfrac{1}{k}$

25-33. Points chosen may vary. Examples are given.

25.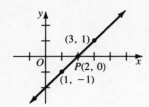

26.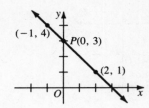

27.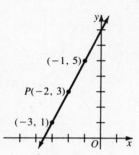

28.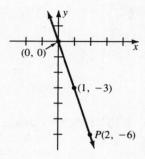

29.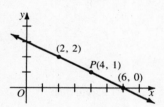

30.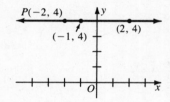

31.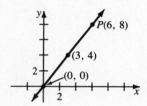

32.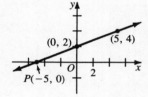

33.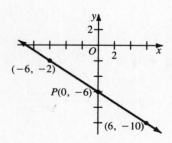

34. $\dfrac{6-10}{2-0} = -2$; $\dfrac{2-6}{4-2} = -2$; $\dfrac{-2-2}{6-4} = -2$; the points lie on a line with slope -2.

35. $\dfrac{-1-3}{0-(-3)} = -\dfrac{4}{3}$; $\dfrac{-3-(-1)}{3-0} = -\dfrac{2}{3}$; the points do not lie on a line.

36. $\dfrac{4 - 2}{2 - 1} = 2;\ \dfrac{8 - 4}{4 - 2} = 2;\ \dfrac{12 - 8}{8 - 4} = 1$; the points do not lie on a line.

37. $\dfrac{5 - 2}{2 - 0} = \dfrac{3}{2};\ \dfrac{8 - 5}{4 - 2} = \dfrac{3}{2};\ \dfrac{14 - 8}{8 - 4} = \dfrac{3}{2}$; the points lie on a line with slope $\dfrac{3}{2}$.

38. Let y = distance in kilometers; $\dfrac{y}{8} = 0.14$; $y = 1.12$; 1.12 km

39. Let x = distance in feet; $\dfrac{6}{x} = 0.2$; $x = 30$; 30 ft

40. $12x - ky = 5$; $-\dfrac{A}{B} = 3$; $-\dfrac{12}{-k} = 3$; $\dfrac{12}{k} = 3$; $k = 4$

41. $kx + 2y = 8$; $-\dfrac{A}{B} = -3$; $-\dfrac{k}{2} = -3$; $k = 6$

42. $kx + 2y = 6$; $-\dfrac{A}{B} = k + 1$; $-\dfrac{k}{2} = k + 1$; $-k = 2k + 2$; $-3k = 2$; $k = -\dfrac{2}{3}$

43. $(k + 6)x - 3y = 1$; $-\dfrac{A}{B} = k$; $-\dfrac{k + 6}{-3} = k$; $\dfrac{k + 6}{3} = k$; $k + 6 = 3k$; $2k = 6$; $k = 3$

44. $\dfrac{3k - k}{-1 - (-4)} = 4$; $\dfrac{2k}{3} = 4$; $k = 6$

45. $\dfrac{2 - k}{-3 - (k + 1)} = 2$; $\dfrac{2 - k}{-4 - k} = 2$; $2 - k = -8 - 2k$; $k = -10$

46. $\dfrac{k - 3k}{-2 - 2} = k + 2$; $\dfrac{-2k}{-4} = k + 2$; $\dfrac{k}{2} = k + 2$; $k = 2k + 4$; $k = -4$

47. $\dfrac{k + 4 - 3k}{k + 2 - k} = k$; $\dfrac{4 - 2k}{2} = k$; $2 - k = k$; $k = 1$

48. $\dfrac{k - |k|}{2} = -1$; $k - |k| = -2$; if $k \geq 0$, $|k| = k$ and $k - |k| = 0$; then $k < 0$;

    $k - |k| = -2$; $k - (-k) = -2$; $2k = -2$; $k = -1$

49. $\dfrac{k - |k|}{-2 - 2} = 2$; $\dfrac{k - |k|}{-4} = 2$; $k - |k| = -8$; if $k \geq 0$, $|k| = k$ and $k - |k| = 0$; then $k < 0$;

    $k - |k| = -8$; $k - (-k) = -8$; $2k = -8$; $k = -4$

50. $y - y_1 = m(x - x_1)$; $y - y_1 = mx - mx_1$; $mx - y = mx_1 - y_1$; $A = m$; $B = -1$;

    $C = mx_1 - y_1$

51. The coordinates of $P(x_1, y_1)$ satisfy the equation in Ex. 50 above; $m(x_1) - y_1 = mx_1 - y_1$

52. slope $= -\dfrac{A}{B} = -\dfrac{m}{-1} = m$

53. Since $P(x_1, y_1)$ and $Q(x', y')$ are points on a line with slope m, $\dfrac{y' - y_1}{x' - x_1} = m$.

54. The coordinates of $Q(x', y')$ satisfy the equation of L.

55. Through any two points there is exactly one line; both L and L' go through P and Q.

Page 114 · CHALLENGE

Let A, B, C, and D represent the people's ages, and let $A < B$? represent the question
"Beth, are you older than Alicia?". First ask the following two questions: $A < B$? $C < D$?
Then compare the two older people in each pair. For example, if $A < B$ and $C < D$, ask
$B < D$? From the answer to this question, you know who the oldest person is. Now compare
the younger person in the pair that contains the oldest person with each of the people in the
other pair. For example, if $B < D$, ask $C < B$? $C < A$? The answers to these two questions
determine the order of the ages. Thus 5 questions suffice to find the age order.

Pages 118-119 · WRITTEN EXERCISES

A   1. $\dfrac{y - 1}{x - 3} = 1;\ y - 1 = x - 3;\ x - y = 2$

    2. $\dfrac{y - 2}{x - 1} = -2;\ y - 2 = -2x + 2;\ 2x + y = 4$

    3. $\dfrac{y - 0}{x - 4} = -1;\ y = -x + 4;\ x + y = 4$

    4. Since $m = 0$, the graph is a horizontal line through $(-3, 2)$ and the line has equation
$y = 2.\ \left(\text{or } \dfrac{y - 2}{x - (-3)} = 0;\ y - 2 = 0;\ y = 2\right)$

    5. $\dfrac{y - (-5)}{x - (-3)} = -3;\ \dfrac{y + 5}{x + 3} = -3;\ y + 5 = -3x - 9;\ 3x + y = -14$

    6. $\dfrac{y - (-2)}{x - 6} = \dfrac{1}{2};\ \dfrac{y + 2}{x - 6} = \dfrac{1}{2};\ 2y + 4 = x - 6;\ x - 2y = 10$

    7. Since $m = 0$, the graph is a horizontal line through $(3, -4)$ and the line has equation
$y = -4.\ \left(\text{or } \dfrac{y - (-4)}{x - 3} = 0;\ y + 4 = 0;\ y = -4\right)$

    8. $\dfrac{y - 2}{x - (-3)} = -\dfrac{2}{3};\ \dfrac{y - 2}{x + 3} = -\dfrac{2}{3};\ 3y - 6 = -2x - 6;\ 2x + 3y = 0$

    9. A vertical line through $(-2, 6)$ has equation $x = -2$.

    10. A vertical line through $(-6, -5)$ has equation $x = -6$.

    11. $\dfrac{y - (-5)}{x - (-1)} = 0.2;\ \dfrac{y + 5}{x + 1} = \dfrac{1}{5};\ 5y + 25 = x + 1;\ x - 5y = 24$

    12. $\dfrac{y - 0}{x - (-3)} = -0.4;\ \dfrac{y}{x + 3} = -\dfrac{2}{5};\ 5y = -2x - 6;\ 2x + 5y = -6$

    13. $y = -2x + 1;\ 2x + y = 1$ 14. $y = x - 4;\ x - y = 4$

    15. $y = \dfrac{1}{2}x - 3;\ 2y = x - 6;\ x - 2y = 6$

16. $y = -\dfrac{2}{3}x + \dfrac{1}{3}$; $3y = -2x + 1$; $2x + 3y = 1$

17. $y = 0.4x + 1.2$; $y = \dfrac{2}{5}x + \dfrac{6}{5}$; $5y = 2x + 6$; $2x - 5y = -6$

18. $y = -1.5x + 2.5$; $y = -\dfrac{3}{2}x + \dfrac{5}{2}$; $2y = -3x + 5$; $3x + 2y = 5$

19. $b = 0$; $m = \dfrac{-3 - 0}{2 - 0} = -\dfrac{3}{2}$; $y = -\dfrac{3}{2}x + 0$; $2y = -3x$; $3x + 2y = 0$

20. $b = 0$; $m = \dfrac{2 - 0}{-4 - 0} = -\dfrac{1}{2}$; $y = -\dfrac{1}{2}x + 0$; $2y = -x$; $x + 2y = 0$

21. $b = -3$; $m = \dfrac{-3 - 0}{0 - 4} = \dfrac{3}{4}$; $y = \dfrac{3}{4}x - 3$; $4y = 3x - 12$; $3x - 4y = 12$

22. $b = 6$; $m = \dfrac{6 - 0}{0 - (-4)} = \dfrac{3}{2}$; $y = \dfrac{3}{2}x + 6$; $2y = 3x + 12$; $3x - 2y = -12$

23. $m = \dfrac{-3 - (-4)}{4 - 3} = 1$; $y - (-4) = 1(x - 3)$; $y + 4 = x - 3$; $x - y = 7$

24. The line contains two points with y-coordinate -2; its equation is $y = -2$.

25. The line contains two points with x-coordinate -1; its equation is $x = -1$.

26. The line contains two points with x-coordinate 3; its equation is $x = 3$.

27. $m = \dfrac{3 - (-3)}{3 - 1} = 3$; $y - (-3) = 3(x - 1)$; $y + 3 = 3x - 3$; $3x - y = 6$

28. $m = \dfrac{-4 - (-2)}{-3 - (-1)} = 1$; $y - (-2) = 1[x - (-1)]$; $y + 2 = x + 1$; $x - y = 1$

29. $m = \dfrac{\dfrac{1}{6} - \dfrac{2}{3}}{1 - \dfrac{1}{2}} = \dfrac{-\dfrac{3}{6}}{\dfrac{1}{2}} = -1$; $y - \dfrac{2}{3} = -1\left(x - \dfrac{1}{2}\right)$; $y - \dfrac{2}{3} = -x + \dfrac{1}{2}$; $x + y = \dfrac{7}{6}$;

$6x + 6y = 7$

30. $m = \dfrac{-\dfrac{2}{3} - \left(-\dfrac{1}{3}\right)}{1 - \dfrac{5}{3}} = \dfrac{-\dfrac{1}{3}}{-\dfrac{2}{3}} = \dfrac{1}{2}$; $y - \left(-\dfrac{1}{3}\right) = \dfrac{1}{2}\left(x - \dfrac{5}{3}\right)$; $y + \dfrac{1}{3} = \dfrac{1}{2}x - \dfrac{5}{6}$;

$6y + 2 = 3x - 5$; $3x - 6y = 7$

B **31.** slope of $L = -1$ **a.** $m = -1$; $y - 2 = -1(x - 0)$; $y - 2 = -x$; $x + y = 2$
b. $m = 1$; $y - 2 = 1(x - 0)$; $y - 2 = x$; $x - y = -2$

32. slope of $L = 1$ **a.** $m = 1$; $y - (-1) = 1(x - 0)$; $y + 1 = x$; $x - y = 1$
b. $m = -1$; $y - (-1) = -1(x - 0)$; $y + 1 = -x$; $x + y = -1$

33. slope of $L = 2$ **a.** $m = 2$; $y - (-3) = 2(x - 0)$; $y + 3 = 2x$; $2x - y = 3$

    b. $m = -\dfrac{1}{2}$; $y - (-3) = -\dfrac{1}{2}(x - 0)$; $2y + 6 = -x$; $x + 2y = -6$

34. slope of $L = -\dfrac{3}{2}$ **a.** $m = -\dfrac{3}{2}$; $y - 5 = -\dfrac{3}{2}(x - 0)$; $2y - 10 = -3x$; $3x + 2y = 10$

    b. $m = \dfrac{2}{3}$; $y - 5 = \dfrac{2}{3}(x - 0)$; $3y - 15 = 2x$; $2x - 3y = -15$

35. L is horizontal. **a.** A horizontal line through $(2, 5)$ has equation $y = 5$.
    b. A vertical line through $(2, 5)$ has equation $x = 2$.

36. L is vertical. **a.** A vertical line through $(-1, 3)$ has equation $x = -1$.
    b. A horizontal line through $(-1, 3)$ has equation $y = 3$.

37. slope of $L = -\dfrac{3}{5}$

    a. $m = -\dfrac{3}{5}$; $y - (-3) = -\dfrac{3}{5}(x - 2)$; $5y + 15 = -3x + 6$; $3x + 5y = -9$

    b. $m = \dfrac{5}{3}$; $y - (-3) = \dfrac{5}{3}(x - 2)$; $3y + 9 = 5x - 10$; $5x - 3y = 19$

38. slope of $L = \dfrac{1}{3}$ **a.** $m = \dfrac{1}{3}$; $y - 0 = \dfrac{1}{3}[x - (-5)]$; $3y = x + 5$; $x - 3y = -5$

    b. $m = -3$; $y - 0 = -3[x - (-5)]$; $y = -3x - 15$; $3x + y = -15$

39. slope of $L = \dfrac{3}{2}$ **a.** $m = \dfrac{3}{2}$; $y - 0 = \dfrac{3}{2}(x - 4)$; $2y = 3x - 12$; $3x - 2y = 12$

    b. $m = -\dfrac{2}{3}$; $y - 0 = -\dfrac{2}{3}(x - 4)$; $3y = -2x + 8$; $2x + 3y = 8$

40. slope of $L = \dfrac{1}{5}$ **a.** $m = \dfrac{1}{5}$; $y - 3 = \dfrac{1}{5}(x - 1)$; $5y - 15 = x - 1$; $x - 5y = -14$

    b. $m = -5$; $y - 3 = -5(x - 1)$; $y - 3 = -5x + 5$; $5x + y = 8$

41. slope of $\overleftrightarrow{AB} = \dfrac{1 - (-2)}{5 - 4} = 3$; slope of $\overleftrightarrow{DC} = \dfrac{3 - 0}{0 - (-1)} = 3$; $\overleftrightarrow{AB} \| \overleftrightarrow{DC}$; slope of

    $\overleftrightarrow{AD} = \dfrac{0 - (-2)}{-1 - 4} = -\dfrac{2}{5}$; slope of $\overleftrightarrow{BC} = \dfrac{3 - 1}{0 - 5} = -\dfrac{2}{5}$; $\overleftrightarrow{AD} \| \overleftrightarrow{BC}$; $ABCD$ is a

    parallelogram; $-\dfrac{2}{5} \neq -\dfrac{1}{3}$ so $\overleftrightarrow{AD}$ is not perpendicular to $\overleftrightarrow{AB}$; $ABCD$ is not a rectangle.

42. slope of $\overleftrightarrow{AB} = \dfrac{-2 - 2}{0 - (-2)} = -2$; slope of $\overleftrightarrow{DC} = \dfrac{2 - 6}{6 - 4} = -2$; $\overleftrightarrow{AB} \| \overleftrightarrow{DC}$; slope of

    $\overleftrightarrow{AD} = \dfrac{6 - 2}{4 - (-2)} = \dfrac{2}{3}$; slope of $\overleftrightarrow{BC} = \dfrac{2 - (-2)}{6 - 0} = \dfrac{2}{3}$; $\overleftrightarrow{AD} \| \overleftrightarrow{BC}$; $ABCD$ is a parallelogram;

    $\dfrac{2}{3} \neq \dfrac{1}{2}$ so $\overleftrightarrow{AD}$ is not perpendicular to $\overleftrightarrow{AB}$; $ABCD$ is not a rectangle.

43. slope of $\overleftrightarrow{AB} = \dfrac{4 - 1}{3 - 4} = -3$; slope of $\overleftrightarrow{DC} = \dfrac{2 - (-2)}{-4 - (-3)} = -4$; $\overleftrightarrow{AB}$ and $\overleftrightarrow{DC}$ are not parallel; $ABCD$ is not a parallelogram.

44. $\overleftrightarrow{AB}$ and $\overleftrightarrow{DC}$ are horizontal; $\overleftrightarrow{AD}$ and $\overleftrightarrow{BC}$ are vertical; $ABCD$ is a parallelogram; $ABCD$ is a rectangle.

45. slope of $\overleftrightarrow{AB} = \dfrac{6-1}{1-8} = -\dfrac{5}{7}$; slope of $\overleftrightarrow{DC} = \dfrac{-2-(-3)}{-2-5} = -\dfrac{1}{7}$; $\overleftrightarrow{AB}$ and $\overleftrightarrow{DC}$ are not parallel; $ABCD$ is not a parallelogram.

46. slope of $\overleftrightarrow{AB} = \dfrac{5-1}{5-6} = -4$; slope of $\overleftrightarrow{DC} = \dfrac{3-(-1)}{-4-(-2)} = -2$; $\overleftrightarrow{AB}$ and $\overleftrightarrow{DC}$ are not parallel; $ABCD$ is not a parallelogram.

47-48. Note that $m_1 = $ slope of $L_1 = -\dfrac{A_1}{B_1}$ and $m_2 = $ slope of $L_2 = -\dfrac{A_2}{B_2}$ and that B_1 and B_2 are both nonzero.

47. If $A_1B_2 = A_2B_1$, then $\dfrac{A_1B_2}{-B_1B_2} = \dfrac{A_2B_1}{-B_1B_2} (B_1 \neq 0, B_2 \neq 0)$; $-\dfrac{A_1}{B_1} = -\dfrac{A_2}{B_2}$; $m_1 = m_2$; L_1

and L_2 are parallel. If L_1 and L_2 are parallel, $m_1 = m_2$; $-\dfrac{A_1}{B_1} = -\dfrac{A_2}{B_2}$; $\dfrac{A_1}{B_1} = \dfrac{A_2}{B_2}$; $A_1B_2 = A_2B_1$.

48. If $A_1A_2 + B_1B_2 = 0$, $A_1A_2 = -B_1B_2$; $\dfrac{A_1A_2}{A_2B_1} = -\dfrac{B_1B_2}{A_2B_1}$ (since $A_1A_2 = -B_1B_2 \neq 0$,

$A_2 \neq 0$); $\dfrac{A_1}{B_1} = -\dfrac{B_2}{A_2}$; $m_1 = -\dfrac{1}{m_2}$; L_1 and L_2 are perpendicular. If L_1 and L_2 are per-

pendicular, $m_1 = -\dfrac{1}{m_2}$; $-\dfrac{A_1}{B_1} = \dfrac{B_2}{A_2} - A_2B_1\left(-\dfrac{A_1}{B_1}\right) = -A_2B_1\left(\dfrac{B_2}{A_2}\right)$; $A_1A_2 = -B_1B_2$;

$A_1A_2 + B_1B_2 = 0$.

49. slope $= \dfrac{y_2 - y_1}{x_2 - x_1}$; using point-slope form, the equation is $y - y_1 = \dfrac{y_2 - y_1}{x_2 - x_1}(x - x_1)$

50. The line contains $(a, 0)$ and $(0, b)$; $m = \dfrac{b-0}{0-a} = \dfrac{b}{-a} = -\dfrac{b}{a}$; using the slope-intercept

form, the equation is $y = -\dfrac{b}{a}x + b$; $\dfrac{y}{b} = -\dfrac{x}{a} + 1$; $\dfrac{x}{a} + \dfrac{y}{b} = 1$.

51. a. $0 = (A_1x + B_1y - C_1) + k(A_2x + B_2y - C_2) = A_1x + B_1y - C_1 + kA_2x + kB_2y - kC_2$; $0 = (A_1 + kA_2)x + (B_1 + kB_2)y - (C_1 + kC_2)$; $(A_1 + kA_2)x + (B_1 + kB_2)y = C_1 + kC_2$; the graph of the equation is a line.

b. Let $Q = (x', y')$; since Q is on L_1 and L_2, $A_1x' + B_1y' = C_1$ and $A_2x' + B_2y' = C_2$; then $kA_2x' + kB_2y' = kC_2$ and $A_1x' + B_1y' + kA_2x' + kB_2y' = C_1 + kC_2$; $(A_1 + kA_2)x' + (B_1 + kB_2)y = C_1 + kC_2$; thus the line passes through Q.

52. First find k such that $3x + 4y - 7 + k(x + 3y - 4) = 0$ contains $(3, 0)$; $3(3) + 4(0) - 7 + k[3 + 3(0) - 4] = 0$; $9 - 7 + 3k - 4k = 0$; $k = 2$; $3x + 4y - 7 + 2(x + 3y - 4) = 0$; $3x + 4y - 7 + 2x + 6y - 8 = 0$; $5x + 10y - 15 = 0$; $x + 2y - 3 = 0$; the line $x + 2y - 3 = 0$ passes through P and Q.

53. First find k such that $6x - 3y + 2 + k(5x + 2y + 2) = 0$ contains $(0, -2)$;

$6(0) - 3(-2) + 2 + k[5(0) + 2(-2) + 2] = 0$; $6 + 2 - 4k + 2k = 0$; $2k = 8$; $k = 4$;

$6x - 3y + 2 + 4(5x + 2y + 2) = 0$; $6x - 3y + 2 + 20x + 8y + 8 = 0$;

$26x + 5y + 10 = 0$; the line $26x + 5y + 10 = 0$ passes through P and Q.

54. First find k such that $2x - 5y - 6 + k(3x + 2y + 4) = 0$ contains $(0, 0)$;

$2(0) - 5(0) - 6 + k[3(0) + 2(0) + 4] = 0$; $-6 + 4k = 0$; $k = \dfrac{3}{2}$;

$2x - 5y - 6 + \dfrac{3}{2}(3x + 2y + 4) = 0$; $4x - 10y - 12 + 3(3x + 2y + 4) = 0$;

$4x - 10y - 12 + 9x + 6y + 12 = 0$; $13x - 4y = 0$; the line $13x - 4y = 0$ passes through P and Q.

Pages 119-120 · COMPUTER EXERCISES

1. 10 PRINT "ENTER X1, Y1, X2, Y2"
20 INPUT X1, Y1, X2, Y2
30 IF X1 = X2 THEN 70
40 LET M = (Y2 − Y1)/(X2 − X1)
50 PRINT "SLOPE = "; M
60 GOTO 80
70 PRINT "LINE IS VERTICAL"
80 END

2. a. 4.5   **b.** −2.28571429   **c.** vertical   **d.** 1.95555556

3. 10 PRINT "ENTER M, X, Y"
20 INPUT M, X, Y
30 LET B = Y − M * X
40 PRINT "Y = "; M "X + "; B
50 END

4. Y = 1.72X + 17.2

5. 10 PRINT "ENTER X1, Y1, X2, Y2"
20 INPUT X1, Y1, X2, Y2
30 IF X1 = X2 THEN 80
40 LET M = (Y2 − Y1)/(X2 − X1)
50 LET B = Y1 − M * X1
60 PRINT "Y = "; M; "X + "; B
70 GOTO 90
80 PRINT "X = "; X1
90 END

6. a. Y = 4.5X − 14.5   **b.** Y = −2.28571429X − 4.42857143
c. X = 7   **d.** Y = 1.95555556X − 259.755556

Pages 125-126 · WRITTEN EXERCISES

A
1. $3x + 2y = 8$ $9x + 6y = 24$ $11x = 44; x = 4; 4 - 3y = 10; -3y = 6;$
   $x - 3y = 10$; $2x - 6y = 20$;

   $y = -2; (4, -2)$

2. $4x + y = 5$ $8x + 2y = 10$ $11x = 22; x = 2; 4(2) + y = 5; 8 + y = 5;$
   $3x - 2y = 12$; $3x - 2y = 12$;

   $y = -3; (2, -3)$

3. $5x - 2y = 4$ $-10x + 4y = -8$ $-7x = -14; x = 2; 5(2) - 2y = 4;$
   $3x - 4y = -6$; $3x - 4y = -6$;

   $10 - 2y = 4; -2y = -6; y = 3; (2, 3)$

4. $6x + 5y = -2$ $6x + 5y = -2$ $-4y = -20; y = 5; 6x + 5(5) = -2;$
   $2x + 3y = 6$; $-6x - 9y = -18$;

   $6x + 25 = -2; 6x = -27; x = -4\frac{1}{2}; \left(-4\frac{1}{2}, 5\right)$

5. $2x + 3y = 4$ $10x + 15y = 20$ $7y = 14; y = 2; 2x + 3(2) = 4;$
   $5x + 4y = 3$; $-10x - 8y = -6$;

   $2x + 6 = 4; 2x = -2; x = -1; (-1, 2)$

6. $5x - 2y = 17$ $15x - 6y = 51$ $19x = 57; x = 3; 5(3) - 2y = 17;$
   $2x + 3y = 3$; $4x + 6y = 6$;

   $15 - 2y = 17; -2y = 2; y = -1; (3, -1)$

7. $2x - 7y = 8$ $6x - 21y = 24$ $-13y = 26; y = -2; 2x - 7(-2) = 8;$
   $3x - 4y = -1$; $-6x + 8y = 2$;

   $2x + 14 = 8; 2x = -6; x = -3; (-3, -2)$

8. $3x + 4y = -8$ $6x + 8y = -16$ $-7y = -7; y = 1; 3x + 4(1) = -8;$
   $2x + 5y = -3$; $-6x - 15y = 9$;

   $3x + 4 = -8; 3x = -12; x = -4; (-4, 1)$

9. $2x - 7y = 32$ $-6x + 21y = -96$ $26y = -104; y = -4; 2x - 7(-4) = 32;$
   $6x + 5y = -8$; $6x + 5y = -8$;

   $2x + 28 = 32; 2x = 4; x = 2; (2, -4)$

10. $u + 3v = 17$ $u = -3v + 17; 3(-3v + 17) - 2v = -4; -9v + 51 - 2v = -4;$
    $3u - 2v = -4$;

    $-11v = -55; v = 5; u = -3(5) + 17 = -15 + 17 = 2; (2, 5)$

11. $5s + 9t = -6$ $15s + 27t = -18$ $7t = -28; t = -4; 5s + 9(-4) = -6;$
    $3s + 4t = 2$; $-15s - 20t = -10$;

    $5s - 36 = -6; 5s = 30; s = 6; (6, -4)$

12. $3x - 8y = -3$ $\quad$ $6x - 16y = -6$
$ \dfrac{2x - 3y = 5}{}$; $\quad$ $\dfrac{-6x + 9y = -15}{}$; $\quad$ $-7y = -21; y = 3; 3x - 8(3) = -3;$

$ 3x - 24 = -3; 3x = 21; x = 7; (7, 3)$

13. inconsistent

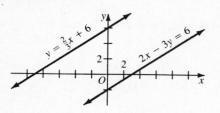

14. consistent

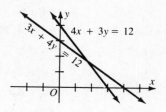

15. consistent

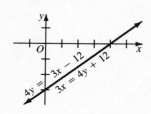

16. consistent

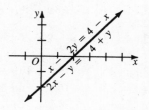

17. $4x = 5y - 5; 5y = 4x + 5; y = \dfrac{4}{5}x + 1; 4y = 5x + 2; y = \dfrac{5}{4}x + \dfrac{1}{2}$; the graphs have different slopes; they are not parallel so they must intersect; then the system has a solution and the equations are consistent.

18. $y - 1 = 4x; y = 4x + 1; y - 5 = 3x; y = 3x + 5$; the graphs have different slopes; they are not parallel so they must intersect; then the system has a solution and the equations are consistent.

19. $6x + y = 7; y = -6x + 7; 6x + y = 2; y = -6x + 2$; since the graphs have the same slope but different y-intercepts, the graphs are parallel; the system has no solution and the equations are inconsistent.

20. $\dfrac{1}{2}x - y = 10; y = \dfrac{1}{2}x - 10; -x + \dfrac{1}{2}y = 8; \dfrac{1}{2}y = x + 8; y = 2x + 16$; the graphs have different slopes; they are not parallel so they must intersect; then the system has a solution and the equations are consistent.

21. $3x + 5y = 6$ $\quad$ $9x + 15y = 18$
$ \dfrac{2x - 3y = 4}{}$; $\quad$ $\dfrac{10x - 15y = 20}{}$; $\quad$ $19x = 38; x = 2; 3(2) + 5y = 6; 6 + 5y = 6;$

$ 5y = 0; y = 0; (2, 0)$

22. $3u - 2v = -6$ $\quad$ $-21u + 14v = 42$
$ \dfrac{21u - 14v = -39}{}$; $\quad$ $\dfrac{21u - 14v = -39}{}$; $\quad$ $0 = 3;$ no solution

23. $6x - 9y = -21$ $12x - 18y = -42$
    $4x - 6y = -14$; $-12x + 18y = 42$; $0 = 0; \{(x, y): 2x - 3y = -7\};$

    examples: $\left(0, \dfrac{7}{3}\right), \left(-\dfrac{1}{2}, 2\right), (1, 3)$

24. $u - 7v = -4$ $u - 7v = -4$
    $7u - v = -4$; $-49u + 7v = 28$; $-48u = 24;\ u = -\dfrac{1}{2};\ -\dfrac{1}{2} - 7v = -4;$

    $-7v = -\dfrac{7}{2};\ v = \dfrac{1}{2};\ \left(-\dfrac{1}{2}, \dfrac{1}{2}\right)$

25. $16s - 6t = 3$ $32s - 12t = 6$
    $6s - 4t = -5$; $-18s + 12t = 15$; $14s = 21;\ s = \dfrac{3}{2};\ 16\left(\dfrac{3}{2}\right) - 6t = 3;$

    $24 - 6t = 3;\ -6t = -21;\ t = \dfrac{7}{2};\ \left(\dfrac{3}{2}, \dfrac{7}{2}\right)$

26. $3p + q = 1$ $3p + q = 1$
    $-p + 3q = 1$; $-3p + 9q = 3$; $10q = 4;\ q = \dfrac{2}{5};\ 3p + \dfrac{2}{5} = 1;\ 3p = \dfrac{3}{5};$

    $p = \dfrac{1}{5};\ \left(\dfrac{1}{5}, \dfrac{2}{5}\right)$

27. $2x - 2y = 5 + 2y$ $2x - 4y = 5$ $2x - 4y = 5$
    $2x + 2y = 5 - 2x$; $4x + 2y = 5$; $8x + 4y = 10$; $10x = 15;\ x = \dfrac{3}{2};$

    $2\left(\dfrac{3}{2}\right) - 4y = 5;\ 3 - 4y = 5;\ -4y = 2;\ y = -\dfrac{1}{2};\ \left(\dfrac{3}{2}, -\dfrac{1}{2}\right)$

28. $2x - 6 = 3y + 6$ $2x - 3y = 12$
    $2x + 6 = 3y + 18$; $2x - 3y = 12$; $\{(x, y): 2x - 3y = 12\};$

    examples: $(0, -4), (6, 0), (3, -2)$

29. $x + y = 4y - 8$ $x - 3y = -8$ $x - 3y = -8$
    $x - y = 2y + 8$; $x - 3y = 8$; $-x + 3y = -8$; $0 = -16;$ no solution

30. $x - 5y = 1$ $x - 5y = 1$
    $x + y = -1$; $5x + 5y = -5$; $6x = -4;\ x = -\dfrac{2}{3};\ -\dfrac{2}{3} - 5y = 1;$

    $-5y = \dfrac{5}{3};\ y = -\dfrac{1}{3};\ \left(-\dfrac{2}{3}, -\dfrac{1}{3}\right)$

31. $2x - 3y = 3x + 3y - 6$ $-x - 6y = -6$
    $3x - 2y = 2x + 2y - 6$; $x - 4y = -6$; $-10y = -12;\ y = \dfrac{6}{5};$

    $-x - 6\left(\dfrac{6}{5}\right) = -6;\ -x - \dfrac{36}{5} = -6;\ -x = \dfrac{6}{5};\ x = -\dfrac{6}{5};\ \left(-\dfrac{6}{5}, \dfrac{6}{5}\right)$

32. $5x + 2y = 3x - 3y + 6$ $2x + 5y = 6$ $2x + 5y = 6$
    $2x - 5y = 3x + 3y - 6$; $-x - 8y = -6$; $-2x - 16y = -12$;

    $-11y = -6;\ y = \dfrac{6}{11};\ 2x + 5\left(\dfrac{6}{11}\right) = 6;\ 2x + \dfrac{30}{11} = 6;\ 2x = \dfrac{36}{11};\ x = \dfrac{18}{11};\ \left(\dfrac{18}{11}, \dfrac{6}{11}\right)$

B **33.** Let $x = \dfrac{1}{u}$ and $y = \dfrac{1}{v}$; $\dfrac{6x + 3y = 2}{2x - 9y = 4}$; $\dfrac{18x + 9y = 6}{2x - 9y = 4}$; $\quad 20x = 10$; $x = \dfrac{1}{2}$;

$2\left(\dfrac{1}{2}\right) - 9y = 4$; $1 - 9y = 4$; $-9y = 3$; $y = -\dfrac{1}{3}$; $\dfrac{1}{2} = \dfrac{1}{u}$; $u = 2$; $-\dfrac{1}{3} = \dfrac{1}{v}$; $v = -3$

$(2, -3)$

34. Let $x = \dfrac{1}{u}$ and $y = \dfrac{1}{v}$; $\dfrac{2x + y = 4}{4x + 3y = 11}$; $\dfrac{-4x - 2y = -8}{4x + 3y = 11}$; $\quad y = 3$; $2x + 3 = 4$

$2x = 1$; $x = \dfrac{1}{2}$; $\dfrac{1}{2} = \dfrac{1}{u}$; $u = 2$; $3 = \dfrac{1}{v}$; $v = \dfrac{1}{3}$; $\left(2, \dfrac{1}{3}\right)$

35. Let $x = \dfrac{1}{u}$ and $y = \dfrac{1}{v}$; $\dfrac{3x + 8y = 1}{5x + 4y = 1}$; $\dfrac{3x + 8y = 1}{-10x - 8y = -2}$; $\quad -7x = -1$; $x = \dfrac{1}{7}$

$3\left(\dfrac{1}{7}\right) + 8y = 1$; $\dfrac{3}{7} + 8y = 1$; $8y = \dfrac{4}{7}$; $y = \dfrac{1}{14}$; $\dfrac{1}{7} = \dfrac{1}{u}$; $u = 7$; $\dfrac{1}{14} = \dfrac{1}{v}$; $v = 14$

$(7, 14)$

36. Let $x = \dfrac{1}{u}$ and $y = \dfrac{1}{v}$; $\dfrac{6x + 5y = 1}{3x - 10y = 3}$; $\dfrac{12x + 10y = 2}{3x - 10y = 3}$; $\quad 15x = 5$; $x = \dfrac{1}{3}$;

$3\left(\dfrac{1}{3}\right) - 10y = 3$; $1 - 10y = 3$; $-10y = 2$; $y = -\dfrac{1}{5}$; $\dfrac{1}{3} = \dfrac{1}{u}$; $u = 3$; $-\dfrac{1}{5} = \dfrac{1}{v}$

$v = -5$; $(3, -5)$

37. Let $x = \dfrac{1}{u}$ and $y = \dfrac{1}{v}$; $\dfrac{x - y = 5}{5x + 3y = -3}$; $\dfrac{3x - 3y = 15}{5x + 3y = -3}$; $\quad 8x = 12$; $x = \dfrac{3}{2}$;

$\dfrac{3}{2} - y = 5$; $-y = \dfrac{7}{2}$; $y = -\dfrac{7}{2}$; $\dfrac{3}{2} = \dfrac{1}{u}$; $u = \dfrac{2}{3}$; $-\dfrac{7}{2} = \dfrac{1}{v}$; $v = -\dfrac{2}{7}$; $\left(\dfrac{2}{3}, -\dfrac{2}{7}\right)$

38. Let $x = \dfrac{1}{u}$ and $y = \dfrac{1}{v}$; $\dfrac{5x + 2y = 5}{7x - 2y = -1}$; $\quad 12x = 4$; $x = \dfrac{1}{3}$; $5\left(\dfrac{1}{3}\right) + 2y = 5$;

$\dfrac{5}{3} + 2y = 5$; $2y = \dfrac{10}{3}$; $y = \dfrac{5}{3}$; $\dfrac{1}{3} = \dfrac{1}{u}$; $u = 3$; $\dfrac{5}{3} = \dfrac{1}{v}$; $v = \dfrac{3}{5}$; $\left(3, \dfrac{3}{5}\right)$

39. $\dfrac{A + 3B = 13}{4A - B = 13}$; $\dfrac{A + 3B = 13}{12A - 3B = 39}$; $\quad 13A = 52$; $A = 4$; $4 + 3B = 13$; $3B = 9$;

$B = 3$; $(4, 3)$

40. $\dfrac{-3A + B = -17}{2A + 5B = -17}$; $\dfrac{-6A + 2B = -34}{6A + 15B = -51}$; $\quad 17B = -85$; $B = -5$;

$-3A - 5 = -17$; $-3A = -12$; $A = 4$; $(4, -5)$

41. $\dfrac{-3 = A + B}{5 = 9A + B}$; $\dfrac{-A - B = 3}{9A + B = 5}$; $\quad 8A = 8$; $A = 1$; $-3 = 1 + B$; $B = -4$; $(1, -4$

42. $\dfrac{2 = 4A + 2B}{-18 = 9A - 3B}$; $\dfrac{4A + 2B = 2}{6A - 2B = -12}$; $\quad 10A = -10$; $A = -1$; $2 = 4(-1) + 2B$

$2 = -4 + 2B$; $2B = 6$; $B = 3$; $(-1, 3)$

43. $ax + y = b$ $ax + y = b$ $(a - b)x = b - a$; if $a \neq b$, $x = -1$;
$bx + y = a$; $-bx - y = -a$;

$-a + y = b$; $y = a + b$; if $a \neq b$, the system has the unique solution $(-1, a + b)$

44. $ax - by = c$ $a^2x - aby = ac$ $(a^2 + b^2)x = ac + bd$; if a and b are not both
$bx + ay = d$; $\quad b^2x + aby = bd$;

zero, $x = \dfrac{ac + bd}{a^2 + b^2}$; $a\left(\dfrac{ac + bd}{a^2 + b^2}\right) - by = c$; $-by = c - \dfrac{a^2c + abd}{a^2 + b^2} =$

$\dfrac{a^2c + b^2c - a^2c - abd}{a^2 + b^2} = \dfrac{b^2c - abd}{a^2 + b^2}$; $y = \dfrac{ad - bc}{a^2 + b^2}$; if a and b are not both zero,

the system has the unique solution $\left(\dfrac{ac + bd}{a^2 + b^2}, \dfrac{ad - bc}{a^2 + b^2}\right)$.

45. $ax + by = e$ $adx + bdy = de$ $(ad - bc)x = de - bf$; if $ad \neq bc$,
$cx + dy = f$; $\quad -bcx - bdy = -bf$;

$x = \dfrac{de - bf}{ad - bc}$; $a\left(\dfrac{de - bf}{ad - bc}\right) + by = e$; $by = e - \dfrac{ade - abf}{ad - bc} =$

$\dfrac{ade - bce - ade + abf}{ad - bc} = \dfrac{abf - bce}{ad - bc}$; $y = \dfrac{af - ce}{ad - bc}$; if $ad \neq bc$ the system has the

unique solution $\left(\dfrac{de - bf}{ad - bc}, \dfrac{af - ce}{ad - bc}\right)$

46. $y = mx + b_1$ $y = mx + b_1$ $0 = b_1 - b_2$, but $b_1 \neq b_2$ so the system has
$y = mx + b_2$; $\quad -y = -mx - b_2$;

no solution.

47. $m_1x - y = -b_1$ $m_1x - y = -b_1$ $(m_1 - m_2)x = -b_1 + b_2$; if $m_1 \neq m_2$,
$m_2x - y = -b_2$; $\quad -m_2x + y = b_2$;

$x = \dfrac{b_2 - b_1}{m_1 - m_2}$; $m_1\left(\dfrac{b_2 - b_1}{m_1 - m_2}\right) - y = -b_1$; $-y = -b_1 - \dfrac{m_1b_2 - m_1b_1}{m_1 - m_2}$;

$y = \dfrac{m_1b_1 - m_2b_1 + m_1b_2 - m_1b_1}{m_1 - m_2} = \dfrac{m_1b_2 - m_2b_1}{m_1 - m_2}$; if $m_1 \neq m_2$, the system has the

unique solution $\left(\dfrac{b_2 - b_1}{m_1 - m_2}, \dfrac{m_1b_2 - m_2b_1}{m_1 - m_2}\right)$; that is, L_1 and L_2 have a common solution.

Pages 128-130 · PROBLEMS

1. Let l = length in centimeters and w = width in centimeters;
$2l + 2w = 18$ $l + w = 9$
$l - w = 5$; $\quad l - w = 5$; $2l = 14$; $l = 7$; $7 - w = 5$; $w = 2$; 7 cm by 2 cm

2. Let w = number of women, m = number of men;
$w + m = 137$
$w - m = 11$; $2w = 148$; $w = 74$; $74 - m = 11$; $m = 63$; 63 men, 74 women

3. Let x = length in centimeters of the sides of the shorter-legged triangle, and y th

length of the bases; $\dfrac{2x + y = 21}{4x + y = 37}$; $\dfrac{-2x - y = -21}{4x + y = 37}$; $2x = 16$; $x = 8$;

$2(8) + y = 21$; $16 + y = 21$; $y = 5$; 8 cm, 8 cm, 5 cm and 16 cm, 16 cm, 5 cm

4. Let x = measure in degrees of each base angle and y = measure of vertex angle;

$\dfrac{2x + y = 180}{2x - y = 36}$; $4x = 216$; $x = 54$; $2(54) + y = 180$; $108 + y = 180$; $y = 72$; 54

54°, 72°

5. Let x = number of round trips made by smaller truck and y = number made by large

$\dfrac{x + y = 20}{12x + 15y = 273}$; $\dfrac{-12x - 12y = -240}{12x + 15y = 273}$; $3y = 33$; $y = 11$; $x + 11 = 20$;

$x = 9$; the smaller truck made 9 trips, the larger, 11 trips

6. Let g = number of glasses of lemonade sold and c = number of cookies;

$\dfrac{35g + 25c = 350}{30g + 30c = 360}$; $\dfrac{7g + 5c = 70}{-5g - 5c = -60}$; $2g = 10$; $g = 5$; $35(5) + 25c = 350$;

$175 + 25c = 350$; $25c = 175$; $c = 7$; 5 lemonades, 7 cookies

7. Let w = wind speed and a = air speed in kilometers per hour;

$\dfrac{2(a + w) = 120}{2.5(a - w) = 120}$; $\dfrac{a + w = 60}{a - w = 48}$; $2a = 108$; $a = 54$; $54 + w = 60$; $w = 6$;

plane's air speed = 54 km/h; wind speed = 6 km/h

8. Let w = wind speed and a = air speed in kilometers per hour;

$\dfrac{5(a - w) = 500}{\dfrac{25}{6}(a + w) = 500}$; $\dfrac{a - w = 100}{a + w = 120}$; $2a = 220$; $a = 110$; $a - w = 100$; $w = 1$

plane's air speed = 110 km/h; wind speed = 10 km/h

9. Let e = cost in cents of a dozen eggs and m = cost in cents of a carton of milk;

$\dfrac{4m + 3e = 485}{5m + 2e = 440}$; $\dfrac{8m + 6e = 970}{-15m + 6e = -1320}$; $-7m = -350$; $m = 50$;

$4(50) + 3e = 485$; $200 + 3e = 485$; $3e = 285$; $e = 95$; a carton of milk costs 50¢, a doze

eggs, 95¢

10. Let d = distance in miles and s = speed in miles per hour;

$\dfrac{2.5(s - 10) = d}{1.5(s + 10) = d}$; $\dfrac{2.5s - 25 = d}{1.5s + 15 = d}$; $\dfrac{2.5s - 25 = d}{-1.5s - 15 = -d}$; $s - 40 = 0$; $s = 4$

$2.5(40) - 25 = d$; $100 - 25 = d$; $d = 75$; speed of ultralight = 40 mph; distance to nex

town = 75 mi

11. Let x = number of milliliters of 60% solution and y = number of milliliters of 40%

solution; $\begin{array}{l} x + y = 200 \\ 0.60x + 0.40y = 0.48(200) \end{array}$; $\begin{array}{l} x + y = 200 \\ 60x + 40y = 9600 \end{array}$;

$\begin{array}{l} -40x - 40y = -8000 \\ 60x + 40y = 9600 \end{array}$; $20x = 1600; x = 80; 80 + y = 200; y = 120; 80$ mL of 60%

solution; 120 mL of 40% solution

12. Let x = number of kilograms of 45% compound, y = number of kilograms of 70%

compound; $\begin{array}{l} x + y = 10 \\ 0.45x + 0.70y = 0.60(10) \end{array}$; $\begin{array}{l} x + y = 10 \\ 45x + 70y = 600 \end{array}$;

$\begin{array}{l} -45x - 45y = -450 \\ 45x + 70y = 600 \end{array}$; $25y = 150; y = 6; x + 6 = 10; x = 4; 4$ kg of

45% compound; 6 kg of 70% compound

13. $\begin{array}{l} 25 = v_0 + 5a \\ 33 = v_0 + 7a \end{array}$; $\begin{array}{l} -25 = -v_0 - 5a \\ 33 = v_0 + 7a \end{array}$; $2a = 8; a = 4; 25 = v_0 + 5(4); 25 = v_0 + 20;$

$v_0 = 5$

14. Let x = cost in tiaras for first 30 g and y = cost for each additional 10 g or fraction

thereof; $\begin{array}{l} x + 2y = 312 \\ x + 5y = 600 \end{array}$; $\begin{array}{l} -x - 2y = -312 \\ x + 5y = 600 \end{array}$; $3y = 288; y = 96;$

$x + 2(96) = 312; x + 192 = 312; x = 120; 117 = 30 + 8.7(10);$

$120 + 9(96) = 120 + 864 = 984; 984$ tiaras

15. Let w = walking rate and r = riding rate in kilometers per hour;

$\begin{array}{l} \dfrac{r}{2} + \dfrac{w}{3} = 9.5 \\[2mm] \dfrac{r}{6} + \dfrac{7w}{6} = 9.5 \end{array}$; $\begin{array}{l} 3r + 2w = 57 \\ -3r - 21w = -171 \end{array}$; $-19w = -114; w = 6; 3r + 2(6) = 57;$

$3r + 12 = 57; 3r = 45; r = 15;$ walking rate = 6 km/h; riding rate = 15 km/h

16. Let a, b, and c be the amounts in dollars Alan, Betty, and Chris have, respectively;

$\begin{array}{l} a + b + c = 31 \\ a - b = 3; \\ c - (a + b) = 1 \end{array}$ $\begin{array}{l} a + b + c = 31 \\ a + b - c = -1 \end{array}$; $2a + 2b = 30;$ $\begin{array}{l} a + b = 15 \\ a - b = 3 \end{array}$;

$2a = 18; a = 9; 9 - b = 3; b = 6; c - (9 + 6) = 1; c - 15 = 1; c = 16;$ Alan has \$9,

Betty has \$6, and Chris has \$16.

17. Let p, n, d, and q be the numbers of pennies, nickels, dimes, and quarters, respectively;

$p = 2n$ and $d = q + 2;$ $p + n + d + q = 30;$ $2n + n + q + 2 + q = 30;$

$3n + 2q = 28;$ also, $2n + 5n + 10(q + 2) + 25q = 237; 7n + 35q = 217;$

$\begin{array}{l} 3n + 2q = 28 \\ 7n + 35q = 237 \end{array}$; $\begin{array}{l} -21n - 14q = -196 \\ 21n + 105q = 651 \end{array}$; $91q = 455; q = 5; d = 5 + 2 = 7;$

$3n + 2(5) = 28; 3n + 10 = 28; 3n = 18; n = 6; p = 2(6) = 12; 12$ pennies, 6 nickels,

7 dimes, 5 quarters

18. Let a = plane's air speed in kilometers per hour and t = time for first leg of trip;

$$t\left(a - \frac{a}{10}\right) = 495 \qquad\qquad t\left(\frac{9}{10}a\right) = 495 \qquad\qquad at = 550$$

$$(5 - t)\left(a + \frac{a}{10}\right) = 495 \;;\quad (5 - t)\left(\frac{11a}{10}\right) = 495 \;;\quad 55a - 11at = 4950 \;;$$

$$\frac{11at = 6050}{55a - 11at = 4950}\;;\quad 55a = 11{,}000;\; a = 200;\; 200 \text{ km/h}$$

19. $\frac{1}{4}x + 4 = \frac{1}{2}x$; $\frac{1}{4}x = 4$; $x = 16$; $\frac{1}{2}x = 8$; the break-even point is $(16, 8000)$; for $x > 16$, $R - C$ = profit

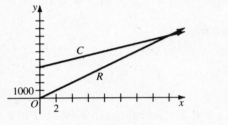

Ex. 19

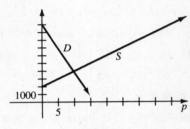

Ex. 20

20. $0.2p + 2 = -0.6p + 10$; $0.8p = 8$; $p = 10$ = the equilibrium price; at prices greater than the equilibrium price, supply will exceed demand.

21. Let c and r be the speeds of the current and the canoe in still water, respectively in kilometers per hour, and let t = time it takes log to travel 2 km; $2 + 1(r - c) =$ $(r + c)(t - 1)$; $2 + r - c = rt + ct - r - c$; $2r - rt - ct = -2$; but $ct = 2$ $2r - rt = 0$; $r(2 - t) = 0$; $2 - t = 0$; $t = 2$; $c(2) = 2$; $c = 1$; 1 km/h

Pages 134–135 · WRITTEN EXERCISES

A **1.**
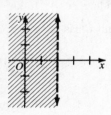

2.
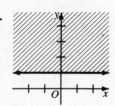

3.
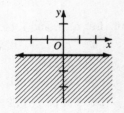

4.
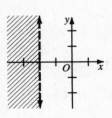

5.
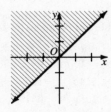

6.
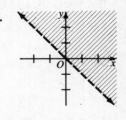

7.
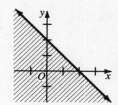

8.
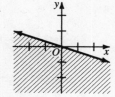

9.
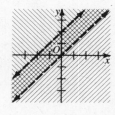

10.
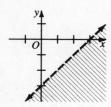

11.
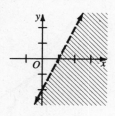

12.
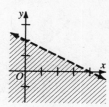

13.
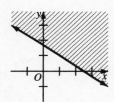

14.
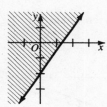

15.
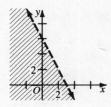

16.
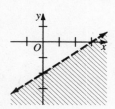

17.
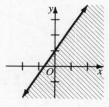

18.
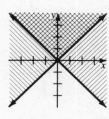

19.
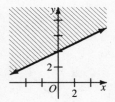

20.
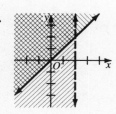

21.
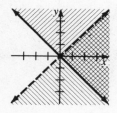

22.
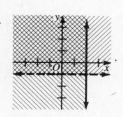

23.
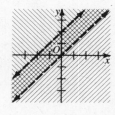

24.
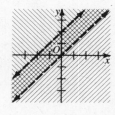

25.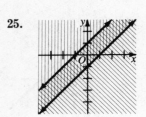

26.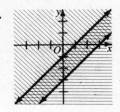

27.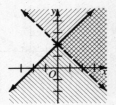

28.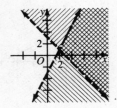

29.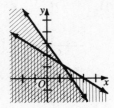

30-34. Note: Only graph of system is shaded

30.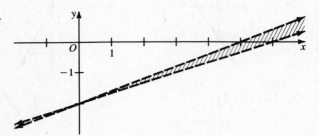

B **31.**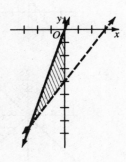

32.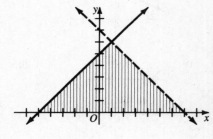

33.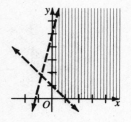

34.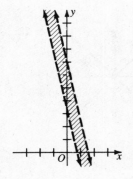

35.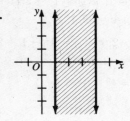

36.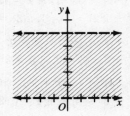

37.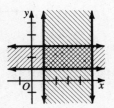

38.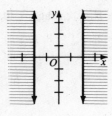

39.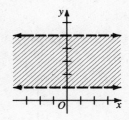

40.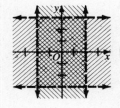

41-42. Note: Only graph of system is shaded.

41.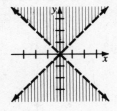

42.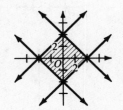

43.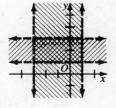

Pages 139-140 · WRITTEN EXERCISES

A **1.** $f(0) = 2(0) - 3 = -3; f(1) = 2(1) - 3 = -1; f(2) = 2(2) - 3 = 1; f(3) = 2(3) - 3 = 3;$
range $= \{-3, -1, 1, 3\}$

2. $g(-1) = 4 - 3(-1) = 7; g(0) = 4 - 3(0) = 4; g(1) = 4 - 3(1) = 1;$
$g(2) = 4 - 3(2) = -2;$ range $= \{7, 4, 1, -2\}$

3. $\varphi(-1) = (-1)^2 - 1 = 0; \varphi(0) = 0^2 - 1 = -1; \varphi(1) = 1^2 - 1 = 0; \varphi(2) = 2^2 - 1 = 3;$
range $= \{-1, 0, 3\}$

4. $G(-1) = 2 - (-1)^2 = 1; G(0) = 2 - 0^2 = 2; G(1) = 2 - 1^2 = 1; G(2) = 2 - 2^2 = -2;$
range $= \{-2, 1, 2\}$

5. $F(0) = 4(0) - 0^2 = 0; F(1) = 4(1) - 1^2 = 3; F(2) = 4(2) - 2^2 = 4;$
$F(3) = 4(3) - 3^2 = 3; F(4) = 4(4) - 4^2 = 0;$ range $= \{0, 3, 4\}$

6. $k(-1) = (-1)^2 - 2(-1) + 1 = 4$; $k(0) = 0^2 - 2(0) + 1 = 1$; $k(1) = 1^2 - 2(1) + 1 = 0$;
$k(2) = 2^2 - 2(2) + 1 = 1$; $k(3) = 3^2 - 2(3) + 1 = 4$; range $= \{0, 1, 4\}$

7. $s(-1) = (-1)^2 - (-1) - 2 = 0$; $s(0) = 0^2 - 0 - 2 = -2$; $s(1) = 1^2 - 1 - 2 = -2$;
$s(2) = 2^2 - 2 - 2 = 0$; $s(3) = 3^2 - 3 - 2 = 4$; range $= \{-2, 0, 4\}$

8. $v(-1) = (-1)^3 - (-1)^2 = -2$; $v(0) = 0^3 - 0^2 = 0$; $v(1) = 1^3 - 1^2 = 0$;
$v(2) = 2^3 - 2^2 = 4$; range $= \{-2, 0, 4\}$

9. $k(-2) = |-2 + 1| = 1$; $k(-1) = |-1 + 1| = 0$; $k(0) = |0 + 1| = 1$; $k(1) = |1 + 1| = 2$;
$k(2) = |2 + 1| = 3$; range $= \{0, 1, 2, 3\}$

10. $m(-2) = |-2| + 1 = 3$; $m(-1) = |-1| + 1 = 2$; $m(0) = |0| + 1 = 1$;
$m(1) = |1| + 1 = 2$; $m(2) = |2| + 1 = 3$; range $= \{1, 2, 3\}$

11.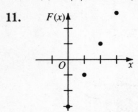

12.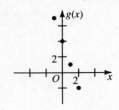

13.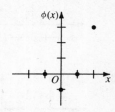

14.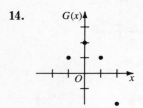

15.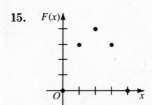

16.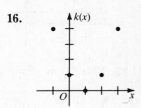

17.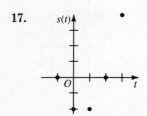

18.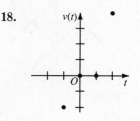

19.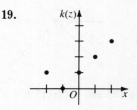

20.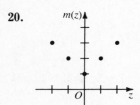

B **21.** $f(x) = x^2$ **22.** $f(x) = 3x + 1$ **23.** $f(x) = -5x + 1$

24. $f(x) = 12^x$ **25.** $f(g(2)) = f[1 - 2(2)] = f(-3) = 1 - (-3)^2 = -8$

26. $g(f(5)) = g(1 - 5^2) = g(-24) = 1 - 2(-24) = 49$

27. $f(g(1)) = f[1 - 2(1)] = f(-1) = 1 - (-1)^2 = 0; g(f(1)) = g(1 - 1^2) = g(0) =$
$1 - 2(0) = 1$

28. $f(h(1)) = f\left(\dfrac{1}{1^2 + 1}\right) = f\left(\dfrac{1}{2}\right) = 1 - \left(\dfrac{1}{2}\right)^2 = \dfrac{3}{4}; h(f(1)) = h(1 - 1^2) = h(0) =$
$\dfrac{1}{0^2 + 1} = 1$

C   **29.** $f(g(a + 1)) = f[1 - 2(a + 1)] = f(-1 - 2a) = 1 - (-2a - 1)^2 =$
$1 - (4a^2 + 4a + 1) = -4a^2 - 4a$

30. $g\left[\dfrac{1}{h(z)}\right] = g(z^2 + 1) = 1 - 2(z^2 + 1) = -2z^2$

31.   **a.** $f(0) = f(0 + 0) = f(0) + f(0); f(0) - f(0) = f(0) + f(0) - f(0); 0 = f(0)$
     b. $f(2a) = f(a + a) = f(a) + f(a) = 2f(a)$
     c. $f(0) = f[a + (-a)] = f(a) + f(-a); f(a) + f(-a) = f(0) = 0$ (from part (a), above);
        $f(-a) = -f(a)$

32.   **a.** For every x, $E(x) = E(0 + x) = E(0)E(x);$ then $E(0) = 1$ since $E(x) \neq 0$.
     b. $E(2a) = E(a + a) = E(a)E(a) = [E(a)]^2$
     c. $E(0) = E(-a + a) = E(-a)E(a);$ but $E(0) = 1$ (from part (a), above);
        $1 = E(-a)E(a); E(-a) = \dfrac{1}{E(a)}.$

33.   **a.** $L(1) = L(1 \cdot 1) = L(1) + L(1); 0 = L(1)$
     b. $L(1) = L\left(\dfrac{1}{a} \cdot a\right) = L\left(\dfrac{1}{a}\right) + L(a);$ but $L(1) = 0$ (from part (a), above);
        $0 = L\left(\dfrac{1}{a}\right) + L(a); L\left(\dfrac{1}{a}\right) = -L(a).$
     c. $L(a^2) = L(a \cdot a) = L(a) + L(a) = 2L(a)$

34.

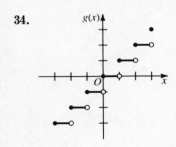

35. The function $x \to \dfrac{x}{|x|}$ is not defined
for $x = 0$.

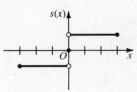

Page 140 · CHALLENGE

$f(n + 1) = \dfrac{n}{f(n)}; f(n + 2) = \dfrac{n + 1}{f(n + 1)} = \dfrac{(n + 1)f(n)}{n}; f(n + 3) = \dfrac{n + 2}{f(n + 2)} = \dfrac{(n + 2)n}{(n + 1)f(n)};$

$f(n + 4) = \dfrac{n + 3}{f(n + 3)} = \dfrac{(n + 3)(n + 1)f(n)}{(n + 2)n};$

for k even, $f(n + k) = \dfrac{(n + k - 1)(n + k - 3)\cdots(n + 1)f(n)}{(n + k - 2)(n + k - 4)\cdots(n + 2)n}$;

for k odd, $f(n + k) = \dfrac{(n + k - 1)(n + k - 3)\cdots(n)}{(n + k - 2)(n + k - 4)\cdots(n + 1)f(n)}$;

$f(12) = f(1 + 11) = \dfrac{11 \cdot 9 \cdot 7 \cdot 5 \cdot 3 \cdot 1}{10 \cdot 8 \cdot 6 \cdot 4 \cdot 2 \cdot f(1)} = \dfrac{11 \cdot 9 \cdot 7}{2 \cdot 8 \cdot 2 \cdot 4 \cdot 2 \cdot 2} = \dfrac{693}{512}$

Page 144 · WRITTEN EXERCISES

A   1. $f(0) = 1; b = 1; f(x) = mx + b = 2x + 1$

     2. $f(0) = 3; b = 3; f(x) = mx + b = -x + 3$

     3. $f(0) = -1; b = -1; f(x) = mx + b = -\dfrac{1}{2}x - 1$

     4. $f(0) = -2; b = -2; f(x) = mx + b = \dfrac{2}{3}x - 2$

     5. $m = \dfrac{1}{2}; f(0) = -1; b = -1; f(x) = mx + b = \dfrac{1}{2}x - 1$

     6. $m = -\dfrac{1}{3}; f(0) = 2; b = 2; f(x) = mx + b = -\dfrac{1}{3}x + 2$

     7. $-1(2) + b = 1; -2 + b = 1; b = 3; f(x) = mx + b = -x + 3$

     8. $1(-1) + b = 2; -1 + b = 2; b = 3; f(x) = mx + b = x + 3$

     9. $\dfrac{2}{3}(-1) + b = -3; -\dfrac{2}{3} + b = -3; b = -\dfrac{7}{3}; f(x) = mx + b = \dfrac{2}{3}x - \dfrac{7}{3}$

   10. $\dfrac{5}{2}(2) + b = -1; 5 + b = -1; b = -6; f(x) = mx + b = \dfrac{5}{2}x - 6$

   11. $m = \dfrac{3 - 1}{1 - 0} = 2; f(0) = 1; b = 1; f(x) = mx + b = 2x + 1$

   12. $m = \dfrac{2 - 3}{1 - 0} = -1; f(0) = 3; b = 3; f(x) = mx + b = -x + 3$

   13. $m = \dfrac{2 - 2}{3 - 1} = 0; 0 + b = 2; b = 2; f(x) = mx + b = 2$

   14. $m = \dfrac{0 - (-2)}{-2 - 0} = -1; f(0) = -2; b = -2; f(x) = mx + b = -x - 2$

   15. $m = \dfrac{0 - 1}{4 - 3} = -1; -1(3) + b = 1; -3 + b = 1; b = 4; f(x) = mx + b = -x + 4$

   16. $m = \dfrac{-2 - (-2)}{1 - (-1)} = 0; 0(-1) + b = -2; 0 + b = -2; b = -2; f(x) = mx + b = -2$

   17. $m = \dfrac{3 - 5}{5 - (-1)} = -\dfrac{1}{3}; -\dfrac{1}{3}(-1) + b = 5; \dfrac{1}{3} + b = 5; b = \dfrac{14}{3};$

       $f(x) = mx + b = -\dfrac{1}{3}x + \dfrac{14}{3}$

18. $m = \dfrac{1 - (-2)}{4 - 2} = \dfrac{3}{2}; \dfrac{3}{2}(2) + b = -2; 3 + b = -2; b = -5;$

$f(x) = mx + b = \dfrac{3}{2}x - 5$

19.

x	2	6	0	8
$g(x)$	3	1	4	0

20.

x	3	6	0	0
$g(x)$	1	2	0	0

21.

x	-2	3	0	$-\dfrac{9}{2}$
$g(x)$	1	3	$\dfrac{9}{5}$	0

22.

x	-1	3	0	1
$g(x)$	-4	4	-2	0

B   **23.** $m = \dfrac{24 - 10}{7 - 4} = \dfrac{14}{3}; \dfrac{14}{3}(4) + b = 10; \dfrac{56}{3} + b = 10; b = -\dfrac{26}{3}; f(x) = \dfrac{14}{3}x - \dfrac{26}{3};$

$f(6) = \dfrac{14}{3}(6) - \dfrac{26}{3} = \dfrac{84}{3} - \dfrac{26}{3} = \dfrac{58}{3}; f(100) = \dfrac{14}{3}(100) - \dfrac{26}{3} = \dfrac{1400}{3} - \dfrac{26}{3} = 458$

24. $m = \dfrac{-20 - (-5)}{8 - 3} = -3; -3(3) + b = -5; -9 + b = -5; b = 4; f(x) = -3x + 4;$

$f(5) = -3(5) + 4 = -11; f(98) = -3(98) + 4 = -290$

25. $m = \dfrac{18 - 15}{10 - 0} = \dfrac{3}{10}; f(0) = 15; b = 15; f(x) = \dfrac{3}{10}x + 15;$

$f(5) = \dfrac{3}{10}(5) + 15 = \dfrac{3}{2} + 15 = \dfrac{33}{2}; f(-5) = \dfrac{3}{10}(-5) + 15 = -\dfrac{3}{2} + 15 = \dfrac{27}{2}$

26. $m = \dfrac{22 - 6}{2 - (-2)} = 4; 4(-2) + b = 6; -8 + b = 6; b = 14; f(x) = 4x + 14;$

$f(1) = 4(1) + 14 = 18; f(1000) = 4(1000) + 14 = 4014$

C   **27.** $\dfrac{f(x + k) - f(x)}{k} = \dfrac{m(x + k) + b - (mx + b)}{k} = \dfrac{mx + mk + b - mx - b}{k}$

$= \dfrac{mk}{k} = m$

28. $\dfrac{f(x_2) - f(x_1)}{x_2 - x_1} = \dfrac{mx_2 + b - (mx_1 + b)}{x_2 - x_1} = \dfrac{mx_2 + b - mx_1 - b}{x_2 - x_1} = \dfrac{m(x_2 - x_1)}{x_2 - x_1} = m$

29. Let $f(x) = mx + b$, $m > 0$, and $x_2 > x_1$; $f(x_2) - f(x_1) = mx_2 + b - (mx_1 + b) = mx_2 - mx_1 = m(x_2 - x_1) > 0$ since $m > 0$ and $x_2 > x_1$; thus $f(x_2) > f(x_1)$ and f is increasing; if $m < 0$ and $x_2 > x_1$, $f(x_2) - f(x_1) = mx_2 + b - (mx_1 + b) = mx_2 - mx_1 = m(x_2 - x_1) < 0$ since $m < 0$ and $x_2 - x_1 > 0$; thus $f(x_2) < f(x_1)$ and the function is decreasing.

Pages 145-146 · PROBLEMS

A 1. Let $C(x)$ = amount charged in dollars for x shares traded; $C(x) = 25 + 0.24x$; domain = natural numbers; $C(1300) = 25 + 0.24(1300) = 25 + 312 = 337$; $337

2. Let $v(t)$ = value in dollars after t years; $v(t) = 1200 - 50t$;

$$v\left(2\frac{3}{4}\right) = 1200 - 50\left(2\frac{3}{4}\right) = 1200 - 137.50 = 1062.50; \quad \$1062.50; \quad 300 = 1200 - 50t;$$

$50t = 900; \; t = 18; \; 18$ yr

3. Let $c(h)$ = amount charged in dollars for h hours; $r = c(h) = mh + 5$; $c(8) = 13 = 8m + 5$; $m = 1$; $c(h) = 5 + h$; $c(4) = 5 + 4 = 9$; $9

4. Let $a(t)$ = number of liters in tank after t minutes; tank will be empty in $\dfrac{288}{4} = 72$ min

so it will be half empty in 36 min; $a(t) = 288 - 4t$; $a(60) = 288 - 4(60) = 288 - 240 = 48$; yes, if amount in tank to begin with is at least 240 L

5. Let $f(x)$ = length of spring in centimeters stretched by a load of x kg; $f(2.5) = 70$ and $f(4.5) = 82$; $m = \dfrac{82 - 70}{4.5 - 2.5} = \dfrac{12}{2} = 6$; $82 = 6(4.5) + b$; $82 = 27 + b$; $b = 55$; $f(x) = 6x + 55$; unstretched length $= f(0) = b = 55$; 55 cm

6. Let $f(x)$ = amount in dollars after x months; $f(8) = 780$ and $f(18) = 855$; $m = \dfrac{855 - 780}{18 - 8} = \dfrac{75}{10} = 7.5$; $780 = 8(7.5) + b$; $780 = 60 + b$; $b = 720$; $f(x) = 7.5x + 720$; original amount $= f(0) = b = 720$; $720

7. Let $f(x)$ = weight in kilograms after x days; $f(15) = 80$ and $f(40) = 77.5$; $m = \dfrac{80 - 77.5}{15 - 40} = \dfrac{2.5}{-25} = -0.1$; $80 = 0.1(15) + b$; $80 = -1.5 + b$; $b = 81.5$;

$f(x) = -0.1x + 81.5$

a. weight at beginning $= f(0) = b = 81.5$; 81.5 kg

b. $70 = -0.1x + 81.5$; $0.1x = 11.5$; $x = 115$; 115 days

8. Let $f(x)$ = height in meters reached after x hours; $f(x) = 220x + b$, where b = base-camp elevation

a. $6400 = 220(3) + b$; $6400 = 660 + b$; $b = 5740$; 5740 m

b. $7500 = 220x + 5740$; $220x = 1760$; $x = 8$; 8 h after 5:00 A.M. is 1:00 P.M.

B 9. **a.** $3 \cdot 50 = 150$ **b.** $-1 \cdot 50 = -50$ **c.** $3(40) - 1(6) = 120 - 6 = 114$

d. Let $f(r)$ = score on new scale of raw score of r; $f(150) = 100$ and $f(-50) = 0$;

$$m = \frac{100 - 0}{150 - (-50)} = \frac{100}{200} = \frac{1}{2}; \; 100 = \frac{1}{2}(150) + b; \; 100 = 75 + b; \; b = 25;$$

$$f(r) = \frac{1}{2}r + 25$$

e. $f(114) = \dfrac{1}{2}(114) + 25 = 57 + 25 = 82$

10. a. Let $f(x)$ = Z-scale temperature equal to $x°C$; $f(-40) = 0$ and $f(360) = 100$;

$$m = \frac{100 - 0}{360 - (-40)} = \frac{100}{400} = \frac{1}{4}; \quad 100 = \frac{1}{4}(360) + b; \quad 100 = 90 + b; \quad b = 10;$$

$$f(x) = \frac{1}{4}x + 10$$

b. $f(0) = \frac{1}{4}(0) + 10 = 0 + 10 = 10;$ $0°C = 10°Z;$

$$f(100) = \frac{1}{4}(100) + 10 = 25 + 10 = 35; \quad 100°C = 35°Z$$

C **11. a.** $c = 4.5 + 0.062n$

  b. $c = 4.5 + 0.062(800) + 0.055(n - 800) = 4.5 + 49.6 + 0.055n - 44$
  $= 10.1 + 0.055n$

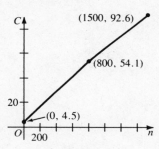

Ex. 11c

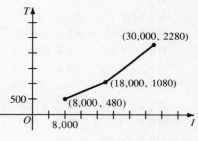

Ex. 12c

12. a. $T = 0.06I$

  b. $T = 0.06(18,000) + 0.1(I - 18,000) = 1080 + 0.1I - 1800 = 0.1I - 720$

Pages 146-147 · COMPUTER EXERCISES

1.
```
10 PRINT "ENTER KILOWATT HOURS"
20 INPUT K
30 LET K2 = K - 350
40 IF K2 < 0 THEN 70
50 LET K1 = 350
60 GOTO 90
70 LET K2 = 0
80 LET K1 = K
90 LET C1 = K1 * .068479
100 LET C2 = K2 * .083479
110 LET C = C1 + C2 + 6.12
120 LET C = INT(C * 100 + .5)/100
130 PRINT K, "$"; C
140 END
```

2. a. $25.16   **b.** $37.52

3. 10 PRINT "ENTER KILOWATT HOURS"
20 INPUT K
30 LET K3 = K − 750
40 IF K3 < 0 THEN 80
50 LET K2 = 400
60 LET K1 = 350
70 GOTO 150
80 LET K3 = 0
90 LET K2 = K − 350
100 IF K2 < 0 THEN 130
110 LET K1 = 350
120 GOTO 150
130 LET K2 = 0
140 LET K1 = K
150 LET C1 = K1 ∗ .053479
160 LET C2 = K2 ∗ .068479
170 LET C3 = K3 ∗ .083479
180 LET C = C1 + C2 + C3 + 6.12
190 LET C = INT(C ∗ 100 + .5)/100
200 PRINT K, "$"; C
210 END

4. a. $22.70   **b.** $36.62   **c.** $56.74   **d.** $52.23

Pages 151-152 · WRITTEN EXERCISES

A   **1.** function

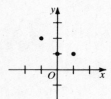

2. not a function

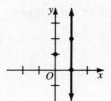

3. not a function

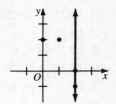

4. function

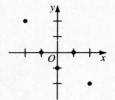

5. not a function

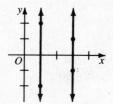

6. not a function

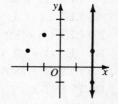

7. $x + y \leq 2$ and $x + y \geq 0$; $y \leq -x + 2$ or $y \geq -x$; domain = all integers; the relation is not a function; the figure shows the graph of the relation for $-3 \leq x \leq 3$.

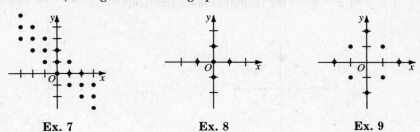

Ex. 7   Ex. 8   Ex. 9

8. $|x| + |y| \leq 1$; $|x| \leq 1 - |y|$; $|y| - 1 \leq x \leq 1 - |y|$; $|y| \leq x + 1$ and $|y| \leq 1 - x$; $-x - 1 \leq y \leq x + 1$ and $x - 1 \leq y \leq 1 - x$; domain = $\{-1, 0, 1\}$; the realtion is not a function.

9. $|x| + |y| = 2$; $|y| = -|x| + 2$; $|y| \geq 0$ so $-|x| + 2 \geq 0$; $|x| \leq 2$; domain = $\{-2, -1, 0, 1, 2\}$; $x = -|y| + 2$ or $x = |y| - 2$; $|y| = -x + 2$ or $|y| = x + 2$; $y = -x + 2$, or $y = x - 2$; or $y = x + 2$, or $y = -x - 2$; the relation is not a function.

10. $x \leq 3$; domain = $\{0, 1, 2, 3\}$; $|y| = x$; $y = x$ or $y = -x$; the relation is not a function.

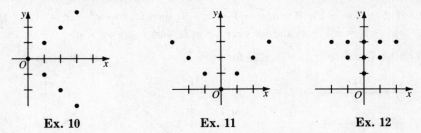

Ex. 10   Ex. 11   Ex. 12

11. $y = |x|$; $y \leq 3$; $|x| \leq 3$; domain = $\{-3, -2, -1, 0, 1, 2, 3\}$; $y = x$ or $y = -x$; the relation is a function.

12. $|x| < y$ and $y \leq 3$; $|x| < 3$; domain = $\{-2, -1, 0, 1, 2\}$; $-y < x < y$; $y > -x$ and $y > x$; the relation is not a function.

13. $|x| \leq 2$; domain = $\{-2, -1, 0, 1, 2\}$; $|y| = |x|$; $y = x$ or $y = -x$; the relation is not a function.

Ex. 13   Ex. 14

14. $|x| = 2$; domain = $\{-2, 2\}$; $|y| \leq 2$; $-2 \leq y \leq 2$; the relation is not a function.

B   **15.** $0 < |x| \le 3$; $-3 \le x \le 3$; domain = $\{-3, -2, -1, 1, 2, 3\}$; $|xy| = 6$; $xy = 6$ or $xy = -6$;

$y = \dfrac{6}{x}$ or $y = -\dfrac{6}{x}$; the relation is not a function.

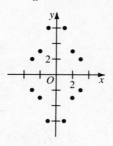

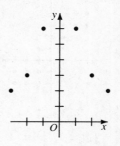

Ex. 15   **Ex. 16**

16. $0 < |x| \le 3$; $-3 \le x \le 3$; domain = $\{-3, -2, -1, 1, 2, 3\}$; $y|x| = 6$; $y = \dfrac{6}{|x|}$; the relation is a function.

17. f: $-1 \to 0$; g: $-1 \to 4$; $f \ne g$

18. f: $-1 \to 1$; g: $-1 \to 1$; f: $0 \to 0$; g: $0 \to 0$; f: $1 \to 1$; g: $1 \to 1$; $f = g$

19. f: $-2 \to 0$; g: $-2 \to 4$; $f \ne g$

20. If $x \ge 1$, $x - 1 \ge 0$ and $|x - 1| = x - 1$; then f: $x \to x^2 - x = x(x - 1) = x|x - 1| = x|1 - x|$ and for every x in D, $f(x) = g(x)$; $f = g$.

21. not a function   **22.** function   **23.** function

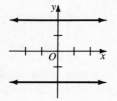

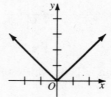

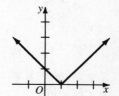

24. not a function   **25.** function   **26.** not a function

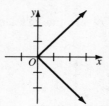

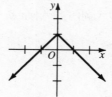

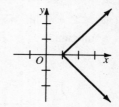

C   **27.** not a function

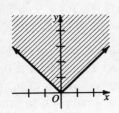

28. not a function

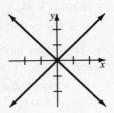

29. not a function

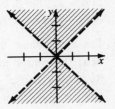

30. not a function

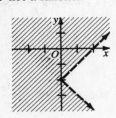

31. not a function

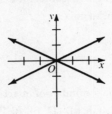

32. not a function

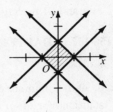

33. a. $\{\{5,3\},5\}; \{5,\{5,3\}\}; \{5,\{3,5\}\}$ **b.** $(4,1)$ **c.** $(a,b,c) = \{a,\{b,\{b,c\}\}\}$

Page 152 · CHALLENGE

1 g, 3 g, and 9 g; in the following let the numbers on either side of the equal sign represent the weights on either side of the balance; the underlined number represents the weight of the object;

$\underline{1} = 1$; $1, \underline{2} = 3$; $\underline{3} = 3$; $\underline{4} = 1, 3$, $1, 3, \underline{5} = 9$; $3, \underline{6} = 9$; $3, \underline{7} = 1, 9$;

$1, \underline{8} = 9$; $\underline{9} = 9$; $\underline{10} = 1, 9$; $1, \underline{11} = 3, 9$; $\underline{12} = 3, 9$; $\underline{13} = 1, 3, 9$

Pages 153-155 · APPLICATION

1. $P(0,0) = 3(0) + 4(0) = 0$; $P(0,90) = 3(0) + 4(90) = 360$; $P(50,80) = 3(50) + 4(80) = 470$; $P(70,20) = 3(70) + 4(20) = 290$; $P(70,0) = 3(70) + 4(0) = 210$; maximum value = 470; minimum value = 0.

2. $P(10,0) = 13(10) - 5(0) = 130$; $P(10,40) = 13(10) - 5(40) = -70$; $P(30,50) = 13(30) - 5(50) = 140$; $P(40,20) = 13(40) - 5(20) = 420$; maximum value = 420; minimum value = -70.

3. The vertices of the feasible region are $(0,5)$, $(0,10)$, $(10,7)$, and $(10,5)$; $S(0,5) = 10(0) + 3(5) = 15$; $S(0,10) = 10(0) + 3(10) = 30$; $S(10,7) = 10(10) + 3(7) = 121$; $S(10,5) = 10(10) + 3(5) = 115$; maximum value = 121; minimum value = 15.

4. The vertices of the feasible region are $(2, 0)$, $(-3, 10)$, $(1, 10)$, and $(6, 0)$; $S(2, 0) = 6(2) - 2(0) = 12$; $S(-3, 10) = 6(-3) - 2(10) = -38$; $S(1, 10) = 6(1) - 2(10) = -14$; $S(6, 0) = 6(6) - 2(0) = 36$; maximum value $= 36$, minimum value $= -38$.

5. Let x = number of packages of Trailblazer mix, y = number of packages of Frontier Mix; the center must maximize $I = 9.75x + 9.50y$ subject to $x \geq 0$, $y \geq 0$, $4x + 3y \leq 120$, and $x + 2y \leq 60$; the vertices of the feasible region are $(0, 0)$, $(0, 30)$, $(12, 24)$, and $(30, 0)$; $I(0, 0) = 9.75(0) + 9.50(0) = 0$; $I(0, 30) = 9.75(0) + 9.50(30) = 285$; $I(12, 24) = 9.75(12) + 9.50(24) = 117 + 228 = 345$; $I(30, 0) = 9.75(30) + 9.50(0) = 292.5$; maximum occurs at $(12, 24)$; the center should sell 12 packages of Trailblazer mix and 24 packages of Frontier mix.

Pages 156-157 · CHAPTER REVIEW

1. b

2. d; let d = number of dimes, q = number of quarters; $10d + 25q = 235$; $d = \dfrac{235 - 25q}{10}$ solutions for (d, q) are $(21, 1)$, $(16, 3)$, $(11, 5)$, $(6, 7)$, and $(1, 9)$

3. d; $2x - y = 3$; $y = 2x - 3$; slope $= 2$, y-intercept $= -3$

4. a; $5(4) + k(3) = 8$; $3k = -12$; $k = -4$ 5. b; $m = \dfrac{-3 - 1}{2 - (-4)} = \dfrac{-4}{6} = -\dfrac{2}{3}$

6. d; $3x + 5y = 15$; $5y = -3x + 15$; $y = -\dfrac{3}{5}x + 3$

7. a; $y + 1 = -2(x - 3)$; $y + 1 = -2x + 6$; $2x + y = 5$

8. b; $y = -3x + 4$ has slope -3; $y + 3 = -3(x - 2)$; $y + 3 = -3x + 6$; $3x + y = 3$

9. a; $2x + 4y = 1$; $y = -\dfrac{1}{2}x + 4$ has slope $-\dfrac{1}{2}$; $y - 5 = 2(x - 2)$; $y - 5 = 2x - 4$; $y - 2x = 1$

10. c; $\begin{array}{l} 3x + 2y = 1 \\ 2x + y = 5 \end{array}$; $\begin{array}{l} 3x + 2y = 1 \\ -4x - 2y = -10 \end{array}$; $-x = -9$; $x = 9$; $2x + y = 5$; $18 + y = 5$; $y = -13$

11. d; $3 = -1^2 + 4$, $0 = -2^2 + 4$

12. c; let x = cost of pencil, y = cost of pad.
$\begin{array}{l} 6x + 2y = 230 \\ 4x + 3y = 270 \end{array}$; $\begin{array}{l} 18x + 6y = 690 \\ -8x - 6y = -540 \end{array}$; $10x = 150$; $x = 15$; $6(15) + 2y = 230$; $y = 70$

13. b; $3 - 2(-1) = 5 \not< 5$

14. a; $g(-1) = 1 - (-1) = 2$; $f(g(-1)) = f(2) = 4 - 2^2 = 4 - 4 = 0$

15. d; if $x \geq 0$, $\phi : x \to x - x = 0$; if $x < 0$, $\phi : x \to -x - x = -2x$; $\{0, -2, -4\}$

16. c; $m = \dfrac{7 - 1}{-1 - 2} = -2$; $-2 = \dfrac{f(4) - 1}{4 - 2}$; $f(4) - 1 = -4$; $f(4) = -3$

17. b; $\dfrac{722 - 200}{800 - 200} = \dfrac{522}{600} = \dfrac{87}{100}$ **18.** d

Page 158 · CHAPTER TEST

1. $2(3) + k(2) = k + 1$; $6 + 2k = k + 1$; $k = -5$

2.

x	$y = -\dfrac{2x + 12}{3}$
0	4
3	2
6	0

If $x > 3$, $y < 0$; $\{(0, 4), (3, 2), (6, 0)\}$

3. a.   **b.**   **c.**

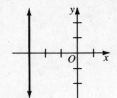   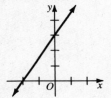   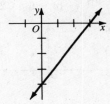

4. a. -2 **b.** $\dfrac{3}{5}$

5. $\dfrac{3}{-(k + 1)} = 2$; $3 = -2(k + 1)$; $3 = -2k - 2$; $2k = -5$; $k = -\dfrac{5}{2}$

6. a. $\dfrac{y - (-2)}{x - 1} = 3$; $\dfrac{y + 2}{x - 1} = 3$; $y + 2 = 3x - 3$; $3x - y = 5$

b. $m = \dfrac{6 - 0}{0 - (-2)} = 3$; $b = 6$; $y = 3x + 6$; $3x - y = -6$

7. slope of given line $= \dfrac{-2}{-4} = \dfrac{1}{2}$

a. $m = \dfrac{1}{2}$; $\dfrac{y - (-1)}{x - 3} = \dfrac{1}{2}$; $\dfrac{y + 1}{x - 3} = \dfrac{1}{2}$; $2y + 2 = x - 3$; $x - 2y = 4$

b. $m = -2$; $\dfrac{y + 1}{x - 3} = -2$; $y + 1 = -2x + 6$; $2x + y = 5$

8. $\dfrac{3x - 2y = 16}{5x + 3y = -5}$; $\dfrac{9x - 6y = 48}{10x + 6y = -10}$; $19x = 38$; $x = 2$; $3(2) - 2y = 16$;

$6 - 2y = 16$; $-2y = 10$; $y = -5$; $(2, -5)$

9. Let c = speed of the current and r = speed of the riverboat in kilometers per hour;

$\dfrac{6(r - c) = 120}{4(r + c) = 120}$; $\dfrac{r - c = 20}{r + c = 30}$; $2r = 50$; $r = 25$; $25 - c = 20$; $c = 5$; speed of

riverboat = 25 km/h; speed of current = 5 km/h

10.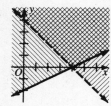

11. $f(0) = 2; f(1) = 1; f(2) = 0; f(3) = 1;$
$f(4) = 2;$ range $= \{0, 1, 2\}$

12. $f(g(x)) = (x + 1)^2 - 1 = x^2 + 2x + 1 - 1 = x^2 + 2x; g(f(x)) = (x^2 - 1) + 1 = x^2$

13. $m = \dfrac{-7 - 2}{4 - 1} = -3; 2 = -3(1) + b; 2 = -3 + b; b = 5; \varphi(x) = -3x + 5;$

$\varphi(3) = -3(3) + 5 = -9 + 5 = -4$

14. Let $f(x) =$ length of spring in centimeters with a load of x kg; $f(6) = 30; f(10) = 40;$

$m = \dfrac{40 - 30}{10 - 6} = \dfrac{5}{2}; 30 = \dfrac{5}{2}(6) + b; 30 = 15 + b; b = 15; f(0) = b = 15;$ 15 cm

15.   function

Page 159 · CUMULATIVE REVIEW (Chapters 1-3)

1. $-5[9 - 16] \div 14 \cdot 6 = -5(-7) \div 14 \cdot 6 = -35 \div 14 \cdot 6 = \dfrac{5}{2} \cdot 6 = 15$

2. $|-4| \cdot (-4) + 9 = 4(-4) + 9 = -16 + 9 = -7$

3. $2(-x^2 + 5x) - 3(6x - 1) = -2x^2 + 10x - 18x + 3 = -2x^2 - 8x + 3$

4. $\dfrac{3(-4)^2 - 5(-4) - 6}{-\dfrac{2}{3}(-4 + 1)} = \dfrac{3(16) + 20 - 6}{-\dfrac{2}{3}(-3)} = \dfrac{62}{2} = 31$

5. (1) $1 > 0$ (Oral Ex. 1, page 87);   (2) $a > 1$ (Given);

(3) $a > 0$ (Trans. prop. of order);   (4) $\dfrac{1}{a} > 0$ (Ex. 15, page 89);

(5) $a \cdot \dfrac{1}{a} > 1 \cdot \dfrac{1}{a}$ (Mult. prop. of order); (6) $1 > 1 \cdot \dfrac{1}{a}$ (Prop. of recip.; Subst.);

(7) $1 > \dfrac{1}{a}$ or $\dfrac{1}{a} < 1$ (Ident. prop. for mult.; Subst.)

6. $\dfrac{3}{4}(5t - 2) = 4t; 15t - 6 = 16t; t = -6; \{-6\}$

Ex. 6   Ex. 7

7. $7(2r - 6) - 14r = -42; 14r - 42 - 14r = -42; -42 = -42;$ true for all real numbers

8. $-7k + 7 > k + 15$; $-8k > 8$; $k < -1$; $\{k : k < -1\}$

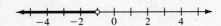

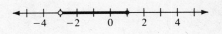

Ex. 8   **Ex. 9**

9. $u - 3 < 2u \le u + 1$; $-3 < u \le 1$; $\{u : -3 < u \le 1\}$

10. $\left| \dfrac{z - 1}{3} \right| > \dfrac{1}{2}$; $\dfrac{z - 1}{3} > \dfrac{1}{2}$ or $\dfrac{z - 1}{3} < -\dfrac{1}{2}$; $z - 1 > \dfrac{3}{2}$ or $z - 1 < -\dfrac{3}{2}$; $z > \dfrac{5}{2}$ or

$z < -\dfrac{1}{2}$; $\left\{ z : z < -\dfrac{1}{2} \text{ or } z > \dfrac{5}{2} \right\}$

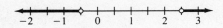

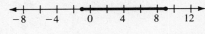

Ex. 10   **Ex. 11**

11. $|4 - d| \le 5$; $-5 \le 4 - d \le 5$; $-9 \le -d \le 1$; $-1 \le d \le 9$; $\{d : -1 \le d \le 9\}$

12.

x	$\dfrac{-5x + 10}{3}$	$y \le \dfrac{-5x + 10}{3}$
1	$\dfrac{5}{3}$	1

If $x > 1$, $y \le 0$; $(1, 1)$

13. $3x + ky = -2$; $ky = -3x - 2$; $y = \dfrac{-3}{k}x - \dfrac{2}{k}$; $\dfrac{-3}{k} = \dfrac{1}{2}$; $k = -6$

14. $y = -3x + 4$; $3x + y = 4$

15. slope of $L_1 = -\dfrac{2}{-3} = \dfrac{2}{3}$; $m = \dfrac{2}{3}$; $\dfrac{y - 0}{x - (-5)} = \dfrac{2}{3}$; $\dfrac{y}{x + 5} = \dfrac{2}{3}$; $3y = 2x + 10$;

$2x - 3y = -10$

16. slope of $L_2 = -\dfrac{1}{2}$; $m = 2$; $\dfrac{y - 1}{x - 4} = 2$; $y - 1 = 2x - 8$; $2x - y = 7$

17. $m = \dfrac{\dfrac{2}{3} - (-2)}{-\dfrac{1}{3} - (-7)} = \dfrac{\dfrac{8}{3}}{\dfrac{20}{3}} = \dfrac{8}{20} = \dfrac{2}{5}$; $\dfrac{y - (-2)}{x - (-7)} = \dfrac{2}{5}$; $\dfrac{y + 2}{x + 7} = \dfrac{2}{5}$; $5y + 10 = 2x + 14$;

$2x - 5y = -4$

18. $\begin{array}{l} x + y = -6 \\ x - y = 6 \end{array}$; $2x = 0$; $x = 0$; $0 + y = -6$; $y = -6$; $(0, -6)$

19. $\begin{array}{l} 4a - 2b = 2 \\ 2a - b = -3 \end{array}$; $\begin{array}{l} 2a - b = 1 \\ 2a - b = -3 \end{array}$; $0 = -2$; no solution

20. $2m + 2n + 2 = m - n$ $m + 3n = -2$ $\dfrac{3}{2}n = -1;\ n = -\dfrac{2}{3};$

$-\dfrac{3}{2}n = m + 1$; $-m - \dfrac{3}{2}n = 1$;

$m + 3\left(-\dfrac{2}{3}\right) = -2;\ m = 0;\ \left(0, -\dfrac{2}{3}\right)$

21.

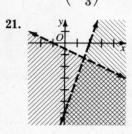

22. Let x = number of milliliters of water to be added; $0.08(100 + x) = 20$; $8(100 + x) = 2000;\ 800 + 8x = 2000;$ $8x = 1200;\ x = 150;$ 150 mL

23. Let x = cost of a bag of apples in cents and y = cost of a carton of yogurt;

$4x + 5y = 776$ $8x + 10y = 1552$

$3x + 2y = 491$; $-15x - 10y = -2455$; $-7x = -903;\ x = 129;\ \$1.29$

24. $f(g(2)) = f\left[\dfrac{1}{2}(2^2) - 7\right] = f(-5) = |5 - 3(-5)| = |5 + 15| = |20| = 20;$

$g(f(2)) = g\left[|5 - 3(2)|\right] = g(1) = \dfrac{1}{2}(1^2) - 7 = \dfrac{1}{2} - 7 = -\dfrac{13}{2}$

25. $m = \dfrac{-3 - 0}{2 - (-4)} = \dfrac{-3}{6} = -\dfrac{1}{2};\ 0 = -\dfrac{1}{2}(-4) + b;\ 0 = 2 + b;\ b = -2;$

$h(x) = -\dfrac{1}{2}x - 2;\ h(-1) = -\dfrac{1}{2}(-1) - 2 = \dfrac{1}{2} - 2 = -\dfrac{3}{2}$

26. function

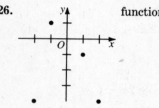

CHAPTER 4 · Products and Factors of Polynomials

Page 163 · WRITTEN EXERCISES

A

1. $5x^2 \cdot 2x^5 = 10 \cdot x^{2+5} = 10x^7$ 2. $6t^2 \cdot t^3 = 6 \cdot t^{2+3} = 6t^5$

3. $(-a^3)^3 = (-1)^3(a^3)^3 = -1 \cdot a^{3\cdot3} = -a^9$ 4. $(-2c^3)^2 = (-2)^2(c^3)^2 = 4 \cdot c^{3\cdot2} = 4c^6$

5. $(xy^2)(2x^2y) = 2 \cdot x^{1+2} \cdot y^{2+1} = 2x^3y^3$ 6. $(2u^2v)(u^2v^3) = 2 \cdot u^{2+2} \cdot v^{1+3} = 2u^4v^4$

7. $(2pq^2)(p^2q^3)(3p^3q) = 2 \cdot 3 \cdot p^{1+2+3} \cdot q^{2+3+1} = 6p^6q^6$

8. $(st^2)(2s^3t)(-3st) = -6 \cdot s^{1+3+1} \cdot t^{2+1+1} = -6s^5t^4$

9. $(x^2y^3)^2 = (x^2)^2(y^3)^2 = x^{2\cdot2} \cdot y^{3\cdot2} = x^4y^6$ 10. $(2pq^3)^2 = 2^2(p^2)(q^3)^2 = 4p^2 \cdot q^{3\cdot2} = 4p^2q^6$

11. $(-2a)(-a^2)^3 = -2a(-1)^3(a^2)^3 = -2a(-1)(a^{2\cdot3}) = 2a \cdot a^6 = 2 \cdot a^{1+6} = 2a^7$

12. $(-x^2)(-x)^2 = (-1)(x^2)(-1)^2(x^2) = (-1)(x^2)(1)(x^2) = (-1)(x^{2+2}) = -x^4$

13. $(-z)^2(-z)^3(-z)^4 = (-1)^2(z^2)(-1)^3(z^3)(-1)^4(z^4) = (1)(z^2)(-1)(z^3)(1)(z^4)$
    $= (-1)(z^{2+3+4}) = -z^9$

14. $-x(x^2)^2(x^3)^3 = (-1)(x)(x^{2\cdot2})(x^{3\cdot3}) = (-1)(x)(x^4)(x^9) = (-1)(x^{1+4+9}) = -x^{14}$

15. $(a^2b)^2(ab^2)^3 = (a^2)^2(b^2)(a^3)(b^2)^3 = (a^{2\cdot2})(a^3)(b^2)(b^{2\cdot3}) = (a^4)(a^3)(b^2)(b^6) = (a^{4+3})(b^{2+6})$
    $= a^7b^8$

16. $(2uv^3)^2(u^2v)^3 = (2^2)(u^2)(v^3)^2(u^2)^3(v^3) = 4(u^2)(u^{2\cdot3})(v^{3\cdot2})(v^3) = 4(u^2)(u^6)(v^6)(v^3)$
    $= 4(u^{2+6})(v^{6+3}) = 4u^8v^9$

17. $2x(x^2 - 3x + 2) = 2x(x^2) - 2x(3x) + 2x(2) = 2 \cdot x^{1+2} - 6x^{1+1} + 4x$
    $= 2x^3 - 6x^2 + 4x$

18. $x^2(x^3 - 2x^2 + 1) = x^2(x^3) - x^2(2x^2) + x^2(1) = x^{2+3} - 2 \cdot x^{2+2} + x^2$
    $= x^5 - 2x^4 + x^2$

19. $x^2y(xy + y^2) = x^2y(xy) + x^2y(y^2) = x^{2+1} \cdot y^{1+1} + x^2 \cdot y^{1+2} = x^3y^2 + x^2y^3$

20. $ab(a^2 - ab + b^2) = ab(a^2) - ab(ab) + ab(b^2) = a^{1+2} \cdot b - a^{1+1} \cdot b^{1+1} + a \cdot b^{1+2}$
    $= a^3b - a^2b^2 + ab^3$

21. $t^3t^{n-3} = t^{3+(n-3)} = t^n$ 22. $x^{n-2}x^{n+2} = x^{(n-2)+(n+2)} = x^{2n}$

23. $a^n \cdot a \cdot a^{n-1} = a^{(n+1)+(n-1)} = a^{2n}$ 24. $z^{m+k} \cdot z^m \cdot z^{m-k} = z^{(m+k)+m+(m-k)} = z^{3m}$

25. $(x^m)^3(x^3)^m = x^{m\cdot3} \cdot x^{3\cdot m} = x^{3m} \cdot x^{3m} = x^{3m+3m} = x^{6m}$

26. $u^2(u^{n-1})^2 = u^2 \cdot u^{2(n-1)} = u^2 \cdot u^{2n-2} = u^{2+(2n-2)} = u^{2n}$

B

27. $z^2(z^{n-2} + 2z^{n-1} + z^n) = z^2(z^{n-2}) + z^2(2z^{n-1}) + z^2(z^n) = z^{2+(n-2)} + 2z^{2+(n-1)} + z^{2+n}$
    $= z^n + 2z^{n+1} + z^{n+2}$

28. $x(x^{m+1} + x^m + x^{m-1}) = x(x^{m+1}) + x(x^m) + x(x^{m-1}) = x^{1+(m+1)} + x^{1+m} + x^{1+(m-1)}$
    $= x^{m+2} + x^{m+1} + x^m$

29. $a^n(a^{m-n+1} + a^{m-n} + a^{m-n-1}) = a^n(a^{m-n+1}) + a^n(a^{m-n}) + a^n(a^{m-n-1})$
    $= a^{n+(m-n+1)} + a^{n+(m-n)} + a^{n+(m-n-1)} = a^{m+1} + a^m + a^{m-1}$

79

30. $t^{m-n}(t^{m+n} + t^n) = t^{m-n}(t^{m+n}) + t^{m-n}(t^n) = t^{(m-n)+(m+n)} + t^{(m-n)+n} = t^{2m} + t^m$

31. $(x^m)^n(x^n)^{n-m} = x^{mn} \cdot x^{n(n-m)} = x^{mn} \cdot x^{n2-mn} = x^{mn+(n2-mn)} = x^{n2}$

32. $(z^{h-k})^h(z^{h+k})^k = z^{h(h-k)} \cdot z^{k(h+k)} = z^{h2-kh} \cdot z^{kh+k2} = z^{(h2-kh)+(kh+k2)} = z^{h2+k2}$

33. $x^{2n}(x^{n+1} + x^{3n-2}) = x^{2n}(x^{n+1}) + x^{2n}(x^{3n-2}) = x^{2n+(n+1)} + x^{2n+(3n-2)} = x^{3n+1} + x^{5n-2}$

34. $y^{3m}(y^{2m+4} - y^{m+2} + y^{m+n}) = y^{3m}(y^{2m+4}) - y^{3m}(y^{m+2}) + y^{3m}(y^{m+n})$
$= y^{3m+(2m+4)} - y^{3m+(m+2)} + y^{3m+(m+n)} = y^{5m+4} - y^{4m+2} + y^{4m+n}$

35. $5^{3m} = 5^3 \cdot (5^m)^2$; $5^{3m} = 5^3(5^{m \cdot 2})$; $5^{3m} = 5^3 \cdot 5^{2m}$; $5^{3m} = 5^{3+2m}$; $3m = 3 + 2m$; $m = 3$

36. $3 \cdot (9)^{2k} = (3^5)^k$; $3 \cdot (3^2)^{2k} = 3^{5k}$; $3 \cdot 3^{4k} = 3^{5k}$; $3^{1+4k} = 3^{5k}$; $4k + 1 = 5k$; $k = 1$

C   37. 1. $a^m \cdot a^n = (a \cdot a \cdot \ldots \cdot a)(a \cdot a \cdot \ldots \cdot a)$ (Def. of a power)
    m factors n factors

2. $(a \cdot a \cdot \ldots \cdot a)(a \cdot a \cdot \ldots \cdot a) = a \cdot a \cdot \ldots \cdot a$ (Assoc. prop. for mult.)
    m factors n factors $m + n$ factors

3. $a \cdot a \cdot \ldots \cdot a = a^{m+n}$ (Def. of a power)
    $m + n$ factors

4. $a^m \cdot a^n = a^{m+n}$ (Trans. prop. of equal.)

38. 1. $(a^m)^n = a^m \cdot a^m \cdot \ldots \cdot a^m$ (Def. of a power)
    n factors

2. $a^m \cdot a^m \cdot \ldots \cdot a^m = a^{m+m+\ldots+m}$ (First law of exp.)
    n factors n addends

3. $a^{m+m+\ldots+m} = a^{mn}$ (Def. of mult.)   4. $(a^m)^n = a^{mn}$ (Trans. prop. of equal.)
    n addends

39. 1. $((a^m)^n)^r = (a^{mn})^r$ (Third law of exp.)   2. $(a^{mn})^r = a^{(mn)r}$ (Third law of exp.)

3. $a^{(mn)r} = a^{mnr}$ (Assoc. prop. for mult.)   4. $((a^m)^n)^r = a^{mnr}$ (Trans. prop. of equal.)

40. 1. $(a^m)^n = a^{mn}$ (Third law of exp.)   2. $mn = nm$ (Comm. prop. for mult.)
3. $a^{mn} = a^{nm}$ (Subst.)   4. $a^{nm} = (a^n)^m$ (Third law of exp.)
5. $(a^m)^n = (a^n)^m$ (Trans. prop.)

Pages 165-166 · WRITTEN EXERCISES

A   1. $(3x + 2)(4x - 1) = 3x(4x - 1) + 2(4x - 1) = 12x^2 - 3x + 8x - 2$
    $= 12x^2 + 5x - 2$

2. $(2u - 5)(3u + 5) = 2u(3u + 5) - 5(3u + 5) = 6u^2 + 10u - 15u - 25$
    $= 6u^2 - 5u - 25$

3. $(2t - 7)(7t - 2) = 2t(7t - 2) - 7(7t - 2) = 14t^2 - 4t - 49t + 14$
    $= 14t^2 - 53t + 14$

4. $(3x - 5)(2x - 7) = 3x(2x - 7) - 5(2x - 7) = 6x^2 - 21x - 10x + 35$
    $= 6x^2 - 31x + 35$

5. $(5y - 4)(5y + 4) = (5y)^2 - 4^2 = 25y^2 - 16$

6. $(7a + 3)^2 = (7a)^2 + 2(7a)(3) + 3^2 = 49a^2 + 42a + 9$

7. $(10 - 7x)^2 = 10^2 - 2(10)(7x) + (7x)^2 = 100 - 140x + 49x^2$

8. $(2 + 11t)(2 - 11t) = 2^2 - (11t)^2 = 4 - 121t^2$

9. $(9a + 4)(3a + 2) = 9a(3a + 2) + 4(3a + 2) = 27a^2 + 18a + 12a + 8$
$= 27a^2 + 30a + 8$

10. $(6c - 5)(5c + 6) = 6c(5c + 6) - 5(5c + 6) = 30c^2 + 36c - 25c - 30$
$= 30c^2 + 11c - 30$

11. $(12z + 1)(1 - 12z) = (1 + 12z)(1 - 12z) = 1^2 - (12z)^2 = 1 - 144z^2$

12. $(10 - 3t)(3t - 10) = (-1)(3t - 10)(3t - 10) = -(3t - 10)^2 = -(9t^2 - 60t + 100)$
$= -9t^2 + 60t - 100$

13. $(2x - 5y)(3x - 2y) = 2x(3x - 2y) - 5y(3x - 2y) = 6x^2 - 4xy - 15xy + 10y^2$
$= 6x^2 - 19xy + 10y^2$

14. $(7a + 2b)(2a + 5b) = 7a(2a + 5b) + 2b(2a + 5b) = 14a^2 + 35ab + 4ab + 10b^2$
$= 14a^2 + 39ab + 10b^2$

15. $(u + 6v)(2u - 5v) = u(2u - 5v) + 6v(2u - 5v) = 2u^2 - 5uv + 12uv - 30v^2$
$= 2u^2 + 7uv - 30v^2$

16. $(s - t)(11s + 13t) = s(11s + 13t) - t(11s + 13t) = 11s^2 + 13st - 11st - 13t^2$
$= 11s^2 + 2st - 13t^2$

17. $(a^2 - 2)(a^2 + 2) = (a^2)^2 - 2^2 = a^4 - 4$

18. $(2x^2 - 1)^2 = (2x^2)^2 - 2(2x^2)(1) + 1^2 = 4x^4 - 4x^2 + 1$

19. $(s^3 - t^3)^2 = (s^3)^2 - 2(s^3)(t^3) + (t^3)^2 = s^6 - 2s^3t^3 + t^6$

20. $(x^2 - y^2)(y^2 + x^2) = (x^2 - y^2)(x^2 + y^2) = (x^2)^2 - (y^2)^2 = x^4 - y^4$

21. $x(x - 1)(x - 2) = x[x(x - 2) - 1(x - 2)] = x(x^2 - 2x - x + 2) = x(x^2 - 3x + 2)$
$= x^3 - 3x^2 + 2x$

22. $t^2(t - 1)(t + 1) = t^2[t^2 - (1)^2] = t^2(t^2 - 1) = t^4 - t^2$

23. $uv(u + v)^2 = uv(u^2 + 2uv + v^2) = u^3v + 2u^2v^2 + uv^3$

24. $ab(2a - b)^2 = ab[(2a)^2 - 2(2a)(b) + b^2] = ab(4a^2 - 4ab + b^2)$
$= 4a^3b - 4a^2b^2 + ab^3$

25. $(x^2 - 5x + 6)(x^2 + 6x) = x^2(x^2 + 6x) - 5x(x^2 + 6x) + 6(x^2 + 6x)$
$= x^4 + 6x^3 - 5x^3 - 30x^2 + 6x^2 + 36x = x^4 + x^3 - 24x^2 + 36x$

26. $(x^2 + 4x + 7)(x^2 - 5x) = x^2(x^2 - 5x) + 4x(x^2 - 5x) + 7(x^2 - 5x)$
$= x^4 - 5x^3 + 4x^3 - 20x^2 + 7x^2 - 35x = x^4 - x^3 - 13x^2 - 35x$

27. $(7 - 2x - x^2)(x^2 + 4x) = 7(x^2 + 4x) - 2x(x^2 + 4x) - x^2(x^2 + 4x)$
$= 7x^2 + 28x - 2x^3 - 8x^2 - x^4 - 4x^3 = -x^4 - 6x^3 - x^2 + 28x$

28. $(2x^2 - 10x + 3)(6 - x) = 2x^2(6 - x) - 10x(6 - x) + 3(6 - x)$
    $= 12x^2 - 2x^3 - 60x + 10x^2 + 18 - 3x = -2x^3 + 22x^2 - 63x + 18$

29. $(2x + y)(y - 2x) = (y + 2x)(y - 2x) = y^2 - (2x)^2 = y^2 - 4x^2$

30. $(a + bi)(a - bi) = a^2 - (bi)^2 = a^2 - b^2i^2$

B 31. $(a - b)(a + b + 1) = a(a + b + 1) - b(a + b + 1) = a^2 + ab + a - ab - b^2 - b$
    $= a^2 + a - b^2 - b$

32. $(x + y)(x - y + 1) = x(x - y + 1) + y(x - y + 1)$
    $= x^2 - xy + x + xy - y^2 + y = x^2 + x - y^2 + y$

33. $(2x^2 + 5x + 6)(x^2 - 6x + 10) = 2x^2(x^2 - 6x + 10) + 5x(x^2 - 6x + 10)$
    $+ 6(x^2 - 6x + 10) = 2x^4 - 12x^3 + 20x^2 + 5x^3 - 30x^2 + 50x + 6x^2 - 36x + 60$
    $= 2x^4 - 7x^3 - 4x^2 + 14x + 60$

34. $(4t^2 - 7t + 13)(t^2 - 10t - 9) = 4t^2(t^2 - 10t - 9) - 7t(t^2 - 10t - 9)$
    $+ 13(t^2 - 10t - 9) = 4t^4 - 40t^3 - 36t^2 - 7t^3 + 70t^2 + 63t + 13t^2 - 130t - 117$
    $= 4t^4 - 47t^3 + 47t^2 - 67t - 117$

35. $(3y^2 - 7y + 7)(y^2 + 15y + 12) = 3y^2(y^2 + 15y + 12) - 7y(y^2 + 15y + 12)$
    $+ 7(y^2 + 15y + 12) = 3y^4 + 45y^3 + 36y^2 - 7y^3 - 105y^2 - 84y + 7y^2 + 105y$
    $+ 84 = 3y^4 + 38y^3 - 62y^2 + 21y + 84$

36. $(u^2 + 10u - 9)(3u^2 + 7u + 10) = u^2(3u^2 + 7u + 10) + 10u(3u^2 + 7u + 10)$
    $- 9(3u^2 + 7u + 10) = 3u^4 + 7u^3 + 10u^2 + 30u^3 + 70u^2 + 100u - 27u^2 - 63u$
    $- 90 = 3u^4 + 37u^3 + 53u^2 + 37u - 90$

37. $(x^n - 2)^2 = (x^n)^2 - 2(x^n)(2) + 2^2 = x^{2n} - 4x^n + 4$

38. $(z^n + 1)(z^n - 1) = (z^n)^2 - 1^2 = z^{2n} - 1$

39. $(x^n + y^n)(x^n - 2y^n) = x^n(x^n - 2y^n) + y^n(x^n - 2y^n) = x^{2n} - 2x^ny^n + x^ny^n - 2y^{2n}$
    $= x^{2n} - x^ny^n - 2y^{2n}$

40. $(a^{2n} + b^n)^2 = (a^{2n})^2 + 2(a^{2n})(b^n) + (b^n)^2 = a^{4n} + 2a^{2n}b^n + b^{2n}$

41. $(a + b)^3 = (a + b)(a + b)^2 = a + b(a^2 + 2ab + b^2)$
    $= a(a^2 + 2ab + b^2) + b(a^2 + 2ab + b^2) = a^3 + 2a^2b + ab^2 + a^2b + 2ab^2 + b^3$
    $= a^3 + 3a^2b + 3ab^2 + b^3$

42. $(a - b)^3 = (a - b)(a - b)^2 = (a - b)(a^2 - 2ab + b^2)$
    $= a(a^2 - 2ab + b^2) - b(a^2 - 2ab + b^2) = a^3 - 2a^2b + ab^2 - a^2b + 2ab^2 - b^3$
    $= a^3 - 3a^2b + 3ab^2 - b^3$

43. $(a + b)(a^2 - ab + b^2) = a(a^2 - ab + b^2) + b(a^2 - ab + b^2)$
    $= a^3 - a^2b + ab^2 + a^2b - ab^2 + b^3 = a^3 + b^3$

44. $(a - b)(a^2 + ab + b^2) = a(a^2 + ab + b^2) - b(a^2 + ab + b^2)$
    $= a^3 + a^2b + ab^2 - a^2b - ab^2 - b^3 = a^3 - b^3$

45. $(u + v)(u - v)(u^2 + v^2) = (u^2 - v^2)(u^2 + v^2) = (u^2)^2 - (v^2)^2 = u^4 - v^4$

46. $(a + b)^2 - (a - b)^2 = [(a + b) + (a - b)][(a + b) - (a - b)] = 2a(2b) = 4ab$

C **47.** 4 terms   **48.** 9 terms   **49.** 4 terms   **50.** 4 terms

51. $(x - k)(x + 2k) = x(x + 2k) - k(x + 2k) = x^2 + 2kx - kx - 2k^2;\ x^2 + kx - 2k^2$
$= x^2 - 3x - 18;\ k = -3$

52. $(2x + k)(x - 2k) = 2x(x - 2k) + k(x - 2k) = 2x^2 - 4kx + kx - 2k^2$
$= 2x^2 - 3kx - 2k^2;\ 2x^2 - 3kx - 2k^2 = 2x^2 + 3x - 2;\ k = -1$

53. $(x + k)(3x + 2k) = x(3x + 2k) + k(3x + 2k) = 3x^2 + 2kx + 3kx + 2k^2$
$= 3x^2 + 5kx + 2k^2;\ 3x^2 + 5kx + 2k^2 = 3x^2 + 5kx + 50;\ 2k^2 = 50;\ k^2 = 25;\ k = 5$
or $k = -5$

54. $(kx + 3)^2 = (kx)^2 + 2(kx)(3) + 3^2 = k^2x^2 + 6kx + 9;\ k^2x^2 + 6kx + 9$
$= 4x^2 + 6kx + 9;\ k^2 = 4;\ k = 2$ or $k = -2$

Page 167 · READING ALGEBRA

1. a. Two divides eight; true   **b.** Four divides four; true
   c. Two divides one; false   **d.** Two divides zero; true
   e. Zero divides three; false

2. does not equal (or is not equal to); does not divide

3. a. true   **b.** true   **c.** false

4. yes   **5.** no   **6.** $17 \equiv -3 \pmod{5}$

7. $n | (a - b)$ **8.** yes

9. a. One hundred is congruent to twenty-five (mod five); true
   b. Negative three is congruent to three (mod five); false
   c. Six is congruent to one (mod five); true
   d. Zero is congruent to five (mod five); true

10. even integers   **11.** odd integers

12. Answers may vary. Examples: **a.** $n = 2$ **b.** $n = 2$

Pages 170-171 · WRITTEN EXERCISES

A   **1.** $2 \cdot 3 \cdot 5 \cdot 7$ **2.** $2 \cdot 3^2 \cdot 7$ **3.** $3 \cdot 29$

   4. prime   **5.** $3^2 \cdot 11^2$ **6.** $2^2 \cdot 3^5$

   7. $3^4 \cdot 5 \cdot 7$ **8.** $2^2 \cdot 7^2 \cdot 11$

   9. $15 = 3 \cdot 5$ and $35 = 5 \cdot 7$ **a.** 5   **b.** 105

   10. $56 = 2^3 \cdot 7$ and $98 = 2 \cdot 7^2$ **a.** 14   **b.** 392

   11. $72 = 2^3 \cdot 3^2$ and $108 = 2^2 \cdot 3^3$ **a.** 36   **b.** 216

   12. $150 = 2 \cdot 3 \cdot 5^2$ and $315 = 3^2 \cdot 5 \cdot 7$ **a.** 15   **b.** 3150

   13. $280 = 2^3 \cdot 5 \cdot 7$, $168 = 2^3 \cdot 3 \cdot 7$, and $196 = 2^2 \cdot 7^2$ **a.** 28   **b.** 5880

14. $126 = 2 \cdot 3^2 \cdot 7$, $189 = 3^3 \cdot 7$, and $315 = 3^2 \cdot 5 \cdot 7$ **a.** 63 **b.** 1890

15. 5, 7, and 11 are prime and $9 = 3^2$ **a.** 1 **b.** 3465

16. $30 = 2 \cdot 3 \cdot 5$, 11 is prime, $36 = 2^2 \cdot 3^2$, and $66 = 2 \cdot 3 \cdot 11$ **a.** 1 **b.** 1980

17. $6a^3x = 2 \cdot 3a^3x$ and $15a^2x^2 = 3 \cdot 5a^2x^2$ **a.** $3a^2x$ **b.** $30a^3x^2$

18. $12u^3 = 2^2 \cdot 3u^3$ and $18u^2v = 2 \cdot 3^2u^2v$ **a.** $6u^2$ **b.** $36u^3v$

19. $42xyz = 2 \cdot 3 \cdot 7xyz$ and $60xz^2 = 2^2 \cdot 3 \cdot 5xz^2$ **a.** $6xz$ **b.** $420xyz^2$

20. $34x^3y = 2 \cdot 17x^3y$ and $51xy^3 = 3 \cdot 17xy^3$ **a.** $17xy$ **b.** $102x^3y^3$

21. $52a^2st^3 = 2^2 \cdot 13a^2st^3$ and $65as^2t^2 = 5 \cdot 13as^2t^2$ **a.** $13ast^2$ **b.** $260a^2s^2t^3$

22. $132ab^2c^3 = 2^2 \cdot 3 \cdot 11ab^2c^3$ and $-110a^2b^2c^2 = -1 \cdot 2 \cdot 5 \cdot 11a^2b^2c^2$ **a.** $22ab^2c^2$
    b. $660a^2b^2c^3$

23. $4uv^2w = 2^2uv^2w$, $8uvw^2 = 2^3uvw^2$ **a.** $2uvw$ **b.** $8u^2v^2w^2$

24. $6xyz = 2 \cdot 3xyz$ **a.** $3xy$ **b.** $6x^2y^2z$

25. $63a^2b^3c = 3^2 \cdot 7a^2b^3c$, $42a^3b^2c^2 = 2 \cdot 3 \cdot 7a^3b^2c^2$, and $105a^2b^3 = 3 \cdot 5 \cdot 7a^2b^3$
    a. $21a^2b^2$ **b.** $630a^3b^3c^2$

26. $225p^3qr^2 = 3^2 \cdot 5^2p^3qr^2$, $135p^2q^2r^2 = 3^3 \cdot 5p^2q^2r^2$, and $180p^3r^3 = 2^2 \cdot 3^2 \cdot 5p^3r^3$
    a. $45p^2r^2$ **b.** $2700p^3q^2r^3$

B **27.** $1, p, q, pq, p^2, q^2, q^3, pq^2, pq^3, p^2q, p^2q^2, p^2q^3, -1, -p, -q, -pq, -p^2, -q^2, -q^3, -pq^2,$
    $-pq^3, -p^2q, -p^2q^2, -p^2q^3$

28. $496 = 2^4 \cdot 31$; the positive factors of 496 are 1, 2, 4, 8, 16, 31, 62, 124, 248, and 496;
    $1 + 2 + 4 + 8 + 16 + 31 + 62 + 124 + 248 = 496$

29. $6 = 2 \cdot 3$ and $6 = 1 + 2 + 3$; $28 = 2^2 \cdot 7$ and $28 = 1 + 2 + 4 + 7 + 14$

30. The LCM of two numbers is the product of the greatest power of each prime factor of
    both numbers. If the numbers are relatively prime, they have no factors in common and
    the LCM is the product of the prime factors.

31. If the integers are divided by their GCF, the resulting quotients have no common factors
    other than 1 and are relatively prime.

C **32.** False; 2 and 3 are relatively prime, as are 3 and 4, but 2 and 4 are not relatively prime
    since their GCF is 2.

33. Let h, k, m, and n be integers such that $hm - kn = 1$ and suppose m and n are not
    relatively prime. Then there is an integer $x > 1$ and integers y and z such that $m = xy$
    and $n = xz$. Then $hxy - kxz = 1$ or $x(hy - kz) = 1$ and $hy - kz$ is the reciprocal of
    x. Since h, y, k, and z are integers, so is $hy - kz$. There are only two integers whose
    reciprocals are integers, -1 and 1. This contradicts the fact that $x > 1$. It follows that
    m and n are relatively prime.

34. Let m and n be the two integers. Then $m = 84p$ and $n = 84q$, with p, q relatively prime. Since 252 is the LCM of m and n, $\dfrac{252}{84p}$ and $\dfrac{252}{84q}$ are integers. But $\dfrac{252}{84p} = \dfrac{3}{p}$ and $\dfrac{252}{84q} = \dfrac{3}{q}$. Thus $p = 3$ and $q = 1$ or $q = 3$ and $p = 1$. The numbers are 84 and 252.

35. The other monomial has no factor of 3, a factor of 2, a factor of 5, a factor of a and 4 factors of x. The monomial is $10ax^4$.

Page 171 · CALCULATOR KEY-IN

Answers may vary according to the number of digits displayed.

1. 8641.501548	**2.** 43046721	**3.** 1651.501304
4. 140.4831108	**5.** 0.000038416	**6.** 0.089311826
7. 1.068736482	**8.** 2.704813829	**9.** 1.9998957
10. 20674.99195		

Pages 174-175 · WRITTEN EXERCISES

A   **1.** $15z^2(z - 4)$ **2.** $8ab(2a + 3b)$ **3.** $(x + 11)(x - 11)$

4. $(z - 11)^2$ **5.** $(a + 13)^2$ **6.** $(4x + 1)(4x - 1)$

7. $3x(4x^2 - 1) = 3x(2x + 1)(2x - 1)$ **8.** $2t(4t^2 - 4t + 1) = 2t(2t - 1)^2$

9. $(2t - 3)^2$ **10.** $(5x + 2)^2$

11. $9(9a^2 - b^2) = 9(3a + b)(3a - b)$ **12.** $4(x^2 - 4y^2) = 4(x + 2y)(x - 2y)$

13. $(u + 3)(u^2 - 3u + 9)$ **14.** $z(z^3 - 8) = z(z - 2)(z^2 + 2z + 4)$

15. $(x - 10y)^2$ **16.** $uv(u^3 + v^3) = uv(u + v)(u^2 - uv + v^2)$

17. $st(9s^2 - 6st + t^2) = st(3s - t)^2$ **18.** $2(16x^2 - 24xy + 9y^2) = 2(4x - 3y)^2$

19. $2xy(8y^3 - x^3) = 2xy(2y - x)(4y^2 + 2xy + x^2)$

20. $(x^3 - y^2)^2$ **21.** $(x + 2)(y - 1)$ **22.** $(a - 2)(b + 3)$

23. $(x - 2)(y - 1)$ or $(2 - x)(1 - y)$ **24.** $(a + 2)(b - 3)$

25. $xy - 3y + 2x - 6 = y(x - 3) + 2(x - 3) = (y + 2)(x - 3)$

26. $ab + 5b - (2a + 10) = b(a + 5) - 2(a + 5) = (b - 2)(a + 5)$

27. $2xy - 4x + (y - 2) = 2x(y - 2) + 1(y - 2) = (2x + 1)(y - 2)$

28. $3ab + 2b - (3a + 2) = b(3a + 2) - 1(3a + 2) = (b - 1)(3a + 2)$

29. $(u + 1)^2 - v^2 = (u + 1 + v)(u + 1 - v)$

30. $(p - 2)^2 - q^2 = (p - 2 + q)(p - 2 - q)$

31. $u^2 + 4u + 4 - v^2 = (u + 2)^2 - v^2 = (u + 2 + v)(u + 2 - v)$

32. $p^2 + 4p + 4 - 4q^2 = (p + 2)^2 - 4q^2 = (p + 2 + 2q)(p + 2 - 2q)$

B 33. $4(x^4 + 2x^2 + 1) = 4(x^2 + 1)^2$ 34. $(3t^2 - 1)^2$

35. $(x^2 + 3)(x^4 - 3x^2 + 9)$ 36. $(2 + 5y)(4 - 10y + 25y^2)$

37. $(9x^2 + 4)(9x^2 - 4) = (9x^2 + 4)(3x + 2)(3x - 2)$

38. $(a^2 + b^2)(a^2 - b^2) = (a^2 + b^2)(a + b)(a - b)$

39. $(a^3 + b^3)(a^3 - b^3) = (a + b)(a^2 - ab + b^2)(a - b)(a^2 + ab + b^2)$

40. $(x^3 + 8)(x^3 - 8) = (x + 2)(x^2 - 2x + 4)(x - 2)(x^2 + 2x + 4)$

41. $(z^2 + a)(z^4 - z^2a + a^2)$ 42. $(z^3 + a)(z^3 - a)$

43. $[(x + 1) + 1][(x^2 + 2x + 1) - (x + 1) + 1] = (x + 2)(x^2 + x + 1)$

44. $[(u - 2) - 2][(u^2 - 4u + 4) + 2(u - 2) + 4] = (u - 4)(u^2 - 2u + 4)$

45. $[(x + y) - (x - y)][(x^2 + 2xy + y^2) + (x^2 - y^2) + (x^2 - 2xy + y^2)]$
$= 2y(3x^2 + y^2)$

46. $[(x + y) + (x - y)][(x^2 + 2xy + y^2) - (x^2 - y^2) + (x^2 - 2xy + y^2)]$
$= 2x(x^2 + 3y^2)$

C 47. $[(a + d)^2 - (a - d)^2][(a + d)^4 + (a + d)^2(a - d)^2 + (a - d)^4]$
$= [a^2 + 2ad + d^2 - (a^2 - 2ad + d^2)][(a + d)^4 + (a^2 - d^2)^2 + (a - d)^4]$
$= 4ad[(a^4 + 4a^3d + 6a^2d^2 + 4ad^3 + d^4) + (a^4 - 2a^2d^2 + d^4)$
$+ (a^4 - 4a^3d + 6a^2d^2 - 4ad^3 + d^4)] = 4ad(3a^4 + 10a^2d^2 + 3d^4)$
$= 4ad(3a^2 + d^2)(a^2 + 3d^2)$

48. $[r(t + s)]^2 - [r(t - s)]^2 = r^2(t + s)^2 - r^2(t - s)^2 = r^2[(t + s)^2 - (t - s)^2]$
$= r^2[(t + s) + (t - s)][(t + s) - (t - s)] = r^2(2t)(2s) = 4r^2st$

49. $(x^n + 1)(x^n - 1)$ 50. $(x^n - 1)^2$ 51. $(x^n + y^n)(x^n - y^n)$

52. $(x^n + y^n)(x^{2n} - x^ny^n + y^{2n})$ 53. $(x^n - n)(x^{2n} + x^nn + n^2)$

54. $(x^{2n} + n^2)(x^{2n} - n^2) = (x^{2n} + n^2)(x^n + n)(x^n - n)$

55. $x^4 + x^2 + 1 = x^4 + 2x^2 + 1 - x^2 = (x^2 + 1)^2 - x^2 = (x^2 + 1 + x)(x^2 + 1 - x)$

56. $x^4 + 4 = x^4 + 4x^2 + 4 - 4x^2 = (x^2 + 2)^2 - (2x)^2 = (x^2 + 2 + 2x)(x^2 + 2 - 2x)$

57. $x^4 + x^2y^2 + y^4 = x^4 + 2x^2y^2 + y^4 - x^2y^2 = (x^2 + y^2)^2 - (xy)^2$
$= (x^2 + y^2 + xy)(x^2 + y^2 - xy)$

58. $x^4 + 4y^4 = x^4 + 4x^2y^2 + 4y^4 - 4x^2y^2 = (x^2 + 2y^2)^2 - (2xy)^2$
$= (x^2 + 2y^2 + 2xy)(x^2 + 2y^2 - 2xy)$

59. **a.** $x^4 - y^4 = (x^2 - y^2)(x^2 + y^2) = (x - y)(x + y)(x^2 + y^2)$
b. $(x^8 - y^8) = (x^4 - y^4)(x^4 + y^4) = (x^2 - y^2)(x^2 + y^2)(x^4 + y^4)$
$= (x - y)(x + y)(x^2 + y^2)(x^4 + y^4)$
c. $x^n - y^n = (x - y)(x + y)(x^2 + y^2)(x^4 + y^4) \cdots (x^{n/2} + y^{n/2})$

Page 175 · COMPUTER EXERCISES

1. Answers may vary. A sample program is given.

```
10  INPUT A, B, C
20  FOR I = 1 TO A
30  IF I * I = A THEN 60
40  NEXT I
50  GOTO 170
60  FOR J = 1 TO C
70  IF J * J = C THEN 100
80  NEXT J
90  GOTO 170
100 IF B = 2 * I * J THEN 130
110 IF B = −2 * I * J THEN 150
120 GOTO 170
130 PRINT "(";I; "X + ";J; "Y") ("I; "X + ";J "Y")"
140 GOTO 180
150 PRINT "(";I; "X − ";J; "Y") ("I; "X − ";J "Y")"
160 GOTO 180
170 PRINT A; "X ↑ 2 + ";B; "XY + ";C; "NOT A PERFECT SQUARE"
180 END
```

2. **a.** $(1X − 28Y)(1X − 28Y)$ **b.** $(3X + 24Y)(3X + 24Y)$
   c. $64X ↑ 2 + 56XY + 49$ NOT A PERFECT SQUARE
   d. $(25X − 21Y)(25X − 21Y)$

3. Answers may vary. For example, change line 170 and add line 15 and lines 190 through 320, as follows:

```
15  IF B = 0 THEN 190
170 PRINT A; "X ↑ 2 + ";B; "XY + ";C; "NOT A PERFECT SQUARE OR DIFF OF
    SQUARES"
190 IF C < 0 THEN 220
200 PRINT A; "X ↑ 2 + ";B; "XY + ";C; "NOT A PERFECT SQUARE OR DIFF OF
    SQUARES"
210 END
220 FOR I = 1 TO A
230 IF I * I = A THEN 260
240 NEXT I
250 GOTO 200
260 CP = −C
270 FOR J = 1 TO CP
```

(continued)

280 IF J * J = CP THEN 310
290 NEXT J
300 GOTO 200
310 PRINT "(";I; "X + ";J; "Y) (";I; "X − ";J "Y)"
320 END

4. a. $(12X − 2Y)(12X − 2Y)$ **b.** $(12X + 2Y)(12X − 2Y)$

c. $(12X + 2Y)(12X + 2Y)$

d. $144X \uparrow 2 + 0XY + 4$ NOT A PERFECT SQUARE OR DIFF OF SQUARES

Pages 179-180 · WRITTEN EXERCISES

A   **1.** $(x − 7)(x − 1)$ **2.** $(y + 6)(y + 2)$ **3.** $(t + 6)(t + 3)$

4. $(x − 10)(x − 2)$ **5.** $(u + 14)(u + 2)$ **6.** $(x − 11)(x − 1)$

7. $(u + 6)^2$ **8.** prime   **9.** prime

10. $(v + 18)(v + 2)$ **11.** $(4s − 1)(3s + 1)$ **12.** $(5t + 1)(3t + 1)$

13. $(6 + x)(5 − x)$ **14.** $(6 + t)(4 − t)$ **15.** $(x − 5y)(x + 4y)$

16. $(6x + y)(3x + y)$ **17.** $(6 + x)(3 − x)$ **18.** $(z − 15w)(z + 5w)$

19. $(2t + 1)(t + 2)$ **20.** $(3x + 1)(x − 1)$ **21.** $(3 − 2t)(2 + 3t)$

22. $(5 + 2w)(1 − 3w)$ **23.** $(1 − s)(1 + 5s)$ **24.** prime

25. prime   **26.** $(2t − 3)(t + 2)$ **27.** prime

28. $(6x − 5y)(x + y)$ **29.** $(2x − 3)(x + 5)$ **30.** $(5u − 3)(u + 1)$

B   **31.** $(3t + 5)(2t − 3)$ **32.** $(5z + 6)(3z + 1)$ **33.** prime

34. $(2x − 5)^2$ **35.** $(3h + 4k)(2h − 5k)$ **36.** $2(2u + 3v)(u − v)$

37. $x^2(4x^2 − 9) = x^2(2x + 3)(2x − 3)$ **38.** $x(4x − 15)(x − 1)$

39. $x(3x − 1)(2x + 1)$ **40.** $3x^2(x^3 + 8y^3) = 3x^2(x + 2y)(x^2 − 2xy + 4y^2)$

41. $(x^2 + y^2)(x^2 − y^2) = (x^2 + y^2)(x + y)(x − y)$

42. $(x^3 + y^3)(x^3 − y^3) = (x + y)(x^2 − xy + y^2)(x − y)(x^2 + xy + y^2)$

43. $(x^2 − 4)(x^2 − 1) = (x + 2)(x − 2)(x + 1)(x − 1)$

44. $(z^2 − 9)(z^2 + 1) = (z + 3)(z − 3)(z^2 + 1)$

45. $\left(x − \dfrac{1}{3}\right)\left(x + \dfrac{1}{2}\right)$ **46.** $\left(t + \dfrac{2}{3}\right)\left(t − \dfrac{1}{5}\right)$ **47.** $(1.1x + 0.4)^2$

48. $(1.2x + 0.2)^2$

49. $x^2 + x − 6 = (x + 3)(x − 2)$; $x^2 − 4x + 4 = (x − 2)^2$; GCF $= x − 2$

50. $x^2 − 9 = (x + 3)(x − 3)$; $x^2 + 2x − 3 = (x + 3)(x − 1)$; GCF $= x + 3$

51. $z^3 − 4z = z(z + 2)(z − 2)$; $z^3 − 2z^2 = z^2(z − 2)$; $z^3 − z^2 − 2z = z(z − 2)(z + 1)$;
GCF $= z(z − 2)$

52. $(t^2 - t)^2 = (t(t - 1))^2 = t^2(t - 1)^2$; $t^3 - t = t(t^2 - 1) = t(t + 1)(t - 1)$;
   $t^3 + t^2 - 2t = t(t^2 + t - 2) = t(t + 2)(t - 1)$; GCF $= t(t - 1)$

53. $x^2 - y^2 = (x + y)(x - y)$; $x^3 - y^3 = (x - y)(x^2 + xy + y^2)$; GCF $= x - y$

54. $u^2 - v^2 = (u + v)(u - v)$; $u^3 + v^3 = (u + v)(u^2 + uv + v^2)$; GCF $= u + v$

55. Suppose $x^2 + x + k$ is not prime. Then there are integers r and s such that $rs = k$ and
   $r + s = 1$. Since k is positive r and s are both negative or both positive. The sum of two
   negative numbers is negative so r and s must both be positive. But the sum of two
   positive integers is greater than or equal to 2. Thus there can be no such integers r and
   s and $x^2 + x + k$ is prime.

56. $x^2 + (k + 1)x + k = (x + k)(x + 1)$ for all positive integers k.

57. $(x^{2n} + a^{2n})(x^{2n} - a^{2n}) = (x^{2n} + a^{2n})(x^n + a^n)(x^n - a^n)$

58. $(x^{3n} + a^{3n})(x^{3n} - a^{3n}) = (x^n + a^n)(x^{2n} - x^n a^n + a^{2n})(x^n - a^n)(x^{2n} + x^n a^n + a^{2n})$

59. $[(x^2 + 2x - 5) + (x^2 + 1)][(x^2 + 2x - 5) - (x^2 + 1)] = (2x^2 + 2x - 4)(2x - 6)$
   $= [2(x^2 + x - 2)][2(x - 3)] = 4(x + 2)(x - 1)(x - 3)$

60. $[(x^2 + x - 1) + (x^2 - x - 1)][(x^2 + x - 1) - (x^2 - x - 1)] = (2x^2 - 2)(2x)$
   $= [2(x^2 - 1)](2x) = 4x(x + 1)(x - 1)$

61. $(x^{2n} - 4)(x^{2n} - 1) = (x^n + 2)(x^n - 2)(x^n + 1)(x^n - 1)$

62. $(x^{4n} - 1)^2 = [(x^{2n} + 1)(x^{2n} - 1)]^2 = [(x^{2n} + 1)(x^n + 1)(x^n - 1)]^2$
   $= (x^{2n} + 1)^2(x^n + 1)^2(x^n - 1)^2$

63. $[(a + b + c) - (a - b + c)]^2 = (2b)^2 = 4b^2$

64. $x^3 - 2x^2 - 2x - 3 = x^3 - 2x^2 - 3x + x - 3 = x(x^2 - 2x - 3) + (x - 3)$
   $= x(x + 1)(x - 3) + (x - 3) = (x - 3)[x(x + 1) + 1] = (x - 3)(x^2 + x + 1)$;
   the other factor is $x^2 + x + 1$.

Page 182 · COMPUTER KEY-IN

1. $(3 * X + 8) * (4 * X + -15)$

2. $(3 * X + -8) * (-5 * X + -6)$

3. $(1 * X + -8) * (6 * X + -7)$

4. $1X \uparrow 2 + 5 * X + -4$ IS IRREDUCIBLE.

5. $(1 * X + -1) * (2 * X + 10)$

6. $(2 * X + 5) * (2 * X + -5)$

Pages 185-187 · WRITTEN EXERCISES

A 1. $x - 3 = 0$ or $x + 5 = 0$; $x = 3$ or $x = -5$; $\{3, -5\}$

   2. $t = 0$ or $t + 2 = 0$; $t = 0$ or $t = -2$; $\{0, -2\}$

3. $5t + 1 = 0$ or $t - 5 = 0$; $t = -\dfrac{1}{5}$ or $t = 5$; $\left\{-\dfrac{1}{5}, 5\right\}$

4. $2t - 3 = 0$ or $(t - 1)^2 = 0$; $t = \dfrac{3}{2}$ or $t = 1$ (double root); $\left\{\dfrac{3}{2}, 1\right\}$

5. $x^2 = 0$ or $(3x + 2)^2 = 0$; $x = 0$ (double root) or $x = -\dfrac{2}{3}$ (double root); $\left\{0, -\dfrac{2}{3}\right\}$

6. $x + 1 = 0$, $x + 2 = 0$, or $x + 3 = 0$; $x = -1$ or $x = -2$, or $x = -3$; $\{-1, -2, -3\}$

7. $(u - 1)(u - 4) = 0$; $u - 1 = 0$ or $u - 4 = 0$; $u = 1$ or $u = 4$; $\{1, 4\}$

8. $(x + 2)(x + 1) = 0$; $x + 2 = 0$ or $x + 1 = 0$; $x = -2$ or $x = -1$; $\{-2, -1\}$

9. $z(z - 9) = 0$; $z = 0$ or $z - 9 = 0$; $z = 0$ or $z = 9$; $\{0, 9\}$

10. $4z^2 - 16z = 0$; $4z(z - 4) = 0$; $4z = 0$ or $z - 4 = 0$; $z = 0$ or $z = 4$; $\{0, 4\}$

11. $x^2 - 6x + 9 = 0$; $(x - 3)^2 = 0$; $x - 3 = 0$; $x = 3$ (double root); $\{3\}$

12. $(t + 9)^2 = 0$; $t + 9 = 0$; $t = -9$ (double root); $\{-9\}$

13. $y(y^2 - 3y + 2) = 0$; $y(y - 2)(y - 1) = 0$; $y = 0$, $y - 2 = 0$, or $y - 1 = 0$; $y = 0$
    $y = 2$, or $y = 1$; $\{0, 2, 1\}$

14. $x^2(x^2 - 16) = 0$; $x^2(x + 4)(x - 4) = 0$; $x^2 = 0$, $x + 4 = 0$, or $x - 4 = 0$; $x =$
    (double root), $x = -4$, or $x = 4$; $\{0, -4, 4\}$

15. $(3t - 2)(t + 1) = 0$; $3t - 2 = 0$ or $t + 1 = 0$; $t = \dfrac{2}{3}$ or $t = -1$; $\left\{\dfrac{2}{3}, -1\right\}$

16. $(2x - 1)(x - 1) = 0$; $2x - 1 = 0$ or $x - 1 = 0$; $x = \dfrac{1}{2}$ or $x = 1$; $\left\{\dfrac{1}{2}, 1\right\}$

17. $6x^2 - 5x + 1 = 0$; $(2x - 1)(3x - 1) = 0$; $2x - 1 = 0$ or $3x - 1 = 0$;
    $x = \dfrac{1}{2}$ or $x = \dfrac{1}{3}$; $\left\{\dfrac{1}{2}, \dfrac{1}{3}\right\}$

18. $(3z - 2)(z + 3) = 0$; $3z - 2 = 0$ or $z + 3 = 0$; $z = \dfrac{2}{3}$ or $z = -3$; $\left\{\dfrac{2}{3}, -3\right\}$

19. $m^2 + 7m + 10 = 0$; $(m + 5)(m + 2) = 0$; $m + 5 = 0$ or $m + 2 = 0$; $m = -5$ o
    $m = -2$; $\{-5, -2\}$

20. $x^2 - 3x - 4 = 0$; $(x - 4)(x + 1) = 0$; $x - 4 = 0$ or $x + 1 = 0$; $x = 4$ or $x = -1$
    $\{4, -1\}$

21. $10y^2 - 5y = 0$; $5y(2y - 1) = 0$; $5y = 0$ or $2y - 1 = 0$; $y = 0$ or $y = \dfrac{1}{2}$; $\left\{0, \dfrac{1}{2}\right\}$

22. $x^2 - 4x + 4 = 0$; $(x - 2)^2 = 0$; $x - 2 = 0$; $x = 2$ (double root); $\{2\}$

23. $x^2 - 4 = 5$; $x^2 = 9$; $x = 3$ or $x = -3$; $\{3, -3\}$

24. $t^2 - 16 = 9$; $t^2 = 25$; $t = 5$ or $t = -5$; $\{5, -5\}$

25. $t^2 - 12t + 36 = t$; $t^2 - 13t + 36 = 0$; $(t - 9)(t - 4) = 0$; $t - 9 = 0$ or $t - 4 = 0$
    $t = 9$ or $t = 4$; $\{9, 4\}$

26. $x^2 - 8x + 16 = 2x; x^2 - 10x + 16 = 0; (x - 8)(x - 2) = 0; x - 8 = 0$ or $x - 2 = 0;$
$x = 8$ or $x = 2; \{8, 2\}$

27. $(x + 2)(x + 2)(x - 2) = 0; (x + 2)^2(x - 2) = 0; (x + 2)^2 = 0$ or $x - 2 = 0; x = -2$
(double root) or $x = 2; \{-2, 2\}$

28. $(t - 1)(t - 1)(t + 2) = 0; (t - 1)^2(t + 2) = 0; (t - 1)^2 = 0$ or $t + 2 = 0; t = 1$
(double root) or $t = -2; \{1, -2\}$

B **29.** $(x^2 - 4)^2 = 0; [(x + 2)(x - 2)]^2 = 0; (x + 2)^2(x - 2)^2 = 0; (x + 2)^2 = 0$ or
$(x - 2)^2 = 0; x = -2$ (double root) or $x = 2$ (double root); $\{2, -2\}$

30. $(x^2 - 9)(x^2 - 1) = 0; (x + 3)(x - 3)(x + 1)(x - 1) = 0; x + 3 = 0, x - 3 = 0,$
$x + 1 = 0,$ or $x - 1 = 0; x = -3, x = 3, x = -1,$ or $x = 1; \{-3, 3, -1, 1\}$

31. $t^6 - 5t^4 + 4t^2 = 0; t^2(t^4 - 5t^2 + 4) = 0; t^2(t^2 - 4)(t^2 - 1) = 0;$
$t^2(t + 2)(t - 2)(t + 1)(t - 1) = 0; t^2 = 0, t + 2 = 0, t - 2 = 0, t + 1 = 0,$ or
$t - 1 = 0; t = 0$ (double root), $t = -2, t = 2, t = -1,$ or $t = 0; \{0, -2, 2, -1, 1\}$

32. $z^6 + z^2 - 2z^4 = 0; z^2(z^4 - 2z^2 + 1) = 0; z^2(z^2 - 1)^2 = 0; z^2[(z + 1)(z - 1)]^2 = 0;$
$z^2(z + 1)^2(z - 1)^2 = 0; z^2 = 0, (z + 1)^2 = 0,$ or $(z - 1)^2 = 0; z = 0$ (double root),
$z = -1$ (double root), or $z = 1$ (double root); $\{0, -1, 1\}$

33. $10(0.1x^2 + 1.6x + 1.5) = 0; x^2 + 16x + 15 = 0; (x + 15)(x + 1) = 0; x + 15 = 0$ or
$x + 1 = 0; x = -15$ or $x = -1; \{-15, -1\}$

34. $10(0.2x^2 + 0.3x + 0.1) = 0; 2x^2 + 3x + 1 = 0; (2x + 1)(x + 1) = 0; 2x + 1 = 0$ or
$x + 1 = 0; x = -\dfrac{1}{2}$ or $x = -1; \left\{-\dfrac{1}{2}, -1\right\}$

35. $15\left(x^2 + \dfrac{13}{15}x + \dfrac{2}{15}\right) = 0; 15x^2 + 13x + 2 = 0; (5x + 1)(3x + 2) = 0; 5x + 1 = 0$ or

$3x + 2 = 0; x = -\dfrac{1}{5}$ or $x = -\dfrac{2}{3}; \left\{-\dfrac{1}{5}, -\dfrac{2}{3}\right\}$

36. $6\left(2x^2 - \dfrac{2}{3}x - \dfrac{1}{6}\right) = 0; 12x^2 - 4x - 1 = 0; (6x + 1)(2x - 1) = 0; 6x + 1 = 0$ or

$2x - 1 = 0; x = -\dfrac{1}{6}$ or $x = \dfrac{1}{2}; \left\{-\dfrac{1}{6}, \dfrac{1}{2}\right\}$

37. $(x - 2)^2[(x - 2) - 1] = 0; (x - 2)^2(x - 3) = 0; (x - 2)^2$ or $x - 3 = 0; x = 2$ (double
root) or $x = 3; \{2, 3\}$

38. $(x - 2)[(x - 2)^2 - 1] = 0; (x - 2)[(x - 2) + 1][(x - 2) - 1] = 0;$
$(x - 2)(x - 1)(x - 3) = 0; x - 2 = 0, x - 1 = 0,$ or $x - 3 = 0; x = 2, x = 1,$ or
$x = 3; \{2, 1, 3\}$

39. $[(x^2 + 1) - 5][(x^2 + 1) - 2] = 0; (x^2 - 4)(x^2 - 1) = 0;$
$(x + 2)(x - 2)(x + 1)(x - 1) = 0; x + 2 = 0, x - 2 = 0, x + 1 = 0,$ or $x - 1 = 0;$
$x = -2, x = 2, x = -1,$ or $x = 1; \{-2, 2, -1, 1\}$

40. $[(x^2 - 2) - 2][(x^2 - 2) + 1] = 0$; $(x^2 - 4)(x^2 - 1) = 0$;
$(x + 2)(x - 2)(x + 1)(x - 1) = 0$; $x + 2 = 0$, $x - 2 = 0$, $x + 1 = 0$, or $x - 1 = 0$
$x = -2$, $x = 2$, $x = -1$, or $x = 1$; $\{-2, 2, -1, 1\}$

41. $t^3 + 3t^2 + 3t + 1 = t^3 + 7$; $3t^2 + 3t - 6 = 0$; $t^2 + t - 2 = 0$; $(t + 2)(t - 1) = 0$
$t + 2 = 0$ or $t - 1 = 0$; $t = -2$ or $t = 1$; $\{-2, 1\}$

42. $x^3 - 3x^2 + 3x - 1 = x^3 - 19$; $3x^2 - 3x - 18 = 0$; $x^2 - x - 6 = 0$;
$(x - 3)(x + 2) = 0$; $x - 3 = 0$ or $x + 2 = 0$; $x = 3$ or $x = -2$; $\{3, -2\}$

43. $(x - 3)^3 - 4(x - 3) = 0$; $(x - 3)[(x - 3)^2 - 4] = 0$;
$(x - 3)[(x - 3) + 2][(x - 3) - 2] = 0$; $(x - 3)(x - 1)(x - 5) = 0$; $x - 3 = 0$
$x - 1 = 0$, or $x - 5 = 0$; $x = 3$, $x = 1$, or $x = 5$; the zeros are 1, 3, and 5.

44. $(x + 1)^3 + (x + 1)^2 = 0$; $(x + 1)^2[(x + 1) + 1] = 0$; $(x + 1)^2(x + 2) = 0$; $(x + 1)^2 = $
or $x + 2 = 0$; $x = -1$ or $x = -2$; the zeros are -1 (double zero) and -2.

45. $4t^4 - 12t^3 + 9t^2 = 0$; $t^2(4t^2 - 12t + 9) = 0$; $t^2(2t - 3)^2 = 0$; $t^2 = 0$ or $(2t - 3)^2 = 0$
$t = 0$ or $t = \dfrac{3}{2}$; the two double zeros are 0 and $\dfrac{3}{2}$.

46. $4u^4 - 17u^2 + 4 = 0$; $(4u^2 - 1)(u^2 - 4) = 0$; $(2u + 1)(2u - 1)(u + 2)(u - 2) = 0$
$2u + 1 = 0$, $2u - 1 = 0$, $u + 2 = 0$, or $u - 2 = 0$; $u = -\dfrac{1}{2}$, $u = \dfrac{1}{2}$, $u = -2$, o
$u = 2$; the zeros are $-\dfrac{1}{2}$, $\dfrac{1}{2}$, -2, and 2.

47. $(t - 1)^3 = 0$; $t = 1$; 1 is a triple zero.

C   48. $(x + y)^3 = x^3 + 3x^2y + 3xy^2 + y^3$; $x^3 + y^3 = (x + y)^3$ if
$3x^2y + 3xy^2 = 3xy(x + y) = 0$; that is, if $x = 0$, $y = 0$, or $x = -y$.

49. a. false   **b.** If $a > 0$ and $b > 0$, then $ab > 0$; true

50. a. true   **b.** If a and b have opposite signs, then $ab < 0$; true
c. $ab < 0$ if and only if a and b have opposite signs.

51. a. true   **b.** If $-a > -b$, then $a < b$; true
c. $a < b$ if and only if $-a > -b$.

52. a. true   **b.** If $0 < \dfrac{1}{b} < \dfrac{1}{a}$, then $0 < a < b$; true
c. $0 < a < b$ if and only if $0 < \dfrac{1}{b} < \dfrac{1}{a}$.

53. a. true   **b.** If $a^2 = b^2$, then $a = b$; false

54. a. false   **b.** If $a < b < c$, then $a^2 < b^2$ and $b^2 < c^2$; false

Pages 189-191 · PROBLEMS

A
1. Let x = the larger number; then $x - 3$ = the smaller number; $x(x - 3) = 88$; $x^2 - 3x = 88$; $x^2 - 3x - 88 = 0$; $(x - 11)(x + 8) = 0$; $x = 11$ or $x = -8$; if $x = 11$, $x - 3 = 8$; if $x = -8$, $x - 3 = -11$; 11 and 8 or −8 and −11

2. Let x and $x + 2$ be the integers; $x(x + 2) = 99$; $x^2 + 2x = 99$; $x^2 + 2x - 99 = 0$; $(x + 11)(x - 9) = 0$; $x = -11$ or $x = 9$; if $x = -11$, $x + 2 = -9$; if $x = 9$, $x + 2 = 11$; −11 and −9 or 9 and 11

3. Let x and $x + 2$ be the integers; $x^2 + (x + 2)^2 = 74$; $x^2 + x^2 + 4x + 4 = 74$; $2x^2 + 4x - 70 = 0$; $x^2 + 2x - 35 = 0$; $(x + 7)(x - 5) = 0$; $x = -7$ or $x = 5$; if $x = -7$, $x + 2 = -5$; if $x = 5$, $x + 2 = 7$; −7 and −5 or 5 and 7

4. Let x and $x + 2$ be the integers; $|(x + 2)^2 - x^2| = 68$; $x^2 + 4x + 4 - x^2 = 68$ or -68; $4x + 4 = 68$ or -68; $x = 16$ or $x = -18$; if $x = 16$, $x + 2 = 18$; if $x = -18$, $x + 2 = -16$; 16 and 18 or −18 and −16

5. Let w = width in meters; then $w + 7$ = length; $w^2 + (w + 7)^2 = 169$; $w^2 + w^2 + 14w + 49 = 169$; $2w^2 + 14w - 120 = 0$; $w^2 + 7w - 60 = 0$; $(w + 12)(w - 5) = 0$; $w = -12$ (reject) or $w = 5$; $w = 5$; $w + 7 = 12$; 12 m long by 5 m wide

6. Let x and $x + 3$ be the lengths of the legs in centimeters; $x^2 + (x + 3)^2 = 225$; $x^2 + x^2 + 6x + 9 = 225$; $2x^2 + 6x - 216 = 0$; $x^2 + 3x - 108 = 0$; $(x + 12)(x - 9) = 0$; $x = -12$ (reject) or $x = 9$; $x = 9$; $x + 3 = 12$; 12 cm and 9 cm

7. Let n = distance in miles from port of ship nearer to port; $n + 7$ = distance from port of other ship; $n^2 + (n + 7)^2 = 289$; $n^2 + n^2 + 14n + 49 = 289$; $2n^2 + 14n - 240 = 0$; $n^2 + 7n - 120 = 0$; $(n + 15)(n - 8) = 0$; $n = -15$ (reject) or $n = 8$; $n = 8$; $n + 7 = 15$; 8 mi and 15 mi

8. Let x = distance in feet of foot from wall; $x + 4$ = height of top; $x^2 + (x + 4)^2 = 400$; $x^2 + x^2 + 8x + 16 = 400$; $2x^2 + 8x - 384 = 0$; $x^2 + 4x - 192 = 0$; $(x + 16)(x - 12) = 0$; $x = -16$ (reject) or $x = 12$; $x = 12$; 12 ft

9. Let x and $2x - 6$ be the lengths in centimeters of the legs; $x^2 + (2x - 6)^2 = 225$; $x^2 + 4x^2 - 24x + 36 = 225$; $5x^2 - 24x - 189 = 0$; $(5x + 21)(x - 9) = 0$; $x = -\dfrac{21}{5}$ (reject) or $x = 9$; $x = 9$; $2x - 6 = 12$; 9 cm and 12 cm

10. Let h = height in meters; $h - 5$ = length of base; $\dfrac{1}{2}(h - 5)(h) = 42$; $h^2 - 5h = 84$; $h^2 - 5h - 84 = 0$; $(h + 7)(h - 12) = 0$; $h = -7$ (reject) or $h = 12$; $h = 12$; 12 m

11. Let x = length of a side; $x^2 = 4x$; $x^2 - 4x = 0$; $x(x - 4) = 0$; $x = 0$ (reject) or $x = 4$; $x = 4$; 4 by 4

12. Let w = width in centimeters; length = $10 - w$; $(10 - w)w = 21$; $10w - w^2 = 21$; $w^2 - 10w + 21 = 0$; $(w - 7)(w - 3) = 0$; $w = 7$ or $w = 3$; if $w = 7$, $10 - w = 3$; if $w = 3$, $10 - w = 7$; 7 cm by 3 cm

B　**13.** $0.05r^2 + r = 240$; $r^2 + 20r = 4800$; $r^2 + 20r - 4800 = 0$; $(r + 80)(r - 60) = 0$; $r = -80$ (reject) or $r = 60$; $r = 60$; the speed was not within the legal limit.

14. $5200 = (20 - 0.01x)x + 100$; $5200 = 20x - 0.01x^2 + 100$; $0.01x^2 - 20x + 5100 = 0$; $x^2 - 2000x + 510{,}000 = 0$; $(x - 1700)(x - 300) = 0$; $x = 1700$ (reject; $x < 1000$) or $x = 300$; 300

15. Let x = length in centimeters of an edge of the new cube; $x + 1$ = length of an edge of the original cube; $x^3 + 169 = (x + 1)^3$; $x^3 + 169 = x^3 + 3x^2 + 3x + 1$; $3x^2 + 3x - 168 = 0$; $x^2 + x - 56 = 0$; $(x + 8)(x - 7) = 0$; $x = -8$ (reject) or $x = 7$; $x = 7$; volume = 343 cm^3

16. Let x = length of an edge; $x^3 + 6x^2 = 6(12x)$; $x^3 + 6x^2 - 72x = 0$; $x(x^2 + 6x - 72) = 0$; $x(x + 12)(x - 6) = 0$; $x = 0$ (reject), $x = -12$ (reject), or $x = 6$; 6

17. Let x be the length in meters of the side formed by the wall; length of adjacent side = $\dfrac{17 - x}{2}$; $x\left(\dfrac{17 - x}{2}\right) = 35$; $17x - x^2 = 70$; $x^2 - 17x + 70 = 0$; $(x - 7)(x - 10) = 0$; $x = 7$ or $x = 10$; if $x = 7$, $\dfrac{17 - x}{2} = 5$; if $x = 10$, $\dfrac{17 - x}{2} = 3.5$; the pen is 7 m long and 5 m wide, or 10 m long and 3.5 m wide.

18. Let x = length in meters lost on each side; $(50 - x)(60 - x) = \dfrac{2}{3}(50)(60)$; $3000 - 110x + x^2 = 2000$; $x^2 - 110x + 1000 = 0$; $(x - 100)(x - 10) = 0$; $x = 100$ (reject; $x < 50$) or $x = 10$; $x = 10$; $50 - x = 40$; $60 - x = 50$; 40 m by 50 m

19. Let x and $x + 2$ be the width and length and $x + 4$ the diagonal; $x^2 + (x + 2)^2 = (x + 4)^2$; $x^2 + x^2 + 4x + 4 = x^2 + 8x + 16$; $x^2 - 4x - 12 = 0$; $(x + 2)(x - 6) = 0$; $x = -2$ (reject) or $x = 6$; $x = 6$, $x + 2 = 8$, and $x + 4 = 10$; 6, 8, and 10

20. No; the resulting equation would be as in Ex. 19 above with solution $x = 6$.

21. Let n be the number; $n + n^3 = 2n^2$; $n^3 - 2n^2 + n = 0$; $n(n^2 - 2n + 1) = 0$; $n(n - 1)^2 = 0$; $n = 0$ or $n = 1$; 0 or 1

22. Let x, $x + 2$, and $x + 4$ be the numbers; $x(x + 2) + (x + 2)(x + 4) = 648$; $(x + 2)[x + (x + 4)] = 648$; $(x + 2)(2x + 4) = 648$; $2x^2 + 8x + 8 = 648$; $x^2 + 4x + 4 = 324$; $x^2 + 4x - 320 = 0$; $(x - 16)(x + 20) = 0$; $x = 16$ or $x = -20$; if $x = 16$, $x + 2 = 18$, and $x + 4 = 20$; if $x = -20$, $x + 2 = -18$, and $x + 4 = -16$; 16, 18, and 20 or -20, -18, and -16

C　**23.** $98 = 0 + 58.8t - 4.9t^2$; $4.9t^2 - 58.8t + 98 = 0$; $t^2 - 12t + 20 = 0$; $(t - 10)(t - 2) = 0$; $t = 10$ or $t = 2$; 2 s and 10 s; the projectile will be at that height twice, once on the way up and once on the way down.

24. $0 = 49 + 14.7t - 4.9t^2$; $4.9t^2 - 14.7t - 49 = 0$; $t^2 - 3t - 10 = 0$; $(t + 2)(t - 5) = 0$; $t = -2$ (reject) or $t = 5$; $t = 5$; 5 s

25. $500 = 500 + 68.6t - 4.9t^2$; $4.9t^2 - 68.6t = 0$; $t(t - 14) = 0$; $t = 0$ (reject) or $t = 14$; 14 s

26. $100 = 21.6 + 39.2t - 4.9t^2$; $4.9t^2 - 39.2t + 78.4 = 0$; $t^2 - 8t + 16 = 0$; $(t - 4)^2 = 0$; $t = 4$; the arrow achieves a height of 100 m at only one point, thus it must be at the peak of its path.

27. Let w = width in centimeters; length = $2w$; $3(w - 6)(2w - 6) = 168$; $2w^2 - 18w + 36 = 56$; $2w^2 - 18w - 20 = 0$; $w^2 - 9w - 10 = 0$; $(w + 1)(w - 10) = 0$; $w = -1$ (reject) or $w = 10$; $w = 10$; $2w = 20$; 20 cm by 10 cm

28. Let x be the length of a side of a square cut off to form the shorter box; $2x$ = length of side of a square cut off to form the other box; $x(20 - 2x)(16 - 2x) = 2x(20 - 4x)(16 - 4x)$; $x[2(10 - x)(2)(8 - x)] = 2x[4(5 - x)(4)(4 - x)]$; $4x(10 - x)(8 - x) = 32x(5 - x)(4 - x)$; $x(80 - 18x + x^2) = 8x(20 - 9x + x^2)$; $80x - 18x^2 + x^3 = 160x - 72x^2 + 8x^3$; $7x^3 - 54x^2 + 80x = 0$; $x(7x - 40)(x - 2) = 0$; $x = 0$ (reject), $x = \dfrac{40}{7}$ $\left(\text{reject; if } x = \dfrac{40}{7}, 2x = \dfrac{80}{7} \text{ and } 20 - 2(2x) < 0\right)$ or $x = 2$; $x = 2$; the boxes are 2 cm and 4 cm tall.

Page 191 · CHALLENGE

Let x be the number. Since x leaves a remainder of 1 when divided by 2, it is odd. Since x leaves a remainder of 3 when divided by 5, its last digit is 3 or 8. Therefore, the last digit of x is 3. Since x leaves a remainder of 2 when divided by 3 and a remainder of 5 when divided by 7, both 7 and 3 divide $x - 5$ evenly. Thus, x leaves a remainder of 5 when divided by 21, and x is 5 more than a multiple of 21. If $n \cdot 21 + 5 = x$, we want $n \cdot 21 + 5$ to end in the digit 3, so we choose $n = 8$, giving $x = 173$. This is the smallest positive integer meeting the given conditions.

Page 192 · COMPUTER EXERCISES

1. Answers may vary. A sample program is given.

```
10 PRINT "INPUT STARTING VELOCITY, START TIME, END TIME, NUMBER
   OF VALUES"
20 INPUT V, T1, T2, N
30 LET D = (T2 + 1 - T1)/N
40 FOR T = T1 TO T2 STEP D
50 LET H = V * T - 4.9 * T ↑ 2
60 PRINT T, H
70 NEXT T
80 END
```

2. a.

			b.		
1	44.1		1	44.1
2	78.4		2	78.4
3	102.9		3	102.9
4	117.6		4	117.6
5	122.5		5	122.5
6	117.6		6	117.6
7	102.9		7	102.9
8	78.4		8	78.4
9	44.0999999		9	44.0999999
10	0		10	0
			11	-53.9000003
			12	-117.6
			13	-191.1
			14	-274.4
			15	-367.5
			16	-470.4
			17	-583.100002
			18	-705.600001
			19	-837.9
			20	-980.00000

Negative values of h indicate the distance below ground the rocket would reach if allowed to continue in free fall.

3. Answers may vary. For example, add lines 25 and 26, and change lines 50 and 60, as follows:

25 PRINT "INPUT INITIAL HEIGHT"
26 INPUT K
50 LET H = K + V $*$ T $-$ 4.9 $*$ T $\uparrow$ 2
60 PRINT K, T, H

4. a.

50	1	120.1
50	2	180.4
50	3	230.9
50	4	271.6
50	5	302.5
50	6	323.6
50	7	334.9
50	8	336.4
50	9	328.1
50	10	310

Maximum height occurs at approximately 336.4 m.

b.

50	1	125.1
50	2	190.4
50	3	245.9
50	4	291.6
50	5	327.5
50	6	353.6
50	7	369.9
50	8	376.4
50	9	373.1
50	10	360
50	11	337.1
50	12	304.4
50	13	261.9
50	14	209.6
50	15	147.5
50	16	75.5999999
50	17	−6.10000138
50	18	−97.6000009
50	19	−198.9
50	20	−310.000001

Maximum height occurs at approximately 8 seconds.

Page 196 · WRITTEN EXERCISES

A   **1.** $x - 5 > 0$ and $x + 5 > 0$, or $x - 5 < 0$ and $x + 5 < 0$; $x > 5$ and $x > -5$, or $x < 5$ and $x < -5$; $x > 5$ or $x < -5$; $\{x : x < -5 \text{ or } x > 5\}$

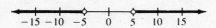

2. $(x - 4)^2 \geq 0$ for every real number x

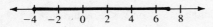

3. $x - 7 \leq 0$ and $x + 4 \geq 0$, or $x - 7 \geq 0$ and $x + 4 \leq 0$; $x \leq 7$ and $x \geq -4$, or $x \geq 7$ and $x \leq -4$; $\{x : -4 \leq x \leq 7\}$

4. $(x - 4) \leq 0$ and $x - 4 \geq 0$; $x \leq 4$ and $x \geq 4$; $\{4\}$

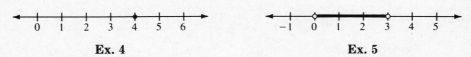

Ex. 4   Ex. 5

5. $x(x - 3) < 0$; $x < 0$ and $x - 3 > 0$, or $x > 0$ and $x - 3 < 0$; $x < 0$ and $x > 3$, or $x > 0$ and $x < 3$; $\{x : 0 < x < 3\}$

6. $x(x + 2) > 0$; $x > 0$ and $x + 2 > 0$, or $x < 0$ and $x + 2 < 0$; $x > 0$ and $x > -2$, or $x < 0$ and $x < -2$; $\{x : x < -2 \text{ or } x > 0\}$

Ex. 6　　　　　　　　　　　**Ex. 7**

7. $9x^2 - 81 \leq 0$; $x^2 - 9 \leq 0$; $(x + 3)(x - 3) \leq 0$; $x + 3 \leq 0$ and $x - 3 \geq 0$, or $x + 3 \geq 0$ and $x - 3 \leq 0$; $x \leq -3$ and $x \geq 3$, or $x \geq -3$ and $x \leq 3$; $\{x : -3 \leq x \leq 3\}$

8. $4t^2 - 64 < 0$; $t^2 - 16 < 0$; $(t + 4)(t - 4) < 0$; $t + 4 > 0$ and $t - 4 < 0$, or $t + 4 < 0$ and $t - 4 > 0$; $t > -4$ and $t < 4$, or $t < -4$ and $t > 4$; $\{t : -4 < t < 4\}$

Ex. 8　　　　　　　　　　　**Ex. 9**

9. $(t - 3)(t + 1) \geq 0$; $t - 3 \geq 0$ and $t + 1 \geq 0$, or $t - 3 \leq 0$ and $t + 1 \leq 0$; $t \geq 3$ and $t \geq -1$, or $t \leq 3$ and $t \leq -1$; $t \geq 3$ or $t \leq -1$; $\{t : t \leq -1 \text{ or } t \geq 3\}$

10. $(x - 3)(x - 1) \leq 0$; $x - 3 \leq 0$ and $x - 1 \geq 0$, or $x - 3 \geq 0$ and $x - 1 \leq 0$; $x \leq 3$ and $x \geq 1$, or $x \geq 3$ and $x \leq 1$; $\{x : 1 \leq x \leq 3\}$

Ex. 10　　　　　　　　　　　**Ex. 11**

11. $x^2 - 10x + 16 < 0$; $(x - 8)(x - 2) < 0$; $x - 8 < 0$ and $x - 2 > 0$, or $x - 8 > 0$ and $x - 2 < 0$; $x < 8$ and $x > 2$, or $x > 8$ and $x < 2$; $\{x : 2 < x < 8\}$

12. $x^2 + 3x \geq 4$; $x^2 + 3x - 4 \geq 0$; $(x + 4)(x - 1) \geq 0$; $x + 4 \geq 0$ and $x - 1 \geq 0$, or $x + 4 \leq 0$ and $x - 1 \leq 0$; $x \geq -4$ and $x \geq 1$, or $x \leq -4$ and $x \leq 1$; $x \geq 1$ or $x \leq -4$; $\{x : x \leq -4 \text{ or } x \geq 1\}$

Ex. 12　　　　　　　　　　　**Ex. 13**

13. $4z^2 + 4z < 3$; $4z^2 + 4z - 3 < 0$; $(2z + 3)(2z - 1) < 0$; $2z + 3 > 0$ and $2z - 1 < 0$, or $2z + 3 < 0$ and $2z - 1 > 0$; $z > -\dfrac{3}{2}$ and $z < \dfrac{1}{2}$, or $z < -\dfrac{3}{2}$ and $z > \dfrac{1}{2}$; $\left\{z : -\dfrac{3}{2} < z < \dfrac{1}{2}\right\}$

14. $2x^2 + 2 > 5x$; $2x^2 - 5x + 2 > 0$; $(2x - 1)(x - 2) > 0$; $2x - 1 > 0$ and $x - 2 > 0$, or $2x - 1 < 0$ and $x - 2 < 0$; $x > \dfrac{1}{2}$ and $x > 2$, or $x < \dfrac{1}{2}$ and $x < 2$; $x > 2$ or $x < \dfrac{1}{2}$; $\left\{x : x < \dfrac{1}{2} \text{ or } x > 2\right\}$

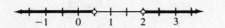

Ex. 14   **Ex. 15**

15. $x(x^2 - 9) > 0$; $x(x + 3)(x - 3) > 0$; true if exactly one factor is positive, or if all three are positive; the conjunctions that yield solutions are (1) $x > 0$, $x + 3 > 0$, and $x - 3 > 0$ or (2) $x < 0$, $x + 3 > 0$, and $x - 3 < 0$; thus (1) $x > 0$, $x > -3$, and $x > 3$; $x > 3$; or (2) $x < 0$, $x > -3$, and $x < 3$; $-3 < x < 0$; $\{x : x > 3 \text{ or } -3 < x < 0\}$

16. $u^3 - 16u < 0$; $u(u^2 - 16) < 0$; $u(u + 4)(u - 4) < 0$; true if exactly one factor is negative or if all three are negative; the conjunctions that yield solutions are (1) $u < 0$, $u + 4 < 0$, and $u - 4 < 0$ or (2) $u > 0$, $u + 4 > 0$, and $u - 4 < 0$; thus (1) $u < 0$, $u < -4$, and $u < 4$; $u < -4$; or (2) $u > 0$, $u > -4$, and $u < 4$; $0 < u < 4$; $\{u : u < -4 \text{ or } 0 < u < 4\}$

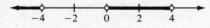

Ex. 16   **Ex. 17**

17. $t^3 - 6t - t^2 < 0$; $t(t^2 - t - 6) < 0$; $t(t - 3)(t + 2) < 0$; true if exactly one factor is negative or if all three are negative; the conjunctions that yield solutions are (1) $t < 0$, $t - 3 < 0$, and $t + 2 < 0$ or (2) $t > 0$, $t - 3 < 0$, and $t + 2 > 0$; thus (1) $t < 0$, $t < 3$, and $t < -2$; $t < -2$; or (2) $t > 0$, $t < 3$, and $t > -2$; $0 < t < 3$; $\{t : t < -2 \text{ or } 0 < t < 3\}$

18. $x^3 - 4x^2 + 3x > 0$; $x(x^2 - 4x + 3) > 0$; $x(x - 3)(x - 1) > 0$; true if exactly one factor is positive or if all three are positive; the conjunctions that yield solutions are (1) $x > 0$, $x - 3 > 0$, and $x - 1 > 0$ or (2) $x > 0$, $x - 3 < 0$, and $x - 1 < 0$; thus (1) $x > 0$, $x > 3$, and $x > 1$; $x > 3$; or (2) $x > 0$, $x < 3$, $x < 1$; $0 < x < 1$; $\{x : x > 3 \text{ or } 0 < x < 1\}$

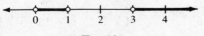

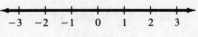

Ex. 18   **Ex. 19**

19. $x^2 - 4x + 4 \geq 0$; $(x - 2)^2 \geq 0$ for every real number x.

20. $x^2 - 6x + 9 \leq 0$; $(x - 3)^2 \leq 0$; $x - 3 \leq 0$ and $x - 3 \geq 0$; $x \leq 3$ and $x \geq 3$; $\{3\}$

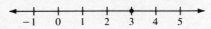

21. $t^2 - t - 30 \le 0$; $(t - 6)(t + 5) \le 0$; $t - 6 \le 0$ and $t + 5 \ge 0$, or $t - 6 \ge 0$ and $t + 5 \le 0$; $t \le 6$ and $t \ge -5$, or $t \ge 6$ and $t \le -5$; $\{t : -5 \le t \le 6\}$

Ex. 21   **Ex. 22**

22. $2t^2 + 5t - 12 > 0$; $(2t - 3)(t + 4) > 0$; $2t - 3 > 0$ and $t + 4 > 0$, or $2t - 3 < 0$ and $t + 4 < 0$; $t > \dfrac{3}{2}$ and $t > -4$, or $t < \dfrac{3}{2}$ and $t < -4$; $\left\{t : t < -4 \text{ or } t > \dfrac{3}{2}\right\}$

B **23.** $58.8t - 4.9t^2 > 98$; $4.9t^2 - 58.8t + 98 < 0$; $t^2 - 12t + 20 < 0$; $(t - 10)(t - 2) < 0$; $t - 10 < 0$ and $t - 2 > 0$, or $t - 10 > 0$ and $t - 2 < 0$; $t < 10$ and $t > 2$, or $t > 10$ and $t < 2$; $\{t : 2 < t < 10\}$; between 2 and 10 seconds after firing.

24. $49 + 14.7t - 4.9t^2 \ge 49$; $14.7t - 4.9t^2 \ge 0$; $t^2 - 3t \le 0$; $t(t - 3) \le 0$; $t \le 0$ and $t - 3 \ge 0$, or $t \ge 0$ and $t - 3 \le 0$; $t \le 0$ and $t \ge 3$, or $t \ge 0$ and $t \le 3$; $\{t : 0 \le t \le 3\}$; the first 3 seconds after tossing.

25. True if all factors are positive, all factors are negative, or two factors are positive; drawing a sign graph yields the solution set $\{x : x < -2, 0 < x < 1, \text{ or } x > 3\}$.

Ex. 25   **Ex. 26**

26. $x(x + 4)(x^2 + 4) < 0$; true if one factor is negative or all factors are negative; however, $x^2 + 4 > 0$ for every real number x, and if $x + 4 < 0$, then $x < 0$; thus $x(x + 4)(x^2 + 4) < 0$ only if $x < 0$ and $x + 4 > 0$; $x < 0$ and $x > -4$; $\{x : -4 < x < 0\}$.

27. $48x^2 + 2x - 1 \ge 0$; $(6x + 1)(8x - 1) \ge 0$; $6x + 1 \ge 0$ and $8x - 1 \ge 0$, or $6x + 1 \le 0$ and $8x - 1 \le 0$; $x \ge -\dfrac{1}{6}$ and $x \ge \dfrac{1}{8}$, or $x \le -\dfrac{1}{6}$ and $x \le \dfrac{1}{8}$; $\left\{x : x \le -\dfrac{1}{6} \text{ or } x \ge \dfrac{1}{8}\right\}$

28. $60x^2 - 37x - 6 < 0$; $(15x + 2)(4x - 3) < 0$; $15x + 2 < 0$ and $4x - 3 > 0$, or $15x + 2 > 0$ and $4x - 3 < 0$; $x < -\dfrac{2}{15}$ and $x > \dfrac{3}{4}$, or $x > -\dfrac{2}{15}$ and $x < \dfrac{3}{4}$; $\left\{x : -\dfrac{2}{15} < x < \dfrac{3}{4}\right\}$

C 29. $(x^2 - 25)(x^2 - 1) < 0$; $(x + 5)(x - 5)(x + 1)(x - 1) < 0$; true if exactly one factor is negative or exactly three are negative; drawing a sign graph yields the solution set $\{x : -5 < x < -1 \text{ or } 1 < x < 5\}$

Ex. 29   Ex. 30

30. $x^4 - 13x^2 + 36 > 0$; $(x^2 - 9)(x^2 - 4) > 0$; $(x + 3)(x - 3)(x + 2)(x - 2) > 0$; true if all factors are positive, exactly two factors are positive, or if all are negative; drawing a sign graph yields the solution set $\{x : x < -3, -2 < x < 2, \text{ or } x > 3\}$

31. $(x - 2)(x + 1)(x - 2)^2 > 0$; $(x - 2)^3(x + 1) > 0$; $(x - 2)^3 > 0$ and $x + 1 > 0$, or $(x - 2)^3 < 0$ and $x + 1 < 0$; $x > 2$ and $x > -1$, or $x < 2$ and $x < -1$; $\{x : x < -1 \text{ or } x > 2\}$

Ex. 31   Ex. 32

32. $(x - 2)(x + 1)(x + 1)^2 < 0$; $(x - 2)(x + 1)^3 < 0$; $x - 2 < 0$ and $(x + 1)^3 > 0$, or $x - 2 > 0$ and $(x + 1)^3 < 0$; $x < 2$ and $x > -1$, or $x > 2$ and $x < -1$; $\{x : -1 < x < 2\}$

33. $x + p > 0$ and $x + q < 0$, or $x + q > 0$ and $x + p < 0$; $x > -p$ and $x < -q$, or $x > -q$ and $x < -p$; solutions exist if $-p < -q$ or if $-q < -p$, that is if $p > q$ or $q > p$. Then $(x + p)(x + q) < 0$ has a solution for all real numbers p and q such that $p \neq q$.

Page 198 · CHAPTER REVIEW

1. d; $(-a^2)^3 a^4 = (-a^6)a^4 = -a^{10}$

2. b; $2x^2y(xy + y^2) = 2x^2y(xy) + 2x^2y(y^2) = 2x^3y^2 + 2x^2y^3$

3. c; $x^2(x - 3)^2 = x^2(x^2 - 6x + 9) = x^4 - 6x^3 + 9x^2$

4. b; $at(t + a)(t - a) = at(t^2 - a^2) = at^3 - a^3t$

5. d; $1764 = 2 \cdot 882 = 2 \cdot 2 \cdot 441 = 2 \cdot 2 \cdot 3 \cdot 147 = 2 \cdot 2 \cdot 3 \cdot 3 \cdot 49 = 2 \cdot 2 \cdot 3 \cdot 3 \cdot 7 \cdot 7$
   $= 2^2 \cdot 3^2 \cdot 7^2$

6. b; $48x^2y^3 = 2^4 \cdot 3 \cdot x^2y^3$; $72x^3y^2 = 2^3 \cdot 3^2 \cdot x^3y^2$; $36xy^4 = 2^2 \cdot 3^2 \cdot xy^4$;
   GCF $= 2^2 \cdot 3 \cdot xy^2 = 12xy^2$

7. b; $6ax^3 = 2 \cdot 3 \cdot ax^3$; $3 \cdot a^2x^2$; $10x^4 = 2 \cdot 5 \cdot x^4$; LCM $= 2 \cdot 3 \cdot 5a^2x^4 = 30a^2x^4$

8. a   9. c; $2t^3 - 8t = 2t(t^2 - 4) = 2t(t + 2)(t - 2)$

10. a   11. c   12. c; $x^2 = 4x$; $x^2 - 4x = 0$; $x(x - 4) = 0$; $x = 0$ or $x = 4$

13. b; $6x^2 = x + 2$; $6x^2 - x - 2 = 0$; $(3x - 2)(2x + 1) = 0$; $x = \dfrac{2}{3}$ or $x = -\dfrac{1}{2}$

14. d; let x = length of minute hand, $x - 7$ = length of hour hand; $x^2 + (x - 7)^2 = 17^2$; $2x^2 - 14x - 240 = 0$; $x^2 - 7x - 120 = 0$; $(x - 15)(x + 8) = 0$; $x = 15$ or $x = -8$ (reject); 15 cm

15. b; $x^3 - x^2 - 2x \le 0$; $x(x^2 - x - 2) \le 0$; $x(x - 2)(x + 1) \le 0$; ($x \le 0$ and $x \le 2$ and $x \le -1$) or ($x \le 0$ and $x \ge 2$ and $x \ge -1$) or ($x \ge 0$ and $x \le 2$ and $x \ge -1$) or ($x \ge 0$ and $x \ge 2$ and $x \le -1$); $x \le -1$ or $0 \le x \le 2$

Page 199 · CHAPTER TEST

1. $(9x^2y^4)(-5x^2y) = -45 \cdot x^{2+2}y^{4+1} = -45x^4y^5$

2. $2 \cdot u^{2+1}v^{1+1} - 2 \cdot 2 \cdot u^2v^{1+2} = 2u^3v^2 - 4u^2v^3$

3. $t(2t + 1) - 3(2t + 1) = 2t^2 + t - 6t - 3 = 2t^2 - 5t - 3$

4. $ax(2x - a)(2x - a) = ax[(2x)^2 - 2(2x)(a) + a^2] = ax(4x^2 - 4ax + a^2)$
$= ax(4x^2) - ax(4ax) + ax(a^2) = 4ax^3 - 4a^2x^2 + a^3x$

5. $140 = 2^2 \cdot 5 \cdot 7$ and $168 = 2^3 \cdot 3 \cdot 7$ **a.** 28 **b.** 840

6. $12x^2y = 2^2 \cdot 3 \cdot x^2y$, $18y^3 = 2 \cdot 3^2 \cdot y^3$, and $24xy^2 = 2^3 \cdot 3 \cdot xy^2$ **a.** $6y$ **b.** $72x^2y^3$

7. $(10x - 1)^2$ **8.** $(2x^2 - 6x) - (xy - 3y) = 2x(x - 3) - y(x - 3) = (2x - y)(x - 3)$

9. $(s - 2t)(s + 9t)$ **10.** $(2u + 1)(6u - 7)$ **11.** $(x^2 - 2)(x^2 + 1)$

12. $ax(x^2 - 4a^2 + 4ax) = ax(x^2 + 4ax - 4a^2)$

13. $x = 0$, $x + 1 = 0$, or $x - 2 = 0$; $x = 0$, $x = -1$, or $x = 2$; $\{0, -1, 2\}$

14. $2t^2 - 5t + 2 = 0$; $(2t - 1)(t - 2) = 0$; $2t - 1 = 0$ or $t - 2 = 0$; $t = \dfrac{1}{2}$ or $t = 2$; $\left\{\dfrac{1}{2}, 2\right\}$

15. Let w = width in meters of deck; $2w(2w + 9) + 2w(6) = 54$; $w(2w + 9) + 6w = 27$; $2w^2 + 9w + 6w = 27$; $2w^2 + 15w - 27 = 0$; $(w + 9)(2w - 3) = 0$; $w = -9$ (reject) or $w = \dfrac{3}{2}$; 1.5 m

16. $x^2 - x - 6 < 0$; $(x - 3)(x + 2) < 0$; $x - 3 < 0$ and $x + 2 > 0$, or $x - 3 > 0$ and $x + 2 < 0$; $x < 3$ and $x > -2$, or $x > 3$ and $x < -2$; $\{x : -2 < x < 3\}$

Pages 199–200 · MIXED REVIEW

1. $5 - 4.2 - 27 \div \dfrac{1}{2} = 5 - 4.2 - 54 = -53.2$ **2.** $\left(\dfrac{1}{8} - \dfrac{4}{8}\right)(6) = -\dfrac{3}{8} \cdot 6 = -\dfrac{9}{4}$

3. $10 + 6 = 16$ **4.** $-5.41, -5.4, -5.14, -5.1$

5. $-5[2x - 6 + 8y - 8x + 10xy] - 12xy = -5[-6x - 6 + 8y + 10xy] - 12xy$
$= 30x + 30 - 40y - 50xy - 12xy = 30x + 30 - 40y - 62xy$

6. $3a - 10a - 5 = 86$; $-7a = 91$; $a = -13$

7. $-3 \le x + 1 < 6$; $-4 \le x < 5$; $\{x : -4 \le x < 5\}$

Ex. 7   **Ex. 8**

8. $|2t - 1| > 5$; $2t - 1 < -5$ or $2t - 1 > 5$; $t < -2$ or $t > 3$; $\{t : t < -2 \text{ or } t > 3\}$

9. Let w = width in meters; length = $w + 8$; $(w + 8)^2 = w(w + 8) + 224$;
$w^2 + 16w + 64 = w^2 + 8w + 224$; $8w = 160$; $w = 20$; $w + 8 = 28$; 28 m by 20 m

10. Let n = number of nickels; number of dimes = $n + 4$; number of
quarters = $4(n + 4) = 4n + 16$; $1000 < 5n + 10(n + 4) + 25(4n + 16) < 1100$;
$1000 < 5n + 10n + 40 + 100n + 400 < 1100$; $1000 < 115n + 440 < 1100$;
$560 < 115n < 660$; $4\dfrac{20}{23} < n < 5\dfrac{17}{23}$; $n = 5$; $n + 4 = 9$; $4n + 16 = 36$; 5 nickels,
9 dimes, 36 quarters

11.
$$
\begin{aligned}
b(-a + a) &= b(-a) + ba && \text{(Dist. prop.)} \\
&= (-a)b + ab && \text{(Comm. prop. for mult.)} \\
&= (-1 \cdot a)b + ab && \text{(Mult. prop. of } -1) \\
&= -1(ab) + ab && \text{(Assoc. prop. for mult.)} \\
&= -ab + ab && \text{(Mult. prop. of } -1) \\
&= 0 && \text{(Prop. of opp.)}
\end{aligned}
$$

12. Substitute for x beginning with $x = 1$ and determine corresponding values of y; solution: $\{(1, 1), (2, 1)\}$

13. $x + 3y = 0$; $3y = -x$; $y = -\dfrac{1}{3}x$; $m = 3$; $\dfrac{y - (-3)}{x - 2} = 3$; $\dfrac{y + 3}{x - 2} = 3$; $3x - 6 = y + 3$;
$3x - y = 9$

14. $1 \cdot A + 4 \cdot B = 17$ and $4 \cdot A + (-1)B = 17$; $A + 4B = 17$ and $4A - B = 7$; $B = 4A - 17$; $A + 4(4A - 17) = 17$; $17A - 68 = 17$; $17A = 85$; $A = 5$; $B = 4(5) - 17 = 3$

15. a. $21x + 6y = 33$
$$\underline{10x - 6y = 60}$$
$31x \quad\quad = 93; \quad x = 3$; $63 + 6y = 33$; $6y = -30$; $y = -5$; $(3, -5)$

b. $9w - 6t = 4t + 10$; $9w - 10t = 10$
$$18w - 20t = 20$$
$$\underline{18w - 24t = 27}$$
$4t = -7; \quad t = -\dfrac{7}{4}$; $6w + 14 = 9$; $6w = -5$; $w = -\dfrac{5}{6}$; $\left(-\dfrac{7}{4}, -\dfrac{5}{6}\right)$

16.

17. $-3t^2(-8t^6) = 24t^8$

18. $3y^{n-1+1} - 5y^{n-1+2} = 3y^n - 5y^{n+1}$

19. $(3x^2)^2 - 2(3x^2)(5y) + (5y)^2$
$= 9x^4 - 30x^2y + 25y^2$

20. $(r - 2w)(r^2 - 4rw + 4w^2) = r(r^2 - 4rw + 4w^2) - 2w(r^2 - 4rw + 4w^2)$
$= r^3 - 4r^2w + 4rw^2 - 2r^2w + 8rw^2 - 8w^3 = r^3 - 6r^2w + 12rw^2 - 8w^3$

21. $63a^3b^5c = 3^2 \cdot 7 \cdot a^3b^5c$ and $147ab^4 = 3 \cdot 7^2 \cdot ab^4$ **a.** $21ab^4$ **b.** $441a^3b^5c$

22. $t(t^3 - 64) = t(t - 4)(t^2 + 4t + 16)$

23. $a^2(a + 3) - 9(a + 3) = (a^2 - 9)(a + 3) = (a - 3)(a + 3)(a + 3)$
$= (a - 3)(a + 3)^2$

24. $(2r + 3)(3r - 7)$

25. $2m^3 - 20m^2 + 50m = 0$; $2m(m^2 - 10m + 25) = 0$; $2m(m - 5)^2 = 0$; $m = 0$ or
$m = 5$; $\{0, 5\}$

26. $9x^2 - 24x + 16 = 6x + 16$; $9x^2 - 30x = 0$; $3x(3x - 10) = 0$; $x = 0$ or $x = \dfrac{10}{3}$;
$\left\{0, \dfrac{10}{3}\right\}$

27. $(y + 2)(y + 3) > 0$; $y + 2 > 0$ and $y + 3 > 0$, or $y + 2 < 0$ and $y + 3 < 0$; $y > -2$
and $y > -3$, or $y < -2$ and $y < -3$; $\{y : y < -3 \text{ or } y > -2\}$

28. Let x, $x + 2$, and $x + 4$ be the integers; $x^2 + (x + 4)^2 = 170$; $x^2 + x^2 + 8x + 16 = 170$; $2x^2 + 8x - 154 = 0$; $x^2 + 4x - 77 = 0$; $(x + 11)(x - 7) = 0$; $x = -11$ or $x = 7$;
if $x = -11$, $x + 2 = -9$, and $x + 4 = -7$; if $x = 7$, $x + 2 = 9$, and $x + 4 = 11$; -11,
-9, and -7 or 7, 9, and 11

Page 201 · PREPARING FOR COLLEGE ENTRANCE EXAMS

1. B   **2.** C   **3.** C   **4.** B

5. A   **6.** D   **7.** D

Pages 205-206 · WRITTEN EXERCISES

A 1. $\dfrac{12}{4} \cdot \dfrac{x^3}{x} = 3x^2$ 2. $\dfrac{15}{5} \cdot \dfrac{z^3}{z^5} = \dfrac{3}{z^2}$ 3. $\dfrac{-2}{14} \cdot \dfrac{a^2}{a} \cdot \dfrac{b^3}{b^4} = -\dfrac{1}{7} \cdot a \cdot \dfrac{1}{b} = -\dfrac{a}{7b}$

4. $\dfrac{40}{-8} \cdot \dfrac{p^3}{p} \cdot \dfrac{q^2}{q^4} = -5 \cdot p^2 \cdot \dfrac{1}{q^2} = -\dfrac{5p^2}{q^2}$ 5. $\dfrac{-18}{-6} \cdot \dfrac{x^3}{x^4} \cdot \dfrac{y^5}{y^4} = 3 \cdot \dfrac{1}{x} \cdot y = \dfrac{3y}{x}$

6. $\dfrac{24}{16} \cdot \dfrac{a^3}{a^4} \cdot \dfrac{c^6}{c^3} = \dfrac{3}{2} \cdot \dfrac{1}{a} \cdot c^3 = \dfrac{3c^3}{2a}$ 7. $\left(\dfrac{2a}{b^2}\right)^3 = \dfrac{(2a)^3}{(b^2)^3} = \dfrac{8a^3}{b^6}$

8. $\left(\dfrac{3r^3}{-s^2}\right)^2 = \dfrac{(3r^3)^2}{(-s^2)^2} = \dfrac{9r^6}{s^4}$ 9. $\dfrac{2x^2}{3y} \cdot \dfrac{x}{2y^2} = \dfrac{2}{3 \cdot 2} \cdot \dfrac{x^2 \cdot x}{y \cdot y^2} = \dfrac{1}{3} \cdot \dfrac{x^3}{y^3} = \dfrac{x^3}{3y^3}$

10. $\dfrac{a^3}{2b^2} \cdot \dfrac{2a^2}{b} = \dfrac{2}{2} \cdot \dfrac{a^3 \cdot a^2}{b^2 \cdot b} = \dfrac{a^5}{b^3}$ 11. $\dfrac{2p}{q^2} \cdot \dfrac{2q}{p^2} = 2 \cdot 2 \cdot \dfrac{p}{p^2} \cdot \dfrac{q}{q^2} = 4 \cdot \dfrac{1}{p} \cdot \dfrac{1}{q} = \dfrac{4}{pq}$

12. $\dfrac{(5x^2y^4)^2}{(-xy^5)^3} = \dfrac{25x^4y^8}{-x^3y^{15}} = -25 \cdot x \cdot \dfrac{1}{y^7} = -\dfrac{25x}{y^7}$

13. $\dfrac{(-3m^2n)^2}{(2mn^2)^3} = \dfrac{9}{8} \cdot \dfrac{m^4}{m^3} \cdot \dfrac{n^2}{n^6} = \dfrac{9}{8} \cdot m \cdot \dfrac{1}{n^4} = \dfrac{9m}{8n^4}$

14. $\dfrac{r^2}{s^3}\left(\dfrac{2s}{r^2}\right)^3 = \dfrac{r^2}{s^3}\left(\dfrac{8s^3}{r^6}\right) = 8 \cdot \dfrac{r^2}{r^6} \cdot \dfrac{s^3}{s^3} = 8 \cdot \dfrac{1}{r^4} \cdot 1 = \dfrac{8}{r^4}$

15. $\dfrac{2x^5}{y^3}\left(\dfrac{y^2}{2x^3}\right)^3 = \dfrac{2x^5}{y^3}\left(\dfrac{y^6}{8x^9}\right) = \dfrac{2}{8} \cdot \dfrac{x^5}{x^9} \cdot \dfrac{y^6}{y^3} = \dfrac{1}{4} \cdot \dfrac{1}{x^4} \cdot y^3 = \dfrac{y^3}{4x^4}$

16. $\dfrac{4x^2y^2}{(4x^2y)^2} = \dfrac{4}{16} \cdot \dfrac{x^2}{x^4} \cdot \dfrac{y^2}{y^2} = \dfrac{1}{4} \cdot \dfrac{1}{x^2} \cdot 1 = \dfrac{1}{4x^2}$ 17. $2 \cdot \dfrac{a}{a^3} \cdot \dfrac{b^2}{b^2} \cdot \dfrac{c^3}{c} = 2 \cdot \dfrac{1}{a^2} \cdot 1 \cdot c^2 = \dfrac{2c^2}{a^2}$

18. $\dfrac{x^3}{x} \cdot \dfrac{y}{y^2} \cdot \dfrac{z^2}{z^3} = x^2 \cdot \dfrac{1}{y} \cdot \dfrac{1}{z} = \dfrac{x^2}{yz}$ 19. $\dfrac{(x^2yz)^2}{(xyz^2)^2} = \dfrac{x^4}{x^2} \cdot \dfrac{y^2}{y^2} \cdot \dfrac{z^2}{z^4} = x^2 \cdot 1 \cdot \dfrac{1}{z^2} = \dfrac{x^2}{z^2}$

20. $\dfrac{(ab^3z^2)^3}{(ab^2z^3)^2} = \dfrac{a^3}{a^2} \cdot \dfrac{b^9}{b^4} \cdot \dfrac{z^6}{z^6} = a \cdot b^5 \cdot 1 = ab^5$

B 21. $\dfrac{x^{2n}y^{2n+1}}{(x^ny^n)^2} = \dfrac{x^{2n}}{x^{2n}} \cdot \dfrac{y^{2n+1}}{y^{2n}} = 1 \cdot y^{2n+1-2n} = y$

22. $\dfrac{r^n}{r^{n-1}} \cdot \dfrac{s^{n+1}}{s^n} = r^{n-(n-1)} \cdot s^{n+1-n} = r^1 \cdot s^1 = rs$

23. $\dfrac{(ab)^m}{ab^m} = \dfrac{a^m}{a} \cdot \dfrac{b^m}{b^m} = a^{m-1} \cdot 1 = a^{m-1}$ 24. $\dfrac{(x^n)^3}{x^nx^3} = \dfrac{x^{3n}}{x^{n+3}} = x^{3n-(n+3)} = x^{2n-3}$

25. $\dfrac{x^{m+1}x^{m-1}}{x^m} = \dfrac{x^{m+1+(m-1)}}{x^m} = \dfrac{x^{2m}}{x^m} = x^{2m-m} = x^m$

26. $\dfrac{a^{n-1}b^{2n}}{a^{n+1}(b^2)^{n-1}} = \dfrac{a^{n-1}}{a^{n+1}} \cdot \dfrac{b^{2n}}{b^{2n-2}} = a^{n-1-(n+1)} \cdot b^{2n-(2n-2)} = a^{-2} \cdot b^2 = \dfrac{b^2}{a^2}$

27. $\dfrac{x^{n+2} - x^n}{x^{n+1} - x^n} = \dfrac{x^n \cdot x^2 - x^n}{x^n \cdot x - x^n} = \dfrac{x^n(x^2 - 1)}{x^n(x - 1)} = \dfrac{x^n}{x^n} \cdot \dfrac{(x + 1)(x - 1)}{x - 1} = 1(x + 1) = x + 1$

28. $\dfrac{x^{n+1} + x^{n-1}}{x^n} = \dfrac{x^n \cdot x + x^n \cdot x^{-1}}{x^n} = \dfrac{x^n(x + x^{-1})}{x^n} = \dfrac{x^n}{x^n}(x + x^{-1}) = 1(x + x^{-1})$

$= x + \dfrac{1}{x}$

29. $(p - q) + (r - s) = (p + r) - (q + s)$; $(p - q) + (r - s) = p + r - q - s$;
$(p - q) + (r - s) = (p - q) + (r - s)$; yes

30. a. $(p \cdot r) \div (q \cdot r) = p \div q$

b. $(p + r) - (q + r) = p - q$; $(p + r) - (q + r) = p + r - q - r = p - q$; yes

31. (1) $ma + na = (m + n)a$; yes;   **(2)** $m(a + b) = ma + mb$; yes;
(3) $n(ma) = (mn)a$; yes;   **(4a)** If $m > n$, $ma - na = (m - n)a$; yes;
(4b) If $n > m$, $ma - an = 1 - (n - m)a = 1 - (na - ma) = 1 - na + ma = ma - na + 1$; no;   **(5)** $m(a - b) = ma - mb$; yes

32. (1) Def. of div.;   **(2)** Comm. prop. for mult.; assoc. prop. for mult.;
(3) Prop. of the recip. of a product; **(4)** Def. of div.

33. (1) Def. of a power;   **(2)** Rule for mult. fractions

34. (1) $m > n$ or $m - n > 0$ (Given); **(2)** $a^{m-n} \cdot a^n = a^{m-n+n} = a^m$ (Law 1 of exp.);

(3) $a^{m-n} = \dfrac{a^m}{a^n}$ (Div. prop. of equality)

Page 207 · COMPUTER KEY-IN

1. a. 48   **b.** 2   **c.** 37   **d.** 6   **e.** 18   **f.** 1   **g.** 1009

2. a. GCF = 87; $\dfrac{1}{19}$ **b.** GCF = 512; $\dfrac{23}{31}$ **c.** GCF = 396; $\dfrac{7}{15}$ **d.** GCF = 1; $\dfrac{2048}{40{,}387}$

Pages 210-211 · WRITTEN EXERCISES

A   **1.** $5 \cdot 3^{-1} = 5 \cdot \dfrac{1}{3} = \dfrac{5}{3}$ **2.** $(2 \cdot 7)^{-1} = \dfrac{1}{2 \cdot 7} = \dfrac{1}{14}$

3. $(-2^{-1})^{-2} = (-1)^{-2} \cdot (2^{-1})^{-2} = 1 \cdot 2^2 = 4$

4. $(-3^{-2})^{-1} = (-1)^{-1} \cdot (3^{-2})^{-1} = -1 \cdot 3^2 = -9$

5. $(2^{-1} \cdot 3^0 \cdot 5^{-1})^{-1} = (2^{-1})^{-1} \cdot (3^0)^{-1} \cdot (5^{-1})^{-1} = 2 \cdot 1 \cdot 5 = 10$

6. $2^{-1}(3^{-1} \cdot 5^{-1})^0 = 2^{-1} \cdot 1 = \dfrac{1}{2} \cdot 1 = \dfrac{1}{2}$ **7.** $3\left(\dfrac{3}{5}\right)^{-2} = 3\left(\dfrac{5}{3}\right)^2 = 3 \cdot \dfrac{25}{9} = \dfrac{25}{3}$

8. $\left(\dfrac{5}{8}\right)^{-1} \cdot \left(\dfrac{8}{5}\right)^{-2} = \left(\dfrac{5}{8}\right)^{-1}\left(\dfrac{5}{8}\right)^2 = \left(\dfrac{5}{8}\right)^{-1+2} = \dfrac{5}{8}$

9. $602 \times 10^{-2} = 602 \times \dfrac{1}{10^2} = \dfrac{602}{100} = 6.02$ **10.** $436 \times 10^{-3} = 436 \times \dfrac{1}{10^3} = \dfrac{436}{1000} = 0.436$

11. $5.61 \times 10^{-3} = 5.61 \times \dfrac{1}{10^3} = \dfrac{5.61}{1000} = 0.00561$

12. $7.15 \times 10^{-2} = 7.15 \times \dfrac{1}{10^2} = \dfrac{7.15}{100} = 0.0715$

13. $\left(-\dfrac{2}{3}\right)^{-3} = \left(-\dfrac{3}{2}\right)^{3} = (-1)^3\left(\dfrac{3}{2}\right)^{3} = -1 \cdot \dfrac{27}{8} = -\dfrac{27}{8} = -3.375$

14. $\left(-\dfrac{5}{3}\right)^{-2} = \left(-\dfrac{3}{5}\right)^{2} = (-1)^2\left(\dfrac{3}{5}\right)^{2} = 1 \cdot \dfrac{9}{25} = 0.36$

15. $(2 \cdot 7^{-1})^{-2} = \left(\dfrac{2}{7}\right)^{-2} = \left(\dfrac{7}{2}\right)^{2} = \dfrac{49}{4} = 12.25$

16. $(2^2 \cdot 3^{-2} \cdot 5^2)^{-1} = (2^2)^{-1} \cdot (3^{-2})^{-1} \cdot (5^2)^{-1} = 2^{-2} \cdot 3^2 \cdot 5^{-2} = \dfrac{3^2}{2^2 \cdot 5^2} = \dfrac{9}{4 \cdot 25} = \dfrac{9}{100}$
$= 0.09$

17. $\dfrac{2x^{-1}}{y^{-2}} = \dfrac{2y^2}{x}$ **18.** $\dfrac{3a^2x^{-2}}{axy^{-1}} = 3 \cdot a^{2-1} \cdot x^{-2-1} \cdot y^{-(-1)} = 3a^1 x^{-3} y^1 = \dfrac{3ay}{x^3}$

19. $\dfrac{p^2 q^{-3}}{q^{-4} r^5} = p^2 \cdot q^{-3-(-4)} \cdot r^{-5} = p^2 \cdot q^1 \cdot r^{-5} = \dfrac{p^2 q}{r^5}$

20. $\dfrac{(2u^2)^{-2}}{u^{-2}v^{-2}} = 2^{-2} \cdot (u^2)^{-2} \cdot u^{-(-2)} \cdot v^{-(-2)} = \dfrac{1}{4} \cdot u^{-4} \cdot u^2 \cdot v^2 = \dfrac{1}{4} \cdot u^{-4+2} \cdot v^2$
$= \dfrac{1}{4} \cdot u^{-2} \cdot v^2 = \dfrac{v^2}{4u^2}$

21. $\left(\dfrac{a}{b^{-1}}\right)^{-1} = \dfrac{b^{-1}}{a} = \dfrac{1}{ab}$ **22.** $\left(\dfrac{1}{ab^{-1}}\right)^{-2} = \left(\dfrac{1}{\dfrac{a}{b}}\right)^{-2} = \left(\dfrac{b}{a}\right)^{-2} = \dfrac{b^{-2}}{a^{-2}} = \dfrac{a^2}{b^2}$

23. $(a^{-1}z^2)^{-3} = (a^{-1})^{-3} \cdot (z^2)^{-3} = a^3 \cdot z^{-6} = \dfrac{a^3}{z^6}$

24. $(u^{-2}v^2)^{-2} = (u^{-2})^{-2} \cdot (v^2)^{-2} = u^4 \cdot v^{-4} = \dfrac{u^4}{v^4}$

25. $2x(2xy)^{-2} = 2 \cdot x \cdot 2^{-2} \cdot x^{-2} \cdot y^{-2} = \dfrac{2x}{2^2 x^2 y^2} = \dfrac{1}{2xy^2}$

26. $4p^2(2p^2q)^{-1} = 4 \cdot p^2 \cdot 2^{-1} \cdot (p^2)^{-1} \cdot q^{-1} = 4 \cdot \dfrac{1}{2} \cdot p^2 \cdot p^{-2} \cdot q^{-1} = 2 \cdot p^{2+(-2)} \cdot q^{-1}$
$= 2 \cdot p^0 \cdot q^{-1} = \dfrac{2}{q}$

27. $\left(\dfrac{2x^{-1}}{y}\right)^{-3} = \left(\dfrac{y}{2x^{-1}}\right)^{3} = \dfrac{y^3}{(2x^{-1})^3} = \dfrac{y^3}{8x^{-3}} = \dfrac{1}{8} \cdot y^3 \cdot x^{-(-3)} = \dfrac{x^3 y^3}{8}$

28. $\left(\dfrac{3p^{-1}}{2q^2}\right)^{-3} = \left(\dfrac{2q^2}{3p^{-1}}\right)^{3} = \dfrac{8q^6}{27p^{-3}} = \dfrac{8}{27} \cdot q^6 \cdot p^{-(-3)} = \dfrac{8p^3 q^6}{27}$

29. $\left(\dfrac{a}{b^2}\right)^{-1}\left(\dfrac{a^2}{b}\right)^{-2} = \dfrac{b^2}{a} \cdot \left(\dfrac{b}{a^2}\right)^2 = \dfrac{b^2}{a} \cdot \dfrac{b^2}{a^4} = \dfrac{b^{2+2}}{a^{1+4}} = \dfrac{b^4}{a^5}$

30. $\left(\dfrac{2}{x}\right)^{-2}\left(\dfrac{x}{2}\right)^{-3} = \left(\dfrac{x}{2}\right)^2\left(\dfrac{2}{x}\right)^3 = \dfrac{x^2}{4} \cdot \dfrac{8}{x^3} = \dfrac{8}{4}x^2 \cdot x^{-3} = 2 \cdot x^{2+(-3)} = 2 \cdot x^{-1} = \dfrac{2}{x}$

31. $\dfrac{(ax^2)^{-1}}{a^2 x^{-2}} = \dfrac{a^{-1} \cdot x^{-2}}{a^2 x^{-2}} = a^{-1} \cdot a^{-2} \cdot x^{-2} \cdot x^{-(-2)} = a^{-1+(-2)} \cdot x^{-2+2} = a^{-3} \cdot x^0 = a^{-3} = \dfrac{1}{a^3}$

32. $\dfrac{(pq^{-2})^{-1}}{(p^2 q)^{-2}} = \dfrac{p^{-1} \cdot q^2}{p^{-4} q^{-2}} = p^{-1} \cdot p^{-(-4)} \cdot q^2 \cdot q^{-(-2)} = p^{-1} \cdot p^4 \cdot q^2 \cdot q^2 = p^{-1+4} \cdot q^{2+2}$

$= p^3 q^4$

33. $\dfrac{x^2}{y}\left(\dfrac{2x}{y^2}\right)^{-2} = \dfrac{x^2}{y}\left(\dfrac{y^2}{2x}\right)^2 = \dfrac{x^2}{y} \cdot \dfrac{y^4}{4x^2} = \dfrac{1}{4} \cdot x^2 \cdot x^{-2} \cdot y^4 \cdot y^{-1} = \dfrac{1}{4}x^{2+(-2)} \cdot y^{4+(-1)}$

$= \dfrac{1}{4} \cdot x^0 \cdot y^3 = \dfrac{y^3}{4}$

34. $\dfrac{a^{-1}}{b^2}\left(\dfrac{a^2}{b^{-1}}\right)^{-1} = \dfrac{a^{-1}}{b^2} \cdot \dfrac{b^{-1}}{a^2} = a^{-1} \cdot a^{-2} \cdot b^{-1} \cdot b^{-2} = a^{-1+(-2)} \cdot b^{-1+(-2)} = a^{-3} \cdot b^{-3}$

$= \dfrac{1}{a^3 b^3}$

35. $\dfrac{u}{v^{-2}}\left(\dfrac{u^{-1}}{v^2}\right)^{-1} = \dfrac{u}{v^{-2}} \cdot \dfrac{v^2}{u^{-1}} = u \cdot u^{-(-1)} \cdot v^2 \cdot v^{-(-2)} = u^{1+1} \cdot v^{2+2} = u^2 v^4$

36. $\left(\dfrac{x^{-2}}{y^{-3}}\right)^{-1}\left(\dfrac{x^{-3}}{y^{-2}}\right)^2 = \dfrac{y^{-3}}{x^{-2}}\left(\dfrac{x^{-6}}{y^{-4}}\right) = y^{-3} \cdot y^{-(-4)} \cdot x^{-6} \cdot x^{-(-2)} = y^{-3+4} \cdot x^{-6+2} = y \cdot x^{-4}$

$= \dfrac{y}{x^4}$

37. $3x^2 y^{-6} + (x^{-1}y^3)^{-2} = 3x^2 y^{-6} + x^2 y^{-6} = 4x^2 y^{-6} = \dfrac{4x^2}{y^6}$

38. $\left(\dfrac{a^2}{y}\right)^2 + \left(\dfrac{y}{2a^2}\right)^{-2} = \dfrac{a^4}{y^2} + \left(\dfrac{2a^2}{y}\right)^2 = \dfrac{a^4}{y^2} + \dfrac{4a^4}{y^2} = \dfrac{5a^4}{y^2}$

39-42. Answers may vary; examples are given.

39. Let $x = 1$ and $y = 2$; $(x + y)^{-1} = (1 + 2)^{-1} = 3^{-1} = \dfrac{1}{3}$; $x^{-1} + y^{-1} = 1 + \dfrac{1}{2} = \dfrac{3}{2}$;

$\dfrac{1}{3} \neq \dfrac{3}{2}$

40. Let $x = 2$ and $y = 3$; $(xy)^{-1} = (2 \cdot 3)^{-1} = 6^{-1} = \dfrac{1}{6}$; $\dfrac{x}{y} = \dfrac{2}{3}$; $\dfrac{1}{6} \neq \dfrac{2}{3}$

41. Let $x = 2$ and $y = 3$; $xy^{-1} = 2 \cdot 3^{-1} = \dfrac{2}{3}$; $\dfrac{1}{xy} = \dfrac{1}{2 \cdot 3} = \dfrac{1}{6}$; $\dfrac{2}{3} \neq \dfrac{1}{6}$

42. Let $x = -1$; $(1 - x)^{-2} = \dfrac{1}{(1-x)^2} = \dfrac{1}{(1-(-1))^2} = \dfrac{1}{2^2} = \dfrac{1}{4}$; $1 - x^{-2} = 1 - \dfrac{1}{x^2}$

$= 1 - \dfrac{1}{(-1)^2} = 1 - 1 = 0$; $\dfrac{1}{4} \neq 0$

B 43. $x^{-1} + 4x^{-2} + 4x^{-3} = x^{-3}(x^2 + 4x + 4)$ 44. $1 - 3x^{-1} + 4x^{-2} = x^{-2}(x^2 - 3x + 4)$

45. $1 - 2x^{-2} + x^{-4} = x^{-4}(x^4 - 2x^2 + 1)$ 46. $x^{-3} - 3x^{-2} + 2 = x^{-3}(1 - 3x + 2x^3)$

47. $x(x + 1)^{-2} - 2(x + 1)^{-1} = (x + 1)^{-2}[x - 2(x + 1)] = (x + 1)^{-2}(-x - 2)$

48. $x^2(x^2 + 1)^{-2} - (x^2 + 1)^{-1} = (x^2 + 1)^{-2}[x^2 - (x^2 + 1)] = (x^2 + 1)^{-2}(-1)$

49. $x(x + 3)^{-1} + 2 = (x + 3)^{-1}[x + 2(x + 3)] = (x + 3)^{-1}(3x + 6)$

50. $x^2(x^2 - 4)^{-1} - 1 = (x^2 - 4)^{-1}[x^2 - (x^2 - 4)] = (x^2 - 4)^{-1}(4)$

C 51. (1) m and n are positive integers; $m > n$ (Given)

(2) $a^m \cdot a^{-n} = a^m \cdot \dfrac{1}{a^n}$ (Def. of neg. exp.)

(3) $= \dfrac{a^m}{a^n}$ (Def. of div.)

(4) $= a^{m-n}$ (Law 4a of pos. exp.)

(5) $= a^{m+(-n)}$ (Def. of subtr.)

(6) $\therefore a^m \cdot a^{-n} = a^{m+(-n)}$ (Trans. prop. of equality)

52. (1) m and n are positive integers; $m > n$ (Given)

(2) $a^{-m}a^n = \dfrac{1}{a^m} \cdot a^n$ (Def. of neg. exp.)

(3) $= \dfrac{a^n}{a^m}$ (Def. of div.)

(4) $= \dfrac{1}{a^{m-n}}$ (Law 4b of pos. exp.)

(5) $= a^{-(m-n)}$ (Def. of neg. exp.)

(6) $= a^{-(m+(-n))}$ (Def. of subtr.)

(7) $= a^{(-m)+[-(-n)]}$ (Prop. of the opp. of a sum)

(8) $= a^{(-m)+n}$ (For every real number x, $-(-x) = x$.)

(9) $\therefore a^{-m}a^n = a^{(-m)+n}$ (Trans. prop. of equality)

53. (1) $(a^{-m})^n = \left(\dfrac{1}{a^m}\right)^n$ (Def. of neg. exp.)

(2) $= \dfrac{1^n}{(a^m)^n}$ (Law 5 of pos. exp.)

(3) $= \dfrac{1}{a^{mn}}$ (Subst.; Law 3 of neg. exp.)

(4) $= a^{-(mn)}$ (Def. of neg. exp.)

(5) $= a^{(-m)n}$ (The opp. of a prod. is the prod. of the opp. of one factor and the other factors.)

(6) $\therefore (a^{-m})^n = a^{(-m)n}$ (Trans. prop. of equality)

54. (1) $\dfrac{a^{-m}}{a^n} = a^{-m} \cdot \dfrac{1}{a^n}$ (Def. of div.)

(2) $= \dfrac{1}{a^m} \cdot \dfrac{1}{a^n}$ (Def. of neg. exp.)

(3) $\qquad = \dfrac{1}{a^m \cdot a^n}$ (Rule for mult. fractions)

(4) $\qquad = \dfrac{1}{a^{m+n}}$ (Law 1 of pos. exp.)

(5) $\qquad = a^{-(m+n)}$ (Def. of neg. exp.)

(6) $\qquad = a^{(-m)+(-n)}$ (Prop. of the opp. of a sum)

(7) $\qquad = a^{(-m)-n}$ (Def. of subtr.)

(8) $\therefore \dfrac{a^{-m}}{a^n} = a^{(-m)-n}$ (Trans. prop. of equality)

55. (1) $\dfrac{a^m}{a^{-n}} = a^m \div \dfrac{1}{a^n}$ (Def. of neg. exp.)

(2) $\qquad = a^m \cdot \dfrac{1}{\dfrac{1}{a^n}}$ (Def. of div.)

(3) $\qquad = a^m \cdot a^n$ $\left(\text{For every nonzero real number } x,\ \dfrac{1}{\dfrac{1}{x}} = x. \right)$

(4) $\qquad = a^{m+n}$ (Law 1 of pos. exp.)

(5) $\qquad = a^{m+[-(-n)]}$ (For every real number x, $-(-x) = x$.)

(6) $\qquad = a^{m-(-n)}$ (Def. of subtr.)

(7) $\therefore \dfrac{a^m}{a^{-n}} = a^{m-(-n)}$ (Trans. prop. of equality)

56. (1) $\dfrac{a^{-m}}{a^{-n}} = a^{-m} \cdot \dfrac{1}{a^{-n}}$ (Def. of div.)

(2) $\qquad = \dfrac{1}{a^m} \cdot a^n$ (Def. of neg. exp.)

(3) $\qquad = \dfrac{a^n}{a^m}$ (Def. of div.)

(4) $\qquad = \dfrac{1}{a^{m-n}}$ (Law 4b of pos. exp.)

(5) $\qquad = a^{-(m-n)}$ (Def. of neg. exp.)

(6) $\qquad = a^{-[m+(-n)]}$ (Def. of subtr.)

(7) $\qquad = a^{(-m)+[-(-n)]}$ (Prop. of the opp. of a sum)

(8) $\qquad = a^{(-m)-(-n)}$ (Def. of subtr.)

(9) $\therefore \dfrac{a^{-m}}{a^{-n}} = a^{(-m)-(-n)}$ (Trans. prop. of equality)

57. (1) $\left(\dfrac{a}{b}\right)^{-m} = \dfrac{1}{\left(\dfrac{a}{b}\right)^m}$ (Def. of neg. exp.)

(2) $\qquad = \dfrac{1}{\dfrac{a^m}{b^m}}$ (Law 5 for pos. exp.)

(3) $= \dfrac{1}{a^m \cdot \dfrac{1}{b^m}}$ (Def. of div.)

(4) $= \dfrac{1}{a^m} \cdot \dfrac{1}{\dfrac{1}{b^m}}$ (Prop. of the recip. of a product)

(5) $= a^{-m} \cdot \dfrac{1}{b^{-m}}$ (Def. of neg. exp.)

(6) $= \dfrac{a^{-m}}{b^{-m}}$ (Def. of div.)

(7) $\therefore \left(\dfrac{a}{b}\right)^{-m} = \dfrac{a^{-m}}{b^{-m}}$ (Trans. prop. of equality)

Pages 214-215 · WRITTEN EXERCISES

A   1. 20,000

2. 0.0001

3. 0.003

4. 1,000,000

5. 3450

6. 0.502

7. 0.0000360

8. 725,000

9. 1.2×10^4

10. 2.5×10^6

11. 2.05×10^{-1}

12. 1.2×10^{-3}

13. 4.053×10^2

14. 2.650×10^1

15. 2.0×10^{-3}

16. 3.5×10^{-5}

17. 2.75×10^4

18. 8.4×10^{-4}

19. 2.65×10^{-4} 20. 4.630×10^1

21. $(3.4 \times 10^5)(2.4 \times 10^3) = (3.4 \times 2.4) \times 10^{5+3} = 8.16 \times 10^8;\ 8.2 \times 10^8$

22. $(6.4 \times 10^{-3})(7.7 \times 10^1) = (6.4 \times 7.7) \times 10^{-3+1} = 49.28 \times 10^{-2};\ 4.9 \times 10^{-1}$

23. $(2.653 \times 10^3)(2.52 \times 10^{-1}) = (2.653 \times 2.52) \times 10^{3+(-1)} = 6.68556 \times 10^2;\ 6.69 \times 10^2$

24. $(3.67 \times 10^{-3})(3.587 \times 10^{-2}) = (3.67 \times 3.587) \times 10^{-3+(-2)} = 13.16429 \times 10^{-5};$
1.32×10^{-4}

25. $\dfrac{(5.26 \times 10^{-2})(6.3 \times 10^{-3})}{4.06 \times 10^{-4}} = \dfrac{5.26 \times 6.3}{4.06} \times 10^{-2+(-3)-(-4)} = 8.2 \times 10^{-1}$

26. $\dfrac{(3.200 \times 10^3)(8.72 \times 10^4)}{5.66 \times 10^5} = \dfrac{3.200 \times 8.72}{5.66} \times 10^{3+4-5} = 4.93 \times 10^2$

B   27. $\dfrac{473 \times 0.276}{28.3 \times 0.0580} = \dfrac{4.73 \times 10^2 \times 2.76 \times 10^{-1}}{2.83 \times 10^1 \times 5.80 \times 10^{-2}} \approx \dfrac{5 \times 10^2 \times 3 \times 10^{-1}}{3 \times 10^1 \times 6 \times 10^{-2}}$

$= \dfrac{5 \times 3}{3 \times 6} \times 10^{2+(-1)-[1+(-2)]} \approx 0.8 \times 10^2;\ 8 \times 10^1$ or 80

28. $\dfrac{80{,}300 \times 0.0526}{0.00385 \times 47.0} = \dfrac{8.03 \times 10^4 \times 5.26 \times 10^{-2}}{3.85 \times 10^{-3} \times 4.70 \times 10^1} \approx \dfrac{8 \times 10^4 \times 5 \times 10^{-2}}{4 \times 10^{-3} \times 5 \times 10^1}$

$= \dfrac{8 \times 5}{4 \times 5} \times 10^{4+(-2)-(-3+1)} = 2 \times 10^4$ or 20,000

29. $\dfrac{52.65 \times (0.371)^2}{0.087 \times (61.67)^2} = \dfrac{5.265 \times 10^1 \times (3.71 \times 10^{-1})^2}{8.7 \times 10^{-2} \times (6.167 \times 10^1)^2} \approx \dfrac{5 \times 10^1 \times (4 \times 10^{-1})^2}{9 \times 10^{-2} \times (6 \times 10^1)^2}$

$= \dfrac{5 \times 10^1 \times 16 \times 10^{-2}}{9 \times 10^{-2} \times 36 \times 10^2} = \dfrac{5 \times 16}{9 \times 36} \times 10^{1+(-2)-(-2+2)} \approx 0.2 \times 10^{-1}; \; 2 \times 10^{-2} \text{ or } 0.02$

30. $\dfrac{0.000729 \times (478)^2}{46,800 \times (0.0871)^2} = \dfrac{7.29 \times 10^{-4} \times (4.78 \times 10^2)^2}{4.68 \times 10^4 \times (8.71 \times 10^{-2})^2} \approx \dfrac{7 \times 10^4 \times (5 \times 10^2)^2}{5 \times 10^4 \times (9 \times 10^{-2})^2}$

$= \dfrac{7 \times 10^4 \times 25 \times 10^4}{5 \times 10^4 \times 81 \times 10^{-4}} = \dfrac{7 \times 25}{5 \times 81} \times 10^{4+4-(4-(-4))} \approx 0.4 \times 10^0; \; 4 \times 10^{-1} \text{ or } 0.4$

Pages 215-216 · PROBLEMS

A **1.**

	1983 Population	Land Area (km²)
U.S.	234,000,000	9,370,000
India	740,000,000	3,290,000
World	4,720,000,000	149,000,000

2. a. $\dfrac{9.37 \times 10^6}{1.49 \times 10^8} = \dfrac{9.37}{1.49} \times 10^{6-8} \approx 6.29 \times 10^{-2} = 0.0629 = 6.29\%$

   b. $\dfrac{3.29 \times 10^6}{1.49 \times 10^8} = \dfrac{3.29}{1.49} \times 10^{6-8} \approx 2.21 \times 10^{-2} = 0.0221 = 2.21\%$

3. a. $\dfrac{2.34 \times 10^8}{4.72 \times 10^9} = \dfrac{2.34}{4.72} \times 10^{8-9} \approx 0.496 \times 10^{-1} = 0.0496 = 4.96\%$

   b. $\dfrac{7.40 \times 10^8}{4.72 \times 10^9} = \dfrac{7.40}{4.72} \times 10^{8-9} \approx 1.57 \times 10^{-1} = 0.157 = 15.7\%$

4. a. $\dfrac{2.34 \times 10^8}{9.37 \times 10^6} = \dfrac{2.34}{9.37} \times 10^{8-6} \approx 0.250 \times 10^2; \text{ about 25 persons per km}^2$

   b. $\dfrac{7.40 \times 10^8}{3.29 \times 10^6} = \dfrac{7.40}{3.29} \times 10^{8-6} \approx 2.25 \times 10^2; \text{ about 225 persons per km}^2$

   c. $\dfrac{4.72 \times 10^9}{1.49 \times 10^8} = \dfrac{4.72}{1.49} \times 10^{9-8} \approx 3.17 \times 10^1; \text{ about 32 persons per km}^2$

5. $\dfrac{1.38 \times 10^{12}}{2.34 \times 10^8} = \dfrac{1.38}{2.34} \times 10^{12-8} \approx 0.590 \times 10^4 = 5900; \text{ about \$5900}$

6. Let d = distance between components; $\dfrac{d}{2.4 \times 10^{10}} \leq 4 \times 10^{-9}$; $d \leq 2.4 \times 10^{10} \times 4 \times$

$10^{-9} = 9.6 \times 10 = 96$; components must be less than 100 cm or 1 m apart.

7.

	AU	parsec	lt.-yr.
1 AU	1	4.85×10^{-6}	1.58×10^{-5}
1 parsec	2.06×10^5	1	3.26
1 lt.-yr.	6.33×10^4	0.307	1

8. 1 AU $\approx 1.58 \times 10^{-5}$ light-years $\approx (1.58 \times 10^{-5} \times 9.46 \times 10^{12})$ km $\approx 14.9 \times 10^7$ or 1.49×10^8 km; 1 parsec ≈ 3.26 light-years $\approx (3.26 \times 9.46 \times 10^{12})$ km $\approx 30.8 \times 10^{12}$ or 3.08×10^{13} km

B **9.** Wages on n-th day $= 2^{n-1}$ cents; $2^{31-1} = 2^{30} = 2^{10 \cdot 3} = (2^{10})^3 = (10^3)^3 = 10^9$; 10^9 cents $= 10^7$ dollars; $10,000,000$

10. $\dfrac{100 \text{ watts}}{125 \text{ volts}} = 0.8$ amperes; $0.8 \times 6.2 \times 10^{18} = 8 \times 10^{-1} \times 6.2 \times 10^{18}$
$= 8 \times 6.2 \times 10^{-1+18} = 49.6 \times 10^{17}$ electrons/second; 1 h $= 60$ min $= 3600$ s, $4.96 \times 10^{18} \times 3.6 \times 10^3 \approx 17.9 \times 10^{21}$; 1.79×10^{22} electrons

11. Volume of sun $= \dfrac{4}{3} \pi (7.0 \times 10^8)^3 = \dfrac{4}{3} \pi (343 \times 10^{24})$; density of

sun $= \dfrac{2.0 \times 10^{30}}{\dfrac{4}{3} \pi (3.43 \times 10^{26})}$; volume of Earth $= \dfrac{4}{3} \pi (6.4 \times 10^6)^3 \approx \dfrac{4}{3} \pi (262 \times 10^{18})$

$= \dfrac{4}{3} \pi (2.62 \times 10^{20})$; density of Earth $\approx \dfrac{6.0 \times 10^{24}}{\dfrac{4}{3} \pi (2.62 \times 10^{20})}$; $\dfrac{\text{density of Earth}}{\text{density of sun}}$

$\approx \dfrac{6.0 \times 10^{24}}{\dfrac{4}{3} \pi (2.62 \times 10^{20})} \div \dfrac{2.0 \times 10^{30}}{\dfrac{4}{3} \pi (3.43 \times 10^{26})} = \dfrac{6.0 \times 10^{24}}{\dfrac{4}{3} \pi (2.62 \times 10^{20})} \cdot \dfrac{\dfrac{4}{3} \pi (3.43 \times 10^{26})}{2.0 \times 10^{30}}$

$= \dfrac{6.0 \times 3.43}{2.62 \times 2.0} \times 10^{24+26-(20+30)} \approx 3.9 \times 10^0 \approx 4$

Page 216 · COMPUTER EXERCISES

1.
```
10  PRINT "ENTER X, M, Y, N"
20  INPUT X, M, Y, N
30  LET L = M + N
40  LET Z = X * Y
50  IF Z < 10 THEN 90
60  LET Z = Z/10
70  LET L = L + 1
80  GOTO 50
90  PRINT Z; "TIMES 10 TO THE ";L;" POWER"
100 END
```

   2. **a.** 3.746316 TIMES 10 TO THE 13 POWER

      b. 1.142547 TIMES 10 TO THE −7 POWER

      c. 8.635432 TIMES 10 TO THE −7 POWER

      d. 2.005728 TIMES 10 TO THE 1 POWER

   3. Answers may vary. For example, add lines 25, 26, and 85, and change line 50 as follows.

      25 PRINT "ENTER NUMBER OF SIGNIFICANT DIGITS"

      26 INPUT S

      85 LET Z = INT(Z ∗ 10 ↑ (S − 1) + .5)/10 ↑ (S − 1)

      50 IF Z < 10 THEN 85

   4. **a.** 4 TIMES 10 TO THE 13 POWER

         1 TIMES 10 TO THE −7 POWER

         9 TIMES 10 TO THE −7 POWER

         2 TIMES 10 TO THE 1 POWER

      b. 3.75 TIMES 10 TO THE 13 POWER

         1.14 TIMES 10 TO THE −7 POWER

         8.64 TIMES 10 TO THE −7 POWER

         2.01 TIMES 10 TO THE 1 POWER

Page 217 · CALCULATOR KEY-IN

   1. 1,000,000,000 or 1×10^9 **2.** 1.4655151×10^{11} **3.** 1×10^{-10}

   4. 4.246×10^{18} **5.** 1.081×10^{-4} **6.** 5.194×10^{-6}

   7. 9.517×10^0

   8. a. (1) 0.6666 . . . . 6 or (2) 0.6666 . . . 7   **b.** (1) truncates (2) rounds

Pages 220-221 · WRITTEN EXERCISES

A **1.** $\dfrac{3x^2}{6x^2 - 9x} = \dfrac{3x^2}{3x(2x - 3)} = \dfrac{x}{2x - 3}$ **2.** $\dfrac{4x^4 - 2x^3}{2x^2} = \dfrac{2x^2(2x^2 - x)}{2x^2} = 2x^2 - x$

  3. $\dfrac{t^2 + 2t}{t + t - 2} = \dfrac{t(t + 2)}{(t + 2)(t - 1)} = \dfrac{t}{t - 1}$

  4. $\dfrac{x^3 - 4x}{x^3 - 4x^2 + 4x} = \dfrac{x(x^2 - 4)}{x(x^2 - 4x + 4)} = \dfrac{x(x - 2)(x + 2)}{x(x - 2)^2} = \dfrac{x + 2}{x - 2}$

  5. $(a - x)(x - a)^{-1} = \dfrac{a - x}{x - a} = \dfrac{-1(x - a)}{x - a} = -1$

  6. $(t^2 - at)t^{-2} = \dfrac{t^2 - at}{t^2} = \dfrac{t(t - a)}{t^2} = \dfrac{t - a}{t}$ **7.** $\dfrac{(x + 1)^2}{x^2 - 1} = \dfrac{(x + 1)^2}{(x + 1)(x - 1)} = \dfrac{x + 1}{x - 1}$

  8. $\dfrac{u^2 - 9}{(u - 3)^2} = \dfrac{(u - 3)(u + 3)}{(u - 3)^2} = \dfrac{u + 3}{u - 3}$ **9.** $\dfrac{a^2 - t^2}{(a - t)^2} = \dfrac{(a - t)(a + t)}{(a - t)^2} = \dfrac{a + t}{a - t}$

10. $\dfrac{(x+y)^2}{x^2-y^2} = \dfrac{(x+y)^2}{(x-y)(x+y)} = \dfrac{x+y}{x-y}$ **11.** $\dfrac{2x^2-5x+2}{2x^2-3x-2} = \dfrac{(2x-1)(x-2)}{(2x+1)(x-2)} = \dfrac{2x-1}{2x+1}$

12. $\dfrac{4t^2+3t-1}{4t^2-5t+1} = \dfrac{(4t-1)(t+1)}{(4t-1)(t-1)} = \dfrac{t+1}{t-1}$

13. $(u^2-u-6)(u+2)^{-2} = \dfrac{u^2-u-6}{(u+2)^2} = \dfrac{(u-3)(u+2)}{(u+2)^2} = \dfrac{u-3}{u+2}$

14. $(x^2+4x-5)(x-1)^{-2} = \dfrac{x^2+4x-5}{(x-1)^2} = \dfrac{(x+5)(x-1)}{(x-1)^2} = \dfrac{x+5}{x-1}$

15. $\dfrac{x^2+x-6}{(x-3)(2-x)} = \dfrac{(x+3)(x-2)}{-(x-3)(x-2)} = -\dfrac{x+3}{x-3}$

16. $\dfrac{(x-1)(x+1)^2}{(x+1)(x^2-1)} = \dfrac{(x-1)(x+1)^2}{(x+1)(x-1)(x+1)} = \dfrac{(x-1)(x+1)^2}{(x-1)(x+1)^2} = 1$

17. $(x^4-x^2)(x^4-1)^{-1} = \dfrac{x^4-x^2}{x^4-1} = \dfrac{x^2(x^2-1)}{(x^2-1)(x^2+1)} = \dfrac{x^2}{x^2+1}$

18. $(x^3+1)(x+1)^{-3} = \dfrac{x^3+1}{(x+1)^3} = \dfrac{(x+1)(x^2-x+1)}{(x+1)^3} = \dfrac{x^2-x+1}{(x+1)^2}$

19. $\dfrac{t^3-1}{t^4-1} = \dfrac{(t-1)(t^2+t+1)}{(t^2-1)(t^2+1)} = \dfrac{(t-1)(t^2+t+1)}{(t-1)(t+1)(t^2+1)} = \dfrac{t^2+t+1}{(t+1)(t^2+1)}$

20. $\dfrac{x^4-y^4}{(x+y)^2(x^2+y^2)} = \dfrac{(x^2-y^2)(x^2+y^2)}{(x+y)^2(x^2+y^2)} = \dfrac{(x+y)(x-y)(x^2+y^2)}{(x+y)^2(x^2+y^2)} = \dfrac{x-y}{x+y}$

21. $f(x) = \dfrac{x^2-4}{x^2-4x} = \dfrac{(x+2)(x-2)}{x(x-4)}$ **a.** all real numbers except 0 and 4   **b.** 2 and -2

22. $f(t) = \dfrac{t^3+t}{t^2-1} = \dfrac{t(t^2+1)}{(t+1)(t-1)}$ **a.** all real numbers except 1 and -1 **b.** 0

23. $g(t) = \dfrac{t^3-8}{t^4-1} = \dfrac{t^3-8}{(t^2+1)(t^2-1)} = \dfrac{(t-2)(t^2+2t+4)}{(t^2+1)(t+1)(t-1)}$

a. all real numbers except 1 and -1 **b.** 2

24. $\varphi(x) = \dfrac{x^3+8}{(x-2)^3} = \dfrac{(x+2)(x^2-2x+4)}{(x-2)^3}$ **a.** all real numbers except 2   **b.** -2

25. $F(x) = \dfrac{(x+1)^2+(x-1)^2}{(x+1)^2-(x-1)^2} = \dfrac{x^2+2x+1+x^2-2x+1}{[(x+1)-(x-1)][(x+1)+(x-1)]} = \dfrac{2x^2+2}{2(2x)}$

$= \dfrac{x^2+1}{2x}$ **a.** all real numbers except 0   **b.** $x^2+1>0$ for all real numbers; there are no zeros.

26. $h(u) = \dfrac{3u^2+8u-3}{u^2-6u+9} = \dfrac{(3u-1)(u+3)}{(u-3)^2}$ **a.** all real numbers except 3   **b.** $\dfrac{1}{3}$ and -3

B **27.** $G(x) = \dfrac{x^3+3x^2+x+3}{x^4+2x-3} = \dfrac{x^2(x+3)+(x+3)}{(x^2+3)(x^2-1)} = \dfrac{(x^2+1)(x+3)}{(x^2+3)(x+1)(x-1)}$

a. all real numbers except -1 and 1   **b.** -3

28. $f(t) = \dfrac{t^3 + t^2 - 4t - 4}{t^3 - 4t^2 + t - 4} = \dfrac{t^2(t + 1) - 4(t + 1)}{t^2(t - 4) + (t - 4)} = \dfrac{(t^2 - 4)(t + 1)}{(t^2 + 1)(t - 4)}$

$\qquad = \dfrac{(t + 2)(t - 2)(t + 1)}{(t^2 + 1)(t - 4)}$ **a.** all real numbers except 4 **b.** $-2, 2$, and -1

29. $\dfrac{x^3 - x^2 - x + 1}{x^3 + x^2 - x - 1} = \dfrac{x^2(x - 1) - (x - 1)}{x^2(x + 1) - (x + 1)} = \dfrac{(x^2 - 1)(x - 1)}{(x^2 - 1)(x + 1)} = \dfrac{x - 1}{x + 1}$

30. $\dfrac{x^4 - 1}{x^3 + x^2 + x + 1} = \dfrac{(x^2 - 1)(x^2 + 1)}{x^2(x + 1) + (x + 1)} = \dfrac{(x + 1)(x - 1)(x^2 + 1)}{(x^2 + 1)(x + 1)} = x - 1$

31. $\dfrac{x^3 + x^2 y - xy^2 - y^3}{x^2 - y^2} = \dfrac{x^3 - xy^2 + x^2 y - y^3}{x^2 - y^2} = \dfrac{x(x^2 - y^2) + y(x^2 - y^2)}{x^2 - y^2}$

$\qquad = \dfrac{(x + y)(x^2 - y^2)}{x^2 - y^2} = x + y$

32. $\dfrac{s^4 - s^3 t - st^3 + t^4}{(s^2 - t^2)^2} = \dfrac{s^4 - st^3 - s^3 t + t^4}{[(s + t)(s - t)]^2} = \dfrac{s(s^3 - t^3) - t(s^3 - t^3)}{(s + t)^2(s - t)^2}$

$\qquad = \dfrac{(s - t)(s^3 - t^3)}{(s + t)^2(s - t)^2} = \dfrac{(s - t)(s^2 + st + t^2)}{(s + t)^2(s - t)} = \dfrac{s^2 + st + t^2}{(s + t)^2}$

33. $\dfrac{u^4 - 2u^2 v^2 + v^4}{u^4 - v^4} = \dfrac{(u^2 - v^2)^2}{(u^2 + v^2)(u^2 - v^2)} = \dfrac{u^2 - v^2}{u^2 + v^2} = \dfrac{(u + v)(u - v)}{u^2 + v^2}$

34. $\dfrac{x^4 + 2x^2 y^2 + y^4}{x^4 - y^4} = \dfrac{(x^2 + y^2)^2}{(x^2 - y^2)(x^2 + y^2)} = \dfrac{x^2 + y^2}{x^2 - y^2} = \dfrac{x^2 + y^2}{(x + y)(x - y)}$

35. $\dfrac{x^3 - y^3}{x^4 - y^4} = \dfrac{(x - y)(x^2 + xy + y^2)}{(x^2 + y^2)(x^2 - y^2)} = \dfrac{(x - y)(x^2 + xy + y^2)}{(x^2 + y^2)(x + y)(x - y)}$

$\qquad = \dfrac{x^2 + xy + y^2}{(x^2 + y^2)(x + y)}$

36. $\dfrac{x^2 - 12y^2 + xy}{x^2 - 6y^2 - xy} = \dfrac{(x + 4y)(x - 3y)}{(x - 3y)(x + 2y)} = \dfrac{x + 4y}{x + 2y}$

37. $\dfrac{(x - y)[z^2 - (x + y)z + xy]}{(x - z)[y^2 - (x + z)y + xz]} = \dfrac{(x - y)[z^2 - xz - yz + xy]}{(x - z)[y^2 - xy - yz + xz]}$

$\qquad = \dfrac{(x - y)[z(z - y) - x(z - y)]}{(x - z)[y(y - z) - x(y - z)]} = \dfrac{(x - y)(z - x)(z - y)}{(x - z)(y - z)(y - x)}$

$\qquad = \dfrac{(x - y)(x - z)(y - z)}{-(x - z)(y - z)(x - y)} = -1$

38. $\dfrac{ax - by + bx - ay}{ax + by - bx - ay} = \dfrac{x(a + b) - y(a + b)}{x(a - b) - y(a - b)} = \dfrac{(x - y)(a + b)}{(x - y)(a - b)} = \dfrac{a + b}{a - b}$

39. $\dfrac{x^2(x+3)(x^2-9) + 2x(x-3)^2(x+3)}{x^2+2x-3}$

$= \dfrac{x^2(x+3)(x+3)(x-3) + 2x(x-3)^2(x+3)}{(x+3)(x-1)}$

$= \dfrac{x(x+3)(x-3)[x(x+3)+2(x-3)]}{(x+3)(x-1)} = \dfrac{x(x-3)[x^2+3x+2x-6]}{x-1}$

$= \dfrac{x(x-3)(x^2+5x-6)}{x-1} = \dfrac{x(x-3)(x+6)(x-1)}{x-1} = x(x-3)(x+6)$

C 40. $\dfrac{x(x+3)(x^2+2x-3) - 2(x-1)(x^2+4x+3)}{(x^2+x-2)^2}$

$= \dfrac{x(x+3)(x+3)(x-1) - 2(x-1)(x+3)(x+1)}{[(x+2)(x-1)]^2}$

$= \dfrac{(x+3)(x-1)[x(x+3)-2(x+1)]}{(x+2)^2(x-1)^2} = \dfrac{(x+3)(x^2+3x-2x-2)}{(x+2)^2(x-1)}$

$= \dfrac{(x+3)(x^2+x-2)}{(x+2)^2(x-1)} = \dfrac{(x+3)(x+2)(x-1)}{(x+2)^2(x-1)} = \dfrac{x+3}{x+2}$

41. $\dfrac{x^4+x^2y^2+y^4}{x^3+y^3} = \dfrac{x^4+2x^2y^2+y^4-x^2y^2}{(x+y)(x^2-xy+y^2)} = \dfrac{(x^2+y^2)^2-(xy)^2}{(x+y)(x^2-xy+y^2)}$

$= \dfrac{(x^2+y^2-xy)(x^2+y^2+xy)}{(x+y)(x^2-xy+y^2)} = \dfrac{x^2+xy+y^2}{x+y}$

42. $\dfrac{x^{2n}+5x^n+6}{x^{2n}+2x^n-3} = \dfrac{(x^n+3)(x^n+2)}{(x^n+3)(x^n-1)} = \dfrac{x^n+2}{x^n-1}$

43. $\dfrac{x^{2n}+3x^n-4}{x^{2n}-2x^n+1} = \dfrac{(x^n+4)(x^n-1)}{(x^n-1)^2} = \dfrac{x^n+4}{x^n-1}$

Page 221 · BIOGRAPHICAL NOTE

An integer of the form $7k+2$ satisfies the third condition. Trial and error shows that $7(3)+2 = 23$ satisfies the other conditions as well. Since 105 is the LCM of 3, 5, and 7, any integer of the form $105n+23$ satisfies all three conditions as well. Since the number must be positive, $n \geq 0$.

Page 224 · WRITTEN EXERCISES

A 1. $\dfrac{12}{35} \div \dfrac{9}{14} \cdot \left(-\dfrac{15}{16}\right) = \dfrac{12}{35} \cdot \dfrac{14}{9} \cdot \left(-\dfrac{15}{16}\right) = -\dfrac{1}{2}$

2. $\dfrac{56}{39} \cdot \left(-\dfrac{9}{98}\right) \div \left(-\dfrac{12}{91}\right) = \dfrac{56}{39} \cdot \left(-\dfrac{9}{98}\right) \cdot \left(-\dfrac{91}{12}\right) = 1$

3. $\dfrac{3x^3}{-2} \cdot \dfrac{-4}{9x} = \dfrac{3(-4)x^3}{-2 \cdot 9 \cdot x} = \dfrac{2x^2}{3}$

4. $\dfrac{21t^2}{-5} \cdot \dfrac{10}{7t^3} = \dfrac{21 \cdot 10 \cdot t^2}{-5 \cdot 7 \cdot t^3} = -\dfrac{6}{t}$

5. $\dfrac{2u^2}{3} \div \dfrac{6u^3}{5} = \dfrac{2u^2}{3} \cdot \dfrac{5}{6u^3} = \dfrac{2 \cdot 5 \cdot u^2}{3 \cdot 6 \cdot u^3} = \dfrac{5}{9u}$

6. $\dfrac{15x^3}{14} \div \dfrac{18x}{7} = \dfrac{15x^2}{14} \cdot \dfrac{7}{18x} = \dfrac{15 \cdot 7 \cdot x^3}{14 \cdot 18 \cdot x} = \dfrac{5x^2}{12}$

7. $\dfrac{xy^2}{2} \cdot \dfrac{x^2}{2y} \cdot \left(\dfrac{x^2y}{2}\right)^{-1} = \dfrac{xy^2}{2} \cdot \dfrac{x^2}{2y} \cdot \dfrac{2}{x^2y} = \dfrac{2x^3y^2}{4x^2y^2} = \dfrac{x}{2}$

8. $axy \div \dfrac{ax}{y} \div \dfrac{ay}{x} = axy \cdot \dfrac{y}{ax} \cdot \dfrac{x}{ay} = \dfrac{ax^2y^2}{a^2xy} = \dfrac{xy}{a}$

9. $\dfrac{9u^2}{28v} \div \dfrac{27u^2}{8v^2} \div \dfrac{4u^2}{21} = \dfrac{9u^2}{28v} \cdot \dfrac{8v^2}{27u^2} \cdot \dfrac{21}{4u^2} = \dfrac{9 \cdot 8 \cdot 21 \cdot u^2v^2}{28 \cdot 27 \cdot 4 \cdot u^4v} = \dfrac{v}{2u^2}$

10. $\dfrac{4s^2}{5t^2} \cdot \dfrac{9st}{14} \cdot \left(\dfrac{6s}{35t}\right)^{-1} = \dfrac{4s^2}{5t^2} \cdot \dfrac{9st}{14} \cdot \dfrac{35t}{6s} = \dfrac{4 \cdot 9 \cdot 35 \cdot s^3t^2}{5 \cdot 14 \cdot 6 \cdot st^2} = 3s^2$

11. $\dfrac{x+2}{x-3} \cdot \dfrac{x^2-4x+3}{x^2+6x+8} = \dfrac{x+2}{x-3} \cdot \dfrac{(x-3)(x-1)}{(x+4)(x+2)} = \dfrac{x-1}{x+4}$

12. $\dfrac{s^2-4}{4s^2-1} \cdot \dfrac{2s-1}{s+2} = \dfrac{(s+2)(s-2)}{(2s+1)(2s-1)} \cdot \dfrac{2s-1}{s+2} = \dfrac{s-2}{2s+1}$

13. $\dfrac{t^2-1}{2t^2-t-1} \div \dfrac{t^2-4}{2t^2-3t-2} = \dfrac{(t+1)(t-1)}{(2t+1)(t-1)} \cdot \dfrac{(2t+1)(t-2)}{(t+2)(t-2)} = \dfrac{t+1}{t+2}$

14. $\dfrac{2x^2+x-1}{2x^2+3x-2} \div \dfrac{x^2-2x+1}{x^2+x-2} = \dfrac{(2x-1)(x+1)}{(2x-1)(x+2)} \cdot \dfrac{(x+2)(x-1)}{(x-1)^2} = \dfrac{x+1}{x-1}$

B 15. **a.** $f(x) \cdot g(x) = \dfrac{x^2-3x+2}{x^2+3x+2} \cdot \dfrac{x^2-1}{x^2-4} = \dfrac{(x-2)(x-1)}{(x+2)(x+1)} \cdot \dfrac{(x+1)(x-1)}{(x+2)(x-2)} = \dfrac{(x-1)^2}{(x+2)^2}$

b. $f(x) \div g(x) = \dfrac{(x-2)(x-1)}{(x+2)(x+1)} \div \dfrac{(x+1)(x-1)}{(x+2)(x-2)}$

$= \dfrac{(x-2)(x-1)}{(x+2)(x+1)} \cdot \dfrac{(x+2)(x-2)}{(x+1)(x-1)} = \dfrac{(x-2)^2}{(x+1)^2}$

16. **a.** $f(x) \cdot g(x) = \dfrac{4x^2-1}{x^2+x-2} \cdot \dfrac{2x^2-x-1}{2x^2+3x-2} = \dfrac{(2x+1)(2x-1)}{(x+2)(x-1)} \cdot \dfrac{(2x+1)(x-1)}{(2x-1)(x+2)}$

$= \dfrac{(2x+1)^2}{(x+2)^2}$ **b.** $f(x) \div g(x) = \dfrac{(2x+1)(2x-1)}{(x+2)(x-1)} \div \dfrac{(2x+1)(x-1)}{(2x-1)(x+2)}$

$= \dfrac{(2x+1)(2x-1)}{(x+2)(x-1)} \cdot \dfrac{(2x-1)(x+2)}{(2x+1)(x-1)} = \dfrac{(2x-1)^2}{(x-1)^2}$

17. $\dfrac{u^4-v^4}{(u+v)^2} \div \dfrac{u^2+v^2}{u-v} = \dfrac{u^4-v^4}{(u+v)^2} \cdot \dfrac{u-v}{u^2+v^2} = \dfrac{(u^2+v^2)(u^2-v^2)}{(u+v)^2} \cdot \dfrac{u-v}{u^2+v^2}$

$= \dfrac{(u-v)(u+v)(u-v)}{(u+v)^2} = \dfrac{(u-v)^2}{u+v}$

18. $\dfrac{x^4-y^4}{x^3+y^3} \div \dfrac{x^2-y^2}{x+y} = \dfrac{x^4-y^4}{x^3+y^3} \cdot \dfrac{x+y}{x^2-y^2} = \dfrac{(x^2+y^2)(x^2-y^2)}{(x+y)(x^2-xy+y^2)} \cdot \dfrac{x+y}{x^2-y^2}$

$= \dfrac{x^2+y^2}{x^2-xy+y^2}$

19. $\dfrac{st^2}{s - t} \div (s - t) \cdot \dfrac{s^2 - 2st + t^2}{st^2 + s^2 t} = \dfrac{st^2}{s - t} \cdot \dfrac{1}{s - t} \cdot \dfrac{(s - t)^2}{st(s + t)} = \dfrac{t}{s + t}$

20. $\dfrac{x^2 + 2ax}{2a - x} \cdot \dfrac{x^2 - 3ax + 2a^2}{a^2 - x^2} \div \dfrac{x + 2a}{x + a} = \dfrac{x(x + 2a)}{2a - x} \cdot \dfrac{(x - 2a)(x - a)}{(a + x)(a - x)} \cdot \dfrac{x + a}{x + 2a}$

$= \dfrac{x(x + 2a)(x - 2a)(x - a)(x + a)}{-(x - 2a)(x + a)[-(x - a)](x + 2a)} = x$

21. $\dfrac{2x^2 - xy - 3y^2}{2x^2 + xy - 3y^2} \div \dfrac{6x^2 - 7xy - 3y^2}{x^2 + 2xy - 3y^2} \div \dfrac{x + 3y}{2x + 3y}$

$= \dfrac{(2x - 3y)(x + y)}{(2x + 3y)(x - y)} \cdot \dfrac{(x + 3y)(x - y)}{(2x - 3y)(3x + y)} \cdot \dfrac{2x + 3y}{x + 3y} = \dfrac{x + y}{3x + y}$

22. $\dfrac{u^2 + 5uv + 6v^2}{u^2 + 4uv + 3v^2} \cdot (u + 2v) \cdot \left(\dfrac{u^2 + 4uv + 4v^2}{u + v} \right)^{-1}$

$= \dfrac{(u + 3v)(u + 2v)}{(u + 3v)(u + v)} \cdot (u + 2v) \cdot \dfrac{u + v}{(u + 2v)^2} = 1$

23. $\dfrac{s^3 + t^3}{s^2 + st - 6t^2} \div \dfrac{s^2 - 2st - 3t^2}{s^2 + 2st - 8t^2} \cdot \left(\dfrac{s^2 + 6st + 8t^2}{s - 3t} \right)^{-1}$

$= \dfrac{(s + t)(s^2 - st + t^2)}{(s + 3t)(s - 2t)} \cdot \dfrac{(s + 4t)(s - 2t)}{(s - 3t)(s + t)} \cdot \dfrac{s - 3t}{(s + 4t)(s + 2t)} = \dfrac{s^2 - st + t^2}{(s + 3t)(s + 2t)}$

C **24. a.** Since f has zeros 1 and 2, the numerator of f has factors $(x - 2)$ and $(x - 1)$; these factors are not in the denominator of f; similarly g has $(x + 2)(x - 3)$ in the numerator but not in the denominator. Since $f \cdot g$ has only 1 and 3 as zeros, the denominator of $f \cdot g$ must have factors $x - 2$ and $x + 2$; let $f(x) = \dfrac{(x - 1)(x - 2)}{x + 2}$ and $g(x) = \dfrac{(x + 2)(x - 3)}{x - 2}$.

b. If $f(x) = \dfrac{x - k}{x - h}$ and $g(x) = \dfrac{x - h}{x - k}$, with $k = n$, the conditions will be satisfied; for example, let $f(x) = \dfrac{x - 2}{x - 1}$ and $g(x) = \dfrac{x - 1}{x - 2}$.

c. If $f(x)$ is constant and $g(x) = \dfrac{1}{(x - n)(x - m)}$, $n \neq m$, the conditions will be satis-

fied; for example, let $f(x) = 2$ and $g(x) = \dfrac{1}{(x - 2)(x - 1)}$; neither f nor g has a zero but $f \div g$ has zeros 2 and 1.

Pages 226-227 · WRITTEN EXERCISES

A **1.** $\dfrac{1}{2} - \dfrac{1}{3} + \dfrac{1}{6} = \dfrac{3}{6} - \dfrac{2}{6} + \dfrac{1}{6} = \dfrac{2}{6} = \dfrac{1}{3}$ **2.** $\dfrac{2}{3} - \dfrac{1}{5} - \dfrac{1}{15} = \dfrac{10}{15} - \dfrac{3}{15} - \dfrac{1}{15} = \dfrac{6}{15} = \dfrac{2}{5}$

3. $\dfrac{4}{15} + \dfrac{5}{12} - \dfrac{1}{2} = \dfrac{16}{60} + \dfrac{25}{60} - \dfrac{30}{60} = \dfrac{11}{60}$ **4.** $1 - \dfrac{5}{6} + \dfrac{3}{14} = \dfrac{42}{42} - \dfrac{35}{42} + \dfrac{9}{42} = \dfrac{16}{42} = \dfrac{8}{21}$

5. $\dfrac{x - 2}{3} + \dfrac{x + 4}{6} = \dfrac{2(x - 2)}{6} + \dfrac{x + 4}{6} = \dfrac{2x - 4 + x + 4}{6} = \dfrac{3x}{6} = \dfrac{x}{2}$

6. $\dfrac{a+1}{5} - \dfrac{2a-3}{10} = \dfrac{2(a+1)}{10} - \dfrac{2a-3}{10} = \dfrac{2a+2-2a+3}{10} = \dfrac{5}{10} = \dfrac{1}{2}$

7. $\dfrac{12}{7d} - \dfrac{3}{14d} = \dfrac{24}{14d} - \dfrac{3}{14d} = \dfrac{21}{14d} = \dfrac{3}{2d}$ 8. $\dfrac{3}{10v} + \dfrac{2}{15v} = \dfrac{9}{30v} + \dfrac{4}{30v} = \dfrac{13}{30v}$

9. $\dfrac{x+1}{x} - \dfrac{x-1}{x^2} = \dfrac{x(x+1)}{x^2} - \dfrac{x-1}{x^2} = \dfrac{x^2+x-x+1}{x^2} = \dfrac{x^2+1}{x^2}$

10. $\dfrac{t+1}{t^2} + \dfrac{t-2}{2t} = \dfrac{2(t+1)}{2t^2} + \dfrac{t(t-2)}{2t^2} = \dfrac{2t+2+t^2-2t}{2t^2} = \dfrac{t^2+2}{2t^2}$

11. $\dfrac{3u+8}{4u} - \dfrac{u+6}{3u} = \dfrac{3(3u+8)}{12u} - \dfrac{4(u+6)}{12u} = \dfrac{9u+24-4u-24}{12u} = \dfrac{5u}{12u} = \dfrac{5}{12}$

12. $\dfrac{2x+1}{4x^2} - \dfrac{x+3}{6x} = \dfrac{3(2x+1)}{12x^2} - \dfrac{2x(x+3)}{12x^2} = \dfrac{6x+3-2x^2-6x}{12x^2} = \dfrac{3-2x^2}{12x^2}$

13. $\dfrac{1}{2uv^4} + \dfrac{1}{u^3v^2} = \dfrac{u^2}{2u^3v^4} + \dfrac{2v^2}{2u^3v^4} = \dfrac{u^2+2v^2}{2u^3v^4}$

14. $\dfrac{1}{2x^2y^2} - \dfrac{2}{5x^3y} = \dfrac{5x}{10x^3y^2} - \dfrac{4y}{5x^3y} = \dfrac{5x-4y}{10x^3y^2}$

15. $4s^{-2} - t^{-2} = \dfrac{4}{s^2} - \dfrac{1}{t^2} = \dfrac{4t^2}{s^2t^2} - \dfrac{s^2}{s^2t^2} = \dfrac{4t^2-s^2}{s^2t^2} = \dfrac{(2t-s)(2t+s)}{s^2t^2}$

16. $xy^{-1} + x^{-1}y = \dfrac{x}{y} + \dfrac{y}{x} = \dfrac{x^2}{xy} + \dfrac{y^2}{xy} = \dfrac{x^2+y^2}{xy}$

17. $\dfrac{x}{yz} + \dfrac{y}{zx} + \dfrac{z}{xy} = \dfrac{x^2}{xyz} + \dfrac{y^2}{xyz} + \dfrac{z^2}{xyz} = \dfrac{x^2+y^2+z^2}{xyz}$

18. $\dfrac{y-z}{x} + \dfrac{z-x}{y} + \dfrac{x-y}{z} = \dfrac{yz(y-z)}{xyz} + \dfrac{xz(z-x)}{xyz} + \dfrac{xy(x-y)}{xyz}$

$= \dfrac{y^2z - yz^2 + xz^2 - x^2z + x^2y - xy^2}{xyz}$

19. $\dfrac{1}{4x^2} - \dfrac{1}{xy} + \dfrac{1}{y^2} = \dfrac{y^2}{4x^2y^2} - \dfrac{4xy}{4x^2y^2} + \dfrac{4x^2}{4x^2y^2} = \dfrac{y^2-4xy+4x^2}{4x^2y^2} = \dfrac{(y-2x)^2}{4x^2y^2}$

20. $\dfrac{1}{3v^2} + \dfrac{1}{uv} + \dfrac{3}{4u^2} = \dfrac{4u^2}{12u^2v^2} + \dfrac{12uv}{12u^2v^2} + \dfrac{9v^2}{12u^2v^2} = \dfrac{4u^2+12uv+9v^2}{12u^2v^2} = \dfrac{(2u+3v)^2}{12u^2v^2}$

21. $\dfrac{4}{t-3} + \dfrac{1}{3-t} = \dfrac{4}{t-3} + \dfrac{-1}{t-3} = \dfrac{3}{t-3}$

22. $\dfrac{x}{x-1} + \dfrac{1}{1-x} = \dfrac{x}{x-1} + \dfrac{-1}{x-1} = \dfrac{x-1}{x-1} = 1$

23. $\dfrac{5}{x} - \dfrac{3}{x+5} = \dfrac{5(x+5)}{x(x+5)} - \dfrac{3x}{x(x+5)} = \dfrac{5x+25-3x}{x(x+5)} = \dfrac{2x+25}{x(x+5)}$

24. $\dfrac{1}{z} - \dfrac{1}{z+4} = \dfrac{z+4}{z(z+4)} - \dfrac{z}{z(z+4)} = \dfrac{z+4-z}{z(z+4)} = \dfrac{4}{z(z+4)}$

25. $\dfrac{1}{s^2 - s} + \dfrac{1}{s^2 + s} = \dfrac{1}{s(s-1)} + \dfrac{1}{s(s+1)} = \dfrac{s+1}{s(s-1)(s+1)} + \dfrac{s-1}{s(s-1)(s+1)}$

$= \dfrac{s+1+s-1}{s(s-1)(s+1)} = \dfrac{2s}{s(s-1)(s+1)} = \dfrac{2}{(s-1)(s+1)}$

26. $\dfrac{1}{x^2 - x} - \dfrac{1}{x^2 - 1} = \dfrac{1}{x(x-1)} - \dfrac{1}{(x+1)(x-1)} = \dfrac{x+1}{x(x-1)(x+1)} - \dfrac{x}{x(x-1)(x+1)}$

$= \dfrac{x+1-x}{x(x-1)(x+1)} = \dfrac{1}{x(x-1)(x+1)}$

27. $\dfrac{1}{x^2 - 1} - \dfrac{1}{(x-1)^2} = \dfrac{1}{(x-1)(x+1)} - \dfrac{1}{(x-1)^2} = \dfrac{x-1}{(x-1)^2(x+1)} - \dfrac{x+1}{(x-1)^2(x+1)}$

$= \dfrac{x-1-x-1}{(x-1)^2(x+1)} = -\dfrac{2}{(x-1)^2(x+1)}$

28. $\dfrac{1}{u^2 + u - 2} + \dfrac{1}{u^2 - u} = \dfrac{1}{(u+2)(u-1)} + \dfrac{1}{u(u-1)}$

$= \dfrac{u}{u(u+2)(u-1)} + \dfrac{u+2}{u(u+2)(u-1)} = \dfrac{u+u+2}{u(u+2)(u-1)} = \dfrac{2u+2}{u(u+2)(u-1)}$

$= \dfrac{2(u+1)}{u(u+2)(u-1)}$

B **29.** $\dfrac{a+b}{a-b} + \dfrac{a-b}{a+b} + \dfrac{b-a}{a-b} + \dfrac{b-a}{a+b} = \dfrac{a+b+b-a}{a-b} + \dfrac{a-b+b-a}{a+b} = \dfrac{2b}{a-b} + 0$

$= \dfrac{2b}{a-b}$

30. $\dfrac{a+b}{a-b} - \dfrac{a-b}{a+b} - \dfrac{b-a}{a-b} + \dfrac{b-a}{a+b} = \dfrac{a+b-b+a}{a-b} + \dfrac{-a+b+b-a}{a+b}$

$= \dfrac{2a}{a-b} + \dfrac{-2a+2b}{a+b} = \dfrac{(a+b)2a}{(a-b)(a+b)} + \dfrac{(a-b)(-2a+2b)}{(a-b)(a+b)}$

$= \dfrac{2a^2 + 2ab - 2a^2 + 4ab - 2b^2}{(a-b)(a+b)} = \dfrac{6ab - 2b^2}{(a-b)(a+b)} = \dfrac{2b(3a-b)}{(a-b)(a+b)}$

31. $\dfrac{3}{x^2 + 5ax + 6a^2} + \dfrac{2}{x^2 - 4a^2} = \dfrac{3}{(x+3a)(x+2a)} + \dfrac{2}{(x-2a)(x+2a)}$

$= \dfrac{3(x-2a)}{(x+3a)(x+2a)(x-2a)} + \dfrac{2(x+3a)}{(x+3a)(x+2a)(x-2a)}$

$= \dfrac{3x - 6a + 2x + 6a}{(x+3a)(x+2a)(x-2a)} = \dfrac{5x}{(x+3a)(x+2a)(x-2a)}$

32. $\dfrac{6}{4u^2 - 12uv + 9v^2} + \dfrac{2}{2uv - 3v^2} = \dfrac{6}{(2u-3v)^2} + \dfrac{2}{v(2u-3v)}$

$= \dfrac{6v}{v(2u-3v)^2} + \dfrac{2(2u-3v)}{v(2u-3v)^2} = \dfrac{6v + 4u - 6v}{v(2u-3v)^2} = \dfrac{4u}{v(2u-3v)^2}$

33. $(x + y)^{-1} + (x - y)^{-1} = \dfrac{1}{x + y} + \dfrac{1}{x - y} = \dfrac{x - y}{(x + y)(x - y)} + \dfrac{x + y}{(x + y)(x - y)}$

$= \dfrac{x - y + x + y}{(x + y)(x - y)} = \dfrac{2x}{(x + y)(x - y)}$

34. $(x + y)^{-2} - (x - y)^{-2} = \dfrac{1}{(x + y)^2} - \dfrac{1}{(x - y)^2} = \dfrac{(x - y)^2}{(x + y)^2(x - y)^2} - \dfrac{(x + y)^2}{(x + y)^2(x - y)^2}$

$= \dfrac{(x - y)^2 - (x + y)^2}{(x + y)^2(x - y)^2} = \dfrac{[(x - y) - (x + y)][(x - y) + (x + y)]}{(x + y)^2(x - y)^2} = \dfrac{-2y(2x)}{(x + y)^2(x - y)^2}$

$= \dfrac{-4xy}{(x + y)^2(x - y)^2}$

35. $\dfrac{3s}{2s - t} - \dfrac{2s}{2s + t} + \dfrac{2t^2}{4s^2 - t^2} = \dfrac{3s}{2s - t} - \dfrac{2s}{2s + t} + \dfrac{2t^2}{(2s - t)(2s + t)}$

$= \dfrac{3s(2s + t)}{(2s - t)(2s + t)} - \dfrac{2s(2s - t)}{(2s - t)(2s + t)} + \dfrac{2t^2}{(2s - t)(2s + t)}$

$= \dfrac{6s^2 + 3st - 4s^2 + 2st + 2t^2}{(2s - t)(2s + t)} = \dfrac{2s^2 + 5st + 2t^2}{(2s - t)(2s + t)} = \dfrac{(2s + t)(s + 2t)}{(2s - t)(2s + t)} = \dfrac{s + 2t}{2s - t}$

36. $\dfrac{a}{a - x} - \dfrac{a^2 + x^2}{a^2 - x^2} + \dfrac{x}{a + x} = \dfrac{a}{a - x} - \dfrac{a^2 + x^2}{(a - x)(a + x)} + \dfrac{x}{a + x}$

$= \dfrac{a(a + x)}{(a - x)(a + x)} - \dfrac{a^2 + x^2}{(a - x)(a + x)} + \dfrac{x(a - x)}{(a - x)(a + x)}$

$= \dfrac{a^2 + ax - a^2 - x^2 + ax - x^2}{(a - x)(a + x)} = \dfrac{2ax - 2x^2}{(a - x)(a + x)} = \dfrac{2x(a - x)}{(a - x)(a + x)} = \dfrac{2x}{a + x}$

37. $\dfrac{4u}{u^2 - 4uv + 4v^2} + \dfrac{1}{u + 2v} + \dfrac{4u}{u^2 - 4v^2} = \dfrac{4u}{(u - 2v)^2} + \dfrac{1}{u + 2v} + \dfrac{4u}{(u - 2v)(u + 2v)}$

$= \dfrac{4u(u + 2v)}{(u - 2v)^2(u + 2v)} + \dfrac{(u - 2v)^2}{(u - 2v)^2(u + 2v)} + \dfrac{4u(u - 2v)}{(u - 2v)^2(u + 2v)}$

$= \dfrac{4u^2 + 8uv + u^2 - 4uv + 4v^2 + 4u^2 - 8uv}{(u - 2v)^2(u + 2v)} = \dfrac{9u^2 - 4uv + 4v^2}{(u - 2v)^2(u + 2v)}$

38. $\dfrac{5}{2x^2 + 3xy - 2y^2} - \dfrac{3}{x^2 - 4y^2} + \dfrac{3}{2x^2 - 5xy + 2y^2} = \dfrac{5}{(2x - y)(x + 2y)}$

$- \dfrac{3}{(x - 2y)(x + 2y)} + \dfrac{3}{(2x - y)(x - 2y)} = \dfrac{5(x - 2y)}{(2x - y)(x + 2y)(x - 2y)}$

$- \dfrac{3(2x - y)}{(2x - y)(x + 2y)(x - 2y)} + \dfrac{3(x + 2y)}{(2x - y)(x + 2y)(x - 2y)}$

$= \dfrac{5x - 10y - 6x + 3y + 3x + 6y}{(2x - y)(x + 2y)(x - 2y)} = \dfrac{2x - y}{(2x - y)(x + 2y)(x - 2y)}$

$= \dfrac{1}{(x + 2y)(x - 2y)}$

39. $\dfrac{x - 7}{x^2 + x - 6} = \dfrac{A}{x + 3} + \dfrac{B}{x - 2}$; $\dfrac{x - 7}{(x + 3)(x - 2)} = \dfrac{A}{x + 3} + \dfrac{B}{x - 2}$; $\dfrac{x - 7}{(x + 3)(x - 2)}$

$= \dfrac{A(x - 2)}{(x + 3)(x - 2)} + \dfrac{B(x + 3)}{(x + 3)(x - 2)}$; $x - 7 = Ax - 2A + Bx + 3B$;

$x - 7 = (A + B)x - (2A - 3B)$; $A + B = 1$; $2A - 3B = 7$; solving the system

gives $A = 2, B = -1$.

40. $\dfrac{x + 5}{x^2 - 5x + 4} = \dfrac{A}{x - 1} + \dfrac{B}{x - 4} = \dfrac{x + 5}{(x - 1)(x - 4)} = \dfrac{A}{x - 1} + \dfrac{B}{x - 4}$; $\dfrac{x + 5}{(x - 1)(x - 4)}$

$= \dfrac{A(x - 4)}{(x - 1)(x - 4)} + \dfrac{B(x - 1)}{(x - 1)(x - 4)}$; $x + 5 = A(x - 4) + B(x - 1)$;

$x + 5 = Ax - 4A + Bx - B$; $x + 5 = (A + B)x + (-4A - B)$; $A + B = 1$;

$-4A - B = 5$; solving the system gives $A = -2, B = 3$.

C 41. $\dfrac{x^2 + 2}{x(x + 1)(x + 2)} = \dfrac{A}{x} + \dfrac{B}{x + 1} + \dfrac{C}{x + 2}$; $\dfrac{x^2 + 2}{x(x + 1)(x + 2)} = \dfrac{A(x + 1)(x + 2)}{x(x + 1)(x + 2)}$

$+ \dfrac{Bx(x + 2)}{x(x + 1)(x + 2)} + \dfrac{Cx(x + 1)}{x(x + 1)(x + 2)}$; $x^2 + 2 = A(x^2 + 3x + 2) + Bx^2 + 2Bx$

$+ Cx^2 + Cx$; $x^2 + 2 = Ax^2 + 3Ax + 2A + Bx^2 + 2Bx + Cx^2 + Cx$; $x^2 + 2$

$= (A + B + C)x^2 + (3A + 2B + C)x + 2A$; $2A = 2$; $A = 1$; $A + B + C = 1$;

$B + C = 0$; $3A + 2B + C = 0$; $2B + C = -3$; solving the system gives $B = -3$

and $C = 3$.

Pages 229-230 · WRITTEN EXERCISES

A 1. $\dfrac{\left(1 + \dfrac{1}{2}\right) \cdot 4}{\left(1 - \dfrac{1}{4}\right) \cdot 4} = \dfrac{4 + 2}{4 - 1} = \dfrac{6}{3} = 2$

2. $\dfrac{\left(\dfrac{1}{2} + \dfrac{1}{3}\right) \cdot 6}{\left(1 - \dfrac{1}{6}\right) \cdot 6} = \dfrac{3 + 2}{6 - 1} = \dfrac{5}{5} = 1$

3. $\dfrac{\left(\dfrac{5}{6} - \dfrac{1}{2}\right) \cdot 6}{\left(\dfrac{2}{3} + 1\right) \cdot 6} = \dfrac{5 - 3}{4 + 6} = \dfrac{2}{10} = \dfrac{1}{5}$

4. $\dfrac{\left(\dfrac{2}{3} + \dfrac{4}{9}\right) \cdot 18}{\left(\dfrac{11}{6} - \dfrac{1}{2}\right) \cdot 18} = \dfrac{12 + 8}{33 - 9} = \dfrac{20}{24} = \dfrac{5}{6}$

5. $\dfrac{(x - 1)x}{\left(1 - \dfrac{1}{x}\right)x} = \dfrac{(x - 1)x}{x - 1} = x$

6. $\dfrac{\left(t - \dfrac{1}{t}\right)t}{\left(1 - \dfrac{1}{t}\right)t} = \dfrac{t^2 - 1}{t - 1} = \dfrac{(t + 1)(t - 1)}{t - 1} = t + 1$

7. $\dfrac{(u + v)uv}{\left(\dfrac{1}{u} + \dfrac{1}{v}\right)uv} = \dfrac{(u + v)uv}{v + u} = uv$

8. $\dfrac{\left(\dfrac{1}{a} - \dfrac{1}{b}\right)ab}{\left(1 - \dfrac{a}{b}\right)ab} = \dfrac{b - a}{ab - a^2} = \dfrac{b - a}{a(b - a)} = \dfrac{1}{a}$

9. $\dfrac{\left(\dfrac{1}{x}+\dfrac{1}{y}\right)x^2y^2}{\left(\dfrac{1}{x^2}-\dfrac{1}{y^2}\right)x^2y^2} = \dfrac{xy^2+x^2y}{y^2-x^2} = \dfrac{xy(y+x)}{(y+x)(y-x)} = \dfrac{xy}{y-x}$

10. $\dfrac{\left(\dfrac{1}{s^2}-\dfrac{1}{t^2}\right)s^2t^2}{\left(\dfrac{1}{s^2}-\dfrac{1}{st}-\dfrac{2}{t^2}\right)s^2t^2} = \dfrac{t^2-s^2}{t^2-st-2s^2} = \dfrac{(t+s)(t-s)}{(t-2s)(t+s)} = \dfrac{t-s}{t-2s}$

11. $\dfrac{\left(\dfrac{1}{u^2}-\dfrac{1}{v^2}\right)u^2v^2}{\left(\dfrac{1}{u^2}-\dfrac{2}{uv}+\dfrac{1}{v^2}\right)u^2v^2} = \dfrac{v^2-u^2}{v^2-2uv+u^2} = \dfrac{(v-u)(v+u)}{(v-u)^2} = \dfrac{v+u}{v-u}$

12. $\dfrac{\left(\dfrac{1}{a^2}-\dfrac{1}{b^2}\right)}{\left(\dfrac{1}{a}-\dfrac{1}{b}\right)^2} = \dfrac{\dfrac{1}{a^2}-\dfrac{1}{b^2}}{\left(\dfrac{1}{a^2}-\dfrac{2}{ab}+\dfrac{1}{b^2}\right)} = \dfrac{b+a}{b-a}$ (See Ex. 11, above.)

13. $\dfrac{\left(\dfrac{1}{x^2}-y^2\right)x^2}{\left(\dfrac{1}{x}-y\right)x^2} = \dfrac{1-x^2y^2}{x-x^2y} = \dfrac{(1-xy)(1+xy)}{x(1-xy)} = \dfrac{1+xy}{x}$

14. $\dfrac{\left(c-\dfrac{1}{c^2}\right)c^2}{\left(1-\dfrac{1}{c}\right)c^2} = \dfrac{c^3-1}{c^2-c} = \dfrac{(c-1)(c^2+c+1)}{c(c-1)} = \dfrac{c^2+c+1}{c}$

15. $\dfrac{\left(\dfrac{b^2}{a^2}-\dfrac{a^2}{b^2}\right)a^2b^2}{\left(\dfrac{b}{a}-\dfrac{a}{b}\right)a^2b^2} = \dfrac{b^4-a^4}{ab^3-a^3b} = \dfrac{(b^2-a^2)(b^2+a^2)}{ab(b^2-a^2)} = \dfrac{b^2+a^2}{ab}$

16. $\dfrac{\dfrac{1}{x+y}}{\dfrac{1}{x}+\dfrac{1}{y}} = \dfrac{\dfrac{1}{x+y}}{\dfrac{y}{xy}+\dfrac{x}{xy}} = \dfrac{\dfrac{1}{x+y}}{\dfrac{x+y}{xy}} = \dfrac{1}{x+y}\cdot\dfrac{xy}{x+y} = \dfrac{xy}{(x+y)^2}$

17. $\dfrac{\left(\dfrac{1}{x-1}+\dfrac{1}{x+1}\right)(x-1)(x+1)}{\left(\dfrac{1}{x-1}-\dfrac{1}{x+1}\right)(x-1)(x+1)} = \dfrac{(x+1)+(x-1)}{(x+1)-(x-1)} = \dfrac{2x}{2} = x$

18. $\dfrac{\left(1 - \dfrac{1}{x+1}\right)(x+1)(x-1)}{\left(1 + \dfrac{1}{x-1}\right)(x+1)(x-1)} = \dfrac{(x+1)(x-1) - (x-1)}{(x+1)(x-1) + (x+1)} = \dfrac{x^2 - 1 - x + 1}{x^2 - 1 + x + 1}$

$= \dfrac{x^2 - x}{x^2 + x} = \dfrac{x(x-1)}{x(x+1)} = \dfrac{x-1}{x+1}$

B 19. $\dfrac{\left(1 + \dfrac{1}{x^2 - 1}\right)(x^2 - 1)}{\left(1 + \dfrac{1}{x-1}\right)(x^2 - 1)} = \dfrac{x^2 - 1 + 1}{x^2 - 1 + x + 1} = \dfrac{x^2}{x^2 + x} = \dfrac{x^2}{x(x+1)} = \dfrac{x}{x+1}$

20. $\dfrac{\dfrac{1}{x} - \dfrac{1}{x+1}}{\dfrac{1}{x} - \dfrac{1}{x-1}} = \dfrac{\dfrac{x+1-x}{x(x+1)}}{\dfrac{x-1-x}{x(x-1)}} = \dfrac{1}{x(x+1)} \cdot \dfrac{x(x-1)}{-1} = -\dfrac{x-1}{x+1}$

21. $\dfrac{\dfrac{u}{v} + \dfrac{u+v}{u-v}}{\dfrac{u}{v} - \dfrac{u-v}{u+v}} = \dfrac{\dfrac{u^2 - uv + uv + v^2}{v(u-v)}}{\dfrac{u^2 + uv - uv + v^2}{v(u+v)}} = \dfrac{u^2 + v^2}{v(u-v)} \cdot \dfrac{v(u+v)}{u^2 + v^2} = \dfrac{u+v}{u-v}$

22. $\dfrac{\left(\dfrac{a+b}{a-b} + \dfrac{a-b}{a+b}\right)(a-b)(a+b)}{\left(\dfrac{a+b}{a-b} - \dfrac{a-b}{a+b}\right)(a-b)(a+b)} = \dfrac{(a+b)^2 + (a-b)^2}{(a+b)^2 - (a-b)^2}$

$= \dfrac{a^2 + 2ab + b^2 + a^2 - 2ab + b^2}{[(a+b) + (a-b)][(a+b) - (a-b)]} = \dfrac{2a^2 + 2b^2}{2a \cdot 2b} = \dfrac{2(a^2 + b^2)}{4ab} = \dfrac{a^2 + b^2}{2ab}$

23. $\dfrac{1 + \dfrac{2 + \dfrac{1}{x}}{x}}{1 + \dfrac{1}{x}} = \dfrac{1 + \dfrac{\left(2 + \dfrac{1}{x}\right)x}{x \cdot x}}{1 + \dfrac{1}{x}} = \dfrac{\left(1 + \dfrac{2x+1}{x^2}\right)x^2}{\left(1 + \dfrac{1}{x}\right)x^2} = \dfrac{x^2 + 2x + 1}{x^2 + x} = \dfrac{(x+1)^2}{x(x+1)}$

$= \dfrac{x+1}{x}$

24. $\dfrac{\dfrac{1}{x-1}}{x + \dfrac{1}{x - \dfrac{1}{x}}} = \dfrac{\dfrac{1}{x-1}}{x + \dfrac{1 \cdot x}{\left(x - \dfrac{1}{x}\right)x}} = \dfrac{\left(\dfrac{1}{x-1}\right)(x^2 - 1)}{\left(x + \dfrac{x}{x^2 - 1}\right)(x^2 - 1)} = \dfrac{x+1}{x(x^2 - 1) + x}$

$= \dfrac{x+1}{x^3 - x + x} = \dfrac{x+1}{x^3}$

25. $1 + \cfrac{1}{1 + \cfrac{1}{1 + \cfrac{1}{1 + \cfrac{1}{1}}}} = 1 + \cfrac{1}{1 + \cfrac{1}{1 + \cfrac{1}{1 + 1}}} = 1 + \cfrac{1}{1 + \cfrac{1}{1 + \cfrac{1}{2}}} = 1 + \cfrac{1}{1 + \cfrac{1}{\cfrac{3}{2}}}$

$= 1 + \cfrac{1}{1 + \cfrac{2}{3}} = 1 + \cfrac{1}{\cfrac{5}{3}} = 1 + \cfrac{3}{5} = \cfrac{8}{5}$

26. $x + \cfrac{1}{x + \cfrac{1}{x + \cfrac{(1)x}{\left(x + \cfrac{1}{x}\right)x}}} = x + \cfrac{1}{x + \cfrac{(1)(x^2 + 1)}{\left(x + \cfrac{x}{x^2 + 1}\right)(x^2 + 1)}}$

$= x + \cfrac{1}{x + \cfrac{x^2 + 1}{x^3 + x + x}} = x + \cfrac{1}{x + \cfrac{(1)(x^3 + 2x)}{\cfrac{(x^2 + 1)}{(x^3 + 2x)}(x^3 + 2x)}} = x + \cfrac{x^3 + 2x}{x^4 + 2x^2 + x^2 + 1}$

$= x + \cfrac{x^3 + 2x}{x^4 + 3x^2 + 1} = \cfrac{x^5 + 3x^3 + x + x^3 + 2x}{x^4 + 3x^2 + 1} = \cfrac{x^5 + 4x^3 + 3x}{x^4 + 3x^2 + 1}$

$= \cfrac{x(x^4 + 4x^2 + 3)}{x^4 + 3x^2 + 1} = \cfrac{x(x^2 + 1)(x^2 + 3)}{x^4 + 3x^2 + 1}$

27. a. $1 + \cfrac{1}{2} = 1.500$ **b.** $1 + \cfrac{1}{2 + \cfrac{1}{2}} = 1 + \cfrac{1 \cdot 2}{\left(2 + \cfrac{1}{2}\right)2} = 1 + \cfrac{2}{4 + 1} = 1 + \cfrac{2}{5} = 1.400$

c. $1 + \cfrac{1}{2 + \cfrac{1}{2 + \cfrac{1}{2}}} = 1 + \cfrac{1}{2 + \cfrac{1 \cdot 2}{\left(2 + \cfrac{1}{2}\right)2}} = 1 + \cfrac{1}{2 + \cfrac{2}{5}} = 1 + \cfrac{1 \cdot 5}{\left(2 + \cfrac{2}{5}\right)5}$

$= 1 + \cfrac{5}{10 + 2} = 1 + \cfrac{5}{12} = \cfrac{17}{12} \approx 1.417$

d. $1 + \cfrac{1}{2 + \cfrac{1}{2 + \cfrac{1 \cdot 2}{\left(2 + \cfrac{1}{2}\right)2}}} = 1 + \cfrac{1}{2 + \cfrac{1}{2 + \cfrac{2}{4 + 1}}} = 1 + \cfrac{1}{2 + \cfrac{1 \cdot 5}{\left(2 + \cfrac{2}{5}\right)5}}$

$= 1 + \cfrac{1}{2 + \cfrac{5}{10 + 2}} = 1 + \cfrac{1 \cdot 12}{\left(2 + \cfrac{5}{12}\right)12} = 1 + \cfrac{12}{24 + 5} = 1 + \cfrac{12}{29} = \cfrac{41}{29} \approx 1.414$

C **28.** $\cfrac{f(x + h) - f(x)}{h} = \cfrac{\cfrac{1}{x + h} - \cfrac{1}{x}}{h} = \cfrac{\cfrac{x}{x(x + h)} - \cfrac{x + h}{x(x + h)}}{h} = \cfrac{x - (x + h)}{hx(x + h)}$

$= \cfrac{-h}{hx(x + h)} = -\cfrac{1}{x(x + h)}$

29. $\dfrac{f(x+h)-f(x)}{h} = \dfrac{\dfrac{1}{x+h+1} - \dfrac{1}{x+1}}{h} = \dfrac{\dfrac{x+1}{(x+1)(x+h+1)} - \dfrac{x+h+1}{(x+1)(x+h+1)}}{h}$

$= \dfrac{x+1-(x+h+1)}{h(x+1)(x+h+1)} = \dfrac{-h}{h(x+1)(x+h+1)} = -\dfrac{1}{(x+1)(x+h+1)}$

30. $\dfrac{f(x+h)-f(x)}{h} = \dfrac{\dfrac{1-(x+h)}{x+h} - \dfrac{1-x}{x}}{h} = \dfrac{\dfrac{x[1-(x+h)]}{x(x+h)} - \dfrac{(x+h)(1-x)}{x(x+h)}}{h}$

$= \dfrac{x - x^2 - xh + x^2 + xh - x - h}{hx(x+h)} = \dfrac{-h}{hx(x+h)} = -\dfrac{1}{x(x+h)}$

31. $\dfrac{f(x+h)-f(x)}{h} = \dfrac{\dfrac{1}{(x+h)^2} - \dfrac{1}{x^2}}{h} = \dfrac{\dfrac{x^2}{x^2(x+h)^2} - \dfrac{(x+h)^2}{x^2(x+h)^2}}{h} = \dfrac{x^2 - x^2 - 2hx - h^2}{hx^2(x+h)^2}$

$= \dfrac{-h(2x+h)}{hx^2(x+h)^2} = -\dfrac{2x+h}{x^2(x+h)^2}$

32. $f(f(x)) = f\left(\dfrac{1}{x+1}\right) = \dfrac{1}{\dfrac{1}{x+1}+1} = \dfrac{1(x+1)}{\left(\dfrac{1}{x+1}+1\right)(x+1)} = \dfrac{x+1}{1+x+1} = \dfrac{x+1}{x+2}$

33. $f(f(x)) = f\left(\dfrac{x}{x+1}\right) = \dfrac{\dfrac{x}{x+1}}{\dfrac{x}{x+1}+1} = \dfrac{\left(\dfrac{x}{x+1}\right)(x+1)}{\left(\dfrac{x}{x+1}+1\right)(x+1)} = \dfrac{x}{x+x+1} = \dfrac{x}{2x+1}$

34. $f(f(x)) = f\left(\dfrac{1+x}{1-x}\right) = \dfrac{1+\dfrac{1+x}{1-x}}{1-\dfrac{1+x}{1-x}} = \dfrac{\left(1+\dfrac{1+x}{1-x}\right)(1-x)}{\left(1-\dfrac{1+x}{1-x}\right)(1-x)} = \dfrac{1-x+1+x}{1-x-1-x} = -\dfrac{1}{x}$

35. $f(f(x)) = f(1-x)^{-1} = [1-(1-x)^{-1}]^{-1} = \dfrac{1}{1-\dfrac{1}{1-x}} = \dfrac{1(1-x)}{\left(1-\dfrac{1}{1-x}\right)(1-x)}$

$= \dfrac{1-x}{1-x-1} = \dfrac{-(x-1)}{-x} = \dfrac{x-1}{x}$

Page 231 · COMPUTER EXERCISES

1.
```
10 INPUT H
20 LET A = 2
30 LET S = A
40 FOR N = 1 TO H
50 LET S = 1/S + A
60 NEXT N
70 LET S = S - A + 1
80 PRINT S
90 END
```

2. a. 1.5   **b.** 1.414286   **c.** 1.414214   **d.** 1.414214   **e.** $\sqrt{2}$

3. Change line 20 to: 20 INPUT A

4. a. 1.617978   **b.** 1.302776   **c.** 1.099019

Pages 234-235 · WRITTEN EXERCISES

A **1.** $\dfrac{x}{6} - \dfrac{1}{4} = \dfrac{2}{3}$; $12\left(\dfrac{x}{6} - \dfrac{1}{4}\right) = 12\left(\dfrac{2}{3}\right)$; $2x - 3 = 8$; $2x = 11$; $x = \dfrac{11}{2}$; $\left\{\dfrac{11}{2}\right\}$

2. $\dfrac{3t}{4} + \dfrac{5}{6} = \dfrac{t}{8}$; $24\left(\dfrac{3t}{4} + \dfrac{5}{6}\right) = 24\left(\dfrac{t}{8}\right)$; $18t + 20 = 3t$; $15t = -20$; $t = -\dfrac{20}{15} = -\dfrac{4}{3}$; $\left\{-\dfrac{4}{3}\right\}$

3. $\dfrac{z-1}{6} = \dfrac{z+2}{9} + \dfrac{1}{2}$; $18\left(\dfrac{z-1}{6}\right) = 18\left(\dfrac{z+2}{9} + \dfrac{1}{2}\right)$; $3z - 3 = 2z + 4 + 9$; $z = 16$; $\{16\}$

4. $\dfrac{z-3}{5} - \dfrac{z+5}{3} = \dfrac{4}{9}$; $45\left(\dfrac{z-3}{5} - \dfrac{z+5}{3}\right) = 45\left(\dfrac{4}{9}\right)$; $9z - 27 - 15(z+5) = 20$;

$9z - 27 - 15z - 75 = 20$; $-6z = 122$; $z = -\dfrac{122}{6} = -\dfrac{61}{3}$; $\left\{-\dfrac{61}{3}\right\}$

5. $\dfrac{x}{2} + \dfrac{2}{3} > \dfrac{1}{6}$; $6\left(\dfrac{x}{2} + \dfrac{2}{3}\right) > 6\left(\dfrac{1}{6}\right)$; $3x + 4 > 1$; $3x > -3$; $x > -1$; $\{x : x > -1\}$

6. $1 - \dfrac{t}{9} \le \dfrac{5}{6}$; $18\left(1 - \dfrac{t}{9}\right) \le 18\left(\dfrac{5}{6}\right)$; $18 - 2t \le 15$; $-2t \le -3$; $t \ge \dfrac{3}{2}$; $\left\{t : t \ge \dfrac{3}{2}\right\}$

7. $\dfrac{t-5}{10} \le \dfrac{4t}{15} - 2$; $30\left(\dfrac{t-5}{10}\right) \le 30\left(\dfrac{4t}{15} - 2\right)$; $3t - 15 \le 8t - 60$; $-5t \le -45$; $t \ge 9$; $\{t : t \ge 9\}$

8. $\dfrac{3x+1}{6} > \dfrac{x-2}{8} - \dfrac{1}{3}$; $24\left(\dfrac{3x+1}{6}\right) > 24\left(\dfrac{x-2}{8} - \dfrac{1}{3}\right)$; $12x + 4 > 3x - 6 - 8$; $9x > -18$; $x > -2$; $\{x : x > -2\}$

9. $\dfrac{x^2}{8} - \dfrac{3x}{4} + 1 = 0$; $8\left(\dfrac{x^2}{8} - \dfrac{3x}{4} + 1\right) = 0$; $x^2 - 6x + 8 = 0$; $(x-4)(x-2) = 0$; $x = 4$ or $x = 2$; $\{4, 2\}$

10. $\dfrac{x^2}{6} + \dfrac{x}{3} - \dfrac{1}{2} = 0$; $6\left(\dfrac{x^2}{6} + \dfrac{x}{3} - \dfrac{1}{2}\right) = 0$; $x^2 + 2x - 3 = 0$; $(x+3)(x-1) = 0$; $x = -3$ or $x = 1$; $\{-3, 1\}$

11. $\dfrac{t^2}{6} - \dfrac{t}{3} + \dfrac{1}{8} = 0$; $24\left(\dfrac{t^2}{6} - \dfrac{t}{3} + \dfrac{1}{8}\right) = 0$; $4t^2 - 8t + 3 = 0$; $(2t-1)(2t-3) = 0$; $t = \dfrac{1}{2}$ or $t = \dfrac{3}{2}$; $\left\{\dfrac{1}{2}, \dfrac{3}{2}\right\}$

12. $\dfrac{u^2}{9} - \dfrac{u}{6} - \dfrac{1}{2} = 0$; $18\left(\dfrac{u^2}{9} - \dfrac{u}{6} - \dfrac{1}{2}\right) = 0$; $2u^2 - 3u - 9 = 0$; $(2u + 3)(u - 3)$;

$u = -\dfrac{3}{2}$ or $u = 3$; $\left\{-\dfrac{3}{2}, 3\right\}$

13. $\dfrac{x^2}{5} + \dfrac{x - 5}{6} = 0$; $30\left(\dfrac{x^2}{5} + \dfrac{x - 5}{6}\right) = 0$; $6x^2 + 5x - 25 = 0$; $(3x - 5)(2x + 5) = 0$;

$x = \dfrac{5}{3}$ or $x = -\dfrac{5}{2}$; $\left\{\dfrac{5}{3}, -\dfrac{5}{2}\right\}$

14. $\dfrac{x(x + 1)}{3} = \dfrac{x + 2}{2}$; $6\left[\dfrac{x(x + 1)}{3}\right] = 6\left(\dfrac{x + 2}{2}\right)$; $2x(x + 1) = 3x + 6$;

$2x^2 + 2x = 3x + 6$; $2x^2 - x - 6 = 0$; $(2x + 3)(x - 2)$; $x = -\dfrac{3}{2}$ or $x = 2$; $\left\{-\dfrac{3}{2}, 2\right\}$

15. $\dfrac{x(x + 1)}{2} = \dfrac{3x + 1}{9}$; $18\left[\dfrac{x(x + 1)}{2}\right] = 18\left(\dfrac{3x + 1}{9}\right)$; $9x(x + 1) = 6x + 2$; $9x^2 + 9x$

$= 6x + 2$; $9x^2 + 3x - 2 = 0$; $(3x - 1)(3x + 2) = 0$; $x = \dfrac{1}{3}$ or $x = -\dfrac{2}{3}$; $\left\{\dfrac{1}{3}, -\dfrac{2}{3}\right\}$

16. $\dfrac{z^2}{6} = \dfrac{3(z + 5)}{4}$; $12\left(\dfrac{z^2}{6}\right) = 12\left[\dfrac{3(z + 5)}{4}\right]$; $2z^2 = 9(z + 5)$; $2z^2 = 9z + 45$;

$2z^2 - 9z - 45 = 0$; $(2z - 15)(z + 3) = 0$; $z = \dfrac{15}{2}$ or $z = -3$; $\left\{\dfrac{15}{2}, -3\right\}$

17. $\dfrac{u(u - 1)}{3} + \dfrac{1}{2} = \dfrac{u + 1}{4}$; $12\left[\dfrac{u(u - 1)}{3} + \dfrac{1}{2}\right] = 12\left(\dfrac{u + 1}{4}\right)$; $4u(u - 1) + 6 = 3u + 3$;

$4u^2 - 4u + 6 = 3u + 3$; $4u^2 - 7u + 3 = 0$; $(4u - 3)(u - 1) = 0$; $u = \dfrac{3}{4}$ or $u = 1$;

$\left\{\dfrac{3}{4}, 1\right\}$

18. $\dfrac{t(t + 1)}{5} = \dfrac{t + 1}{6} + \dfrac{1}{3}$; $30\left[\dfrac{t(t + 1)}{5}\right] = 30\left(\dfrac{t + 1}{6} + \dfrac{1}{3}\right)$; $6t(t + 1) = 5t + 5 + 10$;

$6t^2 + 6t = 5t + 15$; $6t^2 + t - 15 = 0$; $(3t + 5)(2t - 3) = 0$; $t = -\dfrac{5}{3}$ or $t = \dfrac{3}{2}$;

$\left\{-\dfrac{5}{3}, \dfrac{3}{2}\right\}$

19. $\dfrac{5x - 5}{3} - \dfrac{4 - 2x}{5} = 20$; $15\left(\dfrac{5x - 5}{3} - \dfrac{4 - 2x}{5}\right) = 15(20)$; $25x - 25 - 12 + 6x = 300$;

$31x = 337$; $x = \dfrac{337}{31}$; $\left\{\dfrac{337}{31}\right\}$

20. $\dfrac{4t - 2}{5} + \dfrac{14 - 3t}{4} = 3$; $20\left(\dfrac{4t - 2}{5} + \dfrac{14 - 3t}{4}\right) = 20(3)$; $16t - 8 + 70 - 15t = 60$;

$t = -2$; $\{-2\}$

B 21. $-\dfrac{1}{4} \le \dfrac{2x + 1}{2} \le \dfrac{1}{4}$; $4\left(-\dfrac{1}{4}\right) \le 4\left(\dfrac{2x + 1}{2}\right) \le 4\left(\dfrac{1}{4}\right)$; $-1 \le 4x + 2 \le 1$;

$-3 \le 4x \le -1$; $-\dfrac{3}{4} \le x \le -\dfrac{1}{4}$; $\left\{x : -\dfrac{3}{4} \le x \le -\dfrac{1}{4}\right\}$

22. $-4t \le \dfrac{5t-1}{3} < 2 - 4t$; $3(-4t) \le 3\left(\dfrac{5t-1}{3}\right) < 3(2-4t)$; $-12t \le 5t - 1 < 6 - 12t$;

$0 \le 17t - 1 < 6$; $1 \le 17t < 7$; $\dfrac{1}{17} \le t < \dfrac{7}{17}$; $\left\{t : \dfrac{1}{17} \le t < \dfrac{7}{17}\right\}$

23. $\dfrac{x^2+1}{6} + \dfrac{x+1}{3} < \dfrac{1}{2}$; $6\left(\dfrac{x^2+1}{6} + \dfrac{x+1}{3}\right) < 6\left(\dfrac{1}{2}\right)$; $x^2 + 1 + 2x + 2 < 3$;

$x^2 + 2x < 0$; $x(x+2) < 0$; $x > 0$ and $x + 2 < 0$ or $x < 0$ and $x + 2 > 0$; $x > 0$ and $x < -2$ (reject) or $x < 0$ and $x > -2$; $\{x : -2 < x < 0\}$

24. $\dfrac{x^2-4}{6} - \dfrac{2x-3}{4} > \dfrac{1}{12}$; $12\left(\dfrac{x^2-4}{6} - \dfrac{2x-3}{4}\right) > 12\left(\dfrac{1}{12}\right)$; $2x^2 - 8 - 6x + 9 > 1$;

$2x^2 - 6x > 0$; $2x(x-3) > 0$; $x > 0$ and $x - 3 > 0$ or $x < 0$ and $x - 3 < 0$; $x > 3$ or $x < 0$; $\{x : x > 3 \text{ or } x < 0\}$

25. $\dfrac{t^2}{15} + \dfrac{2}{5} \ge \dfrac{t+2}{6}$; $30\left(\dfrac{t^2}{15} + \dfrac{2}{5}\right) \ge 30\left(\dfrac{t+2}{6}\right)$; $2t^2 + 12 \ge 5t + 10$; $2t^2 - 5t + 2 \ge 0$;

$(2t-1)(t-2) \ge 0$; $2t - 1 \ge 0$ and $t - 2 \ge 0$ or $2t - 1 \le 0$ and $t - 2 \le 0$; $t \ge \dfrac{1}{2}$ and

$t \ge 2$ or $t \le \dfrac{1}{2}$ and $t \le 2$; $t \ge 2$ or $t \le \dfrac{1}{2}$; $\left\{t : t \le \dfrac{1}{2} \text{ or } t \ge 2\right\}$

26. $\dfrac{x^2}{6} + \dfrac{x-2}{4} \le \dfrac{x+1}{3}$; $12\left(\dfrac{x^2}{6} + \dfrac{x-2}{4}\right) \le 12\left(\dfrac{x+1}{3}\right)$; $2x^2 + 3x - 6 \le 4x + 4$;

$2x^2 - x - 10 \le 0$; $(2x-5)(x+2) \le 0$; $2x - 5 \ge 0$ and $x + 2 \le 0$ or $2x - 5 \le 0$ and

$x + 2 \ge 0$; $x \ge \dfrac{5}{2}$ and $x \le -2$ (reject) or $x \le \dfrac{5}{2}$ and $x \ge -2$; $\left\{x : -2 \le x \le \dfrac{5}{2}\right\}$

Pages 235-236 · PROBLEMS

A **1-6.** Let n be the number.

1. $\dfrac{2}{5} \cdot \dfrac{3}{8}n = 12$; $\dfrac{3}{20}n = 12$; $3n = 240$; $n = 80$; 80

2. $\dfrac{5}{6} \cdot \dfrac{3}{4}n = 10$; $\dfrac{5}{8}n = 10$; $5n = 80$; $n = 16$; 16

3. $30 = 0.20(0.30n)$; $30 = 0.06n$; $500 = n$; 500

4. $10 = 0.60\left(\dfrac{2}{3}n\right)$; $10 = 0.4n$; $25 = n$; 25

5. $n + \dfrac{n^2}{2} = 24$; $2n + n^2 = 48$; $n^2 + 2n - 48 = 0$; $(n+8)(n-6) = 0$; $n = -8$ or

$n = 6$; 6 or -8

6. $\dfrac{n+n^2}{2} = 36$; $n + n^2 = 72$; $n^2 + n - 72 = 0$; $(n+9)(n-8) = 0$; $n = -9$ or $n = 8$;

-9 or 8

7. Let h = Jim's height in centimeters; $\frac{7}{8}h$ = Jan's height; $\dfrac{\frac{7}{8}h + h}{2} = 165$; $\frac{7}{8}h + h =$

330; $\frac{15h}{8} = 330$; $15h = 2640$; $h = 176$; $\frac{7}{8}h = 154$; Jim is 176 cm tall; Jan is 154 cm tall.

8. Let t = Jan's score; $\frac{4}{5}t$ = Jim's score; $\dfrac{t + \frac{4}{5}t}{2} = 0.81$; $t + \frac{4}{5}t = 1.62$; $\frac{9}{5}t = 1.62$;

$9t = 8.1$; $t = 0.90$; $\frac{4}{5}t = 0.72$; Jan's score was 90%, Jim's was 72%.

9. Let n = number of hours job takes when both belts are used; $\frac{n}{20} + \frac{n}{12} = 1$; $3n + 5n =$
60; $8n = 60$; $n = 7.5$; 7.5 h

10. Let n = number of liters to be added; present solution contains 0.08(6) = 0.48 L of
alcohol; $\frac{0.48}{n + 6} = 0.05$; $\frac{48}{n + 6} = 5$; $5n + 30 = 48$; $5n = 18$; $n = 3.6$; 3.6 L

11. Let n = number of liters to be evaporated; present solution contains 0.03(250) = 7.5 L
of salt; $\frac{7.5}{250 - n} = 0.05$; $\frac{750}{250 - n} = 5$; $1250 - 5n = 750$; $-5n = -500$; $n = 100$; 100 L

12. Let b = number of bleacher tickets sold; $18,000 - b$ = number of grandstand tickets;
$4.25b + 6.50(18,000 - b) = 103,050$; $425b + 650(18,000 - b) = 10,305,000$;
$425b + 11,700,000 - 650b = 10,305,000$; $-225b = -1,395,000$; $b = 6200$;
$18,000 - b = 11,800$; 6200 bleacher tickets, 11,800 grandstand

13. Let n = time taken if both pumps are used; $\frac{n}{36} + \frac{n}{24} = 1$; $2n + 3n = 72$; $5n = 72$;
$n = 14.4$; 14.4 h

14. Let d = distance in kilometers; $\frac{3}{2} = \dfrac{\frac{d}{2}}{6} + \dfrac{\frac{d}{2}}{10}$; $\frac{3}{2} = \frac{d}{12} + \frac{d}{20}$; $90 = 5d + 3d$; $8d = 90$;
$d = 11.25$; 11.25 km

15. Let d = distance traveled upstream in kilometers; $6 = \frac{d}{4} + \frac{d}{6} + 1$; $\frac{d}{4} + \frac{d}{6} = 5$;
$3d + 2d = 60$; $5d = 60$; $d = 12$; 12 km

16. Let x = amount invested at 9%; $2400 - x$ = amount invested at 12%;
$0.09x + 0.12(2400 - x) = 270$; $9x + 12(2400 - x) = 27,000$; $9x + 28,800 - 12x =$
$27,000$; $-3x = -1800$; $x = 600$; $2400 - x = 1800$; $600 at 9%; $1800 at 12%

17. Let x = amount invested at 10.5%; $53,650 - x$ = amount invested at 12%; $0.105x =$
$\frac{1}{3}(0.12)(53,650 - x)$; $0.105x = 0.04(53,650 - x)$; $105x = 40(53,650 - x)$; $105x =$
$2,146,000 - 40x$; $145x = 2,146,000$; $x = 14,800$; $53,650 - x = 38,850$; $14,800 at
10.5%, $38,850 at 12%

B **18.** Let n = number of hours, d = distance from Los Angeles to Austin; $d - \dfrac{n}{3}d =$

$\dfrac{1}{2}\left(d - \dfrac{n}{3.5}d\right)$; $d\left(1 - \dfrac{n}{3}\right) = d\left(\dfrac{1}{2} - \dfrac{n}{7}\right)$; $1 - \dfrac{n}{3} = \dfrac{1}{2} - \dfrac{n}{7}$; $42 - 14n = 21 - 6n$;

$-8n = -21$; $n = 2.625$ h; 2.625 or $2\dfrac{5}{8}$ h

19. Let n = number of liters; $\dfrac{0.20n + 0.12(3)}{3 + n} = 0.15$; $\dfrac{20n + 36}{3 + n} = 15$; $20n + 36 =$

$45 + 15n$; $5n = 9$; $n = 1.8$; 1.8 L

20. Let n = number of milliliters of 5% solution; $800 - n$ = number of milliliters of 15%

solution; $\dfrac{0.05n + 0.15(800 - n)}{800} = 0.08$; $0.05n + 0.15(800 - n) = 64$;

$5n + 15(800 - n) = 6400$; $5n + 12{,}000 - 15n = 6400$; $-10n = -5600$; $n = 560$;

$800 - n = 240$; 560 mL of 5% solution, 240 mL of 15% solution

21. Let n = number of hours; $\dfrac{n}{8} + \dfrac{n}{12} = 20$; $3n + 2n = 480$; $5n = 480$; $n = 96$; 96 h

22. Let n = number of hours; $\dfrac{1.5}{6} + \dfrac{n}{6} + \dfrac{n}{9} = 1$; $4.5 + 3n + 2n = 18$; $5n = 13.5$;

$n = 2.7$; pipes are on for 2.7 h = 2 h 42 min after 1:30 P.M., tank is full at 4:12 P.M.;
1612 h

23. Let h = height of tower in meters; $4.5(60) = \dfrac{h}{3} + \dfrac{h}{4} + 60$; $270 = \dfrac{h}{3} + \dfrac{h}{4} + 60$;

$\dfrac{h}{3} + \dfrac{h}{4} = 210$; $4h + 3h = 2520$; $7h = 2520$; $h = 360$; 360 m

C **24.** Let x = shorter distance in kilometers; longer distance = $x + 96$, and total distance =

$2x + 96$; $\dfrac{x}{60} + \dfrac{x + 96}{120} = \dfrac{2x + 96}{100}$; $10x + 5x + 480 = 12x + 576$; $3x = 96$; $x = 32$;

$2x + 96 = 160$; 160 km

25. Let x = number of kilograms of Supermix and y = number of kilograms of Tastimix;
$0.25x + 0.15y = 0.21(15)$ and $0.40x + 0.30y = 0.36(15)$; $25x + 15y = 315$ and
$40x + 30y = 540$; solving the system gives $x = 9$ and $y = 6$; 9 kg of Supermix, 6 kg
of Tastimix

26. Let x = number of liters to be removed; $0.55(5) = 0.75x + 0.25(5 - x)$; $55(5) =$
$75x + 25(5 - x)$; $275 = 75x + 125 - 25x$; $150 = 50x$; $x = 3$; 3 L

Page 239 · WRITTEN EXERCISES

A **1.** $\dfrac{2}{x} - \dfrac{1}{2x} = \dfrac{1}{2}$; $2x\left(\dfrac{2}{x} - \dfrac{1}{2x}\right) = \dfrac{1}{2}$; $4 - 1 = x$; $x = 3$; $\{3\}$

2. $\dfrac{5}{t} + \dfrac{3}{5} = \dfrac{2}{t}$; $5t\left(\dfrac{5}{t} + \dfrac{3}{5}\right) = 5t\left(\dfrac{2}{t}\right)$; $25 + 3t = 10$; $3t = -15$; $t = -5$; $\{-5\}$

3. $\dfrac{2}{u} = \dfrac{1}{u-1}$; $u(u-1)\left(\dfrac{2}{u}\right) = u(u-1)\left(\dfrac{1}{u-1}\right)$; $2u-2 = u$; $u = 2$; $\{2\}$

4. $\dfrac{2}{x-1} - \dfrac{3}{x+1} = 0$; $(x-1)(x+1)\left[\dfrac{2}{x-1} - \dfrac{3}{x+1}\right] = 0$; $2x+2-3x+3 = 0$;

   $-x = -5$; $x = 5$; $\{5\}$

5. $\dfrac{1}{2+3x} + \dfrac{2}{2-3x} = 0$; $(2+3x)(2-3x)\left[\dfrac{1}{2+3x} + \dfrac{2}{2-3x}\right] = 0$;

   $2-3x+4+6x = 0$; $3x = -6$; $x = -2$; $\{-2\}$

6. $\dfrac{3}{x-\dfrac{1}{2}} = \dfrac{5}{x+\dfrac{1}{2}}$; $\left(x+\dfrac{1}{2}\right)\left(x-\dfrac{1}{2}\right)\left(\dfrac{3}{x-\dfrac{1}{2}}\right) = \left(x+\dfrac{1}{2}\right)\left(x-\dfrac{1}{2}\right)\left(\dfrac{5}{x+\dfrac{1}{2}}\right)$

   $= 3x + \dfrac{3}{2} = 5x - \dfrac{5}{2}$; $-2x = -\dfrac{8}{2}$; $x = 2$; $\{2\}$

7. $\dfrac{t}{t-2} = \dfrac{t+3}{t}$; $t(t-2)\left(\dfrac{t}{t-2}\right) = t(t-2)\left(\dfrac{t+3}{t}\right)$; $t^2 = t^2 + t - 6$; $t = 6$; $\{6\}$

8. $\dfrac{x-2}{x} = \dfrac{x-4}{x-6}$; $x(x-6)\left(\dfrac{x-2}{x}\right) = x(x-6)\left(\dfrac{x-4}{x-6}\right)$; $x^2 - 8x + 12 = x^2 - 4x$;

   $-4x = -12$; $x = 3$; $\{3\}$

9. $\dfrac{2z^2 + z - 3}{z^2 + 1} = 2$; $(z^2+1)\left(\dfrac{2z^2+z-3}{z^2+1}\right) = (z^2+1)2$; $2z^2 + z - 3 = 2z^2 + 2$;

   $z = 5$; $\{5\}$

10. $\dfrac{(x-1)^2}{(x+3)^2} = 1$; $(x+3)^2\left[\dfrac{(x-1)^2}{(x+3)^2}\right] = (x+3)^2$; $(x-1)^2 = (x+3)^2$;

    $x^2 - 2x + 1 = x^2 + 6x + 9$; $-8x = 8$; $x = -1$; $\{-1\}$

11. $\dfrac{1}{x} + \dfrac{x}{x+2} = 1$; $x(x+2)\left[\dfrac{1}{x} + \dfrac{x}{x+2}\right] = x(x+2)$; $x+2+x^2 = x^2 + 2x$;

    $-x = -2$; $x = 2$; $\{2\}$

12. $\dfrac{1}{t-1} + \dfrac{t-1}{t+1} = 1$; $(t-1)(t+1)\left[\dfrac{1}{t-1} + \dfrac{t-1}{t+1}\right] = (t-1)(t+1)$;

    $t+1+t^2-2t+1 = t^2 - 1$; $-t = -3$; $t = 3$

13. $\dfrac{1}{u+4} + \dfrac{1}{u-4} = \dfrac{6}{u^2-16}$; $(u+4)(u-4)\left[\dfrac{1}{u+4} + \dfrac{1}{u-4}\right]$

    $= (u+4)(u-4)\left(\dfrac{6}{u^2-16}\right)$; $u-4+u+4 = 6$; $2u = 6$; $u = 3$; $\{3\}$

14. $\dfrac{1}{x+1} + \dfrac{1}{x-1} = \dfrac{2}{x^2-1}$; $(x+1)(x-1)\left[\dfrac{1}{x+1} - \dfrac{1}{x-1}\right]$

    $= (x+1)(x-1)\left(\dfrac{2}{x^2-1}\right)$; $x-1+x+1 = 2$; $2x = 2$; $x = 1$ (reject); no solution; $\emptyset$

15. $\dfrac{1}{t+2} + \dfrac{2}{t-2} = \dfrac{4}{t^2-4}$; $(t+2)(t-2)\left[\dfrac{1}{t+2} + \dfrac{2}{t-2}\right] = (t+2)(t-2)\left(\dfrac{4}{t^2-4}\right)$;

$t - 2 + 2t + 4 = 4$; $3t = 2$; $t = \dfrac{2}{3}$; $\left\{\dfrac{2}{3}\right\}$

16. $\dfrac{1}{x} + \dfrac{1}{x-1} = \dfrac{5}{x(x-1)}$; $x(x-1)\left[\dfrac{1}{x} + \dfrac{1}{x-1}\right] = x(x-1)\left[\dfrac{5}{x(x-1)}\right]$

$= x - 1 + x = 5$; $2x = 6$; $x = 3$; $\{3\}$

17. $\dfrac{2}{x} + \dfrac{1}{x-2} = 1$; $x(x-2)\left[\dfrac{2}{x} + \dfrac{1}{x-2}\right] = x(x-2)$; $2x - 4 + x = x^2 - 2x$;

$-x^2 + 5x - 4 = 0$; $x^2 - 5x + 4 = 0$; $(x-1)(x-4) = 0$; $x = 1$ or $x = 4$; $\{1, 4\}$

18. $\dfrac{1}{x-1} + \dfrac{1}{x+2} = \dfrac{1}{2}$; $2(x-1)(x+2)\left[\dfrac{1}{x-1} + \dfrac{1}{x+2}\right] = 2(x-1)(x+2)\left(\dfrac{1}{2}\right)$;

$2x + 4 + 2x - 2 = x^2 + x - 2$; $-x^2 + 3x + 4 = 0$; $x^2 - 3x - 4 = 0$;

$(x-4)(x+1) = 0$; $x = 4$ or $x = -1$; $\{4, -1\}$

19. $\dfrac{x}{x+1} + \dfrac{3}{x-3} + 1 = 0$; $(x+1)(x-3)\left[\dfrac{x}{x+1} + \dfrac{3}{x-3} + 1\right] = 0$; $x^2 - 3x + 3x$

$+ 3 + x^2 - 2x - 3 = 0$; $2x^2 - 2x = 0$; $2x(x-1) = 0$; $x = 0$ or $x = 1$; $\{0, 1\}$

20. $\dfrac{1}{x-3} + \dfrac{1}{x+5} = \dfrac{x+1}{x-3}$; $(x-3)(x+5)\left[\dfrac{1}{x-3} + \dfrac{1}{x+5}\right]$

$= (x-3)(x+5)\left(\dfrac{x+1}{x-3}\right)$; $x + 5 + x - 3 = x^2 + 6x + 5$; $-x^2 - 4x - 3 = 0$;

$x^2 + 4x + 3 = 0$; $(x+3)(x+1) = 0$; $x = -3$ or $x = -1$; $\{-3, -1\}$

B   21. $\dfrac{5}{(x-3)(x+2)} = \dfrac{1}{x-3} - \dfrac{x}{x+2}$; $(x-3)(x+2)\left(\dfrac{5}{(x-3)(x+2)}\right)$

$= (x-3)(x+2)\left[\dfrac{1}{x-3} - \dfrac{x}{x+2}\right]$; $5 = x + 2 - x^2 + 3x$; $x^2 - 4x + 3 = 0$;

$(x-3)(x-1) = 0$; $x = 3$ (reject) or $x = 1$; $\{1\}$

22. $\dfrac{4}{(x-3)(x+1)} = \dfrac{x}{x-3} - \dfrac{1}{x+1}$; $(x-3)(x+1)\left(\dfrac{4}{(x-3)(x+1)}\right)$

$= (x-3)(x+1)\left[\dfrac{x}{x-3} - \dfrac{1}{x+1}\right]$; $4 = x^2 + x - x + 3$; $-x^2 + 1 = 0$; $x^2 - 1 = 0$;

$(x+1)(x-1) = 0$; $x = -1$ (reject) or $x = 1$; $\{1\}$

23. $\dfrac{5x+2}{(x+2)(x-2)} = \dfrac{5x}{x-2} + \dfrac{2}{x+2}$; $(x+2)(x-2)\left(\dfrac{5x+2}{(x+2)(x-2)}\right)$

$= (x+2)(x-2)\left[\dfrac{5x}{x-2} + \dfrac{2}{x+2}\right]$; $5x + 2 = 5x^2 + 10x + 2x - 4$; $-5x^2 - 7x + 6$

$= 0$; $5x^2 + 7x - 6 = 0$; $(x+2)(5x-3) = 0$; $x = -2$ (reject) or $x = \dfrac{3}{5}$; $\left\{\dfrac{3}{5}\right\}$

24. $\dfrac{3x}{(x+4)(x-2)} = \dfrac{1}{x-2} + \dfrac{x}{x-4}$; $(x+4)(x-2)\left(\dfrac{3x}{(x+4)(x-2)}\right)$

$= (x+4)(x-2)\left[\dfrac{1}{x-2} + \dfrac{x}{x-4}\right]$; $3x = x+4+x^2-2x$; $-x^2+4x-4 = 0$;

$x^2 - 4x + 4 = 0$; $(x-2)^2 = 0$; $x = 2$ (reject); no solution; $\emptyset$

25. $\dfrac{x}{x+1} + \dfrac{1}{x-2} = \dfrac{3}{x^2-x-2}$; $(x+1)(x-2)\left(\dfrac{x}{x+1} + \dfrac{1}{x-2}\right)$

$= (x+1)(x-2)\left[\dfrac{3}{x^2-x-2}\right]$; $x(x-2)+x+1 = 3$; $x^2-2x+x+1 = 3$;

$x^2 - x - 2 = 0$; $(x-2)(x+1) = 0$; $x = 2$ or $x = -1$ (reject both); no solution; $\emptyset$

26. $\dfrac{(x+3)^2}{(x-1)^2} - 2 = \dfrac{x+3}{x-1}$; $(x-1)^2\left[\dfrac{(x+3)^2}{(x-1)^2} - 2\right] = (x-1)^2\left(\dfrac{x+3}{x-1}\right)$;

$(x+3)^2 - 2(x-1)^2 = (x-1)(x+3)$; $x^2 + 6x + 9 - 2(x^2 - 2x + 1)$

$= x^2 + 2x - 3$; $x^2 + 6x + 9 - 2x^2 + 4x - 2 = x^2 + 2x - 3$; $-2x^2 + 8x + 10 = 0$;

$x^2 - 4x - 5 = 0$; $(x-5)(x+1) = 0$; $x = 5$ or $x = -1$; $\{5, -1\}$

C 27. $\dfrac{\frac{1}{x} + \frac{1}{y}}{\frac{-1}{x+y}} = \dfrac{1}{6}$ and $y = -\dfrac{6}{x}$; $\dfrac{1}{x} + \dfrac{1}{y} = \dfrac{1}{x} - \dfrac{x}{6} = \dfrac{6-x^2}{6x}$; $\dfrac{-1}{x+y} = \dfrac{-1}{x-\frac{6}{x}} = \dfrac{-x}{x^2-6}$;

$\dfrac{\frac{1}{x} + \frac{1}{y}}{\frac{-1}{x+y}} = \dfrac{\frac{6-x^2}{6x}}{\frac{-x}{x^2-6}} = \dfrac{-(x^2-6)^2}{-6x^2} = \dfrac{(x^2-6)^2}{6x^2}$; $\dfrac{(x^2-6)^2}{6x^2} = \dfrac{1}{6}$; $(x^2-6)^2 = x^2$;

$x^4 - 12x^2 + 36 = x^2$; $x^4 - 13x^2 + 36 = 0$; $(x^2-9)(x^2-4) = 0$;

$(x+3)(x-3)(x+2)(x-2) = 0$; $x = -3$, $x = 3$, $x = -2$, or $x = 2$; if $x = -3$,

$y = -\dfrac{6}{-3} = 2$; if $x = 3$, $y = -\dfrac{6}{3} = -2$; if $x = -2$, $y = -\dfrac{6}{-2} = 3$;

if $x = 2$, $y = -\dfrac{6}{2} = -3$; $\{(-3,2), (3,-2), (-2,3), (2,-3)\}$

28. $\dfrac{\frac{1}{x} - \frac{1}{y}}{\frac{1}{x} + \frac{1}{y}} = \dfrac{4}{5}$ and $y = \dfrac{1}{x}$; $\dfrac{1}{x} - \dfrac{1}{y} = \dfrac{1}{x} - x = \dfrac{1-x^2}{x}$; $\dfrac{1}{x} + \dfrac{1}{y} = \dfrac{1}{x} + x = \dfrac{1+x^2}{x}$;

$\dfrac{\frac{1}{x} - \frac{1}{y}}{\frac{1}{x} + \frac{1}{y}} = \dfrac{\frac{1-x^2}{x}}{\frac{1+x^2}{x}} = \dfrac{1-x^2}{1+x^2}$; $\dfrac{1-x^2}{1+x^2} = \dfrac{4}{5}$; $5(1-x^2) = 4(1+x^2)$; $5 - 5x^2 = 4 + 4x^2$;

$-9x^2 + 1 = 0$; $9x^2 - 1 = 0$; $(3x-1)(3x+1) = 0$; $x = \dfrac{1}{3}$ or $x = -\dfrac{1}{3}$; if $x = \dfrac{1}{3}$,

$y = 3$; if $x = -\dfrac{1}{3}$, $y = -3$; $\left\{\left(\dfrac{1}{3}, 3\right), \left(-\dfrac{1}{3}, -3\right)\right\}$

Pages 239-241 · PROBLEMS

A   **1.** Let n be the smaller number, $n + 9$ the larger; $\dfrac{1}{n} - \dfrac{1}{n+9} = 10$; $10(n + 9) - 10n = n(n + 9)$; $10n + 90 - 10n = n^2 + 9n$; $n^2 + 9n - 90 = 0$; $(n + 15)(n - 6) = 0$; $n = -15$ (reject) or $n = 6$; $n + 9 = 15$; 6 and 15

2. Let n and $25 - n$ be the numbers; $\dfrac{1}{n} + \dfrac{1}{25-n} = \dfrac{1}{4}$; $4(25 - n) + 4n = n(25 - n)$; $100 - 4n + 4n = 25n - n^2$; $n^2 - 25n + 100 = 0$; $(n - 20)(n - 5) = 0$; $n = 20$ or $n = 5$; if $n = 20$, $25 - n = 5$; if $n = 5$; $25 - n = 20$; 20 and 5

3. Let n be the number; $\dfrac{1}{\frac{n}{2}} - \dfrac{1}{2}\left(\dfrac{1}{n}\right) = \dfrac{1}{2}$; $\dfrac{2}{n} - \dfrac{1}{2n} = \dfrac{1}{2}$; $4 - 1 = n$; $n = 3$; 3

4. Let n and $n + 2$ be the integers; $\dfrac{1}{n} - \dfrac{1}{n+2} = \dfrac{1}{60}$; $60(n + 2) - 60n = n(n + 2)$; $60n + 120 - 60n = n^2 + 2n$; $n^2 + 2n - 120 = 0$; $(n + 12)(n - 10) = 0$; $n = -12$ (reject) or $n = 10$; $n + 2 = 12$; 10 and 12

5. Let n = number of hours for new sweeper alone; $\dfrac{7.5}{30} + \dfrac{7.5}{n} = 1$; $7.5n + 225 = 30n$; $22.5n = 225$; $n = 10$; 10 h

6. Let n = number of hours for outlet pipe to empty tank; $\dfrac{n}{4} - \dfrac{n}{6} = 1$; $3n - 2n = 12$; $n = 12$; 12 h

7. Let n = average highway fuel consumption in km/L; $\dfrac{100}{8} + \dfrac{300}{n} = \dfrac{400}{12}$; $300n + 7200 = 800n$; $500n = 7200$; $n = 14.4$; 14.4 km/L

8. Let r = speed in km/h; r = 110% of usual speed; usual speed $= \dfrac{r}{1.1}$; $\dfrac{4400}{r} = \dfrac{4400}{\frac{r}{1.1}} - \dfrac{1}{2}$; $\dfrac{4400}{r} = \dfrac{4840}{r} - \dfrac{1}{2}$; $8800 = 9680 - r$; $r = 880$; 880 km/h

9. Let c = speed of current in kilometers per hour; $\dfrac{30}{16-c} + \dfrac{30}{16+c} = 4$; $30(16 + c) + 30(16 - c) = 4(16 - c)(16 + c)$; $480 + 30c + 480 - 30c = 1024 - 4c^2$; $4c^2 - 64 = 0$; $c^2 - 16 = 0$; $(c + 4)(c - 4) = 0$; $c = -4$ (reject) or $c = 4$; 4 km/h

10. Let r = speed in still water in kilometers per hour; $\dfrac{10}{r-3} + \dfrac{10}{r+3} = 3.5$; $10r + 30 + 10r - 30 = 3.5(r^2 - 9)$; $20r = 3.5r^2 - 31.5$; $35r^2 - 200r - 315 = 0$; $7r^2 - 40r - 63 = 0$; $(7r + 9)(r - 7) = 0$; $r = -\dfrac{9}{7}$ (reject) or $r = 7$; $7(3.5) = 24.5$; 24.5 km

11. Let n = number of members now; $\dfrac{900}{n-6} - 7.5 = \dfrac{900}{n}$; $900n - 7.5n^2 + 45n = 900n - 5400$; $-7.5n^2 + 45n + 5400 = 0$; $n^2 - 6n - 720 = 0$; $(n + 24)(n - 30) = 0$; $n = -24$ (reject) or $n = 30$; 30 members

12. Let x = number that went; $\dfrac{1500}{x+4} + 12.5 = \dfrac{1500}{x}$; $1500x + 12.5x^2 + 50x =$

$1500x + 6000$; $12.5x^2 + 50x - 6000 = 0$; $x^2 + 4x - 480 = 0$; $(x+24)(x-20) = 0$;

$x = -24$ (reject) or $x = 20$; 20

13. Let r = speed of new planes in kilometers per hour; $\dfrac{2800}{r} = \dfrac{2800}{r-100} - \dfrac{1}{2}$;

$5600r - 560{,}000 = 5600r - r^2 + 100r$; $r^2 - 100r - 560{,}000 = 0$;

$(r+700)(r-800) = 0$; $r = -700$ (reject) or $r = 800$; 800 km/h

14. Let x = numbers of hours for one machine; $6 - x$ = number of hours for other;

$\dfrac{\frac{4}{3}}{x} + \dfrac{\frac{4}{3}}{6-x} = 1$; $\dfrac{4}{3x} + \dfrac{4}{3(6-x)} = 1$; $24 - 4x + 4x = 18x - 3x^2$; $3x^2 - 18x + 24 =$

0; $x^2 - 6x + 8 = 0$; $(x-4)(x-2) = 0$; $x = 4$ or $x = 2$; if $x = 4$, $6 - x = 2$; if $x = 2$,

$6 - x = 4$; 2 h and 4 h

B 15. Let d = distance from A to B and x = average speed for whole trip; $\dfrac{d}{x} = \dfrac{\frac{d}{2}}{45} + \dfrac{\frac{d}{2}}{90}$;

$\dfrac{d}{x} = \dfrac{d}{90} + \dfrac{d}{180}$; $180d = 2dx + dx$; $3dx = 180d$; $x = 60$; 60 km/h

16. Let d = length of whole trip and x = average speed for remainder; $\dfrac{d}{60} = \dfrac{\frac{d}{2}}{50} + \dfrac{\frac{d}{2}}{x}$;

$\dfrac{d}{60} = \dfrac{d}{100} + \dfrac{d}{2x}$; $5dx = 3dx + 150d$; $2dx = 150d$; $x = 75$; 75 km/h

17. Let d = length of whole trip and x = average speed for last 20%; $\dfrac{d}{90} = \dfrac{\frac{4}{5}d}{120} + \dfrac{\frac{d}{5}}{x}$;

$\dfrac{d}{90} = \dfrac{4d}{600} + \dfrac{d}{5x}$; $\dfrac{d}{90} = \dfrac{d}{150} + \dfrac{d}{5x}$; $5dx = 3dx + 90d$; $2dx = 90d$; $x = 45$; 45 km/h

18. Let n = number of hours for pipe C to empty tank; $n - 2$ = number of hours for B to

fill tank; $\dfrac{10}{3}\left(\dfrac{1}{6} + \dfrac{1}{n-2} - \dfrac{1}{n}\right) = 1$; $\dfrac{1}{6} + \dfrac{1}{n-2} - \dfrac{1}{n} = \dfrac{3}{10}$; $\dfrac{1}{n-2} - \dfrac{1}{n} = \dfrac{4}{30}$;

$30n - 30n + 60 = 4n^2 - 8n$; $-4n^2 + 8n + 60 = 0$; $n^2 - 2n - 15 = 0$;

$(n+3)(n-5) = 0$; $n = -3$ (reject) or $n = 5$; 5 h

19. Let r = rate of ascent in meters per second; $r + 1$ = rate of descent; $120 =$

$\dfrac{140}{r} + 24 + \dfrac{140}{r+1}$; $\dfrac{140}{r} + \dfrac{140}{r+1} = 96$; $140r + 140 + 140r = 96r^2 + 96r$;

$96r^2 - 184r - 140 = 0$; $24r^2 - 46r - 35 = 0$; $(12r+7)(2r-5) = 0$; $r = -\dfrac{7}{12}$

(reject) or $r = \dfrac{5}{2}$; 2.5 m/s; $r + 1 = \dfrac{7}{2}$; 3.5 m/s

20. Let w = wind speed in kilometers per hour; $\dfrac{480}{200-w} + \dfrac{240}{200+w} = 4$;

$96{,}000 + 480w + 48{,}000 - 240w = 160{,}000 - 4w^2$; $4w^2 + 240w - 16{,}000 = 0$;

$w^2 + 60w - 4000 = 0$; $(w+100)(w-40) = 0$; $w = -100$ (reject) or $w = 40$; 40 km/h

21. Let j = number of jackets; $\left[\dfrac{3000}{j} + 25\right](j - 10) - 3000 = 750;$

$\left(\dfrac{3000 + 25j}{j}\right)(j - 10) = 3750; (3000 + 25j)(j - 10) = 3750j;$

$3000j + 25j^2 - 30{,}000 - 250j = 3750j; 25j^2 - 1000j - 30{,}000 = 0;$

$j^2 - 40j + 1200 = 0; (j + 20)(j - 60) = 0; j = -20 \text{ (reject) or } j = 60; 60$

22. Let x = amount invested in dollars and $r\%$ be the interest rate; $\dfrac{xr}{100} = 660; x = \dfrac{66{,}000}{r};$

$\dfrac{(x + 500)(r - 1)}{100} = 660; \left(\dfrac{66{,}000}{r} + 500\right)(r - 1) = 66{,}000;$

$66{,}000r + 500r^2 - 66{,}000 - 500r = 66{,}000r; 500r^2 - 500r - 66{,}000 = 0;$

$r^2 - r - 132 = 0; (r + 11)(r - 12) = 0; r = -11 \text{ (reject) or } r = 12; x = \dfrac{66{,}000}{12} =$

$5500; \$5500$ was invested at 12%.

23. $\dfrac{1}{4} = \dfrac{\dfrac{1}{3} + \dfrac{1}{y}}{2}; \dfrac{1}{2} = \dfrac{1}{3} + \dfrac{1}{y}; 3y = 2y + 6; y = 6$

24. Let x and $x + 8$ be the numbers; $\dfrac{1}{6} = \dfrac{\dfrac{1}{x} + \dfrac{1}{x + 8}}{2}; \dfrac{1}{3} = \dfrac{1}{x} + \dfrac{1}{x + 8}; x^2 + 8x =$

$3x + 24 + 3x; x^2 + 2x - 24 = 0; (x + 6)(x - 4) = 0; x = -6 \text{ or } x = 4; \text{ if } x = -6,$

$x + 8 = 2; \text{ if } x = 4, x + 8 = 12; -6 \text{ and } 2 \text{ or } 4 \text{ and } 12$

Page 241 · CALCULATOR KEY-IN

$x = \sqrt{2} \approx 1.41; \text{ minimum value} = x + \dfrac{2}{x} = \sqrt{2} + \dfrac{2}{\sqrt{2}} = 2\sqrt{2} \approx 2.83$

Page 243 · APPLICATION

1. $\dfrac{1}{R_c} = \dfrac{1}{10} + \dfrac{1}{15} = \dfrac{1}{6}; R_c = 6; R = 6 + 8 + 4 = 18; x = \dfrac{27}{18} = 1.5; 1.5A$

2. $\dfrac{1}{R} = \dfrac{1}{15} + \dfrac{1}{15} + \dfrac{1}{15} = \dfrac{3}{15} = \dfrac{1}{5}; R = 5; 2.5 = \dfrac{E}{5}; E = 12.5; 12.5V$

3. $\dfrac{1}{R} = \dfrac{1}{x} + \dfrac{1}{x + 5} = \dfrac{x + 5 + x}{x^2 + 5x}; R = \dfrac{x^2 + 5x}{2x + 5}; 2 = \dfrac{12}{\dfrac{x^2 + 5x}{2x + 5}}; 2\left(\dfrac{x^2 + 5x}{2x + 5}\right) = 12;$

$\dfrac{x^2 + 5x}{2x + 5} = 6; x^2 + 5x = 12x + 30; x^2 - 7x - 30 = 0; (x + 3)(x - 10) = 0; x = -3$

(reject) or $x = 10; 10 \ \Omega$

4. $\dfrac{1}{R_c} = \dfrac{1}{x} + \dfrac{1}{x} = \dfrac{2}{x}; R_c = \dfrac{x}{2}; R = \dfrac{x}{2} + 5 = \dfrac{x + 10}{2}; 1.5 = \dfrac{24}{\dfrac{x + 10}{2}}; 1.5\left(\dfrac{x + 10}{2}\right) =$

$24; \dfrac{x + 10}{2} = 16; x + 10 = 32; x = 22; 22 \ \Omega$

1. c

2. d; $\dfrac{(xy^2z)^2}{(-xy)^3} = \dfrac{x^2y^4z^2}{-x^3y^3} = -\dfrac{yz^2}{x}$

3. a; $\dfrac{ax^{-3}}{(ax)^{-3}} = \dfrac{ax^{-3}}{a^{-3}x^{-3}} = a^4$

4. b; $\dfrac{(-2a^2x^{-1})^0}{(a^{-1}x^2)^{-1}} \cdot \left(\dfrac{ax^{-1}}{2a^{-1}x}\right)^{-2} = \dfrac{1}{ax^{-2}} \cdot \dfrac{a^{-2}x^2}{2^{-2}a^2x^{-2}} = \dfrac{x^2}{a} \cdot \dfrac{4x^4}{a^4} = \dfrac{4x^6}{a^5}$

5. d   **6.** c

7. d; $(0.00571)(224) \div 0.039 \approx (6 \times 10^{-3})(2 \times 10^2) \div (4 \times 10^{-2}) = 3 \times 10^1$

8. d; $\dfrac{x^2 - x}{x^2 - 1} = \dfrac{x(x - 1)}{(x + 1)(x - 1)} = \dfrac{x}{x + 1}$

9. a; $f(t) = \dfrac{t^2 + 4t + 3}{t^2 + 5t + 6} = \dfrac{(t + 3)(t + 1)}{(t + 3)(t + 2)}, \; t \neq -3, \; t \neq -2; f(t) = \dfrac{t + 1}{t + 2}, \; t \neq -3,$

$t \neq -2; f(t) = 0 \text{ if } t + 1 = 0$

10. b; $\dfrac{x^2 - 2x}{x^2 + x - 2} \cdot \dfrac{x^2 + 5x + 6}{x^2 + x - 6} = \dfrac{x(x - 2)}{(x + 2)(x - 1)} \cdot \dfrac{(x + 2)(x + 3)}{(x + 3)(x - 2)} = \dfrac{x}{x - 1}$

11. d; $\dfrac{uv}{u - v} \div \dfrac{u^2v^2}{u^2 - v^2} = \dfrac{uv}{u - v} \cdot \dfrac{(u + v)(u - v)}{u^2v^2} = \dfrac{u + v}{uv}$

12. c; $\dfrac{s + 2}{6s} - \dfrac{s + 1}{3s^2} = \dfrac{s^2 + 2s}{6s^2} - \dfrac{2s + 2}{6s^2} = \dfrac{s^2 - 2}{6s^2}$

13. a; $\dfrac{3}{x^2 + x - 2} + \dfrac{1}{x^2 - x} - \dfrac{3}{x^2 + 2x} = \dfrac{3}{(x + 2)(x - 1)} + \dfrac{1}{x(x - 1)} - \dfrac{3}{x(x + 2)}$

$= \dfrac{3x + x + 2 - 3(x - 1)}{x(x + 2)(x - 1)} = \dfrac{x + 5}{x(x + 2)(x - 1)}$

14. c; $\dfrac{a^{-2} - b^{-2}}{a - b} \cdot \dfrac{a^2b^2}{a^2b^2} = \dfrac{b^2 - a^2}{(a - b)(a^2b^2)} = -\dfrac{(a + b)(a - b)}{(a - b)(a^2b^2)} = -\dfrac{a + b}{a^2b^2}$

15. d; $\dfrac{x - \dfrac{3}{x - 2}}{1 - \dfrac{1}{x - 2}} \cdot \dfrac{x - 2}{x - 2} = \dfrac{x^2 - 2x - 3}{x - 2 - 1} = \dfrac{(x - 3)(x + 1)}{x - 3} = x + 1$

16. d; $36\left(\dfrac{x - 2}{18}\right) < 36\left(1 - \dfrac{x + 5}{12}\right); 2x - 4 < 36 - 3x - 15; 5x < 25; x < 5$

17. b; $12\left(\dfrac{s^2}{4} + \dfrac{4s}{3}\right) = 12; 3s^2 + 16s - 12 = 0; (3s - 2)(s + 6) = 0; s = \dfrac{2}{3} \text{ or } s = -6$

18. b; let x = amount of 85% solution; $.85x + (.45)5 = .60(x + 5)$;

$85x + 225 = 60x + 300; 25x = 75; x = 3$

19. b; $\dfrac{2}{x(x - 1)} = \dfrac{1}{x} + \dfrac{4}{(x + 1)(x - 1)}; 2(x + 1) = (x + 1)(x - 1) + 4x$;

$2x + 2 = x^2 + x - x - 1 + 4x; x^2 + 2x - 3 = 0; (x + 3)(x - 1) = 0; x = -3 \text{ or }$

$x = 1 \text{ (reject)}; x = -3$

20. c; let x = speed in still water; $d = rt$; $t = \dfrac{d}{r}$; $\dfrac{24}{x-3} + \dfrac{24}{x+3} = 6$;

$24(x+3) + 24(x-3) = 6(x+3)(x-3)$; $48x = 6x^2 - 54$; $8x = x^2 - 9$;

$x^2 - 8x - 9 = 0$; $(x-9)(x+1) = 0$; $x = 9$ or $x = -1$ (reject); 9 km/h

Page 247 · CHAPTER TEST

1. $\dfrac{3u^4v^2}{(2uv^3)^2}\left(\dfrac{2v}{u}\right)^3 = \dfrac{3u^4v^2}{4u^2v^6} \cdot \dfrac{8v^3}{u^3} = \dfrac{24u^4v^5}{4u^5v^6} = \dfrac{6}{uv}$

2. $\left(\dfrac{x^2y^{-1}}{x^{-1}y^2}\right)^{-2} = \left(\dfrac{x^{-1}y^2}{x^2y^{-1}}\right)^2 = \dfrac{x^{-2}y^4}{x^4y^{-2}} = x^{-6}y^6 = \dfrac{y^6}{x^6}$

3. $\dfrac{(6.4 \times 10^{-3})(8.2 \times 10^5)}{2.1 \times 10^{-2}} = \dfrac{6.4 \times 8.2}{2.1} \times 10^{-3+5-(-2)} \approx 25 \times 10^4 = 2.5 \times 10^5$

4. $\dfrac{4x^2 - 2x}{2x^2 + 3x - 2} = \dfrac{2x(2x-1)}{(2x-1)(x+2)} = \dfrac{2x}{x+2}$

5. $\dfrac{2x^2}{y} \div \dfrac{x}{2y} \div 2xy = \dfrac{2x^2}{y} \cdot \dfrac{2y}{x} \cdot \dfrac{1}{2xy} = \dfrac{4x^2y}{2x^2y^2} = \dfrac{2}{y}$

6. $\dfrac{2t^2 - 5t + 2}{t^2 - 1} \cdot \dfrac{t^2 + t - 2}{4t^2 - 1} \div \dfrac{t+2}{2t+1} = \dfrac{(2t-1)(t-2)}{(t+1)(t-1)} \cdot \dfrac{(t+2)(t-1)}{(2t-1)(2t+1)} \cdot \dfrac{2t+1}{t+2}$

$= \dfrac{t-2}{t+1}$

7. $\dfrac{x}{x-y} - \dfrac{y}{x+y} = \dfrac{x(x+y) - y(x-y)}{(x-y)(x+y)} = \dfrac{x^2 + xy - xy + y^2}{(x-y)(x+y)} = \dfrac{x^2 + y^2}{(x-y)(x+y)}$

8. $\dfrac{x+1}{2x+6} + \dfrac{2x}{x^2 - 9} = \dfrac{x+1}{2(x+3)} + \dfrac{2x}{(x+3)(x-3)} = \dfrac{(x+1)(x-3) + 4x}{2(x+3)(x-3)}$

$= \dfrac{x^2 - 2x - 3 + 4x}{2(x+3)(x-3)} = \dfrac{x^2 + 2x - 3}{2(x+3)(x-3)} = \dfrac{(x+3)(x-1)}{2(x+3)(x-3)} = \dfrac{x-1}{2(x-3)}$

9. $\dfrac{\dfrac{1}{1 - \dfrac{1}{x}} + 1}{\dfrac{1}{1 - \dfrac{1}{x}} - 1} = \dfrac{\dfrac{x}{x-1} + 1}{\dfrac{x}{x-1} - 1} = \dfrac{x + x - 1}{x - x + 1} = \dfrac{2x - 1}{1} = 2x - 1$

10. $\dfrac{2x+1}{3} - 1 \ge \dfrac{3x-1}{5}$; $\dfrac{2x+1-3}{3} \ge \dfrac{3x-1}{5}$; $\dfrac{2x-2}{3} \ge \dfrac{3x-1}{5}$;

$10x - 10 \ge 9x - 3$: $x \ge 7$; $\{x : x \ge 7\}$

11. Let n = number of hours job took; $\dfrac{x}{3} + \dfrac{x - \dfrac{1}{2}}{2} = 1$; $2x + 3x - \dfrac{3}{2} = 6$; $5x = 7.5$;

$x = 1.5$; 1.5 hours after 7 A.M. is 8:30 A.M.

12. $\dfrac{1}{(2x-1)(x-1)} + \dfrac{1}{2x+1} + \dfrac{4}{(2x-1)(2x+1)} = 0;$

$(2x+1)(2x-1)(x-1)\left[\dfrac{1}{(2x-1)(x-1)} + \dfrac{1}{2x+1} + \dfrac{4}{(2x-1)(2x+1)}\right] = 0;$

$2x + 1 + 2x^2 - 3x + 1 + 4x - 4 = 0; \quad 2x^2 + 3x - 2 = 0; \quad (2x-1)(x+2) = 0;$

$x = \dfrac{1}{2}$ (reject) or $x = -2; \{-2\}$

13. Let n = number of members now; $\dfrac{600}{n} + 5 = \dfrac{600}{n-6};$ $600n - 3600 + 5n^2 - 30n =$

$600n; \; 5n^2 - 30n - 3600 = 0; \; n^2 - 6n - 720 = 0; \; (n+24)(n-30) = 0; \; n = -24$

(reject) or $n = 30; 30$

CHAPTER 6 · Irrational and Complex Numbers

A **1. a.** 8   **b.** not real   **c.** -8 **d.** -4

2. a. 4   **b.** $\sqrt{16} = 4$ **c.** $\sqrt[3]{-64} = -4$ **d.** -4

3. a. 0.1   **b.** not real   **c.** -0.06 **d.** 0.0036

4. a. 0.04   **b.** 0.2   **c.** not real   **d.** -0.2

5. a. $\sqrt{9+16} = \sqrt{25} = 5$ **b.** $\sqrt{7^2} = 7$ **c.** $\sqrt{(-1)^2} = \sqrt{1} = 1$
  d. $\sqrt{9-16} = \sqrt{-7}$; not real

6. a. $\sqrt{169-144} = \sqrt{25} = 5$ **b.** $\sqrt{1^2} = 1$ **c.** $\sqrt{(-1)^2} = \sqrt{1} = 1$ **d.** $\sqrt{(25)^2} = 25$

7. a. $10^2 = 100$ **b.** $10^2 = 100$ **c.** $2 \times 10 = 20$
  d. $\sqrt[4]{1.6 \times 10^5} = \sqrt[4]{16 \times 10^4} = 2 \times 10 = 20$

8. a. $\dfrac{1}{5}$ **b.** $\dfrac{3}{5}$ **c.** $\sqrt{\dfrac{9}{16}} = \dfrac{3}{4}$ **d.** $\sqrt[3]{-\dfrac{1}{8}} = -\dfrac{1}{2}$

9. a. $|x|$ **b.** x^2 **c.** $|x^3|$ **d.** $|x^3|$

10. a. y^2 **b.** y^2 **c.** y^4 **d.** $-y^2$

11. 2000   **12.** 5000   **13.** $\sqrt{\sqrt[3]{N}} = 5$; $\sqrt[3]{N} = 25$; $N = (25)^3 = 15{,}625$

14. $\sqrt[3]{\sqrt{N}} = 5$; $\sqrt{N} = 5^3 = 125$; $N = (125)^2 = 15{,}625$

15. $x = \pm 5$ **16.** $y^2 = \dfrac{25}{4}$; $y = \pm\dfrac{5}{2}$ **17.** $x^2 = -9$; no real roots

18. $a^3 = -8$; $a = -2$ **19.** $n^3 = 2$; $n = \sqrt[3]{2}$ **20.** $z^4 = 9$; $z^2 = \pm 3$; $z = \pm\sqrt{3}$

21. $a^2 = 900$; $a = \pm 30$ **22.** $x^6 = -64$; no real roots   **23.** $|x+7| = x+7$; $x \geq -7$

24. $|a-5| = |5-a| = 5-a$; $a \leq 5$ **25.** $\sqrt[5]{(n-6)^5} = n-6$; true for all real numbers

26. $\sqrt{n^4} = \sqrt{(n^2)^2} = |n^2| = n^2$; true for all real numbers

B **27.** $\sqrt{a^2 + 2a + 1} = \sqrt{(a+1)^2} = |a+1|$; true for all real numbers

28. $\sqrt{b^2 - 6b + 9} = \sqrt{(b-3)^2} = |b-3| = b-3$; $b \geq 3$

29. $(\sqrt{n^2 + 4})^2 = (n+2)^2$; $n^2 + 4 = n^2 + 4n + 4$; $n = 0$

30. $(\sqrt[3]{8 - b^3})^3 = (2-b)^3$; $8 - b^3 = 8 - 12b + 6b^2 - b^3$; $-12b + 6b^2 = -6b(2-b) = 0$;
  $b = 0, b = 2$

31. a. $x \geq -9$ **b.** $x \geq 9$ **c.** all real numbers **d.** $x^2 - 9 \geq 0$; $x^2 \geq 9$; $x \leq -3$ or $x \geq 3$

32. a. $x \leq 4$ **b.** $4 - x^2 \geq 0$; $4 \geq x^2$; $-2 \leq x \leq 2$ **c.** all real numbers
  d. all real numbers

C **33.** $\sqrt{x} - x \geq 0$; $x \geq 0$; $\sqrt{x} \geq x \geq 0$; $(\sqrt{x})^2 \geq x^2$; $x \geq x^2$; $x^2 - x \leq 0$; $x(x-1) \leq 0$;
  $0 \leq x \leq 1$

34. $x^3 - 3x \geq 0$; $x(x^2 - 3) \geq 0$; $x \geq 0$ and $x^2 \geq 3$ or $x \leq 0$ and $x^2 \leq 3$; $x \geq \sqrt{3}$ or
  $-\sqrt{3} \leq x \leq 0$

Pages 255-257 · WRITTEN EXERCISES

A 1. $2\sqrt{2}$ 　　　　　　　 2. $10\sqrt{5}$ 　　　　　　　 3. $\dfrac{2\sqrt{2}}{3}$

4. $\dfrac{5\sqrt{2}}{7}$ 　　　 5. $\dfrac{\sqrt{5}}{\sqrt{2}}\cdot\dfrac{\sqrt{2}}{\sqrt{2}}=\dfrac{\sqrt{10}}{2}$ 　　　 6. $\dfrac{\sqrt{7}}{\sqrt{3}}\cdot\dfrac{\sqrt{3}}{\sqrt{3}}=\dfrac{\sqrt{21}}{3}$

7. $\dfrac{8}{\sqrt{2}}\cdot\dfrac{\sqrt{2}}{\sqrt{2}}=4\sqrt{2}$ 　　 8. $\dfrac{15}{\sqrt{3}}\cdot\dfrac{\sqrt{3}}{\sqrt{3}}=5\sqrt{3}$ 　　 9. $\dfrac{10\sqrt{3}}{\sqrt{5}}\cdot\dfrac{\sqrt{5}}{\sqrt{5}}=2\sqrt{15}$

10. $\dfrac{4\sqrt{7}}{2\sqrt{2}}\cdot\dfrac{\sqrt{2}}{\sqrt{2}}=\sqrt{14}$ 　　 11. $2\sqrt[3]{2}$ 　　　　 ·12. $\sqrt[3]{(27)(10)}=3\sqrt[3]{10}$

13. $\dfrac{\sqrt[3]{5}}{\sqrt[3]{2}}\cdot\dfrac{\sqrt[3]{4}}{\sqrt[3]{4}}=\dfrac{\sqrt[3]{20}}{2}$ 　　　　　　 14. $\dfrac{\sqrt[3]{7}}{\sqrt[3]{9}}\cdot\dfrac{\sqrt[3]{3}}{\sqrt[3]{3}}=\dfrac{\sqrt[3]{21}}{3}$

15. $6\sqrt[3]{\dfrac{1}{3}}=\sqrt[3]{216}\cdot\sqrt[3]{\dfrac{1}{3}}=\sqrt[3]{72}=\sqrt[3]{8}\cdot\sqrt[3]{9}=2\sqrt[3]{9}$

16. $\dfrac{6}{\sqrt[3]{54}}=\dfrac{\sqrt[3]{216}}{\sqrt[3]{54}}=\sqrt[3]{4}$ 　　 17. a. $4\sqrt{2}$ 　　　 b. $2\sqrt[3]{4}$ 　　　 c. $2\sqrt[4]{2}$ 　　　 d. 2

18. a. $\sqrt{\dfrac{3}{8}\cdot\dfrac{2}{2}}=\dfrac{\sqrt{6}}{4}$ 　 b. $\dfrac{\sqrt[3]{3}}{2}$ 　 c. $\sqrt[4]{\dfrac{3}{8}\cdot\dfrac{2}{2}}=\dfrac{\sqrt[4]{6}}{2}$ 　 d. $\sqrt[5]{-\dfrac{3}{8}\cdot\dfrac{4}{4}}=-\dfrac{\sqrt[5]{12}}{2}$

19. 7.141 　　　　　 20. 17.03 　　　　　 21. 1.474

22. 22.89 　　 23. $\sqrt{7}\cdot\sqrt{7}\cdot\sqrt{5}=7\sqrt{5}$ 　 24. $\sqrt{12\cdot\dfrac{2}{3}\cdot\dfrac{3}{4}}=\sqrt{6}$

25. $\sqrt[3]{3}\cdot\sqrt[3]{3}\cdot\sqrt[3]{3}\cdot\sqrt[3]{2}=3\sqrt[3]{2}$ 　　 26. $\sqrt[3]{\dfrac{3}{4}}\cdot\sqrt[3]{8}\cdot\sqrt[3]{9}=\sqrt[3]{\dfrac{8}{4}\cdot27}=3\sqrt[3]{2}$

27. $5^3\cdot4=500$ 　　 28. $(-2)^3(\sqrt{5})^3=-40\sqrt{5}$ 　 29. $\dfrac{3}{\sqrt{3}}\cdot\dfrac{\sqrt{3}}{\sqrt{3}}=\sqrt{3}$

30. $\dfrac{2\sqrt{3}}{\sqrt{2}}\cdot\dfrac{\sqrt{2}}{\sqrt{2}}=\sqrt{6}$ 　　 31. $3|x|\sqrt{2}$ 　　　　　 32. $2x\sqrt{2x}$

33. $5a^2\sqrt[3]{2a}$ 　　　 34. $2c\sqrt[3]{2c}$ 　 35. $\dfrac{\sqrt{x^2}}{\sqrt{y^3}}=\dfrac{|x|}{y\sqrt{y}}\cdot\dfrac{\sqrt{y}}{\sqrt{y}}=\dfrac{|x|\sqrt{y}}{y^2}$

36. $\dfrac{2}{x^2\sqrt{5x}}\cdot\dfrac{\sqrt{5x}}{\sqrt{5x}}=\dfrac{2\sqrt{5x}}{5x^3}$ 　 37. $\sqrt[3]{\dfrac{a}{2b^4}\cdot\dfrac{4b^2}{4b^2}}=\dfrac{\sqrt[3]{4ab^2}}{2b^2}$ 　 38. $\sqrt[3]{\dfrac{8c}{9d^5}\cdot\dfrac{3d}{3d}}=\dfrac{2\sqrt[3]{3cd}}{3d^2}$

B 39. $\sqrt{4(a+b)}=2\sqrt{a+b}$ 　　　 40. $\sqrt{9(a^2-b^2)}=3\sqrt{a^2-b^2}$

41. $\sqrt{2(a+1)^2}=|a+1|\sqrt{2}$ 　　 42. $\sqrt{3(x-2)^2}=|x-2|\sqrt{3}$

43. $\sqrt{\dfrac{1}{36}}=\dfrac{1}{6}$ 　 44. $\sqrt[3]{\dfrac{1}{32}\cdot\dfrac{2}{2}}=\dfrac{\sqrt[3]{2}}{4}$ 　 45. $\sqrt[3]{\dfrac{1}{4}+\dfrac{1}{8}}=\sqrt[3]{\dfrac{3}{8}}=\dfrac{\sqrt[3]{3}}{2}$

46. $\sqrt{\dfrac{1}{16}+\dfrac{1}{9}}=\sqrt{\dfrac{25}{144}}=\dfrac{5}{12}$ 　　 47. $\sqrt[4]{(-32)^{-4}}=\sqrt[4]{\dfrac{1}{(-32)^4}}=\dfrac{1}{32}$

48. $\sqrt{64}=8$ 　　　 49. $\sqrt[6]{(12)^8}=\sqrt[6]{(12)^6}\cdot\sqrt[6]{12^2}=12\sqrt[6]{144}$

50. $\sqrt[4]{4 \cdot 3^8} = \sqrt[4]{3^8} \cdot \sqrt[4]{4} = 3^2 \cdot \sqrt[4]{4} = 9\sqrt[4]{4}$ **51.** $\dfrac{2x\sqrt{2x}}{y^2}$ **52.** $\dfrac{2b\sqrt[3]{4b}}{a}$

53. $\sqrt{50a^3} = 5a\sqrt{2a}$ **54.** $\sqrt{12x^4} = 2x^2\sqrt{3}$ **55.** $\sqrt[3]{54y^4} = 3y\sqrt[3]{2y}$

56. $\sqrt[4]{48c^7} = 2c\sqrt[4]{3c^3}$ **57.** $\sqrt{\dfrac{1}{4b} \cdot \dfrac{b}{b}} = \dfrac{\sqrt{b}}{2b}$ **58.** $\sqrt{\dfrac{a^4 - 1}{(a+1)^2}} = \dfrac{\sqrt{a^4 - 1}}{|a+1|}$

C 59. a. $(\sqrt[n]{a} \cdot \sqrt[n]{b})^n = (\sqrt[n]{a})^n(\sqrt[n]{b})^n = ab$

b. If n is odd, $\sqrt[n]{a} \cdot \sqrt[n]{b}$ is the only root and, therefore, the principal root. If n is even, $\sqrt[n]{a}$ and $\sqrt[n]{b}$ are both nonnegative; thus, $\sqrt[n]{a} \cdot \sqrt[n]{b}$ is the nonnegative nth root of ab.

60. $\left(\dfrac{\sqrt[n]{a}}{\sqrt[n]{b}}\right)^n = \dfrac{(\sqrt[n]{a})^n}{(\sqrt[n]{b})^n} = \dfrac{a}{b}$. Thus, $\dfrac{\sqrt[n]{a}}{\sqrt[n]{b}}$ is an nth root of $\dfrac{a}{b}$. If n is odd, $\dfrac{\sqrt[n]{a}}{\sqrt[n]{b}}$ is the only nth

root of $\dfrac{a}{b}$. If n is even, both $\sqrt[n]{a}$ and $\sqrt[n]{b}$ are nonnegative and so is $\dfrac{\sqrt[n]{a}}{\sqrt[n]{b}}$.

61. 1. $\left(\sqrt[n]{\sqrt[q]{b}}\right)^{nq} = \left[\left(\sqrt[n]{\sqrt[q]{b}}\right)^n\right]^q$ $((b^m)^n = b^{mn})$

2. $= (\sqrt[q]{b})^q$ (Rule 1, p. 250)

3. $= b$ (Rule 1, p. 250)

If $b < 0$, q and n are both odd and there is only one root. If $b \geq 0$, then $\sqrt[q]{b}$, $\sqrt[n]{\sqrt[q]{b}}$, and $\sqrt[nq]{b}$ are all nonnegative.

62. 1. $[(\sqrt[n]{b})^m]^n = (\sqrt[n]{b})^{mn} = [(\sqrt[n]{b})^n]^m$; $((b^m)^n = b^{mn}$, Comm. prop. for mult.)

2. $[(\sqrt[n]{b})^n]^m = b^m$ (Rule 1, p. 250)

If n is odd, there is only one nth root of b^m. If n is even then $\sqrt[n]{b}$ is nonnegative and so is $(\sqrt[n]{b})^m$.

Page 257 · COMPUTER EXERCISES

1.
```
10   PRINT "ENTER N"
20   INPUT N
30   LET Z1 = INT(SQR(N + 1))
40   FOR Z = Z1 TO 2 STEP −1
50   LET Q = N/(Z * Z)
60   IF Q = INT(Q) THEN 100
70   NEXT Z
80   PRINT "SQR(";N;") ALREADY SIMPLIFIED"
90   GOTO 10
100 IF Q <> 1 THEN 130
110 PRINT "SQR(";N;") = "; Z
120 GOTO 10
130 IF Z <> 1 THEN 160
140 PRINT "SQR(";N;") = SQR(";Q;")"
150 GOTO 10
160 PRINT "SQR(";N;") = ";Z;" * SQR(";Q;")"
170 GOTO 10
```

2. a. SRQ(612) = 6 * SQR(17)
   b. SQR(4961) = 11 * SQR(41)
   c. SQR(11466) = 21 * SQR(26)
   d. SQR(574452) = 54 * SQR(197)

3. 10   PRINT "ENTER M,N"
   20   INPUT M,N
   30   LET Z1 = INT((N + 1) ↑ (1/M))
   40   FOR Z = Z1 TO 2 STEP −1
   42   LET T = Z
   43   FOR L = 2 TO M
   44   LET T = T * Z
   45   NEXT L
   50   LET Q = N/T
   60   IF Q = INT(Q) THEN 100
   70   NEXT Z
   80   PRINT M; "TH ROOT OF"; N; "ALREADY SIMPLIFIED"
   90   GOTO 10
   100 IF Q <> 1 THEN 130
   110 PRINT M; "TH ROOT OF"; N; " = "; Z
   120 GOTO 10
   130 IF Z <> 1 THEN 160
   140 PRINT M; "TH ROOT OF"; N; " = "; M; "TH ROOT OF"; Q
   150 GOTO 10
   160 PRINT M; "TH ROOT OF"; N; " = "; Z; " * ("; M; "TH ROOT OF"; Q; ")"
   170 GOTO 10

4. a. 3TH ROOT OF 3087 = 7 * (3TH ROOT OF 9)
   b. 5TH ROOT OF 93312 = 6 * (5TH ROOT OF 12)
   c. 4TH ROOT OF 50625 = 15
   d. 10TH ROOT OF 7168 = 2 * (10TH ROOT OF 7)

Page 257 · CALCULATOR KEY-IN

1. 0.01033	**2.** 4.784	**3.** 1.908×10^{10}
4. 5.300×10^7	**5.** 7.312×10^1	**6.** 1000
7. 7.80	**8.** 13.2	**9.** 1

Page 259 · WRITTEN EXERCISES

A   **1.** $5\sqrt{2} + 3\sqrt{2} - 2\sqrt{2} = 6\sqrt{2}$ **2.** $3\sqrt{5} - 2\sqrt{5} + 5\sqrt{5} = 6\sqrt{5}$

3. $3\sqrt{3} - 5\sqrt{3} + 4\sqrt{3} = 2\sqrt{3}$ **4.** $3\sqrt{2} + 2\sqrt{6} - 3\sqrt{6} = 3\sqrt{2} - \sqrt{6}$

5. $3\sqrt[3]{3} + 2\sqrt[3]{2} - 2\sqrt[3]{3} = \sqrt[3]{3} + 2\sqrt[3]{2}$ **6.** $3\sqrt[3]{2} - 2\sqrt[3]{3} + 4\sqrt[3]{5}$

7. $2\sqrt{7} - 14\sqrt{2} + 3\sqrt{7} = 5\sqrt{7} - 14\sqrt{2}$ **8.** $2\sqrt{6} + 5\sqrt{6} - 4\sqrt{6} = 3\sqrt{6}$

9. $\dfrac{\sqrt{6}}{3} + \dfrac{\sqrt{6}}{2} + \dfrac{\sqrt{6}}{6} = \sqrt{6}$ 　　　　　**10.** $\dfrac{\sqrt{10}}{2} + \dfrac{\sqrt{10}}{5} - \dfrac{2\sqrt{10}}{10} = \dfrac{\sqrt{10}}{2}$

11. $\sqrt[3]{4} + 3\sqrt[3]{4} = 4\sqrt[3]{4}$ 　　**12.** $2\sqrt[3]{3} - 2 \cdot \dfrac{2}{\sqrt[3]{9}} \cdot \dfrac{\sqrt[3]{3}}{\sqrt[3]{3}} = 2\sqrt[3]{3} - \dfrac{4}{3}\sqrt[3]{3} = \dfrac{2}{3}\sqrt[3]{3} = \dfrac{2\sqrt[3]{3}}{3}$

13. $\sqrt{45} + \sqrt{75} - \sqrt{27} = 3\sqrt{5} + 5\sqrt{3} - 3\sqrt{3} = 3\sqrt{5} + 2\sqrt{3}$

14. $2\sqrt{36} - \sqrt{24} = 12 - 2\sqrt{6}$ 　　　　**15.** $6\sqrt{3} + 12\sqrt{3} - 3\sqrt{3} = 15\sqrt{3}$

16. $\dfrac{\sqrt{12}}{\sqrt{3}} + \dfrac{2\sqrt{27}}{\sqrt{3}} = \sqrt{4} + 2\sqrt{9} = 2 + 6 = 8$ 　　　　**17.** $\sqrt{3} - \sqrt{9} = \sqrt{3} - 3$

18. $6\sqrt{50} - 2\sqrt{75} + 2\sqrt{200} + 3\sqrt{8} = 30\sqrt{2} - 10\sqrt{3} + 20\sqrt{2} + 6\sqrt{2} = 56\sqrt{2} - 10\sqrt{3}$

B 　**19.** $5 + \sqrt[3]{35}$ 　　　　　**20.** $\sqrt[3]{3} + \sqrt[3]{24} + \sqrt[3]{54} = \sqrt[3]{3} + 2\sqrt[3]{3} + 3\sqrt[3]{2} = 3\sqrt[3]{3} + 3\sqrt[3]{2}$

21. $|p|\sqrt{pr} + |r|\sqrt{pr} = \sqrt{pr}\,(|p| + |r|)$ 　　**22.** $|a|b^2\sqrt{2} + 2|a|b^2\sqrt{2} = 3|a|b^2\sqrt{2}$

23. $\dfrac{4}{9}\sqrt{3a} + \dfrac{2}{3}\sqrt{3a} - \dfrac{1}{3}\sqrt{3a} = \dfrac{7}{9}\sqrt{3a} = \dfrac{7\sqrt{3a}}{9}$

24. $\sqrt{6x} + \dfrac{1}{3}\sqrt{6x} - \dfrac{1}{2}\sqrt{6x} = \dfrac{5}{6}\sqrt{6x} = \dfrac{5\sqrt{6x}}{6}$

25. $x^2 = (\sqrt{2})^2 + 10^2;\; x^2 = 2 + 100 = 102;\; x = \sqrt{102}$

26. $x^2 + (2\sqrt{5})^2 = (5\sqrt{2})^2;\; x^2 + 20 = 50;\; x^2 = 30;\; x = \sqrt{30}$

27. $(AC)^2 = (2x)^2 + (6x)^2;\; (AC)^2 = 40x^2;\; AC = \sqrt{40x^2} = 2x\sqrt{10};$
　　　$(AE)^2 = (AC)^2 + (3x)^2 = 40x^2 + 9x^2 = 49x^2;\; AE = \sqrt{49x^2} = 7x$

Page 259 · CHALLENGE

If $a = 2$, $b = 3$, and $c = 6$, then $\dfrac{1}{a} + \dfrac{1}{b} + \dfrac{1}{c} = \dfrac{1}{2} + \dfrac{1}{3} + \dfrac{1}{6} = 1.$

Pages 261-262 · WRITTEN EXERCISES

A 　**1.** $\sqrt{12} + \sqrt{18} = 2\sqrt{3} + 3\sqrt{2}$ 　　　　　**2.** $\sqrt{147} + \sqrt{98} = 7\sqrt{3} + 7\sqrt{2}$

　　3. $4 + 4\sqrt{2}$ 　　　　**4.** $6\sqrt{6} + 12$ 　　　　**5.** $4 - 3 = 1$

　　6. $25 - 2 = 23$ 　　　　**7.** $7 - 11 = -4$ 　　　　**8.** $40 - 5 = 35$

　　9. $25 - 28 = -3$ 　　　**10.** $45 - 12 = 33$ 　　　**11.** $\dfrac{4}{4} = 1$

12. $\dfrac{54 - 12}{36} = \dfrac{42}{36} = \dfrac{7}{6}$ 　　**13.** $5 + 2\sqrt{5} + 1 = 6 + 2\sqrt{5}$ 　**14.** $3 - 4\sqrt{3} + 4 = 7 - 4\sqrt{3}$

15. $12 + 4\sqrt{3} + 1 = 13 + 4\sqrt{3}$ 　　　　**16.** $16 - 16\sqrt{5} + 20 = 36 - 16\sqrt{5}$

17. $(\sqrt{2} - \sqrt{8})^2 = (\sqrt{2} - 2\sqrt{2})^2 = (-\sqrt{2})^2 = 2$

18. $3 + 2\sqrt{18} + 6 = 9 + 2\sqrt{18} = 9 + 6\sqrt{2}$ 　**19.** $3 + 4\sqrt{2} + 2 = 5 + 4\sqrt{2}$

20. $24 + 2\sqrt{3} - 3 = 21 + 2\sqrt{3}$ 　　　　**21.** $6 + 5\sqrt{3} - 12 = -6 + 5\sqrt{3}$

22. $15 + 13\sqrt{2} + 4 = 19 + 13\sqrt{2}$

23. $\dfrac{1}{3 + \sqrt{7}} \cdot \dfrac{3 - \sqrt{7}}{3 - \sqrt{7}} = \dfrac{3 - \sqrt{7}}{2}$

24. $\dfrac{1}{2 + \sqrt{3}} \cdot \dfrac{2 - \sqrt{3}}{2 - \sqrt{3}} = 2 - \sqrt{3}$

25. $\dfrac{3}{\sqrt{5} - \sqrt{2}} \cdot \dfrac{\sqrt{5} + \sqrt{2}}{\sqrt{5} + \sqrt{2}} = \dfrac{3(\sqrt{5} + \sqrt{2})}{3} = \sqrt{5} + \sqrt{2}$

26. $\dfrac{10}{2\sqrt{3} - \sqrt{7}} \cdot \dfrac{2\sqrt{3} + \sqrt{7}}{2\sqrt{3} + \sqrt{7}} = \dfrac{10(2\sqrt{3} + \sqrt{7})}{5} = 4\sqrt{3} + 2\sqrt{7}$

27. $\dfrac{\sqrt{23} + 4}{\sqrt{23} - 4} \cdot \dfrac{\sqrt{23} + 4}{\sqrt{23} + 4} = \dfrac{23 + 8\sqrt{23} + 16}{23 - 16} = \dfrac{39 + 8\sqrt{23}}{7}$

28. $\dfrac{\sqrt{5} - \sqrt{3}}{3\sqrt{5} + 4\sqrt{3}} \cdot \dfrac{3\sqrt{5} - 4\sqrt{3}}{3\sqrt{5} - 4\sqrt{3}} = \dfrac{27 - 7\sqrt{15}}{-3} = \dfrac{-27 + 7\sqrt{15}}{3}$

B **29.** $f(2 + \sqrt{3}) = (2 + \sqrt{3}) + \dfrac{1}{2 + \sqrt{3}} \cdot \dfrac{2 - \sqrt{3}}{2 - \sqrt{3}} = 2 + \sqrt{3} + (2 - \sqrt{3}) = 4$

30. $g(2 + \sqrt{5}) = 2 + \sqrt{5} - \dfrac{1}{2 + \sqrt{5}} \cdot \dfrac{2 - \sqrt{5}}{2 - \sqrt{5}} = 2 + \sqrt{5} - \dfrac{2 - \sqrt{5}}{-1}$

$= 2 + \sqrt{5} + 2 - \sqrt{5} = 4$

31. $(3 + \sqrt{5})^2 - 6(3 + \sqrt{5}) + 4 = 14 + 6\sqrt{5} - 18 - 6\sqrt{5} + 4 = 0;$

$(3 - \sqrt{5})^2 - 6(3 - \sqrt{5}) + 4 = 14 - 6\sqrt{5} - 18 + 6\sqrt{5} + 4 = 0$

32. $1 \pm \dfrac{\sqrt{2}}{2} = \dfrac{2 \pm \sqrt{2}}{2}; 2\left(\dfrac{2 \pm \sqrt{2}}{2}\right)^2 - 4\left(\dfrac{2 \pm \sqrt{2}}{2}\right) + 1 = \dfrac{6 \pm 4\sqrt{2}}{2} - 2(2 \pm \sqrt{2}) + 1$

$= 3 \pm 2\sqrt{2} - 4 \pm 2\sqrt{2} + 1 = 0$

33. $(4 - \sqrt{2})^2 + (4 + \sqrt{2})^2 = x^2; (16 - 8\sqrt{2} + 2) + (16 + 8\sqrt{2} + 2) = x^2; x^2 = 36;$

$x = 6$

34. $x^2 + (3 - \sqrt{3})^2 = 9^2; x^2 = 81 - (3 - \sqrt{3})^2 = 81 - (12 - 6\sqrt{3}) = 69 + 6\sqrt{3};$

$x = \sqrt{69 + 6\sqrt{3}}$

35-36. Answers may vary.

35. Let $a = 8, b = 1$; then $\sqrt[3]{8} - \sqrt[3]{1} = 2 - 1 = 1; \sqrt[3]{8 - 1} = 7; 1 \neq 7$

36. Let $a = 4, b = 9$; then $\dfrac{1}{\sqrt{4}} + \dfrac{1}{\sqrt{9}} = \dfrac{1}{2} + \dfrac{1}{3} = \dfrac{5}{6}; \dfrac{\sqrt{4 + 9}}{\sqrt{4 \cdot 9}} = \dfrac{\sqrt{13}}{6}; \dfrac{5}{6} \neq \dfrac{\sqrt{13}}{6}$

37. $(\sqrt{n + 1})^2 - (\sqrt{n})^2 = n + 1 - n = 1$

38. $a + 2\sqrt{ab} + b - (a - 2\sqrt{ab} + b) = 4\sqrt{ab}$

39. $\dfrac{1}{\sqrt{x} - 4} \cdot \dfrac{\sqrt{x} + 4}{\sqrt{x} + 4} = \dfrac{\sqrt{x} + 4}{x - 16}$

40. $\dfrac{2}{\sqrt{x + 2} + \sqrt{x}} \cdot \dfrac{\sqrt{x + 2} - \sqrt{x}}{\sqrt{x + 2} - \sqrt{x}} = \dfrac{2(\sqrt{x + 2} - \sqrt{x})}{(x + 2) - x} = \sqrt{x + 2} - \sqrt{x}$

41. $\dfrac{\sqrt{n} - 3}{\sqrt{n} + 3} \cdot \dfrac{\sqrt{n} - 3}{\sqrt{n} - 3} + \dfrac{6\sqrt{n}}{n - 9} = \dfrac{n - 6\sqrt{n} + 9 + 6\sqrt{n}}{n - 9} = \dfrac{n + 9}{n - 9}$

42. $\sqrt{\dfrac{a^2 + b^2}{ab} \cdot \dfrac{ab}{ab} \cdot \dfrac{1}{\sqrt{ab}}} = \dfrac{1}{ab}\sqrt{\dfrac{ab(a^2 + b^2)}{ab}} = \dfrac{\sqrt{a^2 + b^2}}{ab}$

43. $\sqrt{1 - x^2} \cdot \dfrac{\sqrt{1 - x^2}}{\sqrt{1 - x^2}} + \dfrac{x^2}{\sqrt{1 - x^2}} = \dfrac{1 - x^2 + x^2}{\sqrt{1 - x^2}} = \dfrac{1}{\sqrt{1 - x^2}} \cdot \dfrac{\sqrt{1 - x^2}}{\sqrt{1 - x^2}} = \dfrac{\sqrt{1 - x^2}}{1 - x^2}$

44. $\dfrac{\sqrt{x}\,(\sqrt{x} - 1)}{(\sqrt{x} + 1)(\sqrt{x} - 1)} + \dfrac{\sqrt{x}\,(\sqrt{x} + 1)}{(\sqrt{x} - 1)(\sqrt{x} + 1)} = \dfrac{x - \sqrt{x} + x + \sqrt{x}}{x - 1} = \dfrac{2x}{x - 1}$

C 45. $\sqrt{(12 - 2\sqrt{11})(12 + 2\sqrt{11})} = \sqrt{144 - 44} = \sqrt{100} = 10$

46. $\dfrac{1}{(\sqrt{2} + \sqrt{3}) + \sqrt{5}} \cdot \dfrac{(\sqrt{2} + \sqrt{3}) - \sqrt{5}}{(\sqrt{2} + \sqrt{3}) - \sqrt{5}} = \dfrac{\sqrt{2} + \sqrt{3} - \sqrt{5}}{(\sqrt{2} + \sqrt{3})^2 - (\sqrt{5})^2} = \dfrac{\sqrt{2} + \sqrt{3} - \sqrt{5}}{5 + 2\sqrt{6} - 5}$

$= \dfrac{\sqrt{2} + \sqrt{3} - \sqrt{5}}{2\sqrt{6}} \cdot \dfrac{\sqrt{6}}{\sqrt{6}} = \dfrac{\sqrt{12} + \sqrt{18} - \sqrt{30}}{12} = \dfrac{2\sqrt{3} + 3\sqrt{2} - \sqrt{30}}{12}$

47. $(a + \sqrt{b})^3 + (a - \sqrt{b})^3 = a^3 + 3a^2\sqrt{b} + 3ab + b\sqrt{b} + a^3 - 3a^2\sqrt{b} + 3ab - b\sqrt{b}$
$= 2a^3 + 6ab$, which is rational if a and b are rational.

Page 262 · CALCULATOR KEY-IN

1. a. 1.710   **b.** 4.642   **2.** 2.100

Pages 265-266 · WRITTEN EXERCISES

A 1. $x - 2 = 36;\ x = 38$ **2.** $3x + 1 = 16;\ 3x = 15;\ x = 5$

3. $2t = 4^3;\ t = \dfrac{64}{2} = 32$ **4.** $3y - 7 = 2^3;\ 3y = 15;\ y = 5$

5. $\sqrt[4]{2n} = -1;\ 2n = (-1)^4;\ n = \dfrac{1}{2};$ but $\sqrt[4]{2 \cdot \dfrac{1}{2}} = 1 \neq -1;$ no real solution

6. $4x^2 = 36;\ x^2 = 9;\ x = \pm 3$ **7.** $5x^2 - 4 = 16;\ 5x^2 = 20;\ x^2 = 4;\ x = \pm 2$

8. $2y^2 - 9 = y^2;\ y^2 = 9;\ y = \pm 3;\ y = 3$ **9.** $4x^{-1} = 2^3;\ \dfrac{4}{x} = 8;\ x = \dfrac{1}{2}$

10. $(2x)^{-2} = \left(\dfrac{1}{2}\right)^4;\ \dfrac{1}{(2x)^2} = \dfrac{1}{16};\ 4x^2 = 16;\ x^2 = 4;\ x = \pm 2$

11. $3x = 1 - x;\ 4x = 1;\ x = \dfrac{1}{4}$

12. $\dfrac{x}{3} = \dfrac{2x + 1}{4};\ 4x = 6x + 3;\ 2x = -3;\ x = -\dfrac{2}{3};$ no real solution

13. a. $4x = 25;\ x = \dfrac{25}{4}$ **b.** $x = \dfrac{5}{\sqrt{2}} = \dfrac{5\sqrt{2}}{2}$

14. a. $9x = 144;\ x = 16$ **b.** $x = \dfrac{12}{\sqrt{3}} = \dfrac{12\sqrt{3}}{3} = 4\sqrt{3}$

15. a. $2\sqrt{x} = 2;\ 4x = 4;\ x = 1$ **b.** $x\sqrt{2} = 2;\ x = \dfrac{2}{\sqrt{2}} = \dfrac{2\sqrt{2}}{2} = \sqrt{2}$

16. a. $x(3 - \sqrt{3}) = 6$; $x = \dfrac{6}{3 - \sqrt{3}} \cdot \dfrac{3 + \sqrt{3}}{3 + \sqrt{3}} = \dfrac{6(3 + \sqrt{3})}{6} = 3 + \sqrt{3}$

   b. $x - 6 = \sqrt{x}$; $x^2 - 12x + 36 = x$; $x^2 - 13x + 36 = 0$; $(x - 9)(x - 4) = 0$; $x = 9$
   (reject) or $x = 4$; $x = 4$

17. a. $x - 3 = 2\sqrt{x}$; $x^2 - 6x + 9 = 4x$; $x^2 - 10x + 9 = 0$; $(x - 9)(x - 1) = 0$; $x = 1$
   (reject) or $x = 9$; $x = 9$

   b. $x(1 - \sqrt{2}) = 3$; $x = \dfrac{3}{1 - \sqrt{2}} \cdot \dfrac{1 + \sqrt{2}}{1 + \sqrt{2}} = \dfrac{3 + 3\sqrt{2}}{1 - 2} = -3 - 3\sqrt{2}$

18. a. $2x + 2 = 5\sqrt{x}$; $4x^2 + 8x + 4 = 25x$; $4x^2 - 17x + 4 = 0$; $(4x - 1)(x - 4) = 0$;
   $x = \dfrac{1}{4}$ or $x = 4$

   b. $2x - x\sqrt{5} = -2$; $x(2 - \sqrt{5}) = -2$; $x = \dfrac{-2}{2 - \sqrt{5}} \cdot \dfrac{2 + \sqrt{5}}{2 + \sqrt{5}} = \dfrac{-2(2 + \sqrt{5})}{-1}$
   $= 2(2 + \sqrt{5}) = 4 + 2\sqrt{5}$

19. $x + 2 = x^2$; $x^2 - x - 2 = 0$; $(x - 2)(x + 1) = 0$; $x = -1$ (reject) or $x = 2$; $x = 2$

20. $n^2 - 5n + 4 = 0$; $(n - 4)(n - 1) = 0$; $n = 4$ or $n = 1$

21. $t - 2 = (4 - t)^2 = 16 - 8t + t^2$; $t^2 - 9t + 18 = 0$; $(t - 6)(t - 3) = 0$; $t = 6$ (reject)
   or $t = 3$; $t = 3$

22. $a - 5 = a^2 - 14a + 49$; $a^2 - 15a + 54 = 0$; $(a - 6)(a - 9) = 0$; $a = 6$ (reject) or
   $a = 9$; $a = 9$

23. $2x + 5 = x^2 + 2x + 1$; $x^2 = 4$; $x = -2$ (reject) or $x = 2$; $x = 2$

24. $n - 2 = 16 - 8n + n^2$; $n^2 - 9n + 18 = 0$; $(n - 6)(n - 3) = 0$; $n = 3$ (reject) or
   $n = 6$; $n = 6$

B 25. $a^2 + a + 4 = 16$; $a^2 + a - 12 = 0$; $(a + 4)(a - 3) = 0$; $a = -4$ or $a = 3$

26. $\dfrac{x^2}{81} = \dfrac{x - 4}{2}$; $2x^2 - 81x + 324 = 0$; $(2x - 9)(x - 36) = 0$; $x = 36$ or $x = 4\dfrac{1}{2}$

27. $64x^2 - x^5 = 0$; $x^2(64 - x^3) = 0$; $x = 0$ or $x = 4$

28. $\sqrt{y} + \sqrt{y + 5} = 5$; $y + 2\sqrt{y} \cdot \sqrt{y + 5} + y + 5 = 25$; $2\sqrt{y(y + 5)} = 20 - 2y$;
   $\sqrt{y^2 + 5y} = 10 - y$; $y^2 + 5y = 100 - 20y + y^2$; $25y = 100$; $y = 4$

29. $x + 4 + 2\sqrt{x^2 + 4x} + x = 9$; $2\sqrt{x^2 + 4x} = 5 - 2x$; $4x^2 + 16x = 25 - 20x + 4x^2$;
   $36x = 25$; $x = \dfrac{25}{36}$

30. $x - 3 + 2\sqrt{x^2 - 3x} + x = 1$; $\sqrt{x^2 - 3x} = 2 - x$; $x^2 - 3x = 4 - 4x + x^2$; no real
   solution

31. $3a - 2 - 2\sqrt{(3a - 2)(2a - 3)} + 2a - 3 = 1$; $5a - 6 = 2\sqrt{6a^2 - 13a + 6}$;
   $25a^2 - 60a + 36 = 24a^2 - 52a + 24$; $a^2 - 8a + 12 = 0$; $(a - 6)(a - 2) = 0$; $a = 6$
   or $a = 2$

32. $3b - 2 - 2\sqrt{6b^2 + 11b - 10} + 2b + 5 = 1$; $(5b + 2)^2 = 4(6b^2 + 11b - 10)$;
$25b^2 + 20b + 4 = 24b^2 + 44b - 40$; $b^2 - 24b + 44 = 0$; $(b - 2)(b - 22) = 0$; $b = 2$
(reject) or $b = 22$; $b = 22$

33. $\sqrt{3y + 3} = 2 + \sqrt{y + 5}$; $3y + 3 = 4 + 4\sqrt{y + 5} + y + 5$; $2y - 6 = 4\sqrt{y + 5}$;
$y - 3 = 2\sqrt{y + 5}$; $y^2 - 6y + 9 = 4y + 20$; $y^2 - 10y - 11 = 0$; $(y - 11)(y + 1)$
$= 0$; $y = -1$ (reject) or $y = 11$; $y = 11$

34. $x^2 + 2x\sqrt{2} + 2 = x + 2$; $x^2 + (2\sqrt{2} - 1)x = 0$; $x[x + (2\sqrt{2} - 1)] = 0$; $x = 0$ or
$x = 1 - 2\sqrt{2}$ (reject); $x = 0$

35. $n + 6 - 2\sqrt{n^2 + 6n} + n = 6$; $2n = 2\sqrt{n^2 + 6n}$; $n = \sqrt{n^2 + 6n}$; $n^2 = n^2 + 6n$;
$6n = 0$; $n = 0$

36. a. $x + x + x\sqrt{2} = 2x + x\sqrt{2} = 10$; $x(2 + \sqrt{2}) = 10$; $x = \dfrac{10}{2 + \sqrt{2}} = \dfrac{10(2 - \sqrt{2})}{2}$
$= 10 - 5\sqrt{2}$

b. $\dfrac{1}{2}x^2 = 12$; $x^2 = 24$; $x = 2\sqrt{6}$

37. $x + x + x\sqrt{2} = 4$; $x(2 + \sqrt{2}) = 4$; $x = \dfrac{4}{2 + \sqrt{2}} = \dfrac{4(2 - \sqrt{2})}{2} = 4 - 2\sqrt{2}$

38. $r^2 = \dfrac{km}{F}$; $F = \dfrac{km}{r^2}$ **39.** $s^2 = \dfrac{1}{1 - t^2}$; $1 - t^2 = \dfrac{1}{s^2}$; $t = \pm\sqrt{1 - \dfrac{1}{s^2}} = \pm\dfrac{\sqrt{s^2 - 1}}{|s|}$

40. $V^2 = V_0^2 + 2uS$; $S = \dfrac{V^2 - V_0^2}{2u}$ **41.** $T^2 = 4\pi^2\dfrac{l}{g}$; $l = \dfrac{T^2g}{4\pi^2}$

42. a. Let the length of each leg $= y$; $y^2 = 10^2 + x^2 = 100 + x^2$; $y = \sqrt{100 + x^2}$.
b. $2y + 20 = 3x$; $2\sqrt{100 + x^2} = 3x - 20$; $400 + 4x^2 = 9x^2 - 120x + 400$;
$5x(x - 24) = 0$; $x = 0$ (reject) or $x = 24$; $x = 24$; 24 cm

C **43.** $\sqrt{(x + 1)^2 - x^2} + \sqrt{(x + 3)^2 - x^2} = 14$; $\sqrt{6x + 9} = 14 - \sqrt{2x + 1}$; $6x + 9$
$= 196 - 28\sqrt{2x + 1} + 2x + 1$; $x - 47 = -7\sqrt{2x + 1}$; $x^2 - 94x + (47)^2$
$= 49(2x + 1)$; $x^2 - 192x + 2160 = 0$; $(x - 12)(x - 180) = 0$; $x = 12$ or $x = 180$
(reject); $x = 12$

44. a. $V = \dfrac{1}{3}Bh = \dfrac{1}{3}(x^2)h$; $AC = x\sqrt{2}$; let F be the foot of the altitude and G be the
midpoint of $\overline{BC}$; $(EG)^2 = (EC)^2 - (GC)^2 = x^2 - \left(\dfrac{x}{2}\right)^2 = \dfrac{3x^2}{4}$; $h^2 = (EG)^2 - (FG)^2$
$= \dfrac{3x^2}{4} - \left(\dfrac{x}{2}\right)^2 = \dfrac{x^2}{2}$; $h = \dfrac{x}{\sqrt{2}} = \dfrac{x\sqrt{2}}{2}$; $V = \dfrac{1}{3} \cdot x^2 \cdot \dfrac{x\sqrt{2}}{2} = \dfrac{x^3\sqrt{2}}{6}$

b. $\dfrac{x^3\sqrt{2}}{6} = 9$; $x^3\sqrt{2} = 54$; $x^3 = \dfrac{54}{\sqrt{2}} \cdot \dfrac{\sqrt{2}}{\sqrt{2}} = 27\sqrt{2}$; $x = \sqrt[3]{27\sqrt{2}} = 3\sqrt[6]{2}$

Page 267 · CHALLENGE

The program finds and prints the quotient and remainder when any positive integer x is
divided by 17; 123.

Pages 271-273 · WRITTEN EXERCISES

1. **a.** rational **b.** irrational 2. **a.** rational **b.** rational 3. **a.** irrational **b.** irrational

4. **a.** $\dfrac{\sqrt{2}}{2} + \dfrac{\sqrt{2}}{4} = \dfrac{3\sqrt{2}}{4}$; irrational   **b.** $\sqrt{\dfrac{1}{2}} \cdot \sqrt{\dfrac{1}{8}} = \sqrt{\dfrac{1}{16}} = \dfrac{1}{4}$; rational

5. **a.** rational   **b.** irrational   6. **a.** rational   **b.** irrational

7. 0.625 8. $0.\overline{45}$ 9. $-1.\overline{571428}$

10. 31.75 11. $\dfrac{472}{100} = \dfrac{118}{25}$ 12. $\dfrac{1375}{10{,}000} = \dfrac{11}{80}$

13. $18.271 = \dfrac{18{,}271}{1000}$ 14. $0.014 = \dfrac{7}{500}$ 15. $\dfrac{2}{9}$

16. $N = 0.8\overline{3};\ 10N = 8.\overline{3};\ 9N = 7.5;\ N = \dfrac{7.5}{9} = \dfrac{75}{90} = \dfrac{5}{6}$

17. $N = 0.\overline{36};\ 100N = 36.\overline{36};\ 99N = 36;\ N = \dfrac{4}{11}$

18. $N = 1.\overline{27};\ 100N = 127.\overline{27};\ 99N = 126;\ N = \dfrac{14}{11}$

19. $N = 3.1\overline{81};\ 100N = 318.\overline{18};\ 99N = 315;\ N = \dfrac{35}{11}$

20. $N = 0.\overline{123};\ 1000N = 123.\overline{123};\ 999N = 123;\ N = \dfrac{41}{333}$

21. $N = 3.\overline{033};\ 1000N = 3033.\overline{033};\ 999N = 3030;\ N = \dfrac{1010}{333}$

22. $N = 0.\overline{1001};\ 10{,}000N = 1001.\overline{1001};\ 9999N = 1001;\ N = \dfrac{1001}{9999}$

23. Yes. If $x = \dfrac{a}{b}$ and $y = \dfrac{c}{d}$ (a, b, c, and d are integers), then $\dfrac{x+y}{2} = \dfrac{ad+bc}{2bd}$; $ad + bc$ and $2bd$ are integers, so $\dfrac{x+y}{2}$ is a quotient of 2 integers.

24. **a.** Answers will vary. For example, $x = 1 + \sqrt{2}$, $y = 1 - \sqrt{2}$; $\dfrac{x+y}{2} = 1$.

    b. Answers will vary. For example, $a = \sqrt{2}$, $b = \sqrt{3}$; $\dfrac{a+b}{2} = \dfrac{\sqrt{2}+\sqrt{3}}{2}$.

25. **a.** infinitely many   **b.** Answers will vary; e.g., 0.000015

26. **a.** (1), (4)   **b.** infinitely many   **c.** infinitely many

27-34. Answers may vary; examples are given.

27. **a.** 0.15 **b.** $\dfrac{\sqrt{2}}{10}$ 28. **a.** 0.00515 **b.** $0.515115111\ldots$

29. a. $\sqrt{5\frac{4}{9}} = \sqrt{\frac{49}{9}} = \frac{7}{3}$ **b.** $\sqrt{5\frac{1}{2}} = \frac{\sqrt{22}}{2}$ **30. a.** 3.1   **b.** $\frac{3 + \pi}{2}$

31. a. 0.0000001   **b.** 0.000000121221222...   **32. a.** $\frac{7}{9.5} = \frac{14}{19}$ **b.** 0.717117111..

33. a. $3\frac{2}{13}$ **b.** $\pi + 0.002$ **34. a.** 0.45   **b.** 0.454454445..

35. a. There can be no more than 16.   **b.** $0.\overline{0588235294117647}$

B   **36.** Any fraction with numerator 1 and denominator a number whose only prime factors ar

2 or 5. For example: $\frac{1}{16}, \frac{1}{32}, \frac{1}{10}, \frac{1}{50}$.

37. $x + y = \frac{a}{b} + \frac{c}{d} = \frac{ad + bc}{bd}$; $ad + bc$ and bd are integers, so $x + y$ is rational.

38. a. $xy = \frac{a}{b} \cdot \frac{c}{d} = \frac{ac}{bd}$. Since ac and bd are integers, xy is rational.

    b. The product may be either rational or irrational.

C   **39.** Suppose $x + z$ is rational. Then $x + z = \frac{c}{d}$, where c and d are integers. Let $x = \frac{a}{b}$

where a and b are integers. Then $\frac{a}{b} + z = \frac{c}{d}$; $z = \frac{c}{d} - \frac{a}{b} = \frac{bc - ad}{bd}$, which is r

tional. This contradicts the hypothesis, which states that z is irrational. Thus, $x +$

cannot be rational, so $x + z$ must be irrational.

40. If x is rational ($x \neq 0$) and z is irrational, then xz is irrational. Proof: Suppose xz wer

rational. Then $xz = \frac{c}{d}$ and $x = \frac{a}{b}$ (a, b, c, and d are integers) and $\frac{a}{b} \cdot z = \frac{c}{d}$. Thu

$z = \frac{bc}{ad}$, which is rational. This contradicts the hypothesis; therefore, xz must b

irrational.

Page 273 · CHALLENGE

Place 1 at any point and then place the integers 2 through 10 alternately to one side an

the other.

Page 276 · WRITTEN EXERCISES

A   **1.** $4i$ **2.** $7i$ **3.** $10i$

    4. $6i$ **5.** $-3i$ **6.** $6i\sqrt{2}$

    7. $10i\sqrt{3}$ **8.** $3i\sqrt{5}$ **9.** -4

  10. -9 **11.** -16 **12.** -6

  13. -15 **14.** -14 **15.** -4

  16. -12 **17.** $-\frac{3}{i} \cdot \frac{i}{i} = 3i$

18. $\dfrac{8}{i\sqrt{2}} \cdot \dfrac{i\sqrt{2}}{i\sqrt{2}} = \dfrac{8i\sqrt{2}}{-2} = -4i\sqrt{2}$ **19.** $\dfrac{20}{i\sqrt{5}} \cdot \dfrac{i\sqrt{5}}{i\sqrt{5}} = \dfrac{20i\sqrt{5}}{-5} = -4i\sqrt{5}$

20. $\dfrac{10}{i\sqrt{2}} \cdot \dfrac{i\sqrt{2}}{i\sqrt{2}} = \dfrac{10i\sqrt{2}}{-2} = -5i\sqrt{2}$

21. $i^2 = -1$; $i^3 = -i$; $i^4 = 1$; $i^5 = i$; $i^6 = -1$; $i^7 = -i$; $i^8 = 1$; $i^9 = i$; $i^{10} = -1$; $i^{11} = -i$; $i^{12} = 1$. If $n = 4k + r$ (k and r are integers), then $i^n = i^r$.

22. a. $i^{20} = i^4 = 1$ **b.** $i^{21} = i$ **c.** $i^{100} = i^4 = 1$ **d.** $i^{150} = i^2 = -1$

23. a. $4i + 2i = 6i$ **b.** $4i \cdot 2i = -8$

24. a. $i\sqrt{3} + 3i\sqrt{3} = 4i\sqrt{3}$ **b.** $i\sqrt{3} \cdot 3i\sqrt{3} = -9$

25. a. $i\sqrt{2} + 5i\sqrt{2} = 6i\sqrt{2}$ **b.** $i\sqrt{2} \cdot 5i\sqrt{2} = -10$

26. a. $10i\sqrt{3} - 5i\sqrt{5} = (10\sqrt{3} - 5\sqrt{5})i$ **b.** $(10i\sqrt{3})(-5i\sqrt{5}) = 50\sqrt{15}$

27. a. $3i\sqrt{2} + 2i\sqrt{2} = 5i\sqrt{2}$ **b.** $3i\sqrt{2} \cdot 2i\sqrt{2} = -12$

28. a. $8i^2\sqrt{2} - 8\sqrt{2} = -8\sqrt{2} - 8\sqrt{2} = -16\sqrt{2}$ **b.** $(8i^2\sqrt{2})(-8\sqrt{2}) = 128$

29. $x = \pm 11i$ **30.** $x = \pm 20i$ **31.** $x = \pm i\sqrt{6}$

32. $x = \pm 4i$ **33.** $x^2 = -\dfrac{1}{4}$; $x = \pm i\sqrt{\dfrac{1}{4}} = \pm\dfrac{1}{2}i$

34. $x^2 = -\dfrac{16}{9}$; $x = \pm i\sqrt{\dfrac{16}{9}} = \pm\dfrac{4}{3}i$

35. $3i\sqrt{a} \cdot 2i\sqrt{a} = -6a$ **36.** $(3\sqrt{2c})(ic\sqrt{2c}) = 6c^2 i$

37. $i\sqrt{\dfrac{r}{5}} \cdot i\sqrt{\dfrac{20}{r}} = i^2\sqrt{4} = -2$ **38.** $i\sqrt{\dfrac{a^5}{b}} \cdot i\sqrt{\dfrac{b}{a^3}} = i^2\sqrt{a^2} = ai^2 = -a$

39. $3ci + 7ci - 2ci = 8ci$ **40.** $t^2 i\sqrt{2t} + 2t^2 i\sqrt{2t} - 3t^2 i\sqrt{2t} = 0$

41. $ri\sqrt{r} + 2ri\sqrt{r} - 3ri\sqrt{r} = 0$ **42.** $5ai\sqrt{a} - 15ai\sqrt{a} + 20ai\sqrt{a} = 10ai\sqrt{a}$

43. $\dfrac{1}{i} \cdot \dfrac{i}{i} - \dfrac{i}{2} + \dfrac{3}{2i} \cdot \dfrac{i}{i} = -i - \dfrac{i}{2} - \dfrac{3i}{2} = -3i$

44. $\dfrac{\sqrt{3}}{i} \cdot \dfrac{i}{i} + \dfrac{i}{\sqrt{3}} \cdot \dfrac{\sqrt{3}}{\sqrt{3}} - \dfrac{\sqrt{3}}{3i} \cdot \dfrac{i}{i} = -i\sqrt{3} + \dfrac{i\sqrt{3}}{3} + \dfrac{i\sqrt{3}}{3} = -\dfrac{i\sqrt{3}}{3}$

45. $x^2 i\sqrt{x} + 5x^2 i\sqrt{x} - 5x^2 i\sqrt{x} = x^2 i\sqrt{x}$

46. $2t^2 i^2 + 2t^2 - 3t^2 i^2 = -2t^2 + 2t^2 + 3t^2 = 3t^2$

Pages 280-281 · WRITTEN EXERCISES

A   **1.** $9 + i$ **2.** $-2 - 6i$ **3.** $-3 - 9i$

     4. $10 - 5i$ **5.** $17 + 3i$ **6.** -8

     7. $-4 + 3i$ **8.** $6 + 18i$ **9.** $-6 - 16i$

     10. $-6 - 2i$ **11.** 2 **12.** 17

13. 29

14. 7

15. $20 - 12i + 5i - 3i^2 = 23 - 7i$

16. $6 + 12i - 14i - 28i^2 = 34 - 2i$

17. $-2 - 6i + 5i + 15i^2 = -17 - i$

18. $-6 - 3i + 12i + 6i^2 = -12 + 9i$

19. $18i^2 + 12i - 12i - 8 = -26$

20. $-10 + 15i + 6i - 9i^2 = -1 + 21i$

21. $4 - 16i + 16i^2 = -12 - 16i$

22. $16 - 40i + 25i^2 = -9 - 40i$

23. $1 + 2i\sqrt{6} + 6i^2 = -5 + 2i\sqrt{6}$

24. $9 + 6i\sqrt{5} + 5i^2 = 4 + 6i\sqrt{5}$

25. $(1 + i)^2(1 + i) = 2i(1 + i) = 2i + 2i^2 = -2 + 2i$

26. $(-2 + 2i)^4 = [(-2 + 2i)^2]^2 = [(4 - 8i + 4i^2)]^2 = (-8i)^2 = 64i^2 = -64$

27. $[(3 + 2i)(3 - 2i)]^2 = (13)^2 = 169$

28. $[(2 - i)(2 + i)]^3 = 5^3 = 125$

29. $(\sqrt{2} - i\sqrt{5})(\sqrt{2} + i\sqrt{5}) = 2 - 5i^2 = 7$

30. $(\sqrt{7} - i\sqrt{6})(\sqrt{7} + i\sqrt{6}) = 7 - 6i^2 = 13$

31. $5x = 3y, -2y = -3x - 1; x = \dfrac{3}{5}y, -2y = -\dfrac{9}{5}y - 1; 10y = 9y + 1; y = 5, x =$

32. $2x + y = 5, 3y = -x; x = -3y; 2(-3y) + y = 5; -5y = 5; y = -1, x = 3$

33. $\dfrac{5}{3 + 4i} \cdot \dfrac{3 - 4i}{3 - 4i} = \dfrac{5(3 - 4i)}{25} = \dfrac{3}{5} - \dfrac{4}{5}i$ **34.** $\dfrac{10}{2 + i} \cdot \dfrac{2 - i}{2 - i} = \dfrac{20 - 10i}{5} = 4 - 2i$

35. $\dfrac{2}{3 - i} \cdot \dfrac{3 + i}{3 + i} = \dfrac{6 + 2i}{10} = \dfrac{3}{5} + \dfrac{1}{5}i$

36. $\dfrac{5i}{6 - 2i} \cdot \dfrac{6 + 2i}{6 + 2i} = \dfrac{-10 + 30i}{40} = -\dfrac{1}{4} + \dfrac{3}{4}i$ **37.** $\dfrac{7}{i} \cdot \dfrac{i}{i} = -7i$

38. $\dfrac{8}{-2i} \cdot \dfrac{i}{i} = \dfrac{8i}{2} = 4i$ **39.** $\dfrac{7 + i}{3 - 4i} \cdot \dfrac{3 + 4i}{3 + 4i} = \dfrac{17 + 31i}{25} = \dfrac{17}{25} + \dfrac{31}{25}i$

40. $\dfrac{5 + i}{5 - i} \cdot \dfrac{5 + i}{5 + i} = \dfrac{24 + 10i}{26} = \dfrac{12}{13} + \dfrac{5}{13}i$

41. $\dfrac{6 - i\sqrt{2}}{6 + i\sqrt{2}} \cdot \dfrac{6 - i\sqrt{2}}{6 - i\sqrt{2}} = \dfrac{34 - 12i\sqrt{2}}{38} = \dfrac{17}{19} - \dfrac{6\sqrt{2}}{19}i$

42. $\dfrac{-3 + i\sqrt{5}}{-3 - i\sqrt{5}} \cdot \dfrac{-3 + i\sqrt{5}}{-3 + i\sqrt{5}} = \dfrac{4 - 6i\sqrt{5}}{14} = \dfrac{2}{7} - \dfrac{3\sqrt{5}}{7}i$

B **43.** $(2 + i)^2 - 4(2 + i) + 5 = 4 + 4i + i^2 - 8 - 4i + 5 = 4 - 1 - 8 + 5 = 0$

44. $2\left(\dfrac{1 - i}{2}\right)^2 - 2\left(\dfrac{1 - i}{2}\right) + 1 = -i - (1 - i) + 1 = -i - 1 + i + 1 = 0$

45. $f(1 + 3i) = 1 + 3i + \dfrac{1}{1 + 3i} \cdot \dfrac{1 - 3i}{1 - 3i} = 1 + 3i + \dfrac{1 - 3i}{10} = \dfrac{11}{10} + \dfrac{27i}{10}$

46. $f(2 + i) = \dfrac{(2 + i)^2 - 1}{2 + i} = \dfrac{2 + 4i}{2 + i} \cdot \dfrac{2 - i}{2 - i} = \dfrac{8 + 6i}{5} = \dfrac{8}{5} + \dfrac{6}{5}i$

47. $f(1 + i\sqrt{3}) = 1 + i\sqrt{3} + \dfrac{4}{1 + i\sqrt{3}} \cdot \dfrac{1 - i\sqrt{3}}{1 - i\sqrt{3}} = 1 + i\sqrt{3} + \dfrac{4(1 - i\sqrt{3})}{4}$

$= 1 + i\sqrt{3} + (1 - i\sqrt{3}) = 2$

48. $f(1 - i) = \dfrac{2 + 1 - i}{2 - (1 - i)} = \dfrac{3 - i}{1 + i} \cdot \dfrac{1 - i}{1 - i} = \dfrac{3 - 4i + i^2}{1 - i^2} = \dfrac{2 - 4i}{2} = 1 - 2i$

49. $\dfrac{5}{2 + 6i} \cdot \dfrac{2 - 6i}{2 - 6i} = \dfrac{10 - 30i}{40} = \dfrac{1}{4} - \dfrac{3}{4}i$

50. $\left(\dfrac{1}{2} + i\dfrac{\sqrt{3}}{2}\right)\left(\dfrac{1}{2} - i\dfrac{\sqrt{3}}{2}\right) = \dfrac{1}{4} - i^2\left(\dfrac{3}{4}\right) = \dfrac{1}{4} + \dfrac{3}{4} = 1$

51. Answers may vary. $-\dfrac{1}{2} + i\dfrac{\sqrt{3}}{2}$ and $-\dfrac{1}{2} - i\dfrac{\sqrt{3}}{2}$

52. a. $\left(\dfrac{\sqrt{2}}{2} + \dfrac{i\sqrt{2}}{2}\right)^2 = \dfrac{1}{2} + i + \dfrac{i^2}{2} = \dfrac{1}{2} + i - \dfrac{1}{2} = i$ **b.** $\dfrac{\sqrt{2}}{2} + \dfrac{i\sqrt{2}}{2}$

c. $-\left(\dfrac{\sqrt{2}}{2} + \dfrac{i\sqrt{2}}{2}\right) = -\dfrac{\sqrt{2}}{2} - \dfrac{i\sqrt{2}}{2}$

53. a. $(-1 + i\sqrt{3})^3 = (-1 + i\sqrt{3})^2(-1 + i\sqrt{3}) = (-2 - 2i\sqrt{3})(-1 + i\sqrt{3})$

$= 2 - 2i\sqrt{3} + 2i\sqrt{3} - 6i^2 = 8$ **b.** $(-1 + i\sqrt{3})^3 = 8$

c. $(-1 - i\sqrt{3})^3 = (-1 - i\sqrt{3})^2(-1 - i\sqrt{3}) = (-2 + 2i\sqrt{3})(-1 - i\sqrt{3})$

$= 2 + 2i\sqrt{3} - 2i\sqrt{3} + 6 = 8$; yes

Page 283 · EXTRA

1. 3 **2.** 5 **3.** 13

4. 13 **5.** $\sqrt{2}$ **6.** 2

7. 1 **8.** $\dfrac{\sqrt{3}}{2}$ **9. a.** 10 **b.** 8 **10 a.** 4 **b.** 2

11. Let $z = u + vi$; $\bar{z} = u - vi$; $|\bar{z}| = \sqrt{u^2 + (-v)^2} = \sqrt{u^2 + v^2}$; $|z| = \sqrt{u^2 + v^2}$

12. Let $z = u + vi$; $z + \bar{z} = (u + vi) + (u - vi) = 2u$

13. a. Let $z = u + vi$; $z - \bar{z} = (u + vi) - (u - vi) = 2vi$; $v = \dfrac{z - \bar{z}}{2i} \cdot \dfrac{i}{i} = \dfrac{(z - \bar{z})i}{-2}$

$= \dfrac{(\bar{z} - z)i}{2}$

b. Let $z = u + vi$. If $z = \bar{z}$, then $u + vi = u - vi$; $v = 0$. If $v = 0$, then

$z = u + 0 = u$ and $\bar{z} = u - 0 = u$; $z = \bar{z}$.

14. Let $w = u + vi$ and $z = x + yi$; $\overline{w + z} = \overline{(u + x) + (v + y)i} = (u + x) - (v + y)i$;

$\bar{w} + \bar{z} = (u - vi) + (x - yi) = (u + x) + (-v - y)i = (u + x) - (v + y)i$

15. $\overline{w - z} = \overline{(u + vi) - (x + yi)} = \overline{(u - x) + (v - y)i} = (u - x) + (y - v)i$;

$\bar{w} - \bar{z} = (u - vi) - (x - yi) = (u - x) + (-v + y)i = (u - x) + (y - v)i$

16. Let $z = u + vi$; $\left(\dfrac{1}{z}\right) = \left(\dfrac{1}{u + vi} \cdot \dfrac{u - vi}{u - vi}\right) = \left(\dfrac{u - vi}{u^2 + v^2}\right) = \dfrac{u}{u^2 + v^2} + \dfrac{v}{u^2 + v^2}i$;

$\dfrac{1}{\overline{z}} = \dfrac{1}{u - vi} \cdot \dfrac{u + vi}{u + vi} = \dfrac{u + vi}{u^2 + v^2} = \dfrac{u}{u^2 + v^2} + \dfrac{v}{u^2 + v^2}i$

17. $\left(\overline{\dfrac{w}{z}}\right) = \left(\overline{w \cdot \dfrac{1}{z}}\right) = \overline{w} \cdot \left(\overline{\dfrac{1}{z}}\right) = \overline{w} \cdot \dfrac{1}{\overline{z}} = \dfrac{\overline{w}}{\overline{z}}$

18. $\left|\dfrac{w}{z}\right|^2 = \dfrac{w}{z}\left(\overline{\dfrac{w}{z}}\right) = \dfrac{w}{z} \cdot \dfrac{\overline{w}}{\overline{z}} = \dfrac{|w|^2}{|z|^2} \cdot \left|\dfrac{w}{z}\right| = \dfrac{|w|}{|z|}$

19. $w\overline{z} + \overline{w}z = w\overline{z} + \overline{w\overline{z}}$ = twice the real part of $w\overline{z}$ (see Exercise 12). Let $w\overline{z} = u + vi$

then $w\overline{z} + \overline{w}z = 2u$. $u \le \sqrt{u^2 + v^2} = |w\overline{z}|$; $u \le |w\overline{z}|$;

$w\overline{z} + \overline{w}z = 2u \le 2|w\overline{z}| = 2|w||\overline{z}| = 2|w||z|$

20. $|w + z|^2 = (w + z)(\overline{w + z})$ (If z is a complex number, then $|z|^2 = z\overline{z}$.)

$\qquad\qquad = (w + z)(\overline{w} + \overline{z})$ (If w and z are complex numbers, then $\overline{w + z} =$

$\qquad\qquad\qquad\qquad\qquad\qquad\qquad$ $\overline{w} + \overline{z}$.)

$\qquad\qquad = w\overline{w} + w\overline{z} + \overline{w}z + z\overline{z}$ (Distributive prop.)

$\qquad\qquad \le w\overline{w} + 2|w||z| + z\overline{z}$ (Exercise 19)

$\qquad\qquad \le |w|^2 + 2|w||z| + |z|^2$ (If z is a complex number, then $|z|^2 = z\overline{z}$.)

$\qquad\qquad \le (|w| + |z|)^2$ (Distributive prop.)

$\therefore |w + z| \le |w| + |z|$ (If a and $b \ge 0$ and $a^2 < b^2$, then $a < b$.)

Pages 286-287 · CHAPTER REVIEW

1. c; $\sqrt[3]{-64a^6} = \sqrt[3]{-64}\,\sqrt[3]{a^6} = -4a^2$ **2.** b; $3x^2 - 27 = 0$; $x^2 - 9 = 0$; $x^2 = 9$; $x = \pm$

3. d; $\sqrt{8x^5z^8} = \sqrt{4x^4z^8}\,\sqrt{2x} = 2x^2z^4\sqrt{2x}$

4. b; $\sqrt[4]{32x^5y} \cdot \sqrt[4]{2xy^4} = \sqrt[4]{64x^6y^5} = \sqrt[4]{16x^4y^4}\,\sqrt[4]{4x^2y} = 2xy\sqrt[4]{4x^2y}$

5. a; $\dfrac{1}{\sqrt{3}} - \dfrac{2}{\sqrt{12}} + 2\sqrt{3} = \dfrac{1}{\sqrt{3}} - \dfrac{2}{2\sqrt{3}} + 2\sqrt{3} = \dfrac{1}{\sqrt{3}} - \dfrac{1}{\sqrt{3}} + 2\sqrt{3} = 2\sqrt{3}$

6. c; $\dfrac{\sqrt{3}}{4 - \sqrt{3}} \cdot \dfrac{4 + \sqrt{3}}{4 + \sqrt{3}} = \dfrac{4\sqrt{3} + 3}{4^2 - (\sqrt{3})^2} = \dfrac{4\sqrt{3} + 3}{13}$

7. d; $(\sqrt{8} - \sqrt{3})^2 = 8 - 2\sqrt{24} + 3 = 11 - 4\sqrt{6}$

8. a; $\sqrt[3]{y^{-1}} = -3$; $y^{-1} = (-3)^3$; $\dfrac{1}{y} = -27$; $y = -\dfrac{1}{27}$

9. d; $(\sqrt{k - 3} + \sqrt{k})^2 = (\sqrt{2})^2$; $k - 3 + 2\sqrt{k(k - 3)} + k = 2$; $2\sqrt{k(k - 3)} = 5 - 2k$;

$4k(k - 3) = 25 - 20k + 4k^2$; $4k^2 - 12k = 25 - 20k + 4k^2$; $8k = 25$; $k = \dfrac{25}{8}$;

$\sqrt{\dfrac{25}{8} - 3} + \sqrt{\dfrac{25}{8}} = \sqrt{\dfrac{1}{8}} + \sqrt{\dfrac{25}{8}} = \dfrac{1}{\sqrt{8}} + \dfrac{5}{\sqrt{8}} = \dfrac{6}{\sqrt{8}} = \dfrac{6\sqrt{8}}{8} = \dfrac{3\sqrt{2}}{2} \ne \sqrt{2}$;

no solution

10. b; $N = 0.7\overline{3}$; $10N = 7.\overline{3}$; $10N - N = 7.\overline{3} - 0.7\overline{3}$; $9N = 6.6$; $N = \dfrac{6.6}{9} = \dfrac{66}{90} = \dfrac{11}{15}$

11. c

12. d; $i\sqrt{-3} \cdot \sqrt{-12} = i(i\sqrt{3})(i\sqrt{12}) = i^3\sqrt{36} = (-i)6 = -6i$

13. d; $9x^2 = -8$; $x^2 = -\dfrac{8}{9}$; $x = \pm\sqrt{-\dfrac{8}{9}} = \pm i\sqrt{\dfrac{8}{9}} = \pm\dfrac{2i\sqrt{2}}{3}$

14. b; $7x = 9$; $x = \dfrac{9}{7}$; $-3y = -2$; $y = \dfrac{2}{3}$

15. c; $(5 - 7i)(2 + 2i) = 10 + 10i - 14i - 14i^2 = 10 - 4i + 14 = 24 - 4i$

16. c; $\dfrac{2 - i}{3 + 2i} \cdot \dfrac{3 - 2i}{3 - 2i} = \dfrac{6 - 7i + 2i^2}{3^2 - (2i)^2} = \dfrac{6 - 7i - 2}{9 - (-4)} = \dfrac{4 - 7i}{13}$

Page 287 · CHAPTER TEST

1. $\sqrt[3]{0.125} = 0.5$ **2.** $z^3 = -\dfrac{1}{27}$; $z = -\dfrac{1}{3}$ **3.** $\sqrt[3]{8x^3y^6} = 2xy^2$

4. $\sqrt[4]{\dfrac{16a^4b^5}{c^3} \cdot \dfrac{c}{c}} = 2\left|\dfrac{ab}{c}\right|\sqrt[4]{bc}$ **5.** $\sqrt{3(p + 3)^2} = |p + 3|\sqrt{3}$

6. $3y^2\sqrt{3} - 4y^2\sqrt{3} + 18y^2\sqrt{2} = -y^2\sqrt{3} + 18y^2\sqrt{2} = y^2(18\sqrt{2} - \sqrt{3})$

7. $6\sqrt{2} + 6\sqrt{2} - 48\sqrt{2} = -36\sqrt{2}$ **8.** $24 + 4\sqrt{30} + 5 = 29 + 4\sqrt{30}$

9. $\dfrac{5}{\sqrt{2} - \sqrt{6}} \cdot \dfrac{\sqrt{2} + \sqrt{6}}{\sqrt{2} + \sqrt{6}} = \dfrac{5\sqrt{2} + 5\sqrt{6}}{-4} = -\dfrac{5\sqrt{2} + 5\sqrt{6}}{4}$

10. $x^2 + 2 = 27$; $x^2 = 25$; $x = \pm 5$

11. $13 - x = -3x + 2\sqrt{-3x} + 1$; $12 + 2x = 2\sqrt{-3x}$; $144 + 48x + 4x^2 = -12x$;
$4x^2 + 60x + 144 = 0$; $x^2 + 15x + 36 = 0$; $(x + 3)(x + 12) = 0$; $x = -3$ or $x = -12$
(reject); $x = -3$

12. $\dfrac{9}{22}$ **13.** Answers will vary; e.g. 2.23; 2.212112111...

14. $x^2 = -3$; $x = \pm i\sqrt{3}$ **15.** $i\sqrt{5} \cdot 3i\sqrt{5} = -15$ **16.** $\dfrac{6}{3i\sqrt{2}} = \dfrac{2}{i\sqrt{2}} \cdot \dfrac{i\sqrt{2}}{i\sqrt{2}} = -i\sqrt{2}$

17. $5i\sqrt{2} + 4i\sqrt{2} = 9i\sqrt{2}$ **18.** $2 - 3i$ **19.** $10^2 - i^2 = 101$

20. $(1 - i)^3 = (1 - i)^2(1 - i) = (-2i)(1 - i) = -2 - 2i$

21. $\dfrac{9 - i}{6 - i} \cdot \dfrac{6 + i}{6 + i} = \dfrac{55 + 3i}{37} = \dfrac{55}{37} + \dfrac{3}{37}i$

Page 288 · MIXED REVIEW

1. $\dfrac{(-3)^2 - \left(\dfrac{1}{2}\right)(-6)}{-6 - (-3) + \dfrac{1}{2}} = \dfrac{12}{-2\dfrac{1}{2}} = 12\left(-\dfrac{2}{5}\right) = -\dfrac{24}{5}$

2. $\dfrac{1}{2}[z - (z - 2)] = \dfrac{1}{2}(z - z + 2) = \dfrac{1}{2} \cdot 2 = 1$

3. Let a = the number of adult tickets; $5a + 3(285 - a) = 1045$; $2a + 855 = 1045$; $2a = 190$; $a = 95$; 95 adults

4. $-1 \le 0.2(6 - a) < 0.4$; $-5 \le 6 - a < 2$; $-11 \le -a < -4$; $11 \ge a > 4$, or $4 < a \le 11$

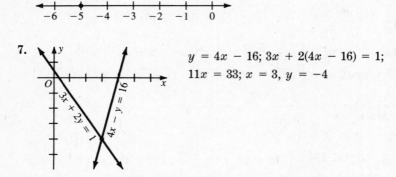

5. $\left|1 - \dfrac{b}{2}\right| > 3$; $1 - \dfrac{b}{2} > 3$ or $1 - \dfrac{b}{2} < -3$; $b < -4$ or $b > 8$.

6. $-8 - 16c = 87 + 3c$; $-95 = 19c$; $c = -5$

7. $y = 4x - 16$; $3x + 2(4x - 16) = 1$;
$11x = 33$; $x = 3$, $y = -4$

8. $m = \dfrac{6 - (-6)}{-4 - (-1)} = -4$; $y - 2 = -4(x - 5)$; $y - 2 = -4x + 20$; $4x + y = 22$

9. $f(1) = m \cdot 1 + b = 10$; $f(7) = m \cdot 7 + b = 2$; $m = -\dfrac{4}{3}$, $b = \dfrac{34}{3}$; $f(x) = -\dfrac{4}{3}x + \dfrac{34}{3}$

10. a. $8r^{10}s^4$ **b.** $5w^2(6w^2 + 5wz - 4z^2) = 30w^4 + 25w^3z - 20w^2z^2$

11. $8x^3(x - 1) - (x - 1) = (x - 1)(8x^3 - 1) = (x - 1)(2x - 1)(4x^2 + 2x + 1)$

12. $(4r^2 - 9t^2)(4r^2 + 9t^2) = (2r + 3t)(2r - 3t)(4r^2 + 9t^2)$

13. $(5a - b)(3a + 2b)$ **14.** $\dfrac{(-4)^{-3}x^6y^{-3}}{8^{-2}x^{-2}y^{-4}} = \dfrac{64x^8y}{-64} = -x^8y$

15. a. $\dfrac{(5 + x)(5 - x)}{(x - 5)(x - 5)} \cdot \dfrac{(5x - 1)(x - 5)}{-x(x + 5)} = \dfrac{(5 - x)(5x - 1)}{-x(x - 5)} = \dfrac{5x - 1}{x}$

b. $\dfrac{y}{2(y - 2)} - \dfrac{2}{y(y - 2)} = \dfrac{y^2 - 4}{2y(y - 2)} = \dfrac{(y + 2)(y - 2)}{2y(y - 2)} = \dfrac{y + 2}{2y}$

16. Let x = the number of minutes they would need working together; $\dfrac{x}{120} + \dfrac{x}{105} = 1$;
$7x + 8x = 840$; $x = 56$; 56 min

17. $\dfrac{2x^2}{2x(x+2)} + \dfrac{x+2}{2x(x+2)} = \dfrac{4-2x}{2x(x+2)}$; $2x^2 + 3x - 2 = 0$; $(2x-1)(x+2) = 0$; $x = \dfrac{1}{2}$

or $x = -2$ (reject); $x = \dfrac{1}{2}$

18. $y^4 = 81$; $y = \pm 3$

19. $\sqrt{z} = 2 + \sqrt{z-1}$; $z = 4 + 4\sqrt{z-1} + z - 1$; $-3 = 4\sqrt{z-1}$; $\sqrt{z-1} = -\dfrac{3}{4}$;

no real roots

20. $\sqrt[3]{\dfrac{27 \cdot 5}{25 \cdot 5}} = \dfrac{3\sqrt[3]{5}}{5}$ **21.** $3\sqrt{6} - \dfrac{\sqrt{6}}{2} = \dfrac{5\sqrt{6}}{2}$

22. $\dfrac{3+\sqrt{3}}{3-\sqrt{3}} \cdot \dfrac{3+\sqrt{3}}{3+\sqrt{3}} = \dfrac{9 + 6\sqrt{3} + 3}{6} = 2 + \sqrt{3}$

23. $(2+3i)(4-i) = 8 - 2i + 12i - 3i^2 = 11 + 10i$

24. $f(2-i) = 2 - i - \dfrac{1}{2-i} \cdot \dfrac{2+i}{2+i} = 2 - i - \dfrac{2+i}{5} = \dfrac{8}{5} - \dfrac{6}{5}i$

Page 289 · PREPARING FOR COLLEGE ENTRANCE EXAMS

1. C   **2.** D   **3.** D   **4.** D

5. B   **6.** A   **7.** C

Page 294 · WRITTEN EXERCISES

A 1. **a.** $x = \pm 5$; $\{\pm 5\}$ **b.** $x - 1 = \pm 5$; $x = 1 \pm 5$; $x = 6$ or $x = -4$; $\{6, -4\}$

2. **a.** $y = \pm \sqrt{-7}$; $y = \pm i\sqrt{7}$; $\{\pm i\sqrt{7}\}$
   b. $y + 3 = \pm i\sqrt{7}$; $y = -3 \pm i\sqrt{7}$; $\{-3 \pm i\sqrt{7}\}$

3. **a.** $z = \pm\sqrt{8} = \pm 2\sqrt{2}$; $\{\pm 2\sqrt{2}\}$ **b.** $z - 4 = \pm 2\sqrt{2}$; $z = 4 \pm 2\sqrt{2}$; $\{4 \pm 2\sqrt{2}\}$

4. $x + 7 = \pm\sqrt{\dfrac{16}{9}}$; $x + 7 = \pm\dfrac{4}{3}$; $x = -7 \pm \dfrac{4}{3}$; $x = -\dfrac{25}{3}$ or $-\dfrac{17}{3}$; $\left\{-\dfrac{25}{3}, -\dfrac{17}{3}\right\}$

5. $(y - 2)^2 = 7$; $y - 2 = \pm\sqrt{7}$; $y = 2 \pm \sqrt{7}$; $\{2 \pm \sqrt{7}\}$

6. $(y + 1)^2 = 20$; $y + 1 = \pm\sqrt{20}$; $y + 1 = \pm 2\sqrt{5}$; $y = -1 \pm 2\sqrt{5}$; $\{-1 \pm 2\sqrt{5}\}$

7. $z - 5 = \pm\sqrt{-4} = \pm 2i$; $z = 5 \pm 2i$; $\{5 \pm 2i\}$

8. $t - 3 = \pm\sqrt{-12} = \pm 2i\sqrt{3}$; $t = 3 \pm 2i\sqrt{3}$; $\{3 \pm 2i\sqrt{3}\}$

9. $2x - 1 = \pm 5$; $2x = 1 \pm 5$; $x = \dfrac{1 \pm 5}{2}$; $x = 3$ or $x = -2$; $\{3, -2\}$

10. $3x - 4 = \pm\sqrt{10}$; $3x = 4 \pm \sqrt{10}$; $x = \dfrac{4 \pm \sqrt{10}}{3}$; $\left\{\dfrac{4 \pm \sqrt{10}}{3}\right\}$

11. $(x + 1)^2 = 4$; $x + 1 = \pm 2$; $x = -1 \pm 2$; $x = 1$ or $x = -3$; $\{1, -3\}$

12. $6(u + 5)^2 = -18$; $(u + 5)^2 = -3$; $u + 5 = \pm\sqrt{-3} = \pm i\sqrt{3}$; $u = -5 \pm i\sqrt{3}$; $\{-5 \pm i\sqrt{3}\}$

13. $(x - 7)^2 = 60$; $x - 7 = \pm\sqrt{60} = \pm 2\sqrt{15}$; $x = 7 \pm 2\sqrt{15}$; $\{7 \pm 2\sqrt{15}\}$

14. $(y + 4)^2 = 10$; $y + 4 = \pm\sqrt{10}$; $y = -4 \pm \sqrt{10}$; $\{-4 \pm \sqrt{10}\}$

15. $(2x - 1)^2 = \dfrac{25}{4}$; $2x - 1 = \pm\sqrt{\dfrac{25}{4}} = \pm\dfrac{5}{2}$; $2x = 1 \pm \dfrac{5}{2}$; $2x = \dfrac{7}{2}$ or $2x = -\dfrac{3}{2}$; $x = \dfrac{7}{4}$
    or $x = -\dfrac{3}{4}$; $\left\{\dfrac{7}{4}, -\dfrac{3}{4}\right\}$

16. $x^2 - 2x = 4$; $x^2 - 2x + 1 = 5$; $(x - 1)^2 = 5$; $x - 1 = \pm\sqrt{5}$; $x = 1 \pm \sqrt{5}$; $\{1 \pm \sqrt{5}$

17. $x^2 + 4x = 96$; $x^2 + 4x + 4 = 100$; $(x + 2)^2 = 100$; $x + 2 = \pm 10$; $x = -2 \pm 10$;
    $x = -12$ or $x = 8$; $\{8, -12\}$

18. $y^2 + 6y = -10$; $y^2 + 6y + 9 = -1$; $(y + 3)^2 = -1$; $y + 3 = \pm\sqrt{-1} = \pm i$;
    $y = -3 \pm i$; $\{-3 \pm i\}$

19. $z^2 - 10z = -30$; $z^2 - 10z + 25 = -5$; $(z - 5)^2 = -5$; $z - 5 = \pm\sqrt{-5} = \pm i\sqrt{5}$;
    $z = 5 \pm i\sqrt{5}$; $\{5 \pm i\sqrt{5}\}$

20. $a^2 - 14a = 1$; $a^2 - 14a + 49 = 50$; $(a - 7)^2 = 50$; $a - 7 = \pm\sqrt{50} = \pm 5\sqrt{2}$;
    $a = 7 \pm 5\sqrt{2}$; $\{7 \pm 5\sqrt{2}\}$

21. $t^2 - 8t = -4$; $t^2 - 8t + 16 = 12$; $(t - 4)^2 = 12$; $t - 4 = \pm\sqrt{12} = \pm 2\sqrt{3}$;
    $t = 4 \pm 2\sqrt{3}$; $\{4 \pm 2\sqrt{3}\}$

22. $y^2 + 2y + 1 = 400; (y + 1)^2 = 400; y + 1 = \pm\sqrt{400} = \pm 20; y = -1 \pm 20; y = 19$ or
$y = -21; \{19, -21\}$

23. $b^2 - b = 1; b^2 - b + \dfrac{1}{4} = \dfrac{5}{4}; \left(b - \dfrac{1}{2}\right)^2 = \dfrac{5}{4}; b - \dfrac{1}{2} = \pm\sqrt{\dfrac{5}{4}} = \pm\dfrac{\sqrt{5}}{2};$

$b = \dfrac{1}{2} \pm \dfrac{\sqrt{5}}{2}; \left\{\dfrac{1 \pm \sqrt{5}}{2}\right\}$

24. $x^2 - 4x = \dfrac{7}{2}; x^2 - 4x + 4 = \dfrac{15}{2}; (x - 2)^2 = \dfrac{15}{2}; x - 2 = \pm\sqrt{\dfrac{15}{2}} = \pm\dfrac{\sqrt{30}}{2};$

$x = 2 \pm \dfrac{\sqrt{30}}{2}; \left\{2 \pm \dfrac{\sqrt{30}}{2}\right\}$

25. $3w^2 - 6w = -5; w^2 - 2w = -\dfrac{5}{3}; w^2 - 2w + 1 = -\dfrac{2}{3}; (w - 1)^2 = -\dfrac{2}{3};$

$w - 1 = \pm\sqrt{-\dfrac{2}{3}} = \pm\dfrac{i\sqrt{6}}{3}; w = 1 \pm \dfrac{i\sqrt{6}}{3}; \left\{1 + \dfrac{i\sqrt{6}}{3}\right\}$

26. $5v^2 + 5v = 1; v^2 + v = \dfrac{1}{5}; v^2 + v + \dfrac{1}{4} = \dfrac{9}{20}; \left(v + \dfrac{1}{2}\right)^2 = \dfrac{9}{20};$

$v + \dfrac{1}{2} = \pm\sqrt{\dfrac{9}{20}} = \pm\dfrac{3\sqrt{5}}{10}; v = -\dfrac{1}{2} \pm \dfrac{3\sqrt{5}}{10}; \left\{-\dfrac{1}{2} \pm \dfrac{3\sqrt{5}}{10}\right\}$

27. $2x^2 - 4x = -8; x^2 - 2x = -4; x^2 - 2x + 1 = -3; (x - 1)^2 = -3;$
$x - 1 = \pm\sqrt{-3} = \pm i\sqrt{3}; x = 1 \pm i\sqrt{3}; \{1 \pm i\sqrt{3}\}$

B   **28.** $\dfrac{y^2}{4} - \dfrac{y}{2} - \dfrac{1}{8} = 0; \dfrac{y^2}{4} - \dfrac{y}{2} = \dfrac{1}{8}; y^2 - 2y = \dfrac{1}{2}; y^2 - 2y + 1 = \dfrac{3}{2}; (y - 1)^2 = \dfrac{3}{2};$

$y - 1 = \pm\sqrt{\dfrac{3}{2}} = \pm\dfrac{\sqrt{6}}{2}; y = 1 \pm \dfrac{\sqrt{6}}{2}; \left\{1 \pm \dfrac{\sqrt{6}}{2}\right\}$

29. $\dfrac{x^2}{2} - \dfrac{x}{5} = \dfrac{1}{10}; x^2 - \dfrac{2x}{5} = \dfrac{1}{5}; x^2 - \dfrac{2x}{5} + \dfrac{1}{25} = \dfrac{1}{5} + \dfrac{1}{25}; \left(x - \dfrac{1}{5}\right)^2 = \dfrac{6}{25};$

$x - \dfrac{1}{5} = \pm\sqrt{\dfrac{6}{25}} = \pm\dfrac{\sqrt{6}}{5}; x = \dfrac{1}{5} \pm \dfrac{\sqrt{6}}{5}; \left\{\dfrac{1 \pm \sqrt{6}}{5}\right\}$

30. $7x - 7x^2 = 5x - 10; 7x^2 - 2x = 10; x^2 - \dfrac{2}{7}x = \dfrac{10}{7}; x^2 - \dfrac{2}{7}x + \dfrac{1}{49} = \dfrac{10}{7} + \dfrac{1}{49};$

$\left(x - \dfrac{1}{7}\right)^2 = \dfrac{71}{49}; x - \dfrac{1}{7} = \pm\sqrt{\dfrac{71}{49}} = \pm\dfrac{\sqrt{71}}{7}; x = \dfrac{1}{7} \pm \dfrac{\sqrt{71}}{7}; \left\{\dfrac{1 \pm \sqrt{71}}{7}\right\}$

31. $2x^2 - 8x = 3 - 3x; 2x^2 - 5x = 3; x^2 - \dfrac{5}{2}x = \dfrac{3}{2}; x^2 - \dfrac{5}{2}x + \dfrac{25}{16} = \dfrac{3}{2} + \dfrac{25}{16};$

$\left(x - \dfrac{5}{4}\right)^2 = \dfrac{49}{16}; x - \dfrac{5}{4} = \pm\sqrt{\dfrac{49}{16}} = \pm\dfrac{7}{4}; x = \dfrac{5}{4} \pm \dfrac{7}{4}; x = 3$ or $x = -\dfrac{1}{2}; \left\{3, -\dfrac{1}{2}\right\}$

32. $5x^2 = x^2 + 4x + 4; 4x^2 - 4x = 4; x^2 - x = 1; x^2 - x + \dfrac{1}{4} = \dfrac{5}{4}; \left(x - \dfrac{1}{2}\right)^2 = \dfrac{5}{4};$

$x - \dfrac{1}{2} = \pm\sqrt{\dfrac{5}{4}} = \pm\dfrac{\sqrt{5}}{2}; x = \dfrac{1}{2} \pm \dfrac{\sqrt{5}}{2}; \left\{\dfrac{1 \pm \sqrt{5}}{2}\right\}$

33. $3x^2 = x^2 + 6x + 9$; $2x^2 - 6x = 9$; $x^2 - 3x = \dfrac{9}{2}$; $x^2 - 3x + \dfrac{9}{4} = \dfrac{9}{2} + \dfrac{9}{4}$;

$\left(x - \dfrac{3}{2}\right)^2 = \dfrac{27}{4}$; $\quad x - \dfrac{3}{2} = \pm\sqrt{\dfrac{27}{4}} = \pm\dfrac{3\sqrt{3}}{2}$; $x = \dfrac{3}{2} \pm \dfrac{3\sqrt{3}}{2}$; $\left\{\dfrac{3 \pm 3\sqrt{3}}{2}\right\}$

34. $x - 1 + x + 1 = (x - 1)(x + 1)$; $2x = x^2 - 1$; $x^2 - 2x = 1$; $x^2 - 2x + 1 = 1 + 1$;
$(x - 1)^2 = 2$; $x - 1 = \pm\sqrt{2}$; $x = 1 \pm \sqrt{2}$; $\{1 \pm \sqrt{2}\}$

35. $y + 6 + y + 2 = (y + 2)(y + 6)$; $2y + 8 = y^2 + 8y + 12$; $y^2 + 6y = -4$;
$y^2 + 6y + 9 = -4 + 9$; $(y + 3)^2 = 5$; $y + 3 = \pm\sqrt{5}$; $y = -3 \pm \sqrt{5}$; $\{-3 \pm \sqrt{5}\}$

36. $x + 3 = 4x^2$; $4x^2 - x = 3$; $x^2 - \dfrac{x}{4} = \dfrac{3}{4}$; $x^2 - \dfrac{x}{4} + \dfrac{1}{64} = \dfrac{3}{4} + \dfrac{1}{64}$; $\left(x - \dfrac{1}{8}\right)^2 = \dfrac{49}{64}$;
$x - \dfrac{1}{8} = \pm\dfrac{7}{8}$; $x = \dfrac{1}{8} \pm \dfrac{7}{8}$; $\{1\}$

37. $\left(\sqrt{x - 4} - \dfrac{2}{\sqrt{x - 4}}\right)^2 = 1^2$; $x - 4 - 4 + \dfrac{4}{x - 4} = 1$; $x + \dfrac{4}{x - 4} = 9$;

$x^2 - 4x + 4 = 9x - 36$; $x^2 - 13x = -40$; $x^2 - 13x + \dfrac{169}{4} = -40 + \dfrac{169}{4}$;
$\left(x - \dfrac{13}{2}\right)^2 = \dfrac{9}{4}$; $x - \dfrac{13}{2} = \pm\dfrac{3}{2}$; $x = \dfrac{13}{2} \pm \dfrac{3}{2}$; $\{8\}$

38. $(x + 2)^2 + (x - 2)^2 = 8 - 4x$; $x^2 + 4x + 4 + x^2 - 4x + 4 = 8 - 4x$; $2x^2 + 4x = 0$;
$x^2 + 2x = 0$; $x^2 + 2x + 1 = 1$; $(x + 1)^2 = 1$; $x + 1 = \pm1$; $x = -1 \pm 1$; $\{0\}$

39. $\dfrac{x}{x - 1} - \dfrac{x}{x + 1} = 3 - \dfrac{2x^2}{x^2 - 1}$; $x(x + 1) - x(x - 1) = 3(x - 1)(x + 1) - 2x^2$;
$x^2 + x - x^2 + x = 3x^2 - 3 - 2x^2$; $x^2 - 2x = 3$; $x^2 - 2x + 1 = 4$; $(x - 1)^2 = 4$;
$x - 1 = \pm2$; $x = 1 \pm 2$; $\{3\}$

C 40. $x^2 - 4x + y^2 - 2y = 4$; $x^2 - 4x + 4 + y^2 - 2y + 1 = 9$; $(x - 2)^2 + (y - 1)^2 = 9$

41. $x^2 + 2x + y^2 - 8y = -8$; $x^2 + 2x + 1 + y^2 - 8y + 16 = 9$;
$(x + 1)^2 + (y - 4)^2 = 9$

42. $y - 3 = x^2 + 8x$; $y - 3 + 16 = x^2 + 8x + 16$; $y + 13 = (x + 4)^2$

43. $y - 2 = x^2 + 3x$; $y - 2 + \dfrac{9}{4} = x^2 + 3x + \dfrac{9}{4}$; $y + \dfrac{1}{4} = \left(x + \dfrac{3}{2}\right)^2$

44. $3x^2 - 12x + 4y^2 + 8y = -4$; $3(x^2 - 4x) + 4(y^2 + 2y) = -4$;
$3(x^2 - 4x + 4) + 4(y^2 + 2y + 1) = -4 + 12 + 4$; $3(x - 2)^2 + 4(y + 1)^2 = 12$;
$\dfrac{(x - 2)^2}{4} + \dfrac{(y + 1)^2}{3} = 1$

45. $5x^2 + 30x + 2y^2 - 16y = -67$; $5(x^2 + 6x) + 2(y^2 - 8y) = -67$;
$5(x^2 + 6x + 9) + 2(y^2 - 8y + 16) = -67 + 45 + 32$; $5(x + 3)^2 + 2(y - 4)^2 = 10$;
$\dfrac{(x + 3)^2}{2} + \dfrac{(y - 4)^2}{5} = 1$

Pages 297-298 · WRITTEN EXERCISES

A

1. $x = \dfrac{-6 \pm \sqrt{(6)^2 - 4(1)(2)}}{2} = \dfrac{-6 \pm \sqrt{28}}{2} = \dfrac{-6 \pm 2\sqrt{7}}{2} = -3 \pm \sqrt{7}; \{-3 \pm \sqrt{7}\}$

2. $x = \dfrac{-3 \pm \sqrt{3^2 - 4(1)(-5)}}{2} = \dfrac{-3 \pm \sqrt{29}}{2}; \left\{\dfrac{-3 \pm \sqrt{29}}{2}\right\}$

3. $t = \dfrac{4 \pm \sqrt{(-4)^2 - 4(1)(8)}}{2} = \dfrac{4 \pm \sqrt{-16}}{2} = \dfrac{4 \pm 4i}{2} = 2 \pm 2i; \{2 \pm 2i\}$

4. $y = \dfrac{6 \pm \sqrt{(-6)^2 - 4(1)(-3)}}{2} = \dfrac{6 \pm \sqrt{48}}{2} = \dfrac{6 \pm 4\sqrt{3}}{2} = 3 \pm 2\sqrt{3}; \{3 \pm 2\sqrt{3}\}$

5. $x = \dfrac{6 \pm \sqrt{(-6)^2 - 4(2)(5)}}{2(2)} = \dfrac{6 \pm \sqrt{-4}}{4} = \dfrac{6 \pm 2i}{4} = \dfrac{3 \pm i}{2}; \left\{\dfrac{3}{2} \pm \dfrac{1}{2}i\right\}$

6. $15z^2 + 14z - 16 = 0; z = \dfrac{-14 \pm \sqrt{14^2 - 4(15)(-16)}}{2(15)} = \dfrac{-14 \pm \sqrt{1156}}{30} = \dfrac{-14 \pm 34}{30}$
$= -\dfrac{8}{5}, \dfrac{2}{3}; \left\{-\dfrac{8}{5}, \dfrac{2}{3}\right\}$

7. $5u^2 + 12u + 8 = 0; u = \dfrac{-12 \pm \sqrt{12^2 - 4(5)(8)}}{2(5)} = \dfrac{-12 \pm \sqrt{-16}}{10} = \dfrac{-12 \pm 4i}{10}$
$= \dfrac{-6 \pm 2i}{5}; \left\{-\dfrac{6}{5} \pm \dfrac{2}{5}i\right\}$

8. $2y^2 + 4y + 3 = 0; y = \dfrac{-4 \pm \sqrt{4^2 - 4(2)(3)}}{2(2)} = \dfrac{-4 \pm \sqrt{-8}}{4} = \dfrac{-4 \pm 2i\sqrt{2}}{4}$
$= \dfrac{-2 \pm i\sqrt{2}}{2}; \left\{-1 \pm \dfrac{i\sqrt{2}}{2}\right\}$

9. $3r^2 + 4r - 1 = 0; r = \dfrac{-4 \pm \sqrt{4^2 - 4(3)(-1)}}{2(3)} = \dfrac{-4 \pm \sqrt{28}}{6} = \dfrac{-4 \pm 2\sqrt{7}}{6}$
$= \dfrac{-2 \pm \sqrt{7}}{3}; \left\{\dfrac{-2 \pm \sqrt{7}}{3}\right\}$

10. $4t^2 - 5t - 7 = 0; t = \dfrac{5 \pm \sqrt{(-5)^2 - 4(4)(-7)}}{2(4)} = \dfrac{5 \pm \sqrt{137}}{8}; \left\{\dfrac{5 \pm \sqrt{137}}{8}\right\}$

11. $2x^2 + 2x - 7 = 0; x = \dfrac{-2 \pm \sqrt{2^2 - 4(2)(-7)}}{2(2)} = \dfrac{-2 \pm \sqrt{60}}{4}$
$= \dfrac{-2 \pm 2\sqrt{15}}{4} = \dfrac{-1 \pm \sqrt{15}}{2}; \left\{\dfrac{-1 \pm \sqrt{15}}{2}\right\}$

12. $8y^2 + 12y - 5 = 0; y = \dfrac{-12 \pm \sqrt{(12)^2 - 4(8)(-5)}}{2(8)} = \dfrac{-12 \pm \sqrt{304}}{16} = \dfrac{-12 \pm 4\sqrt{19}}{16}$
$= \dfrac{-3 \pm \sqrt{19}}{4}; \left\{\dfrac{-3 \pm \sqrt{19}}{4}\right\}$

13. $4x^2 - 4x - 1 = 0; x = \dfrac{4 \pm \sqrt{(-4)^2 - 4(4)(-1)}}{2(4)} = \dfrac{4 \pm \sqrt{32}}{8} = \dfrac{4 \pm 4\sqrt{2}}{8} = \dfrac{1 \pm \sqrt{2}}{2};$
$\left\{\dfrac{1 \pm \sqrt{2}}{2}\right\}$

14. $3y^2 - 12y = 10 - 5y$; $3y^2 - 7y - 10 = 0$; $y = \dfrac{7 \pm \sqrt{(-7)^2 - 4(3)(-10)}}{2(3)}$

$= \dfrac{7 \pm \sqrt{169}}{6} = \dfrac{7 \pm 13}{6} = \dfrac{10}{3}, -1$; $\left\{\dfrac{10}{3}, -1\right\}$

15. $2x^2 - 4x = 3$; $2x^2 - 4x - 3 = 0$; $x = \dfrac{4 \pm \sqrt{(-4)^2 - 4(2)(-3)}}{2(2)} = \dfrac{4 \pm \sqrt{40}}{4}$

$= \dfrac{4 \pm 2\sqrt{10}}{4} = \dfrac{2 \pm \sqrt{10}}{2}$; $\left\{\dfrac{2 \pm \sqrt{10}}{2}\right\}$

16. $5z^2 + 10 = 2z$; $5z^2 - 2z + 10 = 0$; $z = \dfrac{2 \pm \sqrt{(-2)^2 - 4(5)(10)}}{2(5)} = \dfrac{2 \pm \sqrt{-196}}{10}$

$= \dfrac{2 \pm 14i}{10} = \dfrac{1 \pm 7i}{5}$; $\left\{\dfrac{1}{5} \pm \dfrac{7}{5}i\right\}$

17. $x + 4 + x + 2 = (x + 2)(x + 4)$; $2x + 6 = x^2 + 6x + 8$; $x^2 + 4x + 2 = 0$;

$x = \dfrac{-4 \pm \sqrt{4^2 - 4(1)(2)}}{2(1)} = \dfrac{-4 \pm \sqrt{8}}{2} = \dfrac{-4 \pm 2\sqrt{2}}{2} = -2 \pm \sqrt{2}$; $\{-2 \pm \sqrt{2}\}$

18. $(2x - 1)(x + 2) - x(x - 1) = 1$; $2x^2 + 3x - 2 - x^2 + x = 1$; $x^2 + 4x - 3 = 0$;

$x = \dfrac{-4 \pm \sqrt{4^2 - 4(1)(-3)}}{2(1)} = \dfrac{-4 \pm \sqrt{28}}{2} = \dfrac{-4 \pm 2\sqrt{7}}{2} = -2 \pm \sqrt{7}$; $\{-2 \pm \sqrt{7}\}$

19. $y = \dfrac{6 \pm \sqrt{(-6)^2 - 4(3)(-7)}}{2(3)} = \dfrac{6 \pm \sqrt{120}}{6} = \dfrac{6 \pm 2\sqrt{30}}{6} = \dfrac{3 \pm \sqrt{30}}{3}$; $\{2.83, -0.83\}$

20. $2t^2 - 8t + 3 = 0$; $t = \dfrac{8 \pm \sqrt{(-8)^2 - 4(2)(3)}}{2(2)} = \dfrac{8 \pm \sqrt{40}}{4} = \dfrac{8 \pm 2\sqrt{10}}{4} = \dfrac{4 \pm \sqrt{10}}{2}$;

$\{3.58, 0.42\}$

21. $4x^2 + 4x = 2.75$; $4x^2 + 4x - 2.75 = 0$; $x = \dfrac{-4 \pm \sqrt{(4)^2 - 4(4)(-2.75)}}{2(4)} = \dfrac{-4 \pm \sqrt{60}}{8}$

$= \dfrac{-4 \pm 2\sqrt{15}}{8} = \dfrac{-2 \pm \sqrt{15}}{4}$; $\{0.47, -1.47\}$

22. $3x^2 + 6x + 2.5 = 0$; $x = \dfrac{-6 \pm \sqrt{6^2 - 4(3)(2.5)}}{2(3)} = \dfrac{-6 \pm \sqrt{6}}{6} = -0.59, -1.41$;

$\{-0.59, -1.41\}$

23. $(3x + 1)(x - 1) = 0$; $3x + 1 = 0$ or $x - 1 = 0$; $x = -\dfrac{1}{3}$ or $x = 1$; $\left\{-\dfrac{1}{3}, 1\right\}$;

$x = \dfrac{2 \pm \sqrt{(-2)^2 - 4(3)(-1)}}{2(3)} = \dfrac{2 \pm \sqrt{16}}{6} = \dfrac{2 \pm 4}{6} = -\dfrac{1}{3}, 1$; $\left\{-\dfrac{1}{3}, 1\right\}$

24. $(2x - 3)(2x + 5) = 0$; $2x - 3 = 0$ or $2x + 5 = 0$; $x = \dfrac{3}{2}$ or $x = -\dfrac{5}{2}$; $\left\{\dfrac{3}{2}, -\dfrac{5}{2}\right\}$;

$x = \dfrac{-4 \pm \sqrt{4^2 - 4(4)(-15)}}{2(4)} = \dfrac{-4 \pm \sqrt{256}}{8} = \dfrac{-4 \pm 16}{8} = \dfrac{3}{2}, -\dfrac{5}{2}$; $\left\{\dfrac{3}{2}, -\dfrac{5}{2}\right\}$

B   **25.** $x = \dfrac{\sqrt{2} \pm \sqrt{2 - 4(-1)}}{2(1)} = \dfrac{\sqrt{2} \pm \sqrt{6}}{2}$; $\left\{\dfrac{\sqrt{2} \pm \sqrt{6}}{2}\right\}$

26. $x = \dfrac{\sqrt{5} \pm \sqrt{5 - 4(-1)}}{2(1)} = \dfrac{\sqrt{5} \pm \sqrt{9}}{2} = \dfrac{\sqrt{5} \pm 3}{2}$; $\left\{\dfrac{\sqrt{5} \pm 3}{2}\right\}$

27. $t = \dfrac{2\sqrt{2} \pm \sqrt{(2\sqrt{2})^2 - 4(1)}}{2(1)} = \dfrac{2\sqrt{2} \pm \sqrt{4}}{2} = \dfrac{2\sqrt{2} \pm 2}{2} = \sqrt{2} \pm 1; \{\sqrt{2} \pm 1\}$

28. $h = \dfrac{-2\sqrt{3} \pm \sqrt{(2\sqrt{3})^2 - 4(-3)}}{2(1)} = \dfrac{-2\sqrt{3} \pm \sqrt{24}}{2} = \dfrac{-2\sqrt{3} \pm 2\sqrt{6}}{2} = -\sqrt{3} \pm \sqrt{6};$

$\{-\sqrt{3} \pm \sqrt{6}\}$

29. $x = \dfrac{-5 \pm \sqrt{5^2 - 4(\sqrt{2})(2\sqrt{2})}}{2(\sqrt{2})} = \dfrac{-5 \pm \sqrt{9}}{2\sqrt{2}} = \dfrac{-5 \pm 3}{2\sqrt{2}} = -\dfrac{2}{2\sqrt{2}}, \quad -\dfrac{8}{2\sqrt{2}} = -\dfrac{\sqrt{2}}{2},$

$-2\sqrt{2}; \left\{-\dfrac{\sqrt{2}}{2}, -2\sqrt{2}\right\}$

30. $x = \dfrac{2 \pm \sqrt{2^2 - 4(\sqrt{3})(2\sqrt{3})}}{2(\sqrt{3})} = \dfrac{2 \pm \sqrt{-20}}{2\sqrt{3}} = \dfrac{2 \pm 2i\sqrt{5}}{2\sqrt{3}} = \dfrac{1 \pm i\sqrt{5}}{\sqrt{3}} = \dfrac{\sqrt{3} \pm i\sqrt{15}}{3};$

$\left\{\dfrac{\sqrt{3}}{3} \pm \dfrac{i\sqrt{15}}{3}\right\}$

31. $z = \dfrac{-i \pm \sqrt{i^2 - 4(1)(2)}}{2(1)} = \dfrac{-i \pm \sqrt{-9}}{2} = \dfrac{-i \pm 3i}{2} = i, -2i; \{i, -2i\}$

32. $z = \dfrac{-2i \pm \sqrt{(2i)^2 - 4(-1)}}{2(1)} = \dfrac{-2i \pm \sqrt{0}}{2} = -\dfrac{2i}{2} = -i; \{-i\}$

33. $2w^2 + 7iw + 3i^2 = 3w^2 + iw - 4i^2; w^2 - 6iw - 7i^2 = 0; w^2 - 6iw + 7 = 0;$

$w = \dfrac{6i \pm \sqrt{(-6i)^2 - 4(7)}}{2(1)} = \dfrac{6i \pm \sqrt{-64}}{2} = \dfrac{6i \pm 8i}{2} = 7i, -i; \{7i, -i\}$

34. $(2z - i)(z + 2i) + (2z + i)(z + 2i) = 4(2z + i)(2z - i);$

$2z^2 + 3iz - 2i^2 + 2z^2 + 5iz + 2i^2 = 16z^2 - 4i^2; 12z^2 - 8iz - 4i^2 = 0;$

$12z^2 - 8iz + 4 = 0; 3z^2 - 2iz + 1 = 0;$

$z = \dfrac{2i \pm \sqrt{(-2i)^2 - 4(3)}}{6} = \dfrac{2i \pm \sqrt{-16}}{6} = \dfrac{2i \pm 4i}{6} = i, -\dfrac{1}{3}i; \left\{i, -\dfrac{1}{3}i\right\}$

35. $x = \dfrac{-q \pm \sqrt{q^2 - 4pr}}{2p}; \left\{\dfrac{-q \pm \sqrt{q^2 - 4pr}}{2p}\right\}$

36. $x = \dfrac{r(p + q) \pm \sqrt{[r(p + q)]^2 - 4r^2pq}}{2r^2} = \dfrac{r(p + q) \pm \sqrt{r^2(p^2 - 2pq + q^2)}}{2r^2}$

$= \dfrac{r(p + q) \pm \sqrt{r^2(p - q)^2}}{2r^2} = \dfrac{r(p + q) \pm r(p - q)}{2r^2}; x = \dfrac{rp + rq - rp + rq}{2r^2} = \dfrac{2rq}{2r^2}$

$= \dfrac{q}{r} \text{ or } x = \dfrac{rp + rq + rp - rq}{2r^2} = \dfrac{2rp}{2r^2} = \dfrac{p}{r}; \left\{\dfrac{q}{r}, \dfrac{p}{r}\right\}$

Pages 298-299 · PROBLEMS

A   1. Let x = width of deck in meters; total area of deck and pool = $(8 + 2x)(10 + 2x) =$ $80 + 36x + 4x^2$; area of pool = 80; area of deck = $4x^2 + 36x + 80 - 80 = 4x^2 + 36x$; $4x^2 + 36x = 72; 4x^2 + 36x - 72 = 0; x^2 + 9x - 18 = 0; x =$ $\dfrac{-9 \pm \sqrt{9^2 - 4(1)(-18)}}{2 \cdot 1} = \dfrac{-9 \pm \sqrt{153}}{2}$. Since $x > 0$, $x = \dfrac{-9 + \sqrt{153}}{2} \approx 1.68$; 1.68 m

2. Let w = width in meters; then $\dfrac{300}{2} - w$ = length; $w(150 - w) = 5000$; $150w - w^2 =$ 5000; $w^2 - 150w + 5000 = 0$; $(w - 100)(w - 50) = 0$; $w = 100$ or $w = 50$; 50 m wide by 100 m long

3. Let w = width in meters; then $8 - w$ = length. $w(8 - w) = 4$; $8w - w^2 = 4$;

$$w^2 - 8w + 4 = 0; \quad w = \frac{8 \pm \sqrt{(-8)^2 - 4(1)(4)}}{2 \cdot 1} = \frac{8 \pm \sqrt{48}}{2} = \frac{8 \pm 4\sqrt{3}}{2} = 4 \pm 2\sqrt{3}$$

Since $w > 0$, $w = 4 + 2\sqrt{3}$; $l = \dfrac{4}{4 + 2\sqrt{3}} = \dfrac{4(4 - 2\sqrt{3})}{(4 + 2\sqrt{3})(4 - 2\sqrt{3})} = \dfrac{16 - 8\sqrt{3}}{16 - 4 \cdot 3} =$ $\dfrac{16 - 8\sqrt{3}}{4} = 4 - 2\sqrt{3}$. The numbers $4 + 2\sqrt{3}$ and $4 - 2\sqrt{3}$ are irrational conjugates

4. $x + 6$ = length of side of new square in meters. $(x + 6)^2 = 2(6^2)$; $x^2 + 12x + 36 = 72$;

$$x^2 + 12x - 36 = 0; x = \frac{-12 \pm \sqrt{12^2 - 4(1)(-36)}}{2 \cdot 1} = \frac{-12 \pm \sqrt{288}}{2} = \frac{-12 \pm 12\sqrt{2}}{2} =$$

$-6 \pm 6\sqrt{2}$; since $x > 0$, $x = -6 + 6\sqrt{2} \approx 2.49$.

5. Let x = the number; then $\dfrac{1}{x}$ = its reciprocal; $x - 1 = \dfrac{1}{x}$; $x^2 - x = 1$; $x^2 - x - 1 =$

0; $x = \dfrac{1 \pm \sqrt{(-1)^2 - 4(1)(-1)}}{2 \cdot 1} = \dfrac{1 \pm \sqrt{5}}{2}$. Since $x > 0$, $x = \dfrac{1 + \sqrt{5}}{2} \approx 1.62$.

6.

Area of trapezoid $= \dfrac{1}{2} \cdot x(x + 6) + x(x + 6) =$

$\dfrac{x^2 + 6x}{2} + x^2 + 6x; \dfrac{x^2 + 6x}{2} + x^2 + 6x = 90;$

$x^2 + 6x + 2x^2 + 12x = 180; 3x^2 + 18x - 180 = 0;$

$x^2 + 6x - 60 = 0; x = \dfrac{-6 \pm \sqrt{6^2 - 4(1)(-60)}}{2 \cdot 1} =$

$\dfrac{-6 \pm \sqrt{276}}{2} = \dfrac{-6 \pm 2\sqrt{69}}{2} = -3 \pm \sqrt{69}$. Since $x > 0$, $x = -3 + \sqrt{69} \approx 5.31$.

B 7. $S.A. = 2[2x(x + 2)] + 2[x(x + 2)] + 2[2x(x)] = 4x^2 + 8x + 2x^2 + 4x + 4x^2 =$ $10x^2 + 12x; 10x^2 + 12x = 36; 10x^2 + 12x - 36 = 0; 5x^2 + 6x - 18 = 0;$

$$x = \frac{-6 \pm \sqrt{6^2 - 4(5)(-18)}}{2 \cdot 5} = \frac{-6 \pm \sqrt{396}}{10}; \text{ since } x > 0, x = \frac{-6 + \sqrt{396}}{10} \approx 1.39.$$

8. Volume of first box $= x^2(x + 5) = x^3 + 5x^2$; volume of second box $=$ $(x + 2)(x + 1)^2 = x^3 + 4x^2 + 5x + 2; x^3 + 5x^2 = x^3 + 4x^2 + 5x + 2;$

$x^2 - 5x - 2 = 0; x = \dfrac{5 \pm \sqrt{(-5)^2 - 4(1)(-2)}}{2 \cdot 1}$; since $x > 0$, $x = \dfrac{5 + \sqrt{33}}{2} \approx 5.37$.

9. Let x = length of side of square piece of metal in centimeters; volume $=$ $5(x - 10)(x - 10) = 5x^2 - 100x + 500; 5x^2 - 100x + 500 = 100; x^2 - 20x + 80 =$

$0; x = \dfrac{20 \pm \sqrt{(-20)^2 - 4(1)(80)}}{2 \cdot 1} = \dfrac{20 \pm \sqrt{80}}{2} = \dfrac{20 \pm 4\sqrt{5}}{2} = 10 \pm 2\sqrt{5} \approx 5.53$ or

14.5; since it is impossible to cut two 5-cm squares from a 5.53-cm square, $x \approx 14.5$; 14.5 cm by 14.5 cm

10. Let x = number of hours it took going out; then $4 - x$ = number of hours for the return trip; $\dfrac{72}{x} = \dfrac{72}{4 - x} + 15$; $72(4 - x) = 72x + 15x(4 - x)$; $288 - 72x = 72x + 60x - 15x^2$; $15x^2 - 204x + 288 = 0$; $5x^2 - 68x + 96 = 0$; $x = \dfrac{68 \pm \sqrt{(-68)^2 + 4(5)(96)}}{2 \cdot 5} = \dfrac{68 \pm \sqrt{2704}}{10} = \dfrac{68 \pm 52}{10}$; $x = 12$ or $x = 1.6$; since $x < 4$, $x = 1.6$; average speed going out $= \dfrac{72}{1.6} = 45$ km/h; average return speed $= 45 - 15 = 30$ km/h.

11. Let l = length and w = width; $\dfrac{l}{w} = \dfrac{l + w}{l}$; $l^2 = wl + w^2$; $l^2 - wl - w^2 = 0$; $l = \dfrac{w \pm \sqrt{(-w)^2 - 4(1)(-w^2)}}{2 \cdot 1} = \dfrac{w \pm \sqrt{5w^2}}{2} = \dfrac{w + w\sqrt{5}}{2}$; since $w > 0$, $l = \dfrac{w + w\sqrt{5}}{2}$; thus, the golden ratio $= \dfrac{l}{w} = \dfrac{\dfrac{w + w\sqrt{5}}{2}}{w} = \dfrac{1 + \sqrt{5}}{2} \approx 1.62$.

12. Let r = monthly payment on the refrigerator; then $r + 10$ = monthly payment on the oven; let m = number of months it took to pay for the refrigerator; then $m - 2$ = number of months it took to pay for the oven; $r = m = 370$ and $(r + 10)(m - 2) = 513$; $m = \dfrac{370}{r}$, so $(r + 10)\left(\dfrac{370}{r} - 2\right) = 513$; $370 + \dfrac{3700}{r} - 2r - 20 = 513$; $370r + 3700 - 2r^2 - 20r = 513r$; $2r^2 + 163r - 3700 = 0$; $r = \dfrac{-163 \pm \sqrt{163^2 - 4(2)(-3700)}}{2 \cdot 2} = \dfrac{-163 \pm \sqrt{56{,}169}}{4} = \dfrac{-163 \pm 237}{4}$; thus, Samantha paid \$18.50 per month for the refrigerator and \$28.50 per month for the oven.

Pages 302-303 · WRITTEN EXERCISES

A

1. $9 + 28 = 37$; two different irrational real roots

2. $25 - 16 = 9$; two different rational real roots

3. $64 + 80 = 144$; two different rational real roots

4. $64 + 60 = 124$; two different irrational real roots

5. $1.44 + 2.56 = 4$; two different rational real roots

6. $0.36 - 2 = -1.64$; two conjugate imaginary roots

7. $z^2 - z + \dfrac{5}{4} = 0$; $1 - 5 = -4$; two conjugate imaginary roots

8. $\dfrac{r^2}{4} - r + 1 = 0$; $1 - 1 = 0$; a double rational real root

9. $d^2 + \dfrac{7}{3}d - 2 = 0$; $\dfrac{49}{9} + 8 = \dfrac{121}{9}$; two different real rational roots

10. $4\sqrt{2} \cdot \sqrt{8} = 4 \cdot 4 = 16$; 2 different irrational real roots (Note: Since $a = \sqrt{2}$, these roots are not rational even though the discriminant is a perfect square.)

11. $25 - 8\sqrt{8}$; two different irrational real roots

12. $7y^2 - 2\sqrt{14}\,y + 2 = 0$; $4 \cdot 14 - 56 = 0$; a double irrational real root

13. $(x + 5)^2 = 0$; $x + 5 = 0$; $x = -5$; $\{-5\}$

14. $x^2 - 2x = 899$; $x^2 - 2x + 1 = 900$; $(x - 1)^2 = 900$; $x - 1 = \pm\sqrt{900}$; $x = 1 \pm \sqrt{900}$; $x = 1 \pm 30$; $x = 31$ or $x = -29$; $\{-29, 31\}$

15. $x^2 - 6x = -10$; $x^2 - 6x + 9 = -10 + 9$; $(x - 3)^2 = -1$; $x - 3 = \pm\sqrt{-1}$; $x = 3 \pm \sqrt{-1}$; $x = 3 \pm i$; $\{3 \pm i\}$

16. $x = \dfrac{q \pm \sqrt{q^2 - 4r^2}}{2r}$; $\left\{\dfrac{q \pm \sqrt{q^2 - 4r^2}}{2r}\right\}$

17. $2x - 4 = \pm\sqrt{50}$; $2x = 4 \pm 5\sqrt{2}$; $x = \dfrac{4 \pm 5\sqrt{2}}{2}$; $\left\{\dfrac{4 \pm 5\sqrt{2}}{2}\right\}$

18. $x^2 + 4x = 2496$; $x^2 + 4x + 4 = 2500$; $(x + 2)^2 = 2500$; $x + 2 = \pm\sqrt{2500}$; $x + 2 = \pm 50$; $x = -2 \pm 50$; $x = -52$ or $x = 48$; $\{-52, 48\}$

19. $x = \dfrac{6a \pm \sqrt{36a^2 - 20t^2}}{2} = \dfrac{6a \pm \sqrt{4(9a^2 - 5t^2)}}{2} = \dfrac{6a \pm 2\sqrt{9a^2 - 5t^2}}{2}$

$= 3a \pm \sqrt{9a^2 - 5t^2}$; $\{3a \pm \sqrt{9a^2 - 5t^2}\}$

20. $3x^2 - 5x - 2 = 18$; $3x^2 - 5x - 20 = 0$; $x = \dfrac{5 \pm \sqrt{(-5)^2 - 4(3)(-20)}}{6} = \dfrac{5 \pm \sqrt{265}}{6}$; $\left\{\dfrac{5 \pm \sqrt{265}}{6}\right\}$

21. $2x^2 - x - 15 = 6$; $2x^2 - x - 21 = 0$; $(2x - 7)(x + 3) = 0$; $2x - 7 = 0$ or $x + 3 = 0$; $x = \dfrac{7}{2}$ or $x = -3$; $\left\{-3, \dfrac{7}{2}\right\}$

B   22. $5(x + 2) - 5(x - 2) = 3(x - 2)(x + 2)$; $5x + 10 - 5x + 10 = 3(x^2 - 4)$;

$20 = 3x^2 - 12$; $3x^2 = 32$; $x^2 = \dfrac{32}{3}$; $x = \pm\sqrt{\dfrac{32}{3}} = \pm 4\sqrt{\dfrac{2}{3} \cdot \dfrac{3}{3}} = \pm\dfrac{4\sqrt{6}}{3}$; $\left\{\pm\dfrac{4\sqrt{6}}{3}\right\}$

23. $3(x + 1) = x(x - 1) + 2(3)$; $3x + 3 = x^2 - x + 6$; $x^2 - 4x + 3 = 0$; $(x - 1)(x - 3) = 0$; $x = 1$ (reject) or $x = 3$; $\{3\}$

24. $x(x - 1) + 2x(x - 2) = 6(x - 2)(x - 1)$; $x^2 - x + 2x^2 - 4x = 6(x^2 - 3x + 2)$; $x^2 - x + 2x^2 - 4x = 6x^2 - 18x + 12$; $3x^2 - 13x + 12 = 0$; $(3x - 4)(x - 3) = 0$; $3x - 4 = 0$ or $x - 3 = 0$; $x = \dfrac{4}{3}$ or $x = 3$; $\left\{\dfrac{4}{3}, 3\right\}$

25. **a.** $6^2 - 4(3)(k) = 36 - 12k$ **b.** $36 - 12k = 0$; $12k = 36$; $k = 3$

26. **a.** $(-10)^2 - 4(1)k = 100 - 4k$ **b.** $100 - 4k > 0$; $-4k > -100$; $k < 25$

27. **a.** $8^2 - 4(k)(-4) = 64 + 16k$ **b.** $64 + 16k < 0$; $16k < -64$; $k < -4$

28. **a.** $(-4)^2 - 4(k)(8) = 16 - 32k$ **b.** $16 - 32k = 0$; $32k = 16$; $k = \dfrac{1}{2}$

29. **a.** $6^2 - 4(k)(k) = 36 - 4k^2$ **b.** $36 - 4k^2 < 0$; $-4k^2 < -36$; $k^2 > 9$; $k < -3$ or $k > 3$

30. a. $(-8)^2 - 4(k^2)(4) = 64 - 16k^2$

b. $64 - 16k^2 > 0; -16k^2 > -64; k^2 < 4; -2 < k < 2$

31. a. $(-k)^2 - 4\left(\dfrac{1}{k}\right)(k) = k^2 - 4$ **b.** $k^2 - 4 > 0; k^2 > 4; k < -2$ or $k > 2$

32. $x^2 + \sqrt{5}x - x + 1 = 0; x^2 + (\sqrt{5} - 1)x + 1 = 0$; the discriminant is $(\sqrt{5} - 1)^2 - 4 = 5 - 2\sqrt{5} + 1 - 4 = 2 - 2\sqrt{5}$, which is negative; therefore, the roots are imaginary.

C   **33.** $rx = r(x + r) + x(x + r); rx = rx + r^2 + x^2 + rx; x^2 + rx + r^2 = 0$; the discriminant is $r^2 - 4r^2 = -3r^2$; since $r \neq 0, r^2 > 0$ so $-3r^2 < 0$. Therefore, the roots are imaginary.

34. The discriminant is $h^2 - 4(h - 1) = h^2 - 4h + 4 = (h - 2)^2$; if h is an integer, then $h - 2$ is an integer, and $(h - 2)^2$ is a perfect square. Therefore, the roots are rational.

35. a. $(-3)^2 - 4(i)(-2i) = 9 + 8i^2 = 9 - 8 = 1$

b. $z = \dfrac{3 \pm 1}{2i}; z = \dfrac{4}{2i} = \dfrac{2i}{i^2} = -2i$ or $z = \dfrac{2}{2i} = \dfrac{i}{i^2} = -i; -2i$ and $-i$

c. The rule applies only to quadratic equations with real coefficients.

Page 303 · COMPUTER EXERCISES

1.
```
10  PRINT "ENTER COEFFICIENTS A, B, C"
20  INPUT A, B, C
30  LET D = B * B - 4 * A * C
40  IF D < 0 THEN 70
50  IF D = 0 THEN 90
60  IF D > 0 THEN 110
70  PRINT "ROOTS ARE IMAGINARY."
80  GOTO 10
90  PRINT "ROOT IS A DOUBLE REAL ROOT."
100 GOTO 10
110 LET R = INT(SQR(D) + .5)
120 IF R * R = D THEN 150
130 PRINT "ROOTS ARE REAL AND IRRATIONAL."
140 GOTO 10
150 PRINT "ROOTS ARE REAL AND RATIONAL."
160 GOTO 10
```

2. a. real, irrational   **b.** real, irrational   **c.** imaginary

3.
```
10  PRINT "ENTER COEFFICIENTS A, B, C"
20  INPUT A, B, C
30  LET D = B * B - 4 * A * C
40  IF D < 0 THEN 70
50  IF D = 0 THEN 90
```

(continued)

```
 60  IF D > 0 THEN 110
 70  PRINT "ROOTS ARE IMAGINARY."
 80  GOTO 10
 90  PRINT "ROOT IS A DOUBLE REAL ROOT."
100 GOTO 135
110 LET R = INT(SQR(D) + .5)
120 IF R * R = D THEN 150
130 PRINT "ROOTS ARE REAL AND IRRATIONAL."
135 LET R1 = (−B + SQR(D))/(2 * A)
136 LET R2 = (−B − SQR(D))/(2 * A)
137 PRINT "ROOTS = "; R1; ","; R2
140 GOTO 10
150 PRINT "ROOTS ARE REAL AND RATIONAL."
160 GOTO 135
```

4. **a.** ROOTS ARE REAL AND RATIONAL.
   ROOTS = 5, −2.33333334
   b. ROOTS ARE REAL AND IRRATIONAL.
   ROOTS = 0.192582404, −5.1925824
   c. ROOTS ARE REAL AND IRRATIONAL.
   ROOTS = 5.10977223, −4.10977223

5.
```
 10  PRINT "ENTER COEFFICIENTS A, B, C"
 20  INPUT A, B, C
 30  LET D = B * B − 4 * A * C
 40  IF D < 0 THEN 70
 50  IF D = 0 THEN 90
 60  IF D > 0 THEN 110
 70  PRINT "ROOTS ARE IMAGINARY."
 80  GOTO 170
 90  PRINT "ROOT IS A DOUBLE REAL ROOT."
100 GOTO 135
110 LET R = INT(SQR(D) + .5)
120 IF R * R = D THEN 150
130 PRINT "ROOTS ARE REAL AND IRRATIONAL."
135 LET R1 = (−B + SQR(D))/(2 * A)
136 LET R2 = (−B − SQR(D))/(2 * A)
137 PRINT "ROOTS = "; R1; ","; R2
140 GOTO 10
150 PRINT "ROOTS ARE REAL AND RATIONAL."
160 GOTO 135
170 LET RT = −B/(2 * A)
180 PRINT "R1 = "; RT; " + "; SQR(ABS(D))/(2 * A); "I"
```

190 PRINT "R2 = "; RT; " − "; SQR(ABS(D))/(2 * A); "I"
200 GOTO 10

6. **a.** ROOTS ARE IMAGINARY.
   R1 = −1 + 2.6457131I
   R2 = −1 − 2.6457131I

  b. ROOTS ARE REAL AND IRRATIONAL.
   ROOTS = 2.39718086, −1.14718086

  c. ROOTS ARE IMAGINARY.
   R1 = 1.5 + 1.11803399I
   R2 = 1.5 − 1.11803399I

Page 303 · CHALLENGE

If $[a] = 1$ and $a = \dfrac{1}{a - [a]}$, then $a = \dfrac{1}{a - 1}$, or $a^2 - a = 1$; $a^2 - a - 1 = 0$; $a =$
$\dfrac{1 \pm \sqrt{(-1)^2 - 4(1)(-1)}}{2 \cdot 1} = \dfrac{1 \pm \sqrt{5}}{2}$. Since $[a] = 1$, $1 \le a < 2$. Therefore, the solution

is $\dfrac{1 + \sqrt{5}}{2}$.

Pages 306-307 · WRITTEN EXERCISES

A   1. $-\dfrac{b}{a} = \dfrac{7}{2}$; $\dfrac{c}{a} = \dfrac{4}{2} = 2$ 2. $-\dfrac{b}{a} = -\dfrac{5}{4}$; $\dfrac{c}{a} = -\dfrac{2}{4} = -\dfrac{1}{2}$

  3. $x^2 - 3x + 5 = 0$; $-\dfrac{b}{a} = 3$; $\dfrac{c}{a} = 5$

  4. $2x^2 - x - 4 = 0$; $-\dfrac{b}{a} = \dfrac{1}{2}$; $\dfrac{c}{a} = \dfrac{-4}{2} = -2$

  5. $-2 + (-1) = -3$; $(-2)(-1) = 2$; $x^2 + 3x + 2 = 0$

  6. $5 + 8 = 13$; $5 \cdot 8 = 40$; $x^2 - 13x + 40 = 0$

  7. $7 + (-3) = 4$; $7(-3) = -21$; $x^2 - 4x - 21 = 0$

  8. $5 + (-5) = 0$; $5(-5) = -25$; $x^2 - 25 = 0$

  9. $-2 + \dfrac{5}{2} = \dfrac{1}{2}$; $(-2)\left(\dfrac{5}{2}\right) = -5$; $x^2 - \dfrac{1}{2}x - 5 = 0$; $2x^2 - x - 10 = 0$

 10. $\dfrac{3}{2} + (-1) = \dfrac{1}{2}$; $\left(\dfrac{3}{2}\right)(-1) = -\dfrac{3}{2}$; $x^2 - \dfrac{1}{2}x - \dfrac{3}{2} = 0$; $2x^2 - x - 3 = 0$

 11. $-\dfrac{1}{2} + \left(-\dfrac{3}{2}\right) = -2$; $\left(-\dfrac{1}{2}\right)\left(-\dfrac{3}{2}\right) = \dfrac{3}{4}$; $x^2 + 2x + \dfrac{3}{4} = 0$; $4x^2 + 8x + 3 = 0$

 12. $\dfrac{2}{3} + \dfrac{4}{3} = 2$; $\left(\dfrac{2}{3}\right)\left(\dfrac{4}{3}\right) = \dfrac{8}{9}$; $x^2 - 2x + \dfrac{8}{9} = 0$; $9x^2 - 18x + 8 = 0$

 13. $4 + \sqrt{3} + 4 - \sqrt{3} = 8$; $(4 + \sqrt{3})(4 - \sqrt{3}) = 16 - 3 = 13$; $x^2 - 8x + 13 = 0$

14. $(-5 + \sqrt{7}) + (-5 - \sqrt{7}) = -10$; $(-5 + \sqrt{7})(-5 - \sqrt{7}) = 25 - 7 = 18$;
$x^2 + 10x + 18 = 0$

15. $\dfrac{1 + \sqrt{2}}{3} + \dfrac{1 - \sqrt{2}}{3} = \dfrac{2}{3}$; $\left(\dfrac{1 + \sqrt{2}}{3}\right)\left(\dfrac{1 - \sqrt{2}}{3}\right) = \dfrac{1 - 2}{9} = -\dfrac{1}{9}$; $x^2 - \dfrac{2}{3}x - \dfrac{1}{9} = 0$;
$9x^2 - 6x - 1 = 0$

16. $\dfrac{-2 + \sqrt{5}}{4} + \dfrac{-2 - \sqrt{5}}{4} = \dfrac{-4}{4} = -1$; $\left(\dfrac{-2 + \sqrt{2}}{4}\right)\left(\dfrac{-2 - \sqrt{5}}{4}\right) = \dfrac{4 - 5}{16} = -\dfrac{1}{16}$;
$x^2 + x - \dfrac{1}{16} = 0$; $16x^2 + 16x - 1 = 0$

17. $3 + i + 3 - i = 6$; $(3 + i)(3 - i) = 9 - i^2 = 9 + 1 = 10$; $x^2 - 6x + 10 = 0$

18. $4 + 2i + 4 - 2i = 8$; $(4 + 2i)(4 - 2i) = 16 - 4i^2 = 16 + 4 = 20$; $x^2 - 8x + 20 = 0$

19. $5 + i\sqrt{2} + 5 - i\sqrt{2} = 10$; $(5 + i\sqrt{2})(5 - i\sqrt{2}) = 25 - i^2 \cdot 2 = 25 + 2 = 27$;
$x^2 - 10x + 27 = 0$

20. $(-2 + i\sqrt{3}) + (-2 - i\sqrt{3}) = -4$; $(-2 + i\sqrt{3})(-2 - i\sqrt{3}) = 4 - i^2 \cdot 3 = 4 + 3$
$= 7$; $x^2 + 4x + 7 = 0$

21. $\dfrac{1 + i\sqrt{3}}{3} + \dfrac{1 - i\sqrt{3}}{3} = \dfrac{2}{3}$; $\left(\dfrac{1 + i\sqrt{3}}{3}\right)\left(\dfrac{1 - i\sqrt{3}}{3}\right) = \dfrac{1 - i^2 \cdot 3}{9} = \dfrac{1 + 3}{9} = \dfrac{4}{9}$;
$x^2 - \dfrac{2}{3}x + \dfrac{4}{9} = 0$; $9x^2 - 6x + 4 = 0$

22. $\dfrac{-2 + i\sqrt{2}}{5} + \dfrac{-2 - i\sqrt{2}}{5} = -\dfrac{4}{5}$; $\left(\dfrac{-2 + i\sqrt{2}}{5}\right)\left(\dfrac{-2 - i\sqrt{2}}{5}\right) = \dfrac{4 - i^2 \cdot 2}{25} = \dfrac{4 + 2}{25}$
$= \dfrac{6}{25}$; $x^2 + \dfrac{4}{5}x + \dfrac{6}{25} = 0$; $25x^2 + 20x + 6 = 0$

B **23.** $\sqrt{3} + \sqrt{2} + \sqrt{3} - \sqrt{2} = 2\sqrt{3}$; $(\sqrt{3} + \sqrt{2})(\sqrt{3} - \sqrt{2}) = 3 - 2 = 1$;
$x^2 - 2x\sqrt{3} + 1 = 0$

24. $\sqrt{5} - 2 + \sqrt{5} + 2 = 2\sqrt{5}$; $(\sqrt{5} - 2)(\sqrt{5} + 2) = 5 - 4 = 1$; $x^2 - 2x\sqrt{5} + 1 = 0$

25. $1 + \sqrt[4]{2} + 1 - \sqrt[4]{2} = 2$; $(1 + \sqrt[4]{2})(1 - \sqrt[4]{2}) = 1 - \sqrt{2}$; $x^2 - 2x + 1 - \sqrt{2} = 0$

26. $5 + i\sqrt{6} + 5 - i\sqrt{6} = 10$; $(5 + i\sqrt{6})(5 - i\sqrt{6}) = 25 - i^2 \cdot 6 = 25 + 6 = 31$;
$x^2 - 10x + 31 = 0$

27-30. Let r = the other root.   **27.** $2 + r = 5$; $r = 3$; $c = 2 \cdot 3 = 6$

28. $3.25r = \dfrac{26}{2} = 13$; $r = 4$; $3.25 + 4 = -\dfrac{b}{2}$; $b = -2(7.25) = -14.5$

29. $\dfrac{3}{2} + r = -\dfrac{6}{3} = -2$; $r = -\dfrac{7}{2}$; $\dfrac{c}{3} = -\dfrac{7}{2} \cdot \dfrac{3}{2} = -\dfrac{21}{4}$; $4c = -63$; $c = -\dfrac{63}{4}$

30. $r(1 + i) = 2i$; $r = \dfrac{2i}{1 + i} = \dfrac{2i(1 - i)}{(1 + i)(1 - i)} = \dfrac{2i - 2i^2}{1 - i^2} = \dfrac{2i + 2}{2} = i + 1$;
$1 + i + 1 + i = -b$; $b = -2 - 2i$

31. Let r and $r + 8$ represent the roots; then $r + r + 8 = \dfrac{12}{3} = 4$; $2r + 8 = 4$; $2r = -4$;

$r = -2$; $r + 8 = 6$; $\dfrac{c}{3} = (-2)(6)$; $c = -36$

32. Let r = the root. $r + r = \dfrac{8}{2} = 4$; $2r = 4$; $r = 2$; $\dfrac{c}{2} = r \cdot r = r^2$; $c = 2r^2 = 2(2)^2 = 8$

C **33.** **a.** $\dfrac{2m - n}{m} + \dfrac{n}{2m - m} = \dfrac{2m - n}{m} + \dfrac{n}{m} = \dfrac{2m - n + n}{m} = \dfrac{2m}{m} = 2$; therefore,

$2m$ is a root.

  b. $(x - n)(x - m) + mn = 2m(x - m)$; $x^2 - nx - mx + mn + mn$

$= 2mx - 2m^2$; $x^2 - nx - 3mx + 2mn + 2m^2 = 0$;

$x^2 - (3m + n)x + 2m(m + n) = 0$. Let r = other root; $2m \cdot r = 2m(m + n)$;

$r = m + n$

34. $\dfrac{1}{r_1} + \dfrac{1}{r_2} = \dfrac{r_2 + r_1}{r_1 r_2} = \dfrac{-\dfrac{b}{a}}{\dfrac{c}{a}} = -\dfrac{b}{c}$

35. $r + s = -\dfrac{b}{a}$; $s = -\dfrac{b}{a} - r$; $rs = \dfrac{c}{a}$; $r\left(-\dfrac{b}{a} - r\right) = \dfrac{c}{a}$; $-\dfrac{br}{a} - r^2 = \dfrac{c}{a}$;

$-br - ar^2 = c$; $ar^2 + br + c = 0$; $r = \dfrac{-b \pm \sqrt{b^2 - 4ac}}{2a}$; if

$r = \dfrac{-b + \sqrt{b^2 - 4ac}}{2a}$, then $s = -\dfrac{b}{a} - \left(\dfrac{-b + \sqrt{b^2 - 4ac}}{2a}\right)$

$= \dfrac{-2b + b - \sqrt{b^2 - 4ac}}{2a} = \dfrac{-b - \sqrt{b^2 - 4ac}}{2a}$; likewise, if $r = \dfrac{-b - \sqrt{b^2 - 4ac}}{2a}$,

then $s = -\dfrac{b}{a} - \left(\dfrac{-b - \sqrt{b^2 - 4ac}}{2a}\right) = \dfrac{-2b + b + \sqrt{b^2 - 4ac}}{2a} = \dfrac{-b + \sqrt{b^2 - 4ac}}{2a}$;

since $\dfrac{-b \pm \sqrt{b^2 - 4ac}}{2a}$ are the roots of $ax^2 + bx + c = 0$; r and s are the roots.

36-38. Answers may vary.

36. $\dfrac{2 + \sqrt{2}}{2} + \dfrac{2 - \sqrt{2}}{2} = \dfrac{4}{2} = 2$; $\left(\dfrac{2 + \sqrt{2}}{2}\right)\left(\dfrac{2 - \sqrt{2}}{2}\right) = \dfrac{4 - 2}{4} = \dfrac{1}{2}$; $x^2 - 2x + \dfrac{1}{2} = 0$;

$2x^2 - 4x + 1 = 0$; $(x - 4)(2x^2 - 4x + 1) = 0(x - 4)$; $2x^3 - 12x^2 + 17x - 4 = 0$

37. $3 + i\sqrt{2} + 3 - i\sqrt{2} = 6$; $(3 + i\sqrt{2})(3 - i\sqrt{2}) = 9 - i^2 \cdot 2 = 9 + 2 = 11$;

$x^2 - 6x + 11 = 0$; $(x - 1)(x^2 - 6x + 11) = 0(x - 1)$; $x^3 - 7x^2 + 17x - 11 = 0$

38. $1 + \sqrt{5} + 1 - \sqrt{5} = 2$; $(1 + \sqrt{5})(1 - \sqrt{5}) = 1 - 5 = -4$; $x^2 - 2x - 4 = 0$;

$3 + (-4) = -1$; $3(-4) = -12$; $x^2 + x - 12 = 0$; $(x^2 - 2x - 4)(x^2 + x - 12) = 0$;

$x^4 - x^3 - 18x^2 + 20x + 48 = 0$

39. If the coefficients are integers and $1 + \sqrt{2}$ is a root, then $1 - \sqrt{2}$ is a root. Also, if $2 - i\sqrt{3}$ is a root, then $2 + i\sqrt{3}$ is a root. $1 + \sqrt{2} + 1 - \sqrt{2} = 2$; $(1 + \sqrt{2})(1 - \sqrt{2}) = 1 - 2 = -1$; $x^2 - 2x - 1 = 0$; $2 + i\sqrt{3} + 2 - i\sqrt{3} = 4$; $(2 + i\sqrt{3})(2 - i\sqrt{3}) = 4 - i^2 \cdot 3 = 4 + 3 = 7$; $x^2 - 4x + 7 = 0$; $(x^2 - 2x - 1)(x^2 - 4x + 7) = 0$; $x^4 - 6x^3 + 14x^2 - 10x - 7 = 0$

Page 310 · WRITTEN EXERCISES

A **1.** Let $z = x^2$; $z^2 - 5z + 4 = 0$; $(z - 4)(z - 1) = 0$; $z = 4$ or $z = 1$; $x^2 = 4$ or $x^2 = 1$; $x = \pm 2$ or $x = \pm 1$; $\{\pm 1, \pm 2\}$

2. Let $z = x^3$; $z^2 - 9z + 8 = 0$; $(z - 8)(z - 1) = 0$; $z = 1$ or $z = 8$; $x^3 = 1$ or $x^3 = 8$; $x = 1$ or $x = 2$; $\{1, 2\}$

3. Let $z = \sqrt{x}$; $z^2 - 4z + 3 = 0$; $(z - 3)(z - 1) = 0$; $z = 3$ or $z = 1$; $\sqrt{x} = 3$ or $\sqrt{x} = 1$; $x = 9$ or $x = 1$; $\{9, 1\}$

4. Let $z = x^{-1}$; $2z^2 + 3z - 2 = 0$; $(2z - 1)(z + 2) = 0$; $z = \dfrac{1}{2}$ or $z = -2$; $x^{-1} = \dfrac{1}{2}$ or $x^{-1} = -2$; $x = 2$ or $x = -\dfrac{1}{2}$; $\left\{2, -\dfrac{1}{2}\right\}$

5. Let $z = n^4$; $4z^2 - 37z + 9 = 0$; $(4z - 1)(z - 9) = 0$; $4z = 1$ or $z = 9$; $z = \dfrac{1}{4}$ or $z = 9$; $n^4 = \dfrac{1}{4}$ or $n^4 = 9$. If $n^4 = \dfrac{1}{4}$, $n^4 - \dfrac{1}{4} = 0$; $\left(n^2 + \dfrac{1}{2}\right)\left(n^2 - \dfrac{1}{2}\right) = 0$; $n = \pm\sqrt{-\dfrac{1}{2}}$, which is not real, or $n = \pm\sqrt{\dfrac{1}{2}} = \pm\dfrac{1}{\sqrt{2}} \cdot \dfrac{\sqrt{2}}{\sqrt{2}} = \pm\dfrac{\sqrt{2}}{2}$. If $n^4 = 9$, $n^4 - 9 = 0$; $(n^2 + 3)(n^2 - 3) = 0$; $n = \pm\sqrt{-3}$, which is not real, or $n = \pm\sqrt{3}$; $\left\{\pm\dfrac{\sqrt{2}}{2}, \pm\sqrt{3}\right\}$

6. Let $z = \dfrac{1}{x}$; $9z^2 - 8z + 1 = 0$; $z = \dfrac{8 \pm \sqrt{(-8)^2 - 4(9)(1)}}{2 \cdot 9} = \dfrac{8 \pm \sqrt{28}}{18} = \dfrac{8 \pm 2\sqrt{7}}{18} = \dfrac{4 \pm \sqrt{7}}{9}$; $z = \dfrac{1}{\dfrac{4 \pm \sqrt{7}}{9}} = \dfrac{9}{4 \pm \sqrt{7}}$; $z = \dfrac{9}{4 + \sqrt{7}} \cdot \dfrac{4 - \sqrt{7}}{4 - \sqrt{7}} = \dfrac{9(4 - \sqrt{7})}{16 - 7} = \dfrac{9(4 - \sqrt{7})}{9} = 4 - \sqrt{7}$ or $z = \dfrac{9}{4 - \sqrt{7}} \cdot \dfrac{4 + \sqrt{7}}{4 + \sqrt{7}} = \dfrac{9(4 + \sqrt{7})}{16 - 7} = \dfrac{9(4 + \sqrt{7})}{9} = 4 + \sqrt{7}$; $\{4 \pm \sqrt{7}\}$

7. Let $x = z^{-1}$; $3x^2 - 4x + 1 = 0$; $(3x - 1)(x - 1) = 0$; $x = \dfrac{1}{3}$ or $x = 1$; $z^{-1} = \dfrac{1}{3}$ or $z^{-1} = 1$; $z = 3$ or $z = 1$; $\{3, 1\}$

8. Let $z = t^3$; $z^2 - 5z + 6 = 0$; $(z - 2)(z - 3) = 0$; $z = 2$ or $z = 3$; $t^3 = 2$ or $t^3 = 3$; $t = \sqrt[3]{2}$ or $t = \sqrt[3]{3}$; $\{\sqrt[3]{2}, \sqrt[3]{3}\}$

9. Let $z = \sqrt{u}$; $z^2 - 3z + 2 = 0$; $(z - 2)(z - 1) = 0$; $z = 2$ or $z = 1$; $\sqrt{u} = 2$ or $\sqrt{u} = 1$; $u = 4$ or $u = 1$; $\{4, 1\}$

10. Let $x = \sqrt{3z}$; $x^2 + 2x - 8 = 0$; $(x + 4)(x - 2) = 0$; $x = -4$ (reject) or $x = 2$. If $\sqrt{3z} = 2$, $3z = 4$; $z = \dfrac{4}{3}$; $\left\{\dfrac{4}{3}\right\}$

11. Let $z = (t^2 - 2)$; $z^2 - z - 2 = 0$; $(z - 2)(z + 1) = 0$; $z = 2$ or $z = -1$; $t^2 - 2 = 2$ or $t^2 - 2 = -1$; $t^2 = 4$ or $t^2 = 1$; $t = \pm 2$ or $t = \pm 1$; $\{\pm 2, \pm 1\}$

12. Let $z = \dfrac{x + 2}{x}$; $z^2 - z - 3 = 0$; $z = \dfrac{1 \pm \sqrt{(-1)^2 - 4(1)(-3)}}{2 \cdot 1} = \dfrac{1 \pm \sqrt{13}}{2}$;

$\dfrac{x + 2}{x} = \dfrac{1 + \sqrt{13}}{2}$ or $\dfrac{x + 2}{x} = \dfrac{1 - \sqrt{13}}{2}$; $x = \dfrac{4}{-1 + \sqrt{13}}$ or $x = \dfrac{4}{-1 - \sqrt{13}}$;

$x = \dfrac{4}{-1 + \sqrt{13}} \cdot \dfrac{-1 - \sqrt{13}}{-1 - \sqrt{13}} = \dfrac{-4 - 4\sqrt{13}}{1 - 13} = \dfrac{-4 - 4\sqrt{13}}{-12} = \dfrac{1 + \sqrt{13}}{3}$ or

$x = \dfrac{4}{-1 - \sqrt{13}} \cdot \dfrac{-1 + \sqrt{13}}{-1 + \sqrt{13}} = \dfrac{-4 + 4\sqrt{13}}{1 - 13} = \dfrac{-4 + 4\sqrt{13}}{-12} = \dfrac{1 - \sqrt{13}}{3}$; $\left\{\dfrac{1 \pm \sqrt{13}}{3}\right\}$

13. Let $z = x^2$; $z^2 - 3z - 10 = 0$; $(z - 5)(z + 2) = 0$; $z = 5$ or $z = -2$; $x^2 = 5$ or $x^2 = -2$; $x = \pm\sqrt{5}$ or $x = \pm i\sqrt{2}$; $\{\pm\sqrt{5}, \pm i\sqrt{2}\}$

14. Let $z = m^4$; $z^2 - 13z + 36 = 0$; $(z - 9)(z - 4) = 0$; $z = 9$ or $z = 4$. If $m^4 = 9$, $m^4 - 9 = 0$; $(m^2 + 3)(m^2 - 3) = 0$; $m^2 = 3$ or $m^2 = -3$; $m = \pm\sqrt{3}$ or $m = \pm\sqrt{-3} = \pm i\sqrt{3}$. If $m^4 = 4$, $m^4 - 4 = 0$; $(m^2 - 2)(m^2 + 2) = 0$; $m = \pm\sqrt{2}$ or $m = \pm i\sqrt{2}$; $\{\pm\sqrt{3}, \pm i\sqrt{3}, \pm\sqrt{2}, \pm i\sqrt{2}\}$

15. Let $z = x^{-2}$; $36z^2 - 5z - 1 = 0$; $(9z + 1)(4z - 1) = 0$; $z = -\dfrac{1}{9}$ or $z = \dfrac{1}{4}$. If $x^{-2} = \dfrac{1}{x^2} = -\dfrac{1}{9}$, $x^2 = -9$ and $x = \pm 3i$. If $x^{-2} = \dfrac{1}{x^2} = \dfrac{1}{4}$, $x^2 = 4$ and $x = \pm 2$; $\{\pm 3i, \pm 2\}$

16. Let $z = r^2$; then $r^4 - 10 = 3r^2$ is equivalent to $z^2 - 3z - 10 = 0$; $(z - 5)(z + 2) = 0$; $z = 5$ or $x = -2$; $x^2 = 5$ or $x^2 = -2$; $x = \pm\sqrt{5}$ or $x = \pm i\sqrt{2}$; $\{\pm\sqrt{5}, \pm i\sqrt{2}\}$

17. Let $z = \sqrt{t}$, then $2t + 5\sqrt{2} + 3 = 2z^2 + 5z + 3 = 0$; $(2z + 3)(z + 1) = 0$; $z = -\dfrac{3}{2}$ (reject) or $z = -1$ (reject); no solution

18. Let $z = \sqrt{y}$; then $2y + 3\sqrt{2} - 2 = 2z$; $3z - 2 = 0$; $(2z - 1)(z + 2) = 0$; $z = \dfrac{1}{2}$ or $z = -2$ (reject). If $\sqrt{y} = \dfrac{1}{2}$, $y = \dfrac{1}{4}$; $\left\{\dfrac{1}{4}\right\}$

19. Let $x = \dfrac{1}{\sqrt{z}}$, then $\dfrac{2}{z} + \dfrac{1}{\sqrt{z}} - 1 = 2x^2 + x - 1 = 0$; $(2x - 1)(x + 1) = 0$; $x = \dfrac{1}{2}$ or $x = -1$ (reject). If $\dfrac{1}{\sqrt{z}} = \dfrac{1}{2}$, $\sqrt{z} = 2$ and $z = 4$; $\{4\}$

20. Let $z = \dfrac{1}{\sqrt{p}}$; then $\dfrac{3}{p} - \dfrac{7}{\sqrt{p}} - 6 = 3z^2 - 7z - 6 = 0$; $(3z + 2)(z - 3) = 0$; $z = -\dfrac{2}{3}$ (reject) or $z = 3$. If $\dfrac{1}{\sqrt{p}} = 3$, then $\sqrt{p} = \dfrac{1}{3}$ and $p = \dfrac{1}{9}$; $\left\{\dfrac{1}{9}\right\}$

B 21. $z(z^4 - 11z^2 + 10) = 0$. Let $x = z^2$. $z^4 - 11z^2 + 10 = x^2 - 11x + 10 = 0$. $(x - 10)(x - 1) = 0$; $x = 10$ or $x = 1$; if $z^2 = 10$, $z = \pm\sqrt{10}$; if $z^2 = 1$, $z = \pm 1$; $\{0, \pm\sqrt{10}, \pm 1\}$

22. $x^2(x^4 + 7x^2 + 12) = 0$. Let $z = x^2$, then $x^4 + 7x^2 + 12 = z^2 + 7z + 12 = 0$;

$(z + 4)(z + 3) = 0$; $z = -4$ or $z = -3$; if $x^2 = -4$, $x = \pm 2i$; if $x^2 = -3$; $x = \pm i\sqrt{3}$

$\{0, \pm 2i, \pm i\sqrt{3}\}$

23. Let $z = x^2 - 2x$. Then $(x^2 - 2x)^2 - 2(x^2 - 2x) - 3 = z^2 - 2z - 3 = 0$;

$(z - 3)(z + 1) = 0$; $z = 3$ or $z = -1$. If $x^2 - 2x = 3$, $x^2 - 2x - 3 = 0$;

$(x - 3)(x + 1) = 0$; $x = -1$ or $x = 3$. If $x^2 - 2x = -1$, $x^2 - 2x + 1 = 0$;

$(x - 1)^2 = 0$; $x = 1$; $\{-1, 1, 3\}$

24. Let $z = (1 + 2y^2)$. Then $(1 + 2y^2)^2 + 6(1 + 2y^2) - 7 = z^2 + 6z - 7 = 0$;

$(z + 7)(z - 1) = 0$; $z = -7$ or $z = 1$. If $1 + 2y^2 = -7$, $2y^2 + 8 = 0$; $2(y^2 + 4) = 0$;

$y = \pm 2i$. If $1 + 2y^2 = 1$, $2y^2 = 0$; $y^2 = 0$; $y = 0$; $\{\pm 2i, 0\}$

25. Let $z = \dfrac{1}{x - 1}$. Then $\left(\dfrac{1}{x - 1}\right)^2 - \dfrac{1}{x - 1} - 2 = z^2 - z - 2 = 0$; $(z - 2)(z + 1) = 0$

$z = 2$ or $z = -1$. If $\dfrac{1}{x - 1} = 2$, $x - 1 = \dfrac{1}{2}$; $x = \dfrac{3}{2}$. If $\dfrac{1}{x - 1} = -1$, $x - 1 = -1$ and

$x = 0$; $\left\{\dfrac{3}{2}, 0\right\}$

26. Let $x = \dfrac{1}{z - 1}$. Then $\dfrac{6}{(z - 1)^2} - \dfrac{1}{z - 1} - 1 = 6x^2 - x - 1 = 0$; $(3x + 1)(2x - 1) = $

0; $x = \dfrac{1}{2}$ or $x = -\dfrac{1}{3}$. If $\dfrac{1}{z - 1} = \dfrac{1}{2}$, then $z - 1 = 2$ and $z = 3$. If $\dfrac{1}{z - 1} = -\dfrac{1}{3}$, then

$z - 1 = -3$ and $z = -2$; $\{3, -2\}$

27. Let $z = \dfrac{1 + t}{t}$. Then $\left(\dfrac{1 + t}{t}\right)^2 - 4\left(\dfrac{1 + t}{t}\right) + 3 = z^2 - 4z + 3 = 0$. $(z - 3)(z - 1) = $

0; $z = 3$ or $z = 1$ (reject). If $\dfrac{1 + t}{t} = 3$, $1 + t = 3t$; $2t = 1$; $t = \dfrac{1}{2}$; $\left\{\dfrac{1}{2}\right\}$

28. Let $z = \dfrac{x - 1}{x + 3}$. Then $\left(\dfrac{x - 1}{x + 3}\right)^2 + 4\left(\dfrac{x - 1}{x + 3}\right) + 3 = z^2 + 4z + 3 = 0$.

$(z + 3)(z + 1) = 0$; $z = -1$ or $z = -3$. If $\dfrac{x - 1}{x + 3} = -1$, $-(x + 3) = x - 1$; $-x - 3 = $

$x - 1$; $2x = -2$; $x = -1$. If $\dfrac{x - 1}{x + 3} = -3$, $x - 1 = -3x - 9$; $4x = -8$; $x = -2$

$\{-1, -2\}$

C 29. Let $z = \sqrt[4]{x + 6}$. Then $\sqrt{x + 6} - 6\sqrt[4]{x + 6} + 8 = z^2 - 6z + 8 = 0$;

$(z - 4)(z - 2) = 0$; $z = 4$ or $z = 2$. If $\sqrt[4]{x + 6} = 4$, $x + 6 = 4^4 = 256$; $x = 250$. If

$\sqrt[4]{x + 6} = 2$, $x + 6 = 2^4 = 16$; $x = 10$; $\{250, 10\}$

30. Let $z = \sqrt[4]{x - 2}$. Then $\sqrt{x - 2} + \sqrt{\sqrt{x - 2}} - 2 = z^2 + z - 2 = 0$;

$(z + 2)(z - 1) = 0$; $z = -2$ (reject) or $z = 1$. If $\sqrt[4]{x - 2} = 1$, $x - 2 = 1$; $x = 3$; $\{3\}$

31. $(s^2 - 9)(s^4 - 3s^2 - 2) - 2(s^2 - 9) = (s^2 - 9)(s^4 - 3s^2 - 2 - 2)$

$= (s^2 - 9)(s^4 - 3s^2 - 4) = 0$; $s^2 - 9 = 0$ and $s = \pm 3$ or $s^4 - 3s^2 - 4 = 0$. Let $z = $

s^2; $z^2 - 3z - 4 = 0$; $(z - 4)(z + 1) = 0$; $z = 4$ or $z = -1$. If $s^2 = 4$, $s = \pm 2$; if

$s^2 = -1$, $s = \pm i$; $\{\pm i, \pm 3, \pm 2\}$

32. $(\sqrt{y} - 3)(y - \sqrt{y} - 1) - (\sqrt{y} - 3) = (\sqrt{y} - 3)(y - \sqrt{y} - 1 - 1)$
$= (\sqrt{y} - 3)(y - \sqrt{y} - 2) = 0.$ $\sqrt{y} - 3 = 0$ and $y = 9$ or $y - \sqrt{y} - 2 = 0.$ Let
$z = \sqrt{y}.$ Then $z^2 - z - 2 = 0;$ $(z - 2)(z + 1) = 0;$ $z = 2$ or $z = -1$ (reject). If
$\sqrt{y} = 2,$ $y = 4;$ $\{9, 4\}$

Pages 315-316 · WRITTEN EXERCISES

A **1.**
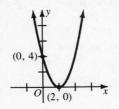

2.
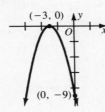

3.
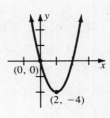

4.
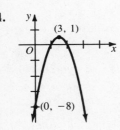

5.
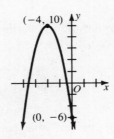

6.
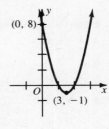

7.
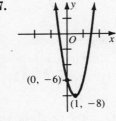

8.
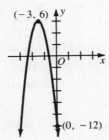

9.
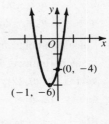

10.
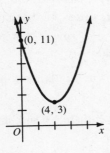

11.
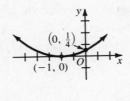

12.
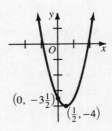

13. $h = 5$ **14.** If $x = 0$ and $y = 0,$ $0 - k = -2(0 - 3)^2 = -2(9) = -18;$ $k = 18$

15. If $y = 5$ and $x = 2,$ $5 - 3 = a(2 - 1)^2;$ $2 = a(1)^2;$ $a = 2$

16. If $x = 0$ and $y = 4,$ $4 + 5 = a(0 + 2)^2;$ $9 = a(4);$ $a = \dfrac{9}{4}$

17. Since the vertex is the origin, $h = 0$, $k = 0$, so $y = ax^2$; since $(2, -2)$ is on the parabola,
$$-2 = a \cdot 2^2; \; -2 = 4a; \; a = -\frac{1}{2}; \; y = -\frac{1}{2}x^2$$

18. $h = -2$, $k = 8$; $y - 8 = a(x + 2)^2$; since $(0, 0)$ is on the parabola, $-8 = a(2)^2$ or $4a = -8$; $a = -2$; $y - 8 = -2(x + 2)^2$

19. $h = 3$, $k = -2$; $y + 2 = a(x - 3)^2$; since $(1, 10)$ is on the parabola, $10 + 2 = a(-2)^2$ $12 = 4a$; $a = 3$; $y + 2 = 3(x - 3)^2$

20. $h = 4$, $k = 5$; $y - 5 = a(x - 4)^2$; since $(5, 3)$ is on the parabola, $-2 = a(5 - 4)^2$; $-2 = a$; $y - 5 = -2(x - 4)^2$

B **21.** $h = 3$, $k = 7$; since $(0, 4)$ is on the parabola, $y - 7 = a(x - 3)^2$; $-3 = a(-3)^2$; $-3 = 9a$; $a = -\frac{1}{3}$; $y - 7 = -\frac{1}{3}(x - 3)^2$

22. Since the parabola opens downward, $a < 0$; since it is congruent to $y = x^2$, $|a| = 1$ and $a = -1$; $h = 2$, $k = -5$; $y + 5 = -(x - 2)^2$

23. $h = -2$; $0 - k = a(0 - h)^2$ and $5 - k = a(1 - h)^2$ are true; $-k = a(2)^2$ and $5 - k = a(3)^2$; $-k = 4a$ and $5 - k = 9a$; $5 + 4a = 9a$; $5a = 5$; $a = 1$. $-k = 4 \cdot 1$; $k = -4$. $y + 4 = 1(x + 2)^2$

24. $h = 1$; $(0, -2)$ and $(1, 0)$ are on the parabola, so $-2 - k = a(0 - h)^2$ and $0 - k = a(1 - h)^2$; $-2 - k = a(-1)^2$ and $-k = a(0)^2$; $k = 0$ and $-2 - 0 = a$ or $a = -2$; $y = -2(x - 1)^2$

25. Since parabolas are symmetric and $(-2, 0)$ and $(2, 0)$ are on the given parabola, the axis must be midway between -2 and 2, or at $x = 0$; since $(0, 12)$ is on the parabola, the vertex is $(0, 12)$; $y - 12 = a(x - 0)^2$; substituting $(2, 0)$ for (x, y), $0 - 12 = a(2)^2$; $4a = -12$, $a = -3$; $y - 12 = -3x^2$

26. Since parabolas are symmetric and $(1, 0)$ and $(3, 0)$ are points on the parabola, the axis must be midway between 1 and 3, or at $x = 2$; since a parabola with equation $y - k = a(x - h)^2$ is tangent to a *horizontal* line only at its vertex, the y-coordinate of the vertex is -4 and the vertex is $(2, -4)$; $h = 2$; $k = -4$, so $y + 4 = a(x - 2)^2$; substituting $(1, 0)$ for (x, y), $4 = a(-1)^2$; $a = 4$; $y + 4 = 4(x - 2)^2$

27. Let $y = 0$; $1 = (x - 3)^2$; $x - 3 = \pm 1$; $x = \pm 1 + 3$; $x = 4$ or $x = 2$; the x-intercepts are 2 and 4.

28. Let $y = 0$; $4 = -2(x + 1)^2$; $(x + 1)^2 = -2$; $x + 1 = \pm i\sqrt{2}$; there are no x-intercepts.

29. Let $y = 0$; $1 = \frac{1}{4}(x + 1)^2$; $4 = (x + 1)^2$; $x + 1 = \pm 2$; $x = -1 \pm 2$; $x = -3$ or $x = 1$; the x-intercepts are -3 and 1.

30. Let $y = 0$; $-3 = -\frac{2}{3}(x - 1)^2$; $\frac{9}{2} = (x - 1)^2$; $x - 1 = \pm\sqrt{\frac{9}{2}} = \pm\frac{3}{2}\sqrt{2}$; $x = 1 \pm \frac{3}{2}\sqrt{2}$; the x-intercepts are $1 \pm \frac{3}{2}\sqrt{2}$.

31. Let $x = h + r$, $y = s$. Then $s - k = (h + r - h)^2$; $s - k = (r)^2$. Since $(-r)^2 = (r)^2$, $s - k = (h - r - h)^2$ is also true. Thus $(h - r, s)$ is on the parabola. This proves that the parabola is symmetric about the axis, $x = h$.

32. a. 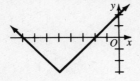   **b.**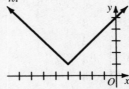

33. a.

y	x
-3	9
-2	4
-1	1
0	0
1	1
2	4
3	9

b.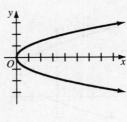

c. No; two values of y correspond to every nonzero value of x.

34. a.

y	x
-3	-9
-2	-4
-1	-1
0	0
1	-1
2	-4
3	-9

b.

y	x
-3	11
-2	6
-1	3
0	2
1	3
2	6
3	11

c.

y	x
-4	9
-3	4
-2	1
-1	0
0	1
1	4
2	9

d.

y	x
-4	11
-3	6
-2	3
-1	2
0	3
1	6
2	11

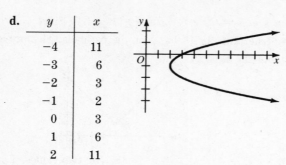

e.

y	x
-1	$-\dfrac{3}{2}$
0	1
1	$\dfrac{5}{2}$
2	3
3	$\dfrac{5}{2}$
4	1
5	$-\dfrac{3}{2}$

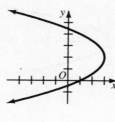

35. a. vertex $(0, 0)$, $y = 0$
   b. vertex $(2, 0)$, $y = 0$
   c. vertex $(0, -1)$, $y = -1$
   d. vertex $(2, -1)$, $y = -1$
   e. vertex $(3, 2)$, $y = 2$

36. a. $x - h = a(y - k)^2$ where (h, k) is the vertex and $y = k$ is the axis.
   b. One; either 2 (if $h < 0$ and $a > 0$ or $h > 0$ and $a < 0$), 1 (if $h = 0$), or 0 (if $h < 0$ and $a < 0$ or $h > 0$ and $a > 0$).

Pages 320-321 · WRITTEN EXERCISES

A   **1.** $y - 11 = x^2 - 6x$; $y - 11 + 9 = x^2 - 6x + 9$; $y - 2 = (x - 3)^2$

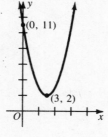   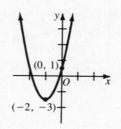   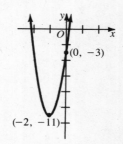

   Ex. 1   Ex. 2   Ex. 3

2. $y - 1 = x^2 + 4x$; $y - 1 + 4 = x^2 + 4x + 4$; $y + 3 = (x + 2)^2$

3. $y + 3 = 2x^2 + 8x$; $y + 3 = 2(x^2 + 4x)$; $y + 3 + 8 = 2(x^2 + 4x + 4)$;
   $y + 11 = 2(x + 2)^2$

4. $y - 5 = 3x^2 - 6x$; $y - 5 = 3(x^2 - 2x)$; $y - 5 + 3 = 3(x^2 - 2x + 1)$;
   $y - 2 = 3(x - 1)^2$

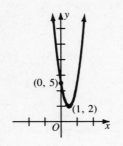

Ex. 4

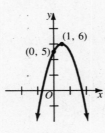

Ex. 5

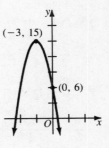

Ex. 6

5. $y - 5 = -x^2 + 2x;\ y - 5 = -(x^2 - 2x);\ y - 5 - 1 = -(x^2 - 2x + 1);$
$y - 6 = -(x - 1)^2$

6. $y - 6 = -x^2 - 6x;\ y - 6 = -(x^2 + 6x);\ y - 6 - 9 = -(x^2 + 6x + 9);$
$y - 15 = -(x + 3)^2$

7. $y - 9 = -3x^2 - 6x;\ y - 9 = -3(x^2 + 2x);\ y - 9 - 3 = -3(x^2 + 2x + 1);$
$y - 12 = -3(x + 1)^2$

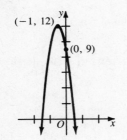

Ex. 7

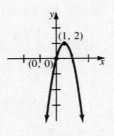

Ex. 8

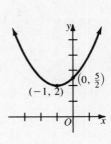

Ex. 9

8. $y = -2x^2 + 4x;\ y = -2(x^2 - 2x);\ y - 2 = -2(x^2 - 2x + 1);\ y - 2 = -2(x - 1)^2$

9. $y - \dfrac{5}{2} = \dfrac{1}{2}x^2 + x;\ y - \dfrac{5}{2} = \dfrac{1}{2}(x^2 + 2x);\ y - \dfrac{5}{2} + \dfrac{1}{2} = \dfrac{1}{2}(x^2 + 2x + 1);$

$y - 2 = \dfrac{1}{2}(x + 1)^2$

10. $y + \dfrac{1}{3} = -\dfrac{1}{3}x^2 + \dfrac{4}{3}x;\ y + \dfrac{1}{3} = -\dfrac{1}{3}(x^2 - 4x^2);\ y + \dfrac{1}{3} - \dfrac{4}{3} = -\dfrac{1}{3}(x^2 - 4x + 4);$

$y - 1 = -\dfrac{1}{3}(x - 2)^2$

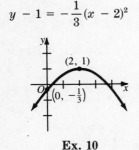

Ex. 10

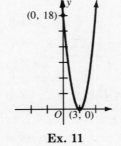

Ex. 11

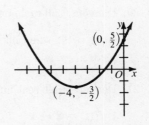

Ex. 12

11. $y - 18 = 2x^2 - 12x$; $y - 18 = 2(x^2 - 6x)$; $y - 18 + 18 = 2(x^2 - 6x + 9)$;
$y = 2(x - 3)^2$

12. $y - \dfrac{5}{2} = \dfrac{1}{4}x^2 + 2x$; $y - \dfrac{5}{2} = \dfrac{1}{4}(x^2 + 8x)$; $y - \dfrac{5}{2} + 4 = \dfrac{1}{4}(x^2 + 8x + 16)$;

$y + \dfrac{3}{2} = \dfrac{1}{4}(x + 4)^2$

13. $-\dfrac{b}{2a} = \dfrac{-6}{2 \cdot 2} = -\dfrac{3}{2}$; $f\left(-\dfrac{3}{2}\right) = 2\left(\dfrac{9}{4}\right) + 6\left(-\dfrac{3}{2}\right) = -\dfrac{9}{2}$; vertex $= \left(-\dfrac{3}{2}, -\dfrac{9}{2}\right)$; since

$a > 0$, the minimum value of the function is $-\dfrac{9}{2}$.

14. $-\dfrac{b}{2a} = \dfrac{3}{2}$; $g\left(\dfrac{3}{2}\right) = \left(\dfrac{3}{2}\right)^2 - 3\left(\dfrac{3}{2}\right) + 10 = 7\dfrac{3}{4}$; vertex $= \left(\dfrac{3}{2}, 7\dfrac{3}{4}\right)$; since $a > 0$, the

minimum value of g is $7\dfrac{3}{4}$.

15. $-\dfrac{b}{2a} = \dfrac{3}{2(-3)} = -\dfrac{1}{2}$; $f\left(-\dfrac{1}{2}\right) = 12 - 3\left(-\dfrac{1}{2}\right) - 3\left(\dfrac{1}{4}\right) = 12\dfrac{3}{4}$;

vertex $= \left(-\dfrac{1}{2}, 12\dfrac{3}{4}\right)$; since $a < 0$, the maximum value of f is $12\dfrac{3}{4}$.

16. $-\dfrac{b}{2a} = \dfrac{-9}{2(-3)} = \dfrac{3}{2}$; $h\left(\dfrac{3}{2}\right) = 9\left(\dfrac{3}{2}\right) - 3\left(\dfrac{3}{2}\right)^2 = \dfrac{27}{4}$; vertex $= \left(\dfrac{3}{2}, 6\dfrac{3}{4}\right)$; since $a < 0$,

the maximum value of h is $6\dfrac{3}{4}$.

17. $p(x) = 4x^2 - 4x - 15$; $-\dfrac{b}{2a} = \dfrac{4}{8} = \dfrac{1}{2}$; $p\left(\dfrac{1}{2}\right) = 4\left(\dfrac{1}{4}\right) - 4\left(\dfrac{1}{2}\right) - 15 = -16$;

vertex $= \left(\dfrac{1}{2}, -16\right)$; since $a > 0$, the minimum value of p is -16.

18. $g(x) = 9x^2 - 9x - 10$; $-\dfrac{b}{2a} = \dfrac{9}{18} = \dfrac{1}{2}$; $g\left(\dfrac{1}{2}\right) = 9\left(\dfrac{1}{4}\right) - 9\left(\dfrac{1}{2}\right) - 10 = -12\dfrac{1}{4}$;

vertex $= \left(\dfrac{1}{2}, -12\dfrac{1}{4}\right)$; since $a > 0$, the minimum value of g is $-12\dfrac{1}{4}$.

19. Domain $=$ all real numbers; $-\dfrac{b}{2a} = \dfrac{6}{6} = 1$; $f(1) = 3 - 6 - 9 = -12$; $a > 0$; range is

$\{y : y \geq -12\}$; when $f(x) = 0$, $3(x^2 - 2x - 3) = 0$; $3(x - 3)(x + 1) = 0$; $x = 3$ or $x = -1$; zeros are 3 and -1.

20. Domain $=$ all real numbers; $-\dfrac{b}{2a} = \dfrac{2}{-2} = -1$; $g(-1) = 8 + 2 - 1 = 9$; $a < 0$; range is

$\{y : y \leq 9\}$; when $g(x) = 0$, $x^2 + 2x - 8 = 0$; $(x + 4)(x - 2) = 0$; $x = 2$ or $x = -4$; zeros are 2 and -4.

21. Domain $=$ all real numbers; $H(x) = 2(x^2 - 2x - 35) = 2x^2 - 4x - 70$; $-\dfrac{b}{2a} = \dfrac{4}{4} = $

1; $H(1) = 2 - 4 - 70 = -72$; $a > 0$; range is $\{y : y \geq -72\}$; when $H(x) = 0$,
$2(x - 7)(x + 5) = 0$; $x = 7$ or $x = -5$; zeros are 7 and -5.

22. Domain = all real numbers; $f(x) = \frac{1}{2}(24 + 10x + x^2) = 12 + 5x + \frac{1}{2}x^2$; $-\frac{b}{2a} =$

$\dfrac{-5}{2\left(\frac{1}{2}\right)} = -5$; $f(-5) = 12 + 5(-5) + \frac{1}{2}(25) = -\frac{1}{2}$; $a > 0$, range is $\left\{y : y \geq -\frac{1}{2}\right\}$;

when $f(x) = 0$, $\frac{1}{2}(6 + x)(4 + x) = 0$; $x = -6$ or $x = -4$; zeros are -6 and -4.

23. Domain = all real numbers; $F(x) = 9 - (x^2 + 12x + 36) = -x^2 - 12x - 27$; $-\frac{b}{2a} =$

$\dfrac{12}{-2} = -6$; $F(-6) = -36 + 72 - 27 = 9$; $a < 0$; range is $\{y : y \leq 9\}$; when $F(x) = 0$,

$x^2 + 12x + 27 = 0$; $(x + 3)(x + 9) = 0$; $x = -3$ or $x = -9$; zeros are -3 and -9.

24. Domain = all real numbers; $G(x) = 2(x^2 - 10x + 25) - 8 = 2x^2 - 20x + 42$; $-\frac{b}{2a} =$

$\dfrac{20}{4} = 5$; $G(5) = 50 - 100 + 42 = -8$; $a > 0$; range is $\{y : y \geq -8\}$; when $G(x) = 0$,

$2x^2 - 20x + 42 = 0$; $2(x^2 - 10x + 21) = 0$; $2(x - 3)(x - 7) = 0$; $x = 3$ or $x = 7$;

zeros are 3 and 7.

B 25. $b^2 - 4ac = 64 - 4 \cdot 2 \cdot 9 = -8 < 0$; the graph of F has no x-intercepts.

26. $b^2 - 4ac = 25 - 4(3)(2) = 1 > 0$; the graph of g has 2 x-intercepts.

27. $b^2 - 4ac = 144 - 4(-4)(-9) = 0$; the graph of f has 1 x-intercept.

28. $b^2 - 4ac = 81 - 4(-3)(-7) = -3 < 0$; the graph of G has no x-intercepts.

29. $b^2 - 4ac = 49 - 4(4)(3) = 1 > 0$; the graph of h has 2 x-intercepts.

30. $b^2 - 4ac = 576 - 4(-9)(-16) = 0$; the graph of f has 1 x-intercept.

31. **a.** $y - c = ax^2 + bx$; $y - c = a\left(x^2 + \frac{b}{a}x\right)$; $y - c + a\left(\frac{b}{2a}\right)^2 =$

$a\left(x^2 + \frac{b}{a}x + \left(\frac{b}{2a}\right)^2\right)$; $y - c + \frac{ab^2}{4a^2} = a\left(x + \frac{b}{2a}\right)^2$; $y - \left(c - \frac{ab^2}{4a^2}\right) =$

$a\left(x + \frac{b}{2a}\right)^2$; $y + \left(\frac{b^2 - 4ac}{4a}\right) = a\left(x + \frac{b}{2a}\right)^2$

b. $\left(-\dfrac{b}{2a}, -\dfrac{b^2 - 4ac}{4a}\right)$

32. The discriminant of $x^2 - 6x + 10 = 0$ is $36 - 40 = -4 < 0$; the parabola does not intersect the x-axis. The discriminant of $x^2 - 6x + 10 = 1$ or $x^2 - 6x + 9 = 0$ is $36 - 36 = 0$; the parabola intersects $y = 1$ once. The discriminant of $x^2 - 6x + 9 = 2$ or $x^2 - 6x + 7 = 0$ is $36 - 28 = 8 > 0$; the parabola intersects $y = 2$ twice.

33. **a.** No zeros, so $b^2 - 4ac < 0$.   **b.** $c = y$-intercept > 0

c. opens upward, $a > 0$ **d.** Since $-\dfrac{b}{2a} = 0$, $b = 0$.

34. a. 2 zeros, $b^2 - 4ac > 0$ **b.** $c = y$-intercept $= 0$ **c.** opens downward, $a < 0$

d. $-\dfrac{b}{2a} > 0$ and $a < 0$, so $-b < 0$ and $b > 0$

35. a. Double root, $b^2 - 4ac = 0$ **b.** $c = y$-intercept > 0

   c. opens upward, $a > 0$ **d.** $-\dfrac{b}{2a} < 0$ and $a > 0$, so $-b < 0$ and $b >$

C **36.** The equation of the parabola has roots 1 and 5, and is of the form $y = a(x - 1)(x - 5$
or $y = a(x^2 - 6x + 5)$; since $(0, 2)$ also satisfies the equation, $a(0^2 - 6 \cdot 0 + 5) =$
and $a = \dfrac{2}{5}$; $y = \dfrac{2}{5}(x^2 - 6x + 5)$ or $y = \dfrac{2}{5}x^2 - \dfrac{12}{5}x + 2$.

37. Since the maximum value occurs at $x = -2$, $x = -2$ is the axis and the roots are
symmetric about -2, so the second zero is -5; $(x + 5)(x - 1) = 0$; $x^2 + 4x - 5 = 0$
$y = ax^2 + bx + c$ must have coefficients in the same ratio and $(-2, 8)$ must satisfy
the equation; let k = ratio; $y = k(x^2 + 4x - 5)$; $y = kx^2 + 4kx - 5k$;
$k(-2)^2 + k(4)(-2) - 5k = 8$; $4k - 8k - 5k = 8$; $-9k = 8$; $k = -\dfrac{8}{9}$;
$y = -\dfrac{8}{9}(x^2 + 4x - 5)$; $y = -\dfrac{8}{9}x^2 - \dfrac{32}{9}x + \dfrac{40}{9}$

38. Since the zeros are symmetric about the axis, the axis is $x = \dfrac{3 - 1}{2} = 1$ and the vertex
is $(1, 10)$; $(x - 3)(x + 1) = 0$; $x^2 - 2x - 3 = 0$; $y = k(x^2 - 2x - 3)$;
$y = kx^2 - 2kx - 3k$; $k(1)^2 - 2(1)k - 3k = 10$; $k - 2k - 3k = 10$; $-4k = 10$;
$k = -\dfrac{5}{2}$; $y = -\dfrac{5}{2}x^2 + 5x + \dfrac{15}{2}$

39. If $f(-x) = f(x)$, $a(-x)^2 + b(-x) + c = ax^2 + bx + c$; $ax^2 - bx + c = ax^2 + bx + c$
$-bx = bx$; $2bx = 0$ for all x, so $b = 0$; if $b = 0$, then $f(-x) = a(-x)^2 + 0(-x) + c =$
$ax^2 + c = ax^2 + 0x + c = f(x)$.

Pages 321-323 · PROBLEMS

A **1.** Let x and $40 - x$ be the numbers; $x(40 - x) = P(x)$; $P(x) = 40x - x^2$; since $a < 0$, P
has a maximum value at its vertex; $x = \dfrac{-40}{-2} = 20$; $P(20) = 400$; the greatest product
is 400.

2. Let x and $20 - x$ be the numbers; $x^2 + (20 - x)^2 = S(x)$; $S(x) = x^2 + 400 - 40x + x^2$
$S(x) = 2x^2 - 40x + 400$; since $a > 0$, S has a minimum value at its vertex; $x = \dfrac{40}{4} =$
10; the numbers are 10 and 10.

3. The lengths of the three fenced sides are x, x and $100 - 2x$; $A(x) = x(100 - 2x)$
$100x - 2x^2$; the greatest area occurs at $x = \dfrac{-100}{-4} = 25$; $A(25) = 25(50) = 1250$
1250 m^2

4. The rectangle has perimeter 32, so the sum of the lengths of its sides is 16; let x and $16 - x$ be the lengths of the sides; then $A(x) = x(16 - x) = 16x - x^2$; the greatest area occurs at $x = \dfrac{-16}{-2} = 8$; $A(8) = 64$; 64 cm^2

5. Maximum power occurs at $I = \dfrac{-120}{-32} = \dfrac{15}{4} = 3.75$; maximum power is $P\left(\dfrac{15}{4}\right) = 120\left(\dfrac{15}{4}\right) - 16\left(\dfrac{15}{4}\right)^2 = 450 - 225 = 225$; a current of 3.75 amps produces the maximum power of 225 watts.

6. $x = $ length of 2 short sides and partitioning side, so the length of each long side is $\dfrac{800 - 3x}{2}$; $A(x) = x\left(\dfrac{800 - 3x}{2}\right) = \dfrac{800}{2}x - \dfrac{3}{2}x^2 = 400x - \dfrac{3}{2}x^2$; the maximum area occurs at $x = \dfrac{-400}{-3} = \dfrac{400}{3}$; $A(x) = \dfrac{160,000}{3} - \dfrac{160,000}{6} = \dfrac{80,000}{3}$; $26,666\dfrac{2}{3}$ m^2

7. **a.** Maximum height occurs at $t = \dfrac{-80}{-32} = \dfrac{5}{2}$; $h = 80\left(\dfrac{5}{2}\right) - 16\left(\dfrac{25}{4}\right) = 200 - 100 = 100$; 100 ft

   b. The ball hits the ground when $h = 0$, so $0 = 80t - 16t^2 = t(80t - 16)$; $t = 0$ or $t = 5$; the ball will hit the ground 5 s after it is thrown.

8. **a.** Maximum height occurs at $x = \dfrac{-\dfrac{4}{3}}{-\dfrac{2}{90}} = 60$; $y = \dfrac{4}{3}(60) - \dfrac{(60)^2}{90} = 40$; maximum height is 40 ft.

   b. When $x = 105$, $y = \dfrac{4}{3}(105) - \dfrac{(105)^2}{90} = 140 - 122\dfrac{1}{2} = 17\dfrac{1}{2}$ ft; the ball will clear the crossbar.

9. If there is 300 m of fencing and a 12 m opening, the lot perimeter will be 312 m with width $= x$ and length $= \dfrac{312}{2} - x$ or $156 - x$; $A(x) = x(156 - x) = 156x - x^2$; the maximum area will occur at $x = \dfrac{-156}{-2} = 78$; 78 m by 78 m.

10. The area of the rectangle is $x \cdot y$; since $3x + 2y = 12$, $y = \dfrac{12 - 3x}{2}$, so $A(x) = x\left(\dfrac{12 - 3x}{2}\right) = 6x - \dfrac{3}{2}x^2$; the maximum area occurs at $x = -\dfrac{6}{-3} = 2$; $A(2) = 12 - 6 = 6$; the maximum area is 6.

11. Let $x = $ number of passengers above 20; then $20 + x = $ total number of passengers and $(60 - 2x) = $ amount each person will pay; revenue $= (20 + x)(60 - 2x) = 1200 + 20x - 2x^2$; maximum revenue occurs when $x = \dfrac{-20}{-2 \cdot 2} = 5$; 25 passengers would produce the greatest revenue.

12. Let $x = $ number of dollars of increase; then $10 + x = $ new fare and $300 - 15x = $ number of passengers per day; income $= (10 + x)(300 - 15x) = 3000 + 150x - 15x^2$; maximum income occurs at $x = \dfrac{-150}{-30} = 5$. The fare yielding the greatest income is \$15.

13. If the height of the triangle is 8, the height of $\triangle APQ$ is $8 - y$; $\triangle APQ$ is similar t$\bullet$

$\triangle ABC$, so $\dfrac{x}{10} = \dfrac{8-y}{8}$; $8x = 80 - 10y$; $8x - 80 = -10y$; $y = 8 - \dfrac{4}{5}x$; $A = xy =$

$x\left(8 - \dfrac{4}{5}x\right) = 8x - \dfrac{4}{5}x^2$; maximum area occurs at $x = -\dfrac{8}{-\dfrac{8}{5}} = 5$; $A =$

$8(5) - \dfrac{4}{5} \cdot 25 = 20$; maximum area of the rectangle is 20.

Pages 324-325 · CHAPTER REVIEW

1. d; $(x - 3)^2 = -8$; $x - 3 = \pm\sqrt{-8}$; $x = 3 \pm 2i\sqrt{2}$

2. c; $z^2 + 3z + \dfrac{d}{4}$; $\left(\dfrac{3}{2}\right)^2 = \dfrac{d}{4}$; $\dfrac{9}{4} = \dfrac{d}{4}$; $d = 9$

3. b; $3y^2 - 8y + 5 = 0$; $(3y - 5)(y - 1) = 0$; $y = 1, \dfrac{5}{3}$

4. d; Let x = increase; $(6 + x)(4 + x) = 48$; $24 + 10x + x^2 = 48$; $x^2 + 10x - 24 = 0$
   $(x + 12)(x - 2) = 0$; $x = -12, 2$

5. a; Discriminant is $9 - 4 \cdot 5 \cdot 2 = -31$ 6. c; Discriminant is $49 - 4 \cdot 3 \cdot 4 = 1$

7. d; If the equation has a double root, the discriminant $[-(k - 3)]^2 - 4k = 0$;
   $k^2 - 6k + 9 - 4k = 0$; $k^2 - 10k + 9 = 0$; $(k - 1)(k - 9) = 0$; $k = 1, 9$

8. b; sum $= \dfrac{4}{4} = 1$; product $= -\dfrac{3}{4}$

9. a; $\dfrac{2 + i\sqrt{3}}{2} + \dfrac{2 - i\sqrt{3}}{2} = 2 = -b$; $b = -2$;

   $\left(\dfrac{2 + i\sqrt{3}}{2}\right)\left(\dfrac{2 - i\sqrt{3}}{2}\right) = \dfrac{4 - 3i^2}{4} = \dfrac{7}{4} = c$; $x^2 - 2x + \dfrac{7}{4} = 0$; $4x^2 - 8x + 7 = 0$

10. d; Let r be the other root; $r + \dfrac{2}{3} = \dfrac{18}{9}$; $r = 2 - \dfrac{2}{3} = \dfrac{4}{3}$

11. c; Let $z = x^2 + 2x$; $z^2 + 2z - 3 = 0$; $(z + 3)(z - 1) = 0$; $z = -3$ or $z = 1$; $x^2 - 2x =$
    -3 or $x^2 - 2x = 1$; $x^2 - 2x + 3 = 0$ or $x^2 - 2x - 1 = 0$; by the quadratic formul$\bullet$
    $x = \dfrac{2 \pm 2i\sqrt{2}}{2}$ or $x = \dfrac{2 \pm 2\sqrt{2}}{2}$; $x = 1 \pm i\sqrt{2}$ or $1 \pm \sqrt{2}$

12. b; $y - 2 = -\dfrac{1}{2}(x - 4)^2$; vertex $= (4, 2)$

13. c; $y + 1 = a(x - 1)^2$; $1 + 1 = a(3 - 1)^2$; $2 = a(4)$; $a = \dfrac{1}{2}$; $y + 1 = \dfrac{1}{2}(x - 1)^2$

14. d; $(0, -2)$ is a point on the parabola, so $-4 = a(2)^2$; $4a = -4$; $a = -1$

15. d; Minimum occurs at $x = \dfrac{-8}{2 \cdot 4} = -1$; $f(-1) = 4(-1)^2 + 8(-1) - 5 = -9$

16. b; The function contains $(0, 0)$ and has a maximum.

17. b; discriminant $= 144 - 4(-4)(-9) = 0$

Page 326 · CHAPTER TEST

1. $z + 7 = \pm\sqrt{5}$; $z = -7 \pm \sqrt{5}$

2. $3m^2 + 4m = 15$; $m^2 + \dfrac{4}{3}m = 5$; $m^2 + \dfrac{4}{3}m + \dfrac{4}{9} = 5 + \dfrac{4}{9}$; $\left(m + \dfrac{2}{3}\right)^2 = \dfrac{49}{9}$;

$m + \dfrac{2}{3} = \pm\sqrt{\dfrac{49}{9}}$; $m = -\dfrac{2}{3} \pm \dfrac{7}{3}$; $m = -3$ or $m = \dfrac{5}{3}$

3. $w = \dfrac{-3 \pm \sqrt{9 - 4(2)(3)}}{2 \cdot 2} = \dfrac{-3 \pm i\sqrt{15}}{4}$

4. a. $b^2 - 4ac = 121 - 4 \cdot 3 \cdot 4 = 73 > 0$; the equation has two different (irrational) real roots.

   b. $b^2 - 4ac = 4 - 4 \cdot 1 \cdot 5 = -16$; the equation has conjugate imaginary roots.

5. $b^2 - 4ac = 100 - 4 \cdot 5k = 100 - 20k$; if the equation has 2 real roots, $100 - 20k > 0$; $-20k > -100$; $k < 5$; $\{k : k < 5\}$

6. $7p^2 - 5p + 2 = 0$; sum $= \dfrac{5}{7}$; product $= \dfrac{2}{7}$

7. Answers may vary; $4 - \sqrt{3} + 4 + \sqrt{3} = 8$; $(4 - \sqrt{3})(4 + \sqrt{3}) = 16 - 3 = 13$; $x^2 - 8x + 13 = 0$

8. Let $z = c^2$; $z^2 - 6z + 8 = 0$; $(z - 4)(z - 2) = 0$; $z = 2$ or $z = 4$; $c^2 = 2$ or $c^2 = 4$; $c = \pm\sqrt{2}$ or $c = \pm 2$; $\{\pm\sqrt{2}, \pm 2\}$

9. Vertex: $(5, 0)$; axis: $x = 5$

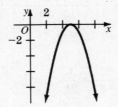

10. $y + 2 = a(x + 4)^2$; $5 + 2 = a(-1 + 4)^2$; $7 = 9a$; $a = \dfrac{7}{9}$; $y + 2 = \dfrac{7}{9}(x + 4)^2$

11. a. $\dfrac{3}{4} > 0$; minimum value

   b. Minimum occurs at $x = -\dfrac{b}{2a} = \dfrac{6}{\dfrac{3}{2}} = 4$; $f(4) = \dfrac{3}{4} \cdot 16 - 6 \cdot 4 + 12 = 0$.

12. Domain $=$ all real numbers; $a < 0$, so f has a maximum value at $x = \dfrac{-4}{-2} = 2$; $f(2) =$

$3 + 8 - 4 = 7$; range $= \{y : y \le 7\}$; $-x^2 + 4x + 3 = 0$; $x = \dfrac{-4 \pm \sqrt{16 - 4(-1)(3)}}{2(-1)} =$

$\dfrac{-4 \pm \sqrt{28}}{-2} = \dfrac{-4 \pm 2\sqrt{7}}{-2} = 2 \pm \sqrt{7}$; zeros are $2 \pm \sqrt{7}$.

13. Let x and $16 - x$ be the numbers; $P(x) = x(16 - x) = 16x - x^2$; the maximum valu

occurs at $x = \dfrac{-16}{-2} = 8$; $P(8) = 16 \cdot 8 - 8^2 = 64$; the greatest possible product is 64

Page 327 · CUMULATIVE REVIEW

1. a. $\left(\dfrac{2}{3}a^2b\right)(36a^6b^2) = 24a^8b^3$ **b.** $5t(6t^2 + 13t - 5) = 30t^3 + 65t^2 - 25t$

2. a. $4x - 4x^3 = 4x(1 - x^2) = 4x(1 - x)(1 + x)$; $6x^4 + 12x^3 + 6x^2 =$
$6x^2(x^2 + 2x + 1) = 6x^2(x + 1)(x + 1)$; GCF $= 2x(x + 1)$
    b. LCM $= 12x^2(1 - x)(1 + x)^2$

3. a. $z^3(5z - 2) + 1(5z - 2) = (5z - 2)(z^3 + 1) = (5z - 2)(z + 1)(z^2 - z + 1)$
    b. $(7m - 2n)(2m + 3n)$

4. Let s = length of side of cube; $(s + 2)(s + 3)(s - 4) = s^3 - 73$;
$(s + 2)(s^2 - s - 12) = s^3 - 73$; $s^3 + s^2 - 14s - 24 = s^3 - 73$; $s^2 - 14s + 49 =$ (
$(s - 7)^2 = 0$; $s = 7$; the original volume is 343 cm³.

5. $y^2 + 3y - 10 > 0$; $(y + 5)(y - 2) > 0$; $(y + 5 > 0$ and $y - 2 > 0)$ or $(y + 5 <$
and $y - 2 < 0)$; $(y > -5$ and $y > 2)$ or $(y < -5$ and $y < 2)$; $y > 2$ or $y < -5$
$\{y : y < -5$ or $y > 2\}$

$$\xleftarrow[\;]{} \quad \overset{-6}{|} \; \diamond \; \overset{-4}{|} \; | \; | \; \overset{-2}{|} \; | \; \overset{0}{|} \; | \; \overset{2}{|} \; \diamond \; \overset{4}{|} \; | \xrightarrow[\;]{}$$

6. $\dfrac{216m^6n^3}{81m^6n^8} = \dfrac{8}{3n^5}$ **7.** $\dfrac{8y}{3x} \cdot 2^{-2}x^{-3(-2)}y^{0(-2)} = \dfrac{8y}{3x} \cdot \dfrac{x^6}{4} = \dfrac{2x^5y}{3}$

8. $\dfrac{(z^2 + 4)(z^2 - 4)}{(4z - 1)(z + 2)} = \dfrac{(z^2 + 4)(z + 2)(z - 2)}{(4z - 1)(z + 2)} = \dfrac{(z^2 + 4)(z - 2)}{4z - 1}$

9. $\dfrac{3a(a + 3)}{6a(1 - 9a^2)} \cdot \dfrac{1}{3a^2 + 10a + 3} = \dfrac{3a(a + 3)}{6a(1 - 3a)(1 + 3a)} \cdot \dfrac{1}{(3a + 1)(a + 3)}$

$= \dfrac{1}{2(1 - 3a)(1 + 3a)^2}$

10. $\dfrac{1}{2(t - 2)} + \dfrac{1}{t(2 - t)} = \dfrac{t - 2}{2t(t - 2)} = \dfrac{1}{2t}$

11. $\dfrac{\left(\dfrac{1}{x + 1} - \dfrac{1}{(x + 1)^2}\right)(x + 1)^2(x - 1)}{\left(1 + \dfrac{1}{x - 1}\right)(x + 1)^2(x - 1)} = \dfrac{(x + 1)(x - 1) - (x - 1)}{(x + 1)^2(x - 1) + (x + 1)^2} = \dfrac{x - 1}{(x + 1)^2}$

12. Let x = number of mL of 5% solution; then $500 - x$ = number of mL of 25% solution
$0.05x + 0.25(500 - x) = 0.1(500)$; $5x + 25(500 - x) = 10(500)$; $5x + 12{,}500 - 25x =$
5000; $-20x = -7500$; $x = 375$; $500 - 375 = 125$; 375 mL of 5% solution, 125 mL o
25% solution

13. $2(x + 2)^2 - 2(x - 1)^2 = 3(x - 1)(x + 2)$; $2(x^2 + 4x + 4) - 2(x^2 - 2x + 1) =$
$3(x^2 + x - 2)$; $2x^2 + 8x + 8 - 2x^2 + 4x - 2 = 3x^2 + 3x - 6$; $12x + 6 =$
$3x^2 + 3x - 6$; $3x^2 - 9x - 12 = 0$; $x^2 - 3x - 4 = 0$; $(x - 4)(x + 1) = 0$; $x = 4$ or
$x = -1$; $\{4, -1\}$

14. $2y^3 = 16$; $y^3 = 8$; $y^3 - 8 = 0$; $(y - 2)(y^2 + 2y + 4) = 0$; $y = 2$ or

$$y = \frac{-2 \pm \sqrt{4 - 4(1)(4)}}{2} = \frac{-2 \pm \sqrt{-12}}{2} = \frac{-2 \pm 2i\sqrt{3}}{2} = -1 \pm i\sqrt{3}; \{2, -1 \pm i\sqrt{3}\}$$

15. $1 - 5k = (k + 7)^2$; $1 - 5k = k^2 + 14k + 49$; $k^2 + 19k + 48 = 0$;

$(k + 3)(k + 16) = 0$; $k = -3$ or $k = -16$ (reject); $k = -3$

16. $\sqrt{\dfrac{9}{2} \cdot \dfrac{2}{2}} - \sqrt{9 \cdot 2} = \dfrac{3}{2}\sqrt{2} - 3\sqrt{2} = -\dfrac{3}{2}\sqrt{2}$ **17.** $3 + 2\sqrt{45} + 15 = 18 + 6\sqrt{5}$

18. $\dfrac{9}{3\sqrt{2} - 2\sqrt{3}} \cdot \dfrac{3\sqrt{2} + 2\sqrt{3}}{3\sqrt{2} + 2\sqrt{3}} = \dfrac{27\sqrt{2} + 18\sqrt{3}}{18 - 12} = \dfrac{27\sqrt{2} + 18\sqrt{3}}{6} = \dfrac{9\sqrt{2} + 6\sqrt{3}}{2}$

19. $\dfrac{1 - i}{2 + i} \cdot \dfrac{(2 - i)}{(2 - i)} = \dfrac{2 - 3i + i^2}{4 - i^2} = \dfrac{1 - 3i}{5}$

20. $x^2 + 4x = \dfrac{9}{4}$; $x^2 + 4x + 4 = \dfrac{9}{4} + 4$; $(x + 2)^2 = \dfrac{25}{4}$; $x + 2 = \pm\sqrt{\dfrac{25}{4}}$; $x + 2 = \pm\dfrac{5}{2}$;

$x = -2 \pm \dfrac{5}{2}$; $x = -\dfrac{9}{2}$ or $x = \dfrac{1}{2}$; $\left\{-\dfrac{9}{2}, \dfrac{1}{2}\right\}$

21. $\dfrac{5}{2}y^2 - 4y + 1 = 0$; $y = \dfrac{4 \pm \sqrt{16 - 4\left(\dfrac{5}{2}\right)(1)}}{2\left(\dfrac{5}{2}\right)} = \dfrac{4 \pm \sqrt{6}}{5}$; $\left\{\dfrac{4 \pm \sqrt{6}}{5}\right\}$

22. $b^2 - 4ac < 0$; $(-2)^2 - 4(3)(k) < 0$; $4 - 12k < 0$; $-12k < -4$; $k > \dfrac{1}{3}$; $\left\{k : k > \dfrac{1}{3}\right\}$

23. Sum $= \dfrac{4}{6} = \dfrac{2}{3}$; product: $-\dfrac{9}{6} = -\dfrac{3}{2}$

24. $\dfrac{3 + 2i}{4} + \dfrac{3 - 2i}{4} = \dfrac{6}{4} = \dfrac{3}{2}$; $\left(\dfrac{3 + 2i}{4}\right)\left(\dfrac{3 - 2i}{4}\right) = \dfrac{9 - 4i^2}{16} = \dfrac{9 + 4}{16} = \dfrac{13}{16}$;

$x^2 - \dfrac{3}{2}x + \dfrac{13}{16} = 0$; $16x^2 - 24x + 13 = 0$

25.

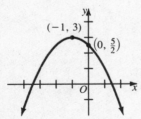

26. Domain = all real numbers; $a > 0$, so f has a minimum value at $x = -\dfrac{b}{2a} = -\dfrac{b}{a} =$

$-\dfrac{4}{4} = -1$; $f(-1) = 2 - 4 + 3 = 1$; range is $\{y : y \geq 1\}$; since $b^2 - 4ac =$

$16 - 4(2)(3) = -8 < 0$ the function has no zeros.

27. Let x and $x - 6$ be the numbers; $P(x) = x(x - 6) = x^2 - 6x$; the minimum value

occurs at $x = \dfrac{6}{2} = 3$; $P(3) = 9 - 18 = -9$; the least possible value of the product is -9.

Pages 332-333 · WRITTEN EXERCISES

A 1. $15 = \dot{m}(10)$; $m = \dfrac{15}{10} = \dfrac{3}{2}$; $y = \dfrac{3}{2}(14) = 21$

2. $15 = m(24)$; $m = \dfrac{15}{24} = \dfrac{5}{8}$; $25 = \dfrac{5}{8}t$; $t = \dfrac{8}{5}(25) = 40$

3. $\dfrac{4.8}{3} = \dfrac{z}{12.5}$; $3z = 60$; $z = 20$

4. $\dfrac{12}{10\frac{2}{3}} = \dfrac{p}{24}$; $\dfrac{32}{3}p = 288$; $p = \dfrac{3}{22}(288) = 27$

5. $\dfrac{20}{4} = \dfrac{v}{16}$; $4v = 320$; $v = 80$

6. $\dfrac{6}{2} = \dfrac{y}{4}$; $2y = 24$; $y = 12$

7. $\dfrac{6}{2} = \dfrac{w}{8}$; $2w = 48$; $w = 24$

8. $\dfrac{9}{3} = \dfrac{15}{2t-1}$; $18t - 9 = 45$; $18t = 54$; $t = 3$

9-12. $\dfrac{a}{b} = \dfrac{b}{c}$; $b^2 = ac$; $b = \sqrt{ac}$

9. $b = \sqrt{4 \cdot 9} = \sqrt{36} = 6$

10. $b = \sqrt{8 \cdot 18} = \sqrt{144} = 12$

11. $b = \sqrt{6 \cdot 10} = \sqrt{60} = 2\sqrt{15}$

12. $b = \sqrt{4 \cdot 12} = \sqrt{48} = 4\sqrt{3}$

B 13. 1. $\dfrac{a}{b} = \dfrac{c}{d}$; a, b, c, and d nonzero (Given)

   2. $\dfrac{bd}{1}\left(\dfrac{a}{b}\right) = \dfrac{bd}{1}\left(\dfrac{c}{d}\right)$ (Mult. prop. of equal.) 3. $\dfrac{bda}{b} = \dfrac{bdc}{d}$ (Rule for mult. of fractions)

   4. $da = bc$ (Canc. rule for fractions)   5. $ad = bc$ (Comm. prop. for mult.)

14. 1. $\dfrac{a}{b} = \dfrac{c}{d}$; a, b, c, and d nonzero (Given)

   2. $\dfrac{b}{c}\left(\dfrac{a}{b}\right) = \dfrac{b}{c}\left(\dfrac{c}{d}\right)$ (Mult. prop. of equal.) 3. $\dfrac{ba}{cb} = \dfrac{bc}{cd}$ (Rule for mult. of fractions)

   4. $\dfrac{a}{c} = \dfrac{b}{d}$ (Canc. rule for fractions)

15. 1. $\dfrac{a}{b} = \dfrac{c}{d}$; a, b, c, and d nonzero (Given)

   2. $\dfrac{d}{a}\left(\dfrac{a}{b}\right) = \dfrac{d}{a}\left(\dfrac{c}{d}\right)$ (Mult. prop. of equal.)

   3. $\dfrac{da}{ab} = \dfrac{dc}{ad}$ (Rule for mult. of fractions)   4. $\dfrac{d}{b} = \dfrac{c}{a}$ (Canc. rule for fractions)

16. 1. $\dfrac{a}{b} = \dfrac{c}{d}$; a, b, c, and d nonzero (Given) 2. $\dfrac{db}{ac}\left(\dfrac{a}{b}\right) = \dfrac{db}{ac}\left(\dfrac{c}{d}\right)$ (Mult. prop. of equal.)

   3. $\dfrac{dba}{acb} = \dfrac{dbc}{acd}$ (Rule for mult. of fractions) 4. $\dfrac{d}{c} = \dfrac{b}{a}$ (Canc. rule for fractions)

17. 1. $\dfrac{a}{b} = \dfrac{c}{d}$; a, b, c, and d nonzero (Given)   2. $\dfrac{a}{b} + 1 = \dfrac{c}{d} + 1$ (Add. prop. of equal.)

3. $\dfrac{a}{b} + b \cdot \dfrac{1}{b} = \dfrac{c}{d} + d \cdot \dfrac{1}{d}$ (Prop. of recip.)   4. $\dfrac{a}{b} + \dfrac{b}{b} = \dfrac{c}{d} + \dfrac{d}{d}$ (Def. of div.)

5. $\dfrac{a + b}{b} = \dfrac{c + d}{d}$ (Rule for add. of fractions)

18. 1. $\dfrac{a}{b} = \dfrac{c}{d}$; a, b, c, and d nonzero (Given)

2. $\dfrac{a}{b} - 1 = \dfrac{c}{d} - 1$ (Add. prop. of equal.; def. of subtr.)

3. $\dfrac{a}{b} - b \cdot \dfrac{1}{b} = \dfrac{c}{d} - d \cdot \dfrac{1}{d}$ (Prop. of recip.) 4. $\dfrac{a}{b} - \dfrac{b}{b} = \dfrac{c}{d} - \dfrac{d}{d}$ (Def. of div.)

5. $\dfrac{a - b}{b} = \dfrac{c - d}{d}$ (Rule for subtr. of fractions)

19. 1. $\dfrac{a}{b} = \dfrac{c}{d}$; a, b, c, and d nonzero; $c \neq d$ (Given)

2. $\dfrac{a - b}{b} = \dfrac{c - d}{d}$ (Ex. 18)   3. $\dfrac{a - b}{c - d} = \dfrac{b}{d}$ (Ex. 14)

4. $\dfrac{a}{c} = \dfrac{b}{d}$ (Ex. 14)   5. $\dfrac{a - b}{c - d} = \dfrac{a}{c}$ (Subst.)

20. 1. $\dfrac{a}{b} = \dfrac{c}{d}$; a, b, c, and d nonzero; $a \neq b$ and $c \neq d$ (Given)

2. $\dfrac{a + b}{b} = \dfrac{c + d}{d}$ and $\dfrac{a - b}{b} = \dfrac{c - d}{d}$ (Ex. 17 and Ex. 18)

3. $\dfrac{a + b}{c + d} = \dfrac{b}{d}$ and $\dfrac{a - b}{c - d} = \dfrac{b}{d}$ (Ex. 14)

4. $\dfrac{a + b}{c + d} = \dfrac{a - b}{c - d}$ (Trans. prop. of equal.)   5. $\dfrac{a + b}{a - b} = \dfrac{c + d}{c - d}$ (Ex. 14)

C 21. 1. g is a direct variation over the set of real numbers. (Given)

2. There is a real number m such that for every real number x, $g(x) = mx$. (Def. of direct variation)

3. $g(a + c) = m(a + c)$; $g(a) + g(c) = ma + mc$ (Def. of direct variation; a and c are real numbers)

4. $m(a + c) = ma + mc$ (Dist. prop.)   5. $g(a + c) = g(a) + g(c)$ (Subst.)

22. 1. For every real number x, $g(x) = mx + b$, $m \neq 0$, $b \neq 0$. (Def. of linear function; g is not a direct variation, and g is not the constant function 0.)

2. $g(a + c) - [g(a) + g(c)] = m(a + c) + b - (ma + b + mc + b) = ma + mc + b - ma - mc - 2b = -b$ (Subst.; dist. prop.)

3. $b \neq 0$ and $-b \neq 0$ (Step 1)

4. $g(a + c) \neq g(a) + g(c)$ (For real numbers x and y, $x = y$ if and only if $x - y = 0$.)

Pages 333-334 · PROBLEMS

A　**1.** $\dfrac{y}{x} = 0.03$; $\dfrac{2}{x} = 0.03$; $x = \dfrac{2}{0.03} = 66\dfrac{2}{3}$; $66\dfrac{2}{3}$ ft

2. Let t = tax in dollars; $\dfrac{t}{210} = \dfrac{8.25}{150}$; $t = \dfrac{210(8.25)}{150} = 11.55$; \$11.55

3. Let c = commission in dollars; $\dfrac{c}{6500} = \dfrac{756}{5400}$; $c = \dfrac{6500(756)}{5400} = 910$; \$910

4. Let x = resistance in ohms; $\dfrac{x}{150} = \dfrac{6}{90}$; $x = \dfrac{150(6)}{90} = 10$; $10\ \Omega$

5. Let x = cost in cents of the 765 g can if it were priced at the same rate; $\dfrac{x}{765} = \dfrac{56}{432}$; $x = \dfrac{765(56)}{432} = 99\dfrac{1}{6}$; the 765 g can is a better value

6. Let x = length in meters; $\dfrac{x}{7} = \dfrac{1500}{4}$; $x = \dfrac{7(1500)}{4} = 2625$; 2625 m

7. Let n = number of voters likely to support measure; $\dfrac{n}{18,000} = \dfrac{396}{600}$; $n = \dfrac{18,000(396)}{600} = 11,880$; 11,880 voters

8. Let s = speed in meters per second; $\dfrac{s}{4} = \dfrac{24.5}{2.5}$; $s = \dfrac{4(24.5)}{2.5} = 39.2$; 39.2 m/s

9. 7°C ≈ 280°K; 21°C ≈ 294°K; let v = volume in liters; $\dfrac{v}{294} = \dfrac{10}{280}$; $v = \dfrac{294(10)}{280} = 10.5$; 10.5 L

10. Let r = rate of cooling in degrees Celsius per minute; $\dfrac{r}{110 - 20} = \dfrac{40}{260 - 20}$; $\dfrac{r}{90} = \dfrac{40}{240} = \dfrac{1}{6}$; $r = \dfrac{90}{6} = 15$; 15°C/min

B　**11.** Let x = natural length in centimeters; $\dfrac{27 - x}{10} = \dfrac{36 - x}{15}$; $15(27 - x) = 10(36 - x)$; $405 - 15x = 360 - 10x$; $45 = 5x$; $x = 9$; 9 cm

12. Let f = force in newtons; $\dfrac{f}{50^2} = \dfrac{90}{20^2}$; $\dfrac{f}{2500} = \dfrac{90}{400} = \dfrac{9}{40}$; $f = \dfrac{2500(9)}{40} = 562.5$; 562.5 N

13. Let s = initial speed in meters per second; $\dfrac{10}{14^2} = \dfrac{20}{s^2}$; $\dfrac{10}{196} = \dfrac{20}{s^2}$; $s^2 = \dfrac{196(20)}{10} = 392$; $s \approx 19.8$; about 19.8 m/s

14. Let x = length in meters; $\dfrac{6}{\sqrt{x}} = \dfrac{2}{1}$; $\sqrt{x} = \dfrac{6}{2} = 3$; $x = 9$; 9 m

15. $V = kd^3$; $36\pi = k(6^3)$; $k = \dfrac{36\pi}{6^3} = \dfrac{\pi}{6}$; $V = \dfrac{\pi d^3}{6}$

16. Let n = number of red blood cells; $\dfrac{n}{3.5(5,000,000)} = \dfrac{1}{200}$; $n = \dfrac{3.5(5,000,000)}{200} = 87{,}500$; 87,500

C 17. Let E_0 = energy at 35 mph and s = speed when E_0 is doubled; $\dfrac{E_0}{(35)^2} = \dfrac{2E_0}{s^2}$;

$s^2 = \dfrac{1225(2E_0)}{E_0} = 2450$; $s \approx 49.5$; $49.5 - 35 = 14.5$; about 14.5 mph

Page 337 · WRITTEN EXERCISES

A 1. $vu = k$; $60(0.5) = k$; $k = 30$; $12u = 30$; $u = 2.5$

2. $y\sqrt{x} = k$; $4\sqrt{9} = k$; $k = 12$; $y\sqrt{4} = 12$; $y = 6$

3. $s = kuv$; $k = \dfrac{s}{uv} = \dfrac{15}{2(1.5)} = \dfrac{15}{3} = 5$; $s = 5(0.5)(6) = 15$

4. $w = k\dfrac{u}{v^2}$; $k = \dfrac{wv^2}{u} = \dfrac{8(3^2)}{2} = 4 \cdot 9 = 36$; $w = 36\left(\dfrac{3}{2^2}\right) = 36\left(\dfrac{3}{4}\right) = 27$

B 5. $w = k\dfrac{xy}{z}$; $k = \dfrac{wz}{xy} = \dfrac{4(6)}{4(5)} = \dfrac{6}{5}$; $w = \dfrac{6}{5}\left(\dfrac{3 \cdot 10}{3}\right) = \dfrac{6}{5} \cdot 10 = 12$

6. $z = k\dfrac{w^2}{uv}$; $k = \dfrac{zuv}{w^2} = \dfrac{6(3)(5)}{3^2} = \dfrac{18 \cdot 5}{9} = 2 \cdot 5 = 10$; $12 = 10 \cdot \dfrac{w^2}{5(6)}$; $w^2 = \dfrac{12 \cdot 30}{10} = 36$;

$w = 6$

Pages 337-338 · PROBLEMS

A 1. Let c = current in amps and r = resistance in ohms; $c = \dfrac{k}{r}$; $k = cr = 5(24) = 120$;

$6 = \dfrac{120}{r}$; $r = \dfrac{120}{6} = 20$; 20 Ω

2. Let f = frequency in kilohertz and w = wave length in meters; $f = \dfrac{k}{w}$;

$k = fw = 750(400) = 300{,}000$; $f = \dfrac{300{,}000}{600} = 500$; 500 kHz

3. Let s = speed in revolutions per second and d = diameter in centimeters; $s = \dfrac{k}{d}$;

$k = sd = 25(18) = 450$; $s = \dfrac{450}{10} = 45$; 45 r/s

4. Let r = resistance in ohms, l = length in meters, and d = diameter in millimeters;

$r = k\dfrac{l}{d^2}$; $k = \dfrac{rd^2}{l} = \dfrac{9(2^3)}{50} = \dfrac{9 \cdot 4}{50} = \dfrac{18}{25}$; $r = \dfrac{18}{25}\left(\dfrac{120}{3^2}\right) = \dfrac{18}{25} \cdot \dfrac{120}{9} = 9.6$; 9.6 Ω

5. Let h = heat loss in British thermal units, a = area in square meters, and t =

temperature difference in degrees Celsius; $h = kat$; $k = \dfrac{h}{at} = \dfrac{700}{(3.2)(12)} = \dfrac{175}{9.6}$; $h =$

$\dfrac{175}{9.6}(4.4)(15) = 1203.125$; 1203.125 BTU/hr

6. Let I = intensity in lux and d = distance in meters; $I = \dfrac{k}{d^2}$; $k = Id^2 = 20(10^2) = 2000$;
$I = \dfrac{2000}{20^2} = \dfrac{2000}{400} = 5$; 5 lx

7. Let I = intensity in lux and d = distance in feet; $I = \dfrac{k}{d^2}$; $k = Id^2 = 20(4^2) = 320$; for
a point on the edge of the table, $d = \sqrt{4^2 + 3^2} = \sqrt{25} = 5$; $I = \dfrac{320}{5^2} = \dfrac{320}{25} \approx 12.8$;
about 12.8 lx

8. Let V = volume, h = height, and r = base radius; $V = khr^2$; $k = \dfrac{V}{hr^2} = \dfrac{15\pi}{5 \cdot 3^2} = \dfrac{\pi}{3}$;
$V = \dfrac{\pi}{3} hr^2 \left(\text{or } V = \dfrac{1}{3} \pi r^2 h \right)$

9. 17°C $\approx$ 290°K and 7°C $\approx$ 280°K; let V = volume in liters, t = temperature in degrees
Kelvin (absolute temperature), and p = pressure in atmospheres; $V = k \dfrac{t}{p}$; $k = \dfrac{Vp}{t} = $
$\dfrac{14(1.7)}{290} = \dfrac{2.38}{29}$; $V = \dfrac{2.38}{29} \left(\dfrac{280}{1} \right) \approx 23$; about 23 L

10-11. Let s = load, w = width, d = depth, and l = length; $s = k \dfrac{wd^2}{l}$; $k = \dfrac{sl}{wd^2}$

10. $k = \dfrac{sl}{wd^2} = \dfrac{540l}{4 \cdot 6^2} = 3.75l$; $s = 3.75l \left(\dfrac{6 \cdot 4^2}{l} \right) = 360$; 360 kg

11. ratio $= \dfrac{k(2w)(2d)^2}{2l} : \dfrac{kwd^2}{l} = \dfrac{4kwd^2}{l} : \dfrac{kwd^2}{l} = 4:1$

C 12. Let p = period in hours and r = radius in kilometers; $p^2 = kr^3$; $k = \dfrac{p^2}{r^3} = $
$\dfrac{(6.14)^2}{(10,600 + 6400)^3} \approx \dfrac{(6.14 \times 10^0)^2}{(1.70 \times 10^4)^3} \approx \dfrac{3.77 \times 10^1}{4.91 \times 10^{12}} \approx 7.68 \times 10^{-12}$;
$24^2 = (7.68 \times 10^{-12})(r^3)$; $r^3 \approx \dfrac{5.76 \times 10^2}{7.68 \times 10^{-12}} = 7.50 \times 10^{13}$; $r \approx 4.22 \times 10^4$;
$42,200 - 6400 = 35,800$; about 35,800 km

13. Using the formula on page 336, the force between the people is $F_1 = k \dfrac{70 \cdot 70}{100} = 49k$;
the gravitational force on each is $F_2 = k \dfrac{70(6 \times 10^{24})}{(6400 \times 10^3)^2} = k \dfrac{4.2 \times 10^{26}}{6.4^2 \times 10^{12}} \approx$
$1.025 \times 10^{13} k$; $\dfrac{F_2}{F_1} \approx \dfrac{(1.025 \times 10^{13})k}{49k} \approx .0209 \times 10^{13}$; about 2×10^{11} times

Pages 342-343 · WRITTEN EXERCISES

A 1. $x + 3 \overline{\smash{\big)}\, \begin{array}{r} x - 1 \\ x^2 + 2x - 1 \end{array}}$
$\underline{x^2 + 3x}$
$-x - 1$
$\underline{-x - 3}$
2

$x - 1 + \dfrac{2}{x + 3}$

2. $x + 1 \overline{\smash{\big)}\, \begin{array}{r} x - 3 \\ x^2 + 2x + 1 \end{array}}$
$\underline{x^2 + x}$
$-3x + 1$
$\underline{-3x - 3}$
4

$x - 3 + \dfrac{4}{x + 1}$

3. $x - 3 \overline{\smash{\big)}\, \begin{array}{r} x + 4 \\ x^2 + x - 4 \end{array}}$
$\underline{x^2 - 3x}$
$4x - 4$
$\underline{4x - 12}$
8

$x + 4 + \dfrac{8}{x - 3}$

4. $t - 2 \overline{) -t^2 + 4t + 0}$

$$\frac{-t + 2}{}$$

$$\frac{-t^2 + 2t}{2t}$$

$$\frac{2t - 4}{4}$$

$$-t + 2 + \frac{4}{t - 2}$$

5. $3u - 2 \overline{) 6u^2 - \ u - 4}$

$$\frac{2u + 1}{}$$

$$\frac{6u^2 - 4u}{3u - 4}$$

$$\frac{3u - 2}{-2}$$

$$2u + 1 - \frac{2}{3u - 2}$$

6. $3z + 1 \overline{) 6z^2 - 7z + 2}$

$$\frac{2z - 3}{}$$

$$\frac{6z^2 + 2z}{-9z + 2}$$

$$\frac{-9z - 3}{5}$$

$$2z - 3 + \frac{5}{3z + 1}$$

7. $x + 3 \overline{) x^3 + 4x^2 + 3x + 5}$

$$\frac{x^2 + x}{}$$

$$\frac{x^3 + 3x^2}{x^2 + 3x}$$

$$\frac{x^2 + 3x}{0 + 5}$$

$$x^2 + x + \frac{5}{x + 3}$$

8. $x + 2 \overline{) x^3 + 0x^2 - \ x + 6}$

$$\frac{x^2 - 2x + 3}{}$$

$$\frac{x^3 + 2x^2}{-2x^2 - \ x}$$

$$\frac{-2x^2 - 4x}{3x + 6}$$

$$\frac{3x + 6}{0}$$

$$x^2 - 2x + 3$$

9. $3t + 2 \overline{) 15t^3 + \ \ t^2 + 0t + 1}$

$$\frac{5t^2 - 3t + 2}{}$$

$$\frac{15t^3 + 10t^2}{-9t^2}$$

$$\frac{-9t^2 - 6t}{6t + 1}$$

$$\frac{6t + 4}{-3}$$

$$5t^2 - 3t + 2 - \frac{3}{3t + 2}$$

10. $2x - 3 \overline{) 6x^3 - 5x^2 - 10x + 0}$

$$\frac{3x^2 + 2x - 2}{}$$

$$\frac{6x^3 - 9x^2}{4x^2 - 10x}$$

$$\frac{4x^2 - \ 6x}{-4x}$$

$$\frac{-4x + 6}{-6}$$

$$3x^2 + 2x - 2 - \frac{6}{2x - 3}$$

11. $2x^2 - x + 3 \overline{) 6x^3 - 5x^2 + 15x - 5}$

$$\frac{3x - 1}{}$$

$$\frac{6x^3 - 3x^2 + \ 9x}{-2x^2 + \ 6x + 5}$$

$$\frac{-2x^2 + \ \ x - 3}{5x + 8}$$

$$3x - 1 + \frac{5x + 8}{2x^2 - x + 3}$$

12. $3x^2 + 4x - 1 \overline{) 3x^3 - 2x^2 - 8x + 5}$

$$\frac{x \ - 2}{}$$

$$\frac{3x^3 + 4x^2 - \ x}{-6x^2 - 7x + 5}$$

$$\frac{-6x^2 - 8x + 2}{x + 3}$$

$$x - 2 + \frac{x + 3}{3x^2 + 4x - 1}$$

13.
$$x - 2 \overline{)\begin{array}{l} x^3 \qquad\qquad - 2 \\ x^4 - 2x^3 + 0x^2 - 2x + 1 \end{array}}$$

$$\begin{array}{r} x^4 - 2x^3 \\ \hline 0 \qquad\quad -2x + 1 \\ -2x + 4 \\ \hline -3 \end{array}$$

$$x^3 - 2 - \frac{3}{x - 2}$$

14.
$$2t - 1 \overline{)\begin{array}{l} t^3 \qquad + 2t + 1 \\ 2t^4 - t^3 + 4t^2 + 0t + 1 \end{array}}$$

$$\begin{array}{r} 2t^4 - t^3 \\ \hline 0 + 4t^2 \\ 4t^2 - 2t \\ \hline 2t + 1 \\ 2t - 1 \\ \hline 2 \end{array}$$

$$t^3 + 2t + 1 + \frac{2}{2t - 1}$$

15.
$$3z^2 + 2 \overline{)\begin{array}{l} 3z^2 \qquad\qquad + 2z - 2 \\ 9z^4 + 6z^3 + 0z^2 + 4z - 4 \end{array}}$$

$$\begin{array}{r} 9z^4 \qquad + 6z^2 \\ \hline 6z^3 - 6z^2 + 4z \\ 6z^3 \qquad + 4z \\ \hline -6z^2 \qquad - 4 \\ -6z^2 \qquad - 4 \\ \hline 0 \end{array}$$

$$3z^2 + 2z - 2$$

16.
$$x^2 + x - 3 \overline{)\begin{array}{l} 2x^2 - 2x + 5 \\ 2x^4 + 0x^3 - 3x^2 + 7x - 8 \end{array}}$$

$$\begin{array}{r} 2x^4 + 2x^3 - 6x^2 \\ \hline -2x^3 + 3x^2 + 7x \\ -2x^3 - 2x^2 + 6x \\ \hline 5x^2 + \ x - 8 \\ 5x^2 + 5x - 15 \\ \hline - 4x + 7 \end{array}$$

$$2x^2 - 2x + 5 - \frac{4x - 7}{x^2 + x - 3}$$

B 17.
$$2u + 3v \overline{)\begin{array}{l} 2u^2 - uv - 2v^2 \\ 4u^3 + 4u^2v - 7uv^2 - 7v^3 \end{array}}$$

$$\begin{array}{r} 4u^3 + 6u^2v \\ \hline -2u^2v - 7uv^2 \\ -2u^2v - 3uv^2 \\ \hline -4uv^2 - 7v^3 \\ -4uv^2 - 6v^3 \\ \hline -v^3 \end{array}$$

$$2u^2 - uv - 2v^2 - \frac{v^3}{2u + 3v}$$

18.
$$3x - 2y \overline{)\begin{array}{l} x^2 + xy \quad + 4y^2 \\ 3x^3 + \ x^2y + 10xy^2 - 8y^3 \end{array}}$$

$$\begin{array}{r} 3x^3 - 2x^2y \\ \hline 3x^2y + 10xy^2 \\ 3x^2y - 2xy^2 \\ \hline 12xy^2 - 8y^3 \\ 12xy^2 - 8y^3 \\ \hline 0 \end{array}$$

$$x^2 + xy + 4y^2$$

19.
$$x^2 - 2a^2 \overline{)\begin{array}{l} 3x^2 - ax + 6a^2 \\ 3x^4 - ax^3 + 0a^2x^2 + 0a^3x - 9a^4 \end{array}}$$

$$\begin{array}{r} 3x^4 \qquad - 6a^2x^2 \\ \hline -ax^3 + 6a^2x^2 \\ -ax^3 \qquad + 2a^3x \\ \hline 6a^2x^2 - 2a^3x - 9a^4 \\ 6a^2x^2 \qquad - 12a^4 \\ \hline -2a^3x + 3a^4 \end{array}$$

$$3x^2 - ax + 6a^2 - \frac{2a^3x - 3a^4}{x^2 - 2a^2}$$

20.

$$x^2 - ax\,)\overline{\,2x^4 - ax^3 + a^2x^2 - a^3x + 2a^4\,}$$

with quotient $2x^2 + ax + 2a^2$

$$\underline{2x^4 - 2ax^3}$$
$$ax^3 + a^2x^2$$
$$\underline{ax^3 - a^2x^2}$$
$$2a^2x^2 - a^3x$$
$$\underline{2a^2x^2 - 2a^3x}$$
$$a^3x + 2a^4$$

$$2x^2 + ax + 2a^2 + \frac{a^3x + 2a^4}{x^2 - ax}$$

21.

$$x^2 + x + 1\,)\overline{\,x^4 + 0x^3 + x^2 + 0x + 1\,}$$

with quotient $x^2 - x + 1$

$$\underline{x^4 + x^3 + x^2}$$
$$-x^3$$
$$\underline{-x^3 - x^2 - x}$$
$$x^2 + x + 1$$
$$\underline{x^2 + x + 1}$$
$$0$$

$$x^2 - x + 1$$

22.

$$x^2 + 0x + 1\,)\overline{\,x^5 + x^4 + x^3 + x^2 + x + 1\,}$$

with quotient $x^3 + x^2$

$$\underline{x^5 + x^3}$$
$$x^4 + x^2$$
$$\underline{x^4 + x^2}$$
$$0 + x + 1$$

$$x^3 + x^2 + \frac{x + 1}{x^2 + 1}$$

23.

$$x + a\,)\overline{\,x^4 + 0ax^3 + 0a^2x^2 + 0a^3x + a^4\,}$$

with quotient $x^3 - ax^2 + a^2x - a^3$

$$\underline{x^4 + ax^3}$$
$$-ax^3$$
$$\underline{-ax^3 - a^2x^2}$$
$$a^2x^2$$
$$\underline{a^2x^2 + a^3x}$$
$$-a^3x + a^4$$
$$\underline{-a^3x - a^4}$$
$$2a^4$$

$$x^3 - ax^2 + a^2x - a^3 + \frac{2a^4}{x + a}$$

24.

$$x + a \overline{)x^5 + 0ax^4 + 0a^2x^3 + 0a^3x^2 + 0a^4x + a^5}$$

quotient: $x^4 - ax^3 + a^2x^2 - a^3x + a^4$

$$\underline{x^5 + \quad ax^4}$$
$$-ax^4$$
$$\underline{-ax^4 - \quad a^2x^3}$$
$$a^2x^3$$
$$\underline{a^2x^3 + \quad a^3x^2}$$
$$-a^3x^2$$
$$\underline{-a^3x^2 - \quad a^4x}$$
$$a^4x + a^5$$
$$\underline{a^4x + a^5}$$
$$0 \qquad x^4 - ax^3 + a^2x^2 - a^3x + a^4$$

25.

$$x^2 - ax + a^2 \overline{)x^6 + 0ax^5 + 0a^2x^4 + 0a^3x^3 + 0a^4x^2 + 0a^5x - a^6}$$

quotient: $x^4 + ax^3 \qquad - a^3x - a^4$

$$\underline{x^6 - \quad ax^5 + \quad a^2x^4}$$
$$ax^5 - \quad a^2x^4$$
$$\underline{ax^5 - \quad a^2x^4 + \quad a^3x^3}$$
$$-a^3x^3$$
$$\underline{-a^3x^3 + \quad a^4x^2 - \quad a^5x}$$
$$-a^4x^2 + \quad a^5x - a^6$$
$$\underline{-a^4x^2 + \quad a^5x - a^6}$$
$$0$$

$$x^4 + ax^3 - a^3x - a^4$$

26.

$$x^4 - a^2x^2 + a^4 \overline{)x^6 + 0a^2x^4 + 0a^4x^2 + a^6}$$

quotient: $x^2 + a^2$

$$\underline{x^6 - \quad a^2x^4 + \quad a^4x^2}$$
$$a^2x^4 - \quad a^4x^2 + a^6$$
$$\underline{a^2x^4 - \quad a^4x^2 + a^6}$$
$$0 \qquad x^2 + a^2$$

27. $\dfrac{P(x)}{x + 2} = 2x^2 - x - 3 + \dfrac{2}{x + 2}; P(x) = (x + 2)\left(2x^2 - x - 3 + \dfrac{2}{x + 2}\right) =$

$2x^3 + 4x^2 - x^2 - 2x - 3x - 6 + 2 = 2x^3 + 3x^2 - 5x - 4$

C **28.** $\dfrac{x^3 - x + 9}{D(x)} = x^2 - 2x + 3 + \dfrac{3}{D(x)}; x^3 - x + 9 = D(x)\left(x^2 - 2x + 3 + \dfrac{3}{D(x)}\right);$

$x^3 - x + 9 = D(x)(x^2 - 2x + 3) + 3; D(x) = \dfrac{x^3 - x + 6}{x^2 - 2x + 3}$; dividing, $D(x) = x + 2$

29. $\dfrac{2x^2 + x + c}{x + k} = 2x - 5 + \dfrac{8}{x + k}; 2x^2 + x + c = (x + k)\left(2x - 5 + \dfrac{8}{x + k}\right);$

$2x^2 + x + c = (x + k)(2x - 5) + 8; 2x^2 + x + c - 8 = 2x^2 + 2kx - 5x - 5k;$

$x + (c - 8) = (2k - 5)x - 5k; 2k - 5 = 1; 2k = 6; k = 3; c - 8 = -5k = -15;$

$c = -7$

30.
$$\begin{array}{r} x^2 \quad\ + (k-2)x \quad\ -2k \\ x+2\overline{)x^3 \quad\ + kx^2 \qquad\quad -4x + (3-k)} \\ \underline{x^3 \quad\ +2x^2} \\ (k-2)x^2 \qquad\quad -4x \\ \underline{(k-2)x^2 + 2(k-2)x} \\ -2kx + (3-k) \\ \underline{-2kx - \quad\ 4k} \\ 3+3k \end{array}$$

Since $3 + 3k = 0$, $3k = -3$;
$k = -1$.

31.
$$\begin{array}{r} x^2 + 2x + (-k^2 + 4) \\ x-2\overline{)x^3 + 0x^2 \qquad\quad -k^2x \qquad\ + (k+2)} \\ \underline{x^3 - 2x^2} \\ 2x^2 \qquad\quad -k^2x \\ \underline{2x^2 \qquad\quad -\ 4x} \\ (-k^2+4)x \qquad\ + (k+2) \\ \underline{(-k^2+4)x \ - 2(-k^2+4)} \\ -2k^2 + k + 10 \end{array}$$

Since $-2k^2 + k + 10 = 0$,
$(-2k+5)(k+2) = 0$;
$k = \dfrac{5}{2}$ or $k = -2$.

32. $\dfrac{P(x)}{D(x)} = Q(x) + \dfrac{R(x)}{D(x)}$ if and only if $D(x) \neq 0$ and $P(x) = Q(x)D(x) + R(x)$;

$(x^2 + 4x + 5)(x-2) + 6 = x^3 - 2x^2 + 4x^2 - 8x + 5x - 10 + 6 =$

$x^3 + 2x^2 - 3x - 4$; $(x^2 + 4x + 3)(x-2) + 2x + 2 =$

$x^3 - 2x^2 + 4x^2 - 8x + 3x - 6 + 2x + 2 = x^3 + 2x^2 - 3x - 4$; in the second of the

given equations, the degree of R is not less than the degree of D.

age 343 · CHALLENGE

Let n = number in group; $\dfrac{78}{x-2} - \dfrac{78}{x} = 1.3$; $78x - 78x + 156 = 1.3x^2 - 2.6x$;

$1.3x^2 - 2.6x - 156 = 0$; $x^2 - 2x - 120 = 0$; $(x+10)(x-12) = 0$; $x = -10$ (reject) or

$x = 12$; 12 people

age 346 · WRITTEN EXERCISES

1.
$$\begin{array}{r} 3\underline{\rfloor\ 2\ -7\quad 6\ -3} \\ 6\ -3\quad 9 \\ \hline 2\ -1\quad 3\quad 6 \end{array}$$
$2x^2 - x + 3 + \dfrac{6}{x-3}$

2.
$$\begin{array}{r} 2\underline{\rfloor\ 3\ -8\quad 8\ -5} \\ 6\ -4\quad 8 \\ \hline 3\ -2\quad 4\quad 3 \end{array}$$
$3x^2 - 2x + 4 + \dfrac{3}{x-2}$

3.
$$\begin{array}{r} -2\underline{\rfloor\ 1\quad 6\quad 5\ -6} \\ -2\ -8\quad 6 \\ \hline 1\quad 4\ -3\quad 0 \end{array}$$
$y^2 + 4y - 3$

4.
$$\begin{array}{r} -4\underline{\rfloor\ 1\quad 1\ -10\quad 8} \\ -4\quad 12\ -8 \\ \hline 1\ -3\quad 2\quad 0 \end{array}$$
$t^2 - 3t + 2$

5. $\underline{-4}\rfloor$ 1   3 −4   5   5

      −4   4   0 −20

   ‾‾‾‾‾‾‾‾‾‾‾‾‾‾‾‾‾‾‾‾‾‾

   1 −1   0   5 −15

   $z^3 - z^2 + 5 - \dfrac{15}{z+4}$

6. $\underline{5}\rfloor$ 2 −8 −7 −17   10

      10 10   15 −10

   ‾‾‾‾‾‾‾‾‾‾‾‾‾‾‾‾‾‾‾‾‾‾

   2   2   3 −2   0

   $2u^3 + 2u^2 + 3u - 2$

7. $\underline{3}\rfloor$ 2 −5   0 −8 −3

      6   3   9   3

   ‾‾‾‾‾‾‾‾‾‾‾‾‾‾‾‾‾‾‾

   2   1   3   1   0

   $2a^3 + a^2 + 3a + 1$

8. $\underline{-3}\rfloor$ 1   0 −5   7 −20

      −3   9 −12   15

   ‾‾‾‾‾‾‾‾‾‾‾‾‾‾‾‾‾‾‾‾‾‾

   1 −3   4 −5 −5

   $b^3 - 3b^2 + 4b - 5 - \dfrac{5}{b+3}$

9. $\underline{1}\rfloor$ 1   0   0   0   0 −1

      1   1   1   1   1

   ‾‾‾‾‾‾‾‾‾‾‾‾‾‾‾‾‾‾‾‾‾‾

   1   1   1   1   1   0

   $x^4 + x^3 + x^2 + x + 1$

10. $\underline{-1}\rfloor$ 1   0   0   0   0   0 −1

      −1   1 −1   1 −1   1

   ‾‾‾‾‾‾‾‾‾‾‾‾‾‾‾‾‾‾‾‾‾‾‾‾‾‾

   1 −1   1 −1   1 −1   0

   $x^5 - x^4 + x^3 - x^2 + x - 1$

11. $\underline{3i}\rfloor$ 1   2   9   18

      3i   −9 + 6i   −18

   ‾‾‾‾‾‾‾‾‾‾‾‾‾‾‾‾‾‾‾‾‾‾‾‾‾

   1 2 + 3i   6i   0

   $x^2 + (2 + 3i)x + 6i$

12. $\underline{-i}\rfloor$ 1   −2   0   −2   2

      −i   −1 + 2i   i + 2   1

   ‾‾‾‾‾‾‾‾‾‾‾‾‾‾‾‾‾‾‾‾‾‾‾‾‾‾‾‾

   1 −2 − i   −1 + 2i   i   3

   $x^3 - (2 + i)x^2 - (1 - 2i)x + i + \dfrac{3}{x + }$

B 13. $\underline{-\tfrac{1}{2}}\rfloor$ 2   5 −5   7

      −1 −2 $\dfrac{7}{2}$

   ‾‾‾‾‾‾‾‾‾‾‾‾‾‾‾‾‾‾

   2   4 −7 $\dfrac{21}{2}$

   $\dfrac{1}{2}\left(2x^2 + 4x - 7 + \dfrac{\dfrac{21}{2}}{x + \dfrac{1}{2}}\right) = x^2 + 2x - \dfrac{7}{2} + \dfrac{21}{4x + 2}$

14. $\underline{-\tfrac{3}{2}}\rfloor$ 4   0 −5   6

      −6   9 −6

   ‾‾‾‾‾‾‾‾‾‾‾‾‾‾‾

   4 −6   4   0

   $\dfrac{1}{2}(4x^2 - 6x + 4) = 2x^2 - 3x + 2$

15. $\underline{\tfrac{2}{3}}\rfloor$ 3   7   0 −7   2

      2   6   4 −2

   ‾‾‾‾‾‾‾‾‾‾‾‾‾‾‾‾‾‾

   3   9   6 −3   0

   $\dfrac{1}{3}(3x^3 + 9x^2 + 6x - 3) = x^3 + 3x^2 + 2x - 1$

16. $\underline{\tfrac{3}{5}}\rfloor$ 5 12 −34   0 17

      3   9 −15 −9

   ‾‾‾‾‾‾‾‾‾‾‾‾‾‾‾‾‾‾‾‾

   5 15 −25 −15   8

   $\dfrac{1}{5}\left(5x^3 + 15x^2 - 25x - 15 + \dfrac{8}{x - \dfrac{3}{5}}\right) =$

   $x^3 + 3x^2 - 5x - 3 + \dfrac{8}{5x - 3}$

17.
$$\underline{-2}\,\lfloor\,3 \quad 0 \quad -7 \quad 15$$
$$ -6 \quad 12 \quad -10$$
$$\,3 \quad -6 \quad 5 \quad 5$$
$Q(x) = 3x^2 - 6x + 5;$
$R = 5$

18.
$$\underline{4}\,\lfloor\,2 \quad -7 \quad 0 \quad -9$$
$$ 8 \quad 4 \quad 16$$
$$\,2 \quad 1 \quad 4 \quad 7$$
$Q(x) = 2x^2 + x + 4;$
$R = 7$

19.
$$\underline{i}\,\lfloor\,2 \quad\quad -3 \quad 2 \quad\quad 3$$
$$ 2i \quad\quad -2 - 3i \quad 3$$
$$\,2 \quad 2i - 3 \quad\quad -3i \quad 6$$
$Q(x) = 2x^2 - (3 - 2i)x - 3i;$
$R = 6$

20.
$$\underline{1 + i}\,\lfloor\,3 \quad -7 \quad\quad 8 \quad\quad -2$$
$$ 3 + 3i \quad -7 - i \quad 2$$
$$\,3 \quad -4 + 3i \quad 1 - i \quad 0$$
$Q(x) = 3x^2 - (4 - 3i)x + 1 - i;$
$R = 0$

21.
$$\underline{-3}\,\lfloor\,1 \quad 0 \quad -9 \quad k$$
$$ -3 \quad -9 \quad 0$$
$$\,1 \quad -3 \quad 0 \quad k$$
$k = 0$

22.
$$\underline{2}\,\lfloor\,2 \quad -3 \quad 1 \quad k$$
$$ 4 \quad 2 \quad 6$$
$$\,2 \quad 1 \quad 3 \quad k + 6$$
$k + 6 = 0;\ k = -6$

23.
$$\underline{-2}\,\lfloor\,1 \quad 5 \quad k \quad\quad\quad 4$$
$$ -2 \quad\quad -6 \quad -2k + 12$$
$$\,3 \quad k - 6 \quad -2k + 16$$
$-2k + 16 = 0;\ 2k = 16;$
$k = 8$

24.
$$\underline{3}\,\lfloor\,1 \quad -4 \quad k \quad\quad\quad -6$$
$$ 3 \quad\quad -3 \quad 3k - 9$$
$$\,1 \quad -1 \quad k - 3 \quad 3k - 15$$
$3k - 15 = 0;\ 3k = 15;\ k = 5$

ages 346-347 · READING ALGEBRA

1. (1) Find m and, choosing either point, use the point-slope form.

   (2) Find m and z, the y-intercept, using $\dfrac{y - z}{x} = m$, then use the slope-intercept form.

   (3) Find m, z (as above), and w, the x-intercept, using $\dfrac{y}{x - w} = m$, then use the standard form (Ex. 50, page 119).

2. Greater than 20; no; no.

3. Let l and w be the length and width; $2(l + w) = 102$; $l + w = 51$; since the sum of two consecutive odd integers or even integers is even, l and w cannot be consecutive odd integers or consecutive even integers; since the sum of two consecutive integers is odd, l and w could be consecutive integers.

4. Less than 2 km/h; if it were greater than 2 km/h, the log would have reached the starting point before the canoeist returned.

5. The answer must be even since each term of the evaluated polynomial must be even; therefore the answer is not 15.

6. **a.** The slower plumber does less than $\dfrac{1}{2}$ the job in 2 h 55 min, so in 6 h, he does less than the whole job; therefore he takes more than 6 h.

b. The faster plumber does more than $\dfrac{1}{2}$ the job in 2 h 55 min, so in 6 h, he does mor⌇ than the whole job; therefore he takes less than 6 h.

c. 2 hours

d. Let a = time for apprentice; then the slower plumber takes $a - 2$ hours and th⌇ faster plumber takes $a - 4$ hours. $\dfrac{1}{a-2} + \dfrac{1}{a-4} = \dfrac{60}{175}$; $175a - 700 + 175a - 350 = 60a^2 - 360a + 480$; $60a^2 - 710a + 1530 = 0$; $6a^2 - 71a + 153 = 0$; the quadratic formula yields $a = 9$. (The other solution⌇ rejected because it would make the faster plumber's time negative.)

Pages 351-352 · WRITTEN EXERCISES

A

1.
$$\begin{array}{r|rrrr}
5 & 1 & -3 & -7 & 9 \\
  &   & 5 & 10 & 15 \\
\hline
  & 1 & 2 & 3 & 24
\end{array}$$
$P(5) = 24$

2.
$$\begin{array}{r|rrrrr}
-4 & 1 & 3 & 0 & 9 & 7 \\
   &   & -4 & 4 & -16 & 28 \\
\hline
   & 1 & -1 & 4 & -7 & 35
\end{array}$$
$P(-4) = 35$

3.
$$\begin{array}{r|rrrr}
3 & -1 & 1 & -1 & 1 \\
  &   & -3 & -6 & -21 \\
\hline
  & -1 & -2 & -7 & -20
\end{array}$$
$P(3) = -20$

4.
$$\begin{array}{r|rrrr}
2 & -4 & 3 & -2 & 1 \\
  &   & -8 & -10 & -24 \\
\hline
  & -4 & -5 & -12 & -23
\end{array}$$
$P(2) = -23$

5.
$$\begin{array}{r|rrrr}
-\frac{1}{2} & 1 & 0 & -1 & 6 \\
  &   & -\frac{1}{2} & \frac{1}{4} & \frac{3}{8} \\
\hline
  & 1 & -\frac{1}{2} & -\frac{3}{4} & \frac{51}{8}
\end{array}$$
$P\!\left(-\dfrac{1}{2}\right) = \dfrac{51}{8}$

6.
$$\begin{array}{r|rrrr}
\frac{1}{3} & 1 & -2 & -3 & 5 \\
  &   & \frac{1}{3} & -\frac{5}{9} & -\frac{32}{27} \\
\hline
  & 1 & -\frac{5}{3} & -\frac{32}{9} & \frac{103}{27}
\end{array}$$
$P\!\left(\dfrac{1}{3}\right) = \dfrac{103}{27}$

7. $(-1)^5 + (-1)^4 + (-1)^3 + (-1)^2 + (-1) + 1 = -1 + 1 - 1 + 1 - 1 + 1 = 0$; yes

8. $(-1)^{10} - (-1)^9 - (-1) + 1 = 1 + 1 + 1 + 1 = 4$; no

9. $(-2)^{10} + 2(-2)^9 + (-2) + 2 = 2^{10} - 2^{10} - 2 + 2 = 0$; yes

10. $(-1)^{50} + 2(-1)^{13} + 1 = 1 - 2 + 1 = 0$; yes

11. $(-\sqrt{2})^3 - (-\sqrt{2})^2 - 2(-\sqrt{2}) + 2 = -2\sqrt{2} - 2 + 2\sqrt{2} + 2 = 0$; yes

12. $(\sqrt{5})^3 + 3(\sqrt{5})^2 - 5(\sqrt{5}) + 15 = 5\sqrt{5} + 15 - 5\sqrt{5} + 15 = 30$; no

13. $(2i)^3 - (2i)^2 + 4(2i) - 4 = -8i + 4 + 8i - 4 = 0$; yes

14. $i^3 + i^2 + i + 1 = -i - 1 + i + 1 = 0$; yes

15.
$$\underline{-3}\big|\ 2\quad 1\quad -13\quad 6$$
$$-6\quad 15\quad -6$$
$$\overline{2\ -5\quad\ 2\quad\ 0}$$
$$2x^2 - 5x + 2 = 0;$$
$$x = \frac{5 \pm 3}{4} = 2 \text{ or } \frac{1}{2};\ \left\{-3, 2, \frac{1}{2}\right\}$$

16.
$$\underline{2}\big|\ 1\quad -2\quad -3\quad 6$$
$$2\quad\ 0\quad -6$$
$$\overline{1\quad 0\ -3\quad\ 0}$$
$$x^2 - 3 = 0;\ x = \sqrt{3} \text{ or } x = -\sqrt{3};$$
$$\{2, \sqrt{3}, -\sqrt{3}\}$$

17.
$$\underline{4}\big|\ 1\quad 0\quad -11\quad -20$$
$$4\quad\ 16\quad\ 20$$
$$\overline{1\quad 4\quad\ 5\quad\ 0}$$
$$x^2 + 4x + 5 = 0;$$
$$x = \frac{-4 \pm 2i}{2} = -2 \pm i;\ \{4, -2 \pm i\}$$

18.
$$\underline{-\tfrac{1}{3}}\big|\ 3\quad 7\quad -4\quad -2$$
$$-1\quad -2\quad\ 2$$
$$\overline{3\quad 6\quad -6\quad\ 0}$$
$$3x^2 + 6x - 6 = 0;$$
$$x^2 + 2x - 2 = 0;$$
$$x = \frac{-2 \pm 2\sqrt{3}}{2} = -1 \pm \sqrt{3};$$
$$\left\{-\frac{1}{3}, -1 \pm \sqrt{3}\right\}$$

19. $P(x) = (x - 1)(x + 2)(x - 3);\ x^3 - 2x^2 - 5x + 6 = 0$

20. $P(x) = (x - 2)(x + 3)(x + 4);\ x^3 + 5x^2 - 2x - 24 = 0$

21. $P(x) = x(x - 2)(x + 2)(x - 5);\ x^4 - 5x^3 - 4x^2 + 20x = 0$

22. $P(x) = (x - 3)^2(x + 1)(x - 4);\ x^4 - 9x^3 + 23x^2 - 3x - 36 = 0$

23. $P(x) = \left(x - \dfrac{3}{2}\right)(x - 2)(x - 1) \text{ or } (2x - 3)(x - 2)(x - 1);$
$$2x^3 - 9x^2 + 13x - 6 = 0$$

24. $P(x) = \left(x - \dfrac{2}{3}\right)(x + 1)(x - 3) \text{ or } (3x - 2)(x + 1)(x - 3);\ 3x^3 - 8x^2 - 5x + 6 = 0$

25. $P(x) = (x - 2)(x - 2 - i)(x - 2 + i);\ x^3 - 6x^2 + 13x - 10 = 0$

26. $P(x) = (x + 3)(x + i)(x - i);\ x^3 + 3x^2 + x + 3 = 0$

27.
$$\underline{-1}\big|\ 1\quad -1\quad 0\quad -2\quad -4$$
$$-1\quad\ 2\quad -2\quad\ 4$$
$$\underline{2}\big|\ \overline{1\ -2\quad\ 2\quad -4\quad\ 0}$$
$$2\quad\ 0\quad\ 4$$
$$\overline{1\quad 0\quad 2\quad\ 0}$$
$$x^2 + 2 = 0;\ x = \pm i\sqrt{2};$$
$$\{-1, 2, \pm i\sqrt{2}\}$$

28.
$$\underline{2}\big|\ 2\quad 5\quad -11\quad -20\quad 12$$
$$4\quad 18\quad\ 14\quad -12$$
$$\underline{-3}\big|\ \overline{2\quad 9\quad\ 7\quad -6\quad\ 0}$$
$$-6\quad -9\quad\ 6$$
$$\overline{2\quad 3\quad -2\quad\ 0}$$
$$2x^2 + 3x - 2 = 0;$$
$$x = \frac{-3 \pm 5}{4} = -2 \text{ or } \frac{1}{2};$$
$$\left\{2, -3, -2, \frac{1}{2}\right\}$$

29. $\underline{-1}|\ 3\ \ -5\ \ -7\ \ \ 3\ \ \ 2$

$\phantom{\underline{-1}|\ 3}\ \ \ -3\ \ \ \ 8\ \ -1\ \ -2$

$\underline{\tfrac{2}{3}}|\ 3\ \ -8\ \ \ 1\ \ \ 2\ \ \ 0$

$\phantom{\underline{\tfrac{2}{3}}|\ 3\ }\ \ 2\ \ -4\ \ -2$

$3\ \ -6\ \ -3\ \ \ 0$

$3x^2 - 6x - 3 = 0;$

$x^2 - 2x - 1 = 0$

$x = \dfrac{2 \pm 2\sqrt{2}}{2} = 1 \pm \sqrt{2};$

$\left\{-1, \dfrac{2}{3}, 1 \pm \sqrt{2}\right\}$

30. $\underline{-2}|\ 2\ \ \ 3\ \ \ 0\ \ \ 3\ \ -2$

$\phantom{\underline{-2}|\ 2\ }\ -4\ \ \ 2\ \ -4\ \ \ 2$

$\underline{\tfrac{1}{2}}|\ 2\ \ -1\ \ \ 2\ \ -1\ \ \ 0$

$\phantom{\underline{\tfrac{1}{2}}|\ 2\ \ }\ 1\ \ \ 0\ \ \ 1$

$2\ \ \ 0\ \ \ 2\ \ \ 0$

$2x^2 + 2 = 0;\ x^2 + 1 = 0;$

$x = \pm i;\ \left\{-2, \dfrac{1}{2}, \pm i\right\}$

31. $\underline{-2}|\ 1\ \ \ 4\ \ \ 0\ \ -16\ \ -16$

$\phantom{\underline{-2}|\ 1\ }\ -2\ \ -4\ \ \ 8\ \ \ \ 16$

$1\ \ \ 2\ \ -4\ \ -8\ \ \ \ \ 0 = P(-2)$

$\ -2\ \ \ 0\ \ \ 8$

$1\ \ \ 0\ \ -4\ \ \ \ 0\ \ \ \ \ = Q(-2)$

$Q(x) = P(x) \div (x - (-2))$

32. $\underline{\tfrac{3}{2}}|\ 4\ \ \ 0\ \ -19\ \ \ 3\ \ \ \ 18$

$\phantom{\underline{\tfrac{3}{2}}|\ 4\ }\ \ 6\ \ \ \ 9\ \ -15\ \ -18$

$4\ \ \ 6\ \ -10\ \ -12\ \ \ \ \ 0 = P\!\left(\dfrac{3}{2}\right)$

$\ \ \ 6\ \ \ 18\ \ \ 12$

$4\ \ 12\ \ \ \ 8\ \ \ \ 0\ \ \ \ = Q\!\left(\dfrac{3}{2}\right)$

$Q(x) = P(x) \div \left(x - \dfrac{3}{2}\right)$

33. Since $P(x) = 0$ has roots -1, 2, and -2, $P(x) = a(x + 1)(x - 2)(x + 2)$
for some a; since $P(0) = 12$; $a(1)(-2)(2) = -4a = 12$; $a = -3$;
$P(x) = -3(x + 1)(x - 2)(x + 2) = -3x^3 - 3x^2 + 12x + 12$

C 34. $x - a - b = x - (a + b)$ is a factor of $x^3 - a^3 - b^3 - 3ab(a + b)$ if $a + b$ is a root
$x^3 - a^3 - b^3 - 3ab(a + b) = 0;\ (a + b)^3 - a^3 - b^3 - 3ab(a + b) =$
$a^3 + 3a^2b + 3ab^2 + b^3 - a^3 - b^3 - 3a^2b - 3ab^2 = 0.$

35. $x(x - a)$ is a factor of $ax^n - a^n x$ if 0 and a are roots of $ax^n - a^n x = 0$; $a(0^n) - a^n(0)$
$0 - 0 = 0$; for every positive integer n and every nonzero number a, $a(a^n) - a^n(a)$
$a^{n+1} - a^{n+1} = 0.$

Page 352 · CALCULATOR KEY-IN

1. a. 183   **b.** 1433   **2. a.** -9.8512 **b.** 1058   **3. a.** 11.61824   **b.** -86.371

4. Answers may vary.

Pages 356-357 · WRITTEN EXERCISES

A 1. $P(x) = x^4 - x^3 + x^2 - x + 1$ has 4 changes of sign, so $P(x) = 0$ has 4, 2, or 0 po
roots; $P(-x) = x^4 + x^3 + x^2 + x + 1$ has no changes of sign so $P(x) = 0$ has no ne
roots. $P(x) = 0$ has 4 pos. real roots; 2 pos. real roots and 2 imag. roots; or 4 imag. root

2. $P(x) = x^4 - 3x^3 - 5$ has one sign change, so $P(x) = 0$ has one pos. root; $P(-x)$
$x^4 + 3x^3 - 5$ has one sign change, so $P(x) = 0$ has one neg. root; $P(x) = 0$ has one ne
real root, one pos. real root, and 2 imag. roots.

3. $P(x) = x^4 - 6x^2 - 8 = 0$ has one change of sign, so $P(x) = 0$ has one pos. root; $P(-x) = x^4 - 6x^2 - 8 = 0$ has one change of sign so $P(x) = 0$ has one neg. root; $P(x) = 0$ has one pos. real root, one neg. real root, and two imag. roots.

4. $P(x) = x^4 + 2x^3 + 3x^2 + 4$ has no changes of sign, so $P(x) = 0$ has no pos. roots; $P(-x) = x^4 - 2x^3 + 3x^2 + 4$ has 2 changes of sign so $P(x) = 0$ has 2 or 0 neg. roots; $P(x) = 0$ has 2 neg. real roots and 2 imag. roots, or 4 imag. roots.

5. $P(x) = x^5 - 6x^2 + 3x - 2 = 0$ has 3 changes of sign, so $P(x) = 0$ has 3 pos. roots or 1; $P(-x) = -x^5 - 6x^2 - 3x - 2$ has no changes of sign, so $P(x) = 0$ has no neg. roots; $P(x) = 0$ has 3 pos. real roots and 2 imag. roots, or 1 pos. real root and 4 imag. roots.

6. $P(x) = x^5 + x^3 - x - 2$ has one change of sign, so $P(x) = 0$ has one pos. root; $P(-x) = -x^5 - x^3 + x - 2$ has 2 changes of sign, so $P(x) = 0$ has 2 or 0 neg. roots; $P(x) = 0$ has 1 pos. real root, 2 neg. real roots, and 2 imag. roots, or 1 pos. real root and 4 imag. roots.

7. $P(x) = x^5 - x^3 + 2x^2 + x + 3$ has 2 changes of sign, so $P(x) = 0$ has 2 or 0 pos. roots; $P(-x) = -x^5 + x^3 + 2x^2 - x + 3$ has 3 changes of sign, so $P(x) = 0$ has 3 neg. roots or 1; the possibilities are:

No. of pos. real roots	No. of neg. real roots	No. of imag. roots
2	3	0
2	1	2
0	3	2
0	1	4

8. $P(x) = x^6 - x^5 + 2x^4 - x - 2$ has 3 changes of sign, so $P(x) = 0$ has 3 pos. roots or 1; $P(-x) = x^6 + x^5 + 2x^4 + x - 2$ has 1 change of sign, so $P(x) = 0$ has 1 neg. root; $P(x) = 0$ has 3 pos. real roots, 1 neg. real root, and 2 imag. roots; or 1 pos. real root, 1 neg. real root, and 4 imag. roots.

9. $-i\sqrt{2}$; since $i\sqrt{2}$ is a root, its conjugate must be also; $(-i\sqrt{2})^3 - 3(-i\sqrt{2})^2 + 2(-i\sqrt{2}) - 6 = 2i\sqrt{2} + 6 - 2i\sqrt{2} - 6 = 0$

10. $1 + i$; since $1 - i$ is a root, its conjugate must be also; $(1 + i)^3 - 2(1 + i) + 4 = 1 + 3i - 3 - i - 2 - 2i + 4 = 0$

11. $1 - 2i$; since $1 + 2i$ is a root, its conjugate must be also; $(1 - 2i)^3 + (1 - 2i) + 10 = -11 + 2i + 1 - 2i + 10 = 0$

12. $-i$; since i is a root, its conjugate must be also; $(-i)^4 - (-i)^3 - (-i)^2 - (-i) - 2 = 1 - i + 1 + i - 2 = 0$

13. Since $2 + i$ is a root, $2 - i$ is also; $P(x) = (x - 3)(x - 2 - i)(x - 2 + i)$; $x^3 - 7x^2 + 17x - 15 = 0$

14. Since $i\sqrt{3}$ is a root, $-i\sqrt{3}$ is also; $P(x) = (x + 1)(x - i\sqrt{3})(x + i\sqrt{3})$;
$x^3 + x^2 + 3x + 3 = 0$

15. Since $2i$ is a root, $-2i$ is also; $P(x) = (x + 2)(x - 2i)(x + 2i)$; $x^3 + 2x^2 + 4x + 8 = 0$

16. Since $3 - 2i$ is a root, $3 + 2i$ is also; $P(x) = (x - 1)(x - 3 + 2i)(x - 3 - 2i)$;
$x^3 - 7x^2 + 19x - 13 = 0$

B **17.** Since i and $1 + i$ are roots, $-i$ and $1 - i$ are also;
$P(x) = (x - i)(x + i)(x - 1 - i)(x - 1 + i)$; $x^4 - 2x^3 + 3x^2 - 2x + 2 = 0$

18. Since $1 - i$ and $2 - i$ are roots, $1 + i$ and $2 + i$ are also; $P(x) =$
$(x - 1 + i)(x - 1 - i)(x - 2 + i)(x - 2 - i)$; $x^4 - 6x^3 + 15x^2 - 18x + 10 = 0$

19. Since $i\sqrt{3}$ is a root, $-i\sqrt{3}$ is also and $(x - i\sqrt{3})(x + i\sqrt{3}) = x^2 + 3$ is a factor of the
polynomial; $(x^3 - 4x^2 + 3x - 12) \div (x^2 + 3) = x - 4$; $x - 4 = 0$ is the depressed
equation; $x = 4$; $\{\pm i\sqrt{3}, 4\}$

20. Since $-1 + 2i$ is a root, $-1 - 2i$ is also and $(x + 1 - 2i)(x + 1 + 2i) = x^2 + 2x + 5$
is a factor of the polynomial; $(x^3 + x - 10) \div (x^2 + 2x + 5) = x - 2$; $x - 2 = 0$ is the
depressed equation; $x = 2$; $\{-1 \pm 2i, 2\}$

21. Since $1 - i$ is a root, $1 + i$ is also and $(x - 1 + i)(x - 1 - i) = x^2 - 2x + 2$ is a factor
of the polynomial; $(x^4 + 2x^3 - 2x^2 + 8) \div (x^2 - 2x + 2) = x^2 + 4x + 4$; $(x + 2)^2 = 0$ is the depressed equation; $x = -2$ (double root); $\{1 \pm i, -2\}$

22. Since $2 + i$ is a root, $2 - i$ is also and $(x - 2 - i)(x - 2 + i) = x^2 - 4x + 5$ is a factor
of the polynomial; $(x^4 - 4x^3 + 20x - 25) \div (x^2 - 4x + 5) = x^2 - 5$; $x^2 - 5 = 0$ is the
depressed equation; $x = \pm\sqrt{5}$; $\{2 \pm i, \pm\sqrt{5}\}$

23. **a.** $i^4 + i^2 - i(i) - 1 = 1 - 1 + 1 - 1 = 0$; i is a root.
b. $(-i)^4 + (-i)^2 - i(-i) - 1 = 1 - 1 - 1 - 1 = -2$; $-i$ is not a root.

24. **a.** $(1 - i)^3 - 2(1 - i)^2 + (1 - i) + 1 - i = -2 - 2i + 4i + 1 - i + 1 - i = 0$;
$1 - i$ is a root.
b. $(1 + i)^3 - 2(1 + i)^2 + (1 + i) + 1 - i = -2 + 2i - 4i + 1 + i + 1 - i = -2i$;
$1 + i$ is not a root.

25. The theorem holds for polynomial equations with real coefficients.

26.

No. of pos. real roots	No. of neg. real roots	No. of imag. roots
3	0	0
2	1	0
1	2	0
1	0	2
0	1	2
0	3	0

27. $\overline{c(a + bi)^k} = \overline{c} \cdot \overline{(a + bi)^k} = c \cdot \overline{(a + bi)(a + bi)\cdots(a + bi)} =$

$$\underbrace{}_{k \text{ factors}}$$

$$c\underbrace{(\overline{a + bi})(\overline{a + bi})\cdots(\overline{a + bi})}_{k \text{ factors}} = c \cdot \underbrace{(a - bi)(a - bi)\cdots(a - bi)}_{k \text{ factors}} = c(a - bi)^k$$

28. $P(a + bi) = c_0(a + bi)^n + c_1(a + bi)^{n-1} + \cdots + c_n$; the conjugate of $P(a + bi)$ is $\overline{c_0(a + bi)^n} + \overline{c_1(a + bi)^{n-1}} + \cdots + \overline{c_n} = c_0(a - bi)^n + c_1(a - bi)^{n-1} + \cdots + c_n = P(a - bi)$

29. $P(a + bi) = 0$; $\overline{P(a + bi)} = \overline{0} = 0$; but $\overline{P(a + bi)} = P(a - bi)$ (Ex. 28); $P(a - bi) = 0$

Pages 360-361 · WRITTEN EXERCISES

A

1. The possible rational roots are ± 1, ± 2, ± 3, and ± 6; $P(x)$ has 1 change of sign so $P(x) = 0$ has one pos. root; $P(-x)$ has 2 changes of sign so $P(x) = 0$ has 2 or 0 neg. roots; -1 and -2 satisfy the equation so there are no other neg. roots; 3 is a root, so there are no other roots; $\{-1, -2, 3\}$.

2. The possible rational roots are ± 1, ± 3, ± 5, and ± 15; $P(x)$ has 2 sign changes so $P(x) = 0$ has 2 or 0 pos. roots; $P(-x)$ has 1 sign change so $P(x) = 0$ has 1 neg. root; -1 satisfies the equation so there are no other neg. roots; checking the possible pos. values yields solutions 3 and 5; $\{-1, 3, 5\}$.

3. The possible rational roots are ± 1, ± 2, ± 3, ± 4, ± 6, and ± 12; none of the possible rational roots satisfy the equation; the equation has no rational roots.

4. The possible rational roots are ± 1, ± 2, ± 4, and ± 8; none of the possible rational roots satisfy the equation; the equation has no rational roots.

5. The possible rational roots are ± 1, $\pm \dfrac{1}{2}$, and $\pm \dfrac{1}{4}$; the equation has no neg. roots; $\dfrac{1}{2}$ satisfies the equation; $\dfrac{1}{2}$ also satisfies the first depressed equation so $\dfrac{1}{2}$ is a double root; the second depressed equation, $4x^2 + 4 = 0$, yields the solutions $\pm i$; $\left\{\dfrac{1}{2}, \pm i\right\}$

6. The possible rational roots are ± 1, ± 2, ± 3, ± 6, ± 9, and ± 18; none of the possible rational roots satisfy the equation; the equation has no rational roots.

7. The possible rational roots are ± 1, ± 2, and $\pm \dfrac{1}{2}$; the equation has no neg. roots; $\dfrac{1}{2}$ satisfies the equation; the depressed equation, $2x^2 - 4x + 4 = 0$, yields the solutions $1 \pm i$; $\left\{\dfrac{1}{2}, 1 \pm i\right\}$

8. The possible rational roots are ± 1, ± 3, $\pm \dfrac{1}{2}$, and $\pm \dfrac{3}{2}$; $-\dfrac{1}{2}$ satisfies the equation; the depressed equation, $2x^2 - 6 = 0$, yields the solutions $\pm \sqrt{3}$; $\left\{-\dfrac{1}{2}, \pm\sqrt{3}\right\}$

9. The possible rational roots are ± 1, ± 2, ± 3, ± 6, $\pm \dfrac{1}{2}$, and $\pm \dfrac{3}{2}$; $-\dfrac{3}{2}$ satisfies the equation; the depressed equation, $2x^2 - 4 = 0$, yields the solutions $\pm \sqrt{2}$; $\left\{ -\dfrac{3}{2}, \pm \sqrt{2} \right\}$

10. The possible rational roots are ± 1, ± 2, $\pm \dfrac{1}{2}$, $\pm \dfrac{1}{3}$, $\pm \dfrac{2}{3}$, and $\pm \dfrac{1}{6}$; $\dfrac{2}{3}$ satisfies the equation; the depressed equation, $6x^2 - 3 = 0$, yields the solutions $\pm \dfrac{\sqrt{2}}{2}$; $\left\{ \dfrac{2}{3}, \pm \dfrac{\sqrt{2}}{2} \right\}$

11. The possible rational roots are ± 1, ± 2, ± 4, $\pm \dfrac{1}{2}$, $\pm \dfrac{1}{3}$, $\pm \dfrac{1}{6}$, $\pm \dfrac{2}{3}$, and $\pm \dfrac{4}{3}$; $\dfrac{1}{3}$ satisfies the equation; $-\dfrac{1}{2}$ satisfies the first depressed equation, $6x^3 + 3x^2 + 24x + 12 = 0$; the second depressed equation, $x^2 + 4 = 0$; yields the solutions $\pm 2i$; $\left\{ \dfrac{1}{3}, -\dfrac{1}{2}, \pm 2i \right\}$

12. The possible rational roots are ± 1, ± 3, $\pm \dfrac{1}{2}$, $\pm \dfrac{3}{2}$, $\pm \dfrac{1}{4}$, and $\pm \dfrac{3}{4}$; $-\dfrac{1}{2}$ satisfies the equation; $\dfrac{3}{2}$ satisfies the first depressed equation, $4x^3 - 6x^2 + 4x - 6 = 0$; the second depressed equation, $4x^2 + 4 = 0$, yields the solutions $\pm i$; $\left\{ -\dfrac{1}{2}, \dfrac{3}{2}, \pm i \right\}$

13. $\sqrt{2}$ is a root of the equation $x^2 - 2 = 0$; the only possible rational roots are ± 1 and ± 2, none of which satisfy the equation. Since $x^2 - 2$ has no rational roots, $\sqrt{2}$ is irrational.

14. $\sqrt{3}$ is a root of the equation $x^2 - 3 = 0$; the only possible rational roots are ± 1 and ± 3, none of which satisfy the equation. Since $x^2 - 3 = 0$ has no rational roots, $\sqrt{3}$ is irrational.

15. $\sqrt[3]{5}$ is a root of the equation $x^3 - 5 = 0$; the only possible rational roots are ± 1 and ± 5, none of which satisfy the equation. Since $x^3 - 5 = 0$ has no rational roots, $\sqrt[3]{5}$ is irrational.

16. $\sqrt[3]{-6}$ is a root of the equation $x^3 + 6 = 0$; the only possible rational roots are ± 1, ± 2, ± 3, and ± 6, none of which satisfy the equation. Since $x^3 + 6 = 0$ has no rational roots, $\sqrt[3]{-6}$ is irrational.

17. $\sqrt[5]{-10}$ is a root of the equation $x^5 + 10 = 0$; the only possible rational roots are ± 1, ± 2, ± 5, and ± 10, none of which satisfy the equation. Since $x^5 + 10 = 0$ has no rational roots, $\sqrt[5]{-10}$ is irrational.

18. $\sqrt[4]{8}$ is a root of the equation $x^4 - 8 = 0$; the only possible rational roots are ± 1, ± 2, ± 4, and ± 8, none of which satisfy the equation. Since $x^4 - 8 = 0$ has no rational roots $\sqrt[4]{8}$ is irrational.

19. $(\sqrt{3} - \sqrt{2})^4 - 10(\sqrt{3} - \sqrt{2})^2 + 1 = 49 - 20\sqrt{6} - 10(5 - 2\sqrt{6}) + 1 =$ $49 - 20\sqrt{6} - 50 + 20\sqrt{6} + 1 = 0$; the only possible rational roots of $x^4 - 10x^2 + 1 = 0$ are ± 1. Since $\sqrt{3} - \sqrt{2} \neq 1$ and $\sqrt{3} - \sqrt{2} \neq -1$, $\sqrt{3} - \sqrt{2}$ is irrational.

20. $(\sqrt{5} + \sqrt{2})^4 - 14(\sqrt{5} + \sqrt{2})^2 + 9 = 89 + 28\sqrt{10} - 14(7 + 2\sqrt{10}) + 9 =$
$89 + 28\sqrt{10} - 98 - 28\sqrt{10} + 9 = 0$; the only possible rational roots of
$x^4 - 14x^2 + 9 = 0$ are ± 1, ± 3, and ± 9, none of which satisfy the equation; since the
equation has no rational roots, $\sqrt{5} + \sqrt{2}$ is irrational.

B 21. Multiply both sides of the equation by the LCD of the fractional coefficients to produce
an equivalent equation with integral coefficients. Then use the Rational Root Theorem.

22. $6\left(x^3 - \dfrac{2}{3}x^2 + \dfrac{1}{2}x - \dfrac{1}{3}\right) = 6(0)$; $6x^3 - 4x^2 + 3x - 2 = 0$; the possible rational roots

are ± 1, ± 2, $\pm\dfrac{1}{2}$, $\pm\dfrac{1}{3}$, $\pm\dfrac{1}{6}$, and $\pm\dfrac{2}{3}$; $6x^3 - 4x^2 + 3x - 2 = 0$ has no neg. roots; $\dfrac{2}{3}$

satisfies the equation; the depressed equation, $6x^2 + 3 = 0$, yields the solutions $\pm\dfrac{i\sqrt{2}}{2}$;

$\left\{\dfrac{2}{3}, \pm\dfrac{i\sqrt{2}}{2}\right\}$

23. $6\left(\dfrac{1}{3}x^3 - \dfrac{1}{2}x^2 + \dfrac{2}{3}x - 1\right) = 6(0)$; $2x^3 - 3x^2 + 4x - 6 = 0$; the possible rational

roots are ± 1, ± 2, ± 3, ± 6, $\pm\dfrac{1}{2}$, and $\pm\dfrac{3}{2}$; the equation has no neg. roots; $\dfrac{3}{2}$ satisfies the

equation; the depressed equation, $2x^2 + 4 = 0$, yields the solutions $\pm i\sqrt{2}$; $\left\{\dfrac{3}{2}, \pm i\sqrt{2}\right\}$

24. $24\left(\dfrac{1}{8}x^3 - \dfrac{1}{3}x^2 + \dfrac{1}{8}x + \dfrac{1}{12}\right) = 24(0)$; $3x^3 - 8x^2 + 3x + 2 = 0$; the possible rational

roots are ± 1, ± 2, $\pm\dfrac{1}{3}$, and $\pm\dfrac{2}{3}$; 1 satisfies the equation; $-\dfrac{1}{3}$ satisfies the first

depressed equation, $3x^2 - 5x - 2 = 0$; 2 satisfies the second, $3x - 6 = 0$; $\left\{1, -\dfrac{1}{3}, 2\right\}$

25. $2\left(x^4 + \dfrac{13}{2}x^3 + 9x^2 + \dfrac{15}{2}x\right) = 2(0)$; $2x^4 + 13x^3 + 18x^2 + 15x = 0$; one root is 0; the

first depressed equation is $2x^3 + 13x^2 + 18x + 15 = 0$; the possible rational roots are

± 1, ± 3, ± 5, ± 15, $\pm\dfrac{1}{2}$, $\pm\dfrac{3}{2}$, $\pm\dfrac{5}{2}$, and $\pm\dfrac{15}{2}$; the equation has no pos. roots; -5 satisfies

the equation; the second depressed equation, $2x^2 + 3x + 3 = 0$, yields the solutions

$\dfrac{-3 \pm i\sqrt{15}}{4}$; $\left\{0, -5, \dfrac{-3 \pm i\sqrt{15}}{4}\right\}$

C 26. The possible rational roots of $x^n - k = 0$ are the integral factors of k. Since $\sqrt[n]{k}$ is
rational and $\sqrt[n]{k}$ is a root of $x^n - k = 0$, then $\sqrt[n]{k}$ is an integral factor of k and there

is an integer z such that $\sqrt[n]{k} \cdot z = k$; $\sqrt[n]{k} = \dfrac{k}{z}$ (an integer); $k = \left(\dfrac{k}{z}\right)^n$.

27. $\dfrac{h}{k}$ is a root of the equation; mult. prop. of equality; add. prop. of equality; div. prop. of

equality; closure props. for the integers

28. 1. $a\left(\dfrac{h}{k}\right)^3 + b\left(\dfrac{h}{k}\right)^2 + c\left(\dfrac{h}{k}\right) + d = 0$ $\left(\dfrac{h}{k}\ \text{is a root of the equation}\right)$

2. $ah^3 + bh^2k + chk^2 + dk^3 = 0$ (Mult. prop. of equality)

3. $ah^3 = -bh^2k - chk^2 - dk^3$ (Add. prop. of equality)

4. $\dfrac{ah^3}{k} = -bh^2 - chk - dk^2$ (Div. prop. of equality)

5. $\dfrac{ah^3}{k}$ is an integer. (Closure props. for integers)

6. k is a factor of d. (All prime factors of k cancel with prime factors of ah^3 and h and k are relatively prime.)

Page 361 · CHALLENGE

$N = 1$

Pages 364-365 · WRITTEN EXERCISES

A   1.
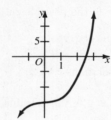
$x \approx 2.5$

2.
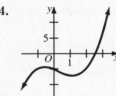
$x \approx -2$

3.
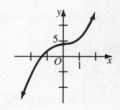
$x \approx 2.5$

4.
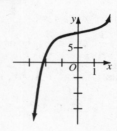
$x \approx 2.5$

5.
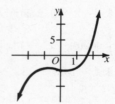
$x \approx 1.5$

6.
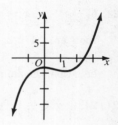
$x \approx -1.5$

7.
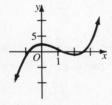
$x \approx -1,\ 1.5,\ 2.5$

8.

$x \approx -1,\ 0.5,\ 3$

9.

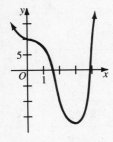

$x \approx 1.5, 4$

10.

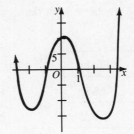

$x \approx -2.5, -1, 1, 3.5$

11. $P(r) = 0$ for some r such that
    $2 < r < 3$.

x	$P(x)$
2.1	-5.739
2.2	-4.352
2.3	-2.833
2.4	-1.176
2.5	0.625

$r \approx 2.5$

12. $P(r) = 0$ for some r such that
    $-3 < r < -2$.

x	$P(x)$
-2.9	-14.389
-2.8	-11.952
-2.7	-9.683
-2.6	-7.576
-2.5	-5.625
-2.4	-3.824
-2.3	-2.167
-2.2	-0.648
-2.1	0.739

$r \approx -2.2$

13. $P(r) = 0$ for some r such that
    $2 < x < 3$.

x	$P(x)$
2.1	-2.559
2.2	-2.032
2.3	-1.413
2.4	-0.696
2.5	0.125

$r \approx 2.5$

14. $P(r) = 0$ for some r such that
    $2 < x < 3$.

x	$P(x)$
2.1	-4.349
2.2	-3.592
2.3	-2.723
2.4	-1.736
2.5	-0.625
2.6	0.616

$r \approx 2.6$

15. $P(r) = 0$ for some r such that $1 < r < 2$.

x	$P(x)$
1.1	-3.559
1.2	-1.032
1.3	-2.413
1.4	-1.696
1.5	-0.875
1.6	0.056

$r \approx 1.6$

16. $P(r) = 0$ for some r such that $-2 < r < -1$.

x	$P(x)$
-1.9	-4.759
-1.8	-3.632
-1.7	-2.613
-1.6	-1.696
-1.5	-0.875
-1.4	-0.144
-1.3	0.503

$r \approx 1.4$

17. $P(x) = 0$ has real roots r_1, r_2, and r_3 such that $-1 < r_1 < 0$, $1 < r_2 < 2$, and $2 < r_3 < 3$.

x	$P(x)$
-0.9	-0.159
-0.8	0.568

$r_1 \approx -0.9$

x	$P(x)$
1.1	0.701
1.2	0.408
1.3	0.127
1.4	-0.136

$r_2 \approx 1.3$

x	$P(x)$
2.1	-0.969
2.2	-0.872
2.3	-0.703
2.4	-0.456
2.5	-0.125
2.6	0.296

$r_3 \approx 2.5$

18. $P(x) = 0$ has real roots $r_1, r_2,$ and r_3 such that $-2 < r_1 < -1, 0 < r_2 < 1,$ and $2 < r_3 < 3$.

x	$P(x)$
-1.9	-7.379
-1.8	-5.912
-1.7	-4.593
-1.6	-3.416
-1.5	-2.375
-1.4	-1.464
-1.3	-0.677
-1.2	-0.008
-1.1	0.549

$r_1 \approx -1.2$

x	$P(x)$
0.1	0.681
0.2	0.328
0.3	-0.053

$r_2 \approx 0.3$

x	$P(x)$
2.1	-4.859
2.2	-4.632
2.3	-4.313
2.4	-3.896
2.5	-3.375
2.6	-2.744
2.7	-1.997
2.8	-1.128
2.9	-0.131
3.0	1

$r_3 \approx 2.9$

19. $P(x) = 0$ has real roots r_1 and r_2 such that $1 < r_1 < 2$ and $3 < r_2 < 4$.

x	$P(x)$
1.1	6.1401
1.2	5.1616
1.3	4.0681
1.4	2.8656
1.5	1.5625
1.6	0.1696
1.7	-1.2999

$r_1 \approx 1.6$

x	$P(x)$
3.1	-16.8119
3.2	-16.2144
3.3	-15.1559
3.4	-13.5824
3.5	-11.4375
3.6	-8.6624
3.7	-5.1959
3.8	-0.9744
3.9	4.0681

$r_2 \approx 3.8$

20. $P(x) = 0$ has real roots r_1, r_2, r_3, and r_4 such that $-3 < r_1 < -2$, $-1 < r_2 < 0$, $1 < r_3 < 2$, and $3 < r_4 < 4$.

x	$P(x)$
-2.9	9.4171
-2.8	3.8176
-2.7	-0.8729

$r_1 \approx -2.7$

x	$P(x)$
-0.9	-0.3149
-0.8	1.3216

$r_2 \approx -0.9$

x	$P(x)$
1.1	2.4331
1.2	0.7456
1.3	-1.0409

$r_3 \approx 1.2$

x	$P(x)$
3.1	-11.1389
3.2	-7.5104
3.3	-3.0449
3.4	2.3296

$r_4 \approx 3.4$

21. $P(1) = 1^2 - 2(1) + 2 = 1$; $P(4) = 4^2 - 2(4) + 2 = 10$; $P(1) < 5 < P(4)$; if $P(c) = c^2 - 2c + 2 = 5$, $c^2 - 2c - 3 = 0$; $(c + 1)(c - 3) = 0$; $c = -1$ (reject) or $c = 3$; $c = 3$

22. $P(-5) = (-5)^2 + (-5) - 2 = 25 - 7 = 18$; $P(-2) = (-2)^2 + (-2) - 2 = 4 - 4 = 0$; $P(-5) > 4 > P(-2)$; if $P(c) = c^2 + c - 2 = 4$, $c^2 + c - 6 = 0$; $(c - 2)(c + 3) = 0$; $c = 2$ (reject) or $c = -3$; $c = -3$

23. $P(-2) = 2(-2)^2 - 5(-2) - 10 = 8 + 10 - 10 = 8$; $P(2) = 2(2)^2 - 5(2) - 10 = 8 - 10 - 10 = -12$; $P(-2) > -7 > P(2)$; if $P(c) = 2c^2 - 5c - 10 = -7$, $2c^2 - 5c - 3 = 0$; $(c - 3)(2c + 1) = 0$; $c = 3$ (reject) or $c = -\dfrac{1}{2}$; $c = -\dfrac{1}{2}$

24. $P(-2) = (-2)^3 - (-2)^2 - 2(-2) + 5 = -8 - 4 + 4 + 5 = -3$; $P(3) = 3^3 - 3^2 - 2(3) + 5 = 27 - 9 - 6 + 5 = 17$; $P(-2) < 5 < P(3)$; if $P(c) = c^3 - c^2 - 2c + 5 = 5$, $c^3 - c^2 - 2c = 0$; $c(c^2 - c - 2) = 0$; $c(c - 2)(c + 1) = 0$; $c = 0$, $c = 2$, or $c = -1$.

C **25.** Let $P(x) = 2x^3 - x^2 - 4x + 2$; since $P(1.4) = -0.072 < 0$ and $P(1.5) = 0.5 > 0$, $P(x)$ has a zero r such that $1.4 < r < 1.5$.

x	$P(x)$
1.41	-0.021658
1.42	0.030176

$r \approx 1.41$

26. In both (a) and (b) we can assume that $Q(x)$ has at least one nonzero coefficient. (If not, then the polynomial P is a nonzero constant and $P(x) = 0$ has no roots, so that any M and L are upper and lower bounds.)

   a. If $x > M$, $x - M > 0$; since $x > 0$ and the coefficients of $Q(x)$ are nonnegative and not all zero, $Q(x) > 0$. Then, since $P(M)$ is nonnegative, $P(x) = (x - M)Q(x) + P(M) > 0$ and x is not a root of $P(x) = 0$.

b. Suppose the *even* powers of x in $Q(x)$ are nonnegative and the *odd* powers non-positive. Then $P(L) \leq 0$. Since the coefficients of Q are not all zero, $Q(x) > 0$ when x is negative. Thus for $x < L < 0$, $P(x) = (x - L)Q(x) + P(L) < 0$ and x is not a root of $P(x) = 0$. A similar argument shows that if the *odd* powers of x in $Q(x)$ are nonnegative, $P(x) > 0$, and again x is not a root of $P(x) = 0$.

c. If $M = 1$, $Q(x) = 3x^3 + 7x^2 + 6x + 10$ and $P(M) = 6$; if $L = -2$, $Q(x) = 3x^3 - 2x^2 + 3x - 2$ and $P(L) = 0$.

Pages 365-366 · COMPUTER KEY-IN

1. a. $x \approx -.7, 2.0, 2.7$ **b.** $x \approx 2.73$

2. a. $x \approx -.2$ **b.** $x \approx -1.6, 2.2$ **c.** $x \approx 3.6, 10.0$

3. $\sqrt[5]{2} \approx 1.149$

Pages 370-371 · WRITTEN EXERCISES

A 1.

Year	Population
1950	151
1955	p
1960	179

$$10\begin{bmatrix} 5\begin{bmatrix} 1950 \\ 1955 \\ 1960 \end{bmatrix} & \begin{bmatrix} 151 \\ p \\ 179 \end{bmatrix}d \end{bmatrix}28$$

$$\frac{d}{28} = \frac{5}{10} = \frac{1}{2};\ 2d = 28;\ d = 14;$$

$p \approx 151 + 14 = 165$; 165 million

2.

$$10\begin{bmatrix} 8\begin{bmatrix} 1900 \\ 1908 \\ 1910 \end{bmatrix} & \begin{bmatrix} 76 \\ p \\ 92 \end{bmatrix}d \end{bmatrix}16$$

$$\frac{d}{16} = \frac{8}{10} = \frac{4}{5};\ 5d = 64;\ d \approx 13;$$

$p \approx 76 + 13 = 89$; 89 million

3.

$$10\begin{bmatrix} 2\begin{bmatrix} 1920 \\ 1922 \\ 1930 \end{bmatrix} & \begin{bmatrix} 106 \\ p \\ 123 \end{bmatrix}d \end{bmatrix}17$$

$$\frac{d}{17} = \frac{2}{10} = \frac{1}{5};\ 5d = 17;\ d \approx 3;$$

$d \approx 3;\ p \approx 106 + 3 = 109$; 109 million

4.

$$10\begin{bmatrix} 4\begin{bmatrix} 1960 \\ 1964 \\ 1970 \end{bmatrix} & \begin{bmatrix} 179 \\ p \\ 203 \end{bmatrix}d \end{bmatrix}24$$

$$\frac{d}{24} = \frac{4}{10} = \frac{2}{5};\ 5d = 48;\ d \approx 10;$$

$p \approx 179 + 10 = 189$; 189 million

5.

$$10\begin{bmatrix} d\begin{bmatrix} 1960 \\ y \\ 1970 \end{bmatrix} & \begin{bmatrix} 179 \\ 200 \\ 203 \end{bmatrix}21 \end{bmatrix}24$$

$$\frac{d}{10} = \frac{21}{24} = \frac{7}{8};\ 8d = 70;\ d \approx 9;$$

$y \approx 1960 + 9 = 1969$

6.

$$10\begin{bmatrix} d\begin{bmatrix} 1940 \\ y \\ 1950 \end{bmatrix} & \begin{bmatrix} 132 \\ 140 \\ 151 \end{bmatrix}8 \end{bmatrix}19$$

$$\frac{d}{10} = \frac{8}{19};\ 19d = 80;\ d \approx 4;$$

$y \approx 1940 + 4 = 1944$

7.

Year	Population
1900	76
y	80
1910	92

$$10\left[d\begin{bmatrix}1900\\y\\1910\end{bmatrix}\begin{matrix}76\\80\\92\end{matrix}\right]4\right]16$$

$\dfrac{d}{10} = \dfrac{4}{16} = \dfrac{1}{4}$; $4d = 10$; $d \approx 3$;

$y \approx 1900 + 3 = 1903$

8.

Year	Population
1950	151
y	160
1960	179

$$10\left[d\begin{bmatrix}1950\\y\\1960\end{bmatrix}\begin{matrix}151\\160\\179\end{matrix}\right]9\right]28$$

$\dfrac{d}{10} = \dfrac{9}{28}$; $28d = 90$; $d \approx 3$;

$y \approx 1950 + 3 = 1953$

9.

Altitude	Density
1000	1.112
1200	y
1500	1.058

$$500\left[200\begin{bmatrix}1000\\1200\\1500\end{bmatrix}\begin{matrix}1.112\\y\\1.058\end{matrix}\right]d\right]0.054$$

$\dfrac{d}{0.054} = \dfrac{200}{500} = \dfrac{2}{5}$; $5d = 0.108$;

$d \approx 0.022$; $y \approx 1.112 - 0.022 = 1.090$;

1.090 kg/m³

10.

Altitude	Density
0	1.225
290	y
500	1.167

$$500\left[290\begin{bmatrix}0\\290\\500\end{bmatrix}\begin{matrix}1.225\\y\\1.167\end{matrix}\right]d\right]0.058$$

$\dfrac{d}{0.058} = \dfrac{290}{500} = \dfrac{29}{50}$; $50d = 1.682$;

$d \approx 0.034$; $y \approx 1.225 - 0.034 = 1.191$;

1.191 kg/m³

11.

Altitude	Density
500	1.167
900	y
1000	1.112

$$500\left[400\begin{bmatrix}500\\900\\1000\end{bmatrix}\begin{matrix}1.167\\y\\1.112\end{matrix}\right]d\right]0.055$$

$\dfrac{d}{0.055} = \dfrac{400}{500} = \dfrac{4}{5}$; $5d = 0.22$; $d = 0.044$;

$y \approx 1.167 - 0.044 = 1.123$;

1.123 kg/m³

12.

Altitude	Density
3000	0.909
3300	y
3500	0.863

$$500\left[300\begin{bmatrix}3000\\3300\\3500\end{bmatrix}\begin{matrix}0.909\\y\\0.863\end{matrix}\right]d\right]0.046$$

$\dfrac{d}{0.046} = \dfrac{300}{500} = \dfrac{3}{5}$; $5d = 0.138$;

$d \approx 0.028$; $y \approx 0.909 - 0.028 = 0.881$;

0.881 kg/m³

13.

Altitude	Density
1000	1.112
x	1.100
1500	1.058

$$500\left[d\begin{bmatrix}1000\\x\\1500\end{bmatrix}\begin{matrix}1.112\\1.100\\1.058\end{matrix}\right]0.012\right]0.054$$

$\dfrac{d}{500} = \dfrac{0.012}{0.054}$; $0.054d = 6$; $d \approx 111$;

$x \approx 1000 + 111 = 1111$; 1111 m

14.

Altitude	Density
1500	1.058
x	1.040
2000	1.007

$$500\left[d\begin{bmatrix}1500\\x\\2000\end{bmatrix}\begin{matrix}1.058\\1.040\\1.007\end{matrix}\right]0.018\right]0.051$$

$\dfrac{d}{500} = \dfrac{0.018}{0.051}$; $0.051d = 9$; $d \approx 176$;

$x \approx 1500 + 176 = 1676$; 1676 m

15.

Altitude	Density
2000	1.007
x	0.980
2500	0.957

$$500\left[d\begin{bmatrix}2000\\x\\2500\end{bmatrix}\begin{matrix}1.007\\0.980\\0.957\end{matrix}\right]0.027\right]0.05$$

$\dfrac{d}{500} = \dfrac{0.027}{0.05}$; $0.05d = 13.5$; $d = 270$;

$x \approx 2000 + 270 = 2270$; 2270 m

16.

Altitude	Density
3000	0.909
x	0.900
3500	0.863

$$500\left[d\begin{bmatrix}3000\\x\\3500\end{bmatrix}\begin{matrix}0.909\\0.900\\0.863\end{matrix}\right]0.009\right]0.046$$

$\dfrac{d}{500} = \dfrac{0.009}{0.046}$; $0.046d = 4.5$; $d \approx 98$;

$x \approx 3000 + 98 = 3098$; 3098 m

17. a. Since $P(1) = -1$ and $P(2) = 8$, $P(x) = 0$ has a real root between 1 and 2; since
$P(1.1) = -0.469$ and $P(1.2) = 0.128$, $P(x) = 0$ has a real root between 1.1 and 1.2.

b.

x	$P(x)$
1.1	-0.469
r	0
1.2	0.128

$0.1 \begin{bmatrix} c\begin{bmatrix}1.1\\r\\1.2\end{bmatrix} \end{bmatrix}$ ... $\begin{bmatrix}-0.469\\0\end{bmatrix}0.469 \Big]0.597$

$\dfrac{c}{0.1} = \dfrac{0.469}{0.597}; \ 0.597c = 0.0469; \ c \approx 0.08;$

$r \approx 1.1 + 0.08 = 1.18$

18. a. Since $P(1) = -3$ and $P(2) = 1$, $P(x) = 0$ has a real root between 1 and 2; since
$P(1.8) = -0.408$ and $P(1.9) = 0.249$, $P(x) = 0$ has a real root between 1.8 and 1.9.

b.

x	$P(x)$
1.8	-0.408
r	0
1.9	0.249

$0.1 \ c\begin{bmatrix}1.8\\r\\1.9\end{bmatrix}$ ... $\begin{bmatrix}-0.408\\0\end{bmatrix}0.408\Big]0.657$

$\dfrac{c}{0.1} = \dfrac{0.408}{0.657}; \ 0.657c = 0.0408; \ c \approx 0.06;$

$r \approx 1.8 + 0.06 = 1.86$

19. a. Since $P(-3) = -4$ and $P(-2) = 5$, $P(x) = 0$ has a real root between -3 and -2;
since $P(-2.7) = -0.103$ and $P(-2.6) = 0.944$, $P(x) = 0$ has a real root between -2.7
and -2.6.

b.

x	$P(x)$
-2.7	-0.103
r	0
-2.6	0.944

$0.1 \ c\begin{bmatrix}-2.7\\r\\-2.6\end{bmatrix}$ ... $\begin{bmatrix}-0.103\\0\end{bmatrix}0.103\Big]1.047$

$\dfrac{c}{0.1} = \dfrac{0.103}{1.047}; \ 1.047c = 0.0103; \ c \approx 0.01;$

$r \approx -2.7 + 0.01 = -2.69$

20. a. Since $P(-2) = -4$ and $P(-1) = 6$, $P(x) = 0$ has a real root between -2 and -1;
since $P(-1.7) = -0.613$ and $P(-1.6) = 0.304$, $P(x) = 0$ has a real root between -1.7
and -1.6.

b.

x	$P(x)$
-1.7	-0.613
r	0
-1.6	0.304

$0.1 \ c\begin{bmatrix}-1.7\\r\\-1.6\end{bmatrix}$ ... $\begin{bmatrix}-0.613\\0\end{bmatrix}0.613\Big]0.917$

$\dfrac{c}{0.1} = \dfrac{0.613}{0.917}; \ 0.917c = 0.0613; \ c \approx 0.07;$

$r \approx -1.7 + 0.07 = -1.63$

21.

N	$\sqrt{N}$
8.7	2.950
8.73	$\sqrt{8.73}$
8.8	2.966

$0.1 \ 0.03\begin{bmatrix}8.7\\8.73\end{bmatrix}$ ... $\begin{bmatrix}2.950\\\sqrt{8.73}\end{bmatrix}d\Big]0.016$

$\dfrac{d}{0.016} = \dfrac{0.03}{0.1} = \dfrac{3}{10}; \ 10d = 0.048;$

$d \approx 0.005; \ \sqrt{8.73} \approx 2.950 + 0.005 = 2.955$

22.

N	$\sqrt{N}$
4.1	2.025
4.17	$\sqrt{4.17}$
4.2	2.049

$0.1 \ 0.07\begin{bmatrix}4.1\\4.17\end{bmatrix}$ ... $\begin{bmatrix}2.025\\\sqrt{4.17}\end{bmatrix}d\Big]0.024$

$\dfrac{d}{0.024} = \dfrac{0.07}{0.1} = \dfrac{7}{10}; \ 10d = 0.168;$

$d \approx 0.017; \ \sqrt{4.17} \approx 2.025 + 0.017 = 2.042$

23.

N	$\sqrt{N}$

$$1.25\begin{bmatrix}0.06\begin{bmatrix}38.44\\38.5\\39.69\end{bmatrix} & \begin{bmatrix}6.2\\\sqrt{38.5}\\6.3\end{bmatrix}d\end{bmatrix}0.1$$

$\dfrac{d}{0.1} = \dfrac{0.06}{1.25} = \dfrac{6}{125}$; $125d = 0.6$;

$d \approx 0.005$; $\sqrt{38.5} \approx 6.2 + 0.005 = 6.205$

24.

N	$\sqrt{N}$

$$1.47\begin{bmatrix}1.01\begin{bmatrix}53.29\\54.3\\54.76\end{bmatrix} & \begin{bmatrix}7.3\\\sqrt{54.3}\\7.4\end{bmatrix}d\end{bmatrix}0.1$$

$\dfrac{d}{0.1} = \dfrac{1.01}{1.47} = \dfrac{101}{147}$; $147d = 10.1$;

$d \approx 0.07$; $\sqrt{54.3} \approx 7.3 + 0.07 = 7.37$

25.

N	$\sqrt[3]{N}$

$$0.1\begin{bmatrix}0.04\begin{bmatrix}5.8\\5.84\\5.9\end{bmatrix} & \begin{bmatrix}1.797\\\sqrt[3]{5.84}\\1.807\end{bmatrix}d\end{bmatrix}0.01$$

$\dfrac{d}{0.01} = \dfrac{0.04}{0.1} = \dfrac{0.004}{0.01}$; $d = 0.004$;

$\sqrt[3]{5.84} \approx 1.797 + 0.004 = 1.801$

26.

N	$\sqrt[3]{N}$

$$20.834\begin{bmatrix}12.13\begin{bmatrix}571.87\\584\\592.704\end{bmatrix} & \begin{bmatrix}8.3\\\sqrt[3]{584}\\8.4\end{bmatrix}d\end{bmatrix}0.1$$

$\dfrac{d}{0.1} = \dfrac{12.13}{20.834}$; $20.834d = 1.213$; $d \approx 0.06$;

$\sqrt[3]{584} \approx 8.3 + 0.06 = 8.36$

27.

N	$\sqrt[3]{N}$

$$4.447\begin{bmatrix}3.528\begin{bmatrix}54.872\\58.4\\59.319\end{bmatrix} & \begin{bmatrix}3.8\\\sqrt[3]{58.4}\\3.9\end{bmatrix}d\end{bmatrix}0.1$$

$\dfrac{d}{0.1} = \dfrac{3.528}{4.447}$; $4.447d = 0.3528$; $d \approx 0.08$;

$\sqrt[3]{58.4} \approx 3.8 + 0.08 = 3.88$

28.

N	$\sqrt[3]{N}$

$$3.367\begin{bmatrix}0.863\begin{bmatrix}35.937\\36.8\\39.304\end{bmatrix} & \begin{bmatrix}3.3\\\sqrt[3]{36.8}\\3.4\end{bmatrix}d\end{bmatrix}0.1$$

$\dfrac{d}{0.1} = \dfrac{0.863}{3.367}$; $3.367d = 0.0863$; $d \approx 0.03$;

$\sqrt[3]{36.8} \approx 3.3 + 0.03 = 3.33$

29.

N	$\sqrt{10N}$

$$0.1\begin{bmatrix}0.04\begin{bmatrix}3.5\\3.54\\3.6\end{bmatrix} & \begin{bmatrix}5.916\\\sqrt{35.4}\\6.000\end{bmatrix}d\end{bmatrix}0.084$$

$\dfrac{d}{0.084} = \dfrac{0.04}{0.1} = \dfrac{2}{5}$; $5d = 0.168$;

$d \approx 0.034$; $\sqrt{35.4} \approx 5.916 + 0.034 =$

5.950; $\sqrt{3540} = \sqrt{35.4 \times 10^2} =$

$\sqrt{35.4} \times 10 \approx 5.950 \times 10 = 59.50$

30.

N	$\sqrt[3]{10N}$

$$0.1\begin{bmatrix}0.06\begin{bmatrix}2.4\\2.46\\2.5\end{bmatrix} & \begin{bmatrix}2.884\\\sqrt[3]{24.6}\\2.924\end{bmatrix}d\end{bmatrix}0.04$$

$\dfrac{d}{0.04} = \dfrac{0.06}{0.1} = \dfrac{0.024}{0.04}$; $d = 0.024$;

$\sqrt[3]{24.6} \approx 2.884 + 0.024 = 2.908$;

$\sqrt[3]{24,600} = \sqrt[3]{24.6 \times 10^3} =$

$\sqrt[3]{24.6} \times 10 \approx 2.908 \times 10 \approx 29.1$

31.

N	$\sqrt{N}$

$$0.1\begin{bmatrix}d\begin{bmatrix}8.6\\x\\8.7\end{bmatrix} & \begin{bmatrix}2.933\\2.941\\2.950\end{bmatrix}0.008\end{bmatrix}0.017$$

$\dfrac{d}{0.1} = \dfrac{0.008}{0.017} = \dfrac{8}{17}$; $17d = 0.8$; $d \approx 0.05$;

$x \approx 8.6 + 0.05 = 8.65$

32.

N	$\sqrt{10N}$

$$0.1\begin{bmatrix}d\begin{bmatrix}3.9\\\dfrac{x}{10}\\4.0\end{bmatrix} & \begin{bmatrix}6.245\\6.298\\6.325\end{bmatrix}0.053\end{bmatrix}0.08$$

$\dfrac{d}{0.1} = \dfrac{0.053}{0.08} = \dfrac{53}{80}$; $80d = 5.3$; $d \approx 0.07$;

$\dfrac{x}{10} \approx 3.9 + 0.07 = 3.97$; $x \approx 39.7$

33.

N	$\sqrt{N}$

$$0.1\begin{bmatrix} d\begin{bmatrix} 5.7 \\ \dfrac{x}{10} \\ 5.8 \end{bmatrix} & \begin{bmatrix} 7.550 \\ 7.566 \end{bmatrix}0.016 \\ & 7.616 \end{bmatrix}0.066$$

$$\frac{d}{0.1} = \frac{0.016}{0.066} = \frac{8}{33};\ 33d = 0.8;\ d \approx 0.02;$$

$$\frac{x}{10} \approx 5.7 + 0.02 = 5.72;\ x \approx 57.2$$

34.

N	$\sqrt[3]{N}$

$$0.1\begin{bmatrix} d\begin{bmatrix} 5.9 \\ x \\ 6.0 \end{bmatrix} & \begin{bmatrix} 1.807 \\ 1.813 \end{bmatrix}0.006 \\ & 1.817 \end{bmatrix}0.01$$

$$\frac{d}{0.1} = \frac{0.006}{0.01} = \frac{0.06}{0.1};\ d = 0.06;$$

$$x \approx 5.9 + 0.06 = 5.96$$

35.

N	$\sqrt[3]{10N}$

$$0.1\begin{bmatrix} d\begin{bmatrix} 7.7 \\ \dfrac{x}{10} \\ 7.8 \end{bmatrix} & \begin{bmatrix} 4.254 \\ 4.262 \end{bmatrix}0.008 \\ & 4.273 \end{bmatrix}0.019$$

$$\frac{d}{0.1} = \frac{0.008}{0.019} = \frac{8}{19};\ 19d = 0.8;\ d \approx 0.04;$$

$$\frac{x}{10} \approx 7.7 + 0.04 = 7.74;\ x \approx 77.4$$

36.

N	$\sqrt[3]{100N}$

$$0.1\begin{bmatrix} d\begin{bmatrix} 5.3 \\ \dfrac{x}{100} \\ 5.4 \end{bmatrix} & \begin{bmatrix} 8.093 \\ 8.135 \end{bmatrix}0.042 \\ & 8.143 \end{bmatrix}0.05$$

$$\frac{d}{0.1} = \frac{0.042}{0.05} = \frac{0.084}{0.1};\ d \approx 0.08;$$

$$\frac{x}{100} \approx 5.3 + 0.08 = 5.38;\ x \approx 538$$

Pages 371-372 · COMPUTER EXERCISES

1. 10 PRINT "ENTER X1, F(X1), X2, F(X2)"
20 INPUT X1, F1, X2, F2
30 PRINT "ENTER VALUE OF X TO BE INTERPOLATED"
40 INPUT X
50 LET F = F1 + (X − X1)/(X2 − X1) * (F2 − F1)
60 PRINT "F("; X;") = "; F
70 GOTO 10

2. a. F(1916) = 100.4
F(1949) = 149.1
F(1972) = 207.8

b. F(1920) = 107.5 The program estimate is greater than the table value by 1.5 million.

3. F(1982) = 231.8
F(1985) = 239
F(2000) = 275
F(1898) = 72.8
F(1879) = 42.4

4. To estimate the function for problem number 5a., use the following program.

```
10 PRINT "ENTER X1, X2"
20 INPUT X1, X2
25 DEF FN Y(X) = X ↑ 3
26 LET F1 = FN Y(X1)
27 LET F2 = FN Y(X2)
30 PRINT "ENTER VALUE OF X TO BE INTERPOLATED"
40 INPUT X
50 LET F = F1 + (X − X1)/(X2 − X1) ∗ (F2 − F1)
60 PRINT "F("; X;") = "; F
65 LET FF = FN Y(X)
66 PRINT "EXACT VALUE IS"; FF
70 END
```

5. **a.** $F(2.8) = 23.2$

EXACT VALUE IS 21.952

b. Change line 25 to: 25 DEF FN Y(X) = 3 ∗ X − 7

$F(7) = 14$

EXACT VALUE IS 14

c. Change line 25 to: 25 DEF FN Y(X) = 1/X

$F(13.71) = .08145$

EXACT VALUE IS .0729394603

d. Change line 25 to: 25 DEF FN Y(X) = X ↑ 5 + 3/4 ∗ X ↑ 3 − X ↑ 2 + 8

$F(14.3) = 606292.576$

EXACT VALUE IS 599967.756

Page 374 · CHAPTER REVIEW

1. a; $s = kt$; $52 = k \cdot 4$; $k = 13$; $s = 13 \cdot 5 = 65$

2. b; $\dfrac{250}{450} = \dfrac{5}{9} = \dfrac{x}{13{,}500}$; $9x = 67{,}500$; $x = 7500$

3. c; $z = kxy^2$; $144 = k \cdot 4 \cdot 3^2$; $k = 4$; $z = 4 \cdot 3 \cdot 4^2 = 192$

4. b; $c = \dfrac{kd^2}{l}$; $0.54 = \dfrac{k \cdot 9}{20}$; $9k = 10.8$; $k = 1.2$; $c = \dfrac{1.2(25)}{50} = 0.6$

5. a;
$$
\begin{array}{r}
2x + 1 \\
x^2 - 2x + 1 \overline{)2x^3 - 3x^2 + 0x + 4} \\
2x^3 - 4x^2 + 2x \\
\hline
x^2 - 2x + 4 \\
x^2 - 2x + 1 \\
\hline
3
\end{array}
$$

6. d;
$$
\begin{array}{r|rrrrr}
-3 & 1 & 2 & -4 & 0 & -5 \\
   &   & -3 & 3 & 3 & -9 \\
\hline
   & 1 & -1 & -1 & 3 & -14
\end{array}
$$

7. d; $x + 1$ is a factor if -1 is a zero;
$(-1)^{21} - 3(-1)^{11} + k = 0$;
$-1 + 3 + k = 0$; $k = -2$

8. c;

$$\underline{-2}\underline{\,|}\ \begin{array}{rrrrr} 1 & 3 & -1 & 0 & 8 \\ & -2 & -2 & 6 & -12 \\ \hline 1 & 1 & -3 & 6 & -4 \end{array}$$

9. c; if $1 - i$ is a root, $1 + i$ is also a root; these are zeros of the quadratic polynomial $x^2 - 2x + 2$, which is a factor of P.

$$\begin{array}{r} 2x^2 - x - 1 \\ x^2 - 2x + 2\overline{\smash{\big)}\,2x^4 - 5x^3 + 5x^2 + 0x - 2} \\ \underline{2x^4 - 4x^3 + 4x^2} \\ -x^3 + x^2 \\ \underline{-x^3 + 2x^2 - 2x} \\ -x^2 + 2x - 2 \\ \underline{-x^2 + 2x - 2} \\ 0 \end{array}$$

$2x^2 - x - 1 = 0$;
$(2x + 1)(x - 1) = 0$;
$x = -\dfrac{1}{2}$, $x = 1$;
$\left\{1 \pm i, 1, -\dfrac{1}{2}\right\}$

10. b; roots are -2, $1 - 2i$, $1 + 2i$; $(x + 2)(x - (1 - 2i))(x - (1 + 2i)) = 0$;
$(x + 2)(x^2 - 2x + 5) = 0$; $x^3 + x + 10 = 0$

11. d; denominator must be a factor of 6   **12.** b; $(1.7)^3 = 4.913$; $(1.8)^3 = 5.832$

13. b; $f(1.43) = 3.16 + \dfrac{0.03}{0.10}(2.92 - 3.16) = 3.16 + 0.3(-0.24) = 3.16 - 0.072 \approx 3.09$

Page 375 · CHAPTER TEST

1. Let d = distance in meters the body has fallen; $\dfrac{19.6}{4} = \dfrac{d}{9}$; $d = 9\left(\dfrac{19.6}{4}\right) = 44.1$; 44.1 m

2. $z = k\dfrac{x}{y^2}$; $k\dfrac{3x}{(2y)^2} = k\dfrac{3x}{4y^2} = \dfrac{3}{4}\left(k\dfrac{x}{y^2}\right)$; z is multiplied by $\dfrac{3}{4}$

3.

$$\begin{array}{r} 3x + 2a \\ 2x^2 - 3ax + 2a^2\overline{\smash{\big)}\,6x^3 - 5ax^2 + 0a^2x + 6a^3} \\ \underline{6x^3 - 9ax^2 + 6a^2x} \\ 4ax^2 - 6a^2x + 6a^3 \\ \underline{4ax^2 - 6a^2x + 4a^3} \\ 2a^3 \end{array}$$

$3x + 2a + \dfrac{2a^3}{2x^2 - 3ax + 2a^2}$

4.

$$\underline{-2}\underline{\,|}\ \begin{array}{rrrrr} 2 & 3 & -1 & 0 & -2 \\ & -4 & 2 & -2 & 4 \\ \hline 2 & -1 & 1 & -2 & 2 \end{array}$$

$2x^3 - x^2 + x - 2 + \dfrac{2}{x + 2}$

5. $P\left(\dfrac{1}{2}\right)$ = remainder when $P(x)$ is divided by $x - \dfrac{1}{2}$.

$$\tfrac{1}{2}\underline{\,|}\ \begin{array}{rrrr} 2 & 3 & -4 & 5 \\ & 1 & 2 & -1 \\ \hline 2 & 4 & -2 & 4 \end{array}$$

$P\left(\dfrac{1}{2}\right) = 4$

6. Since $1 + i\sqrt{2}$ is a root, $1 - i\sqrt{2}$ is also; then $(x - 1 - i\sqrt{2})(x - 1 + i\sqrt{2})$ is a factor of $x^4 - 2x^3 + 6x - 9$; $(x - 1 - i\sqrt{2})(x - 1 + i\sqrt{2}) = x^2 - 2x + 3$; the depressed equation, $x^2 - 3 = 0$, has roots $\pm\sqrt{3}$; $\{1 \pm i\sqrt{2}, \pm\sqrt{3}\}$.

7. The only possible rational roots are ± 1, ± 2, $\pm\dfrac{1}{3}$, and $\pm\dfrac{2}{3}$; $\dfrac{1}{3}$ and -1 satisfy the equation, so $(x + 1)\left(x - \dfrac{1}{3}\right) = x^2 + \dfrac{2}{3}x - \dfrac{1}{3}$ is a factor of

$3x^4 + 2x^3 + 5x^2 + 4x - 2$; the depressed equation, $3x^2 + 6 = 0$, has roots $\pm i\sqrt{2}$; $\left\{\dfrac{1}{3}, -1, \pm i\sqrt{2}\right\}$.

8.

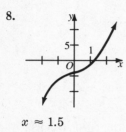

$x \approx 1.5$

9.

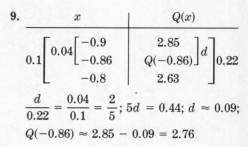

$\dfrac{d}{0.22} = \dfrac{0.04}{0.1} = \dfrac{2}{5};\ 5d = 0.44;\ d \approx 0.09;$

$Q(-0.86) \approx 2.85 - 0.09 = 2.76$

Pages 375-376 · MIXED REVIEW

1.
$$-\tfrac{4}{3}\big|\ \ 6\ \ -13\ \ -73\ \ -60$$
$$\underline{-8\ \ \ 28\ \ \ 60}$$
$$6\ \ -21\ \ -45$$

$6x^2 - 21x - 45 = 0;\ 2x^2 - 7x - 15 = 0;$

$x = \dfrac{7 \pm 13}{4};\ x = 5$ or $x = -\dfrac{3}{2};\ \left\{-\dfrac{4}{3}, 5, -\dfrac{3}{2}\right\}$

2. a. $\dfrac{5}{3r - 2} + \dfrac{3}{r + 2} = -1;\ (3r - 2)(r + 2)\left[\dfrac{5}{3r - 2} + \dfrac{3}{r + 2}\right] = (3r - 2)(r + 2)(-1);$

$5r + 10 + 9r - 6 = -3r^2 - 4r + 4;\ 3r^2 + 18r = 0;\ r^2 + 6r = 0;\ r(r + 6) = 0;$

$r = 0$ or $r = -6;\ \{0, -6\}$

b. $\sqrt{4s - 3} - \sqrt{s + 2} = 2;\ \sqrt{4s - 3} = 2 + \sqrt{s + 2};$

$4s - 3 = 4 + 4\sqrt{s + 2} + s + 2;\ 3s - 9 = 4\sqrt{s + 2};\ 9s^2 - 54s + 81 = 16s + 32;$

$9s^2 - 70s + 49 = 0;\ (9s - 7)(s - 7) = 0;\ s = \dfrac{7}{9}$ (reject) or $s = 7;\ 7$

3. Let n and $n + 2$ be the integers; $n(n + 2) < 35;\ n^2 + 2n < 35;\ n^2 + 2n - 35 < 0;$
$(n + 7)(n - 5) < 0;\ n + 7 < 0$ and $n - 5 > 0$ or $n + 7 > 0$ and $n - 5 < 0;\ n > -7$
and $n < 5;\ n = -5, -3, -1, 1,$ or $3;$ the pairs are -5 and -3, -3 and -1, -1 and 1,
1 and 3, and 3 and 5.

4. $5y^2 - 2y + 4 = 0;\ y = \dfrac{2 \pm \sqrt{4 - 80}}{10} = \dfrac{2 \pm \sqrt{-76}}{10} = \dfrac{2 \pm 2i\sqrt{19}}{10} = \dfrac{1 \pm i\sqrt{19}}{5};$
$\left\{\dfrac{1 \pm i\sqrt{19}}{5}\right\}$

5. $(h, k) = (-1, 3)$; $y = a(x + 1)^2 + 3$; $-5 = a(3 + 1)^2 + 3$; $-5 = 16a + 3$; $16a = -8$;

$a = -\dfrac{1}{2}$; $y = -\dfrac{1}{2}(x + 1)^2 + 3$

6. $m = \dfrac{-\dfrac{5}{2} - (-1)}{-1 - 1} = \dfrac{-\dfrac{3}{2}}{-2} = \dfrac{3}{4}$; $\dfrac{-4 + 1}{a - 1} = \dfrac{3}{4}$; $3a - 3 = -16 + 4$; $3a = -9$; $a = -3$;

$\dfrac{b + 1}{\dfrac{5}{3} - 1} = \dfrac{3}{4}$; $4b + 4 = 2$; $4b = -2$; $b = -\dfrac{1}{2}$

7. Let s = Sue's rate in still water and c = rate of current; Paula's rate in still
water = $s + 2$; $2(s + c) = 11$ and $2(s + 2 - c) = 13$; $s + c = 5.5$ and $s - c = 4.5$;

$$\begin{array}{r} s + c = 5.5 \\ \underline{s - c = 4.5} \\ 2s = 10; \end{array}$$ $s = 5$; $5 + c = 5.5$; $c = 0.5$; 0.5 km/h

8. $(r^{-1} + s^{-1})^{-3} = \left[(-2)^{-1} + \left(\dfrac{2}{5} \right)^{-1} \right]^{-3} = \left(-\dfrac{1}{2} + \dfrac{5}{2} \right)^{-3} = 2^{-3} = \dfrac{1}{8}$

9. $\sqrt{10}(3\sqrt{2} - 2\sqrt{5})^2 = \sqrt{10}(18 - 12\sqrt{10} + 20) = \sqrt{10}(38 - 12\sqrt{10}) = 38\sqrt{10} - 120$

10. $\dfrac{2}{1 + i} - \dfrac{1 + i}{2} = \dfrac{2(1 - i)}{(1 + i)(1 - i)} - \dfrac{1 + i}{2} = \dfrac{2 - 2i}{2} - \dfrac{1 + i}{2} = \dfrac{1 - 3i}{2}$

11. $\sqrt[3]{\dfrac{135}{4}} = \sqrt[3]{\dfrac{5 \cdot 27}{4}} = \sqrt[3]{\dfrac{5 \cdot 27 \cdot 2}{8}} = \dfrac{3\sqrt[3]{10}}{2}$

12. $\dfrac{2}{x^2 - 1} + \dfrac{1}{x + 1} = \dfrac{2}{(x + 1)(x - 1)} + \dfrac{x - 1}{(x + 1)(x - 1)} = \dfrac{x + 1}{(x + 1)(x - 1)} = \dfrac{1}{x - 1}$

13. $\dfrac{8y^3 - 1}{2 + 4y} \div (4y^2 - 1) = \dfrac{(2y - 1)(4y^2 + 2y + 1)}{2(2y + 1)} \cdot \dfrac{1}{(2y + 1)(2y - 1)} = \dfrac{4y^2 + 2y + 1}{2(2y + 1)^2}$

14. $-\dfrac{3}{4}(6 - 7w) > 5(w - 2)$; $-3(6 - 7w) > 20(w - 2)$; $-18 + 21w > 20w - 40$;

$w > -22$; $\{w : w > -22\}$

15. $|3 - 2q| \leq 4$; $-4 \leq 3 - 2q \leq 4$; $-7 \leq -2q \leq 1$; $-\dfrac{1}{2} \leq q \leq \dfrac{7}{2}$; $\left\{ q : -\dfrac{1}{2} \leq q \leq \dfrac{7}{2} \right\}$

16. $m^3 + 6m^2 + 9m = 0$; $m(m^2 + 6m + 9) = 0$; $m(m + 3)^2 = 0$; $m = 0$ or $m = -3$
(double root); $\{0, -3\}$

17. $(8x^3y)^2\left(\dfrac{y}{2x}\right)^4 = (64x^6y^2)\left(\dfrac{y^4}{16x^4}\right) = 4x^2y^6$

18. $(4x - y)^3 = (4x - y)(4x - y)^2 = (4x - y)(16x^2 - 8xy + y^2) =$
$64x^3 - 32x^2y + 4xy^2 - 16x^2y + 8xy^2 - y^3 = 64x^3 - 48x^2y + 12xy^2 - y^3$

19. $(2y^{3/4}z)(3y^{1/4}z^{-1/3}) = 6yz^{2/3}$

20. $f(g(-2)) = f\left[\dfrac{1}{2}(-2) - 5\right] = f(-6) = [3(-6) + 2]^2 = (-16)^2 = 256;$

$g(f(-2)) = g[[3(-2) + 2]^2] = g(16) = \dfrac{1}{2}(16) - 5 = 3$

21. $3x^4 + 5x^3 + 4x^2 + 10x - 4 = 0;$ the possible rational roots are $\pm 1, \pm 2, \pm 4, \pm\dfrac{1}{3},$
$\pm\dfrac{2}{3},$ and $\pm\dfrac{4}{3};$ -2 and $\dfrac{1}{3}$ satisfy the equation.

22. $V = kr^3; 288\pi = k(6^3); 288\pi = 216k; k = \dfrac{288\pi}{216} = \dfrac{4\pi}{3}; 36\pi = \dfrac{4\pi}{3}r^3; r^3 = \dfrac{36\cdot 3}{4} = 27;$
$r = 3; 3$ cm

23.
$$
\begin{array}{r}
5x^2 - 3x\ +\ 4 \\
3x + 4)\overline{15x^3 + 11x^2 + 0x + 20} \\
\underline{15x^3 + 20x^2} \\
-9x^2 \\
\underline{-9x^2 - 12x} \\
12x + 20 \\
\underline{12x + 16} \\
4
\end{array}
$$
$5x^2 - 3x + 4 + \dfrac{4}{3x + 4}$

24. $d^2 + 2d = -2; d^2 + 2d + 1 = -2 + 1; (d + 1)^2 = -1; d + 1 = \pm\sqrt{-1} = \pm i;$
$d = -1 \pm i$

25. $b^2 - 4ac = 9 - 4(1)(-1) = 13;$ the equation has two distinct real roots.

26. product $= \dfrac{-1}{1} = -1;$ sum $= -\dfrac{3}{1} = -3$

27. $P(x) = x^3 - 2x^2 - 9$ so $P(x) = 0$ has one pos. root; $P(-x) = -x^3 - 2x^2 - 9$ so
$P(x) = 0$ has no neg. roots; the possible rational roots are, therefore, 1, 3, and 9; 3
satisfies the equation; the depressed equation, $x^2 + x + 3 = 0,$ has roots $\dfrac{-1 \pm i\sqrt{11}}{2};$
$\left\{3, \dfrac{-1 \pm i\sqrt{11}}{2}\right\}.$

Page 377 · PREPARING FOR COLLEGE ENTRANCE EXAMS

1. B	2. C	3. E
4. D	5. B	6. E
7. C	8. C	

A 1. **a.** $\sqrt{(3-0)^2 + (-1-3)^2} = \sqrt{9+16} = \sqrt{25} = 5$ **b.** $\left(\dfrac{3+0}{2}, \dfrac{-1+3}{2}\right) = \left(\dfrac{3}{2}, 1\right)$

2. **a.** $\sqrt{[0-(-5)]^2 + [6-(-6)]^2} = \sqrt{25+144} = \sqrt{169} = 13$

 b. $\left(\dfrac{0+(-5)}{2}, \dfrac{6+(-6)}{2}\right) = \left(-\dfrac{5}{2}, 0\right)$

3. **a.** $\sqrt{(5-0)^2 + (-1-4)^2} = \sqrt{25+25} = \sqrt{50} = 5\sqrt{2}$

 b. $\left(\dfrac{5+0}{2}, \dfrac{-1+4}{2}\right) = \left(\dfrac{5}{2}, \dfrac{3}{2}\right)$

4. **a.** $\sqrt{(4-0)^2 + (-2-2)^2} = \sqrt{16+16} = \sqrt{32} = 4\sqrt{2}$ **b.** $\left(\dfrac{4+0}{2}, \dfrac{-2+2}{2}\right) = (2,0)$

5. **a.** $\sqrt{\left(2-\dfrac{1}{3}\right)^2 + [2-(-2)]^2} = \sqrt{\dfrac{25}{9}+16} = \sqrt{\dfrac{169}{9}} = \dfrac{13}{3}$

 b. $\left(\dfrac{2+\dfrac{1}{3}}{2}, \dfrac{2+(-2)}{2}\right) = \left(\dfrac{\dfrac{7}{3}}{2}, \dfrac{0}{2}\right) = \left(\dfrac{7}{6}, 0\right)$

6. **a.** $\sqrt{\left[\dfrac{1}{2}-(-1)\right]^2 + (-1-1)^2} = \sqrt{\dfrac{9}{4}+4} = \sqrt{\dfrac{25}{4}} = \dfrac{5}{2}$

 b. $\left(\dfrac{\dfrac{1}{2}+(-1)}{2}, \dfrac{-1+1}{2}\right) = \left(\dfrac{-\dfrac{1}{2}}{2}, \dfrac{0}{2}\right) = \left(-\dfrac{1}{4}, 0\right)$

7. **a.** $\sqrt{(-7-7)^2 + [7-(-7)]^2} = \sqrt{196+196} = \sqrt{392} = 14\sqrt{2}$

 b. $\left(\dfrac{-7+7}{2}, \dfrac{7+(-7)}{2}\right) = (0,0)$

8. **a.** $\sqrt{[12-(-12)]^2 + (5-5)^2} = \sqrt{576} = 24$ **b.** $\left(\dfrac{12+(-12)}{2}, \dfrac{5+5}{2}\right) = (0,5)$

9. **a.** $\sqrt{(0-5)^2 + (0-5)^2} = \sqrt{25+25} = \sqrt{50} = 5\sqrt{2}$ **b.** $\left(\dfrac{0+5}{2}, \dfrac{0+5}{2}\right) = \left(\dfrac{5}{2}, \dfrac{5}{2}\right)$

10. **a.** $\sqrt{(0-\sqrt{2})^2 + (0-\sqrt{2})^2} = \sqrt{2+2} = \sqrt{4} = 2$

 b. $\left(\dfrac{0+\sqrt{2}}{2}, \dfrac{0+\sqrt{2}}{2}\right) = \left(\dfrac{\sqrt{2}}{2}, \dfrac{\sqrt{2}}{2}\right)$

11. **a.** $\sqrt{[\sqrt{2}-(-\sqrt{2})]^2 + (1-0)^2} = \sqrt{8+1} = \sqrt{9} = 3$

 b. $\left(\dfrac{\sqrt{2}+(-\sqrt{2})}{2}, \dfrac{1+0}{2}\right) = \left(0, \dfrac{1}{2}\right)$

12. **a.** $\sqrt{(3-1)^2 + [\sqrt{3}-(-\sqrt{3})]^2} = \sqrt{4+12} = \sqrt{16} = 4$

 b. $\left(\dfrac{3+1}{2}, \dfrac{\sqrt{3}+(-\sqrt{3})}{2}\right) = (2,0)$

13. **a.** $\sqrt{[1+\sqrt{5}-(1-\sqrt{5})]^2 + [2+\sqrt{3}-(-2+\sqrt{3})]^2} = \sqrt{20+16} = \sqrt{36} = 6$

 b. $\left(\dfrac{1+\sqrt{5}+1-\sqrt{5}}{2}, \dfrac{2+\sqrt{3}+(-2+\sqrt{3})}{2}\right) = \left(\dfrac{2}{2}, \dfrac{2\sqrt{3}}{2}\right) = (1, \sqrt{3})$

225

14. a. $\sqrt{[\sqrt{3}+1-(\sqrt{3}-1)]^2 + [\sqrt{2}-\sqrt{3}-(\sqrt{2}+\sqrt{3})]^2} = \sqrt{4+12} = \sqrt{16} = 4$

    b. $\left(\dfrac{\sqrt{3}+1+\sqrt{3}-1}{2}, \dfrac{\sqrt{2}-\sqrt{3}+\sqrt{2}+\sqrt{3}}{2}\right) = \left(\dfrac{2\sqrt{3}}{2}, \dfrac{2\sqrt{2}}{2}\right) = (\sqrt{3}, \sqrt{2})$

15. a. $\sqrt{[a+b-(b-a)]^2 + [a-b-(b+a)]^2} = \sqrt{4a^2+4b^2} = \sqrt{4(a^2+b^2)} =$

    $2\sqrt{a^2+b^2}$ **b.** $\left(\dfrac{a+b+b-a}{2}, \dfrac{a-b+a+b}{2}\right) = \left(\dfrac{2b}{2}, \dfrac{2a}{2}\right) = (b, a)$

16. a. $\sqrt{(a-b)^2 + [\sqrt{ab}-(-\sqrt{ab})]^2} = \sqrt{a^2-2ab+b^2+4ab} = \sqrt{a^2+2ab+b^2}$

    $= \sqrt{(a+b)^2} = |a+b|$ **b.** $\left(\dfrac{a+b}{2}, \dfrac{\sqrt{ab}+(-\sqrt{ab})}{2}\right) = \left(\dfrac{a+b}{2}, 0\right)$

17-22. Let $Q = (x, y)$.   **17.** $\dfrac{x+0}{2} = 2$ and $\dfrac{y+0}{2} = 5$; $x = 4$ and $y = 10$; $Q(4, 10)$

18. $\dfrac{x+(-3)}{2} = 0$ and $\dfrac{y+1}{2} = 0$; $x = 3$ and $y = -1$; $Q(3, -1)$

19. $\dfrac{x+(-1)}{2} = 2$ and $\dfrac{y+0}{2} = 2$; $x = 5$ and $y+0 = 4$; $y = 4$; $Q(5, 4)$

20. $\dfrac{x+4}{2} = 0$ and $\dfrac{y+(-2)}{2} = 3$; $x = -4$ and $y = 8$; $Q(-4, 8)$

21. $\dfrac{x+h}{2} = 0$ and $\dfrac{y+k}{2} = 0$; $x = -h$ and $y = -k$; $Q(-h, -k)$

22. $\dfrac{0+x}{2} = h$ and $\dfrac{0+y}{2} = k$; $x = 2h$ and $y = 2k$; $Q(2h, 2k)$

B   **23. a.** $AB = \sqrt{(-2-2)^2 + (2-1)^2} = \sqrt{16+1} = \sqrt{17}$;

      $BC = \sqrt{(2-1)^2 + [1-(-3)]^2} = \sqrt{1+16} = \sqrt{17}$.

      Since $AB = BC$, $\triangle ABC$ is isosceles.

    b. $AC = \sqrt{(-2-1)^2 + [2-(-3)]^2} = \sqrt{9+25} = \sqrt{34}$; $(AB)^2 + (BC)^2 = 17 + 17$

      $= 34 = (AC)^2$; $\triangle ABC$ is a right triangle.

      Area $= \dfrac{1}{2} \cdot AB \cdot BC = \dfrac{1}{2} \cdot \sqrt{17}\sqrt{17} = \dfrac{17}{2}$.

24. a. $AB = \sqrt{(6-0)^2 + [-4-(-7)]^2} = \sqrt{36+9} = \sqrt{45} = 3\sqrt{5}$;

    $BC = \sqrt{[0-(-6)]^2 + (-7-5)^2} = \sqrt{36+144} = \sqrt{180} = 6\sqrt{5}$;

    $AC = \sqrt{[6-(-6)]^2 + (-4-5)^2} = \sqrt{144+81} = \sqrt{225} = 15$.

    $\triangle ABC$ is not isosceles.

    b. $(AB)^2 + (BC)^2 = 45 + 180 = 225 = (AC)^2$; $\triangle ABC$ is a right triangle.

    Area $= \dfrac{1}{2} \cdot AB \cdot BC = \dfrac{1}{2} \cdot 3\sqrt{5} \cdot 6\sqrt{5} = 45$.

25. a. $AB = \sqrt{[4-(-4)]^2 + (-2-6)^2} = \sqrt{64+64} = \sqrt{128} = 8\sqrt{2}$;

    $BC = \sqrt{[-4-(-3)]^2 + [6-(-1)]^2} = \sqrt{1+49} = \sqrt{50} = 5\sqrt{2}$;

    $AC = \sqrt{[4-(-3)]^2 + [-2-(-1)]^2} = \sqrt{49+1} = \sqrt{50} = 5\sqrt{2}$.

    Since $AB = AC$, $\triangle ABC$ is isosceles.

    b. $(BC)^2 + (AC)^2 = 50 + 50 = 100$; $(AB)^2 = 128$; $\triangle ABC$ is not a right triangle.

26. a. $AB = \sqrt{(2-2)^2 + (-3-3)^2} = \sqrt{36} = 6;$

$BC = \sqrt{(2-5)^2 + (3-0)^2} = \sqrt{9+9} = \sqrt{18} = 3\sqrt{2};$

$AC = \sqrt{(2-5)^2 + (-3-0)^2} = \sqrt{9+9} = \sqrt{18} = 3\sqrt{2}.$

Since $BC = AC$, $\triangle ABC$ is isosceles.

b. $(BC)^2 + (AC)^2 = 18 + 18 = 36 = (AB)^2;$ $\triangle ABC$ is a right triangle.

Area $= \dfrac{1}{2} \cdot BC \cdot AC = \dfrac{1}{2} \cdot 3\sqrt{2} \cdot 3\sqrt{2} = 9$

27. $\sqrt{(0-6)^2 + (1-3)^2} = \sqrt{36+4} = \sqrt{40} = 2\sqrt{10};$

$\sqrt{[6-(-3)]^2 + (3-0)^2} = \sqrt{81+9} = \sqrt{90} = 3\sqrt{10};$

$\sqrt{[0-(-3)]^2 + (1-0)^2} = \sqrt{9+1} = \sqrt{10}; 2\sqrt{10} + \sqrt{10} = 3\sqrt{10}.$

The points are collinear.

28. $\sqrt{[6-(-6)^2 + (0-3)^2} = \sqrt{144+9} = \sqrt{153} = 3\sqrt{17};$

$\sqrt{(-6-2)^2 + (3-1)^2} = \sqrt{64+4} = \sqrt{68} = 2\sqrt{17};$

$\sqrt{(6-2)^2 + (0-1)^2} = \sqrt{16+1} = \sqrt{17}; 2\sqrt{17} + \sqrt{17} = 3\sqrt{17}.$

The points are collinear.

29. $\sqrt{[-4-(-1)]^2 + (-1-2)^2} = \sqrt{9+9} = \sqrt{18} = 3\sqrt{2};$

$\sqrt{(-1-2)^2 + (2-4)^2} = \sqrt{9+4} = \sqrt{13};$

$\sqrt{(-4-2)^2 + (-1-4)^2} = \sqrt{36+25} = \sqrt{61}; \sqrt{61} \neq \sqrt{13} + 3\sqrt{2}.$

The points are not collinear.

30. $\sqrt{(1-2)^2 + (5-0)^2} = \sqrt{1+25} = \sqrt{26};$

$\sqrt{(2-4)^2 + [0-(-10)]^2} = \sqrt{4+100} = \sqrt{104} = 2\sqrt{26};$

$\sqrt{(1-4)^2 + [5-(-10)]^2} = \sqrt{9+225} = \sqrt{234} = 3\sqrt{26}; \sqrt{26} + 2\sqrt{26} = 3\sqrt{26}.$

The points are collinear.

Page 383 · PROBLEMS

A   **1-2.** Let j be the perpendicular bisector.

1. Slope of $\overline{AB} = \dfrac{4-0}{0-(-2)} = 2;$ slope of $j = -\dfrac{1}{2};$ j passes through

$\left(\dfrac{-2+0}{2}, \dfrac{0+4}{2}\right) = (-1, 2); \dfrac{y-2}{x-(-1)} = -\dfrac{1}{2}; 2y - 4 = -x - 1; x + 2y = 3.$

2. Slope of $\overline{AB} = \dfrac{1-(-1)}{3-1} = 1;$ slope of $j = -1;$ j passes through

$\left(\dfrac{1+3}{2}, \dfrac{-1+1}{2}\right) = (2, 0); \dfrac{y-0}{x-2} = -1; y = -x + 2; x + y = 2.$

3-4. Let $(a, 0)$ and $(0, b)$ be the points.

3. $\sqrt{[a-(-2)]^2 + (0-0)^2} = \sqrt{(a-0)^2 + (0-4)^2}; a^2 + 4a + 4 = a^2 + 16; 4a = 12;$

$a = 3; \sqrt{[0-(-2)]^2 + (b-0)^2} = \sqrt{(0-0)^2 + (b-4)^2}; b^2 + 4 = b^2 - 8b + 16;$

$8b = 12; b = 1\dfrac{1}{2}; (3, 0)$ and $\left(0, 1\dfrac{1}{2}\right)$

4. $\sqrt{(a - 1)^2 + [0 - (-1)]^2} = \sqrt{(a - 3)^2 + (0 - 1)^2}$; $\sqrt{a^2 - 2a + 1 + 1} =$
$\sqrt{a^2 - 6a + 9 + 1}$; $a^2 - 2a + 2 = a^2 - 6a + 10$; $4a = 8$; $a = 2$;
$\sqrt{(0 - 1)^2 + [b - (-1)]^2} = \sqrt{(0 - 3)^2 + (b - 1)^2}$; $\sqrt{1 + b^2 + 2b + 1} =$
$\sqrt{9 + b^2 - 2b + 1}$; $b^2 + 2b + 2 = b^2 - 2b + 10$; $4b = 8$; $b = 2$; $(2, 0)$ and $(0, 2)$

5. $(CD)^2 = (4 - 0)^2 + (0 - 0)^2 = 16$; $(DE)^2 = (6 - 4)^2 + (3 - 0)^2 = 4 + 9 = 13$;
$(CD)^2 + (DE)^2 + (EF)^2 + (FC)^2 = 2(CD)^2 + 2(DE)^2 = 2 \cdot 16 + 2 \cdot 13 =$
$32 + 26 = 58$; $(CE)^2 = (6 - 0)^2 + (3 - 0)^2 = 36 + 9 = 45$;
$(DF)^2 = (2 - 4)^2 + (3 - 0)^2 = 4 + 9 = 13$; $(CE)^2 + (DF)^2 = 45 + 13 = 58$;
$(CD)^2 + (DE)^2 + (EF)^2 + (FC)^2 = (CE)^2 + (DF)^2$

6. Let M, N, P, and Q be the midpoints of $\overline{AB}$, $\overline{BC}$, $\overline{CD}$, and $\overline{AD}$, respectively;
$M = \left(\dfrac{0 + 6}{2}, \dfrac{0 + 0}{2} \right) = (3, 0)$; $N = \left(\dfrac{6 + 4}{2}, \dfrac{0 + 8}{2} \right) = (5, 4)$;
$P = \left(\dfrac{4 + (-2)}{2}, \dfrac{8 + 2}{2} \right) = (1, 5)$; $Q = \left(\dfrac{0 + (-2)}{2}, \dfrac{0 + 2}{2} \right) = (-1, 1)$; slope of
$\overline{MN} = \dfrac{4 - 0}{5 - 3} = 2$; slope of $\overline{PQ} = \dfrac{1 - 5}{-1 - 1} = 2$; slope of $\overline{PN} = \dfrac{4 - 5}{5 - 1} = -\dfrac{1}{4}$; slope of
$\overline{QM} = \dfrac{0 - 1}{3 - (-1)} = -\dfrac{1}{4}$; since $\overline{MN} \parallel \overline{PQ}$ and $\overline{PN} \parallel \overline{QM}$, $MNPQ$ is a $\square$.

B   7. Let M, N, and P be the midpoints of $\overline{AB}$, $\overline{BC}$, and $\overline{AC}$, respectively;
$M = \left(\dfrac{0 + a}{2}, \dfrac{0 + 0}{2} \right) = \left(\dfrac{a}{2}, 0 \right)$; $N = \left(\dfrac{a + b}{2}, \dfrac{0 + c}{2} \right) = \left(\dfrac{a + b}{2}, \dfrac{c}{2} \right)$;
$P = \left(\dfrac{0 + b}{2}, \dfrac{0 + c}{2} \right) = \left(\dfrac{b}{2}, \dfrac{c}{2} \right)$; $MN = \sqrt{ \left(\dfrac{a + b}{2} - \dfrac{a}{2} \right)^2 + \left(\dfrac{c}{2} - 0 \right)^2 } = \sqrt{ \dfrac{b^2 + c^2}{4} } =$
$\dfrac{\sqrt{b^2 + c^2}}{2}$; $AC = \sqrt{(b - 0)^2 + (c - 0)^2} = \sqrt{b^2 + c^2}$; slope of $\overline{MN} = \dfrac{\dfrac{c}{2} - 0}{\dfrac{a + b}{2} - \dfrac{a}{2}} = \dfrac{c}{b}$
slope of $\overline{AC} = \dfrac{c - 0}{b - 0} = \dfrac{c}{b}$; $\overline{MN} \parallel \overline{AC}$ and $MN = \dfrac{1}{2} AC$.

8. Methods may vary; example: let M, N, and P be the given points. Draw $\overline{NP}$ and construct j through M parallel to $\overline{NP}$. Draw $\overline{MP}$ and construct k through N parallel to $\overline{MP}$ intersecting j at A. Extend $\overrightarrow{AN}$ through N to B so that $NB = AN$; extend $\overrightarrow{AM}$ through M to C so that $MC = AM$. Draw $\overline{BC}$. $\triangle ABC$ is the desired triangle.

9. Let $P_1 = (x_1, y_1)$, $P_2 = (x_2, y_2)$, then $M = \left(\dfrac{x_1 + x_2}{2}, \dfrac{y_1 + y_2}{2} \right)$.
$MP_1 = \sqrt{ \left(x_1 - \dfrac{x_1 + x_2}{2} \right)^2 + \left(y_1 - \dfrac{y_1 + y_2}{2} \right)^2 } = \sqrt{ \dfrac{(x_1 - x_2)^2}{4} + \dfrac{(y_1 - y_2)^2}{4} } =$
$\dfrac{1}{2} \sqrt{(x_1 - x_2)^2 + (y_1 - y_2)^2} = \dfrac{1}{2} P_1 P_2$; $MP_2 = \sqrt{ \left(x_2 - \dfrac{x_1 + x_2}{2} \right)^2 + \left(y_2 - \dfrac{y_1 + y_2}{2} \right)^2 } =$
$\sqrt{ \dfrac{(x_2 - x_1)^2}{4} + \dfrac{(y_2 - y_1)^2}{4} } = \dfrac{1}{2} \sqrt{(x_1 - x_2)^2 + (y_1 - y_2)^2} = \dfrac{1}{2} P_1 P_2$

10. $(AB)^2 = (0 - a)^2 + (0 - 0)^2 = a^2$; $(AD)^2 = (0 - b)^2 + (0 - c)^2 = b^2 + c^2$;
$(AB)^2 + (BC)^2 + (CD)^2 + (AD)^2 = 2(AB)^2 + 2(AD)^2 = 2a^2 + 2(b^2 + c^2) =$
$2a^2 + 2b^2 + 2c^2$; $(AC)^2 = (a + b - 0)^2 + (c - 0)^2 = (a + b)^2 + c^2$;
$(BD)^2 = (a - b)^2 + (0 - c)^2 = (a - b)^2 + c^2$; $(AC)^2 + (BD)^2 =$
$[(a + b)^2 + c^2] + [(a - b)^2 + c^2] = a^2 + 2ab + b^2 + c^2 + a^2 - 2ab + b^2 + c^2 =$
$2a^2 + 2b^2 + 2c^2$; $(AB)^2 + (BC)^2 + (CD)^2 + (AD)^2 = (AC)^2 + (BD)^2$

11. Let M, N, P, and Q be the midpoints of $\overline{AB}$, $\overline{BC}$, $\overline{CD}$, and $\overline{AD}$, respectively;
$$M = \left(\frac{0 + 2a}{2}, \frac{0 + 0}{2}\right) = (a, 0); \quad N = \left(\frac{2a + 2b}{2}, \frac{0 + 2c}{2}\right) = (a + b, c);$$
$$P = \left(\frac{2b + 2d}{2}, \frac{2c + 2e}{2}\right) = (b + d, c + e); \quad Q = \left(\frac{0 + 2d}{2}, \frac{0 + 2e}{2}\right) = (d, e); \text{ slope of}$$
$$\overline{MN} = \frac{c - 0}{a + b - a} = \frac{c}{b}; \text{ slope of } \overline{PQ} = \frac{e - (c + e)}{d - (b + d)} = \frac{-c}{-b} = \frac{c}{b}; \text{ slope of}$$
$$\overline{PN} = \frac{c + e - c}{b + d - (a + b)} = \frac{e}{d - a}; \text{ slope of } \overline{QM} = \frac{0 - e}{a - d} = \frac{e}{d - a}; \text{ since } \overline{MN} \parallel \overline{PQ} \text{ and}$$
$\overline{PN} \parallel \overline{QM}$, $MNPQ$ is a $\square$.

12. **a.** Since L_1 and L_2 intersect at (r, s), $s = m_1 r + b_1$ and $s = m_2 r + b_2$; let $T_1 = (x_1, y_1)$
and $T_2 = (x_2, y_2)$ since T_1 and T_2 are on $x = r + 1$, $x_1 = r + 1$ and $x_2 = r + 1$;
$y_1 = m_1 x_1 + b_1 = m_1(r + 1) + b_1 = m_1 r + m_1 + b_1 = s + m_1$ and $y_2 =$
$m_2 x_2 + b_2 = m_2(r + 1) + b_2 = m_2 r + m_2 + b_2 = s + m_2$; $T_1 = (r + 1, s + m_1)$
and $T_2 = (r + 1, s + m_2)$.

b. $T_1 T_2 = \sqrt{[r + 1 - (r + 1)]^2 + [s + m_1 - (s + m_2)]^2} = \sqrt{(m_1 - m_2)^2} =$
$|m_1 - m_2|$; $PT_1 = \sqrt{[r - (r + 1)]^2 + [s - (s + m_1)]^2} = \sqrt{1 + m_1^2}$;
$PT_2 = \sqrt{[r - (r + 1)]^2 + [s - (s + m_2)]^2} = \sqrt{1 + m_2^2}$

c. $(T_1 T_2)^2 = (m_1 - m_2)^2 = m_1^2 - 2m_1 m_2 + m_2^2 = m_1^2 - 2(-1) + m_2^2 =$
$m_1^2 + 2 + m_2^2 = m_1^2 + 1 + m_2 + 1 = (PT_1)^2 + (PT_2)^2$

d. Since $\Delta T_1 P T_2$ has a right angle at P, $(T_1 T_2)^2 = (PT_1)^2 + (PT_2)^2$;
$(m_1 - m_2)^2 = 1 + m_1^2 + 1 + m_2^2$; $m_1^2 - 2m_1 m_2 + m_2^2 = 2 + m_1^2 + m_2^2$;
$-2m_1 m_2 = 2$; $m_1 m_2 = -1$.

Page 384 · COMPUTER EXERCISES

1. 10 PRINT "ENTER X1, Y1"
   20 INPUT X1, Y1
   30 PRINT "ENTER X2, Y2"
   40 INPUT X2, Y2
   50 LET D = SQR((Y2 − Y1) ↑ 2 + (X2 − X1) ↑ 2)
   60 PRINT "DISTANCE = "; D
   70 END

2. **a.** 7.07106782   **b.** 18.4390889   **c.** 294.49618   **d.** 61

3. 10 PRINT "ENTER XA, YA"

   20 INPUT XA, YA

   30 PRINT "ENTER XB, YB"

   40 INPUT XB, YB

   50 PRINT "ENTER XC, YC"

   60 INPUT XC, YC

   70 LET AB = SQR((XB − XA)↑2 + (YB − YA)↑2)

   80 LET BC = SQR((XC − XB)↑2 + (YC − YB)↑2)

   90 LET AC = SQR((XC − XA)↑2 + (YC − YA)↑2)

  100 IF ABS(AB − BC − AC) < .00001 THEN 160

  110 IF ABS(AC − BC − AB) < .00001 THEN 160

  120 IF ABS(BC − AC − AB) < .00001 THEN 160

  130 LET P = AB + BC + AC

  140 PRINT "PERIMETER = "; P

  150 GOTO 10

  160 PRINT "A, B, AND C ARE COLLINEAR."

  170 GOTO 10

4. a. PERIMETER = 22.471793   **b.** A, B, AND C ARE COLLINEAR.

   c. PERIMETER = 150.512173

Pages 387-388 · WRITTEN EXERCISES

A

1. $(x − 2)^2 + y^2 = 4$; $x^2 − 4x + 4 + y^2 = 4$; $x^2 + y^2 − 4x = 0$

2. $x^2 + (y + 1)^2 = 1$; $x^2 + y^2 + 2y + 1 = 1$; $x^2 + y^2 + 2y = 0$

3. $(x − 3)^2 + (y + 4)^2 = 25$; $x^2 − 6x + 9 + y^2 + 8y + 16 = 25$;
$x^2 + y^2 − 6x + 8y = 0$

4. $(x + 2)^2 + (y − 1)^2 = 4$; $x^2 + 4x + 4 + y^2 − 2y + 1 = 4$;
$x^2 + y^2 + 4x − 2y + 1 = 0$

5. $x^2 + y^2 = 9$; center = $(0, 0)$; radius = 3   **6.** $x^2 + y^2 = −1$; no graph

7. $x^2 + 4x + y^2 = 0$; $x^2 + 4x + 4 + y^2 = 4$; $(x + 2)^2 + y^2 = 4$; center = $(−2, 0)$;
radius = 2

8. $x^2 + y^2 − 2y = 0$; $x^2 + y^2 − 2y + 1 = 1$; $x^2 + (y − 1)^2 = 1$; center = $(0, 1)$;
radius = 1

9. $x^2 − 4x + y^2 + 2y = 4$; $x^2 − 4x + 4 + y^2 + 2y + 1 = 9$; $(x − 2)^2 + (y + 1)^2 = 9$
center = $(2, −1)$; radius = 3

10. $x^2 − 6x + y^2 − 4y = −12$; $x^2 − 6x + 9 + y^2 − 4y + 4 = 1$;
$(x − 3)^2 + (y − 2)^2 = 1$; center = $(3, 2)$; radius = 1

11. $x^2 + 8x + y^2 + 2y = −18$; $x^2 + 8x + 16 + y^2 + 2y + 1 = −1$;
$(x + 4)^2 + (y + 1)^2 = −1$; no graph

12. $x^2 - 6x + y^2 - 12y = 0$; $x^2 - 6x + 9 + y^2 - 12y + 36 = 45$;
$(x - 3)^2 + (y - 6)^2 = 45$; center $= (3, 6)$; radius $= 3\sqrt{5}$

13. $x^2 + 4x + y^2 - 3y = 0$; $x^2 + 4x + 4 + y^2 - 3y + \dfrac{9}{4} = \dfrac{25}{4}$;
$(x + 2)^2 + \left(y - \dfrac{3}{2}\right)^2 = \dfrac{25}{4}$; center $= \left(-2, \dfrac{3}{2}\right)$; radius $= \dfrac{5}{2}$

14. $x^2 + y^2 - 5y = -4$; $x^2 + y^2 - 5y + \dfrac{25}{4} = \dfrac{9}{4}$; $x^2 + \left(y - \dfrac{5}{2}\right)^2 = \dfrac{9}{4}$; center $= \left(0, \dfrac{5}{2}\right)$;
radius $= \dfrac{3}{2}$

15. $x^2 - \dfrac{2}{3}x + y^2 - \dfrac{2}{3}y = \dfrac{1}{3}$; $x^2 - \dfrac{2}{3}x + \dfrac{1}{9} + y^2 - \dfrac{2}{3}y + \dfrac{1}{9} = \dfrac{5}{9}$;
$\left(x - \dfrac{1}{3}\right)^2 + \left(y - \dfrac{1}{3}\right)^2 = \dfrac{5}{9}$; center $= \left(\dfrac{1}{3}, \dfrac{1}{3}\right)$; radius $= \dfrac{\sqrt{5}}{3}$

16. $x^2 + x + y^2 + 3y = \dfrac{3}{2}$; $x^2 + x + \dfrac{1}{4} + y^2 + 3y + \dfrac{9}{4} = 4$;
$\left(x + \dfrac{1}{2}\right)^2 + \left(y + \dfrac{3}{2}\right)^2 = 4$; center $= \left(-\dfrac{1}{2}, -\dfrac{3}{2}\right)$; radius $= 2$

17. $x^2 + (y - 3)^2 = r^2$; $0^2 + (0 - 3)^2 = r^2$; $9 = r^2$; $x^2 + (y - 3)^2 = 9$

18. $(x + 2)^2 + y^2 = r^2$; $(2 + 2)^2 + 0^2 = r^2$; $4^2 = r^2$; $(x + 2)^2 + y^2 = 16$

19. Center is on the line $y = 1$, 2 units from $(0, 1)$ in the first quadrant; center $= (2, 1)$;
$(x - 2)^2 + (y - 1)^2 = 4$.

20. Center is on the line $y = -1$; center $= (-3, -1)$, radius $= 3$; $(x + 3)^2 + (y + 1)^2 = 9$.

21. Let $A(a, 0)$ and $B(0, b)$ be the points of tangency and C the center of the circle;
$AC = BC$; $a = b$; center $= (a, a)$ and $a + a = 4$; $2a = 4$; $a = 2$; radius $= a$;
$(x - 2)^2 + (y - 2)^2 = 4$.

22. Center is in the third quadrant, 2 units from both axes; center $= (-2, -2)$;
$(x + 2)^2 + (y + 2)^2 = 4$.

23. Circle is tangent to $x = 0$ and $x = 6$ so $2r = 6$ and $r = 3$; center is on $x = 3$ and circle
is tangent to x-axis so center is $(3, 3)$ or $(3, -3)$; $(x - 3)^2 + (y - 3)^2 = 9$ or
$(x - 3)^2 + (y + 3)^2 = 9$.

24. Center $= \left(\dfrac{1 + 5}{2}, \dfrac{6 + 0}{2}\right) = (3, 3)$; radius $= \dfrac{1}{2}\sqrt{(1 - 5)^2 + (6 - 0)^2} = \dfrac{1}{2}\sqrt{16 + 36} =$
$\dfrac{1}{2}\sqrt{52} = \sqrt{13}$; $(x - 3)^2 + (y - 3)^2 = (\sqrt{13})^2$; $(x - 3)^2 + (y - 3)^2 = 13$.

25. $x^2 - 4x + y^2 - 2y = -5$; $x^2 - 4x + 4 + y^2 - 2y + 1 = 0$; $(x - 2)^2 + (y - 1)^2 = 0$
if and only if $x - 2 = 0$ and $y - 1 = 0$; $x = 2$ and $y = 1$; $(2, 1)$

26. $x^2 + 2x + y^2 - 6y = -10$; $x^2 + 2x + 1 + y^2 - 6y + 9 = 0$; $(x + 1)^2 + (y - 3)^2 =$
0 if and only if $x + 1 = 0$ and $y - 3 = 0$; $x = -1$ and $y = 3$; $(-1, 3)$

27. Let $(0, 0)$ and $(3, 0)$ be the positions of the buoys and (x, y) the position of the boat
$\sqrt{(x - 0)^2 + (y - 0)^2} = 2\sqrt{(x - 3)^2 + (y - 0)^2}$; $\sqrt{x^2 + y^2} = 2\sqrt{(x - 3)^2 + y^2}$;
$x^2 + y^2 = 4[(x - 3)^2 + y^2]$; $x^2 + y^2 = 4x^2 - 24x + 36 + 4y^2$; $3x^2 - 24x + 3y^2 =$
-36; $x^2 - 8x + y^2 = -12$; $x^2 - 8x + 16 + y^2 = 4$; $(x - 4)^2 + y^2 = 4$; the path is
circle with center $(4, 0)$ (that is, center 4 mi from the first buoy and 1 mi from the second
and radius 2 mi.

28. Let (x, y) represent the position of the midpoint of the ladder. From a theorem i
geometry, the midpoint of the hypotenuse of a right triangle is equidistant from th
vertices. Then since (x, y) is 3 units from the ends of the ladder, it is 3 units from th
origin of the given coordinate system and its path is along the first-quadrant portion c
a circle with center at the origin and radius 3 m.

C 29.
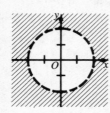

30.
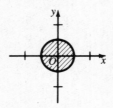

31.
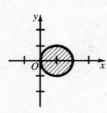

32.
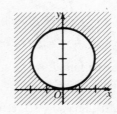

33.
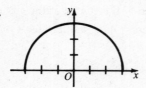

34.
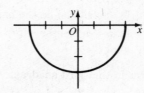

35.

36.
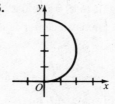

37. The center is 4 units from the first-quadrant portion of the graph of $y = x$ and 4 unit
from the second-quadrant portion of the graph of $y = -x$; the center will be a point o
the y-axis 4 units from the lines $y = x$ and $y = -x$. The origin, the center, and th
points of tangency form a square with sides of length 4 and diagonal on the y-axis c
length $4\sqrt{2}$; center $= (0, 4\sqrt{2})$; $x^2 + (y - 4\sqrt{2})^2 = 16$

38. Let $P(x, y)$ be any point on the semicircle; slope of $\overline{PA} = \dfrac{y - 0}{x - (-r)} = \dfrac{y}{x + r}$; slope of

$\overline{PB} = \dfrac{y - 0}{x - r} = \dfrac{y}{x - r}$; $\dfrac{y}{x + r} \cdot \dfrac{y}{x - r} = \dfrac{y^2}{x^2 - r^2} = \dfrac{y^2}{-(r^2 - x^2)} = \dfrac{y^2}{-y^2} = -1$; since the

product of the slopes of $\overline{PA}$ and $\overline{PB}$ is -1, $\overline{PA} \perp \overline{PB}$ and $\angle P$ is a right angle.

age 388 · CHALLENGE

Answers may vary. Example: the circle with equation $(x - 4)^2 + \left(y - \dfrac{5}{3}\right)^2 = \dfrac{169}{9}$ has

lattice points $(0, 0)$, $(8, 0)$, and $(4, 6)$. The equation was derived as follows: choose points A, B, and C with integer coordinates so that $\triangle ABC$ is neither right nor equilateral. For $A(0, 0)$, $B(8, 0)$, and $C(4, 6)$, the perpendicular bisector, j, of $\overline{AB}$ has equation $x = 4$ and the perpendicular bisector, k, of $\overline{AC}$ has equation $y = -\dfrac{2}{3}x + \dfrac{13}{3}$; j and k intersect at $P\left(4, \dfrac{5}{3}\right)$

and $PC = \dfrac{13}{3}$. By substituting integral values for x, it can be easily shown that

$(x - 4)^2 + \left(y - \dfrac{5}{3}\right)^2 = \dfrac{169}{9}$ has only 3 lattice points.

ages 392-393 · WRITTEN EXERCISES

1. $\sqrt{(x - 0)^2 + (y - 0)^2} = \sqrt{(x - x)^2 + (y + 2)^2}$; $x^2 + y^2 = y^2 + 4y + 4$;
$x^2 = 4y + 4 = 4(y + 1)$

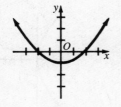   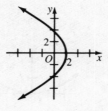   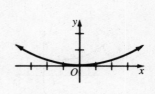

Ex. 1   Ex. 2   Ex. 3

2. $\sqrt{(x - 0)^2 + (y - 0)^2} = \sqrt{(x - 4)^2 + (y - y)^2}$; $x^2 + y^2 = x^2 - 8x + 16$;
$y^2 = -8x + 16 = -8(x - 2)$

3. $D: y = -3$; $\sqrt{(x - 0)^2 + (y - 3)^2} = \sqrt{(x - x)^2 + (y + 3)^2}$;
$x^2 + y^2 - 6y + 9 = y^2 + 6y + 9$; $x^2 = 12y$

4. $D: x = -2$; $\sqrt{(x - 2)^2 + (y - 0)^2} = \sqrt{(x + 2)^2 + (y - y)^2}$;
$x^2 - 4x + 4 + y^2 = x^2 + 4x + 4$; $y^2 = 8x$

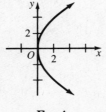   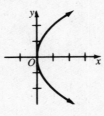   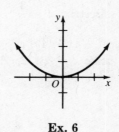

Ex. 4   Ex. 5   Ex. 6

5. $F(1, 0)$; $\sqrt{(x - 1)^2 + (y - 0)^2} = \sqrt{(x + 1)^2 + (y - y)^2}$;
$x^2 - 2x + 1 + y^2 = x^2 + 2x + 1$; $y^2 = 4x$

6. $F(0, 1)$; $\sqrt{(x - 0)^2 + (y - 1)^2} = \sqrt{(x - x)^2 + (y + 1)^2}$;
$x^2 + y^2 - 2y + 1 = y^2 + 2y + 1$; $x^2 = 4y$

7. $\sqrt{(x - 0)^2 + (y - 2)^2} = \sqrt{(x - 2)^2 + (y - y)^2}$; $x^2 + y^2 - 4y + 4 = x^2 - 4x + 4$
$(y - 2)^2 = -4(x - 1)$

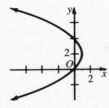
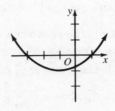
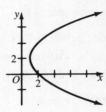

Ex. 7   Ex. 8   Ex. 9

8. $\sqrt{(x + 1)^2 + (y - 0)^2} = \sqrt{(x - x)^2 + (y + 2)^2}$; $(x + 1)^2 + y^2 = y^2 + 4y + 4$;
$(x + 1)^2 = 4(y + 1)$

9. $D : x = 0$; $\sqrt{(x - 2)^2 + (y - 2)^2} = \sqrt{(x - 0)^2 + (y - y)^2}$;
$x^2 - 4x + 4 + (y - 2)^2 = x^2$; $(y - 2)^2 = 4(x - 1)$

10. $D : y = -1$; $\sqrt{(x + 1)^2 + (y - 3)^2} = \sqrt{(x - x)^2 + (y + 1)^2}$;
$(x + 1)^2 + y^2 - 6y + 9 = y^2 + 2y + 1$; $(x + 1)^2 = 8(y - 1)$

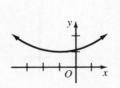
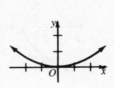
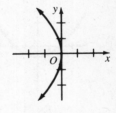

Ex. 10   Ex. 11   Ex. 12

11. $x^2 = 6y$; $x^2 = 4\left(\dfrac{3}{2}\right)y$; $h = 0$, $k = 0$, $c = \dfrac{3}{2}$; axis: $x = 0$; $V(0, 0)$; $F\left(0, \dfrac{3}{2}\right)$;

directrix: $y = -\dfrac{3}{2}$

12. $y^2 = -6x$; $y^2 = 4\left(-\dfrac{3}{2}\right)x$; $h = 0$, $k = 0$, $c = -\dfrac{3}{2}$; axis: $y = 0$; $V(0, 0)$; $F\left(-\dfrac{3}{2}, 0\right)$;

directrix: $x = \dfrac{3}{2}$

13. $x^2 - 4x = 4y$; $x^2 - 4y + 4 = 4y + 4$; $(x - 2)^2 = 4(y + 1)$; $h = 2$, $k = -1$, $c = 1$
axis: $x = 2$; $V(2, -1)$; $F(2, 0)$; directrix: $y = -2$

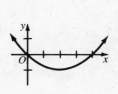

Ex. 13

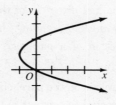

Ex. 14

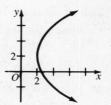

Ex. 15

14. $y^2 - 2y = x$; $y^2 - 2y + 1 = x + 1$; $(y - 1)^2 = x + 1$; $(y - 1)^2 = 4\left[\dfrac{1}{4}(x + 1)\right]$;

$h = -1$, $k = 1$, $c = \dfrac{1}{4}$; axis: $y = 1$; $V(-1, 1)$; $F\left(-\dfrac{3}{4}, 1\right)$; directrix: $x = -\dfrac{5}{4}$

15. $y^2 - 4y = 8x - 20$; $y^2 - 4y + 4 = 8x - 16$; $(y - 2)^2 = 8(x - 2)$; $(y - 2)^2 = 4[2(x - 2)]$; $h = 2$, $k = 2$, $c = 2$; axis: $y = 2$; $V(2, 2)$; $F(4, 2)$; directrix: $x = 0$

16. $x^2 + 4x = 2y - 6$; $x^2 + 4x + 4 = 2y - 2$; $(x + 2)^2 = 2(y - 1)$; $(x + 2)^2 = 4\left[\dfrac{1}{2}(y - 1)\right]$; $h = -2$, $k = 1$, $c = \dfrac{1}{2}$; axis: $x = -2$; $V(-2, 1)$; $F\left(-2, \dfrac{3}{2}\right)$;

directrix: $y = \dfrac{1}{2}$

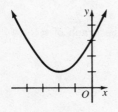

Ex. 16

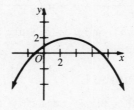

Ex. 17

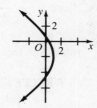

Ex. 18

17. $x^2 - 6x = -8y + 7$; $x^2 - 6x + 9 = -8y + 16$; $(x - 3)^2 = -8(y - 2)$; $(x - 3)^2 = 4[-2(y - 2)]$; $h = 3$, $k = 2$, $c = -2$; axis: $x = 3$; $V(3, 2)$; $F(3, 0)$; directrix: $y = 4$

18. $y^2 + 4y = -8x + 4$; $y^2 + 4y + 4 = -8x + 8$; $(y + 2)^2 = -8(x - 1)$;
$(y + 2)^2 = 4[-2(x - 1)]$; $h = 1$, $k = -2$, $c = -2$; axis: $y = -2$; $V(1, -2)$; $F(-1, -2)$;
directrix: $x = 3$

19.

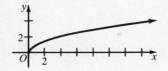

20.

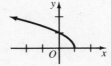

21.

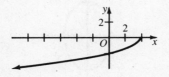

22.

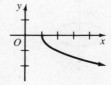

23. Let F and j be the focus and directrix of the parabola and A, B, and C the point
where perpendiculars from P, F, and Q intersect j. Since $\overrightarrow{PQ} \| j$, $PA = FB$ and
$QC = FB$; by the definition of a parabola, $PF = PA$ and $FQ = QC$; then $PQ =$
$PF + FQ = PA + QC = FB + FB = 2 \cdot FB$.

24. Since the center of the circle is on the parabola, the center is equidistant from the focu
and the directrix; the directrix is tangent to the circle.

C 25. The directrix is $x = h - c$; $\sqrt{[x - (h + c)]^2 + (y - k)^2} =$
$\sqrt{[x - (h - c)]^2 + (y - y)^2}$; $x^2 - 2(h + c)x + (h + c)^2 + (y - k)^2 =$
$x^2 - 2(h - c)x + (h - c)^2$; $x^2 - 2hx - 2cx + h^2 + 2ch + c^2 + (y - k)^2 =$
$x^2 - 2hx + 2cx + h^2 - 2ch + c^2$; $(y - k)^2 = 4cx - 4ch$; $(y - k)^2 = 4c(x - h)$

26. The directrix is $y = k - c$; $\sqrt{(x - h)^2 + [y - (k + c)]^2} =$
$\sqrt{(x - x)^2 + [y - (k - c)]^2}$; $(x - h)^2 + y^2 - 2(k + c)y + (k + c)^2 =$
$y^2 - 2(k - c)y + (k - c)^2$; $(x - h)^2 + y^2 - 2ky - 2cy + k^2 + 2ck + c^2 =$
$y^2 - 2ky + 2cy + k^2 - 2ck + c^2$; $(x - h)^2 = 4cy - 4ck$; $(x - h)^2 = 4c(y - k)$

27. Let a be the distance between L and D. Let X be the point where $\overrightarrow{PQ}$ intersects D
$FP + PQ = XP + PQ = XQ = a$.

28. Slope $= \dfrac{b^2 - a^2}{b - (-a)} = \dfrac{b^2 - a^2}{b + a} = b - a$; $\dfrac{y - a^2}{x - (-a)} = b - a$; $y - a^2 = (b - a)(x + a$
$y - a^2 = bx - ax + ab - a^2$; $y = (b - a)x + ab$; the graph of $y = (b - a)x + a$
intersects the y-axis at ab.

Page 399 · WRITTEN EXERCISES

A 1. $c^2 = a^2 - b^2 = 25 - 16 = 9$; $c = \pm 3$; foci: $(3, 0)$, $(-3, 0)$

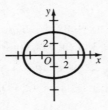

Ex. 1

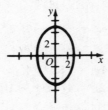

Ex. 2

2. $c^2 = a^2 - b^2 = 25 - 9 = 16$; $c = \pm 4$; foci: $(0, 4)$, $(0, -4)$

3. $\dfrac{x^2}{16} + \dfrac{y^2}{4} = 1$; $c^2 = a^2 - b^2 = 16 - 4 = 12$; $c = \pm 2\sqrt{3}$; foci: $(2\sqrt{3}, 0)$, $(-2\sqrt{3}, 0)$

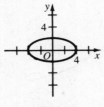

Ex. 3

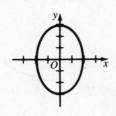

Ex. 4

4. $\dfrac{x^2}{4} + \dfrac{y^2}{9} = 1$; $c^2 = a^2 - b^2 = 9 - 4 = 5$; $c = \pm\sqrt{5}$; foci: $(0, \sqrt{5})$, $(0, -\sqrt{5})$

5. $\dfrac{x^2}{4} + \dfrac{y^2}{8} = 1$; $c^2 = a^2 - b^2 = 8 - 4 = 4$; $c = \pm 2$; foci: $(0, 2)$, $(0, -2)$

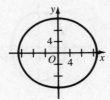

Ex. 5

Ex. 6

6. $\dfrac{x^2}{4} + \dfrac{y^2}{3} = 1$; $c^2 = a^2 - b^2 = 4 - 3 = 1$; $c = \pm 1$; foci: $(1, 0)$, $(-1, 0)$

7. $c^2 = a^2 - b^2 = 169 - 144 = 25$; $c = \pm 5$; foci: $(5, 0)$, $(-5, 0)$

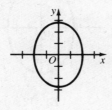

Ex. 7

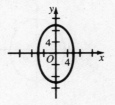

Ex. 8

8. $c^2 = a^2 - b^2 = 100 - 36 = 64$; $c = \pm 8$; foci: $(0, 8)$, $(0, -8)$

9. $\dfrac{x^2}{25} + \dfrac{y^2}{100} = 1$; $c^2 = a^2 - b^2 = 100 - 25 = 75$; $c = \pm 5\sqrt{3}$; foci: $(0, 5\sqrt{3})$, $(0, -5\sqrt{3})$

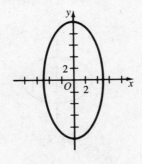

Ex. 9

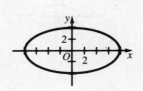

Ex. 10

10. $\dfrac{x^2}{64} + \dfrac{y^2}{16} = 1$; $c^2 = a^2 - b^2 = 64 - 16 = 48$; $c = \pm 4\sqrt{3}$; foci: $(4\sqrt{3}, 0)$, $(-4\sqrt{3}, 0)$

11. $\dfrac{x^2}{12} + \dfrac{y^2}{4} = 1$; $c^2 = a^2 - b^2 = 12 - 4 = 8$; $c = \pm 2\sqrt{2}$; foci: $(2\sqrt{2}, 0)$, $(-2\sqrt{2}, 0)$

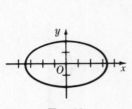

Ex. 11

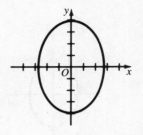

Ex. 12

12. $\dfrac{x^2}{8} + \dfrac{y^2}{16} = 1$; $c^2 = a^2 - b^2 = 16 - 8 = 8$; $c = \pm 2\sqrt{2}$; foci: $(0, 2\sqrt{2})$, $(0, -2\sqrt{2})$

13. $\dfrac{x^2}{12} + \dfrac{y^2}{16} = 1$; $c^2 = a^2 - b^2 = 16 - 12 = 4$; $c = \pm 2$; foci: $(0, 2)$, $(0, -2)$

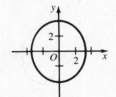

Ex. 13

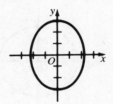

Ex. 14

14. $\dfrac{x^2}{5} + \dfrac{y^2}{9} = 1$; $c^2 = a^2 - b^2 = 9 - 5 = 4$; $c = \pm 2$; foci: $(0, 2)$, $(0, -2)$

15. $x^2 + \dfrac{y^2}{\dfrac{1}{4}} = 1$; $c^2 = a^2 - b^2 = 1 - \dfrac{1}{4} = \dfrac{3}{4}$; $c = \pm \dfrac{\sqrt{3}}{2}$; foci: $\left(\dfrac{\sqrt{3}}{2}, 0\right)$, $\left(-\dfrac{\sqrt{3}}{2}, 0\right)$

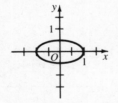

Ex. 15

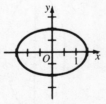

Ex. 16

16. $\dfrac{x^2}{\dfrac{9}{4}} + \dfrac{y^2}{1} = 1$; $c^2 = a^2 - b^2 = \dfrac{9}{4} - 1 = \dfrac{5}{4}$; $c = \pm \dfrac{\sqrt{5}}{2}$; foci: $\left(\dfrac{\sqrt{5}}{2}, 0\right)$, $\left(-\dfrac{\sqrt{5}}{2}, 0\right)$

17. $\dfrac{x^2}{16} + y^2 = 1$ 18. $\dfrac{x^2}{36} + \dfrac{y^2}{4} = 1$ 19. $\dfrac{x^2}{4} + \dfrac{y^2}{8} = 1$ 20. $\dfrac{x^2}{2} + \dfrac{y^2}{5} =$

B   21. Center $= (0, 0)$; distance from focus to center $= 12$; $c = 12$; $2a = 26$; $a = 13$; $b^2 =$

$a^2 - c^2 = 169 - 144 = 25$; foci are on x-axis so major axis is horizontal; $\dfrac{x^2}{169} + \dfrac{y^2}{25} =$

22. Center $= (0,0)$; distance from focus to center $= 3$; $c = 3$; $2a = 10$; $a = 5$; $b^2 = a^2 - c^2 = 25 - 9 = 16$; foci are on y-axis so major axis is vertical; $\dfrac{x^2}{16} + \dfrac{y^2}{25} = 1$

23. Center $= (0,0)$; distance from focus to center $= 5$; $c = 5$; $2a = 20$; $a = 10$; $b^2 = a^2 - c^2 = 100 - 25 = 75$; foci are on y-axis so major axis is vertical; $\dfrac{x^2}{75} + \dfrac{y^2}{100} = 1$

24. Center $= (0,0)$; distance from focus to center $= 7$; $c = 7$; $2a = 16$; $a = 8$; $b^2 = a^2 - c^2 = 64 - 49 = 15$; foci are on x-axis so major axis is horizontal; $\dfrac{x^2}{64} + \dfrac{y^2}{15} = 1$

25. Equation of ellipse: $\dfrac{x^2}{36} + \dfrac{y^2}{16} = 1$;

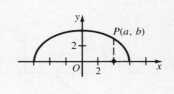

$\dfrac{4^2}{36} + \dfrac{b^2}{16} = 1$; $\dfrac{b^2}{16} = \dfrac{20}{36}$; $b = \sqrt{\dfrac{16 \cdot 20}{36}} = \sqrt{\dfrac{80}{9}} = \dfrac{4\sqrt{5}}{3}$;

$\dfrac{4\sqrt{5}}{3}$ m or about 3 m

26.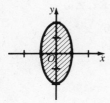

27.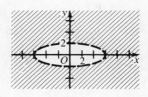

28.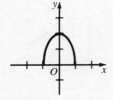

29.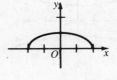

30. $\sqrt{[x - (-c)]^2 + (y - 0)^2} + \sqrt{(x - c)^2 + (y - 0)^2} = 2a$; $\sqrt{(x + c)^2 + y^2} = 2a - \sqrt{(x - c)^2 + y^2}$; $(x + c)^2 + y^2 = 4a^2 - 4a\sqrt{(x - c)^2 + y^2} + (x - c)^2 + y^2$; $x^2 + 2cx + c^2 + y^2 = 4a^2 - 4a\sqrt{(x - c)^2 + y^2} + x^2 - 2cx + c^2 + y^2$; $4a\sqrt{(x - c)^2 + y^2} = 4a^2 - 4cx$; $a\sqrt{(x - c)^2 + y^2} = a^2 - cx$; $a^2(x^2 - 2cx + c^2 + y^2) = a^4 - 2a^2cx + c^2x^2$; $a^2x^2 - 2a^2cx + a^2c^2 + a^2y^2 = a^4 - 2a^2cx + c^2x^2$; $(a^2 - c^2)x^2 + a^2y^2 = a^4 - a^2c^2$; $(a^2 - c^2)x^2 + a^2y^2 = a^2(a^2 - c^2)$; let $b^2 = a^2 - c^2$; $b^2x^2 + a^2y^2 = a^2b^2$; $\dfrac{x^2}{a^2} + \dfrac{y^2}{b^2} = 1$

31. $\sqrt{(x-0)^2 + [y-(-c)]^2} + \sqrt{(x-0)^2 + (y-c)^2} = 2a$;

$\sqrt{x^2 + (y+c)^2} = 2a - \sqrt{x^2 + (y-c)^2}$; $x^2 + y^2 + 2cy + c^2 = $

$4a^2 - 4a\sqrt{x^2 + (y-c)^2} + x^2 + y^2 - 2cy + c^2$; $4a\sqrt{x^2 + (y-c)^2} = 4a^2 - 4cy$;

$a\sqrt{x^2 + (y-c)^2} = a^2 - cy$; $a^2(x^2 + y^2 - 2cy + c^2) = a^4 - 2a^2cy + c^2y^2$;

$a^2x^2 + a^2y^2 - 2a^2cy + a^2c^2 = a^4 - 2a^2cy + c^2y^2$; $a^2x^2 + (a^2 - c^2)y^2 = a^4 - a^2c^2$

$a^2x^2 + (a^2 - c^2)y^2 = a^2(a^2 - c^2)$; let $b^2 = a^2 - c^2$; $a^2x^2 + b^2y^2 = a^2b^2$; $\dfrac{x^2}{b^2} + \dfrac{y^2}{a^2} = 1$

Page 404 · WRITTEN EXERCISES

A　**1. b.** $c^2 = a^2 + b^2 = 4 + 1 = 5$; $c = \pm\sqrt{5}$; foci: $(\sqrt{5}, 0)$, $(-\sqrt{5}, 0)$

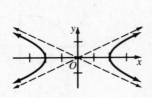

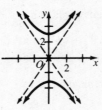

Ex. 1.a.　　　　　　　　　　　　　　　Ex. 2.a.

2. b. $c^2 = a^2 + b^2 = 9 + 16 = 25$; $c = \pm 5$; foci: $(0, 5)$, $(0, -5)$

3. b. $9y^2 - x^2 = 9$; $y^2 - \dfrac{x^2}{9} = 1$; $c^2 = a^2 + b^2 = 1 + 9 = 10$; $c = \pm\sqrt{10}$; foci: $(0, \sqrt{10})$

$(0, -\sqrt{10})$

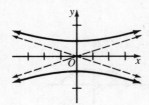

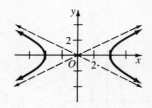

Ex. 3.a.　　　　　　　　　　　　　　　Ex. 4.a.

4. b. $\dfrac{x^2}{16} - \dfrac{y^2}{4} = 1$; $c^2 = a^2 + b^2 = 16 + 4 = 20$; $c = \pm 2\sqrt{5}$; foci: $(2\sqrt{5}, 0)$, $(-2\sqrt{5}, 0)$

5. b. $\dfrac{x^2}{4} - \dfrac{y^2}{25} = 1$; $c^2 = a^2 + b^2 = 4 + 25 = 29$; $c = \pm\sqrt{29}$; foci: $(\sqrt{29}, 0)$, $(-\sqrt{29}, 0)$

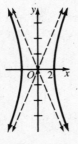

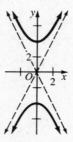

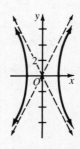

Ex. 5.a.　　　　　　　　Ex. 6.a.　　　　　　　　Ex. 7.a.

6. b. $4y^2 - 16x^2 = 64$; $\dfrac{y^2}{16} - \dfrac{x^2}{4} = 1$; $c^2 = a^2 + b^2 = 16 + 4 = 20$; $c = \pm 2\sqrt{5}$;

foci: $(0, 2\sqrt{5})$, $(0, -2\sqrt{5})$

7. b. $4x^2 - y^2 = 16$; $\dfrac{x^2}{4} - \dfrac{y^2}{16} = 1$; $c^2 = a^2 + b^2 = 4 + 16 = 20$; $c = \pm 2\sqrt{5}$;

foci: $(2\sqrt{5}, 0)$, $(-2\sqrt{5}, 0)$

8. b. $x^2 - 3y^2 = 12$; $\dfrac{x^2}{12} - \dfrac{y^2}{4} = 1$; $c^2 = a^2 + b^2 = 12 + 4 = 16$; $c = \pm 4$; foci: $(4, 0)$,

$(-4, 0)$

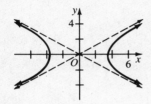

Ex. 8. a.

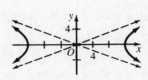

Ex. 9. a.

9. b. $\dfrac{x^2}{144} - \dfrac{y^2}{25} = 1$; $c^2 = a^2 + b^2 = 144 + 25 = 169$; $c = \pm 13$; foci: $(13, 0)$, $(-13, 0)$

10. b. $\dfrac{x^2}{100} - \dfrac{y^2}{75} = 1$; $c^2 = a^2 + b^2 = 100 + 75 = 175$; $c = \pm 5\sqrt{7}$; foci: $(5\sqrt{7}, 0)$,

$(-5\sqrt{7}, 0)$

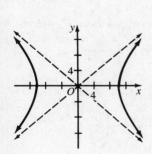

Ex. 10. a.

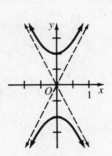

Ex. 11. a.

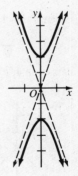

Ex. 12. a.

11. b. $y^2 - 4x^2 = 1$; $y^2 - \dfrac{x^2}{\frac{1}{4}} = 1$; $c^2 = a^2 + b^2 = 1 + \dfrac{1}{4} = \dfrac{5}{4}$; $c = \pm \dfrac{\sqrt{5}}{2}$; foci: $\left(0, \dfrac{\sqrt{5}}{2}\right)$,

$\left(0, -\dfrac{\sqrt{5}}{2}\right)$

12. b. $y^2 - 9x^2 = 4$; $\dfrac{y^2}{4} - \dfrac{x^2}{\frac{4}{9}} = 1$; $c^2 = a^2 + b^2 = 4 + \dfrac{4}{9} = \dfrac{40}{9}$; $c = \pm \dfrac{2\sqrt{10}}{3}$;

foci: $\left(0, \dfrac{2\sqrt{10}}{3}\right)$, $\left(0, -\dfrac{2\sqrt{10}}{3}\right)$

13.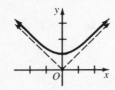

14.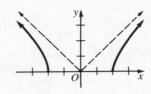

15.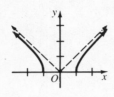

16.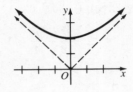

17. Center = $(0,0)$; distance from focus to center = 5; $c = 5$; $2a = 8$; $a = 4$; $b^2 =$
$c^2 - a^2 = 25 - 16 = 9$; the foci are on the y-axis so the y^2 term is positive; $\dfrac{y^2}{16} - \dfrac{x^2}{9} =$

18. Center = $(0,0)$; distance from focus to center = 4; $c = 4$; $2a = 4$; $a = 2$; $b^2 =$
$c^2 - a^2 = 16 - 4 = 12$; the foci are on the x-axis so the x^2 term is positive; $\dfrac{x^2}{4} - \dfrac{y^2}{12} =$

B 19. Since the hyperbola has 2 x-intercepts, it has the form $\dfrac{x^2}{a^2} - \dfrac{y^2}{b^2} = 1$; substituting $(4, 0)$
$\dfrac{16}{a^2} - \dfrac{0}{b^2} = 1$; $16 = a^2$; the asymptotes are $y = \pm\dfrac{b}{a}x = \pm 2x$; $\pm\dfrac{b}{a} = \pm 2$; $\dfrac{b^2}{a^2} = 4$; $b^2 =$
$4a^2 = 4(16) = 64$; $\dfrac{x^2}{16} - \dfrac{y^2}{64} = 1$

20. Since the foci are on the x-axis, the hyperbola has the form $\dfrac{x^2}{a^2} - \dfrac{y^2}{b^2} = 1$; the asymptote
are $y = \pm\dfrac{b}{a}x = \pm x$; $\dfrac{b}{a} = \pm 1$; $\dfrac{b^2}{a^2} = 1$; $b^2 = a^2$; the distance from each focus to th
center is 4; $c = 4$; $c^2 = a^2 + b^2$; $16 = 2a^2$; $a^2 = 8$; $b^2 = 8$; $\dfrac{x^2}{8} - \dfrac{y^2}{8} = 1$

21.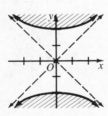

22.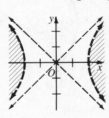

23.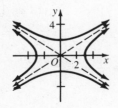

24.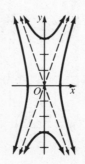

25. Since the foci are on the x-axis, the hyperbola has the form $\dfrac{x^2}{a^2} - \dfrac{y^2}{b^2} = 1$ with asymptotes

$y = \dfrac{b}{a}x$ and $y = -\dfrac{b}{a}x$; the asymptotes are perpendicular, so $\dfrac{b}{a} = -\left(-\dfrac{a}{b}\right);\ \dfrac{b}{a} = \dfrac{a}{b}$;

$a^2 = b^2;\ \dfrac{x^2}{a^2} - \dfrac{y^2}{a^2} = 1.$

26. Since the foci are on the y-axis, the hyperbola has the form $\dfrac{y^2}{a^2} - \dfrac{x^2}{b^2} = 1$ with asymptotes

$y = \dfrac{a}{b}x$ and $y = -\dfrac{a}{b}x$; the asymptotes are perpendicular so $\dfrac{a}{b} = -\left(-\dfrac{b}{a}\right);\ \dfrac{a}{b} = \dfrac{b}{a}$;

$a^2 = b^2;\ \dfrac{y^2}{a^2} - \dfrac{x^2}{a^2} = 1$

27. $\sqrt{(x - 0)^2 + [y - (-3)]^2} - \sqrt{(x - 0)^2 + (y - 3)^2} = 4$;
$\sqrt{x^2 + (y + 3)^2} = 4 + \sqrt{x^2 + (y - 3)^2};\ x^2 + y^2 + 6y + 9 =$
$16 + 8\sqrt{x^2 + (y - 3)^2} + x^2 + y^2 - 6y + 9;\ 12y - 16 = 8\sqrt{x^2 + (y - 3)^2}$;
$3y - 4 = 2\sqrt{x^2 + (y - 3)^2};\ 9y^2 - 24y + 16 = 4(x^2 + y^2 - 6y + 9)$;
$9y^2 - 24y + 16 = 4x^2 + 4y^2 - 24y + 36;\ 5y^2 - 4x^2 = 20;\ \dfrac{y^2}{4} - \dfrac{x^2}{5} = 1$

28. $\sqrt{[x - (-2)]^2 + (y - 0)^2} - \sqrt{(x - 2)^2 + (y - 0)^2} = 2;\ \sqrt{(x + 2)^2 + y^2} =$
$2 + \sqrt{(x - 2)^2 + y^2};\ x^2 + 4x + 4 + y^2 = 4 + 4\sqrt{(x - 2)^2 + y^2} + x^2 - 4x + 4 + y^2$;
$8x - 4 = 4\sqrt{(x - 2)^2 + y^2};\ 2x - 1 = \sqrt{(x - 2)^2 + y^2}$;
$4x^2 - 4x + 1 = x^2 - 4x + 4 + y^2;\ 3x^2 - y^2 = 3;\ x^2 - \dfrac{y^2}{3} = 1$

29. $\sqrt{[x - (-c)]^2 + (y - 0)^2} - \sqrt{(x - c)^2 + (y - 0)^2} = 2a$;
$\sqrt{(x + c)^2 + y^2} = 2a + \sqrt{(x - c)^2 + y^2};\ x^2 + 2cx + c^2 + y^2 =$
$4a^2 + 4a\sqrt{(x - c)^2 + y^2} + x^2 - 2cx + c^2 + y^2;\ 4cx - 4a^2 = 4a\sqrt{(x - c)^2 + y^2}$;
$cx - a^2 = a\sqrt{(x - c)^2 + y^2};\ c^2x^2 - 2a^2cx + a^4 = a^2(x^2 - 2cx + c^2 + y^2)$;
$c^2x^2 - 2a^2cx + a^4 = a^2x^2 - 2a^2cx + a^2c^2 + a^2y^2;\ (c^2 - a^2)x^2 - a^2y^2 = a^2c^2 - a^4$;
$(c^2 - a^2)x^2 - a^2y^2 = a^2(c^2 - a^2);$ let $b^2 = c^2 - a^2;\ b^2x^2 - a^2y^2 = a^2b^2;\ \dfrac{x^2}{a^2} - \dfrac{y^2}{b^2} = 1$

30. $\sqrt{(x - 0)^2 + [y - (-c)]^2} - \sqrt{(x - 0)^2 + (y - c)^2} = 2a$;
$\sqrt{x^2 + (y + c)^2} = 2a + \sqrt{x^2 + (y - c)^2};\ x^2 + y^2 + 2cy + c^2 =$
$4a^2 + 4a\sqrt{x^2 + (y - c)^2} + x^2 + y^2 - 2cy + c^2;\ 4cy - 4a^2 = 4a\sqrt{x^2 + (y - c)^2}$;
$cy - a^2 = a\sqrt{x^2 + (y - c)^2};\ c^2y^2 - 2a^2cy + a^4 = a^2(x^2 + y^2 - 2cy + c^2)$;
$c^2y^2 - 2a^2cy + a^4 = a^2x^2 + a^2y^2 - 2a^2cy + a^2c^2;\ (c^2 - a^2)y^2 - a^2x^2 = a^2c^2 - a^4$;
$(c^2 - a^2)y^2 - a^2x^2 = a^2(c^2 - a^2);$ let $b^2 = c^2 - a^2;\ b^2y^2 - a^2x^2 = a^2b^2;\ \dfrac{y^2}{a^2} - \dfrac{x^2}{b^2} = 1$

31. $\sqrt{(x-a)^2 + (y-a)^2} - \sqrt{[x-(-a)]^2 + [y-(-a)]^2} = 2a;$

$\sqrt{(x-a)^2 + (y-a)^2} = 2a + \sqrt{(x+a)^2 + (y+a)^2};$

$x^2 - 2ax + a^2 + y^2 - 2ay + a^2 =$

$4a^2 + 4a\sqrt{(x+a)^2 + (y+a)^2} + x^2 + 2ax + a^2 + y^2 + 2ay + a^2;$

$-4ax - 4ay - 4a^2 = 4a\sqrt{(x+a)^2 + (y+a)^2}; \, x + y + a =$

$-\sqrt{(x+a)^2 + (y+a)^2}, \, (a \neq 0); \, x^2 + y^2 + a^2 + 2xy + 2ax + 2ay =$

$x^2 + 2ax + a^2 + y^2 + 2ay + a^2; \, 2xy = a^2; \, xy = \dfrac{a^2}{2}$

32. $\sqrt{[x-(-a)]^2 + (y-a)^2} - \sqrt{(x-a)^2 + [y-(-a)]^2} = 2a;$

$\sqrt{(x+a)^2 + (y-a)^2} = 2a + \sqrt{(x-a)^2 + (y+a)^2};$

$x^2 + 2ax + a^2 + y^2 - 2ay + a^2 =$

$4a^2 + 4a\sqrt{(x-a)^2 + (y+a)^2} + x^2 - 2ax + a^2 + y^2 + 2ay + a^2;$

$4ax - 4ay - 4a^2 = 4a\sqrt{(x-a)^2 + (y+a)^2}; \, x - y - a =$

$\sqrt{(x-a)^2 + (y+a)^2} \, (a \neq 0); \, x^2 + y^2 + a^2 - 2xy - 2ax + 2ay =$

$x^2 - 2ax + a^2 + y^2 + 2ay + a^2; \, -2xy = a^2; \, xy = -\dfrac{a^2}{2}$

Pages 406-407 · WRITTEN EXERCISES

A **1-12.** c is the distance from the center to each focus.

1. Center $= \left(\dfrac{0+8}{2}, \dfrac{2+2}{2}\right) = (4, 2); \, 2a = 10; \, a = 5; \, c = 4;$

$b^2 = a^2 - c^2 = 25 - 16 = 9;$ major axis is horizontal; $\dfrac{(x-4)^2}{25} + \dfrac{(y-2)^2}{9} = 1$

2. Center $= \left(\dfrac{0+0}{2}, \dfrac{0+6}{2}\right) = (0, 3); \, 2a = 10; \, a = 5; \, c = 3;$

$b^2 = a^2 - c^2 = 25 - 9 = 16;$ major axis is vertical; $\dfrac{x^2}{16} + \dfrac{(y-3)^2}{25} = 1$

3. Center $= \left(\dfrac{-3+(-3)}{2}, \dfrac{-3+3}{2}\right) = (-3, 0); \, 2a = 8; \, a = 4; \, c = 3;$

$b^2 = a^2 - c^2 = 16 - 9 = 7;$ major axis is vertical; $\dfrac{(x+3)^2}{7} + \dfrac{y^2}{16} = 1$

4. Center $= \left(\dfrac{-4+2}{2}, \dfrac{1+1}{2}\right) = (-1, 1); \, 2a = 8; \, a = 4; \, c = 3;$

$b^2 = a^2 - c^2 = 16 - 9 = 7;$ major axis is horizontal; $\dfrac{(x+1)^2}{16} + \dfrac{(y-1)^2}{7} = 1$

5. Center $= \left(\dfrac{-2+6}{2}, \dfrac{-3+(-3)}{2}\right) = (2, -3); \, 2a = 12; \, a = 6; \, c = 4;$

$b^2 = a^2 - c^2 = 36 - 16 = 20;$ major axis is horizontal; $\dfrac{(x-2)^2}{36} + \dfrac{(y+3)^2}{20} = 1$

6. Center $= \left(\dfrac{-6+(-2)}{2}, \dfrac{1+1}{2}\right) = (-4, 1); \, 2a = 6; \, a = 3; \, c = 2;$

$b^2 = a^2 - c^2 = 9 - 4 = 5;$ major axis is horizontal; $\dfrac{(x+4)^2}{9} + \dfrac{(y-1)^2}{5} = 1$

7. Center $= \left(\dfrac{0+6}{2}, \dfrac{1+1}{2}\right) = (3, 1); \, 2a = 4; \, a = 2; \, c = 3; \, b^2 = c^2 - a^2 = 9 - 4 = 5$

line containing center and foci is horizontal; $\dfrac{(x-3)^2}{4} - \dfrac{(y-1)^2}{5} = 1$

8. Center $= \left(\dfrac{2 + 8}{2}, \dfrac{0 + 0}{2}\right) = (5, 0)$; $2a = 2$; $a = 1$; $c = 3$; $b^2 = c^2 - a^2 = 9 - 1 = 8$; line containing center and foci is horizontal; $\dfrac{(x - 5)^2}{1} - \dfrac{y^2}{8} = 1$

9. Center $= \left(\dfrac{-1 + (-1)}{2}, \dfrac{-4 + 6}{2}\right) = (-1, 1)$; $2a = 6$; $a = 3$; $c = 5$; $b^2 = c^2 - a^2 = 25 - 9 = 16$; line containing center and foci is vertical; $\dfrac{(y - 1)^2}{9} - \dfrac{(x + 1)^2}{16} = 1$

10. Center $= \left(\dfrac{2 + 2}{2}, \dfrac{-3 + 7}{2}\right) = (2, 2)$; $2a = 8$; $a = 4$; $c = 5$; $b^2 = c^2 - a^2 = 25 - 16 = 9$; line containing center and foci is vertical; $\dfrac{(y - 2)^2}{16} - \dfrac{(x - 2)^2}{9} = 1$

11. Center $= \left(\dfrac{3 + 3}{2}, \dfrac{-8 + (-2)}{2}\right) = (3, -5)$; $2a = 4$; $a = 2$; $c = 3$; $b^2 = c^2 - a^2 = 9 - 4 = 5$; line containing center and foci is vertical; $\dfrac{(y + 5)^2}{4} - \dfrac{(x - 3)^2}{5} = 1$

12. Center $= \left(\dfrac{-4 + 4}{2}, \dfrac{-4 + (-4)}{2}\right) = (0, -4)$; $2a = 6$; $a = 3$; $c = 4$; $b^2 = c^2 - a^2 = 16 - 9 = 7$; line containing center and foci is horizontal; $\dfrac{x^2}{9} - \dfrac{(y + 4)^2}{7} = 1$

13. $x^2 - 4x - (y^2 - 2y) = -2$; $x^2 - 4x + 4 - (y^2 - 2y + 1) = 1$; $(x - 2)^2 - (y - 1)^2 = 1$; the conic is a hyperbola with center $(2, 1)$; line containing center and foci is horizontal; $c^2 = a^2 + b^2 = 1 + 1 = 2$; $c = \pm\sqrt{2}$; foci: $(2 + \sqrt{2}, 1)$ and $(2 - \sqrt{2}, 1)$

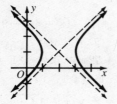

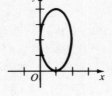

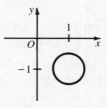

Ex. 13   Ex. 14   Ex. 15

14. $4x^2 - 8x + y^2 - 4y = -4$; $4(x^2 - 2x + 1) + y^2 - 4y + 4 = 4$; $4(x - 1)^2 + (y - 2)^2 = 4$; $(x - 1)^2 + \dfrac{(y - 2)^2}{4} = 1$; the conic is an ellipse with center $(1, 2)$; the major axis is vertical; $c^2 = a^2 - b^2 = 4 - 1 = 3$; $c = \pm\sqrt{3}$; foci: $(1, 2 + \sqrt{3})$, $(1, 2 - \sqrt{3})$

15. $4x^2 - 8x + 4y^2 + 8y = -7$; $4(x^2 - 2x + 1) + 4(y^2 + 2y + 1) = 1$; $4(x - 1)^2 + 4(y + 1)^2 = 1$; $(x - 1)^2 + (y + 1)^2 = \dfrac{1}{4}$; the conic is a circle with center $(1, -1)$.

16. $9x^2 - 18x - (y^2 + 6y) = 9$; $9(x^2 - 2x + 1) - (y^2 + 6y + 9) = 9$; $9(x - 1)^2 - (y + 3)^2 = 9$; $\dfrac{(x - 1)^2}{1} - \dfrac{(y + 3)^2}{9} = 1$; the conic is a hyperbola with center $(1, -3)$; the line containing the center and foci is horizontal; $c^2 = a^2 + b^2 = 10$; $c = \pm\sqrt{10}$; foci: $(1 + \sqrt{10}, -3)$ and $(1 - \sqrt{10}, -3)$

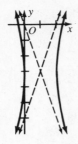
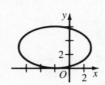
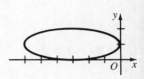

Ex. 16　　　　　　　　　**Ex. 17**　　　　　　　　　**Ex. 18**

17. $9(x^2 + 4x) + 25(y^2 - 6y) = -36$; $9(x^2 + 4x + 4) + 25(y^2 - 6y + 9) = 225$;

$9(x + 2)^2 + 25(y - 3)^2 = 225$; $\dfrac{(x + 2)^2}{25} + \dfrac{(y - 3)^2}{9} = 1$; the conic is an ellipse with

center $(-2, 3)$; the major axis is horizontal; $c^2 = a^2 - b^2 = 25 - 9 = 16$; $c = \pm 4$;

foci: $(2, 3)$ and $(-6, 3)$

18. $x^2 + 6x + 9(y^2 - 2y) = -9$; $x^2 + 6x + 9 + 9(y^2 - 2y + 1) = 9$;

$(x + 3)^2 + 9(y - 1)^2 = 9$; $\dfrac{(x + 3)^2}{9} + \dfrac{(y - 1)^2}{1} = 1$; the conic is an ellipse with cente■

$(-3, 1)$; the major axis is horizontal; $c^2 = a^2 - b^2 = 9 - 1 = 8$; $c = \pm 2\sqrt{2}$;

foci: $\left(-3 + 2\sqrt{2}, 1\right)$ and $\left(-3 - \sqrt{2}, 1\right)$

B **19.** $\sqrt{(x - 1)^2 + (y - 1)^2} + \sqrt{[x - (-1)]^2 + [y - (-1)]^2} = 3$; $\sqrt{(x - 1)^2 + (y - 1)^2} =$

$3 - \sqrt{(x + 1)^2 + (y + 1)^2}$; $x^2 - 2x + 1 + y^2 - 2y + 1 =$

$9 - 6\sqrt{(x + 1)^2 + (y + 1)^2} + x^2 + 2x + 1 + y^2 + 2y + 1$; $-4x - 4y - 9 =$

$-6\sqrt{(x + 1)^2 + (y + 1)^2}$; $16x^2 + 16y^2 + 32xy + 72x + 72y + 81 =$

$36(x^2 + 2x + 1 + y^2 + 2y + 1)$; $16x^2 + 16y^2 + 32xy + 72x + 72y + 81 =$

$36x^2 + 72x + 36y^2 + 72y + 72$; $20x^2 + 20y^2 - 32xy - 9 = 0$

20. $\sqrt{[x - (-1)]^2 + (y - 1)^2} - \sqrt{(x - 1)^2 + [y - (-1)]^2} = 2$; $\sqrt{(x + 1)^2 + (y - 1)^2} =$

$2 + \sqrt{(x - 1)^2 + (y + 1)^2}$; $x^2 + 2x + 1 + y^2 - 2y + 1 =$

$4 + 4\sqrt{(x - 1)^2 + (y + 1)^2} + x^2 - 2x + 1 + y^2 + 2y + 1$; $4x - 4y - 4 =$

$4\sqrt{(x - 1)^2 + (y + 1)^2}$; $x - y - 1 = \sqrt{(x - 1)^2 + (y + 1)^2}$;

$x^2 + y^2 - 2xy - 2x + 2y + 1 = x^2 - 2x + 1 + y^2 + 2y + 1$; $-2xy = 1$; $xy = -\dfrac{1}{2}$

Pages 409–410 · WRITTEN EXERCISES

A **1.** two　　　　　　　**2.** zero　　　　　　　**3.** one

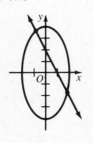
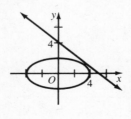
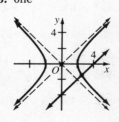

4. two

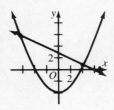

5. four

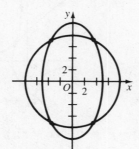

6. four

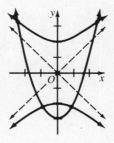

7. zero

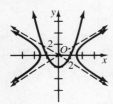

8. two

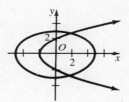

9. three

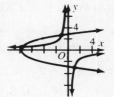

B   10. $\{(4.4, 0.8), (-6.4, 6.2)\}$ **11.** $\{(3.5, 7.2), (3.5, -7.2), (-3.5, 7.2), (-3.5, -7.2)\}$

12. $\{(2.5, 3.2), (-2.5, 3.2), (.9, -2.2), (-.9, -2.2)\}$ **13.** none

14. $\{(1.9, 2.8), (1.9, -2.8)\}$ **15.** $\{(1, -3), (-7.9, 0.4), (-1.1, 2.6)\}$

16.

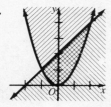

17.

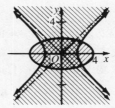

18.

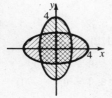

19.

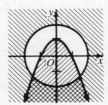

20. a. Let base $= 2x$ and height $= y$; length of leg $= \sqrt{x^2 + y^2}$; area: $xy = 1$;

   perimeter: $x + \sqrt{x^2 + y^2} = 2$

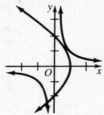

b. $\sqrt{x^2 + y^2} = 2 - x$; $x^2 + y^2 = 4 - 4x + x^2$; $y^2 = -4x + 4$

c. Since the graphs of $xy = 1$ and $y^2 = -4x + 4$ intersect only for negative values of x and y, there is no isosceles triangle with perimeter 4 and area 1.

Page 413 · WRITTEN EXERCISES

A   **1.** $x = -3y + 6$; $y^2 = -3y + 6 + 4$; $y^2 + 3y - 10 = 0$; $(y + 5)(y - 2) = 0$; $y = -5$ or $y = 2$; if $y = -5$, $x = -3(-5) + 6 = 21$; if $y = 2$, $x = -3(2) + 6 = 0$; $\{(0, 2), (21, -5)\}$

2. $2x - y + 2 = 0$; $2x - (x^2 - 1) + 2 = 0$; $2x - x^2 + 3 = 0$; $x^2 - 2x - 3 = 0$; $(x - 3)(x + 1) = 0$; $x = 3$ or $x = -1$; if $x = 3$, $y = 3^2 - 1 = 8$; if $x = -1$, $y = (-1)^2 - 1 = 0$; $\{(3, 8), (-1, 0)\}$

3. $y = 1 - x$; $x^2 - (1 - x)^2 = 9$; $x^2 - (1 - 2x + x^2) = 9$; $x^2 - 1 + 2x - x^2 = 9$; $2x = 10$; $x = 5$; $y = 1 - 5 = -4$; $(5, -4)$

4. $y = x - 5$; $x(x - 5) + 6 = 0$; $x^2 - 5x + 6 = 0$; $(x - 3)(x - 2) = 0$; $x = 3$ or $x = 2$; if $x = 3$, $y = 3 - 5 = -2$; if $x = 2$, $y = 2 - 5 = -3$; $\{(3, -2), (2, -3)\}$

5. $y = -2x + 12$; $x(-2x + 12) = 10$; $-2x^2 + 12x = 10$; $x^2 - 6x + 5 = 0$; $(x - 5)(x - 1) = 0$; $x = 5$ or $x = 1$; if $x = 5$; $y = -2(5) + 12 = 2$; if $x = 1$, $y = -2(1) + 12 = 10$; $\{(5, 2), (1, 10)\}$

6. $x = 3y - 5$; $(3y - 5)^2 + y^2 = 5$; $9y^2 - 30y + 25 + y^2 = 5$; $10y^2 - 30y + 20 = 0$; $y^2 - 3y + 2 = 0$; $(y - 2)(y - 1) = 0$; $y = 2$ or $y = 1$; if $y = 2$, $x = 3(2) - 5 = 1$; if $y = 1$, $x = 3(1) - 5 = -2$; $\{(1, 2), (-2, 1)\}$

7. $y = -x + 3$; $2x^2 + (-x + 3)^2 = 6$; $2x^2 + x^2 - 6x + 9 = 6$; $3x^2 - 6x + 3 = 0$; $x^2 - 2x + 1 = 0$; $(x - 1)^2 = 0$; $x = 1$; $y = -1 + 3 = 2$; $(1, 2)$

8. $y = -x + 3$; $4x^2 - (-x + 3)^2 + 12 = 0$; $4x^2 - (x^2 - 6x + 9) + 12 = 0$; $4x^2 - x^2 + 6x - 9 + 12 = 0$; $3x^2 + 6x + 3 = 0$; $x^2 + 2x + 1 = 0$; $(x + 1)^2 = 0$; $x = -1$; $y = -(-1) + 3 = 4$; $(-1, 4)$

9. $\begin{aligned} x^2 + y^2 &= 25 \\ x^2 - y^2 &= 27 \end{aligned}$; $2x^2 = 32$; $x^2 = 16$; $x = 4$ or -4; $16 + y^2 = 25$; $y^2 = 9$; $y = 3$ or -3;

   $\{(4, 3), (4, -3), (-4, 3), (-4, -3)\}$

10. $4x^2 + y^2 = 52$
    $4x^2 - y^2 = 20$; $8x^2 = 72; x^2 = 9; x = 3$ or $-3; 36 + y^2 = 52; y^2 = 16; y = 4$ or

    $-4; \{(3, 4), (3, -4), (-3, 4), (-3, -4)\}$

11. $y = x^2; y + y^2 = 20; y^2 + y - 20 = 0; (y + 5)(y - 4) = 0; y = -5$ or $y = 4;$ reject
    -5 since $x^2 \geq 0; x^2 = 4; x = 2$ or $-2; \{(2, 4), (-2, 4)\}$

12. $y^2 = 2x; x^2 + 2x = 8; x^2 + 2x - 8 = 0; (x + 4)(x - 2) = 0; x = -4$ or $x = 2;$ reject
    -4 since $y^2 \geq 0; y^2 = 2(2) = 4; y = 2$ or $-2; \{(2, 2), (2, -2)\}$

B 13. $6x^2 + 9y^2 = 51$
    $6x^2 + 2y^2 = 30$; $7y^2 = 21; y^2 = 3; y = \sqrt{3}$ or $-\sqrt{3}; 3x^2 + 3 = 15; 3x^2 = 12;$

    $x^2 = 4; x = 2$ or $-2; \{(2, \sqrt{3}), (2, -\sqrt{3}), (-2, \sqrt{3}), (-2, -\sqrt{3})\}$

14. $4x^2 + 4y^2 = 196$
    $9x^2 + 4y^2 = 36$; $-5x^2 = 160; x^2 = -32;$ no real solution

15. $x^2 + 2y^2 = 12$
    $6x^2 - 2y^2 = 16$; $7x^2 = 28; x^2 = 4; x = 2$ or $-2; 4 + 2y^2 = 12; 2y^2 = 8; y^2 = 4;$

    $y = 2$ or $-2; \{(2, 2), (2, -2), (-2, 2), (-2, -2)\}$

16. $xy = -6; y = -\dfrac{6}{x}; x^2 + \left(-\dfrac{6}{x}\right)^2 = 13; x^2 + \dfrac{36}{x^2} = 13; x^4 + 36 = 13x^2;$

    $x^4 - 13x^2 + 36 = 0; (x^2 - 9)(x^2 - 4) = 0; x^2 = 9$ or $x^2 = 4; x = 3$ or $x = -3, x = 2$
    or $-2;$ if $x = 3, y = -2;$ if $x = -3, y = 2;$ if $x = 2, y = -3;$ if $x = -2, y = 3;$
    $\{(3, -2), (-3, 2), (2, -3), (-2, 3)\}$

17. $xy = 3; y = \dfrac{3}{x}; 2\left(\dfrac{3}{x}\right)^2 - x^2 = 7; 2\left(\dfrac{9}{x^2}\right) - x^2 = 7; \dfrac{18}{x^2} - x^2 = 7; 18 - x^4 = 7x^2;$

    $x^4 + 7x^2 - 18 = 0; (x^2 + 9)(x^2 - 2) = 0; x^2 = -9$ (reject) or $x^2 = 2; x = \sqrt{2}$ or

    $-\sqrt{2};$ if $x = \sqrt{2}; y = \dfrac{3}{\sqrt{2}} = \dfrac{3\sqrt{2}}{2};$ if $x = -\sqrt{2}, y = \dfrac{3}{-\sqrt{2}} = -\dfrac{3\sqrt{2}}{2};$

    $\left\{\left(\sqrt{2}, \dfrac{3\sqrt{2}}{2}\right), \left(-\sqrt{2}, -\dfrac{3\sqrt{2}}{2}\right)\right\}$

18. $y = x^2 + 5; x^2 = y - 5; 16(y - 5) + 9y^2 = 144; 16y - 80 + 9y^2 = 144;$

    $9y^2 + 16y - 224 = 0; y = \dfrac{-8 \pm 4\sqrt{30}}{9};$ reject both since $x^2 = y - 5$ is negative for
    both values; no real solution

19. $y = \dfrac{6}{x}; \left(\dfrac{6}{x}\right)^2 = x + 7; \dfrac{36}{x^2} = x + 7; 36 = x^3 + 7x^2; x^3 + 7x^2 - 36 = 0;$ testing pos-

    sible rational roots yields solutions $x = 2, -3,$ and $-6;$ if $x = 2, y = \dfrac{6}{2} = 3;$ if $x = -3,$

    $y = \dfrac{6}{-3} = -2;$ if $x = -6, y = \dfrac{6}{-6} = -1; \{(2, 3), (-3, -2), (-6, -1)\}$

20. $xy = -6; y = -\dfrac{6}{x}; -\dfrac{6}{x} = x^2 - 1; -6 = x^3 - x; x^3 - x + 6 = 0;$ testing possible rational roots yields the solution $x = -2;$ if $x = -2, y = \dfrac{-6}{-2} = 3; (-2, 3);$ the depressed equation $x^2 - 2x + 3$ has discriminant -8 and therefore has no real roots.

21. $(x^2 - y^2) + 2xyi = 3 - 4i; x^2 - y^2 = 3; 2xy = -4; xy = -2; y = -\dfrac{2}{x};$

$x^2 - \left(-\dfrac{2}{x}\right)^2 = 3; x^2 - \dfrac{4}{x^2} = 3; x^4 - 4 = 3x^2; x^4 - 3x^2 - 4 = 1;$

$(x^2 - 4)(x^2 + 1) = 0; x^2 = -1 \text{ (reject) or } x^2 = 4; x = 2 \text{ or } -2;$ if $x = 2,$

$y = -\dfrac{2}{2} = -1;$ if $x = -2, y = -\dfrac{2}{-2} = 1; \{2 - i, -2 + i\}$

22. $(x^2 - y^2) + 2xyi = -3 + 4i; x^2 - y^2 = -3; 2xy = 4; xy = 2; y = \dfrac{2}{x};$

$x^2 - \left(\dfrac{2}{x}\right)^2 = -3; x^2 - \dfrac{4}{x^2} = -3; x^4 - 4 = -3x^2; x^4 + 3x^2 - 4 = 0;$

$(x^2 + 4)(x^2 - 1) = 0; x^2 = -4 \text{ (reject) or } x^2 = 1; x = 1 \text{ or } -1;$ if $x = 1, y = \dfrac{2}{1} = 2;$ if

$x = -1, y = \dfrac{2}{-1} = -2; \{1 + 2i, -1 - 2i\}$

23. $(x^2 - y^2) + 2xyi = 5 + 12i; x^2 - y^2 = 5; 2xy = 12; xy = 6; y = \dfrac{6}{x}; x^2 - \left(\dfrac{6}{x}\right)^2 = 5;$

$x^2 - \dfrac{36}{x^2} = 5; x^4 - 36 = 5x^2; x^4 - 5x^2 - 36 = 0; (x^2 + 4)(x^2 - 9) = 0; x^2 = -4$

(reject) or $x^2 = 9; x = 3 \text{ or } x = -3;$ if $x = 3, y = \dfrac{6}{3} = 2;$ if $x = -3, y = \dfrac{6}{-3} = -2;$

$\{3 + 2i, -3 - 2i\}$

24. $(x^2 - y^2) + 2xyi = -5 - 12i; x^2 - y^2 = -5; 2xy = -12; xy = -6; y = -\dfrac{6}{x};$

$x^2 - \left(-\dfrac{6}{x}\right)^2 = -5; x^2 - \dfrac{36}{x^2} = -5; x^4 - 36 = -5x^2; x^4 + 5x^2 - 36 = 0;$

$(x^2 + 9)(x^2 - 4) = 0; x^2 = -9 \text{ (reject) or } x^2 = 4; x = 2 \text{ or } x = -2;$ if $x = 2,$

$y = -\dfrac{6}{2} = -3;$ if $x = -2, y = -\dfrac{6}{-2} = 3; \{2 - 3i, -2 + 3i\}$

25. $(x^2 - y^2) + 2xyi = -7 + 24i; x^2 - y^2 = -7; 2xy = 24; xy = 12; y = \dfrac{12}{x};$

$x^2 - \left(\dfrac{12}{x}\right)^2 = -7; x^2 - \dfrac{144}{x^2} = -7; x^4 - 144 = -7x^2; x^4 + 7x^2 - 144 = 0;$

$(x^2 + 16)(x^2 - 9) = 0; x^2 = -16 \text{ (reject) or } x^2 = 9; x = 3 \text{ or } -3;$ if $x = 3, y = \dfrac{12}{x} = 4;$

if $x = -3, y = \dfrac{12}{-3} = -4; \{3 + 4i, -3 - 4i\}$

26. $(x^2 - y^2) + 2xyi = 7 + 24i; x^2 - y^2 = 7; 2xy = 24; xy = 12; y = \dfrac{12}{x};$

$x^2 - \left(\dfrac{12}{x}\right)^2 = 7; x^2 - \dfrac{144}{x^2} = 7; x^4 - 144 = 7x^2; x^4 - 7x^2 - 144 = 0;$

$(x^2 + 9)(x^2 - 16) = 0; x^2 = -9 \text{ (reject) or } x^2 = 16; x = 4 \text{ or } -4;$ if $x = 4, y = \dfrac{12}{4} = 3;$

if $x = -4, y = \dfrac{12}{-4} = -3; \{4 + 3i, -4 - 3i\}$

Pages 414-415 · PROBLEMS

A 1. Let x = frontage on Third Street and y = frontage on D Street; $x = y + 12$; $xy = 640$; $(y + 12)y = 640$; $y^2 + 12y - 640 = 0$; $(y + 32)(y - 20) = 0$; $y = -32$ (reject) or $y = 20$; $x = 20 + 12 = 32$; 32 m by 20 m

2. Let l = length of longer side and w = length of shorter side; $l + w = 7$ and $lw = 12$; $w = \dfrac{12}{l}$; $l + \dfrac{12}{l} = 7$; $l^2 + 12 = 7l$; $l^2 - 7l + 12 = 0$; $(l - 4)(l - 3) = 0$; $l = 4$ or $l = 3$; since l is length of longer side, $l = 4$; $2a = 4$; $a = 2$; $w = 3$; $2b = 3$; $b = \dfrac{3}{2}$; $\dfrac{x^2}{2^2} + \dfrac{y^2}{\left(\dfrac{3}{2}\right)^2} = 1$; $\dfrac{x^2}{4} + \dfrac{y^2}{\dfrac{9}{4}} = 1$; $\dfrac{x^2}{4} + \dfrac{4y^2}{9} = 1$

3. Let l = length and w = width; $l + w = 7$; $w = 7 - l$; $\sqrt{l^2 + w^2} = 5$; $l^2 + w^2 = 25$; $l^2 + (7 - l)^2 = 25$; $l^2 + 49 - 14l + l^2 = 25$; $2l^2 - 14l + 24 = 0$; $l^2 - 7l + 12 = 0$; $(l - 4)(l - 3) = 0$; $l = 4$ or $l = 3$; if $l = 4$, $w = 3$; 4 m by 3 m

4. Let x and y be the lengths of the legs; $x + y + 13 = 30$; $x^2 + y^2 = 169$; $y = 17 - x$; $x^2 + (17 - x)^2 = 169$; $x^2 + 289 - 34x + x^2 = 169$; $2x^2 - 34x + 120 = 0$; $x^2 - 17x + 60 = 0$; $(x - 5)(x - 12) = 0$; $x = 5$ or $x = 12$; if $x = 5$, $y = 12$; if $x = 12$, $y = 5$; 5 m and 12 m

5. Let x be the length of the other leg and y the length of the hypotenuse; $y = x + 1$; $y^2 = x^2 + 49$; $(x + 1)^2 = x^2 + 49$; $x^2 + 2x + 1 = x^2 + 49$; $2x = 48$; $x = 24$; $y = 24 + 1 = 25$; 7 km, 24 km, 25 km

6. $2y + 3x = 180$; $2y = -3x + 180$; $y = -\dfrac{3}{2}x + 90$; $xy = 1350$; $x\left(-\dfrac{3}{2}x + 90\right) = 1350$; $-\dfrac{3}{2}x^2 + 90x = 1350$; $x^2 - 60x + 900 = 0$; $(x - 30)^2 = 0$; $x = 30$; $y = -\dfrac{3}{2}(30) + 90 = 45$; 45 m by 30 m

7. Let x and y be the dimensions; $xy = 560$; $y = \dfrac{560}{x}$; $4(x - 8)(y - 8) = 960$; $(x - 8)(y - 8) = 240$; $xy - 8y - 8x + 64 = 240$; $560 - \dfrac{4480}{x} - 8x + 64 = 240$; $-\dfrac{4480}{x} - 8x + 384 = 0$; $4480 + 8x^2 - 384x = 0$; $x^2 - 48x + 560 = 0$; $(x - 28)(x - 20) = 0$; $x = 28$ or $x = 20$; if $x = 28$, $y = 20$; if $x = 20$, $y = 28$; 28 cm by 20 cm

8. Let x and y be the dimensions; $xy = 10$; $y = \dfrac{10}{x}$; $x^2 + y^2 = 25$; $x^2 + \left(\dfrac{10}{x}\right)^2 = 25$; $x^2 + \dfrac{100}{x^2} = 25$; $x^4 + 100 = 25x^2$; $x^4 - 25x^2 + 100 = 0$; $(x^2 - 20)(x^2 - 5) = 0$; $x^2 = 20$ or $x^2 = 5$; $x = 2\sqrt{5}$ or $x = \sqrt{5}$; if $x = 2\sqrt{5}$, $y = \sqrt{5}$; if $x = \sqrt{5}$, $y = 2\sqrt{5}$; $\sqrt{5}$ by $2\sqrt{5}$

B **9.** Let x and y be the rates of the slower and faster walker, respectively; $y = x + 1$

$x^2 + y^2 = 36$; $x^2 + x^2 + 2x + 1 = 36$; $2x^2 + 2x - 35 = 0$; $x = \dfrac{-1 + \sqrt{71}}{2}$;

$y = \dfrac{-1 + \sqrt{71}}{2} + 1 = \dfrac{1 + \sqrt{71}}{2}$; $\dfrac{-1 + \sqrt{71}}{2}$ km/h and $\dfrac{1 + \sqrt{71}}{2}$ km/h

10. Let $(a, b) = $ center; $(0 - a)^2 + (3 - b)^2 = 25$; $a^2 + 9 - 6b + b^2 = 25$;

$(3 - a)^2 + (0 - b)^2 = 25$; $9 - 6a + a^2 + b^2 = 25$; subtracting, $6a - 6b = 0$; $a = b$

$a^2 + (3 - a)^2 = 25$; $a^2 + 9 - 6a + a^2 = 25$; $2a^2 - 6a - 16 = 0$; $a^2 - 3a - 8 = 0$;

$a = \dfrac{3 + \sqrt{41}}{2}$; $b = \dfrac{3 + \sqrt{41}}{2}$; $\left(x - \dfrac{3 + \sqrt{41}}{2}\right)^2 + \left(y - \dfrac{3 + \sqrt{41}}{2}\right)^2 = 25$

C **11.** Let (x, y) be the point where the line joining the center of the circle and $(4, 3)$ meet

the circle; using similar triangles, $\dfrac{y}{3} = \dfrac{x}{4}$; $y = \dfrac{3x}{4}$; $x^2 + y^2 = 1$; $x^2 + \left(\dfrac{3x}{4}\right)^2 = 1$

$x^2 + \dfrac{9x^2}{16} = 1$; $25x^2 = 16$; $x^2 = \dfrac{16}{25}$; $x = \dfrac{4}{5}$ [(x, y) is in the first quadrant];

$y = \dfrac{3x}{4} = \dfrac{3}{4}\left(\dfrac{4}{5}\right) = \dfrac{3}{5}$; $\left(\dfrac{4}{5}, \dfrac{3}{5}\right)$

12. With the coordinate system described, the sloping side passes through $(10, 0)$ and

$(510, 300)$; $m = \dfrac{300 - 0}{510 - 10} = \dfrac{300}{500} = \dfrac{3}{5}$; $y = \dfrac{3}{5}x + b$; $0 = \dfrac{3}{5}(10) + b$; $0 = 6 + b$;

$b = -6$; equation for sloping wall: $y = \dfrac{3}{5}x - 6$; $\dfrac{3}{5}x - 6 = 300 - \dfrac{x^2}{80}$;

$48x - 480 = 24{,}000 - x^2$; $x^2 + 48x - 24{,}480 = 0$; $x = -24 + 12\sqrt{174}$;

$y = \dfrac{3}{5}(-24 + 12\sqrt{174}) - 6 = \dfrac{-102 + 36\sqrt{174}}{5}$;

distance $= \sqrt{(-24 + 12\sqrt{174} - 0)^2 + \left(\dfrac{-102 + 36\sqrt{174}}{5} - 300\right)^2} = 262.4$ m

Pages 419–420 · WRITTEN EXERCISES

A **1.** $z = 2$; $y + 2 = 3$; $y = 1$; $x - 1 + 4 = 5$; $x = 2$; $(2, 1, 2)$

2. $z = -2$; $2y - 2 = 4$; $2y = 6$; $y = 3$; $x + 6 - 4 = 3$; $x = 1$; $(1, 3, -2)$

3. $2z = 6$; $z = 3$; $2y + 3 = -3$; $2y = -6$; $y = -3$; $2x - 9 + 3 = 2$; $2x = 8$; $x = 4$;

$(4, -3, 3)$

4. $3z = -6$; $z = -2$; $4y + 6 = 10$; $4y = 4$; $y = 1$; $5x - 3 - 8 = 4$; $5x = 15$; $x = 3$

$(3, 1, -2)$

5. $3x = 6$; $x = 2$; $2y - 2 = 4$; $2y = 6$; $y = 3$; $2z - 9 + 4 = 1$; $2z = 6$; $z = 3$; $(2, 3, 3)$

6. $2y = 8$; $y = 4$; $2x + 12 = 10$; $2x = -2$; $x = -1$; $z - 3 + 4 = 3$; $z = 2$; $(-1, 4, 2)$

7. $\begin{bmatrix} 1 & -2 & 1 & 7 \\ -1 & 3 & 4 & 2 \\ 2 & 2 & -3 & -2 \end{bmatrix} \rightarrow \begin{bmatrix} 1 & -2 & 1 & 7 \\ 0 & 1 & 5 & 9 \\ 0 & 6 & -5 & -16 \end{bmatrix} \rightarrow \begin{bmatrix} 1 & -2 & 1 & 7 \\ 0 & 1 & 5 & 9 \\ 0 & 0 & -35 & -70 \end{bmatrix}$; $-35z = -70; z = 2;$

$y + 5(2) = 9; y + 10 = 9; y = -1; x - 2(-1) + 2 = 7; x + 2 + 2 = 7; x = 3;$

$(3, -1, 2)$

8. $\begin{bmatrix} 1 & 3 & 2 & -1 \\ -3 & -2 & 1 & 3 \\ 2 & -1 & 3 & -8 \end{bmatrix} \rightarrow \begin{bmatrix} 1 & 3 & 2 & -1 \\ 0 & 7 & 7 & 0 \\ 0 & -7 & -1 & -6 \end{bmatrix} \rightarrow \begin{bmatrix} 1 & 3 & 2 & -1 \\ 0 & 7 & 7 & 0 \\ 0 & 0 & 6 & -6 \end{bmatrix}$; $6z = -6; z = -1;$

$7y + 7(-1) = 0; 7y = 7; y = 1; x + 3(1) + 2(-1) = -1; x + 3 - 2 = -1; x = -2;$

$(-2, 1, -1)$

9. $\begin{bmatrix} 1 & -2 & 1 & 10 \\ 2 & 1 & 3 & 10 \\ -4 & 3 & 2 & 5 \end{bmatrix} \rightarrow \begin{bmatrix} 1 & -2 & 1 & 10 \\ 0 & 5 & 1 & -10 \\ 0 & -5 & 6 & 45 \end{bmatrix} \rightarrow \begin{bmatrix} 1 & -2 & 1 & 10 \\ 0 & 5 & 1 & -10 \\ 0 & 0 & 7 & 35 \end{bmatrix}$; $7z = 35; z = 5;$

$5y + 5 = -10; 5y = -15; y = -3; x - 2(-3) + 5 = 10; x + 6 + 5 = 10; x = -1;$

$(-1, -3, 5)$

10. $\begin{bmatrix} 1 & 4 & -1 & 3 \\ 2 & 5 & 2 & -5 \\ -3 & 3 & 5 & 2 \end{bmatrix} \rightarrow \begin{bmatrix} 1 & 4 & -1 & 3 \\ 0 & -3 & 4 & -11 \\ 0 & 15 & 2 & 11 \end{bmatrix} \rightarrow \begin{bmatrix} 1 & 4 & -1 & 3 \\ 0 & -3 & 4 & -11 \\ 0 & 0 & 22 & -44 \end{bmatrix}$; $22z = -44; z = -2;$

$-3y + 4(-2) = -11; -3y - 8 = -11; -3y = -3; y = 1; x + 4 - (-2) = 3;$

$x + 6 = 3; x = -3; (-3, 1, -2)$

11. $\begin{bmatrix} 1 & -3 & -2 & 4 \\ 4 & -2 & 5 & 7 \\ -1 & 1 & -2 & 0 \end{bmatrix} \rightarrow \begin{bmatrix} 1 & -3 & -2 & 4 \\ 0 & 10 & 13 & -9 \\ 0 & -2 & -4 & 4 \end{bmatrix} \rightarrow \begin{bmatrix} 1 & -3 & -2 & 4 \\ 0 & 10 & 13 & -9 \\ 0 & 0 & -7 & 11 \end{bmatrix}$; $-7z = 11;$ $z = -\dfrac{11}{7};$

$10y + 13\left(-\dfrac{11}{7}\right) = -9; 10y - \dfrac{143}{7} = -9; 10y = \dfrac{80}{7}; y = \dfrac{8}{7};$

$x - 3\left(\dfrac{8}{7}\right) - 2\left(-\dfrac{11}{7}\right) = 4; x - \dfrac{24}{7} + \dfrac{22}{7} = 4; x = \dfrac{30}{7}; \left(\dfrac{30}{7}, \dfrac{8}{7}, -\dfrac{11}{7}\right)$

12. $\begin{bmatrix} 1 & 3 & -1 & -10 \\ 2 & -1 & -3 & -3 \\ 3 & 2 & -1 & -1 \end{bmatrix} \rightarrow \begin{bmatrix} 1 & 3 & -1 & -10 \\ 0 & -7 & -1 & 17 \\ 0 & -7 & 2 & 29 \end{bmatrix} \rightarrow \begin{bmatrix} 1 & 3 & -1 & -10 \\ 0 & -7 & -1 & 17 \\ 0 & 0 & 3 & 12 \end{bmatrix}$; $3z = 12; z = 4;$

$-7y - 4 = 17; -7y = 21; y = -3; x + 3(-3) - 4 = -10; x - 9 - 4 = -10; x = 3;$

$(3, -3, 4)$

B 13. $\begin{aligned} 2z - 2y + 3x &= 1 \\ -5z + 5y + 2x &= 7; \\ z - 3y + 4x &= -3 \end{aligned}$ $\begin{bmatrix} 1 & -3 & 4 & -3 \\ 2 & -2 & 3 & 1 \\ -5 & 5 & 2 & 7 \end{bmatrix} \rightarrow \begin{bmatrix} 1 & -3 & 4 & -3 \\ 0 & 4 & -5 & 7 \\ 0 & -10 & 22 & -8 \end{bmatrix} \rightarrow$

$\begin{bmatrix} 1 & -3 & 4 & -3 \\ 0 & 4 & -5 & 7 \\ 0 & 0 & 9.5 & 9.5 \end{bmatrix}$; $9.5x = 9.5; x = 1; 4y - 5 = 7; 4y = 12; y = 3;$

$z - 3(3) + 4 = -3; z - 9 + 4 = -3; z = 2; (1, 3, 2)$

14.
$$\begin{aligned} b + 2a - 2c &= 6 \\ -3b + 5a - 3c &= -2; \\ 2b + 3a + 3c &= -7 \end{aligned} \qquad \begin{bmatrix} 1 & 2 & -2 & 6 \\ -3 & 5 & -3 & -2 \\ 2 & 3 & 3 & -7 \end{bmatrix} \to \begin{bmatrix} 1 & 2 & -2 & 6 \\ 0 & 11 & -9 & 16 \\ 0 & -1 & 7 & -19 \end{bmatrix} \to$$

$$\begin{bmatrix} 1 & 2 & -2 & 6 \\ 0 & 11 & -9 & 16 \\ 0 & 0 & \dfrac{68}{11} & -\dfrac{193}{11} \end{bmatrix}; \dfrac{68}{11}c = -\dfrac{193}{11}; c = -\dfrac{193}{68}; 11a - 9\left(-\dfrac{193}{68}\right) = 16;$$

$$11a + \dfrac{1737}{68} = 16; 11a = -\dfrac{649}{68}; a = -\dfrac{59}{68}; b + 2\left(-\dfrac{59}{68}\right) - 2\left(-\dfrac{193}{68}\right) = 6;$$

$$b - \dfrac{59}{34} + \dfrac{193}{34} = 6; b = \dfrac{70}{34} = \dfrac{35}{17}; \left(-\dfrac{59}{68}, \dfrac{35}{17}, -\dfrac{193}{68}\right)$$

15.
$$\begin{aligned} w + 3u + 2v &= 4 \\ -w + 5u + 3v &= -2; \\ w + 2u &= 1 \end{aligned} \qquad \begin{bmatrix} 1 & 3 & 2 & 4 \\ -1 & 5 & 3 & -2 \\ 1 & 2 & 0 & 1 \end{bmatrix} \to \begin{bmatrix} 1 & 3 & 2 & 4 \\ 0 & 8 & 5 & 2 \\ 0 & -1 & -2 & -3 \end{bmatrix} \to$$

$$\begin{bmatrix} 1 & 3 & 2 & 4 \\ 0 & 8 & 5 & 2 \\ 0 & 0 & -\dfrac{11}{8} & -\dfrac{11}{4} \end{bmatrix}; \qquad -\dfrac{11}{8}v = -\dfrac{11}{4}; v = 2; 8u + 5(2) = 2; 8u = -8; u = -1;$$

$$w + 3(-1) + 2(2) = 4; w - 3 + 4 = 4; w = 3; (-1, 2, 3)$$

16.
$$\begin{aligned} y + 3x + 2z &= 3 \\ y + 5x + 5z &= 8; \\ 2y + 7x + 6z &= 9 \end{aligned} \qquad \begin{bmatrix} 1 & 3 & 2 & 3 \\ 1 & 5 & 5 & 8 \\ 2 & 7 & 6 & 9 \end{bmatrix} \to \begin{bmatrix} 1 & 3 & 2 & 3 \\ 0 & 2 & 3 & 5 \\ 0 & 1 & 2 & 3 \end{bmatrix} \to \begin{bmatrix} 1 & 3 & 2 & 3 \\ 0 & 2 & 3 & 5 \\ 0 & 0 & \dfrac{1}{2} & \dfrac{1}{2} \end{bmatrix};$$

$$\dfrac{1}{2}z = \dfrac{1}{2}; z = 1; 2x + 3(1) = 5; 2x = 2; x = 1; y + 3(1) + 2(1) = 3; y + 5 = 3;$$

$$y = -2; (1, -2, 1)$$

17. Let $a = \dfrac{1}{x}, b = \dfrac{1}{y}, c = \dfrac{1}{z};$
$$\begin{aligned} a + 3b + 4c &= 6 \\ a - 2b + c &= 10; \\ 2a + 3b - c &= -12 \end{aligned} \qquad \begin{bmatrix} 1 & 3 & 4 & 6 \\ 1 & -2 & 1 & 10 \\ 2 & 3 & -1 & -12 \end{bmatrix} \to$$

$$\begin{bmatrix} 1 & 3 & 4 & 6 \\ 0 & -5 & -3 & 4 \\ 0 & -3 & -9 & -24 \end{bmatrix} \to \begin{bmatrix} 1 & 3 & 4 & 6 \\ 0 & -5 & -3 & 4 \\ 0 & 0 & -\dfrac{36}{5} & -\dfrac{132}{5} \end{bmatrix}; \qquad -\dfrac{36}{5}c = -\dfrac{132}{5}; c = \dfrac{11}{3}; z = \dfrac{3}{11};$$

$$-5b - 3\left(\dfrac{11}{3}\right) = 4; -5b - 11 = 4; -5b = 15; b = -3; y = -\dfrac{1}{3};$$

$$a + 3(-3) + 4\left(\dfrac{11}{3}\right) = 6; a - 9 + \dfrac{44}{3} = 6; a = \dfrac{1}{3}; x = 3; \left(3, -\dfrac{1}{3}, \dfrac{3}{11}\right)$$

18. Let $x = \dfrac{1}{r}$, $y = \dfrac{1}{s}$, $z = \dfrac{1}{t}$;

$$\begin{array}{c} x + 3y - 2z = 1 \\ 2x + 3y - 4z = 1; \\ x - 6y - 6z = 0 \end{array} \qquad \begin{bmatrix} 1 & 3 & -2 & 1 \\ 2 & 3 & -4 & 1 \\ 1 & -6 & -6 & 0 \end{bmatrix} \rightarrow$$

$$\begin{bmatrix} 1 & 3 & -2 & 1 \\ 0 & -3 & 0 & -1 \\ 0 & -9 & -4 & -1 \end{bmatrix} \rightarrow \begin{bmatrix} 1 & 3 & -2 & 1 \\ 0 & -3 & 0 & -1 \\ 0 & 0 & -4 & 2 \end{bmatrix}; \qquad -4z = 2;\ z = -\dfrac{1}{2};\ t = -2;\ -3y = -1;$$

$y = \dfrac{1}{3}$; $s = 3$; $x + 3\left(\dfrac{1}{3}\right) - 2\left(-\dfrac{1}{2}\right) = 1$; $x + 1 + 1 = 1$; $x = -1$; $r = -1$; $(-1, 3, -2)$

19. a. $\begin{bmatrix} 1 & -2 & -1 & -1 \\ 2 & -1 & 1 & 1 \\ 1 & 4 & 5 & 5 \end{bmatrix} \rightarrow \begin{bmatrix} 1 & -2 & -1 & -1 \\ 0 & 3 & 3 & 3 \\ 0 & 6 & 6 & 6 \end{bmatrix} \rightarrow \begin{bmatrix} 1 & -2 & -1 & -1 \\ 0 & 3 & 3 & 3 \\ 0 & 0 & 0 & 0 \end{bmatrix}$; $\quad 3y + 3z = 3$;

$y + z = 1$; $y = 1 - z$; $x - 2(1 - z) - z = -1$; $x - 2 + 2z - z = -1$; $x = 1 - z$;

$(1 - z, 1 - z, z)$

b. Examples: $(1, 1, 0)$, $(2, 2, -1)$, $(0, 0, 1)$

20. a. $\begin{bmatrix} 1 & 2 & -2 & 3 \\ 1 & 3 & -4 & 6 \\ 4 & 5 & -2 & 3 \end{bmatrix} \rightarrow \begin{bmatrix} 1 & 2 & -2 & 3 \\ 0 & 1 & -2 & 3 \\ 0 & -3 & 6 & -9 \end{bmatrix} \rightarrow \begin{bmatrix} 1 & 2 & -2 & 3 \\ 0 & 1 & -2 & 3 \\ 0 & 0 & 0 & 0 \end{bmatrix}$; $\quad y - 2z = 3$;

$y = 2z + 3$; $x + 2(2z + 3) - 2z = 3$; $x + 4z + 6 - 2z = 3$; $x = -2z - 3$;

$(-2z - 3, 2z + 3, z)$

b. Examples: $\left(-6, 6, \dfrac{3}{2}\right)$, $(-3, 3, 0)$, $(-9, 9, 3)$

C 21. $\begin{bmatrix} 1 & -2 & -1 & -1 \\ 2 & -1 & 1 & 3 \\ 1 & 4 & 5 & 5 \end{bmatrix} \rightarrow \begin{bmatrix} 1 & -2 & -1 & -1 \\ 0 & 3 & 3 & 5 \\ 0 & 6 & 6 & 6 \end{bmatrix} \rightarrow \begin{bmatrix} 1 & -2 & -1 & -1 \\ 0 & 3 & 3 & 5 \\ 0 & 0 & 0 & -4 \end{bmatrix}$; $\quad 0 \neq -4$;

the system is inconsistent.

22. $\begin{bmatrix} 1 & 2 & -2 & 3 \\ 1 & 3 & -4 & 6 \\ 4 & 5 & -2 & 6 \end{bmatrix} \rightarrow \begin{bmatrix} 1 & 2 & -2 & 3 \\ 0 & 1 & -2 & 3 \\ 0 & -3 & 6 & -6 \end{bmatrix} \rightarrow \begin{bmatrix} 1 & 2 & -2 & 3 \\ 0 & 1 & -2 & 3 \\ 0 & 0 & 0 & 3 \end{bmatrix}$; $\quad 0 \neq 3$;

the system is inconsistent.

23. $\begin{bmatrix} 1 & 0 & -2 & 0 \\ 2 & -1 & 1 & 0 \\ 1 & -1 & 3 & 0 \end{bmatrix} \rightarrow \begin{bmatrix} 1 & 0 & -2 & 0 \\ 0 & -1 & 5 & 0 \\ 0 & -1 & 5 & 0 \end{bmatrix} \rightarrow \begin{bmatrix} 1 & 0 & -2 & 0 \\ 0 & -1 & 5 & 0 \\ 0 & 0 & 0 & 0 \end{bmatrix}$; $\quad -y + 5z = 0$; $y = 5z$;

$x - 2z = 0$; $x = 2z$; $(2z, 5z, z)$

24. $\begin{bmatrix} 1 & -2 & 3 & 0 \\ 1 & 0 & 2 & 0 \\ 3 & -4 & 5 & 0 \end{bmatrix} \rightarrow \begin{bmatrix} 1 & -2 & 3 & 0 \\ 0 & 2 & -1 & 0 \\ 0 & 2 & -4 & 0 \end{bmatrix} \rightarrow \begin{bmatrix} 1 & -2 & 3 & 0 \\ 0 & 2 & -1 & 0 \\ 0 & 0 & -3 & 0 \end{bmatrix}$; $\quad (0, 0, 0)$ is the only solution.

25. $\begin{bmatrix} 1 & 2 & -2 & 0 \\ 2 & 5 & 2 & 0 \\ 3 & 4 & -2 & 0 \end{bmatrix} \rightarrow \begin{bmatrix} 1 & 2 & -2 & 0 \\ 0 & 1 & 6 & 0 \\ 0 & -2 & 4 & 0 \end{bmatrix} \rightarrow \begin{bmatrix} 1 & 2 & -2 & 0 \\ 0 & 1 & 6 & 0 \\ 0 & 0 & 16 & 0 \end{bmatrix}$; $\quad (0, 0, 0)$ is the only solution.

26.
$$\begin{bmatrix} 1 & -2 & 4 & 0 \\ 3 & -1 & 2 & 0 \\ 1 & 3 & -6 & 0 \end{bmatrix} \rightarrow \begin{bmatrix} 1 & -2 & 4 & 0 \\ 0 & 5 & -10 & 0 \\ 0 & 5 & -10 & 0 \end{bmatrix} \rightarrow \begin{bmatrix} 1 & -2 & 4 & 0 \\ 0 & 5 & -10 & 0 \\ 0 & 0 & 0 & 0 \end{bmatrix}; \quad 5y - 10z = 0;$$

$5y = 10z; \; y = 2z; \; x - 2(2z) + 4z = 0; \; x = 0; \; (0, 2z, z)$

Pages 420-421 · PROBLEMS

A   **1.** Let x, y, and z be the number of \$1, \$5, and \$10 bills, respectively;

$x + 5y + 10z = 87$

$x - y - z = 0;$

$x + y + z = 24$

$$\begin{bmatrix} 1 & 5 & 10 & 87 \\ 1 & -1 & -1 & 0 \\ 1 & 1 & 1 & 24 \end{bmatrix} \rightarrow \begin{bmatrix} 1 & 5 & 10 & 87 \\ 0 & -6 & -11 & -87 \\ 0 & -4 & -9 & -63 \end{bmatrix} \rightarrow$$

$$\begin{bmatrix} 1 & 5 & 10 & 87 \\ 0 & -6 & -11 & -87 \\ 0 & 0 & \frac{5}{2} & \frac{15}{2} \end{bmatrix}; \quad \frac{5}{2}z = \frac{15}{2}; \; z = 3; \; -6y - 11(3) = -87; \; -6y = -54; \; y = 9;$$

$x + 5(9) + 10(3) = 87; \; x = 12;$ 12 \$1 bills, 9 \$5 bills, 3 \$10 bills

2. Let n, d, and q be the number of nickels, dimes and quarters respectively;

$n + d + q = 28$

$-n + d - q = 4;$

$5n + 10d + 25q = 320$

$$\begin{bmatrix} 1 & 1 & 1 & 28 \\ -1 & 1 & -1 & 4 \\ 5 & 10 & 25 & 320 \end{bmatrix} \rightarrow \begin{bmatrix} 1 & 1 & 1 & 28 \\ 0 & 2 & 0 & 32 \\ 0 & 5 & 20 & 180 \end{bmatrix} \rightarrow$$

$$\begin{bmatrix} 1 & 1 & 1 & 28 \\ 0 & 2 & 0 & 32 \\ 0 & 0 & 20 & 100 \end{bmatrix}; \quad 20q = 100; \; q = 5; \; 2d = 32; \; d = 16; \; n + 16 + 5 = 28; \; n = 7;$$

7 nickels, 16 dimes, 5 quarters

3. Let x, y, and z be the masses of the diamonds in order from least to greatest;

$x + y \quad\quad = 6$

$x \quad\quad + z = 10;$

$\quad y + z = 12$

$\dfrac{x + y = 6}{x + z = 10}; \quad y - z = -4; \quad \dfrac{y - z = -4}{y + z = 12}; \quad 2y = 8;$

$y = 4; \; x + 4 = 6; \; x = 2; \; 2 + z = 10; \; z = 8;$ 2 carats, 4 carats, and 8 carats

4. Let x, y, and z be the masses in order from least to greatest;

$x + y = z + 9$

$y + z = x + 27;$

$x + z = y + 15$

$x + y - z = 9$

$-x + y + z = 27;$

$x - y + z = 15$

$2x = 24; \; x = 12; \; 2y = 36; \; y = 18;$
$2z = 42; \; z = 21;$ 12 g, 18 g, 21 g

5. Let l, w, and h be the length, width, and height;

$l + w + h = 80$

$l - 2w - 2h = -10;$

$2w - h = 6$

$$\begin{bmatrix} 1 & 1 & 1 & 80 \\ 1 & -2 & -2 & -10 \\ 0 & 2 & -1 & 6 \end{bmatrix} \rightarrow \begin{bmatrix} 1 & 1 & 1 & 80 \\ 0 & -3 & -3 & -90 \\ 0 & 2 & -1 & 6 \end{bmatrix} \rightarrow$$

$$\begin{bmatrix} 1 & 1 & 1 & 80 \\ 0 & -2 & -2 & -60 \\ 0 & 2 & -1 & 6 \end{bmatrix} \rightarrow \begin{bmatrix} 1 & 1 & 1 & 80 \\ 0 & -2 & -2 & -60 \\ 0 & 0 & -3 & -54 \end{bmatrix}; \quad -3h = 54; \; h = 18; \; -2w - 2(18) = -60;$$

$-2w = -24; \; w = 12; \; l = 80 - 18 - 12 = 50;$ length = 50, width = 12, height = 18

6. Let r, w, and s be Tom's riding, walking, and swimming speeds, respectively;

$$r + w + 2s = 23$$
$$2r + w + s = 33;$$
$$r + 3w = 33$$

$$\frac{r + w + 2s = 23}{4r + 2w + 2s = 66}; \qquad \frac{-3r - w = -43}{r + 3w = 33};$$

$$\frac{-3r - w = -43}{3r + 9w = 99}; \qquad 8w = 56;\ w = 7;\ r + 21 = 33;\ r = 12;\ 12 + 7 + 2s = 23;$$

$$2s = 4;\ s = 2;\ \text{riding: } 12\text{ km/h; walking: } 7\text{ km/h; swimming: } 2\text{ km/h}$$

B   **7.** Let r, c, and s be the number of regular, children's, and senior citizens' tickets sold;

$$r + c + s = 500$$
$$4r + 2.5c + 3s = 1740; \qquad 2r = 600;\ r = 300;$$
$$r - c - s = 100$$

$$\frac{300 + c + s = 500}{1200 + 2.5c + 3s = 1740};$$

$$\frac{c + s = 200}{2.5c + 3s = 540}; \qquad \frac{3c + 3s = 600}{2.5c + 3s = 540}; \qquad 0.5c = 60;\ c = 120;\ 120 + s = 200;$$

$$s = 80;\ 300\text{ regular tickets, } 120\text{ children's tickets, } 80\text{ senior citizens' tickets}$$

8. Let x, y, and z be the digits of n in order from left to right;

$$x + y + z = 15 \qquad\qquad x + y + z = 15$$
$$100x + 10y + z + (100z + 10y + x) = 1029; \qquad 101x + 20y + 101z = 1029;$$
$$100x + 10y + z - (100z + 10y + x) = 495 \qquad 99x - 99z = 495$$

$$\begin{bmatrix} 1 & 1 & 1 & 15 \\ 101 & 20 & 101 & 1029 \\ 99 & 0 & -99 & 495 \end{bmatrix} \rightarrow \begin{bmatrix} 1 & 1 & 1 & 15 \\ 0 & -81 & 0 & -486 \\ 0 & -99 & -198 & -990 \end{bmatrix}; \qquad -81y = -486;\ y = 6;$$

$$-99z - 198(6) = -990;\ -99z = -198;\ z = 2;\ x + 6 + 2 = 15;\ x = 7;\ n = 762$$

9. $a + b + c = 0$
$$a - b + c = 6; \qquad \frac{2a + 2c = 6}{6a + 3c = 12}; \qquad \frac{2a + 2c = 6}{2a + c = 4}; \qquad c = 2;\ a + 2 = 3;\ a = 1;$$
$$4a + 2b + c = 0$$

$$1 + b + 2 = 0;\ b = -3;\ y = x^2 - 3x + 2$$

10. $a + b + c = 3$
$$4a + 2b + c = 10; \qquad \frac{8a + 2c = 4}{6a + 3c = 0}; \qquad \frac{8a + 2c = 4}{8a + 4c = 0}; \qquad -2c = 4;\ c = -2;$$
$$4a - 2b + c = -6$$

$$4a - 2 = 2;\ 4a = 4;\ a = 1;\ 1 + b - 2 = 3;\ b = 4;\ y = x^2 + 4x - 2$$

11. $4 + 4 - 2a + 2b + c = 0 \qquad 2a - 2b - c = 8$
$$16 + 4 + 4a + 2b + c = 0; \qquad 4a + 2b + c = -20; \qquad 6a = -12;\ a = -2;$$
$$4 + 4 + 2a - 2b + c = 0 \qquad 2a - 2b + c = -8$$

$$6a + 2c = -28;\ -12 + 2c = -28;\ 2c = -16;\ c = -8;\ -4 - 2b + 8 = 8;\ -2b = 4;$$
$$b = -2;\ x^2 + y^2 - 2x - 2y - 8 = 0$$

12. $36 + 9 - 6a - 3b + c = 0$ $6a + 3b - c = 45$

$1 + 16 + a + 4b + c = 0;$ $a + 4b + c = -17;$

$4 + 9 + 2a + 3b + c = 0$ $2a + 3b + c = -13$

$7a + 7b = 28$
$8a + 6b = 32$;

$\dfrac{a + b = 4}{4a + 3b = 16}$; $\dfrac{4a + 4b = 16}{4a + 3b = 16}$; $b = 0; a = 4; 4 + 0 + c = -17; c = -21;$

$x^2 + y^2 + 4x - 21 = 0$

Page 423 · APPLICATION

1. $a = 1; c = 0.017;$ minimum distance $= a - c = 0.983$ AU ≈ 147 million km; maximum distance $= a + c = 1.017$ AU ≈ 153 million km

2. Pluto has the greatest eccentricity, so Pluto has the least circular orbit; length of major axis $= 2a = 78.88$ AU; $\dfrac{c}{a} = 0.250;$ $c = 9.86;$ $b^2 = a^2 - c^2 = 1458;$ $b = 38.19;$ length of minor axis $= 2b = 76.38$ AU; ratio $\approx 1.03{:}1.$

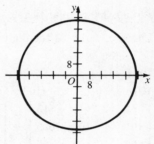

3. $a = 1;$ $c = 0.017;$ $b^2 = a^2 - c^2 = 0.999711;$ $b = 0.9986;$ ratio $= \dfrac{2a}{2b} = \dfrac{a}{b} \approx 1.0001{:}1$

4. $\dfrac{0}{(0.387)^2} + \dfrac{y^2}{(0.379)^2} = 1;$ $y^2 = (0.379)^2$ $d = \sqrt{y^2 + c^2} = \sqrt{(0.379)^2 + (0.080)^2} \approx$ 0.387 AU

5. $a = 1.078;$ $\dfrac{c}{a} = 0.827;$ $c = 0.892;$ $b^2 = a^2 - c^2 = 0.36642;$ $b = 0.605;$
$\dfrac{2a}{2b} = \dfrac{a}{b} \approx 1.78{:}1;$ since the ratio is much larger, the orbit is much more elongated than that of Earth.

Pages 425-426 · CHAPTER REVIEW

1. d; $PQ = \sqrt{(-3 - 1)^2 + (-5 - (-3))^2} = \sqrt{4^2 + 2^2} = \sqrt{20} = 2\sqrt{5}$

2. a; $M = \left(\dfrac{-3 + 1}{2}, \dfrac{-5 + -3}{2}\right) = (-1, -4)$

3. c; $M = (x, y);$ $\dfrac{x + -3}{2} = 1$ and $\dfrac{y + -5}{2} = -3;$ $x = 5$ and $y = -1;$ $M(5, 1)$

4. b; $(x - 4)^2 + (y + 3)^2 = 25;$ $x^2 - 8x + 16 + y^2 + 6y + 9 = 25;$
$x^2 + y^2 - 8x + 6y = 0$

5. b; $x^2 + 4x + y^2 - 6y = -12$; $x^2 + 4x + 4 + y^2 - 6y + 9 = -12 + 4 + 9$;
$(x + 2)^2 + (y - 3)^2 = 1$; center $= (-2, 3)$, radius $= 1$

6. d; center $= (-3, 3)$; $(x + 3)^2 + (y - 3)^2 = 6^2$; $x^2 + 6x + 9 + y^2 - 6y + 9 = 36$;
$x^2 + y^2 + 6x - 6y - 18 = 0$

7. c; $x^2 = 4cy$; $c = -2$; $x^2 = -8y$

8. b; $4x + 4 = y^2 - 4y + 4$; $4(x + 1) = (y - 2)^2$; vertex $= (-1, 2)$

9. b; vertex $= (0, -4)$; $(x - 0)^2 = 4c(y + 4)$; $(2, 0)$ is on the parabola, so
$(2 - 0)^2 = 4c(0 + 4)$; $4 = 16c$; $c = \dfrac{1}{4}$; $x^2 = y + 4$

10. c; $c^2 = 4$, $2a = 8$; $a^2 = 16$; $b^2 = a^2 - c^2 = 12$; $\dfrac{x^2}{12} + \dfrac{y^2}{16} = 1$

11. a; $c^2 = a^2 - b^2 = 20 - 4$; $c = \pm 4$; foci: $(0, 4)$ and $(0, -4)$

12. b; $8y^2 - x^2 = 8$; $\dfrac{y^2}{1} - \dfrac{x^2}{8} = 1$; $c^2 = a^2 + b^2 = 9$; $c = \pm 3$; foci: $(0, 3)$ and $(0, -3)$

13. c; $\pm\dfrac{b}{a} = 1$; $a = \pm b$; $a = 2$; $\dfrac{x^2}{4} - \dfrac{y^2}{4} = 1$; $x^2 - y^2 = 4$

14. d; $x^2 - 6x - 4y^2 - 8y = -1$; $x^2 - 6x + 9 - 4(y^2 + 2y + 1) = -1 + 9 - 4$;
$(x - 3)^2 - 4(y + 1)^2 = 4$; center $= (3, -1)$

15. d; center $= (2, 0)$; $c = 1$; $2a = 4$, $a = 2$; $b^2 = a^2 - c^2 = 3$; $\dfrac{(x - 2)^2}{4} + \dfrac{y^2}{3} = 1$;
$3(x - 2)^2 + 4y^2 = 12$; $3x^2 - 12x + 12 + 4y^2 = 12$; $3x^2 + 4y^2 = 12x$

16. d; $\begin{aligned} x^2 + 4y^2 &= 4; \\ x^2 + y &= 1 \end{aligned}$ $\quad \dfrac{x^2}{4} + \dfrac{y^2}{1} = 1$; $\quad$ the graphs are an ellipse, one of whose
$\qquad\qquad\qquad\qquad y = -x^2 + 1$
y-intercepts is at $(0, 1)$, and a parabola with vertex at $(0, 1)$ that opens downward; the
graphs intersect at $(0, 1)$ and at two other points

17. b; the graphs of both the equations are symmetric to the x-axis.

18. c; $x^2 = 10 - y^2$; $10 - y^2 - 2y = 2$; $y^2 + 2y - 8 = 0$; $(y + 4)(y - 2) = 0$; $y = -4$ or
$y = -2$; if $y = -4$, $x^2 = -6$, no real solution; if $y = 2$, $x^2 = 6$, $x = \pm\sqrt{6}$;
$\{(\sqrt{6}, 2), (-\sqrt{6}, 2)\}$

19. c; $\begin{aligned} x - y + 2z &= 3; \\ 3x + 2y + 2z &= 2 \\ \hline -2x - 3y \phantom{{}+ 2z} &= 1 \end{aligned}$ $\qquad \begin{aligned} 3x + 2y + 2z &= 2; \\ 4x + 6y - 2z &= -8 \\ \hline 7x + 8y \phantom{{}- 2z} &= -6 \end{aligned}$ $\qquad \begin{aligned} -14x - 21y &= 7; \\ 14x + 16y &= -12 \\ \hline -5y &= -5 \\ y &= 1 \end{aligned}$

$7x + 8 = -6$; $7x = -14$; $x = -2$; $z = 2x + 3y + 4 = -4 + 3 + 4 = 3$; $(2, 1, 3)$

Page 427 · CHAPTER TEST

1. **a.** $PQ = \sqrt{(4 - (-2))^2 + (-3 - 5)^2} = \sqrt{6^2 + 8^2} = 10$

   b. $\left(\dfrac{-2 + 4}{2}, \dfrac{5 + (-3)}{2}\right) = (1, 1)$

   c. Let $X = (x, y)$; $\dfrac{x + 4}{2} = -2$ and $\dfrac{y + (-3)}{2} = 5$; $x = -8$ and $y = 13$; $X(-8, 13)$

2. $(x + 1)^2 + (y - 4)^2 = r^2$; $(0 + 1)^2 + (0 - 4)^2 = r^2$; $17 = r^2$; $(x + 1)^2 + (y - 4)^2 = 17$

3. $x^2 - 6x + y^2 + 2y = 0$; $x^2 - 6x + 9 + y^2 + 2y + 1 = 10$;
   $(x - 3)^2 + (y + 1)^2 = 10$; center $= (3, -1)$; radius $= \sqrt{10}$

4. $\sqrt{(x - 0)^2 + (y - 2)^2} = \sqrt{[y - (-2)]^2}$; $x^2 + y^2 - 4y + 4 = y^2 + 4y + 4$; $x^2 = 8y$

5. Vertex $= (-1, 2)$; $c = 1$ and the axis is horizontal, so the focus is $(0, 2)$ and the directrix is $x = -2$.

6. Center $= (0, 0)$; $c = \sqrt{3}$; $2a = 4$; $a = 2$; $b^2 = a^2 - c^2 = 4 - 3 = 1$; major axis is horizontal; $\dfrac{x^2}{4} + y^2 = 1$

7.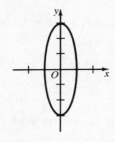

8.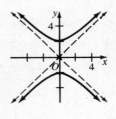

9. Center $= (2, 0)$; $c = 2$; $2a = 8$; $a = 4$; $b^2 = a^2 - c^2 = 16 - 4 = 12$; major axis is horizontal; $\dfrac{x^2}{16} + \dfrac{y^2}{12} = 1$

10. $3(x^2 + 2x) - (y^2 - 4y) = -2$; $3(x^2 + 2x + 1) - (y^2 - 4y + 4) = -3$;
    $3(x + 1)^2 - (y - 2)^2 = -3$; $\dfrac{(y - 2)^2}{3} - (x + 1)^2 = 1$; center $= (-1, 2)$; $c^2 = a^2 + b^2 = 4$; $c = \pm 2$; line containing center and foci is vertical; foci: $(-1, 0)$ and $(-1, 4)$

11.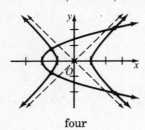

    four

12.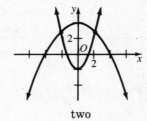

    two

13. $x^2 - 4(x + 2) = 4$; $x^2 - 4x - 8 = 4$; $x^2 - 4x - 12 = 0$; $(x - 6)(x + 2) = 0$; $x = 6$ or $x = -2$; if $x = 6$, $y^2 = 6 + 2 = 8$; $y = \pm 2\sqrt{2}$; if $x = -2$; $y^2 = -2 + 2 = 0$; $y = 0$; $\{(6, 2\sqrt{2}), (6, -2\sqrt{2}), (-2, 0)\}$

14. Let x and y be the lengths of the sides; $xy = 6$; $y = \dfrac{6}{x}$; $\sqrt{x^2 + y^2} = 2\sqrt{5}$;

$x^2 + y^2 = 20$; $x^2 + \left(\dfrac{6}{x}\right)^2 = x^2 + \dfrac{36}{x^2} = 20$; $x^4 + 36 = 20x^2$; $x^4 - 20x^2 + 36 = 0$;

$(x^2 - 18)(x^2 - 2) = 0$; $x^2 = 18$ or $x^2 = 2$; $x = 3\sqrt{2}$ or $x = \sqrt{2}$ (reject negative values

since x represents a length); if $x = 3\sqrt{2}$, $y = \dfrac{6}{3\sqrt{2}} = \sqrt{2}$; if $x = \sqrt{2}$,

$y = \dfrac{6}{\sqrt{2}} = 3\sqrt{2}$; $3\sqrt{2}$ cm by $\sqrt{2}$ m

15. $\begin{bmatrix} 1 & -1 & 3 & 3 \\ 3 & 1 & -1 & 3 \\ 2 & 2 & -3 & -1 \end{bmatrix} \rightarrow \begin{bmatrix} 1 & -1 & 3 & 3 \\ 0 & 4 & -10 & -6 \\ 0 & 4 & -9 & -7 \end{bmatrix} \rightarrow \begin{bmatrix} 1 & -1 & 3 & 3 \\ 0 & 4 & -10 & -6 \\ 0 & 0 & 1 & -1 \end{bmatrix}$; $z = -1$;

$4y - 10(-1) = -6$; $4y + 10 = -6$; $4y = -16$; $y = -4$; $x - (-4) + 3(-1) = 3$; $x = 2$; $(2, -4, -1)$

Page 432 · WRITTEN EXERCISES

A 1. $9^{3/2} = (\sqrt{9})^3 = 3^3 = 27$ 2. $81^{3/4} = (\sqrt[4]{81})^3 = 3^3 = 27$

3. $8^{-4/3} = \dfrac{1}{8^{4/3}} = \dfrac{1}{(\sqrt[3]{8})^4} = \dfrac{1}{2^4} = \dfrac{1}{16}$

4. $4^{-0.5} = \dfrac{1}{4^{1/2}} = \dfrac{1}{\sqrt{4}} = \dfrac{1}{2}$

5. $\left(\dfrac{4}{9}\right)^{-1.5} = \left(\dfrac{9}{4}\right)^{3/2} = \left(\sqrt{\dfrac{9}{4}}\right)^3 = \left(\dfrac{3}{2}\right)^3 = \dfrac{27}{8}$

6. $\left(\dfrac{27}{64}\right)^{-2/3} = \left(\dfrac{64}{27}\right)^{2/3} = \left(\sqrt[3]{\dfrac{64}{27}}\right)^2 = \left(\dfrac{4}{3}\right)^2 = \dfrac{16}{9}$

7. $-125^{-1/3} = -\left(\dfrac{1}{125^{1/3}}\right) = -\dfrac{1}{\sqrt[3]{125}} = -\dfrac{1}{5}$

8. $-8^{2/3} = -[(\sqrt[3]{8})^2] = -(2^2) = -4$

9. $(16^{-5})^{1/20} = 16^{-5 \cdot (1/20)} = 16^{-1/4} = \dfrac{1}{16^{1/4}} = \dfrac{1}{\sqrt[4]{16}} = \dfrac{1}{2}$

10. $(5^{1/2})^{-2} = 5^{1/2(-2)} = 5^{-1} = \dfrac{1}{5}$

11. $(9^{1/2} + 16^{1/2})^2 = (\sqrt{9} + \sqrt{16})^2 = (3 + 4)^2 = 7^2 = 49$

12. $(8^{2/3} - 8^{1/3})^3 = [(\sqrt[3]{8})^2 - \sqrt[3]{8}]^3 = (2^2 - 2)^3 = (4 - 2)^3 = 2^3 = 8$

13. $\sqrt{x^3 y^5} = (x^3 y^5)^{1/2} = x^{3 \cdot (1/2)} y^{5 \cdot (1/2)} = x^{3/2} y^{5/2}$

14. $\sqrt{a^{-2} b^3} = (a^{-2} b^3)^{1/2} = a^{-2 \cdot (1/2)} b^{3 \cdot (1/2)} = a^{-1} b^{3/2}$

15. $\sqrt[3]{p^4 q} = (p^4 q)^{1/3} = p^{4 \cdot (1/3)} q^{1/3} = p^{4/3} q^{1/3}$

16. $(\sqrt{a^{-2} b})^5 = [(a^{-2} b)^{1/2}]^5 = (a^{-2} b)^{(1/2) \cdot 5} = (a^{-2} b)^{5/2} = a^{-2 \cdot (5/2)} b^{5/2} = a^{-5} b^{5/2}$

17. $\sqrt[3]{8 b^6 c^{-4}} = (8 b^6 c^{-4})^{1/3} = 8^{1/3} b^{6 \cdot (1/3)} c^{-4 \cdot (1/3)} = 2 b^2 c^{-4/3}$

18. $\sqrt[4]{\dfrac{16^3 \cdot a^{-2}}{b^6}} = (16^3 a^{-2} b^{-6})^{1/4} = 16^{3 \cdot (1/4)} a^{-2 \cdot (1/4)} b^{-6 \cdot (1/4)} = 16^{3/4} a^{-1/2} b^{-3/2} =$
    $(\sqrt[4]{16})^3 a^{-1/2} b^{-3/2} = 8 a^{-1/2} b^{-3/2}$

19. $2\sqrt{2} = 2^1 \cdot 2^{1/2} = 2^{1+(1/2)} = 2^{3/2}$

20. $9\sqrt{3} = 3^2 \cdot 3^{1/2} = 3^{2+(1/2)} = 3^{5/2}$

21. $2\sqrt[3]{4} = 2^1 \cdot \sqrt[3]{2^2} = 2^1 \cdot 2^{2/3} = 2^{1+(2/3)} = 2^{5/3}$

22. $\sqrt{125} = \sqrt{5^3} = 5^{3/2}$

23. $\sqrt{0.001} = \sqrt{10^{-3}} = 10^{-3/2}$

24. $\dfrac{\sqrt{2}}{8} = \dfrac{2^{1/2}}{2^3} = 2^{1/2} \cdot 2^{-3} = 2^{(1/2)+(-3)} = 2^{-5/2}$

25. $\sqrt{\sqrt[3]{7}} = (7^{1/3})^{1/2} = 7^{(1/3) \cdot (1/2)} = 7^{1/6}$

26. $\sqrt[3]{\sqrt[4]{5}} = (5^{1/4})^{1/3} = 5^{(1/4) \cdot (1/3)} = 5^{1/12}$

27. $9^{1/3} \cdot 9^{1/6} = (3^2)^{1/3}(3^2)^{1/6} = 3^{2 \cdot (1/3)} \cdot 3^{2 \cdot (1/6)} = 3^{2/3} \cdot 3^{1/3} = 3^{(2/3)+(1/3)} = 3^1$

28. $\sqrt{5^{-1}} \cdot \sqrt[3]{25} = (5^{-1})^{1/2} \cdot \sqrt[3]{5^2} = 5^{-1 \cdot (1/2)} \cdot 5^{2/3} = 5^{-1/2} \cdot 5^{2/3} = 5^{-(1/2)+(2/3)} = 5^{1/6}$

29. $9 \cdot \sqrt{\sqrt[3]{9}} = 9\sqrt{\sqrt[3]{3^2}} = 9\sqrt{3^{2/3}} = 9(3^{2/3})^{1/2} = 9(3^{(2/3) \cdot (1/2)})3^2 \cdot 3^{1/3} = 3^{2+(1/3)} = 3^{7/3}$

30. $16^{2/3} \div 16^{1/6} = (2^4)^{2/3} \div (2^4)^{1/6} = 2^{4 \cdot (2/3)} \div 2^{4 \cdot (1/6)} = 2^{8/3} \div 2^{2/3} = 2^{(8/3)-(2/3)} = 2^2$

31. $\sqrt[3]{4} \cdot \sqrt[6]{4} = \sqrt[3]{2^2} \cdot \sqrt[6]{2^2} = 2^{2/3} \cdot 2^{2/6} = 2^{(2/3)+(1/3)} = 2^1 = 2$

32. $\sqrt{8} \cdot \sqrt[6]{8} = \sqrt{2^3} \cdot \sqrt[6]{2^3} = 2^{3/2} \cdot 2^{3/6} = 2^{(3/2)+(1/2)} = 2^2 = 4$

33. $\dfrac{\sqrt[3]{4}}{\sqrt[6]{2}} = \dfrac{\sqrt[3]{2^2}}{\sqrt[6]{2}} = \dfrac{2^{2/3}}{2^{1/6}} = 2^{(2/3)-(1/6)} = 2^{1/2} = \sqrt{2}$

34. $\dfrac{\sqrt[5]{27^3}}{\sqrt[5]{9^2}} = \dfrac{\sqrt[5]{(3^3)^3}}{\sqrt[5]{(3^2)^2}} = \dfrac{\sqrt[5]{3^{3 \cdot 3}}}{\sqrt[5]{3^{2 \cdot 2}}} = \dfrac{\sqrt[5]{3^9}}{\sqrt[5]{3^4}} = \dfrac{3^{9/5}}{3^{4/5}} = 3^{(9/5)-(4/5)} = 3^1 = 3$

35. $\sqrt[10]{32} \div \sqrt[8]{4} = \sqrt[10]{2^5} \div \sqrt[8]{2^2} = 2^{5/10} \div 2^{2/8} = 2^{(1/2)-(1/4)} = 2^{1/4} = \sqrt[4]{2}$

36. $\sqrt[6]{8^3} \div \sqrt[6]{4^2} = \sqrt[6]{(2^3)^3} \div \sqrt[6]{(2^2)^2} = \sqrt[6]{2^{3 \cdot 3}} \div \sqrt[6]{2^{2 \cdot 2}} = \sqrt[6]{2^9} \div \sqrt[6]{2^4} = 2^{9/6} \div 2^{4/6} =$
$2^{(9/6)-(4/6)} = 2^{5/6} = \sqrt[6]{2^5} = \sqrt[6]{32}$

37. $\sqrt[4]{27} \cdot \sqrt[8]{9} = \sqrt[4]{3^3} \cdot \sqrt[8]{3^2} = 3^{3/4} \cdot 3^{2/8} = 3^{(3/4)+(1/4)} = 3^1 = 3$

38. $\sqrt[4]{128} \cdot \sqrt[8]{256} = \sqrt[4]{2^7} \cdot \sqrt[8]{2^8} = 2^{7/4} \cdot 2^{8/8} = 2^{(7/4)+1} = 2^{11/4} = 2^{(8/4)+(3/4)} = 2^2 \cdot 2^{3/4} =$
$4\sqrt[4]{2^3} = 4\sqrt[4]{8}$

B 39. $\sqrt{x} \cdot \sqrt[3]{x} \cdot \sqrt[6]{x} = x^{1/2} \cdot x^{1/3} \cdot x^{1/6} = x^{(1/2)+(1/3)+(1/6)} = x$

40. $\sqrt[3]{a^2} \cdot \sqrt[3]{a^4} = a^{2/3} \cdot a^{4/3} = a^{(2/3)+(4/3)} = a^2$

41. $\sqrt[4]{x} \cdot \sqrt[6]{x} \div \sqrt[3]{x} = x^{1/4} \cdot x^{1/6} \div x^{1/3} = x^{(1/4)+(1/6)-(1/3)} = x^{1/12}$

42. $((b^{1/2})^{-2/3})^{-3/4} = (b^{1/2(-2/3)})^{-3/4} = b^{-1/3(-3/4)} = b^{1/4}$

43. $a^{1/2}(a^{3/2} - 2a^{1/2}) = a^{1/2} \cdot a^{3/2} - 2a^{1/2} \cdot a^{1/2} = a^{(1/2)+(3/2)} - 2a^{(1/2)+(1/2)} = a^2 - 2a$

44. $(x^{3/2} - 2x^{5/2}) \div x^{1/2} = \dfrac{x^{3/2}}{x^{1/2}} - \dfrac{2x^{5/2}}{x^{1/2}} = x^{(3/2)-(1/2)} - 2x^{(5/2)-(1/2)} = x - 2x^2$

45. $y^{-1/2} = 16; (y^{-1/2})^{-2} = 16^{-2}; y = \dfrac{1}{16^2} = \dfrac{1}{256}$

46. $4y^{-1/2} = 16; y^{-1/2} = 4; (y^{-1/2})^{-2} = 4^{-2}; y = \dfrac{1}{4^2} = \dfrac{1}{16}$

47. $(4y)^{-1/2} = 16; [(4y)^{-1/2}]^{-2} = 16^{-2}; 4y = \dfrac{1}{16^2}; 4y = \dfrac{1}{256}; y = \dfrac{1}{1024}$

48. $t^{-2/3} = 4; (t^{-2/3})^{-3/2} = 4^{-3/2}; t = \dfrac{1}{4^{3/2}} = \dfrac{1}{8}$

49. $(x^2 + 9)^{1/2} = 5; [(x^2 + 9)^{1/2}]^2 = 5^2; x^2 + 9 = 25; x^2 = 16; x = 4 \text{ or } x = -4$

50. $(3x - 1)^{4/3} = 16; [(3x - 1)^{4/3}]^{3/4} = 16^{3/4}; 3x - 1 = 8; 3x = 9; x = 3$

C 51. $t^{1/2} + 4t^{-1/2} = 5; t^{1/2}(t^{1/2} + 4t^{-1/2}) = 5t^{1/2}; t + 4 = 5t^{1/2}; (t + 4)^2 = (5t^{1/2})^2;$
$t^2 + 8t + 16 = 25t; t^2 - 17t + 16 = 0; (t - 16)(t - 1) = 0; t = 16 \text{ or } t = 1$

52. $s^{1/4} + 2s^{-1/4} = 3$; $(s^{1/4} + 2s^{-1/4})^2 = 3^2$; $s^{1/2} + 4 + 4s^{-1/2} = 9$; $s^{1/2} + 4s^{-1/2} = 5$;
$s^{1/2}(s^{1/2} + 4s^{-1/2}) = 5s^{1/2}$; $s + 4 = 5s^{1/2}$; $(s + 4)^2 = (5s^{1/2})^2$; $s^2 + 8s + 16 = 25s$;
$s^2 - 17s + 16 = 0$; $(s - 16)(s - 1) = 0$; $s = 16$ or $s = 1$

53. $w^{1/3} - 2w^{1/6} = -1$; $w^{1/3} - 2w^{1/6} + 1 = 0$; $(w^{1/6} - 1)^2 = 0$; $w^{1/6} = 1$; $(w^{1/6})^6 = 1^6$; $w = 1$

Pages 435-436 · WRITTEN EXERCISES

A **1. a.** $5^{\sqrt{2}} \cdot 5^{\sqrt{2}} = 5^{\sqrt{2}+\sqrt{2}} = 5^{2\sqrt{2}}$ **b.** $(5^{\sqrt{2}})^{\sqrt{2}} = 5^{\sqrt{2}\cdot\sqrt{2}} = 5^2 = 25$

 c. $\dfrac{5^{\sqrt{2}+2}}{5^{\sqrt{2}-2}} = 5^{\sqrt{2}+2-(\sqrt{2}-2)} = 5^4 = 625$

2. a. $7^{\sqrt{3}} \cdot 7^{\sqrt{2}} = 7^{\sqrt{3}+\sqrt{2}}$ **b.** $(7^{\sqrt{3}})^{\sqrt{2}} = 7^{\sqrt{3}\cdot\sqrt{2}} = 7^{\sqrt{6}}$

 c. $\dfrac{7^{\sqrt{3}+2}}{49} = \dfrac{7^{\sqrt{3}+2}}{7^2} = 7^{\sqrt{3}+2-2} = 7^{\sqrt{3}}$

3. $(8^\pi)^2 = 8^{2\pi}$ **4.** $\sqrt{6^{2\pi}} = 6^{2\pi/2} = 6^\pi$ **5.** $\sqrt[3]{4^{6\pi}} = 4^{6\pi/3} = 4^{2\pi}$

6. $\dfrac{10^{\sqrt{3}-2}}{10^{\sqrt{3}+2}} = 10^{\sqrt{3}-2-(\sqrt{3}+2)} = 10^{-4} = 0.0001$

7. $\sqrt[4]{\dfrac{9^{1-\pi}}{9^{1+\pi}}} = \sqrt[4]{9^{1-\pi-(1+\pi)}} = \sqrt[4]{9^{-2\pi}} = 9^{-2\pi/4} = 9^{-\pi/2} = (3^2)^{-\pi/2} = 3^{-\pi} = \dfrac{1}{3^\pi}$

8. $\dfrac{6^{\sqrt{2}} \cdot 6^{\sqrt{8}}}{6^{3\sqrt{2}}} = 6^{\sqrt{2}+\sqrt{8}-3\sqrt{2}} = 6^{\sqrt{2}+2\sqrt{2}-3\sqrt{2}} = 6^0 = 1$

9. $(2^{\sqrt{2}})^{-1/\sqrt{2}} = 2^{\sqrt{2}(-1/\sqrt{2})} = 2^{-1} = \dfrac{1}{2}$

10. $8^{1.2} \cdot 2^{-3.6} = (2^3)^{1.2} \cdot 2^{-3.6} = 2^{3.6} \cdot 2^{-3.6} = 2^0 = 1$

11. $[(\sqrt{2})^\pi]^0 = (\sqrt{2})^{\pi\cdot 0} = (\sqrt{2})^0 = 1$

12. $\dfrac{25^{2.4}}{5^{5.8}} = \dfrac{(5^2)^{2.4}}{5^{5.8}} = \dfrac{5^{4.8}}{5^{5.8}} = 5^{4.8-5.8} = 5^{-1} = \dfrac{1}{5}$

13. $\dfrac{(1+\sqrt{3})^{\pi-1}}{(1+\sqrt{3})^{\pi+1}} = (1+\sqrt{3})^{\pi-1-(\pi+1)} = (1+\sqrt{3})^{-2} = \dfrac{1}{(1+\sqrt{3})^2} = \dfrac{1}{4+2\sqrt{3}} = \dfrac{2-\sqrt{3}}{2}$

14. $\dfrac{(\sqrt{2}-1)^{2+\pi}}{(\sqrt{2}-1)^\pi} = (\sqrt{2}-1)^{2+\pi-\pi} = (\sqrt{2}-1)^2 = 3 - 2\sqrt{2}$

15. $3^x = \dfrac{1}{27}$; $3^x = 3^{-3}$; $x = -3$

16. $5^x = \sqrt{125}$; $5^x = \sqrt{5^3} = 5^{3/2}$; $x = \dfrac{3}{2}$

17. $8^{2+x} = 2$; $(2^3)^{2+x} = 2$; $2^{6+3x} = 2^1$; $3x + 6 = 1$; $3x = -5$; $x = -\dfrac{5}{3}$

18. $4^{1-x} = 8$; $(2^2)^{1-x} = 2^3$; $2^{2-2x} = 2^3$; $-2x + 2 = 3$; $2x = -1$; $x = -\dfrac{1}{2}$

19. $27^{2x-1} = 3$; $(3^3)^{2x-1} = 3$; $3^{6x-3} = 3^1$; $6x - 3 = 1$; $6x = 4$; $x = \dfrac{2}{3}$

20. $49^{x-2} = 7\sqrt{7}$; $(7^2)^{x-2} = 7 \cdot 7^{1/2}$; $7^{2x-4} = 7^{3/2}$; $2x - 4 = \dfrac{3}{2}$; $2x = \dfrac{11}{2}$; $x = \dfrac{11}{4}$

21. $4^{2x+5} = 16^{x+1}$; $(2^2)^{2x+5} = (2^4)^{x+1}$; $2^{4x+10} = 2^{4x+4}$; $4x + 10 = 4x + 4$; no solution

22. $3^{-(x+5)} = 9^{4x}$; $3^{-(x+5)} = (3^2)^{4x}$; $3^{-(x+5)} = 3^{8x}$; $-x - 5 = 8x$; $9x = -5$; $x = -\dfrac{5}{9}$

23.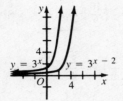

24.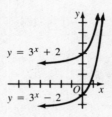

25. $25^{2x} = 5^{x+6}$; $(5^2)^{2x} = 5^{x+6}$; $5^{4x} = 5^{x+6}$; $4x = x + 6$; $3x = 6$; $x = 2$

26. $6^{x+1} = 36^{x-1}$; $6^{x+1} = (6^2)^{x-1}$; $6^{x+1} = 6^{2x-2}$; $2x - 2 = x + 1$; $x = 3$

27. $10^{x-1} = 100^{4-x}$; $10^{x-1} = (10^2)^{4-x}$; $10^{x-1} = 10^{8-2x}$; $x - 1 = 8 - 2x$; $3x = 9$; $x = 3$

28. Let $y = 3^x$; $y^2 - 6y + 9 = 0$; $(y - 3)^2 = 0$; $y - 3 = 0$; $y = 3$; $3^x = 3$; $x = 1$

29. Let $y_{\scriptscriptstyle{\bullet}} = 4^x$; $y^2 - 63y - 64 = 0$; $(y - 64)(y + 1) = 0$; $y = 64$ or
    $y = -1$ (reject); $4^x = 64$; $4^x = 4^3$; $x = 3$

30. Let $y = 3^x$; $y^2 - 10y + 9 = 0$; $(y - 9)(y - 1) = 0$; $y = 9$ or $y = 1$; $3^x = 9$ or $3^x = 1$;
    $3^x = 3^2$ or $3^x = 3^0$; $x = 2$ or $x = 0$

31. $2^{2x-1} - 3 \cdot 2^{x-1} + 1 = 0$; $\dfrac{2^{2x}}{2} - \dfrac{3 \cdot 2^x}{2} + 1 = 0$; let $y = 2^x$; $\dfrac{y^2}{2} - \dfrac{3y}{2} + 1 = 0$;

    $y^2 - 3y + 2 = 0$; $(y - 2)(y - 1) = 0$; $y = 2$ or $y = 1$; $2^x = 2$ or $2^x = 1$; $2^x = 2^1$ or
    $2^x = 2^0$; $x = 1$ or $x = 0$

32. $2^{(2/3)x+1} - 3 \cdot 2^{(1/3)x} - 20 = 0$; $2 \cdot 2^{(2/3)x} - 3 \cdot 2^{(1/3)x} - 20 = 0$; let $y = 2^{(1/3)x}$;

    $2y^2 - 3y - 20 = 0$; $(2y + 5)(y - 4) = 0$; $y = -\dfrac{5}{2}$ (reject) or $y = 4$; $2^{(1/3)x} = 4$;

    $2^{(1/3)x} = 2^2$; $\dfrac{1}{3}x = 2$; $x = 6$

33. $4^x - 9^x = 0$; $4^x = 9^x$; $\dfrac{4^x}{9^x} = 1$; $\left(\dfrac{4}{9}\right)^x = 1$; $\left(\dfrac{4}{9}\right)^x = \left(\dfrac{4}{9}\right)^0$; $x = 0$

Pages 440-441 · WRITTEN EXERCISES

A 1. **a.** $f(g(6)) = f(6 - 3) = f(3) = \dfrac{3}{2}$ **b.** $f(g(-4)) = f(-4 - 3) = f(-7) = -\dfrac{7}{2}$

   c. $f(g(0)) = f(0 - 3) = f(-3) = -\dfrac{3}{2}$ **d.** $f(g(x)) = f(x - 3) = \dfrac{x - 3}{2}$

2. **a.** $g(f(6)) = g\left(\dfrac{6}{2}\right) = g(3) = 3 - 3 = 0$

   b. $g(f(-4)) = g\left(\dfrac{-4}{2}\right) = g(-2) = -2 - 3 = -5$

   c. $g(f(0)) = g\left(\dfrac{0}{2}\right) = g(0) = 0 - 3 = -3$ **d.** $g(f(x)) = g\left(\dfrac{x}{2}\right) = \dfrac{x}{2} - 3$

3. a. $f(h(9)) = f(\sqrt{9}) = f(3) = \dfrac{3}{2}$ **b.** $f(h(4)) = f(\sqrt{4}) = f(2) = \dfrac{2}{2} = 1$

    c. $f(h(-4)) = f(\sqrt{-2})$; no real value   **d.** $f(h(x)) = f(\sqrt{x}) = \dfrac{\sqrt{x}}{2}$

4. a. $h(f(50)) = h\left(\dfrac{50}{2}\right) = h(25) = \sqrt{25} = 5$ **b.** $h(f(16)) = h\left(\dfrac{16}{2}\right) = h(8) = \sqrt{8} = 2\sqrt{2}$

    c. $h(f(x)) = h\left(\dfrac{x}{2}\right) = \sqrt{\dfrac{x}{2}} = \dfrac{\sqrt{2x}}{2}$ **d.** $f(f(x)) = f\left(\dfrac{x}{2}\right) = \dfrac{\frac{x}{2}}{2} = \dfrac{x}{4}$

5. a. $h(g(7)) = h(7 - 3) = h(4) = \sqrt{4} = 2$ **b.** $h(g(2)) = h(2 - 3) = h(-1) = \sqrt{-1}$;

                                                no real value

    c. $h(g(x)) = h(x - 3) = \sqrt{x - 3}$ **d.** $h(h(x)) = h(\sqrt{x}) = \sqrt{\sqrt{x}} = \sqrt[4]{x}$

6. a. $g(h(9)) = g(\sqrt{9}) = g(3) = 3 - 3 = 0$ **b.** $g(h(\sqrt{3})) = g(\sqrt{\sqrt{3}}) = g(\sqrt[4]{3}) = \sqrt[4]{3} - 3$

    c. $g(h(x)) = g(\sqrt{x}) = \sqrt{x} - 3$ **d.** $g(g(x)) = g(x - 3) = x - 3 - 3 = x - 6$

7. $y = 2x - 3$; $x = 2y - 3$; $2y = x + 3$; $y = \dfrac{x + 3}{2}$; $f^{-1}(x) = \dfrac{x + 3}{2}$

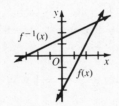

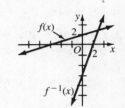

               Ex. 7   **Ex. 8**

8. $y = \dfrac{x + 6}{3}$; $x = \dfrac{y + 6}{3}$; $3x = y + 6$; $y = 3x - 6$; $f^{-1}(x) = 3x - 6$

9. $y = x^3$; $x = y^3$; $y = \sqrt[3]{x}$; $f^{-1}(x) = \sqrt[3]{x}$

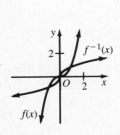

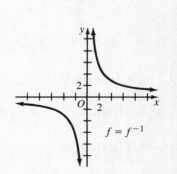

               Ex. 9   **Ex. 10**

10. $y = \dfrac{12}{x}$; $x = \dfrac{12}{y}$; $y = \dfrac{12}{x}$; $f^{-1}(x) = \dfrac{12}{x}$

11. Since g is not one-to-one, g has no inverse.

12. $y = 2x^3 + 1;\ x = 2y^3 + 1;\ 2y^3 = x - 1;\ y^3 = \dfrac{x-1}{2};\ y = \sqrt[3]{\dfrac{x-1}{2}};$

$g^{-1}(x) = \sqrt[3]{\dfrac{x-1}{2}}$

13. $y = \left(\dfrac{4}{x}\right)^3;\ x = \left(\dfrac{4}{y}\right)^3;\ \sqrt[3]{x} = \dfrac{4}{y};\ y = \dfrac{4}{\sqrt[3]{x}};\ g^{-1}(x) = \dfrac{3}{\sqrt[3]{x}}$

14. Since g is not one-to-one, g does not have an inverse.

15. $y = (3x + 7)^5;\ x = (3y + 7)^5;\ \sqrt[5]{x} = 3y + 7;\ 3y = \sqrt[5]{x} - 7;\ y = \dfrac{\sqrt[5]{x} - 7}{3};$

$g^{-1}(x) = \dfrac{\sqrt[5]{x} - 7}{3}$

16. $y = \sqrt[3]{4x - 8};\ x = \sqrt[3]{4y - 8};\ x^3 = 4y - 8;\ 4y = x^3 + 8;\ y = \dfrac{x^3 + 8}{2};$

$g^{-1}(x) = \dfrac{x^3 + 8}{2}$

17. a-b.

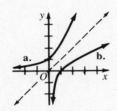

c. $f^{-1}(2) = 1;\ f^{-1}(4) = 2;\ f^{-1}(8) = 3;$

$f^{-1}\left(\dfrac{1}{2}\right) = -1$

d. f: domain = all real numbers; range = $\{y : y > 0\}$; f^{-1}: domain = $\{x : x > 0\}$; range = all real numbers

18. The inverse is $\{(x, x^2) : x \geq 0\}$; it is the function $f(x) = x^2$ with domain restricted to nonnegative numbers.

19. $y = mx + b;\ x = my + b;\ x - b = my;\ y = \dfrac{x - b}{m} = \dfrac{1}{m}x - \dfrac{b}{m};\ f(x) = f^{-1}(x)$ if and only if $m = \dfrac{1}{m}$ and $b = -\dfrac{b}{m};\ m^2 = 1,\ m = 1$ or $m = -1$; if $m = 1,\ b = -\dfrac{b}{1} = -b$, so $b = 0$; if $m = -1,\ b = -\dfrac{b}{-1} = b$, so b can take on any value; $m = 1$ and $b = 0$, or $m = -1$.

20. Let $f(x) = mx + b;\ f^{-1}(x) = \dfrac{1}{m}x - \dfrac{b}{m}$; if the graphs of f and f^{-1} are perpendicular; $m\left(\dfrac{1}{m}\right) = -1$ or $1 = -1$; thus the graphs of a linear function and its inverse are never perpendicular.

Pages 444-445 · WRITTEN EXERCISES

1. $\log_4 16 = \log_4 4^2 = 2$ **2.** $\log_5 125 = \log_5 5^3 = 3$ **3.** $\log_3 81 = \log_3 3^4 = 4$

4. $\log_2 32 = \log_2 2^5 = 5$ **5.** $\log_2 \dfrac{1}{8} = \log_2 2^{-3} = -3$ **6.** $\log_3 \dfrac{1}{9} = \log_3 3^{-2} = -2$

7. $\log_5 \dfrac{1}{25} = \log_5 5^{-2} = -2$ **8.** $\log_8 4 = \log_8 8^{2/3} = \dfrac{2}{3}$ **9.** $\log_6 6\sqrt{6} = \log_6 6^{3/2} = \dfrac{3}{2}$

10. $\log_5 25\sqrt{5} = \log_5 5^{5/2} = \dfrac{5}{2}$ **11.** $\log_4 \sqrt{2} = \log_4 4^{1/4} = \dfrac{1}{4}$

12. $\log_{27} \sqrt{3} = \log_{27} 27^{1/6} = \dfrac{1}{6}$ **13.** $\log_7 \sqrt[3]{49} = \log_7 7^{2/3} = \dfrac{2}{3}$

14. $\log_3 \sqrt[5]{9} = \log_3 3^{2/5} = \dfrac{2}{5}$ **15.** $\log_{1/2} 8 = \log_{1/2}\left(\dfrac{1}{2}\right)^{-3} = -3$

16. $\log_{1/3} 27 = \log_{1/3}\left(\dfrac{1}{3}\right)^{-3} = -3$ **17.** $\log_2 \sqrt[3]{\dfrac{1}{4}} = \log_2 2^{-2/3} = -\dfrac{2}{3}$

18. $\log_{10} \dfrac{1}{\sqrt{1000}} = \log_{10} 10^{-3/2} = -\dfrac{3}{2}$ **19.** $\log_8 x = 2;\ 8^2 = x;\ x = 64$

20. $\log_5 x = 3;\ 5^3 = x;\ x = 125$ **21.** $\log_{16} x = -\dfrac{1}{2};\ 16^{-1/2} = x;\ x = \dfrac{1}{4};$

22. $\log_6 x = 2.5;\ 6^{2.5} = x;\ x = 36\sqrt{6}$ **23.** $\log_4 x = -\dfrac{3}{2};\ 4^{-3/2} = x;\ x = \dfrac{1}{8}$

24. $\log_{1/9} x = -\dfrac{1}{2};\ \left(\dfrac{1}{9}\right)^{-1/2} = x;\ 9^{1/2} = x;\ x = 3$

B   **25.** $\log_x 27 = \dfrac{3}{2};\ x^{3/2} = 27;\ (x^{3/2})^{2/3} = 27^{2/3};\ x = 9$

26. $\log_x 2 = 2;\ x^2 = 2;\ x = \sqrt{2}$ or $x = -\sqrt{2}$ (reject); $x = \sqrt{2}$

27. $\log_x 5 = -\dfrac{1}{2};\ x^{-1/2} = 5;\ (x^{-1/2})^{-2} = 5^{-2};\ x = \dfrac{1}{25}$ **28.** $\log_x 7 = 1;\ x = 7$

29. $\log_x 1 = 0;\ x^0 = 1;$ true for all positive x except 1

30. $\log_x 2 = 0;\ x^0 = 2;$ no solution

31. a. $\log_2 8 = \log_2 2^3 = 3;\ \log_8 2 = \log_8 8^{1/3} = \dfrac{1}{3}$

    b. $\log_3 \sqrt{3} = \log_3 3^{1/2} = \dfrac{1}{2};\ \log_{\sqrt{3}} 3 = \log_{\sqrt{3}} (\sqrt{3})^2 = 2$

    c. For all positive numbers a and b, $a \neq 1$ and $b \neq 1$, $\log_b a = \dfrac{1}{\log_a b}$

32. a. $\log_2 8 + \log_2 4 = \log_2 2^3 + \log_2 2^2 = 3 + 2 = 5 = \log_2 2^5 = \log_2 32$

    b. $\log_9 3 + \log_9 27 = \log_9 9^{1/2} + \log_9 9^{3/2} = \dfrac{1}{2} + \dfrac{3}{2} = 2 = \log_9 9^2 = \log_9 81$

    c. For all positive numbers a, b, and c, $a \neq 1$, $\log_a b + \log_a c = \log_a bc$.

33. a. $\log_5 x$ **b.** f: domain = all real numbers, range = $\{y : y > 0\}$;

        f^{-1}: domain = $\{x : x > 0\}$, range = all real numbers

34. a. 3^x **b.** g: domain = $\{x : x > 0\}$, range = all real numbers;

        g^{-1}: domain = all real numbers; range = $\{y : y > 0\}$

35.

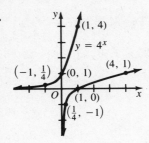

36.

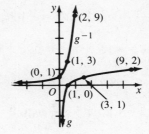

37.

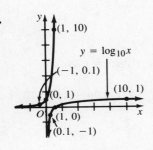

38.

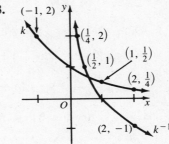

C 39. $\log_5(\log_3 x) = 0$; $\log_3 x = 5^0 = 1$; $3^1 = x$; $x = 3$

40. $\log_4(\log_3(\log_2 x)) = 0$; $\log_3(\log_2 x) = 4^0 = 1$; $3^1 = \log_2 x$; $\log_2 x = 3$; $2^3 = x$; $8 = x$

41. positive; for example, $\log_{1/3} \dfrac{1}{9} = \log_{1/3}\left(\dfrac{1}{3}\right)^2 = 2$

42. negative; for example, $\log_4(\log_4 2) = \log_4(\log_4 4^{1/2}) = \log_4 \dfrac{1}{2} = \log_4 4^{-1/2} = -\dfrac{1}{2}$

Page 449 · WRITTEN EXERCISES

A 1. $\log_2 M^5 N^4 = \log_2 M^5 + \log_2 N^4 = 5 \log_2 M + 4 \log_2 N$

2. $\log_2(MN)^3 = 3 \log_2 MN = 3(\log_2 M + \log_2 N) = 3 \log_2 M + 3 \log_2 N$

3. $\log_2 M\sqrt{N} = \log_2 M + \log_2 N^{1/2} = \log_2 M + \dfrac{1}{2} \log_2 N$

4. $\log_2 \sqrt[3]{M^2 N} = \log_2(M^2 N)^{1/3} = \dfrac{1}{3}(\log_2 M^2 N) = \dfrac{1}{3}(\log_2 M^2 + \log_2 N) =$
$\dfrac{1}{3}(2 \log_2 M + \log_2 N) = \dfrac{2}{3} \log_2 M + \dfrac{1}{3} \log_2 N$

5. $\log_2 \dfrac{M^4}{N^3} = \log_2 M^4 - \log_2 N^3 = 4 \log_2 M - 3 \log_2 N$

6. $\log_2\left(\dfrac{M}{N}\right)^5 = 5 \log_2 \dfrac{M}{N} = 5(\log_2 M - \log_2 N) = 5 \log_2 M - 5 \log_2 N$

7. $\log_2 \sqrt{\dfrac{M}{N^3}} = \log_2\left(\dfrac{M}{N^3}\right)^{1/2} = \dfrac{1}{2} \log_2 \dfrac{M}{N^3} = \dfrac{1}{2}(\log_2 M - \log_2 N^3) =$
$\dfrac{1}{2}(\log_2 M - 3 \log_2 N) = \dfrac{1}{2} \log_2 M - \dfrac{3}{2} \log_2 N$

8. $\log_2 \dfrac{1}{MN} = \log_2(MN)^{-1} = -1(\log_2 M + \log_2 N) = -\log_2 M - \log_2 N$

9. $\log_{10} 81 = \log_{10} 9 \cdot 9 = \log_{10} 9 + \log_{10} 9 = 0.95 + 0.95 = 1.90$

10. $\log_{10} \dfrac{9}{2} = \log_{10} 9 - \log_{10} 2 = 0.95 - 0.30 = 0.65$

11. $\log_{10} \sqrt{2} = \log_{10} 2^{1/2} = \dfrac{1}{2} \log_{10} 2 = \dfrac{1}{2}(0.30) = 0.15$

12. $\log_{10} 3 = \log_{10} 9^{1/2} = \dfrac{1}{2} \log_{10} 9 = \dfrac{1}{2}(0.95) = 0.48$

13. $\log_{10} 8 = \log_{10} 2^3 = 3 \log_{10} 2 = 3(0.30) = 0.90$

14. $\log_{10} 36 = \log_{10} 2^2 \cdot 9 = 2 \log_{10} 2 + \log_{10} 9 = 2(0.30) + 0.95 = 1.56$

15. $\log_{10} \dfrac{20}{9} = \log_{10} \dfrac{10 \cdot 2}{9} = \log_{10} 10 + \log_{10} 2 - \log_{10} 9 = 1 + 0.30 - 0.95 = 0.35$

16. $\log_{10} 900 = \log_{10} 10^2 \cdot 9 = 2 \log_{10} 10 + \log_{10} 9 = 2 + \log_{10} 9 = 2 + 0.95 = 2.95$

17. $\log_{10} \dfrac{1}{9} = \log_{10} 9^{-1} = -\log_{10} 9 = -0.95$

18. $\log_{10} \dfrac{1}{2000} = \log_{10}(10^3 \cdot 2)^{-1} = -\log_{10}(10^3 \cdot 2) = -(\log_{10} 10^3 + \log_{10} 2) =$

    $-\log_{10} 10^3 - \log_{10} 2 = -3 - 0.30 = -3.30$

19. $\log_{10} \sqrt[3]{\dfrac{2}{9}} = \log_{10}\left(\dfrac{2}{9}\right)^{1/3} = \log_{10} \dfrac{2^{1/3}}{9^{1/3}} = \dfrac{1}{3} \log_{10} 2 - \dfrac{1}{3} \log_{10} 9 =$

    $\dfrac{1}{3}(0.30 - 0.95) = -0.22$

20. $\log_{10} 162 = \log_{10} 2 \cdot 9^2 = \log_{10} 2 + 2 \log_{10} 9 = 0.30 + 2(0.95) = 2.20$

21. $3 \log_4 p + \log_4 q = \log_4 p^3 + \log_4 q = \log_4 p^3 q$

22. $\log_{10} x - 5 \log_{10} y = \log_{10} x - \log_{10} y^5 = \log_{10} \dfrac{x}{y^5}$

23. $2 \log_3 A - \dfrac{1}{2} \log_3 B = \log_3 A^2 - \log_3 B^{1/2} = \log_3 \dfrac{A^2}{\sqrt{B}}$

24. $\log_5 M + \dfrac{1}{3} \log_5 N = \log_5 M + \log_5 N^{1/3} = \log_5 M \sqrt[3]{N}$

B 25. $\log_2 M + \log_2 N + 3 = \log_2 M + \log_2 N + \log_2 8 = \log_2 8MN$

26. $\log_5 x - \log_5 y + 2 = \log_5 x - \log_5 y + \log_5 25 = \log_5 x + \log_5 25 - \log_5 y =$

    $\log_5 \dfrac{25x}{y}$

27. $1 - 3 \log_5 x = \log_5 5 - \log_5 x^3 = \log_5 \dfrac{5}{x^3}$

28. $\dfrac{1 + \log_9 x}{2} = \dfrac{1}{2} + \dfrac{1}{2} \log_9 x = \log_9 3 + \log_9 x^{1/2} = \log_9 3\sqrt{x}$

29. $2 \log_3 6 - \log_3 4 = \log_3 \dfrac{6^2}{4} = \log_3 9 = 2$

30. $2 \log_{10} 5 + \log_{10} 4 = \log_{10} 5^2 \cdot 4 = \log_{10} 100 = 2$

31. $\log_4 40 - \log_4 5 = \log_4 4 \cdot 2 \cdot 5 - \log_4 5 = \log_4 4 + \log_4 2 + \log_4 5 - \log_4 5 =$
$1 + \dfrac{1}{2} = \dfrac{3}{2}$

32. $\log_4 3 - \log_4 48 = \log_4 3 - \log_4 4^2 \cdot 3 = \log_4 3 - (\log_4 4^2 + \log_4 3) =$
$\log_4 3 - 2 - \log_4 3 = -2$

33. Let $\log_b M = x$ and $\log_b N = y$; $b^x = M$ and $b^y = N$; $\log_b \dfrac{M}{N} = \log_b \dfrac{b^x}{b^y} =$
$\log_b b^{x-y} = x - y = \log_b M - \log_b N$

34. $\log_a x = 2 \log_a 3 + \log_a 5$; $\log_a x = \log_a 3^2 + \log_a 5$; $\log_a x = \log_a 3^2 \cdot 5 = \log_a 45$;
$x = 45$

35. $\log_a x = \dfrac{3}{2} \log_a 9 + \log_a 2$; $\log_a x = \log_a 9^{3/2} + \log_a 2$; $\log_a x = \log_a 27 \cdot 2 = \log_a 54$;
$x = 54$

36. $\log_b(x + 3) = \log_b 8 - \log_b 2$; $\log_b(x + 3) = \log_b \dfrac{8}{2} = \log_b 4$; $x + 3 = 4$; $x = 1$

37. $\log_b(x^2 + 7) = \dfrac{2}{3} \log_b 64$; $\log_b(x^2 + 7) = \log_b 64^{2/3} = \log_b 16$; $x^2 + 7 = 16$; $x^2 = 9$;
$x = 3$ or $x = -3$

38. $\log_a x - \log_a(x - 5) = \log_a 6$; $\log_a \dfrac{x}{x - 5} = \log_a 6$; $\dfrac{x}{x - 5} = 6$; $x = 6x - 30$; $5x = 30$;
$x = 6$

39. $\log_a(3x + 5) - \log_a(x - 5) = \log_a 8$; $\log_a \dfrac{3x + 5}{x - 5} = \log_a 8$; $\dfrac{3x + 5}{x - 5} = 8$; $3x + 5 =$
$8x - 40$; $5x = 45$; $x = 9$

40. $\log_2(x^2 - 9) = 4$; $\log_2(x^2 - 9) = \log_2 16$; $x^2 - 9 = 16$; $x^2 = 25$; $x = 5$ or $x = -5$

41. $\log_3(x + 2) + \log_3 6 = 3$; $\log_3 6(x + 2) = \log_3 27$; $6x + 12 = 27$; $6x = 15$; $x = \dfrac{15}{6}$

C 42. $\log_6(x + 1) + \log_6 x = 1$; $\log_6 x(x + 1) = \log_6 6$; $x(x + 1) = 6$; $x^2 + x = 6$;
$x^2 + x - 6 = 0$; $(x + 3)(x - 2) = 0$; $x = -3$ (reject) or $x = 2$; $x = 2$

43. $\log_{10}(x + 6) + \log_{10}(x - 6) = 2$; $\log_{10}(x + 6)(x - 6) = \log_{10} 100$; $x^2 - 36 = 100$;
$x^2 = 136$; $x = -\sqrt{136}$ (reject) or $x = \sqrt{136}$; $x = 2\sqrt{34}$

44. $2 \log_3 x - \log_3(x - 2) = 2$; $\log_3 x^2 - \log_3(x - 2) = \log_3 9$; $\log_3 \dfrac{x^2}{x - 2} = \log_3 9$;
$\dfrac{x^2}{x - 2} = 9$; $x^2 = 9x - 18$; $x^2 - 9x + 18 = 0$; $(x - 6)(x - 3) = 0$; $x = 6$ or $x = 3$

45. $\dfrac{1}{2} \log_a(x + 2) + \dfrac{1}{2} \log_a(x - 2) = \dfrac{2}{3} \log_a 27$; $\log_a(x + 2)^{1/2} + \log_a(x - 2)^{1/2} =$
$\log_a 27^{2/3}$; $\log_a(\sqrt{x + 2} \cdot \sqrt{x - 2}) = \log_a 9$; $\sqrt{x + 2} \cdot \sqrt{x - 2} = 9$; $x^2 - 4 = 81$;
$x^2 = 85$; $x = -\sqrt{85}$ (reject) or $x = \sqrt{85}$; $x = \sqrt{85}$

46. $\log_b(x - 1) + \log_b(x + 2) = \log_b(8 - 2x)$; $\log_b(x - 1)(x + 2) = \log_b(8 - 2x)$;

$(x - 1)(x + 2) = 8 - 2x$; $x^2 + x - 2 = 8 - 2x$; $x^2 + 3x - 10 = 0$;

$(x + 5)(x - 2) = 0$; $x = -5$ (reject) or $x = 2$; $x = 2$

47. $4^{\log_2(2\log_2 5)} = 4^{\log_2 5} = (2^2)^{\log_2 5} = 2^{2\log_2 5} = 2^{\log_2 25} = 25$

Pages 454-455 · WRITTEN EXERCISES

1-28. Answers may vary.

A   **1.** Let $x = (1.08)^{10}$; $\log x = 10 \log 1.08 = 10(0.0334) = 0.334$; $x = 2.16$

2. Let $x = \sqrt[5]{786}$; $\log x = \dfrac{1}{5} \log 786 = \dfrac{1}{5}(\log 100 + \log 7.86) = \dfrac{1}{5}(2 + 0.8954) = 0.5791$; $x = 3.79$

3. Let $x = (347)^{1.5}$; $\log x = 1.5(\log 100 + \log 3.47) = 1.5(2 + 0.5403) = 3.810$; $x = 6460$

4. Let $x = (12.7)^{5/2}$; $\log x = \dfrac{5}{2} \log 12.7 = \dfrac{5}{2}(\log 10 + \log 1.27) = \dfrac{5}{2}(1 + 0.1038) = 2.760$; $x = 575$

5. Let $x = \sqrt[3]{(412)^2}$; $\log x = \dfrac{2}{3} \log 412 = \dfrac{2}{3}(\log 100 + \log 4.12) = \dfrac{2}{3}(2 + 0.6149) = 1.743$; $x = 55.3$

6. Let $x = \sqrt[5]{(81.2)^4}$; $\log x = \dfrac{4}{5} \log 81.2 = \dfrac{4}{5}(\log 10 + \log 8.12) = \dfrac{4}{5}(1 + 0.9096) = 1.527$; $x = 33.7$

7. a. $\log 5^x = \log 9$; $x \log 5 = \log 9$; $x = \dfrac{\log 9}{\log 5}$ **b.** $x = \dfrac{0.9542}{0.6990} = 1.37$

8. a. $\log 4.2^t = \log 6$; $t \log 4.2 = \log 6$; $t = \dfrac{\log 6}{\log 4.2}$ **b.** $t = \dfrac{0.7782}{0.6232} = 1.25$

9. a. $\log 8^x = \log 3$; $x \log 8 = \log 3$; $x = \dfrac{\log 3}{\log 8}$ **b.** $x = \dfrac{0.4771}{0.9031} = 0.528$

10. a. $\log(1.02)^x = \log 2$; $x \log 1.02 = \log 2$; $x = \dfrac{\log 2}{\log 1.02}$ **b.** $x = \dfrac{0.3010}{0.0086} = 35.0$

11. a. $\log 30^{-x} = \log 5$; $-x \log 30 = \log 5$; $x = -\dfrac{\log 5}{\log 30}$ **b.** $x = -\dfrac{0.6990}{1.4771} = -0.473$

12. a. $\log 12^{2x} = \log 1000$; $2x \log 12 = 3$; $2x = \dfrac{3}{\log 12}$; $x = \dfrac{3}{2 \log 12}$

b. $x = \dfrac{3}{2(1.0792)} = 1.39$

13. a. $\log 3.5^t = \log 60$; $t \log 3.5 = \log 60$; $t = \dfrac{\log 60}{\log 3.5}$ **b.** $t = \dfrac{1.7782}{0.5441} = 3.27$

14. a. $\log \dfrac{4^{2-t}}{3} = \log 7$; $\log 4^{2-t} - \log 3 = \log 7$; $(2 - t) \log 4 = \log 7 + \log 3$;

$2 - t = \dfrac{\log 7 + \log 3}{\log 4}$; $t = 2 - \dfrac{\log 7 + \log 3}{\log 4}$

b. $t = 2 - \dfrac{0.8451 + 0.4771}{0.6021} = -0.196$

15. $x^{2/5} = 22$; $(x^{2/5})^{5/2} = 22^{5/2}$; $x = 22^{5/2}$; $\log x = \dfrac{5}{2} \log 22 = \dfrac{5}{2}(1.3424) = 3.356$;
$x = 2270$

16. $x^{2/3} = 75$; $(x^{2/3})^{3/2} = 75^{3/2}$; $x = 75^{3/2}$; $\log x = \dfrac{3}{2} \log 75 = \dfrac{3}{2}(1.8751) = 2.8127$; $x = 650$

17. $x^{4/3} = 60$; $(x^{4/3})^{3/4} = 60^{3/4}$; $x = 60^{3/4}$; $\log x = \dfrac{3}{4} \log 60 = \dfrac{3}{4}(1.7782) = 1.3337$; $x = 21.6$

18. $x^{3/5} = 700$; $(x^{3/5})^{5/3} = 700^{5/3}$; $x = 700^{5/3}$; $\log x = \dfrac{5}{3} \log 700 = \dfrac{5}{3}(2.8451) = 4.7418$;
$x = 55{,}200$

B **19.** $2x^5 = 100$; $x^5 = 50$; $(x^5)^{1/5} = 50^{1/5}$; $x = 50^{1/5}$;

$\log x = \dfrac{1}{5} \log 50 = \dfrac{1}{5}(1.6990) = 0.3398$; $x = 2.19$

20. $\dfrac{\sqrt[5]{x}}{9} = 7$; $\sqrt[5]{x} = 63$; $(\sqrt[5]{x})^5 = 63^5$; $x = 63^5$; $\log x = 5 \log 63 = 5(1.7993) = 8.9965$;
$x = 992{,}000{,}000$

21. $(3t - 1)^6 = 80$; $[(3t - 1)^6]^{1/6} = 80^{1/6}$;

$3t - 1 = 80^{1/6}$; $\log(3t - 1) = \dfrac{1}{6} \log 80 = \dfrac{1}{6}(1.9031) = 0.3172$; $3t - 1 = 2.08$;
$3t = 3.08$; $t = 1.03$

22. $\sqrt[3]{4y + 3} = 8.15$; $(\sqrt[3]{4y + 3})^3 = 8.15^3$; $4y + 3 = 8.15^3$;
$\log(4y + 3) = 3 \log 8.15 = 3(0.9112) = 2.7336$; $4y + 3 = 542$; $4y = 539$; $y = 135$

23. Let $y = 3^x$; $y^2 - 7y + 10 = 0$; $(y - 5)(y - 2) = 0$; $y = 5$ or $y = 2$; if $y = 5$, $3^x = 5$;

$\log 3^x = \log 5$; $x \log 3 = \log 5$; $x = \dfrac{\log 5}{\log 3} = \dfrac{0.6990}{0.4771} = 1.47$; if $y = 2$, $3^x = 2$;

$x = \dfrac{\log 2}{\log 3} = \dfrac{0.3010}{0.4771} = 0.631$; $\{1.47, 0.631\}$

24. Let $y = 3^x$; $y^2 - 7y + 12 = 0$; $(y - 4)(y - 3) = 0$; $y = 4$ or $y = 3$; if $y = 4$, $3^x = 4$;

$\log 3^x = \log 4$; $x \log 3 = \log 4$; $x = \dfrac{\log 4}{\log 3} = \dfrac{0.6021}{0.4771} = 1.26$; if $y = 3$, $3^x = 3$; $x = 1$;
$\{1.26, 1\}$

25. $\log_2 9 = \dfrac{\log 9}{\log 2} = \dfrac{0.9542}{0.3010} = 3.1701$

26. $\log_6 8 = \dfrac{\log 8}{\log 6} = \dfrac{0.9031}{0.7782} = 1.1605$

27. $\log_3 40 = \dfrac{\log 40}{\log 3} = \dfrac{1.6021}{0.4771} = 3.3580$

28. $\log_7 \dfrac{1}{2} = \dfrac{\log \dfrac{1}{2}}{\log 7} = \dfrac{-0.3010}{0.8451} = -0.3562$

C 29. By the change-of-base formula, $\log_a b = \dfrac{\log_b b}{\log_b a} = \dfrac{1}{\log_b a}$.

30. Let $\log_b x = y$ and $\log_b a = z$; $b^y = x$ and $b^z = a$; then $a^{y/z} = (b^z)^{y/z} = b^y = x$, so

$$\log_a x = \frac{y}{z} = \frac{\log_b x}{\log_b a}.$$

Page 455 · CALCULATOR KEY-IN

1-2. Answers may vary.

1. a. $(1.36)^x = 18$; $\log(1.36)^x = \log 18$; $x \log 1.36 = \log 18$; $x = \dfrac{\log 18}{\log 1.36} = 9.40$

b. $x = \dfrac{\log 52}{\log 2.15} = 5.16$ **c.** $x = \dfrac{\log 1.49}{\log 5.16} = 0.243$ **d.** $x = \dfrac{\log 0.157}{\log 4.98} = -1.15$

2. a. 6.47   **b.** 45.1   **c.** 0.288

Pages 458-460 · PROBLEMS

The calculations in this section are given to enough places to ensure three-significant-digit accuracy in the final answers. Students using tables may obtain answers that differ in the third significant digit.

A 1. $x = 5 \cdot 2^{-(4.2/3.8)} = 5 \cdot 2^{-1.105}$;

$\log x = \log 5 - 1.105 \log 2 = 0.6990 - 1.105(0.3010) = 0.3664$; $x = 2.32$; 2.32 g

2. $A = 2400\left(1 + \dfrac{0.12}{4}\right)^{4 \cdot (9/2)} = 2400(1.03)^{18}$;

$\log A = \log 2400 + 18 \log 1.03 = 3.38021 + 18(0.01284) = 3.6113$; $A = 4086$;   \$409

3. $30{,}000 = 10{,}000\left(1 + \dfrac{0.12}{12}\right)^{12t}$; $3 = (1.01)^{2t}$; $\log 3 = \log(1.01)^{12t} = 12t \log 1.01$;

$t = \dfrac{\log 3}{12 \log 1.01} = \dfrac{0.4771}{12(0.0043)} = 9.25$; 9 yr and 3 mo

4. $4 \times 10^5 = 3 \times 10^5 \cdot 2^{2k}$; $\dfrac{4}{3} = 2^{2k}$; $2k \log 2 = \log \dfrac{4}{3}$;

$k = \dfrac{\log 4 - \log 3}{2 \log 2} = \dfrac{0.6021 - 0.4771}{2(0.3010)} = 0.208$; $6 \times 10^5 = 3 \times 10^5 \cdot 2^{0.208t}$; $2 = 2^{0.208t}$;

$0.208t = 1$; $t = \dfrac{1}{0.208} = 4.81$; approximately 4:49 P.M.

B 5. $k = \dfrac{1}{50}$; $3n_0 = n_0 \cdot 2^{t/50}$; $3 = 2^{t/50}$; $\dfrac{t}{50} \log 2 = \log 3$;

$t = \dfrac{50 \log 3}{\log 2} = \dfrac{50(0.47711)}{0.30103} = 79.246$; 79.2 yr

6. $8.5 = 10 \cdot 2^{-(2.93/h)}$; $0.85 = 2^{-(2.93/h)}$; $-\dfrac{2.93}{h} \log 2 = \log 0.85$;

$h = \dfrac{-2.93 \log 2}{\log 0.85} = \dfrac{-2.93(0.3010)}{-0.0706} = 12.5$ yr

7. $4 = 3\left(1 + \dfrac{r}{4}\right)^{4 \cdot 5}$; $\dfrac{4}{3} = \left(1 + \dfrac{r}{4}\right)^{20}$; $\left(\dfrac{4}{3}\right)^{1/20} = \left[\left(1 + \dfrac{r}{4}\right)^{20}\right]^{1/20}$; $\dfrac{r}{4} + 1 = \left(\dfrac{4}{3}\right)^{1/20}$;

$\log\left(\dfrac{r}{4} + 1\right) = \dfrac{1}{20}\log\dfrac{4}{3} = \dfrac{1}{20}(0.124938) = 0.006247$; $\dfrac{r}{4} + 1 = 1.014488$; $\dfrac{r}{4} = 0.014488$;

$r = 0.05795$; 5.80%

8. $h = 2$; $0.1x = 0.5x \cdot 2^{-(t/2)}$; $\dfrac{1}{5} = 2^{-(t/2)}$; $-\dfrac{t}{2}\log 2 = \log\dfrac{1}{5}$;

$t = -2\,\dfrac{\log\dfrac{1}{5}}{\log 2} = \dfrac{-2(-0.6990)}{0.3010} = 4.64$; 4.64 min, or 4 min 39 sec

9. $A = \left[2000\left(1 + \dfrac{0.10}{4}\right)^{4 \cdot 2}\right]\left(1 + \dfrac{0.13}{2}\right)^{3 \cdot 2} = 2000(1.025)^8(1.065)^6$; $\log A =$

$\log 2000 + 8\log 1.025 + 6\log 1.065 = 3.3010 + 8(0.0107) + 6(0.0273) = 3.5504$;

$A = 3550$; \$3550

10. $0.92x_0 = x_0 \cdot 2^{-(1/h)}$; $0.92 = 2^{-(1/h)}$; $-\dfrac{1}{h}\log 2 = \log 0.92$; $-\dfrac{1}{h} = \dfrac{\log 0.92}{\log 2} = \dfrac{-0.0362}{0.3010} =$

-0.1203; $x = 12{,}000 \cdot 2^{t(-1/h)} = 12{,}000 \cdot 2^{6.25(-0.1203)} = 12{,}000 \cdot 2^{-0.752}$;

$\log x = \log 12{,}000 - 0.752\log 2 = 4.0792 - 0.752(0.3010) = 3.8528$; $x = 7130$; \$7130

11. $1\left(1 + \dfrac{0.12}{4}\right)^4 = 1.03^4 = 1.1255$; $1.1255 - 1 = 0.1255$; 12.55%

C **12. a.** $I = 10^{12}I_0$; $D = 10\log\left(\dfrac{I}{I_0}\right) = 10\log 10^{12} = 10 \cdot 12 = 120$; 120 dB

    b. Let I_s and I_c be the intensities of the noises of subway trains and normal

       conversations, respectively; $100 = 10\log\dfrac{I_s}{I_0}$; $\log\dfrac{I_s}{I_0} = 10$; $\dfrac{I_s}{I_0} = 10^{10}$; $I_s = 10^{10}I_0$;

       $60 = 10\log\dfrac{I_c}{I_0}$; $\log\dfrac{I_c}{I_0} = 6$; $\dfrac{I_c}{I_0} = 10^6$; $I_c = 10^6I_0$; $I_s = 10^{10}I_0 = 10^4 \cdot 10^6I_0 = 10^4I_c$; the

       noise of a subway train is 10,000 times as intense as normal conversation.

13. $1.2n_0 = 2^{4k}n_0$; $1.2 = 2^{4k}$; $4k\log 2 = \log 1.2$; $k = \dfrac{\log 1.2}{4\log 2} = \dfrac{0.0792}{4(0.3010)} = 0.066$;

original doubling time $= \dfrac{1}{0.066}$; new doubling time $= \dfrac{3}{0.066} = \dfrac{1}{0.022}$;

$12 \times 10^6 = 1.2(2 \times 10^6)2^{0.022t}$; $5 = 2^{0.022t}$; $0.022t\log 2 = \log 5$;

$t = \dfrac{\log 5}{0.022\log 2} = \dfrac{0.6990}{0.022(0.3010)} = 106$; 106 h

Page 460 · COMPUTER EXERCISES

  1. 10 PRINT "ENTER C, B, K, T"
     20 INPUT C, B, K, T
     30 LET A = C * B ↑ (K * T)
     40 PRINT "A = "; A
     50 GOTO 20

  2. 3.26 g

3. $3183.96

4. Add lines 5-8 and 60-100, and change line 50 as follows:

```
5    PRINT "DO YOU WISH TO FIND A OR T?"
6    INPUT X $
7    IF X $ = "A" THEN 10
8    IF X $ = "T" THEN 60
10   PRINT "ENTER C, B, K, T"
20   INPUT C, B, K, T
30   LET A = C ∗ B ↑ (K ∗ T)
40   PRINT "A = "; A
50   GOTO 5
60   PRINT "ENTER A, C, B, K"
70   INPUT A, C, B, K
80   LET T = LOG(A/C)/(K ∗ LOG(B))
90   PRINT "T = "; T
100 GOTO 5
```

5. About 6½ years

6. c ≈ 5000

Page 460 · CHALLENGE

20; first ask "Is the number between 1 and 500,000, inclusive?" thus eliminating 500,000 numbers. Continue asking such questions. For example, if the answer to the above question is yes, the next question should be "Is the number between 1 and 250,000?"

Pages 462-463 · WRITTEN EXERCISES

A **1.** $e^{1.39} = 4$ **2.** $e^{4.61} = 100$ **3.** $e^{-0.69} = \dfrac{1}{2}$ **4.** $e^{-2} = \dfrac{1}{e^2}$

5. $\ln 20.1 = 3$ **6.** $\ln 403 = 6$ **7.** $\ln 1.40 = \dfrac{1}{3}$ **8.** $\ln 1.65 = \dfrac{1}{2}$

9. $\ln e^2 = 2$ **10.** $\ln e^4 = 4$ **11.** $\ln \dfrac{1}{e^3} = \ln e^{-3} = -3$

12. $\ln \dfrac{1}{\sqrt{e}} = \ln e^{-1/2} = -\dfrac{1}{2}$ **13.** $\ln 1 = \ln e^0 = 0$ **14.** $\ln 0$ is not defined.

15. $e^{\ln 2} = 2$ **16.** $e^{\ln 5} = 5$ **17.** $\ln 6 + \ln 5 - \ln 2 = \ln \dfrac{6 \cdot 5}{2} = \ln 15$

18. $\dfrac{1}{2} \ln 9 - \ln 6 = \ln \dfrac{\sqrt{9}}{6} = \ln \dfrac{3}{6} = \ln \dfrac{1}{2} = \ln 1 = \ln 2 = -\ln 2$

19. $\dfrac{3}{2} \ln 4 + 2 = \ln 4^{3/2} + \ln e^2 = \ln 4^{3/2} \cdot e^2 = \ln 8e^2$

20. $-\dfrac{1}{3} \ln 8 + 3 = \ln 8^{-1/3} + \ln e^3 = \ln \dfrac{1}{2} e^3$

21. $\ln x = 5$; $e^{\ln x} = e^5$; $x = e^5$

22. $\ln(x - 3) = 4$; $e^{\ln(x-3)} = e^4$; $x - 3 = e^4$; $x = e^4 + 3$

23. $\ln x^3 = 12$; $e^{\ln x^3} = e^{12}$; $x^3 = e^{12}$; $x = \sqrt[3]{e^{12}} = e^{12/3} = e^4$

24. $\ln \sqrt{x} = 6$; $e^{\ln \sqrt{x}} = e^6$; $\sqrt{x} = e^6$; $x = (e^6)^2 = e^{12}$

B   **25.** $\ln(\ln x) = 0$; $\ln x = 1$; $e^{\ln x} = e$; $x = e$

26. $e^{\ln x} = x$; $\ln x \ln e = \ln x$; $\ln x = \ln x$; true for all positive numbers

27. $\ln x + \ln(x + 2) = \ln 8$; $\ln x(x + 2) = \ln 8$; $e^{\ln x(x+2)} = e^{\ln 8}$; $x(x + 2) = 8$;
$x^2 + 2x - 8 = 0$; $(x + 4)(x - 2) = 0$; $x = -4$ (reject) or $x = 2$; $x = 2$

28. $|\ln x| = 1$; $\ln x = -1$ or $\ln x = 1$; $e^{\ln x} = e^{-1}$ or $e^{\ln x} = e$; $x = e^{-1}$ or $x = e$

29. domain $= \{x : x > 0\}$; range: all real numbers

30. domain $= \{x : x \neq 0\}$; range: all real numbers

31. domain: $\{x : x \neq 0\}$; range: all real numbers

32. domain: $\{x : x > 5\}$; range: all real numbers

33.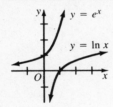

34.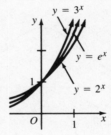

35. a. $e^x = 2$; $x \ln e = \ln 2$; $x = \ln 2$

     b. $e^{2x} = 2$; $2x \ln e = \ln 2$; $2x = \ln 2$; $x = \dfrac{1}{2} \ln 2 = \ln 2^{1/2} = \ln \sqrt{2}$

     c. $e^{x-3} = 2$; $(x - 3) \ln e = \ln 2$; $x - 3 = \ln 2$; $x = \ln 2 + 3 = \ln 2 + \ln e^3 = \ln 2e^3$

36. a. $e^{2t} = 5$; $2t \ln e = \ln 5$; $2t = \ln 5$; $t = \dfrac{1}{2} \ln 5 = \ln 5^{1/2} = \ln \sqrt{5}$

     b. $e^{-t} = 5$; $-t \ln e = \ln 5$; $-t = \ln 5$; $t = -\ln 5 = \ln 5^{-1} = \ln \dfrac{1}{5}$

     c. $e^{4-t} = 5$; $(4 - t) \ln e = \ln 5$; $4 - t = \ln 5$; $t = 4 - \ln 5 = \ln e^4 - \ln 5 = \ln \dfrac{e^4}{5}$

37. Let $y = e^x$; $y^2 - 5y + 6 = 0$; $(y - 3)(y - 2) = 0$; $y = 3$ or $y = 2$; $e^x = 3$ or $e^x = 2$;
$x \ln e = \ln 3$ or $x \ln e = \ln 2$; $x = \ln 3$ or $\ln 2$

38. Let $y = e^x$; $y^2 - y - 6 = 0$; $(y - 3)(y + 2) = 0$; $y = 3$ or $y = -2$ (reject); $e^x = 3$;
$x \ln e = \ln 3$; $x = \ln 3$

C   **39. a.** For n very large, $\left(1 + \dfrac{1}{n}\right)^{5n} = \left[\left(1 + \dfrac{1}{n}\right)^n\right]^5 \approx e^5$

b. For n very large,
$$\left(1 + \frac{2}{n}\right)^n \approx \left(1 + \frac{2}{n} + \frac{1}{n^2}\right)^n = \left[\left(1 + \frac{1}{n}\right)^2\right]^n = \left[\left(1 + \frac{1}{n}\right)^n\right]^2 = e^2$$

c. For n very large, $\left(\dfrac{n}{n+1}\right)^n = \left[\left(\dfrac{n+1}{n}\right)^{-1}\right]^n = \left[\left(\dfrac{n}{n} + \dfrac{1}{n}\right)^{-1}\right]^n =$
$$\left[\left(1 + \frac{1}{n}\right)^n\right]^{-1} = e^{-1}$$

Pages 463-464 · CALCULATOR KEY-IN

1. **a.** $1000e^{0.06} = 1062$; \$1062   **b.** $1000e^{0.06 \cdot 2} = 1000e^{0.12} = 1127$; \$1127
   c. $1000e^{0.06 \cdot 10} = 1000e^{0.6} = 1822$; \$1822

2. Investment A: $P = 1000e^{0.08 \cdot 10} = 1000e^{0.8} = 2226$;
   Investment B: $2000e^{0.08 \cdot 5} = 2000e^{0.4} = 2984$; investment B is worth more.

3. **a.**

x	0	0.1	0.2	0.3	0.4	0.5	0.6	0.7	0.8	0.9	1.0
y	1	0.99	0.96	0.91	0.85	0.78	0.70	0.61	0.53	0.44	0.37

   b.

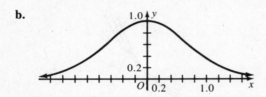

4. **a.** 2.718280469   **b.** the two are equal to 5 decimal places

5. $1 + 1 + \dfrac{1}{2} + \dfrac{1}{6} + \dfrac{1}{24} + \dfrac{1}{120} + \dfrac{1}{720} \approx 2.71805\overline{5} \approx e$

Pages 465-466 · APPLICATION

1. $\dfrac{x}{x_0} = 0.45 = 2^{-t/5730}$; $-\dfrac{t}{5730} = \dfrac{\log 0.45}{\log 2}$;
   $$t = -5730\left(\frac{\log 0.45}{\log 2}\right) = -5730\left(\frac{-0.3468}{0.3010}\right) = 6602; 6600 \text{ years}$$

2. **a.** Ratio $\dfrac{C-14}{C-12}$ in bone sample: $\dfrac{0.08}{10^{12}} = 0.08 \times 10^{-12}$; ratio $\dfrac{C-14}{C-12}$ today: 1×10^{-12}
   $\dfrac{x}{x_0} = 0.08$.

   b. $\dfrac{x}{x_0} = 0.08 = 2^{-t/5730}$; $-\dfrac{t}{5730} = \dfrac{\log 0.8}{\log 2}$;
   $$t = -5730\left(\frac{\log 0.08}{\log 2}\right) = -5730\left(\frac{-1.097}{.3010}\right) \approx 19{,}000; 19{,}000 \text{ years}$$

3. **a.** $\dfrac{x}{x_0} = 2^{-400/5730} = 0.953$; 95.3%   **b.** $\dfrac{x}{x_0} = 2^{-600/5730} = 0.930$; 93.0%

Pages 468-469 · CHAPTER REVIEW

1. b; $(x^{1/2} + y^{1/2})^2 = (x^{1/2})^2 + 2x^{1/2}y^{1/2} + (y^{1/2})^2 = x + 2\sqrt{xy} + y$

2. c; $\dfrac{3}{\sqrt[6]{27}} = \dfrac{3}{\sqrt[6]{3^3}} = \dfrac{3}{3^{3/6}} = 3^{1-1/2} = 3^{1/2} = \sqrt{3}$

3. d; $5^{2(x+2)} = 5^{3x-3}$; $2(x + 2) = 3x - 3$; $2x + 4 = 3x - 3$; $x = 7$

4. c; $\left(\dfrac{3^{1+\sqrt{2}}}{3^{1-\sqrt{2}}}\right)^{\sqrt{2}} = (3^{2\sqrt{2}})^{\sqrt{2}} = 3^{(2\sqrt{2})\sqrt{2}} = 3^4 = 81$ 5. b

6. b; $g(f(x)) = 3(2x + 1) - 4 = 6x - 1$

7. a; $f(g(x)) = \dfrac{5}{3}\left(\dfrac{3(x - 1)}{5}\right) + 1 = x$; $g(f(x)) = \dfrac{3\left(\dfrac{5}{3}x + 1 - 1\right)}{5} = x$

8. c; $y = 9x - 7$; $x = 9y - 7$; $y = \dfrac{x + 7}{9}$; $g(x) = \dfrac{x + 7}{9}$

9. b; $\log_3 81 = \log_3 3^4 = 4$ 10. c; $6^2 = 36 < 180 < 216 = 6^3$

11. a; $\log_6\left(\dfrac{36}{6^{-10}}\right) = \log_6\left(\dfrac{6^2}{6^{-10}}\right) = \log_6 6^{12} = 12$

12. a; $\log_b z = \log_b x^{1/3} + \log_b y = \log_b x^{1/3}y = \log_b y\sqrt[3]{x}$; $z = y\sqrt[3]{x}$

13. d; $10^{3t} = 5$; $3t = \log_{10} 5$; $t = \dfrac{\log_{10} 5}{3} = \dfrac{1}{3}\log_{10} 5$

14. b; $x = x_0 \cdot 2^{-t/h}$; $5 = 40 \cdot 2^{-12/h}$; $\dfrac{1}{8} = 2^{-12/h}$; $2^{-3} = 2^{-12/h}$; $h = 4$

15. b; $\ln\dfrac{1}{e^2} = \ln e^{-2} = -2$ 16. c; $e^{2x-1} = 3$; $2x - 1 = \ln 3$; $x = \dfrac{\ln 3 + 1}{2}$

Page 469 · CHAPTER TEST

1. a. $x = \left(\dfrac{1}{16}\right)^{-3/2} = 16^{3/2} = (\sqrt{16})^3 = 4^3 = 64$
   b. $16^x = 64$; $(4^2)^x = 4^3$; $4^{2x} = 4^3$; $2x = 3$; $x = \dfrac{3}{2}$

2. a. $\sqrt[3]{\sqrt{125y^6}}$; $((5^3y^6)^{1/2})^{1/3} = (5^3y^6)^{1/2 \cdot 1/3} = (5^3y^6)^{1/6} = 5^{3 \cdot 1/6}y^{6 \cdot 1/6} = 5^{1/2}y = y\sqrt{5}$
   b. $(64^{2/3} + 27^{2/3})^{3/2} = [(\sqrt[3]{64})^2 + (\sqrt[3]{27})^2]^{3/2} = (4^2 + 3^2)^{3/2} = 25^{3/2} = (\sqrt{25})^3 = 5^3 = 125$

3. $9^{x-2} = 27^{\pi+1} \div 27^{\pi-1} = 27^{(\pi+1)-(\pi-1)} = 27^2$; $(3^2)^{x-2} = (3^3)^2$; $3^{2x-4} = 3^6$; $2x - 4 = 6$;
   $2x = 10$; $x = 5$

4. a. $f(g(-2)) = 4[(-2)^2 - 3] + 1 = 4(4 - 3) + 1 = 5$
   b. $g(f(x)) = (4x + 1)^2 - 3 = 16x^2 + 8x + 1 - 3 = 16x^2 + 8x - 2$

5. $f(g(x)) = (\sqrt[3]{x + 2})^3 - 2 = x + 2 - 2 = x$; $g(f(x)) = \sqrt[3]{(x^3 - 2) + 2} = \sqrt[3]{x^3} = x$

6. a. $32^{3/5} = 8$; $(2^5)^{3/5} = 8$; $2^3 = 8$; $\log_2 8 = 3$ b. $16^{-3/2} = \dfrac{1}{64}$

7. a. $7^{\log_7 3} = 3$ **b.** $\log_3 27^{\sqrt{2}} = \log_3 (3^3)^{\sqrt{2}} = \log_3 3^{3\sqrt{2}} = 3\sqrt{2}$

8. a. $\log_3 x = \log_3 12 + \log_3 2 - \log_3 6;\ \log_3 x = \log_3 \dfrac{12 \cdot 2}{6} = \log_3 4;\ x = 4$

  b. $\log_4(x - 6) + \log_4 x = 2;\ \log_4(x - 6) + \log_4 x = \log_4 16;\ \log_4 x(x - 6) = \log_4 16;$
    $x(x - 6) = 16;\ x^2 - 6x - 16 = 0;\ (x + 2)(x - 8) = 0;\ x = -2 \text{ (reject) or } x = 8;$
    $x = 8$

9. a. $\log_{10} 9 = \log_{10} 3^2 = 2 \log_{10} 3 = 2(0.477) = 0.954$

  b. $\log_{10} 12 = \log_{10} 2^2 \cdot 3 = 2 \log_{10} 2 + \log_{10} 3 = 2(0.301) + 0.477 = 1.079$

  c. $\log_{10} 15 = \log_{10} \dfrac{10 \cdot 3}{2} = \log_{10} 10 + \log_{10} 3 - \log_{10} 2 = 1 + 0.477 - 0.301 = 1.176$

10. $5^{3t} = 2;\ \log 5^{3t} = \log 2;\ 3t \log 5 = \log 2;\ t = \dfrac{\log 2}{3 \log 5}$

11. $\dfrac{1}{k} = 5;\ k = \dfrac{1}{5};\ 3n_0 = n_0 \cdot 2^{1/5 \cdot t};\ 3 = 2^{t/5};\ \dfrac{t}{5} \log 2 = \log 3;$

    $t = \dfrac{5 \log 3}{\log 2} = \dfrac{5(0.4771)}{0.3010} = 7.9;\ 7.9 \text{ h}$

12. $\ln x^2 = 10;\ e^{10} = x^2;\ x = e^5 \text{ or } -e^5$ **13.** $\dfrac{1}{2} - \ln 7 = \ln e^{1/2} - \ln 7 = \ln \dfrac{e^{1/2}}{7} = \ln \dfrac{\sqrt{e}}{7}$

Page 470 · MIXED REVIEW

1. $-0.35(1.2x - 3) = 6 - 0.409x;\ -0.42x + 1.05 = 6 - 0.409x;\ -0.011x = 4.95;$
  $x = -450$

2. $\dfrac{2m^2}{3} - \dfrac{8m}{9} = \dfrac{1}{6};\ \ 12m^2 - 16m = 3;\ \ 12m^2 - 16m - 3 = 0;\ \ (2m - 3)(6m + 1) = 0;$

  $m = \dfrac{3}{2} \text{ or } m = -\dfrac{1}{6}$

3. $16t^4 + 81 = 72t^2;\ 16t^4 - 72t^2 + 81 = 0;\ (4t^2 - 9)^2 = 0;\ 4t^2 = 9;\ t^2 = \dfrac{9}{4};\ t = \dfrac{3}{2} \text{ or } -\dfrac{3}{2}$

4. $\dfrac{k}{2k - 1} - \dfrac{1}{k} = \dfrac{k^2 - 5k + 2}{2k^2 - k};\ k^2 - 2k + 1 = k^2 - 5k + 2;\ 3k = 1;\ k = \dfrac{1}{3}$

5. $3a^3 + 4 > (a + 2)^2;\ 3a^3 + 4 > a^2 + 4a + 4;\ 3a^3 - a^2 - 4a > 0;\ a(3a^2 - a - 4) > 0;$

  $a(3a - 4)(a + 1) > 0;$ there are variations in signs at $a = 0,\ a = \dfrac{4}{3}$ and $a = -1;$
  $\left\{a: -1 < a < 0 \text{ or } a > \dfrac{4}{3}\right\}$

6. $5|2j + 7| + 1 \le 1;\ 5|2j + 7| \le 0;\ |2j + 7| \le 0;\ |2j + 7| = 0;\ 2j + 7 = 0;$

  $2j = -7;\ j = -\dfrac{7}{2}$

7. $y^2 + 8y + 13 = 0;\ \ y = \dfrac{-8 \pm \sqrt{64 - 4 \cdot 13}}{2} = \dfrac{-8 \pm \sqrt{12}}{2} = \dfrac{-8 \pm 2\sqrt{3}}{2} = -4 \pm \sqrt{3}$

8. $2b - 8 = \sqrt{b^2 - 13}$; $4b^2 - 32b + 64 = b^2 - 13$; $3b^2 - 32b + 77 = 0$;

$b = \dfrac{32 \pm \sqrt{1024 - 4 \cdot 3 \cdot 77}}{2 \cdot 3} = \dfrac{32 \pm \sqrt{100}}{6} = \dfrac{32 \pm 10}{6}$; $b = \dfrac{42}{6} = 7$ or

$b = \dfrac{22}{6} = \dfrac{11}{3}$ (reject); $b = 7$

9. $x^6 + 3x^3 - 40 = 0$; $(x^3 - 5)(x^3 + 8) = 0$; $x^3 = 5$ or $x^3 = -8$; $x = \sqrt[3]{5}$ or $x = -2$

10. Slope of graph of $3x - 5y = 15$ is $\dfrac{3}{5}$; slope of perpendicular line is $-\dfrac{5}{3}$;

$\dfrac{y - (-7)}{x - 3} = -\dfrac{5}{3}$; $\dfrac{y + 7}{x - 3} = -\dfrac{5}{3}$; $3y + 21 = -5x + 15$; $5x + 3y = -6$

11. Let w = speed of head wind, and t_1 and t_2 the time for the first and second legs of the

trip; $t_1 = \dfrac{1050}{450 + w + 20}$; $t_2 = \dfrac{1050}{450 - w}$; $t_1 + t_2 = \dfrac{1050}{470 + w} + \dfrac{1050}{450 - w} = 4.6$;

$(470 + w)(450 - w)(4.6) = (450 - w)(1050) + (470 + w)(1050)$;

$972{,}900 - 92w - 4.6w^2 = 472{,}500 - 1050w + 493{,}500 + 1050w$;

$4.6w^2 + 92w - 6900 = 0$; $w^2 + 20w - 1500 = 0$; $(w + 50)(w - 30) = 0$;

$w = -50$ (reject) or $w = 30$; 30 km/h

12. $\dfrac{(-4x^{-2}y^3)^{-2}}{\left(\dfrac{1}{2}x^0y^{-2}z^{-3}\right)^3} = \dfrac{(-4)^{-2}x^4y^{-6}}{\left(\dfrac{1}{2}\right)^3 x^0 y^{-6} z^{-9}} = \dfrac{x^4 z^9}{(-4)^2 \dfrac{1}{8}} = \dfrac{x^4 z^9}{2}$

13. $\dfrac{c^4 - 16}{c^3 + 8} \div (8 - 4c) = \dfrac{(c^2 + 4)(c + 2)(c - 2)}{(c + 2)(c^2 - 2c + 4)} \cdot \dfrac{1}{-4(c - 2)} = \dfrac{c^2 + 4}{-4(c^2 - 2c + 4)}$

14. $\dfrac{1 - (3n^2)^{-2}}{n^{-2} + (3n^4)^{-1}} = \dfrac{1 - 3^{-2}n^{-4}}{n^{-2} + 3^{-1}n^{-4}} = \dfrac{1 - \dfrac{1}{9n^4}}{\dfrac{1}{n^2} + \dfrac{1}{3n^4}} = \dfrac{\dfrac{9n^4 - 1}{9n^4}}{\dfrac{9n^2 + 3}{9n^4}} =$

$\dfrac{9n^4 - 1}{9n^2 + 3} = \dfrac{(3n^2 + 1)(3n^2 - 1)}{3(3n^2 + 1)} = \dfrac{3n^2 - 1}{3}$

15. $4z^2 + 4z + 26 = 0$; $2z^2 + 2z + 13 = 0$; using the quadratic formula,

$z = \dfrac{-2 \pm \sqrt{4 - 104}}{4} = \dfrac{-2 \pm \sqrt{-100}}{4} = \dfrac{-2 \pm 10i}{4} = \dfrac{-1 \pm 5i}{2}$

16. $f(x) = -2(x + 3)(x - 9) = -2(x^2 - 6x - 27) = -2(x^2 - 6x) + 54 =$

$-2(x^2 - 6x + 9) + 54 + 18 = -2(x - 3)^2 + 72$; domain: all real numbers;

range: $\{y : y \leq 72\}$; zeros: -3 and 9

17. $f(g(1 + i)) = \dfrac{1}{1 + (1 + i)^2} = \dfrac{1}{1 + 1 + 2i - 1} = \dfrac{1}{1 + 2i} = \dfrac{1 - 2i}{5} = \dfrac{1}{5} - \dfrac{2}{5}i$

18. $\sqrt[3]{\dfrac{5}{24}} \cdot \sqrt[3]{\dfrac{25}{3}} = \sqrt[3]{\dfrac{5}{24} \cdot \dfrac{25}{3}} = \sqrt[3]{\dfrac{125}{72}} = \sqrt[3]{\dfrac{125 \cdot 3}{216}} = \dfrac{5}{6}\sqrt[3]{3}$

19. $\dfrac{2\sqrt{5} + 3\sqrt{2}}{2\sqrt{5} - 3\sqrt{2}} = \dfrac{(2\sqrt{5} + 3\sqrt{2})(2\sqrt{5} + 3\sqrt{2})}{(2\sqrt{5} - 3\sqrt{2})(2\sqrt{5} + 3\sqrt{2})} = \dfrac{20 + 12\sqrt{10} + 18}{20 - 18} =$

$\dfrac{38 + 12\sqrt{10}}{2} = 19 + 6\sqrt{10}$

20. $\sqrt{-5}(\sqrt{-4} + \sqrt{-45}) = i\sqrt{5}(2i + 3i\sqrt{5}) = 2i^2\sqrt{5} + 15i^2 = -2\sqrt{5} - 15$

21. Since $2 - i$ is a root, $2 + i$ is also a root and

$[x - (2 - i)][x - (2 + i)] = x^2 - 2x + ix - 2x + ix + 5 = x^2 - 4x + 5$ is a factor,

the depressed equation, $x^2 + 5 = 0$, has roots $\pm i\sqrt{5}$; $\{2 \pm i; \pm i\sqrt{5}\}$

22.

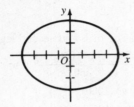

23. $x^2 + y^2 = 100$; $y = -x + 2$; $x^2 + (-x + 2)^2 = 100$; $x^2 + x^2 - 4x + 4 = 100$;

$2x^2 - 4x - 96 = 0$; $x^2 - 2x - 48 = 0$; $(x - 8)(x + 6) = 0$; $x = 8$ or $x = -6$; if

$x = 8$, $y = -8 + 2 = -6$; if $x = -6$, $y = 6 + 2 = 8$; $\{(8, -6), (-6, 8)\}$

24. $\begin{bmatrix} 3 & -2 & 5 & -9 \\ 1 & -7 & 3 & 3 \\ 0 & 5 & -4 & 10 \end{bmatrix} \rightarrow \begin{bmatrix} 1 & -7 & 3 & 3 \\ 0 & 19 & -4 & -18 \\ 0 & 5 & -4 & 10 \end{bmatrix} \rightarrow \begin{bmatrix} 1 & -7 & 3 & 3 \\ 0 & 19 & -4 & -18 \\ 0 & 0 & -\dfrac{56}{19} & \dfrac{280}{19} \end{bmatrix}$

$-\dfrac{56}{19}z = \dfrac{280}{19}$; $z = -5$; $19y + 20 = -18$; $19y = -38$; $y = -2$; $x + 14 - 15 = 3$;

$x = 4$; $(4, -2, -5)$

25. a. $\sqrt{\left(\dfrac{1}{4}\right)^3} \cdot \sqrt[3]{8^{-4}} = 2^x$; $(2^{-2})^{3/2} \cdot (2^3)^{-4/3} = 2^x$; $2^{-3} \cdot 2^{-4} = 2^x$; $2^{-7} = 2^x$; $x = -7$

b. $32(y^2 - 2y)^{-5/3} = 1$; $(y^2 - 2y)^{-5/3} = \dfrac{1}{32}$; $[(y^2 - 2y)^{-5/3}]^{-3/5} = \left(\dfrac{1}{32}\right)^{-3/5}$;

$y^2 - 2y = 8$; $y^2 - 2y - 8 = 0$; $(y + 2)(y - 4) = 0$; $y = -2$ or $y = 4$

26. $y = 2(x - 3)$; $x = 2(y - 3)$; $\dfrac{x}{2} = y - 3$; $\dfrac{x}{2} + 3 = y$; $f^{-1}(x) = \dfrac{x}{2} + 3 = \dfrac{x + 6}{2}$

$f^{-1}(5) = \dfrac{5}{2} + 3 = \dfrac{11}{2}$; $f(f^{-1}(5)) = 5$

27. a. $\log_{1/4} 8 = \log_{1/4} \dfrac{16}{2} = \log_{1/4} \dfrac{\left(\dfrac{1}{4}\right)^{-2}}{\left(\dfrac{1}{4}\right)^{-1/2}} = \log_{1/4}\left(\dfrac{1}{4}\right)^{-3/2} = -\dfrac{3}{2}$

b. $2\log_7 3 - \log_7 63 = \log_7 3^2 - \log_7 63 = \log_7 \dfrac{9}{63} = \log_7 \dfrac{1}{7} = \log_7 7^{-1} = -1$

28. $\sqrt[4]{x^{-3}} = 40$; $x^{-3/4} = 40$; $(x^{-3/4})^{-4/3} = 40^{-4/3}$; $x = 40^{-4/3}$;

$\log x = -\dfrac{4}{3} \log 40 = -\dfrac{4}{3}(1.6021) = -2.1361$; $x = 0.00731$

29. $(18.9)^x = 7$; $x \log 18.9 = \log 7$; $x = \dfrac{\log 7}{\log 18.9} = \dfrac{0.8451}{1.2765} = 0.662$

Page 471 · PREPARING FOR COLLEGE ENTRANCE EXAMS

1. C   2. D   3. E   4. B   5. A   6. E   7. E   8. C

CHAPTER 11 · Sequences and Series

Pages 476-478 · WRITTEN EXERCISES

A **1.** arithmetic; 15, 17   **2.** arithmetic; 20, 28   **3.** geometric; 81, 243

4. geometric; 1, $\dfrac{1}{10}$ **5.** arithmetic; 0, −12   **6.** neither; 1, 16

7. neither; $\dfrac{1}{36}, \dfrac{1}{49}$ **8.** geometric; $\dfrac{25}{2}, -\dfrac{25}{4}$ **9.** neither; $\dfrac{5}{6}, \dfrac{6}{7}$

10. geometric; $4^{7/2}, 4^{9/2}$ **11.** 3, 5, 7, 9; arithmetic   **12.** 2, −1, −4, −7; arithmetic

13. 1, 5, 25, 125; geometric   **14.** 6, 12, 24, 48; geometric   **15.** $-\dfrac{1}{4}, \dfrac{1}{2}, -1, 2$; geometric

16. 20, 28, 36, 44; arithmetic   **17.** 0.3010, 0.4771, 0.6021, 0.6990; neither

18. 1, 2, 3, 4; arithmetic   **19. a.** arithmetic   **b.** geometric

20. a. geometric   **b.** arithmetic

B **21.** 33, 45   **22.** 55, 79   **23.** 8, 6

24. −44, −67   **25.** 63, 127   **26.** $[40 + 3^4] = 121$, $[121 + 3^5] = 364$

27. 21, 34   **28.** $[31 + 25] = 56$, $[56 + 36] = 92$

29. The sequence of the differences is 2, 3, 5, 6, 12, . . . ; the differences of the differences form the sequence 1, 2, 3, 4, . . . ; the next two terms in the sequence of differences are $12 + 5 = 17$ and $17 + 6 = 23$; thus, the next two terms of the sequence are $31 + 17 = 48$ and $48 + 23 = 71$.

30. The sequence of the differences is 3, 4, 7, 12, 19, . . . ; the differences of the differences form the sequence 1, 3, 5, 7, . . . ; the next two terms in the sequence of differences are $19 + 9 = 28$ and $28 + 11 = 39$; thus, the next two terms are $50 + 28 = 78$ and $78 + 39 = 117$.

31. a. $t_5 = 15$ $t_6 = 21$ **b.** $t_{10} = \displaystyle\sum_{n=1}^{10} n = \dfrac{10 \cdot 11}{2} = 55$

32. The sequence of differences is 4, 7, 10, . . . ; the first ten terms of the pentagonal number sequence are 1, 5, 12, 22, 35, 51, 70, 92, 117, 145. The tenth pentagonal number is 145.

33. a. Hexagon drawings will vary; $t_6 = 9$.

b. 0, 2, 5, 9, 14, 20, 27, 35; $t_{10} = 35$

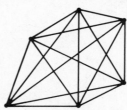

34. a. $t_4 = 11$ regions $t_5 = 16$ regions

b. $16 + 6 = 22$ regions

35. a. 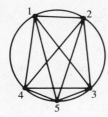 $t_5 = 16$ 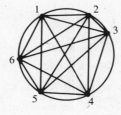 $t_6 = 31$; no

b. The sequence: 1, 2, 4, 8, 16, 31, ...

1st differences: 1, 2, 4, 8, 15, ...

2nd differences: 1, 2, 4, 7, ...

3rd differences: 1, 2, 3, ...

The next 3rd difference is 4, the next 2nd difference is $7 + 4 = 11$, and the next first difference is $15 + 11 = 26$. Therefore, the next term of the sequence is $31 + 26 = 57$; $t_7 = 57$.

Page 478 · CHALLENGE

Examples: 50, 134, and 218

Pages 483-484 · WRITTEN EXERCISES

A   **1.** $8 + (20)(4) = 88$ **2.** $3 + (24)(7) = 171$ **3.** $50 + (15)(-2) = 20$

4. $1.4 + (100)(1.2) = 121.4$ **5.** $-3 + (30)(-9) = -273$ **6.** $7 + (999)(-10) = -9983$

7. $\dfrac{25 - 5}{2} = 10$; $d = 10$; $t_{12} = 5 + (11)(10) = 115$

8. $\dfrac{5 - 4}{2} = \dfrac{1}{2}$; $d = \dfrac{1}{2}$; $t_4 = t_1 + (3)\left(\dfrac{1}{2}\right)$; $5 = t_1 + \dfrac{3}{2}$; $t_1 = 3\dfrac{1}{2}$

9. $\dfrac{36 - 20}{4} = 4$; $d = 4$; $t_5 = t_1 + (4)(4)$; $20 = t_1 + 16$; $t_1 = 4$

10. $\dfrac{50 - 42}{4} = 2$; $d = 2$; $t_8 = t_1 + (7)(2)$; $42 = t_1 + 14$; $t_1 = 28$; $t_{28} = 28 + (27)(2) = 82$

11. $t_9 = 5 \cdot 3^8 = 32{,}805$ **12.** $t_{10} = 2 \cdot 5^9 = 3{,}906{,}250$ **13.** $t_{11} = 64\left(\dfrac{1}{4}\right)^{10} = 0.000061$

14. $t_6 = 3(-3)^5 = -729$ **15.** $t_{11} = 80\left(-\dfrac{1}{2}\right)^{10} = 0.078125$

16. $r = \dfrac{-30}{10} = -3;\ t_6 = 10(-3)^5 = -2430$

17. $6r^2 = 150;\ r^2 = 25;\ r = \pm 5;\ t_2 = 6 \cdot 5 = 30$ or $t_2 = 6(-5) = -30$

18. $4r^2 = 36;\ r^2 = 9;\ r = \pm 3;\ 4 = t_1 \cdot 3$ or $4 = t_1(-3);$ if $r = 3,\ t_1 = \dfrac{4}{3}$, if $r = -3,\ t_1 = -\dfrac{4}{3}$

19. $r = x^4;\ t_{20} = x^2 \cdot (x^4)^{19} = x^2 \cdot x^{76} = x^{78}$

20. $abr^2 = \dfrac{a}{b};\ r^2 = \dfrac{a}{ab^2} = \dfrac{1}{b^2};\ r = \pm\dfrac{1}{b};\ t_{15} = ab\left(\pm\dfrac{1}{b}\right)^{14} = \dfrac{a}{b^{13}}.$

B   **21. a.** $54 = 18 + 2d;\ d = 18;$ the mean is $18 + 18 = 36$

        b. $62 = 2 + (7 - 1)d;\ 62 = 2 + 6d;\ d = 10;$ means are 12, 22, 32, 42, and 52

22. a. $80 = 5r^2;\ r^2 = 16;\ r = 4;\ t_2 = 5 \cdot 4 = 20;$ the mean is 20

     b. $567 = 7r^4;\ r^4 = 81;\ r = 3;$ the means are 21, 63, and 189

23. arithmetic; $t_n = 2 + (n - 1)2 = 2n$ **24.** arithmetic; $3 + (n - 1)2 = 2n + 1$

25. arithmetic; $t_n = 25 + (n - 1)8 = 17 + 8n$

26. arithmetic; $t_n = -17 + (n - 1)6 = -17 + 6n - 6 = -23 + 6n$

27. geometric; $t_n = 200\left(-\dfrac{1}{2}\right)^{n-1} = 200\left(-\dfrac{1}{2}\right)^{-1}\left(-\dfrac{1}{2}\right)^n = -400\left(-\dfrac{1}{2}\right)^n$

28. neither; $t_n = n(n + 1)$ **29.** neither; $(-1)^n n$ **30.** neither; $t_n = \dfrac{n + 1}{n^2}$

31. arithmetic; $t_n = 2a + 1 + (n - 1)(a + 2) = (a - 1) + n(a + 2)$

32. geometric; $t_n = \dfrac{a^2}{2}\left(\dfrac{a^2}{2}\right)^{n-1} = \dfrac{a^2}{2}\left(\dfrac{a^2}{2}\right)^{-1}\left(\dfrac{a^2}{2}\right)^n = \left(\dfrac{a^2}{2}\right)^n$

33. $-10, -20, -30, -40\ldots$ is arithmetic; $t_n = -10 + (n - 1)(-10) = -10n$

34. $1, 5, 9, 13, 17,\ldots$ is arithmetic; $t_n = 1 + (n - 1)(4) = -3 + 4n$

35. neither; $10^n + 1$ **36.** neither; $t_n = (-1)^{n+1}\left(\dfrac{4 + (n - 1)(1)}{5 + (n - 1)(6)}\right) = (-1)^{n+1}\left(\dfrac{3 + n}{-1 + 6n}\right)$

37. $t_1 = 71,\ d = -6;\ -43 = 71 + (n - 1)(-6);\ -43 = 71 - 6n + 6;\ -6n = -120;\ n = 20$

38. $t_1 = 8,\ r = 2;\ 512 = 8 \cdot 2^{n-1};\ 2^{n-1} = 64;\ n - 1 = 6;\ n = 7$

39. The sequence is arithmetic with $t_1 = 18$ and $d = 6;\ 618 = 18 + (n - 1)(6);$
    $600 = (n - 1)(6);\ n - 1 = 100;\ n = 101.$

C   **40.** The multiples of 3 between 100 and 1000 form an arithmetic sequence with $t_1 = 102$
      and $d = 3;$ let t_n be the last term; $t_n = 999 = 102 + (n - 1)3;\ 999 = 102 + 3n - 3;$
      $3n = 900;\ n = 300.$

   41. The multiples of 7 between 50 and 500 form an arithmetic sequence with $t_1 = 56$
      and $d = 7;$ let t_n be the last term; $t_n = 497 = 56 + (n - 1)(7);\ 497 = 56 + 7n - 7;$
      $7n = 448;\ n = 64.$

42. Since 8, x and y form an arithmetic sequence, $\dfrac{8+y}{2} = x$; since x, y and 36 form a geometric sequence, $\dfrac{x}{y} = \dfrac{y}{36}$; so $x = \dfrac{8+y}{2}$ and $y^2 = 36x$; $y^2 = 36\left(\dfrac{8+y}{2}\right) = 18(8+y)$; $y^2 - 18y - 144 = 0$; $(y-24)(y+6) = 0$; $y = -6$ or $y = 24$; if $y = -6$, $x = 1$; if $y = 24$, $x = \dfrac{576}{36} = 16$.

43. $(\sqrt{a} - \sqrt{b})^2 > 0$; $a - 2\sqrt{ab} + b > 0$; $a + b > 2\sqrt{ab}$; $\dfrac{a+b}{2} > \sqrt{ab}$; $\dfrac{a+b}{2} = $ arithmetic mean of a and b; $\sqrt{ab} = $ geometric mean of a and b; therefore the arithmetic mean is greater than the geometric mean.

Pages 484-485 · PROBLEMS

A 1. $t_5 = 14{,}600 + (4)(700) = 17{,}400$; $17{,}400

2. The last "step" is the upper floor, so let $t_n = 330$ and $n - 1 = $ number of steps; $t_n = t_1 + (n-1)d$; $t_n = 330$, $t_1 = 22$ and $d = 22$; $330 = 22 + (n-1)22$; $22n = 330$; $n = 15$; $n - 1 = 14$; 14 steps.

3. On his 21st birthday the son will receive a gift for the tenth time; the amounts of the gifts form a geometric sequence with $t_1 = 3$ and $r = 2$; $t_{10} = 3 \cdot (2)^9 = 1536$; $1536.

4. **a.** The rows are arranged so that the numbers of bricks in the rows form an arithmetic sequence with $t_1 = 85$ and $d = -6$; $t_{12} = 85 + (11)(-6) = 19$; 19 bricks.
   b. $t_n = 1$, so $1 = 85 + (n-1)(-6)$; $1 = 85 - 6n + 6$; $-6n = -90$; $n = 15$; 15

5. $P_2 = P_1(1.06)$ 6. $P_2 = P_1(0.94)$ 7. $P_2 = P_1(0.97)$ 8. $P_2 = P_1(2.5)$

9. The prices form a geometric sequence with $t_1 = 200$ and $r = 1.1$; $t_4 = t_1 \cdot r^3$; $t_4 = 200(1.1)^3 = 266.20$; $266.20

B 10. The prices form a geometric sequence with $r = \dfrac{72{,}000}{60{,}000} = 1.2$; $t_4 = 60{,}000 \cdot (1.2)^3 = 103{,}680$; $103{,}680.

11. **a.** The numbers of ft/sec form an arithmetic sequence with $t_1 = 15{,}840$ and $d = -32$; $t_{45} = 15{,}840 + (44)(-32) = 14{,}432$; 14,432 ft.
   b. The first second of the ninth minute is the $8(60) + 1$ or 481st second; $t_{481} = 15{,}840 + (480)(-32) = 480$; 480 ft.

12. The values of the car each year form a geometric sequence with $t_1 = $ purchase price of the car and $r = 0.75$; $t_7 = 8000(0.75)^6 = 1423.83$; about $1424.

13. The salaries for Job A form an arithmetic sequence with $t_1 = 12{,}000$ and $d = 800$; the salaries for Job B form a geometric sequence with $t_1 = 11{,}000$ and $r = 1.1$. After three years, the salary for Job A $= 12{,}000 + (3)(800) = 14{,}400$, and the salary for Job B $= 11{,}000 \cdot (1.1)^3 = 14{,}641$. After 5 years the salary for Job A $= 12{,}000 + 5(800) = 16{,}000$ and the salary for Job B $= 11{,}000(1.1)^5 = 17{,}715.61$. Job B pays more after 3 years and more after 5 years.

14. The widths at each meter of height form an arithmetic sequence with $t_1 = 229.22$ and $d = -1.57$; let $n =$ height at which width $= 103.62$ m; $t_n = 103.62$; $103.62 = 229.22 + (n - 1)(-1.57)$; $-125.6 = (n - 1)(-1.57)$; $-125.6 = -1.57n + 1.57$; $-1.57n = 127.17$; $n = 81$; 81 m.

C 15. For the given sequence $t_{13} = 440$ and $t_1 = 220$; ratio $= x$; $440 = 220x^{12}$; $x^{12} = 2$;

$x = 2\dfrac{1}{12}$

Pages 490-491 · WRITTEN EXERCISES

A 1. $\displaystyle\sum_{n=1}^{6} (n + 2) = (1 + 2) + (2 + 2) + (3 + 2) + (4 + 2) + (5 + 2) + (6 + 2) =$

$3 + 4 + 5 + 6 + 7 + 8$

2. $\displaystyle\sum_{k=1}^{8} 4k = 4 \cdot 1 + 4 \cdot 2 + 4 \cdot 3 + 4 \cdot 4 + 4 \cdot 5 + 4 \cdot 6 + 4 \cdot 7 + 4 \cdot 8 =$

$4 + 8 + 12 + 16 + 20 + 24 + 28 + 32$

3. $\displaystyle\sum_{t=1}^{5} 2^t = 2 + 2^2 + 2^3 + 2^4 + 2^5 = 2 + 4 + 8 + 16 + 32$

4. $\displaystyle\sum_{n=5}^{10} (2n - 5) = (2 \cdot 5 - 5) + (2 \cdot 6 - 5) + (2 \cdot 7 - 5) + (2 \cdot 8 - 5) + (2 \cdot 9 - 5) +$

$(2 \cdot 10 - 5) = 5 + 7 + 9 + 11 + 13 + 15$

5. $\displaystyle\sum_{n=2}^{\infty} 3^{-n} = \dfrac{1}{3^2} + \dfrac{1}{3^3} + \dfrac{1}{3^4} + \dfrac{1}{3^5} + \cdots = \dfrac{1}{9} + \dfrac{1}{27} + \dfrac{1}{81} + \dfrac{1}{243} + \cdots$

6. $\displaystyle\sum_{j=1}^{\infty} \dfrac{(-1)^{j+1}}{j} = \dfrac{(-1)^2}{1} + \dfrac{(-1)^3}{2} + \dfrac{(-1)^4}{3} + \dfrac{(-1)^5}{4} + \cdots =$

$1 - \dfrac{1}{2} + \dfrac{1}{3} - \dfrac{1}{4} + \dfrac{1}{5} - \dfrac{1}{6} + \cdots$

7. $\displaystyle\sum_{k=2}^{7} |4 - k| = |4 - 2| + |4 - 3| + |4 - 4| + |4 - 5| + |4 - 6| + |4 - 7| =$

$2 + 1 + 0 + 1 + 2 + 3$

8. $\displaystyle\sum_{j=4}^{100} \dfrac{j - 1}{j} = \dfrac{3}{4} + \dfrac{4}{5} + \dfrac{5}{6} + \dfrac{6}{7} + \cdots + \dfrac{99}{100}$ 9. $\displaystyle\sum_{n=1}^{100} 5n$

10. $8 \cdot 1 + 8 \cdot 2 + 8 \cdot 3 + \cdots + 8 \cdot 50 = \displaystyle\sum_{n=1}^{50} 8n$ 11. $\displaystyle\sum_{n=1}^{10} n^4$

12. $\displaystyle\sum_{n=3}^{10} \dfrac{1}{2^n}$ 13. $\displaystyle\sum_{n=0}^{12} 2(5^n)$ 14. $\displaystyle\sum_{n=1}^{24} \dfrac{n}{n + 1}$

15. $\displaystyle\sum_{n=1}^{50} 2n - 1$ 16. $2 \cdot 5 + 2 \cdot 6 + 2 \cdot 7 + \cdots + 2 \cdot 25 = \displaystyle\sum_{n=5}^{25} 2n$

17. $\displaystyle\sum_{n=1}^{7} 2^n$ 18. $\displaystyle\sum_{n=0}^{4} \dfrac{1}{3^n}$ 19. $\displaystyle\sum_{n=2}^{\infty} \dfrac{1}{n}$ 20. $\dfrac{1}{2} + \dfrac{1}{2 \cdot 2} + \dfrac{1}{2 \cdot 3} + \dfrac{1}{2 \cdot 4} = \displaystyle\sum_{n=1}^{\infty} \dfrac{1}{2n}$

B   **21.** $t_1 = -9$; $r = -\dfrac{1}{3}$; $\displaystyle\sum_{n=1}^{\infty} (-9)\left(-\dfrac{1}{3}\right)^{n-1}$ or $\displaystyle\sum_{n=1}^{\infty} -(-3)^{3-n}$

22. $t_1 = 8$, $r = -\dfrac{1}{2}$; $\displaystyle\sum_{n=1}^{\infty} 8\left(-\dfrac{1}{2}\right)^{n-1}$ or $\displaystyle\sum_{n=1}^{\infty} -(-2)^{4-n}$

23. $6 \cdot 1 + 6 \cdot 2 + 6 \cdot 4 + 6 \cdot 8 = \displaystyle\sum_{n=0}^{3} 6(2^n)$ **24.** $\dfrac{1}{1} - \dfrac{1}{3} + \dfrac{1}{5} - \dfrac{1}{7} + \cdots = \displaystyle\sum_{n=1}^{\infty} \dfrac{(-1)^{n+1}}{2n-1}$

25. $1^2 + \left(\dfrac{1}{2}\right)^2 + \left(\dfrac{1}{3}\right)^2 + \left(\dfrac{1}{4}\right)^2 + \cdots = \displaystyle\sum_{n=1}^{\infty} \left(\dfrac{1}{n}\right)^2$

26. $(1^2 + 1) + (2^2 + 1) + (3^2 + 1) + (4^2 + 1) + (5^2 + 1) + (6^2 + 1) = \displaystyle\sum_{n=1}^{6} (n^2 + 1)$

27. $\displaystyle\sum_{n=20}^{199} 5n$ **28.** $\displaystyle\sum_{n=1}^{9} (10n + 2)$ **29.** $\displaystyle\sum_{n=1}^{\infty} \left(\dfrac{1}{4}\right)^{n-1}$

30. $508 = 8 + 10d$; $10d = 500$; $d = 50$; $\displaystyle\sum_{n=1}^{11} 8 + (n-1)50 = \displaystyle\sum_{n=1}^{11} 50n - 42$

31. $\dfrac{j + 4}{j + 8}$ **32.** $\dfrac{k - 2}{k - 3}$

C   **33.** $\displaystyle\sum_{k=1}^{4} k \log 5 = 1 \log 5 + 2 \log 5 + 3 \log 5 + 4 \log 5 = 10 \log 5 = \log 5^{10}$

34. $\log(1 \cdot 2 \cdot 3 \cdot 4 \cdot 5 \cdot 6) = \log 1 + \log 2 + \cdots + \log 6 = \displaystyle\sum_{n=1}^{6} \log n$

35. $\displaystyle\sum_{k=1}^{6} \left(\sum_{j=1}^{k} 1\right) = \sum_{j=1}^{1} 1 + \sum_{j=1}^{2} 1 + \sum_{j=1}^{3} 1 + \sum_{j=1}^{4} 1 + \sum_{j=1}^{5} 1 + \sum_{j=1}^{6} 1 =$

$1 + (1 + 1) + (1 + 1 + 1) + (1 + 1 + 1 + 1) + (1 + 1 + 1 + 1 + 1) +$

$(1 + 1 + 1 + 1 + 1 + 1) = 1 + 2 + 3 + 4 + 5 + 6 = 21$

Page 491 · CHALLENGE

```
30 Prints 1, 1
40 C = 2
50 1, 1, 2
60 A = 1, B = 2
40 C = 3
50 1, 1, 2, 3
```

This program prints the sequence 1, 1, 2, 3, 5, 8, 13, . . . ; the Fibonacci sequence.

Pages 494-496 · WRITTEN EXERCISES

A   **1.** $\dfrac{20(3 + 83)}{2} = 860$ **2.** $\dfrac{40(11 + 89)}{2} = 2000$ **3.** $\dfrac{25(-8 + 66)}{2} = 725$

4. $\dfrac{12(12 - 32)}{2} = -120$ **5.** $n = 25$, $t_1 = 1$, $t_{25} = 49$; $S_{25} = \dfrac{25(1 + 49)}{2} = 625$

6. $n = 13$, $t_1 = 82$, $t_{13} = 46$; $S_{13} = \dfrac{13(82 + 46)}{2} = 832$

7. $n = 50$, $t_1 = 1$, $t_{50} = 148$; $S_{50} = \dfrac{50(1 + 148)}{2} = 3725$

8. $n = 21$, $t_1 = 40$, $t_{21} = 20$; $S_{21} = \dfrac{21(40 + 20)}{2} = 630$

9. $n = 30$, $t_1 = 2$, $t_{30} = 147$; $S_{30} = \dfrac{30(2 + 147)}{2} = 2235$

10. $n = 16$, $t_1 = 20$, $t_{16} = 80$; $S_{16} = \dfrac{16(20 + 80)}{2} = 800$

11. $S_{10} = \dfrac{1(1 - 2^{10})}{1 - 2} = 1023$ **12.** $S_{10} = \dfrac{1(1 - (-2)^{10})}{1 - (-2)} = \dfrac{-1023}{3} = -341$

13. $n = 12$, $r = 3$, $t_1 = 5$; $S_{12} = \dfrac{5(1 - 3^{12})}{1 - 3} = \dfrac{-2{,}657{,}200}{-2} = 1{,}328{,}600$

14. $n = 20$, $r = \dfrac{3}{2}$, $t_1 = 16$; $S_{20} = \dfrac{16\left(1 - \left(\dfrac{3}{2}\right)^{20}\right)}{1 - \dfrac{3}{2}} = \dfrac{16(-3324.2567)}{-\dfrac{1}{2}} = 106{,}376.2$

15. $n = 8$, $r = \dfrac{1}{2}$, $t_1 = 32$; $S_8 = \dfrac{32\left(1 - \left(\dfrac{1}{2}\right)^{8}\right)}{1 - \dfrac{1}{2}} = \dfrac{32\left(\dfrac{255}{256}\right)}{\dfrac{1}{2}} = \dfrac{255}{4} = 63\dfrac{3}{4}$

16. $n = 10$, $r = -\dfrac{1}{2}$, $t_1 = \dfrac{1}{4}$; $S_{10} = \dfrac{\dfrac{1}{4}\left(1 - \left(-\dfrac{1}{2}\right)^{10}\right)}{1 + \dfrac{1}{2}} = \dfrac{\dfrac{1}{4}\left(\dfrac{1023}{1024}\right)}{\dfrac{3}{2}} = \dfrac{341}{2048}$

17. $\dfrac{1}{81} = 1(r^4)$; $r = \pm\dfrac{1}{3}$; if $r = \dfrac{1}{3}$, $S_6 = \dfrac{1\left(1 - \left(\dfrac{1}{3}\right)^{6}\right)}{1 - \dfrac{1}{3}} = \dfrac{\dfrac{728}{729}}{\dfrac{2}{3}} = \dfrac{364}{243}$; if $r = -\dfrac{1}{3}$,

$S_6 = \dfrac{1\left(1 - \left(-\dfrac{1}{3}\right)^{6}\right)}{1 - \left(-\dfrac{1}{3}\right)} = \dfrac{\dfrac{728}{729}}{\dfrac{4}{3}} = \dfrac{182}{243}$; $\dfrac{364}{243}$ or $\dfrac{182}{243}$

18. $\dfrac{8}{9} = 2(r^2)$; $r^2 = \dfrac{4}{9}$; $r = \pm\dfrac{2}{3}$; if $r = \dfrac{2}{3}$, $S_5 = 2\left(1 - \left(\dfrac{2}{3}\right)^{5}\right) = \dfrac{2\left(\dfrac{211}{243}\right)}{\dfrac{1}{3}} = \dfrac{422}{81}$; if

$r = -\dfrac{2}{3}$, $S_5 = \dfrac{2\left(1 - \left(-\dfrac{2}{3}\right)^{5}\right)}{1 - \left(-\dfrac{2}{3}\right)} = \dfrac{2\left(\dfrac{275}{243}\right)}{\dfrac{5}{3}} = \dfrac{110}{81}$; $\dfrac{422}{81}$ or $\dfrac{110}{81}$

19. a. $t_1 = 24$ and $d = -12$; $t_{10} = 24 + 9(-12) = -84$; $S_{10} = \dfrac{(24 - 84)(10)}{2} = -300$

b. $t_1 = 24$ and $r = \dfrac{1}{2}$; $S_{10} = \dfrac{24\left(1 - \left(\dfrac{1}{2}\right)^{10}\right)}{1 - \dfrac{1}{2}} = \dfrac{24\left(\dfrac{1023}{1024}\right)}{\dfrac{1}{2}} = \dfrac{3069}{64}$

20. a. $t_1 = 1$ and $d = 0.1$; $t_{20} = 1 + 19(0.1) = 2.9$, $u = 20$; $S_{20} = \dfrac{20(1 + 2.9)}{2} = 39$

b. $t_1 = 1$ and $r = 1.1$; $S_{20} = \dfrac{1(1 - (1.1)^{20})}{1 - 1.1} = \dfrac{1 - 6.7275}{-0.1} = 57.275$

B 21. $648 = \dfrac{n(3 + 78)}{2}$; $n = 16$; $t_{16} = 78 = 3 + (15)d$; $d = 5$; the first three are 3, 8, and 13

22. $-1975 = \dfrac{25(t_1 + (-151))}{2}$; $-3950 = 25t_1 - 3775$; $25t_1 = -175$; $t_1 = 7$; $-1975 =$

$-7 + (24)d$; $24d = -1968$; $d = -82$; the first three terms are -7, -89, and -171

23. $14 + 24 + \cdots + 94 = \dfrac{9(14 + 94)}{2} = 486$

24. $101 + 103 + 105 + \cdots + 999 = \dfrac{n(101 + 999)}{2}$; $999 = 101 + (n - 1)2$; $2(n - 1) = 898$;

$2n = 900$; $n = 450$; $S_{450} = \dfrac{450(101 + 999)}{2} = 247{,}500$

25. $102 + 108 + 114 + \cdots + 996 = \dfrac{n(102 + 996)}{2}$; $996 = 102 + (n - 1)6$; $894 = 6n - 6$;

$6n = 900$; $n = 150$; $\dfrac{150(102 + 996)}{2} = 82{,}350$

26. a. $2 + 4 + 6 + \cdots + 40 = \dfrac{20(2 + 40)}{2} = 420$

b. $2 + 2^2 + 2^3 + \cdots + 2^{20} = \dfrac{2(1 - 2^{20})}{1 - 2} = 2{,}097{,}150$

27. a. $5^1 + 5^2 + 5^3 + \cdots + 5^{10} = \dfrac{5(1 - 5^{10})}{1 - 5} = \dfrac{5(-9{,}765{,}624)}{-4} = 12{,}207{,}030$

b. $5^2 + 5^4 + 5^6 + \cdots + 5^{20} = \dfrac{5^2(1 - 5^{20})}{1 - 5^2} \approx 9.9341 \times 10^{13}$

28. $10 + 11 + 13 + 14 + 16 + 17 + \cdots + 98 = (10 + 13 + 16 + \cdots + 97) +$

$(11 + 14 + 17 + \cdots + 98) = \dfrac{30(10 + 97)}{2} + \dfrac{30(11 + 98)}{2} = 1605 + 1635 = 3240$

29. a. $\displaystyle\sum_{k=1}^{n} 2^{k-1}$ is a geometric series with $t_1 = 1$ and $r = 2$, so

$\displaystyle\sum_{k=1}^{n} 2^{k-1} = \dfrac{1(1 - 2^n)}{1 - 2} = \dfrac{1 - 2^n}{-1} = 2^n - 1.$

b. $2^n - 1 > 1{,}000{,}000$; $2^n > 1{,}000{,}001$; $n \log 2 > \log 1{,}000{,}001$;

$n > \dfrac{\log 1{,}000{,}001}{\log 2} = 19.93$; $n = 20$

30. (A) is a geometric series with $t_1 = 1$ and $r = \dfrac{1}{2}$; (B) is a geometric series with $t_1 = 1$ an[

$r = -\dfrac{1}{2}$; for n even, the sum of series A is $\dfrac{1\left(1 - \left(\frac{1}{2}\right)^n\right)}{1 - \dfrac{1}{2}} = \dfrac{1 - \left(\frac{1}{2}\right)^n}{\dfrac{1}{2}} = 2\left(1 - \left(\frac{1}{2}\right)^n\right)$

and the sum of series B is $\dfrac{1\left(1 - \left(-\frac{1}{2}\right)^n\right)}{1 + \dfrac{1}{2}} = \dfrac{1 - \left(\frac{1}{2}\right)^n}{\dfrac{3}{2}} = \dfrac{2\left(1 - \left(\frac{1}{2}\right)^n\right)}{3}$.

31. $S_1 = 8(3 - 1) = 16 = t_1$; $S_2 = 8(3^2 - 1) = 64$; $64 - 16 = 48 = t_2$; $S_3 = 8(3^3 - 1) = 208$; $208 - 64 = 144 = t_3$; the first three terms are 16, 48, 144; the series is geometric

32. $S_1 = t_1 = 2 + 5 = 7$; $S_2 = 8 + 10 = 18$; $t_2 = 18 - 7 = 11$; $S_3 = 18 + 15 = 33$;
$t_3 = 33 - 18 = 15$; the series is arithmetic with $t_1 = 7$ and $d = 4$;

$2n^2 + 5n = \dfrac{n(7 + t_n)}{2}$; $7n + nt_n = 4n^2 + 10n$; $t_n = 4n + 3$

33. Answers will vary. **a.** 0.00000095 **b.** 0.00002656 **c.** 0.0000142

C **34. a.** 0 **b.** $\dfrac{t_1}{1 - r}$

35. The series consists of 50 terms, 25 pairs $(2 - 4, 6 - 8, 10 - 12,$ and so on) which eac[
produce a sum of -2; the sum is $25(-2)$ or -50. The sums may also be found as follow[

$(2 + 6 + 10 + \cdots + 98) - (4 + 8 + 12 + \cdots + 100) = \dfrac{25(2 + 98)}{2} - \dfrac{25(4 + 100)}{2} =$
$25(50) - 25(52) = -50$.

36. $(1 + 4 + 7 + 10 + \cdots + 97) + (2 + 5 + 8 + 11 + \cdots + 98) =$

$\dfrac{33(1 + 97)}{2} + \dfrac{33(2 + 98)}{2} = 33[49 + 50] = 3267$

37. $\displaystyle\sum_{k=1}^{20} 2^k + \sum_{k=1}^{20} k = \dfrac{2(1 - 2^{20})}{1 - 2} + \dfrac{20(1 + 20)}{2} = \dfrac{2(-1,048,575)}{-1} = 2,097,150 + 210 =$
$2,097,360$

38. $\displaystyle\sum_{n=1}^{12} (2^n - 1) = \sum_{n=1}^{12} 2^n - \sum_{n=1}^{12} 1 = \dfrac{2(1 - 2^{12})}{1 - 2} - 12 = 8190 - 12 = 8178$

39. The nth term of this series can be written as $1 + \displaystyle\sum_{n=1}^{n} n - 1$ or $1 - n + \sum_{n=1}^{n} n$; since

$\displaystyle\sum_{n=1}^{n} n = \dfrac{n(n + 1)}{2}$, $1 - n + \sum_{n=1}^{n} n = 1 - n + \dfrac{n(n + 1)}{2}$; for $n = 100$,

$1 - 100 + \dfrac{100(101)}{2} = 4951$

Pages 496-498 · PROBLEMS

A

1. $1 + 2 + 3 + \cdots + 12$; $t_1 = 1$; $d = 1$; $t_{12} = 12$; $S_{12} = \dfrac{12(13)}{2} = 78$; 78 times

2. $27 + 29 + 31 + \cdots + t_{20}$; $t_1 = 27$; $d = 2$; $t_{20} = 27 + 2(19) = 65$;

   $S_{20} = \dfrac{20(27 + 65)}{2} = 10(92) = 920$; 920 seats

3. $5 + 8 + 11 + 14 + \cdots + t_{33}$; $t_1 = 5$; $d = 3$; $t_{33} = 5 + (32)3 = 101$;

   $S_{33} = \dfrac{33(5 + 101)}{2} = 1749$; 1749 bricks

4. $2 + 4 + 8 + \cdots + t_{10}$; $t_1 = 2$; $r = 2$; $S_{10} = \dfrac{2(1 - 2^{10})}{1 - 2} = 2046$; 2046 ancestors

5. $t_1 = 12(400) = 4800$; $r = 1.1$; $n = 5$; $S_5 = \dfrac{4800(1 - 1.1^5)}{1 - 1.1} = 29{,}304.48$; \$29,304.48

6. $20 + 40 + 60 + \cdots + t_{12}$; $t_1 = 20$; $d = 20$; $t_{12} = 20 + (11)(20) = 240$;

   $S_{12} = \dfrac{12(20 + 240)}{2} = 1560$; total length needed for both sides $= 2 \cdot 1560 = 3120$ cm

7. $1 + 3 + 9 + 27 + \cdots + t_6$; $t_1 = 1$; $r = 3$; $S_6 = \dfrac{1(1 - 3^6)}{1 - 3} = 364$; 364 people

8. $8000 + 8000(1.05) + 8000(1.05)^2 + \cdots S_8 = \dfrac{8000(1 - (1.05)^8)}{1 - 1.05} = 76{,}392.86$; \$76,392.86

9. $t_3 = 5$; $d = 2$; $t_1 = 5 - 2 \cdot 2 = 1$; $t_{10} = 1 + 2(9) = 19$; $S_{10} = \dfrac{10(1 + 19)}{2} = 100$;

   maximum score $= 100$

10. $100 + 100\left(\dfrac{4}{5}\right) + 100\left(\dfrac{4}{5}\right)^2 + \cdots + t_5$; $t_1 = 100$; $r = \dfrac{4}{5}$;

    $S_5 = \dfrac{100\left(1 - \left(\dfrac{4}{5}\right)^5\right)}{1 - \dfrac{4}{5}} = 336.16$; 336.16 cm

B

11. $t_1 = 5.70$; $d = 0.75$; $t_n = 5.70 + (n - 1)(.75) = 4.95 + 5.70n$;

    $S_n = 66.60 = \dfrac{n[5.70 + (4.95 + .75n)]}{2}$; $(66.60)(2) = 5.70n + 4.95n + 0.75n^2$;

    $0.75n^2 + 10.65n - 133.20 = 0$; $75n^2 + 1065n - 13{,}320 = 0$; $15n^2 + 213n - 2664 = 0$; $(15n + 333)(n - 8) = 0$; $n = -22$ (reject) or $n = 8$, 8 weeks

12. $S_n = 74{,}416 = \dfrac{t_1(1 - (1.2)^5)}{1 - 1.2} = t_1(7.4416)$; $t_1 = 10{,}000$; \$10,000

13. $t_1 = 1000(1.06) = 1060$; $r = 1.06$; $n = 10$; $S_{10} = \dfrac{1060(1 - (1.06)^{10})}{1 - 1.06} = 13{,}971.64$;

    \$13,971.64

14. Suppose the students reach the same page on the same day; for the second student
$t_1 = 10$ and $d = 10$, so $t_n = 10n$; $50n = S_n = \dfrac{n(10 + 10n)}{2}$; $100n = n(10 + 10n)$
$100n = 10n + 10n^2$; $10n^2 - 90n = 0$; $n = 0$ (reject) or $n = 9$; 9 days

15. a. $t_1 = 1$; $d = 1$; $t_n = 1 + (n - 1)(1) = n$; $T_n = \dfrac{n(n + 1)}{2}$ **b.** $\displaystyle\sum_{k=1}^{n} k = \dfrac{n(n + 1)}{2}$

C   **16.** $T_3 + T_4 = 6 + 10 = 16$; 16 is a perfect square. Conjecture: The sum of any two con
secutive triangular numbers is a perfect square. Proof: Let T_n and T_{n+1} be two con
secutive triangular numbers; $T_n + T_{n+1} = \dfrac{n(n + 1)}{2} + \dfrac{(n + 1)(n + 1 + 1)}{2} =$
$\dfrac{n(n + 1)}{2} + \dfrac{(n + 1)(n + 2)}{2} = \dfrac{n^2 + n + n^2 + 3n + 2}{2} = \dfrac{2n^2 + 4n + 2}{2} =$
$n^2 + 2n + 1 = (n + 1)^2$. The sum of 2 consecutive triangular numbers is the square o
the index of the second number.

17. Example: $8(T_3) + 1 = 8 \cdot 6 + 1 = 49$; 49 is a perfect square. Conjecture: One mor
than eight times a triangular number is a perfect square. Proof: Let T_n be a triangula
number; $8(T_n) + 1 = 8\left(\dfrac{n(n + 1)}{2}\right) + 1 = 4(n^2 + n) + 1 = 4n^2 + 4n + 1 =$
$(2n + 1)^2$, a perfect square.

18. $\displaystyle\sum_{k=1}^{n} k^3 = \left(\sum_{k=1}^{n} k\right)^2$

19. a. $n + 2n + 3n + \cdots + n^2$ (the nth row) $= n(1 + 2 + \cdots + n) = n\left[\dfrac{n(n + 1)}{2}\right] =$
$\dfrac{n^3 + n^2}{2}$; the sum at the remainder of the nth column is
$n + 2n + 3n + \cdots + (n - 1)(n) = n\displaystyle\sum_{k=1}^{n-1} k = n\left[\dfrac{(n - 1)(n)}{2}\right] = \dfrac{n^3 - n^2}{2}$;
$\dfrac{n^3 + n^2}{2} + \dfrac{n^3 - n^2}{2} = \dfrac{2n^3}{2} = n^3$

b. second row: $2 + 4 + 6 + \cdots + 2n = 2(1 + 2 + 3 + \cdots + n)$
$= 2\displaystyle\sum_{k=1}^{n} n = 2\left(\dfrac{n(n + 1)}{2}\right) = 2\left(\dfrac{n^2 + n}{2}\right)$;

third row: $3 + 6 + 9 + \cdots + 3n = 3\left(\displaystyle\sum_{k=1}^{n} k\right) = 3\left(\dfrac{n(n + 1)}{2}\right) = 3\left(\dfrac{n^2 + n}{2}\right)$;

fourth row: $4 + 8 + 12 + \cdots + 4n = 4\left(\displaystyle\sum_{k=1}^{n} k\right) = 4\left(\dfrac{n(n + 1)}{2}\right) = 4\left(\dfrac{n^2 + n}{2}\right)$;

nth row: $n + 2n + 3n + \cdots + n^2 = n\left(\displaystyle\sum_{k=1}^{n} k\right) = n\left(\dfrac{nn(n + 1)}{2}\right) = \dfrac{n^3 + n^2}{2}$;

The total of all n rows is

$$\frac{n^2 + n}{2} + 2\left(\frac{n^2 + n}{2}\right) + 3\left(\frac{n^2 + n}{2}\right) + 4\left(\frac{n^2 + n}{2}\right) + \cdots + n\left(\frac{n^2 + n}{2}\right) =$$

$$\frac{n^2 + n}{2}(1 + 2 + 3 + 4 + \cdots + n) = \frac{n^2 + n}{2}\left[\sum_{k=1}^{n} k\right] =$$

$$\left(\frac{n^2 + n}{2}\right)\left(\frac{n^2 + n}{2}\right) = \left(\sum_{k=1}^{n} k\right)^2.$$

c. Since the grids are identical their sums must be equal, that is, $\sum_{k=1}^{n} k^3 = \left(\sum_{k=1}^{n} k\right)^2.$

Pages 498-499 · COMPUTER EXERCISES

1. This program uses the series for exercise 2(a):

```
10 DEF FN Y(N) = 3 * N + 1
20 PRINT "ENTER LOWER AND UPPER SUMMATION LIMITS"
30 INPUT K1, K2
40 LET S = 0
50 FOR K = K1 TO K2
60 LET S = S + FN Y(K)
70 NEXT K
80 PRINT "SUM FROM "; K1; " TO "; K2; " = "; S
90 END
```

2. a. Use program listed for problem (1.), above.
SUM FROM 10 TO 20 = 506

b. Change line 10 to: 10 DEF FN Y(N) = (2/3) ↑ N
SUM FROM 1 TO 30 = 1.99998957

c. Change line 10 to: 10 DEF FN Y(N) = 1/(N * N − 1)
SUM FROM 2 TO 100 = .740049503

3. a. Change line 10 to: 10 DEF FN Y(N) = (−1) ↑ (N + 1)/N
SUM FROM 1 TO 1000 = .69264743

b. Change line 10 to: 10 DEF FN Y(N) = (2 * N + 1)/(2 ↑ N)
SUM FROM 1 TO 100 = 5

c. Change line 10 to: 10 DEF FN Y(N) = 1/((3 * N − 2) * (3 * N + 1))
SUM FROM 1 TO 1000 = .333222257

Pages 502-503 · WRITTEN EXERCISES

1. $S = \dfrac{16}{1 - \dfrac{1}{4}} = 16 \cdot \dfrac{4}{3} = 21\dfrac{1}{3}$

2. $S = \dfrac{16}{1 + \dfrac{1}{4}} = 16 \cdot \dfrac{4}{5} = 12\dfrac{4}{5}$

3. $S = \dfrac{18}{1 + \dfrac{2}{3}} = 18 \cdot \dfrac{3}{5} = 10\dfrac{4}{5}$

4. $S = \dfrac{12}{1 - \dfrac{3}{4}} = 12 \cdot 4 = 48$

5. $r = \dfrac{3}{2}$; no sum

6. $S = \dfrac{45}{1 - \dfrac{2}{3}} = 45 \cdot 3 = 135$

7. $r = \dfrac{8}{7}$; no sum

8. $S = \dfrac{\dfrac{1}{5}}{1 - \dfrac{5}{7}} = \dfrac{1}{5} \cdot \dfrac{7}{2} = \dfrac{7}{10}$

9. $r = -\dfrac{\sqrt{2}}{2}$; $S = \dfrac{2\sqrt{2}}{1 - \left(-\dfrac{\sqrt{2}}{2}\right)} = \dfrac{4\sqrt{2}}{2 + \sqrt{2}} \cdot \dfrac{2 - \sqrt{2}}{2 - \sqrt{2}} = \dfrac{8\sqrt{2} - 8}{4 - 2} = 4\sqrt{2} - 4$

10. $r = 4^{-1} = \dfrac{1}{4}$; $S = \dfrac{4^{-1/2}}{1 - \dfrac{1}{4}} = \dfrac{\dfrac{1}{2}}{\dfrac{3}{4}} = \dfrac{1}{2} \cdot \dfrac{4}{3} = \dfrac{2}{3}$

11. $r = -5$; no sum

12. $\dfrac{3^n}{4^{n-1}} = \dfrac{3^n}{4^n} \cdot \dfrac{1}{4^{-1}} = \left(\dfrac{3}{4}\right)^n \cdot 4$, so $r = \dfrac{3}{4}$; $t_1 = 3$; $S = \dfrac{3}{1 - \dfrac{3}{4}} = 3 \cdot 4 = 12$

13. $S_1 = 8$; $S_2 = 10$; $S_3 = 10\dfrac{1}{2}$; $S_4 = 8 + 2 + \dfrac{1}{2} + \dfrac{1}{8} = 10\dfrac{5}{8}$; $S \approx 10\dfrac{3}{4}$;

$S = \dfrac{8}{1 - \dfrac{1}{4}} = \dfrac{8}{\dfrac{3}{4}} = 10\dfrac{2}{3}$

14. $S_1 = \dfrac{9}{10}$; $S_2 = \dfrac{99}{100}$; $S_3 = \dfrac{999}{1000}$; $S_4 = \dfrac{9999}{10,000}$; $S_5 = \dfrac{99,999}{1,000,000}$; $S \approx 1$;

$S = \dfrac{\dfrac{9}{10}}{1 - \dfrac{1}{10}} = \dfrac{\dfrac{9}{10}}{\dfrac{9}{10}} = 1$

15. $S_1 = \dfrac{3}{4}$; $S_2 = \dfrac{3}{8}$; $S_3 = \dfrac{3}{8} + \dfrac{3}{16} = \dfrac{9}{16}$; $S_4 = \dfrac{9}{16} - \dfrac{3}{32} = \dfrac{15}{32}$; $S_5 = \dfrac{15}{32} + \dfrac{3}{64} = \dfrac{33}{64}$; $S \approx \dfrac{1}{2}$

$S = \dfrac{\dfrac{3}{4}}{1 + \dfrac{1}{2}} = \dfrac{3}{4} \div \dfrac{3}{2} = \dfrac{3}{4} \cdot \dfrac{2}{3} = \dfrac{1}{2}$

16. $S_1 = \dfrac{1}{3}$; $S_2 = \dfrac{4}{9}$; $S_3 = \dfrac{4}{9} + \dfrac{1}{27} = \dfrac{13}{27}$; $S_4 = \dfrac{13}{27} + \dfrac{1}{81} = \dfrac{40}{81}$; $S_5 = \dfrac{40}{81} + \dfrac{1}{243} = \dfrac{121}{243}$;

$S \approx \dfrac{1}{2}$; $S = \dfrac{\dfrac{1}{3}}{1 - \dfrac{1}{3}} = \dfrac{\dfrac{1}{3}}{\dfrac{2}{3}} = \dfrac{1}{2}$

17. $S = \dfrac{t_1}{1 - r}$, so $12 = \dfrac{4}{1 - r}$; $12 - 12r = 4$; $-12r = -8$; $r = \dfrac{2}{3}$; $4, \dfrac{8}{3}, \dfrac{16}{9}$

18. $\dfrac{320}{7} = \dfrac{80}{1 - r}$; $560 = 320 - 320r$; $240 = -320r$; $r = -\dfrac{3}{4}$; $80, -60, 45$

19. $\dfrac{125}{9} = \dfrac{t_1}{1 + 0.8}$; $\dfrac{125}{9} = \dfrac{t_1}{1.8}$; $9t_1 = 225$; $t_1 = \dfrac{225}{9} = 25$; $25, -20, 16$

20. $\dfrac{4}{9} = \dfrac{t_1}{1 - \dfrac{1}{100}}$; $\dfrac{4}{9} = \dfrac{t_1}{\dfrac{99}{100}}$; $9t_1 = 4\left(\dfrac{99}{100}\right)$; $t_1 = \dfrac{11}{25}$; $0.44, 0.0044, 0.000044$

21. $0.6 + 0.06 + 0.006 + \cdots$; $r = 0.2$; $S = \dfrac{0.6}{1 - 0.1} = \dfrac{0.6}{0.9} = \dfrac{2}{3}$

22. $0.777 \ldots = 0.7 + 0.07 + 0.007 + \cdots$; $r = 0.1$; $S = \dfrac{0.7}{1 - 0.1} = \dfrac{7}{9}$

23. $0.4545 \ldots = 0.45 + 0.0045 + \cdots$; $r = 0.01$; $S = \dfrac{0.45}{1 - 0.01} = \dfrac{45}{99} = \dfrac{5}{11}$

24. $0.2272727 = 0.2 + 0.027 + 0.00027 + \cdots = 0.2 + [0.027 + 0.0027 + \cdots]$; $r = 0.01$;

$S = \dfrac{0.027}{1 - 0.01} = \dfrac{27}{990} = \dfrac{3}{110}$; $\dfrac{3}{110} + \dfrac{1}{5} = \dfrac{25}{110} = \dfrac{5}{22}$

25. If $6 = \dfrac{15}{1 - r}$, then $6 - 6r = 15$; $-6r = 9$; $r = -\dfrac{3}{2}$ and $|r| > 1$; this contradicts the fact

that, in order for a series to have a sum, $|r| < 1$.

26. For an arithmetic series, $S_n = \dfrac{n(t_1 + t_n)}{2} = \dfrac{n(t_1 + t_1 + (n - 1)d)}{2}$. If $d \neq 0$, then $|S_n|$

becomes larger than any given number for large enough n.

27. a. $S = \dfrac{1}{1 - \dfrac{2}{3}} = \dfrac{1}{\dfrac{1}{3}} = 3$ **b.** $S_n = \dfrac{1\left(1 - \left(\dfrac{2}{3}\right)^n\right)}{1 - \dfrac{2}{3}} = 3\left(1 - \left(\dfrac{2}{3}\right)^n\right) = 3 - 3\left(\dfrac{2}{3}\right)^n$;

$S - S_n = 3 - \left[3 - 3\left(\dfrac{2}{3}\right)^n\right] = 3 - 3 + 3\left(\dfrac{2}{3}\right)^n = 3\left(\dfrac{2}{3}\right)^n$; if $S - S_n < 0.00001$, then

$3\left(\dfrac{2}{3}\right)^n < 0.00001$; $\log 3 + n \log \dfrac{2}{3} < \log 0.00001$; $0.4771 + n(-0.1761) < -5$;

$n(-0.1761) < -5.4771$; $n > \dfrac{-5.4771}{-0.1761} = 31.1$; $n = 32$

28. $t_1 = 1$, $r = x$; $S = \dfrac{1}{1 - x}$

29. $S = 1 + 3x + 5x^2 + 7x^3 + \cdots$; $xS = x + 3x^2 + 5x^3 + \cdots$;

$S - xS = 1 + 2x + 2x^2 + 2x^3 + \cdots$; $S - xS$ is the geometric series $\displaystyle\sum_{n=0}^{\infty} 2x^n$ where

$r = x$; if $|x| < 1$, $S - xS = \dfrac{1}{1 - x}$; $S(1 - x) = \dfrac{1}{1 - x}$; $S = \dfrac{1}{(1 - x)^2}$.

Pages 503-504 · PROBLEMS

1. $t_1 = 1.5$; $r = \dfrac{14}{15}$; $S = \dfrac{1.5}{1 - \dfrac{14}{15}} = (1.5)15 = 22.5$; 22.5 m

2. $t_1 = 16$; $r = 0.95$; $S = \dfrac{16}{1 - 0.95} = \dfrac{16}{0.05} = 320$; 320 cm

3. The lengths of the sides of the squares are 12, $6\sqrt{2}$, 6, $3\sqrt{2}$, 3, ...; $t_1 = 12$ an

   $r = \dfrac{1}{\sqrt{2}} = \dfrac{\sqrt{2}}{2}$; $S = \dfrac{12}{1 - \dfrac{\sqrt{2}}{2}} = \dfrac{24}{2 - \sqrt{2}} \cdot \dfrac{2 + \sqrt{2}}{2 + \sqrt{2}} = \dfrac{48 + 24\sqrt{2}}{2} = 24 + 12\sqrt{2}$;

   $4S = 96 + 48\sqrt{2}$; $96 + 48\sqrt{2}$ cm.

4.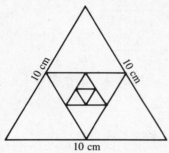

    The lengths of the sides of the triangles are

    10, 5, 2.5, 1.25, ...; $t_1 = 10$ and $r = \dfrac{1}{2}$;

    $S = \dfrac{10}{1 - \dfrac{1}{2}} = 20$; $3S = 60$; 60 cm.

10 cm

5. The areas of the squares are 144, 72, 36, 18, 9, ...; $t_1 = 144$ and $r = \dfrac{1}{2}$;

   $S = \dfrac{144}{1 - \dfrac{1}{2}} = 288$; 288 cm².

6. The areas of the triangle are $25\sqrt{3}$, $6.25\sqrt{3}$, $1.5625\sqrt{3}$, ...; $t_1 = 25\sqrt{3}$ and $r = \dfrac{1}{4}$

   $S = \dfrac{25\sqrt{3}}{1 - \dfrac{1}{4}} = \dfrac{100\sqrt{3}}{3} \approx 57.74$; about 57.74 cm².

B 7. $t_1 = 40$ and $r = \dfrac{2}{5}$; $S = \dfrac{40}{1 - \dfrac{2}{5}} = \dfrac{200}{3} = 66\dfrac{2}{3}$;

   total distance traveled $= 2S - 40 = 133\dfrac{1}{3} - 40 = 93\dfrac{1}{3}$; about $93\dfrac{1}{3}$ cm

8. $t_1 = 30$ and $r = \dfrac{3}{8}$; $S = \dfrac{30}{1 - \dfrac{3}{8}} = 48$;

   total distance traveled $= 2S - 30 = 96 - 30 = 66$; 66 cm

9. **a.** $t_1 = 25{,}000$ and $r = 0.95$; $S = \dfrac{25{,}000}{1 - 0.95} = 500{,}000$; for any integer n, $S_n < S$

b. Let n = number of months; $S_n = \dfrac{25{,}000(1 - (0.95)^n)}{1 - 0.95}$;

$200{,}000 < \dfrac{25{,}000 - 25{,}000(0.95)^n}{.05}$; $10{,}000 < 25{,}000 - 25{,}000(0.95)^n$;

$-15{,}000 < -25{,}000(0.95)^n$; $\dfrac{15{,}000}{25{,}000} > (0.95)^n$; $\dfrac{3}{5} > (0.95)^n$; $\log \dfrac{3}{5} > n \log(0.95)$;

$\dfrac{\log \dfrac{3}{5}}{\log(0.95)} < n$; $9.9589 < n$; $n = 10$; 10 months.

10. a. $S_1 = \dfrac{1}{2}$; $S_2 = \dfrac{1}{2} + \dfrac{1}{6} = \dfrac{2}{3}$; $S_3 = \dfrac{1}{2} + \dfrac{1}{6} + \dfrac{1}{12} = \dfrac{3}{4}$ **b.** $S_n = \dfrac{n}{n+1}$ **c.** 1

11. a. $S_1 = \dfrac{1}{3}$; $S_2 = \dfrac{1}{3} + \dfrac{1}{15} = \dfrac{2}{5}$; $S_3 = \dfrac{1}{3} + \dfrac{1}{15} + \dfrac{1}{35} = \dfrac{3}{7}$ **b.** $S_n = \dfrac{n}{2n+1}$ **c.** $\dfrac{1}{2}$

12. a. $S_1 = \dfrac{1}{4}$; $S_2 = \dfrac{1}{4} + \dfrac{1}{28} = \dfrac{2}{7}$; $S_3 = \dfrac{1}{4} + \dfrac{1}{28} + \dfrac{1}{70} = \dfrac{3}{10}$ **b.** $S_n = \dfrac{n}{3n+1}$ **c.** $\dfrac{1}{3}$

13. An equilateral triangle with sides of length s has area $\dfrac{s^2 \sqrt{3}}{4}$; $A_1 = \dfrac{1^2 \sqrt{3}}{4} = \dfrac{\sqrt{3}}{4}$;

$A_2 = 3\left[\dfrac{\left(\dfrac{1}{3}\right)^2 \sqrt{3}}{4}\right] = \dfrac{\sqrt{3}}{12}$; $A_3 = 12\left[\dfrac{\left(\dfrac{1}{9}\right)^2 \sqrt{3}}{4}\right] = \dfrac{\sqrt{3}}{27}$; $A_4 = 48\left[\dfrac{\left(\dfrac{1}{27}\right)^2 \sqrt{3}}{4}\right] = \dfrac{4\sqrt{3}}{243}$;

thus, $S = \dfrac{\sqrt{3}}{4} + \dfrac{\sqrt{3}}{12} + \dfrac{\sqrt{3}}{27} + \dfrac{4\sqrt{3}}{243} = \dfrac{\sqrt{3}}{4} + \dfrac{\sqrt{3}}{12}\left(1 + \dfrac{4}{9} + \left(\dfrac{4}{9}\right)^2 + \cdots\right) =$

$\dfrac{\sqrt{3}}{4} + \dfrac{\sqrt{3}}{12}\left(\dfrac{1}{1 - \dfrac{4}{9}}\right) = \dfrac{\sqrt{3}}{4} + \dfrac{\sqrt{3}}{12} \cdot \dfrac{9}{5} = \dfrac{8\sqrt{3}}{20} = \dfrac{2\sqrt{3}}{5}$ (square units).

14. $P_1 = 3 - 3 \cdot \dfrac{1}{3} = 2$; $P_2 = 3\left(2 \cdot \dfrac{2}{3} \cdot \dfrac{1}{3}\right) = \dfrac{4}{3}$; $P_3 = 12\left(2 \cdot \dfrac{2}{3} \cdot \dfrac{1}{9}\right) = \dfrac{16}{9}$;

$P_4 = 48\left(2 \cdot \dfrac{2}{3} \cdot \dfrac{1}{27}\right) = \dfrac{64}{27}$; the terms $P_2, P_3, P_4, \ldots$ form an infinite geometric sequence

with $r = \dfrac{4}{3}$; since $\dfrac{4}{3} > 1$, the geometric series $P_1 + P_2 + \cdots$ has no sum; the perimeter

of the curve has no limit.

Page 505 · EXTRA

1. $\dfrac{1}{2} \cdot \dfrac{2}{3} \cdot \dfrac{3}{4} \cdot \dfrac{4}{5} \cdot \dfrac{5}{6} \cdots \cdot \dfrac{99}{100} \cdot \dfrac{100}{101} = \dfrac{1}{101}$ **2.** $\dfrac{1}{2} \cdot \dfrac{1}{3} \cdot \dfrac{1}{4} \cdot \dfrac{1}{5} \cdot \dfrac{1}{6} \cdots = 0$

3. $2 \cdot \dfrac{1}{2} \cdot \dfrac{4}{3} \cdot \dfrac{3}{4} \cdot \dfrac{6}{5} \cdot \dfrac{5}{6} \cdots = 1$

Page 508 · WRITTEN EXERCISES

1. $a^5 - 5a^4b + 10a^3b^2 - 10a^2b^3 + 5ab^4 - b^5$

2. $c^7 + 7c^6d + 21c^5d^2 + 35c^4d^3 + 35c^3d^4 + 21c^2d^5 + 7cd^6 + d^7$

3. $p^8 + 8p^7 + 28p^6 + 56p^5 + 70p^4 + 56p^3 + 28p^2 + 8p + 1$

4. $p^8 - 8p^7 + 28p^6 - 56p^5 + 70p^4 - 56p^3 + 28p^2 - 8p + 1$

5. $(3x)^3 + 3(3x)^2(-2) + 3(3x)(-2)^2 + 1(-2)^3 = 27x^3 - 54x^2 + 36x - 8$

6. $(x^2)^4 + 4(x^2)^3(-1) + 6(x^2)^2(-1)^2 + 4(x^2)(-1)^3 + (-1)^4 = x^8 - 4x^6 + 6x^4 - 4x^2 + 1$

7. $(2a)^6 + 6(2a)^5(3) + 15(2a)^4(3)^2 + 20(2a)^3(3^3) + 15(2a)^2(3)^4 + 6(2a)(3)^5 + 3^6 =$
   $64a^6 + 576a^5 + 2160a^4 + 4320a^3 + 4860a^2 + 2916a + 729$

8. $s^5 + 5s^4(2t) + 10s^3(2t)^2 + 10s^2(2t)^3 + 5s(2t)^4 + (2t)^5 =$
   $s^5 + 10s^4t + 40s^3t^2 + 80s^2t^3 + 80st^4 + 32t^5$

9. $(2p)^5 + 5(2p)^4(-10q) + 10(2p)^3(-10q)^2 + 10(2p)^2(-10q)^3 + 5(2p)(-10q)^4 + (-10q)^5$
   $32p^5 - 800p^4q + 8000p^3q^2 - 40,000p^2q^3 + 100,000pq^4 - 100,000q^5$

10. $(m^2)^6 + 6(m^2)^5(n^2) + 15(m^2)^4(n^2)^2 + 20(m^2)^3(n^2)^3 + 15(m^2)^2(n^2)^4 + 6(m^2)(n^2)^5 +$
    $(n^2)^6 = m^{12} + 6m^{10}n^2 + 15m^8n^4 + 20m^6n^6 + 15m^4n^8 + 6m^2n^{10} + n^{12}$

11. $(a^3)^4 + 4(a^3)^3(b^7) + 6(a^3)^2(b^7)^2 + 4(a^3)(b^7)^3 + (b^7)^4 =$
    $a^{12} + 4a^9b^7 + 6a^6b^{14} + 4a^3b^{21} + b^{28}$

12. $(5m)^4 + 4(5m)^3(-6n) + 6(5m)^2(-6n)^2 + 4(5m)(-6n)^3 + (-6n)^4 =$
    $625m^4 - 3000m^3n + 5400m^2n^2 - 4320mn^3 + 1296n^4$

B 13. $(a)^5 + 5(a^4)\left(\dfrac{1}{a}\right) + 10(a^3)\left(\dfrac{1}{a}\right)^2 + 10(a^2)\left(\dfrac{1}{a}\right)^3 + 5a\left(\dfrac{1}{a}\right)^4 + \left(\dfrac{1}{a}\right)^5 =$

   $a^5 + 5a^3 + 10a + \dfrac{10}{a} + \dfrac{5}{a^3} + \dfrac{1}{a^5}$

14. $(y^2)^4 + 4(y^2)^3(y^{1/2}) + 6(y^2)^2(y^{1/2})^2 + 4(y^2)(y^{1/2})^3 + (y^{1/2})^4 =$
    $y^8 + 4y^{13/2} + 6y^5 + 4y^{7/2} + y^2$

15. $(x^{1/3})^6 + 6(x^{1/3})^5(-2) + 15(x^{1/3})^4(-2)^2 + 20(x^{1/3})^3(-2)^3 + 15(x^{1/3})^2(-2)^4 +$
    $6(x^{1/3})(-2)^5 + (-2)^6 = x^2 - 12x^{5/3} + 60x^{4/3} - 160x + 240x^{2/3} - 192x^{1/3} + 64$

16. $(t^2)^6 + 6(t^2)^5\left(-\dfrac{t}{2}\right) + 15(t^2)^4\left(-\dfrac{t}{2}\right)^2 + 20(t^2)^3\left(-\dfrac{t}{2}\right)^3 + 15(t^2)^2\left(-\dfrac{t}{2}\right)^4 +$

   $6(t^2)\left(-\dfrac{t}{2}\right)^5 + \left(-\dfrac{t}{2}\right)^6 = t^{12} - 3t^{11} + \dfrac{15}{4}t^{10} - \dfrac{5}{2}t^9 + \dfrac{15}{16}t^8 - \dfrac{3}{16}t^7 + \dfrac{t^6}{64}$

17. $136x^2y^{15} + 17xy^{16} + y^{17}$ 18. $231p^2q^{20} - 22pq^{21} + q^{22}$

19. Since the coefficients are symmetric about the eleventh term, the twelfth term
    $167,960x^9$

20. $-729x^5y^7$ 21. $6435p^7q^8$

22. $(2 + 0.1)^7 = (2)^7 + 7(2)^6(0.1) + 21(2)^5 + (0.1)^2 = 128 + 44.8 + 6.72 = 179.52$

C 23. Let $n_1, n_2, n_3, \ldots, n_{n+1}$ be the entries of the nth row of Pascal's Triangle; $(a + b)^n$
    $n_1a^n + n_2a^{n-1}b + n_3a^{n-2}b^2 + \cdots + n_nab^{n-1} + n_{n+1}b^n$; if $a = b = 1$; $(a + b)^n =$

$$(1 + 1)^n = 2^n = n_1 \cdot 1 + n_2 \cdot 1 \cdot 1 + \cdots + n_{n+1} = n_1 + n_2 + n_3 + n_4 + \cdots + n_{n+1};$$

therefore $(1 + 1)^n = 2^n = \displaystyle\sum_{i=1}^{n+1} n_i = $ the sum of the entries of row n.

24. The expansion of $(1 + b)^n$ begins $1 + nb + \ldots$; there is at least one more term since $n \geq 2$, and all terms are positive since $b > 0$; therefore $(1 + b)^n > 1 + bn$.

Pages 511-512 · WRITTEN EXERCISES

A 1. 5040

2. $8(7!) = 8(5040) = 40{,}320$

3. $\dfrac{100 \cdot 99!}{99!} = 100$

4. $\dfrac{100 \cdot 99 \cdot 98!}{98!} = 9900$

5. $\dfrac{7 \cdot 6 \cdot 5 \cdot 4!}{3 \cdot 2 \cdot 1 \cdot 4!} = 35$

6. $\dfrac{9 \cdot 8 \cdot 7 \cdot 6!}{6! \cdot 3 \cdot 2 \cdot 1} = 84$

7. $\dfrac{10 \cdot 9 \cdot 8 \cdot 7 \cdot 6 \cdot 5!}{5 \cdot 4 \cdot 3 \cdot 2 \cdot 1 \cdot 5!} = 252$

8. $\dfrac{10 \cdot 9 \cdot 8 \cdot 7 \cdot 6!}{4 \cdot 3 \cdot 2 \cdot 1 \cdot 6!} = 210$

9. $\dfrac{(n + 1)\,(n!)}{n!} = n + 1$

10. $\dfrac{(n)\,(n - 1)\,(n - 2)!}{(n - 2)!} = n(n - 1) = n^2 - n$

11. $\dfrac{n(n - 1)!}{(n - 1)!\,1!} = n$

12. $\dfrac{n(n - 1)\,(n - 2)\,(n - 3)!}{3!(n - 3)!} = \dfrac{n(n - 1)\,(n - 2)}{6}$

13. **a.** $a^{10} + 10a^9b + \dfrac{10 \cdot 9}{1 \cdot 2}a^8b^2 + \dfrac{10 \cdot 9 \cdot 8}{1 \cdot 2 \cdot 3}a^7b^3 = a^{10} + 10a^9b + 45a^8b^2 + 120a^7b^3$

b. $a^{10} - 10a^9b + 45a^8b^2 - 120a^7b^3$

14. **a.** $a^{12} + 12a^{11}b + \dfrac{12 \cdot 11}{1 \cdot 2}a^{10}b^2 + \dfrac{12 \cdot 11 \cdot 10}{1 \cdot 2 \cdot 3}a^9b^3 =$

$a^{12} + 12a^{11}b + 66a^{10}b^2 + 220a^9b^3$ **b.** $a^{12} - 12a^{11}b + 66a^{10}b^2 - 220a^9b^3$

15. **a.** $a^{11} + 11a^{10}b + \dfrac{11 \cdot 10}{1 \cdot 2}a^9b^2 + \dfrac{11 \cdot 10 \cdot 9}{1 \cdot 2 \cdot 3}a^8b^3 = a^{11} + 11a^{10}b + 55a^9b^2 + 165a^8b^3$

b. $x^{11} + 11x^{10}(-2y) + \dfrac{11 \cdot 10}{1 \cdot 2}x^9(-2y)^2 + \dfrac{11 \cdot 10 \cdot 9}{1 \cdot 2 \cdot 3}x^8(-2y)^3 =$

$x^{11} - 22x^{10}y + 220x^9y^2 - 1320x^8y^3$

16. **a.** $a^{21} + 21a^{20}b + \dfrac{21 \cdot 20}{1 \cdot 2}a^{19}b^2 + \dfrac{21 \cdot 20 \cdot 19}{1 \cdot 2 \cdot 3}a^{18}b^3 =$

$a^{21} + 21a^{20}b + 210a^{19}b^2 + 1330a^{18}b^3$

b. $c^{21} + 21c^{20}(-d^2) + 210c^{19}(-d^2)^2 + 1330c^{18}(-d^2)^3 =$

$c^{21} - 21c^{20}d^2 + 210c^{19}d^4 - 1330c^{18}d^6$

17. $\dfrac{20!}{14!\,6!}a^{14}b^6 = \dfrac{20 \cdot 19 \cdot 18 \cdot 17 \cdot 16 \cdot 15}{1 \cdot 2 \cdot 3 \cdot 4 \cdot 5 \cdot 6}a^{14}b^6 = 38{,}760a^{14}b^6$

18. $\dfrac{15!}{11!\,4!}a^4(-b)^{11} = -\dfrac{15 \cdot 14 \cdot 13 \cdot 12}{4 \cdot 3 \cdot 2 \cdot 1}a^4b^{11} = -1365a^4b^{11}$

19. $\dfrac{14!}{4!\,10!}s^4t^{10} = \dfrac{14 \cdot 13 \cdot 12 \cdot 11}{4 \cdot 3 \cdot 2 \cdot 1}s^4t^{10} = 1001s^4t^{10}$

20. $\dfrac{14!}{13!\,1!}st^{13} = 14st^{13}$

B **21.** $\dfrac{9!}{5!\,4!}\,a^5(2b)^4 = \dfrac{9\cdot 8\cdot 7\cdot 6}{4\cdot 3\cdot 2\cdot 1};\ a^5(16b^4) = 2016a^5b^4$

22. $\dfrac{7!}{5!\,2!}(-y)^5(2x)^2 = \dfrac{7\cdot 6}{2}(-y^5)(4x^2) = -84x^2y^5$

23. The middle term is the fifth term; $\dfrac{8!}{4!\,4!}(c^2)^4(-2d)^4 = \dfrac{8\cdot 7\cdot 6\cdot 5}{4\cdot 3\cdot 2}c^8(16d^4) = 1120c^8d^4$

24. Since $b^{12} = (b^3)^4$, the fifth term contains b^{12}; $\dfrac{5!}{4!\,1!}(a)(3b^3)^4 = 5\cdot a\cdot 81b^{12} = 405ab^{12}$

25. False; let $a = 2$, $b = 3$; $2!\,3! = 12$, $(2\cdot 3)! = 6! = 720$

26. False; let $n = 3$; $(n^2)! = 9! = 362{,}880$; $(3!)^2 = 6^2 = 36$

27. False; let $n = 3$; $(2n)! = 6! = 720$; $2^3(3!)^2 = 8\cdot 6^2 = 288$

C **28.** The sixth term will contain $(y)^{10}$ and $(y^{-2})^5$, so there will be no y;

$$\dfrac{15!}{10!\,5!}\cdot y^{10}(-y^{-2})^5 = -\dfrac{15\cdot 14\cdot 13\cdot 12\cdot 11}{5\cdot 4\cdot 3\cdot 2}y^{10}y^{-10} = -3003$$

29. **a.** $1^{1/2} + \dfrac{1}{2}(1^{-1/2})x^{1/2} + \dfrac{\left(\frac{1}{2}\right)\left(-\frac{1}{2}\right)}{1\cdot 2}(1^{-3/2})x + \dfrac{\left(\frac{1}{2}\right)\left(-\frac{1}{2}\right)\left(-\frac{3}{2}\right)}{1\cdot 2\cdot 3}(1^{-5/2})x^2 =$

$1 + \dfrac{x^{1/2}}{2} - \dfrac{1}{8}x + \dfrac{x^2}{16}$ **b.** $\sqrt{2} = (1 + 1)^{1/2} = 1 + \dfrac{1}{2} - \dfrac{1}{8} + \dfrac{1}{16} \approx 1.4375$

Page 512 · CALCULATOR KEY-IN

1. 3,628,800   **2.** Answers will vary.   **3. a.** 2.433×10^{18} **b.** Answers will vary

4. 8008   **5.** 167,960   **6.** 9.075×10^9

Pages 513-514 · CHAPTER REVIEW

1. b; $r = -3$ **2.** d; $11 + 7 = 18$

3. c; $t_{50} = \dfrac{3}{4} + (49)\left(\dfrac{3}{4}\right) = \dfrac{3}{4} + \dfrac{147}{4} = \dfrac{75}{2}$ **4.** c; $x^2 = 80$; $x = 4\sqrt{5}$

5. d; $t_9 = 5(\sqrt{2})^8 = 5\cdot 16 = 80$ **6.** c

7. d; for n even, $t_n = n^3$; for n odd, $t_n = -n^3$; $\displaystyle\sum_{n=1}^{10}(-1)^n n^3$

8. a; $t_1 = \dfrac{3}{2}$; $d = \dfrac{3}{2}$; $t_n = \dfrac{3}{2} + 19\cdot\dfrac{3}{2} = 30$; $S_{20} = \dfrac{20\left(\dfrac{3}{2} + \dfrac{3}{2}\cdot 20\right)}{2} = 10\left(\dfrac{3}{2} + 30\right) = 315$

9. d; $S_5 = \dfrac{-96\left(1 - \left(-\dfrac{1}{2}\right)^5\right)}{1 - \left(-\dfrac{1}{2}\right)} = \dfrac{-96\left(1 + \dfrac{1}{32}\right)}{\dfrac{3}{2}} = -96\left(\dfrac{33}{32}\right)\left(\dfrac{2}{3}\right) = -66$

10. d; $r = 2$; since $|r| > 1$, the series has no sum.

11. b; $(2x^2)^4 + \dfrac{4!}{3!\,1!}(2x^2)^3(-1) + \dfrac{4!}{2!\,2!}(2x^2)^2(-1)^2 + \dfrac{4!}{1!\,3!}(2x^2)(-1)^3 + \dfrac{4!}{4!}(-1)^4 =$

$16x^8 - 32x^6 + 24x^2 - 8x + 1$

12. b; $\dfrac{6!}{3!\,3!}(2x)^3(-z^2)^3 = \dfrac{6\cdot 5\cdot 4}{3\cdot 2}(8x^3)(-z^6) = -160x^3z^6$

Pages 514-515 · CHAPTER TEST

1. $t_1 = (-1)\dfrac{100}{50} = -100;\;\; t_2 = (-1)^2\dfrac{100}{5} = 20;\;\; t_3 = (-1)\dfrac{100}{5^2} = -4;\;\; t_4 = (-1)^4\dfrac{100}{5^3} = \dfrac{4}{5};$

the sequence $-100,\ 20,\ -4,\ \dfrac{4}{5}$ is geometric with $r = -\dfrac{1}{5}$.

2. The sequence is geometric, with $r = -5;\; t_6 = 1(-5)^5 = -3125$.

3. $t_1 = \dfrac{2(1)}{1};\; t_2 = \dfrac{2(2)}{2(2)-1};\; t_3 = \dfrac{2(3)}{2(3)-1};\; t_n = \dfrac{2n}{2n-1}$

4. $\dfrac{82-2}{4} = 20$; the means are 22, 42, and 62.   **5.** $\displaystyle\sum_{n=1}^{\infty}(-1)^{n+1}\dfrac{2n-1}{2}$

6. $t_{20} = 2 + (19)(-4) = -74;\; S_{20} = \dfrac{20(2-74)}{2} = -720$

7. $1 + 2 + 4 + 8 + 16 + 32 = 63\left(\text{or } S_6 = \dfrac{1(1-2^6)}{1-2} = 63\right)$

8. $r = \dfrac{1}{3};\; S = \dfrac{\dfrac{9}{4}}{1-\dfrac{1}{3}} = \dfrac{9}{4}\cdot\dfrac{3}{2} = \dfrac{27}{8}$

9. $(2s)^5 + \dfrac{5!}{4!\,1!}(2s)^4(t^2) + \dfrac{5!}{3!\,2!}(2s)^3(t^2)^2 + \dfrac{5!}{2!\,3!}(2s)^2(t^2)^3 + \dfrac{5!}{1!\,4!}(2s)(t^2)^4 + (t^2)^5 =$

$32s^5 + 80s^4t^2 + 80s^3t^4 + 40s^2t^6 + 10st^8 + t^{10}$

10. $\dfrac{16!}{13!\,3!}(w)^{13}(2y^2)^3 = \dfrac{16\cdot 15\cdot 14}{3\cdot 2}w^{13}(8y^6) = 4480w^{13}y^6$

Page 515 · CUMULATIVE REVIEW

1. $y_1\sqrt[3]{x_1} = y_2\sqrt[3]{x_2};\; 4\sqrt[3]{125} = y_2\sqrt[3]{1000};\; 4\cdot 5 = y_2\cdot 10;\; y_2 = 2$

2.
$$2x - 1\overline{)6x^3 - 11x^2 + 0x + 4}$$

$$2x^2 - 3x - 1 + \dfrac{3}{3x-1}$$

$\underline{6x^3 - 2x^2}$

$-9x^2 + 0x$

$\underline{-9x^2 + 3x}$

$-3x + 4$

$\underline{-3x + 1}$

3

3. If $3 - i$ is a root, so is $3 + i$;

$[x - (3-i)][x - (3+i)] =$

$x^2 - 6x + 10$ is a factor of

$x^4 - 6x^3 + 6x^2 + 24x - 40$; the other

factor is $\dfrac{x^4 - 6x^3 + 6x^2 + 24x - 40}{x^2 - 6x + 10} =$

$x^2 - 4;\; x^2 - 4 = 0;\; x = \pm 2;\; \{3 \pm i, \pm 2\}.$

4. $x^2 + 4x + 4 + y^2 - 6y + 9 = 36 + 4 + 9$; $(x + 2)^2 + (y - 3)^2 = 49$;
center $= (-2, 3)$ and radius $= 7$

5. Since the vertex is the midpoint of the line segment between the focus and directrix, and
is perpendicular to the directrix, the focus is $(0, 4)$; let (x, y) be a point on the parabola,

$$\sqrt{(x - 0)^2 + (y - 4)^2} = y - 0; \; x^2 + y^2 - 8y + 16 = y^2; \; 8y = x^2 + 16; \; y = \frac{x^2}{8} + 2.$$

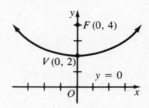

6. $c^2 = a^2 - b^2 = 169 - 144 = 25$; $c = 5$; foci: $(-5, 0)$ and $(5, 0)$

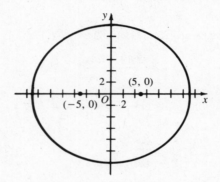

7. $xy + 12 = 0$; $y = -\dfrac{12}{x}$; $\left(-\dfrac{12}{x}\right)^2 - x^2 = -10$; $\dfrac{144}{x^2} - x^2 = -10$; $144 - x^4 = -10x^2$;

$x^4 - 10x^2 - 144 = 0$; $(x^2 + 8)(x^2 - 18) = 0$; $x^2 = -8$ (reject) or $x^2 = 18$;

$x = \pm\sqrt{18} = \pm 3\sqrt{2}$; if $x = 3\sqrt{2}$, $y = \dfrac{-12}{3\sqrt{2}} = -2\sqrt{2}$; if $x = -3\sqrt{2}$,

$y = \dfrac{-12}{-3\sqrt{2}} = 2\sqrt{2}$; $\{(3\sqrt{2}, -2\sqrt{2}), (-3\sqrt{2}, 2\sqrt{2})\}$

8. $x = -4y - 1$; $(-4y - 1)^2 - 2y^2 = 7$; $16y^2 + 8y + 1 - 2y^2 = 7$; $14y^2 + 8y - 6 = 0$;

$7y^2 + 4y - 3 = 0$; $(7y - 3)(y + 1) = 0$; $y = \dfrac{3}{7}$ or $y = -1$; if $y = \dfrac{3}{7}$,

$x = -4\left(\dfrac{3}{7}\right) - 1 = -\dfrac{12}{7} - 1 = -\dfrac{19}{7}$; if $y = -1$, $x = -4(-1) - 1 = 3$;

$\left\{\left(-\dfrac{19}{7}, \dfrac{3}{7}\right), (3, -1)\right\}$

9. $\begin{array}{l} x - y + z = 0 \\ 2x + 3y + 5z = 1 \end{array}$; $\begin{array}{l} 3x - 3y + 3z = 0 \\ 2x + 3y + 5z = 1 \\ \hline 5x \quad + 8z = 1 \end{array}$; $\begin{array}{l} x - y + z = 0 \\ 3x + 2y + 4z = 7 \end{array}$; $\begin{array}{l} 2x - 2y + 2z = 0 \\ 3x + 2y + 4z = 7 \\ \hline 5x \quad + 6z = 7 \end{array}$;

$\begin{array}{l} 5x + 8z = 1 \\ 5x + 6z = 7 \\ \hline 2z = -6 \end{array}$; $z = -3; 5x - 24 = 1; 5x = 25; x = 5; 5 - y - 3 = 0; -y = -2;$

$y = 2; (5, 2, -3)$

10. **a.** $\left(\dfrac{1}{\sqrt[3]{27}} - \dfrac{1}{(\sqrt[3]{27})^2}\right)^{1/2} = \left(\dfrac{1}{3} - \dfrac{1}{9}\right)^{1/2} = \sqrt{\dfrac{2}{9}} = \dfrac{\sqrt{2}}{3}$ **b.** $\dfrac{1}{4^{1/6} \cdot 4^{4/3}} = \dfrac{1}{4^{9/6}} = \dfrac{1}{4^{3/2}} = \dfrac{1}{8}$

11. **a.** $x^{3/4} = 2; \dfrac{3}{4} \log x = \log 2; \log x = \dfrac{4}{3} \log 2; x = 2\sqrt[3]{2}$

b. $x^{-2} = 4; \dfrac{1}{x^2} = 4; \dfrac{1}{x} = 2; x = \dfrac{1}{2}$ **c.** $4^{-2} = x; x = \dfrac{1}{4^2} = \dfrac{1}{16}$

12. $y = \dfrac{1}{2}x - 1; x = \dfrac{1}{2}y - 1; 2x = y - 2; y = 2x + 2; f^{-1}(1) = 4$

13. $\log x = \dfrac{6}{5}\left[\log 24 - \left(\log 3 + \log\left(\dfrac{1}{2}\right)^2\right)\right] = \dfrac{6}{5} \log \dfrac{24}{3 \cdot \dfrac{1}{4}} = \dfrac{6}{5} \log 32 = \log 32^{\frac{6}{5}} = $

$\log 64; x = 64$

14. $t \log 12.5 = \log 720; t = \dfrac{\log 720}{\log 12.5} = \dfrac{2.8573}{1.0969} = 2.6049; 2.60$

15. $t^{2/3} = 0.123; \dfrac{2}{3} \log t = \log 0.123; \log t = (\log 0.123)\dfrac{3}{2} = -1.3651; t = 0.0431$

16. $\log t = 0.12 \log 304; \log t = 0.2979; t = 1.9858; 1.99$

17. $S = 16 = \dfrac{t_1}{1 - \dfrac{3}{4}}; 16 = \dfrac{t_1}{\dfrac{1}{4}}; t_1 = 16 \cdot \dfrac{1}{4} = 4; t_4 = 4\left(\dfrac{3}{4}\right)^3 = \dfrac{27}{16}$

18. $(x^2)^4 + \dfrac{4!}{3! \, 1!}(x^2)^3(-y) + \dfrac{4!}{2! \, 2!}(x^2)^2(-y)^2 + \dfrac{4!}{1! \, 3!}(x^2)(-y)^3 + (-y)^4 = $

$x^8 - 4x^6 y + 6x^4 y^2 - 4x^2 y^3 + y^4$

19. $\dfrac{14!}{4! \, 10!}(-2x)^4(y)^{10} = \dfrac{14 \cdot 13 \cdot 12 \cdot 11}{4 \cdot 3 \cdot 2} \cdot 16x^4 y^{10} = 16{,}016x^4 y^{10}$

Pages 520-521 · WRITTEN EXERCISES

A **1. a.** second quadrant

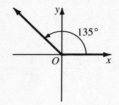

b. third quadrant

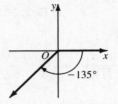

2. a. first quadrant

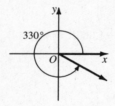

b. fourth quadrant

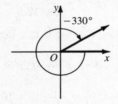

3. a. fourth quadrant

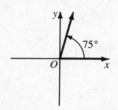

b. first quadrant

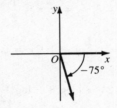

4. a. third quadrant

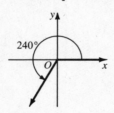

b. second quadrant

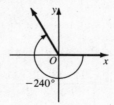

5. quadrantal

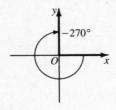

6. fourth quadrant

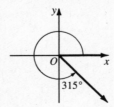

7. fourth quadrant

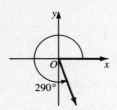

8. quadrantal

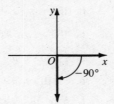

9. second quadrant

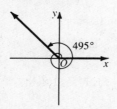

10. quadrantal

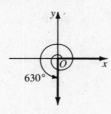

11. quadrantal

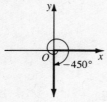

12. first quadrant

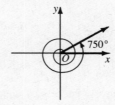

13. $\frac{2}{3} \times 360 = 240;\ 240°$ **14.** $\frac{3}{8} \times 360 = 135;\ 135°$ **15.** $\frac{3}{4} \times (-360) = -270;\ -270°$

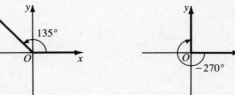

16. $\frac{1}{6} \times (-360) = -60;\ -60°$ **17.** $\frac{8}{5} \times 360 = 576;\ 576°$ **18.** $\frac{7}{3} \times 360 = 840;\ 840°$

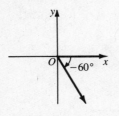

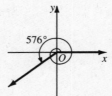

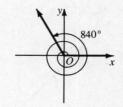

19-26. Answers to part a may vary. Examples are given.

19. a. $375°, -345°$ **b.** $15° + n \cdot 360°$, n an integer

20. a. $525°, -195°$ **b.** $165° + n \cdot 360°$, n an integer

21. a. $260°, -460°$ **b.** $-100° + n \cdot 360° = 260° + n \cdot 360°$, n an integer

22. a. $150°, -570°$ **b.** $-210° + n \cdot 360° = 150° + n \cdot 360°$, n an integer

23. a. $160°, -200°$ **b.** $520° + n \cdot 360° = 160° + n \cdot 360°$, n an integer

24. a. $715°, -5°$ **b.** $355° + n \cdot 360°$, n an integer

25. a. $5°, -355°$ **b.** $3605° + n \cdot 360° = 5° + n \cdot 360°$, n an integer

26. a. $-1°, 359°$ **b.** $-7201° + n \cdot 360° = 359° + n \cdot 360°$, n an integer

29. $72° + \left(\dfrac{40}{60}\right)° = 72.\overline{6}° \approx 72.7°$ **30.** $51° + \left(\dfrac{20}{60}\right)° = 51.\overline{3}° \approx 51.3°$

31. $25° + \left(\dfrac{45}{60}\right)° = 25.75°$ **32.** $33° + \left(\dfrac{15}{60}\right)° = 33.25°$

33. $6° + \left(\dfrac{21}{60}\right)° + \left(\dfrac{30}{3600}\right)° = 6° + 0.35° + 0.008\overline{3}° \approx 6.36°$

34. $0° + \left(\dfrac{42}{60}\right)° + \left(\dfrac{30}{3600}\right)° = 0.7° + 0.008\overline{3}° \approx 0.71°$

35. $65° + (0.4 \times 60)' = 65° + 24' = 65°24'$ **36.** $19° + (0.6 \times 60)' = 19° + 36' = 19°36'$

37. $23° + (0.9 \times 60)' = 23° + 54' = 23°54'$ **38.** $42° + (0.1 \times 60)' = 42° + 6' = 42°6'$

39. $19° + (0.41 \times 60)' = 19° + 24.6' = 19° + 24' + (0.6 \times 60)'' = 19° + 24' + 36'' = 19°24'36''$

40. $32° + (0.27 \times 60)' = 32° + 16.2' = 32° + 16' + (0.2 \times 60)'' = 32° + 16' + 12'' = 32°16'12''$

41. $57° + (0.67 \times 60)' = 57° + 40.2' = 57° + 40' + (0.2 \times 60)'' = 57° + 40' + 12'' = 57°40'12''$

42. $22° + (0.83 \times 60)' = 22° + 49.8' = 22° + 49' + (0.8 \times 60)'' = 22° + 49' + 48'' = 22°49'48''$

43. $135°$ or $-225°$ **44.** $53°$ or $-307°$

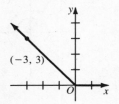

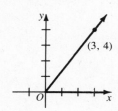

45. 37° or −323°

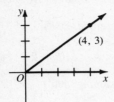

46. 315° or −45°

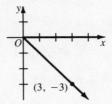

47. 30° or −330°

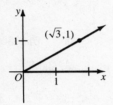

48. 120° or −240°

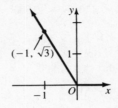

49. 240° or −120°

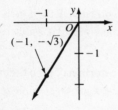

50. 330° or −30°

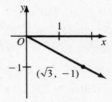

B **51.** $90° + 4n \cdot 360° < 4\theta < 180° + 4n \cdot 360°$; $22.5° + n \cdot 360° < \theta < 45° + n \cdot 360°$, n an integer (for example, 30°)

52. $180° + 4n \cdot 360° < 4\theta < 270° + 4n \cdot 360°$; $45° + n \cdot 360° < \theta < 67.5° + n \cdot 360°$, n an integer (for example, 50°)

53. $270° + 4n \cdot 360° < 4\theta < 360° + 4n \cdot 360°$; $67.5° + n \cdot 360° < \theta < 90° + n \cdot 360°$, n an integer (for example, 70°)

54. $90° + 6n \cdot 360° < 6\theta < 180° + 6n \cdot 360°$, $15° + n \cdot 360° < \theta < 30° + n \cdot 360°$, n an integer (for example, 20°)

55. $180° + 6n \cdot 360° < 6\theta < 270° + 6n \cdot 360°$; $30° + n \cdot 360° < \theta < 45° + n \cdot 360°$, n an integer (for example, 40°)

56. $270° + 6n \cdot 360° < 6\theta < 360° + 6n \cdot 360°$; $45° + n \cdot 360° < \theta < 60° + n \cdot 360°$, n an integer (for example, 50°)

57. $0° + n \cdot 360° < \frac{1}{2}\theta < 90° + n \cdot 360°$; $2n \cdot 360° < \theta < 180° + 2n \cdot 360°$; $n \cdot 720° < \theta < 180° + n \cdot 720°$, n an integer (for example, 120°)

58. $90° + n \cdot 360° < \frac{1}{2}\theta < 180° + n \cdot 360°$; $180° + 2n \cdot 360° < \theta < 360° + 2n \cdot 360°$;

    $180° + n \cdot 720° < \theta < 360° + n \cdot 720°$, n an integer (for example, 200°)

59. $180° + n \cdot 360° < \frac{1}{2}\theta < 270° + n \cdot 360°$; $360° + 2n \cdot 360° < \theta < 540° + 2n \cdot 360°$;

    $360° + n \cdot 720° < \theta < 540° + n \cdot 720°$, n an integer (for example, 400°)

60. $0° + n \cdot 360° < \frac{1}{5}\theta < 90° + n \cdot 360°$; $5n \cdot 360° < \theta < 450° + 5n \cdot 360°$;

    $n \cdot 1800° < \theta < 450° + n \cdot 1800°$, n an integer (for example, 100°)

61. $90° + n \cdot 360° < \frac{1}{5}\theta < 180° + n \cdot 360°$; $450° + 5n \cdot 360° < \theta < 900° + 5n \cdot 360°$;

    $450° + n \cdot 1800° < \theta < 900° + n \cdot 1800°$, n an integer (for example, 500°)

62. $180° + n \cdot 360° < \frac{1}{5}\theta < 270° + n \cdot 360°$; $900° + 5n \cdot 360° < \theta < 1350° + 5n \cdot 360°$;

    $900° + n \cdot 1800° < \theta < 1350° + n \cdot 1800°$, n an integer (for example, 1000°)

C 63. Suppose $\theta = 10° + k \cdot 150°$ and $\varphi = 10° + (k + j)150°$ are coterminal; then their differ-
    ence, $150j$, is divisible by 360. The least such j is 12; that is, there are 12 possible terminal
    sides for the angles $10° + n \cdot 150°$ in standard position.

64. Suppose $\theta = 10° + k \cdot 170°$ and $\varphi = 10° + (k + j)170°$ are coterminal; then their differ-
    ence, $170j$, is divisible by 360. The least such j is 36; that is, there are 36 possible terminal
    sides for the angles $10° + n \cdot 170°$ in standard position.

65. Suppose $\theta = 10° + k \cdot 19°$ and $\varphi = 10° + (k + j)19°$ are coterminal; then their differ-
    ence, $19j$, is divisible by 360. The least such j is 360; that is, there are 360 possible
    terminal sides for the angles $10° + n \cdot 19°$ in standard position.

66. Suppose $\theta = 10° + k\sqrt{2}°$ and $\varphi = 10° + (k + j)\sqrt{2}°$ are coterminal; then their differ-
    ence, $j\sqrt{2}$, is divisible by 360. $j\sqrt{2}$ is not divisible by 360 for any integer j; θ and φ are
    not coterminal and there are an infinite number of possible terminal sides for the angle
    $10° + n\sqrt{2}°$ in standard position.

Page 521 · CHALLENGE

At least 6 cuts are necessary. Dividing the cube as shown produces 27 cubes, the innermost
of which has no painted surfaces.

Pages 526-527 · WRITTEN EXERCISES

A

1. $x = 3$, $y = 4$; $r^2 = 3^2 + 4^2 = 25$; $r = 5$; $\sin \theta = \dfrac{y}{r} = \dfrac{4}{5}$, $\cos \theta = \dfrac{x}{r} = \dfrac{3}{5}$,

$\tan \theta = \dfrac{y}{x} = \dfrac{4}{3}$; $\csc \theta = \dfrac{r}{y} = \dfrac{5}{4}$; $\sec \theta = \dfrac{r}{x} = \dfrac{5}{3}$; $\cot \theta = \dfrac{x}{y} = \dfrac{3}{4}$

2. $x = 8$, $y = 6$; $r^2 = 8^2 + 6^2 = 100$; $r = 10$; $\sin \theta = \dfrac{y}{r} = \dfrac{3}{5}$; $\cos \theta = \dfrac{x}{r} = \dfrac{4}{5}$;

$\tan \theta = \dfrac{y}{x} = \dfrac{3}{4}$; $\csc \theta = \dfrac{r}{y} = \dfrac{5}{3}$; $\sec \theta = \dfrac{r}{x} = \dfrac{5}{4}$; $\cot \theta = \dfrac{x}{y} = \dfrac{4}{3}$

3. $x = 9$, $y = 2$; $r^2 = 9^2 + 2^2 = 85$; $r = \sqrt{85}$; $\sin \theta = \dfrac{y}{r} = \dfrac{2}{\sqrt{85}} = \dfrac{2\sqrt{85}}{85}$;

$\cos \theta = \dfrac{x}{r} = \dfrac{9}{\sqrt{85}} = \dfrac{9\sqrt{85}}{85}$; $\tan \theta = \dfrac{y}{x} = \dfrac{2}{9}$; $\csc \theta = \dfrac{r}{y} = \dfrac{\sqrt{85}}{2}$;

$\sec \theta = \dfrac{r}{x} = \dfrac{\sqrt{85}}{9}$; $\cot \theta = \dfrac{x}{y} = \dfrac{9}{2}$

4. $x = 1$, $y = 1$; $r^2 = 1^2 + 1^2 = 2$; $r = \sqrt{2}$; $\sin \theta = \dfrac{y}{r} = \dfrac{1}{\sqrt{2}} = \dfrac{\sqrt{2}}{2}$;

$\cos \theta = \dfrac{x}{r} = \dfrac{1}{\sqrt{2}} = \dfrac{\sqrt{2}}{2}$; $\tan \theta = \dfrac{y}{x} = 1$; $\csc \theta = \dfrac{r}{y} = \sqrt{2}$; $\sec \theta = \dfrac{r}{x} = \sqrt{2}$;

$\cot \theta = \dfrac{x}{y} = 1$

5. $x = 1$, $y = 2$; $r^2 = 1^2 + 2^2 = 5$; $r = \sqrt{5}$; $\sin \theta = \dfrac{y}{r} = \dfrac{2}{\sqrt{5}} = \dfrac{2\sqrt{5}}{5}$;

$\cos \theta = \dfrac{x}{r} = \dfrac{1}{\sqrt{5}} = \dfrac{\sqrt{5}}{5}$; $\tan \theta = \dfrac{y}{x} = 2$; $\csc \theta = \dfrac{r}{y} = \dfrac{\sqrt{5}}{2}$; $\sec \theta = \dfrac{r}{x} = \sqrt{5}$;

$\cot \theta = \dfrac{x}{y} = \dfrac{1}{2}$

6. $x = 3$, $y = 1$; $r^2 = 3^2 + 1^2 = 10$; $r = \sqrt{10}$; $\sin \theta = \dfrac{y}{r} = \dfrac{1}{\sqrt{10}} = \dfrac{\sqrt{10}}{10}$;

$\cos \theta = \dfrac{x}{r} = \dfrac{3}{\sqrt{10}} = \dfrac{3\sqrt{10}}{10}$; $\tan \theta = \dfrac{y}{x} = \dfrac{1}{3}$; $\csc \theta = \dfrac{r}{y} = \sqrt{10}$; $\sec \theta = \dfrac{r}{x} = \dfrac{\sqrt{10}}{3}$;

$\cot \theta = \dfrac{x}{y} = 3$

7. $x = 6$, $y = 7$; $r^2 = 6^2 + 7^2 = 85$; $r = \sqrt{85}$; $\sin \theta = \dfrac{y}{r} = \dfrac{7}{\sqrt{85}} = \dfrac{7\sqrt{85}}{85}$;

$\cos \theta = \dfrac{x}{r} = \dfrac{6}{\sqrt{85}} = \dfrac{6\sqrt{85}}{85}$; $\tan \theta = \dfrac{y}{x} = \dfrac{7}{6}$; $\csc \theta = \dfrac{r}{y} = \dfrac{\sqrt{85}}{7}$; $\sec \theta = \dfrac{r}{x} = \dfrac{\sqrt{85}}{6}$;

$\cot \theta = \dfrac{x}{y} = \dfrac{6}{7}$

8. $x = 4$, $y = 2$; $r^2 = 4^2 + 2^2 = 20$; $r = \sqrt{20} = 2\sqrt{5}$; $\sin \theta = \dfrac{y}{r} = \dfrac{2}{2\sqrt{5}} = \dfrac{\sqrt{5}}{5}$;

$\cos \theta = \dfrac{x}{r} = \dfrac{4}{2\sqrt{5}} = \dfrac{2\sqrt{5}}{5}$; $\tan \theta = \dfrac{y}{x} = \dfrac{1}{2}$; $\csc \theta = \dfrac{r}{y} = \sqrt{5}$; $\sec \theta = \dfrac{r}{x} = \dfrac{\sqrt{5}}{2}$;

$\cot \theta = \dfrac{x}{y} = 2$

9. $x = \sqrt{2}$, $y = \sqrt{2}$; $r^2 = (\sqrt{2})^2 + (\sqrt{2})^2 = 4$; $r = 2$; $\sin \theta = \dfrac{y}{r} = \dfrac{\sqrt{2}}{2}$;

$\cos \theta = \dfrac{x}{r} = \dfrac{\sqrt{2}}{2}$; $\tan \theta = \dfrac{y}{x} = 1$; $\csc \theta = \dfrac{r}{y} = \dfrac{2}{\sqrt{2}} = \sqrt{2}$; $\sec \theta = \dfrac{r}{x} = \dfrac{2}{\sqrt{2}} = \sqrt{2}$;

$\cot \theta = \dfrac{x}{y} = 1$

10. $x = \sqrt{3}$, $y = 1$; $r^2 = (\sqrt{3})^2 + 1^2 = 4$; $r = 2$; $\sin \theta = \dfrac{y}{r} = \dfrac{1}{2}$; $\cos \theta = \dfrac{x}{r} = \dfrac{\sqrt{3}}{2}$;

$\tan \theta = \dfrac{y}{x} = \dfrac{1}{\sqrt{3}} = \dfrac{\sqrt{3}}{3}$; $\csc \theta = \dfrac{r}{y} = 2$; $\sec \theta = \dfrac{r}{x} = \dfrac{2}{\sqrt{3}} = \dfrac{2\sqrt{3}}{3}$; $\cot \theta = \dfrac{x}{y} = \sqrt{3}$

11. $x = 2\sqrt{5}$, $y = \sqrt{5}$; $r^2 = (2\sqrt{5})^2 + (\sqrt{5})^2 = 25$; $r = 5$; $\sin \theta = \dfrac{y}{r} = \dfrac{\sqrt{5}}{5}$;

$\cos \theta = \dfrac{x}{r} = \dfrac{2\sqrt{5}}{5}$; $\tan \theta = \dfrac{y}{x} = \dfrac{\sqrt{5}}{2\sqrt{5}} = \dfrac{1}{2}$; $\csc \theta = \dfrac{r}{y} = \dfrac{5}{\sqrt{5}} = \sqrt{5}$;

$\sec \theta = \dfrac{r}{x} = \dfrac{5}{2\sqrt{5}} = \dfrac{\sqrt{5}}{2}$; $\cot \theta = \dfrac{x}{y} = 2$

12. $x = \sqrt{7}$, $y = \sqrt{2}$; $r^2 = (\sqrt{7})^2 + (\sqrt{2})^2 = 9$; $r = 3$; $\sin \theta = \dfrac{y}{r} = \dfrac{\sqrt{2}}{3}$;

$\cos \theta = \dfrac{x}{r} = \dfrac{\sqrt{7}}{3}$; $\tan \theta = \dfrac{y}{x} = \dfrac{\sqrt{2}}{\sqrt{7}} = \dfrac{\sqrt{14}}{7}$; $\csc \theta = \dfrac{r}{y} = \dfrac{3}{\sqrt{2}} = \dfrac{3\sqrt{2}}{2}$;

$\sec \theta = \dfrac{r}{x} = \dfrac{3}{\sqrt{7}} = \dfrac{3\sqrt{7}}{7}$; $\cot \theta = \dfrac{x}{y} = \dfrac{\sqrt{7}}{\sqrt{2}} = \dfrac{\sqrt{14}}{2}$

	13.	**14.**	**15.**	**16.**	**17.**	**18.**	**19.**	**20.**
$\sin \theta$	$\dfrac{4}{5}$	$\dfrac{1}{2}$	$\dfrac{\sqrt{3}}{2}$	$\dfrac{3}{5}$	$\dfrac{\sqrt{2}}{2}$	$\dfrac{12}{13}$	$\dfrac{5}{13}$	$\dfrac{\sqrt{2}}{2}$
$\cos \theta$	$\dfrac{3}{5}$	$\dfrac{\sqrt{3}}{2}$	$\dfrac{1}{2}$	$\dfrac{4}{5}$	$\dfrac{\sqrt{2}}{2}$	$\dfrac{5}{13}$	$\dfrac{12}{13}$	$\dfrac{\sqrt{2}}{2}$
$\tan \theta$	$\dfrac{4}{3}$	$\dfrac{\sqrt{3}}{3}$	$\sqrt{3}$	$\dfrac{3}{4}$	1	$\dfrac{12}{5}$	$\dfrac{5}{12}$	1

21. $\sin 30° = \dfrac{a}{18}$; $\dfrac{1}{2} = \dfrac{a}{18}$; $a = 9$; $\cos 30° = \dfrac{b}{18}$; $\dfrac{\sqrt{3}}{2} = \dfrac{b}{18}$; $b = 9\sqrt{3}$;

$\angle B = 90° - 30° = 60°$

22. $\sin 45° = \dfrac{a}{8}$; $\dfrac{\sqrt{2}}{2} = \dfrac{a}{8}$; $a = 4\sqrt{2}$; $\cos 45° = \dfrac{b}{8}$; $\dfrac{\sqrt{2}}{2} = \dfrac{b}{8}$; $b = 4\sqrt{2}$;

$\angle B = 90° - 45° = 45°$

23. $\sin 45° = \dfrac{12}{c}$; $\dfrac{\sqrt{2}}{2} = \dfrac{12}{c}$; $c = \dfrac{24}{\sqrt{2}} = 12\sqrt{2}$; $\tan 45° = \dfrac{12}{b}$; $1 = \dfrac{12}{b}$; $b = 12$;

$\angle B = 90° - 45° = 45°$

24. $\tan 60° = \dfrac{a}{15}$; $\sqrt{3} = \dfrac{a}{15}$; $a = 15\sqrt{3}$; $\sec 60° = \dfrac{c}{15}$; $2 = \dfrac{c}{15}$; $c = 30$;

$\angle B = 90° - 60° = 30°$

25. $\tan A = \dfrac{5}{5} = 1$; $\angle A = 45°$; $\angle B = 90° - 45° = 45°$; $c = \sqrt{5^2 + 5^2} = \sqrt{50} = 5\sqrt{2}$

26. $\sin A = \dfrac{4}{8} = \dfrac{1}{2}$; $\angle A = 30°$; $\angle B = 90° - 30° = 60°$; $b = \sqrt{8^2 - 4^2} = \sqrt{48} = 4\sqrt{3}$

27. Let x_1, x_2, and y be as shown; $\cos 45° = \dfrac{x_1}{15}$; $x_1 = \dfrac{\sqrt{2}}{2} \cdot 15 = \dfrac{15\sqrt{2}}{2}$; $y = x_1 = \dfrac{15\sqrt{2}}{2}$;

$\tan 60° = \dfrac{y}{x_2}$; $\sqrt{3}\,x_2 = \dfrac{15\sqrt{2}}{2}$; $x_2 = \dfrac{15\sqrt{2}}{2\sqrt{3}} = \dfrac{5\sqrt{6}}{2}$;

$x = x_1 + x_2 = \dfrac{15\sqrt{2}}{2} + \dfrac{5\sqrt{6}}{2} = \dfrac{15\sqrt{2} + 5\sqrt{6}}{2}$

28. Let x_1, x_2, and y be as shown; $\cos 30° = \dfrac{x_1}{12}$;

$x_1 = 12\left(\dfrac{\sqrt{3}}{2}\right) = 6\sqrt{3}$; $\sin 30° = \dfrac{y}{12}$; $y = 12\left(\dfrac{1}{2}\right) = 6$;

$x_2 = y = 6$; $x = x_1 + x_2 = 6\sqrt{3} + 6$

29. Let y be as shown; $\tan 45° = \dfrac{x + y}{24}$; $1 = \dfrac{x + y}{24}$; $x + y = 24$;

$x = 24 - y$; $\tan 30° = \dfrac{y}{24}$; $y = 24\left(\dfrac{\sqrt{3}}{3}\right) = 8\sqrt{3}$; $x = 24 - 8\sqrt{3}$

30. Let y be as shown; $\cot 30° = \dfrac{y}{18}$; $y = 18\sqrt{3}$; $\tan 60° = \dfrac{18 + x}{y}$;

$\sqrt{3} = \dfrac{18 + x}{18\sqrt{3}}$; $54 = 18 + x$; $x = 36$

31. Let $R_1 = (x, 0)$ and $R_2 = (x', 0)$. $\triangle OPR_1$, and $\triangle OQR_2$ are right triangles and $\triangle OPR_1 \sim$

$\triangle OQR_2$ by the AA Similarity Theorem. Then $\dfrac{y}{y'} = \dfrac{r}{s}$ and $\dfrac{y}{r} = \dfrac{y'}{s}$. Similarly, $\dfrac{x}{r} = \dfrac{x'}{s}$,

and $\dfrac{y}{x} = \dfrac{y'}{x'}$.

32. $\cos^2\theta = 1 - \sin^2\theta$; $\cos\theta = \sqrt{1 - \sin^2\theta} = \sqrt{1 - u^2}$;

$\tan\theta = \dfrac{\sin\theta}{\cos\theta} = \dfrac{u}{\sqrt{1 - u^2}} = \dfrac{u\sqrt{1 - u^2}}{1 - u^2}$; $\csc\theta = \dfrac{1}{\sin\theta} = \dfrac{1}{u}$;

$\sec\theta = \dfrac{1}{\cos\theta} = \dfrac{1}{\sqrt{1 - u^2}} = \dfrac{\sqrt{1 - u^2}}{1 - u^2}$; $\cot\theta = \dfrac{1}{\tan\theta} = \dfrac{\sqrt{1 - u^2}}{u}$

33. $\sin^2\phi = 1 - \cos^2\phi$; $\sin\phi = \sqrt{1 - \cos^2\phi} = \sqrt{1 - v^2}$; $\tan\phi = \dfrac{\sin\phi}{\cos\phi} = \dfrac{\sqrt{1 - v^2}}{v}$;

$\csc\phi = \dfrac{1}{\sin\phi} = \dfrac{1}{\sqrt{1 - v^2}} = \dfrac{\sqrt{1 - v^2}}{1 - v^2}$; $\sec\phi = \dfrac{1}{\cos\phi} = \dfrac{1}{v}$;

$\cot\phi = \dfrac{1}{\tan\phi} = \dfrac{v}{\sqrt{1 - v^2}} = \dfrac{v\sqrt{1 - v^2}}{1 - v^2}$

Pages 532-533 · WRITTEN EXERCISES

A   **1.** $\alpha = 360° - 272° = 88°$ **2.** $\alpha = 180° - 119° = 61°$ **3.** $\alpha = 48°$

4. $\alpha = -(-211° + 180°) = 31°$ **5.** $473° - 360° = 113°$; $\alpha = 180° - 113° = 67$

6. $619° - 360° = 259°$; $\alpha = 259° - 180° = 79°$

7. $-752° = -720° - 32°$; $\alpha = 32°$ **8.** $-719° = -720° + 1°$; $\alpha = 1°$

9. $\alpha = 180° - 127.3° = 52.7°$ **10.** $\alpha = -(-232.7° + 180°) = 52.7°$

11. $\alpha = 193.25° - 180° = 13.25°$ **12.** $\alpha = 360° - 333.33° = 26.67°$

13. $\alpha = 246°13' - 180° = 66°13'$ **14.** $\alpha = 180° - 163°42' = 16°18'$

15. $\sin 236° = -\sin 56°$ **16.** $\tan(-13°) = -\tan 13°$ **17.** $\sec(-122°) = -\sec 58°$

18. $\cos 323° = \cos 37°$ **19.** $\cot 318.4° = -\cot 41.6°$ **20.** $\csc 123.4° = \csc 56.6°$

21. $\cos(-231.9°) = -\cos 51.9°$ **22.** $\sin(-46.6°) = -\sin 46.6°$

23. $\tan 263°18' = \tan 83°18'$ **24.** $\cot 147°37' = -\cot 32°23'$

25. $\sin 225° = -\sin 45° = -\dfrac{\sqrt{2}}{2}$; $\cos 225° = -\cos 45° = -\dfrac{\sqrt{2}}{2}$; $\tan 225° = 1$;

$\csc 225° = -\sqrt{2}$; $\sec 225° = -\sqrt{2}$; $\cot 225° = 1$

26. $\sin 300° = -\sin 60° = -\dfrac{\sqrt{3}}{2}$; $\cos 300° = \cos 60° = \dfrac{1}{2}$; $\tan 300° = -\sqrt{3}$;

$\csc 300° = -\dfrac{2}{\sqrt{3}} = -\dfrac{2\sqrt{3}}{3}$; $\sec 300° = 2$; $\cot 300° = -\dfrac{1}{\sqrt{3}} = -\dfrac{\sqrt{3}}{3}$

27. $\sin 150° = \sin 30° = \dfrac{1}{2}$; $\cos 150° = -\cos 30° = -\dfrac{\sqrt{3}}{2}$; $\tan 150° = -\dfrac{1}{\sqrt{3}} = -\dfrac{\sqrt{3}}{3}$;

$\csc 150° = 2$; $\sec 150° = -\dfrac{2}{\sqrt{3}} = -\dfrac{2\sqrt{3}}{3}$; $\cot 150° = -\sqrt{3}$

28. $\sin(-45°) = -\sin 45° = -\dfrac{\sqrt{2}}{2}$; $\cos(-45°) = \cos 45° = \dfrac{\sqrt{2}}{2}$; $\tan(-45°) = -1$;

$\csc(-45°) = -\sqrt{2}$; $\sec(-45°) = \sqrt{2}$; $\cot(-45°) = -1$

29. $\sin 330° = -\sin 30° = -\dfrac{1}{2}$; $\cos 330° = \cos 30° = \dfrac{\sqrt{3}}{2}$; $\tan 330° = -\dfrac{1}{\sqrt{3}} = -\dfrac{\sqrt{3}}{3}$;

$\csc 330° = -2$; $\sec 330° = \dfrac{2}{\sqrt{3}} = \dfrac{2\sqrt{3}}{3}$; $\cot 330° = -\sqrt{3}$

30. $\sin 210° = -\sin 30° = -\dfrac{1}{2}$; $\cos 210° = -\cos 30° = -\dfrac{\sqrt{3}}{2}$; $\tan 210° = \dfrac{1}{\sqrt{3}} = \dfrac{\sqrt{3}}{3}$;

$\csc 210° = -2$; $\sec 210° = -\dfrac{2}{\sqrt{3}} = -\dfrac{2\sqrt{3}}{3}$; $\cot 210° = \sqrt{3}$

31. $\sin(-300°) = \sin 60° = \dfrac{\sqrt{3}}{2}$; $\cos(-300°) = \cos 60° = \dfrac{1}{2}$; $\tan(-300°) = \sqrt{3}$;

$\csc(-300°) = \dfrac{2}{\sqrt{3}} = \dfrac{2\sqrt{3}}{3}$; $\sec(-300°) = 2$; $\cot(-300°) = \dfrac{1}{\sqrt{3}} = \dfrac{\sqrt{3}}{3}$

32. $\sin 390° = \sin 30° = \dfrac{1}{2}$; $\cos 390° = \cos 30° = \dfrac{\sqrt{3}}{2}$; $\tan 390° = \dfrac{1}{\sqrt{3}} = \dfrac{\sqrt{3}}{3}$; $\csc 390° = 2$;

$\sec 390° = \dfrac{2}{\sqrt{3}} = \dfrac{2\sqrt{3}}{3}$; $\cot 390° = \sqrt{3}$

33. Choose $(0, 1)$ on the terminal side of the angle; $\sin 90° = \dfrac{1}{1} = 1$; $\cos 90° = \dfrac{0}{1} = 0$; $\tan 90°$ is undefined; $\csc 90° = \dfrac{1}{1} = 1$; $\sec 90°$ is undefined; $\cot 90° = \dfrac{0}{1} = 0$.

34. Choose $(1, 0)$ on the terminal side of the angle; $\sin(-720°) = \dfrac{0}{1} = 0$; $\cos(-720°) =$ $\dfrac{1}{1} = 1$; $\tan(-720°) = \dfrac{0}{1} = 0$; $\csc(-720°)$ is undefined; $\sec(-720°) = \dfrac{1}{1} = 1$; $\cot(-720°)$ is undefined.

35. Choose $(0, -1)$ on the terminal side of the angle; $\sin(-90°) = \dfrac{-1}{1} = -1$; $\cos(-90°) =$ $\dfrac{0}{1} = 0$; $\tan(-90°)$ is undefined; $\csc(-90°) = \dfrac{-1}{1} = -1$; $\sec(-90°)$ is undefined; $\cot(-90°) = \dfrac{0}{-1} = 0$.

36. Choose $(-1, 0)$ on the terminal side of the angle; $\sin 540° = \dfrac{0}{1} = 0$; $\cos 540° = \dfrac{-1}{1} = -1$; $\tan 540° = \dfrac{0}{-1} = 0$; $\csc 540°$ is undefined; $\sec 540° = \dfrac{1}{-1} = -1$; $\cot 540°$ is undefined.

37. **a.** $\cos\theta$ is negative in Quadrants II and III; since $0° < \theta < 180°$, θ is in Quadrant II.

b. $\sin^2\theta = 1 - \left(-\dfrac{12}{13}\right)^2 = 1 - \dfrac{144}{169} = \dfrac{25}{169}$; since θ is in Quadrant II, $\sin\theta = \dfrac{5}{13}$;

$\tan\theta = \dfrac{\sin\theta}{\cos\theta} = -\dfrac{5}{12}$; $\csc\theta = \dfrac{1}{\sin\theta} = \dfrac{13}{5}$; $\sec\theta = \dfrac{1}{\cos\theta} = -\dfrac{13}{12}$;

$\cot\theta = \dfrac{1}{\tan\theta} = -\dfrac{12}{5}$

38. **a.** $\sin\theta$ is negative and $\cos\theta$ positive in Quadrant IV.

b. $\cos^2\theta = 1 - \left(-\dfrac{3}{5}\right)^2 = 1 - \dfrac{9}{25} = \dfrac{16}{25}$; since $\cos\theta > 0$, $\cos\theta = \dfrac{4}{5}$;

$\tan\theta = \dfrac{\sin\theta}{\cos\theta} = -\dfrac{3}{4}$; $\csc\theta = \dfrac{1}{\sin\theta} = -\dfrac{5}{3}$; $\sec\theta = \dfrac{1}{\cos\theta} = \dfrac{5}{4}$;

$\cot\theta = \dfrac{1}{\tan\theta} = -\dfrac{4}{3}$

39. a. $\sin \theta$ and $\cos \theta$ are both negative in Quadrant III.

    b. $\cos^2\theta = 1 - \left(-\dfrac{5}{13}\right)^2 = 1 - \dfrac{25}{169} = \dfrac{144}{169}$; since $\cos \theta < 0$, $\cos \theta = -\dfrac{12}{13}$;

    $\tan \theta = \dfrac{\sin \theta}{\cos \theta} = \dfrac{5}{12}$; $\csc \theta = \dfrac{1}{\sin \theta} = -\dfrac{13}{5}$; $\sec \theta = \dfrac{1}{\cos \theta} = -\dfrac{13}{12}$; $\cot \theta = \dfrac{1}{\tan \theta} = \dfrac{12}{5}$

40. a. $\cos \theta$ is positive in Quadrants I and IV; since $180° < \theta < 360°$, θ is in Quadrant IV.

    b. $\sin^2\theta = 1 - \left(\dfrac{12}{13}\right)^2 = 1 - \dfrac{144}{169} = \dfrac{25}{169}$; $\sin \theta < 0$ for θ in Quadrant IV, so $\sin \theta =$

    $-\dfrac{5}{13}$; $\tan \theta = \dfrac{\sin \theta}{\cos \theta} = -\dfrac{5}{12}$; $\csc \theta = \dfrac{1}{\sin \theta} = -\dfrac{13}{5}$; $\sec \theta = \dfrac{1}{\cos \theta} = \dfrac{13}{12}$;

    $\cot \theta = \dfrac{1}{\tan \theta} = -\dfrac{12}{5}$

41. a. $\cos \theta$ is positive in Quadrants I and IV; since $0° < \theta < 270°$, θ is in Quadrant I.

    b. $\sin^2\theta = 1 - \left(\dfrac{2}{3}\right)^2 = 1 - \dfrac{4}{9} = \dfrac{5}{9}$; $\sin \theta > 0$ for θ in Quadrant I, so $\sin \theta = \dfrac{\sqrt 5}{3}$;

    $\tan \theta = \dfrac{\sin \theta}{\cos \theta} = \dfrac{\sqrt 5}{2}$; $\csc \theta = \dfrac{1}{\sin \theta} = \dfrac{3}{\sqrt 5} = \dfrac{3\sqrt 5}{5}$; $\sec \theta = \dfrac{1}{\cos \theta} = \dfrac{3}{2}$;

    $\cot \theta = \dfrac{1}{\tan \theta} = \dfrac{2}{\sqrt 5} = \dfrac{2\sqrt 5}{5}$

42. a. $\sin \theta$ is negative in Quadrants III and IV; since $-90° < \theta < 180°$, θ is in Quadrant IV.

    b. $\cos^2\theta = 1 - \left(-\dfrac{2}{5}\right)^2 = 1 - \dfrac{4}{25} = \dfrac{21}{25}$; $\cos \theta > 0$ for θ in Quadrant IV, so

    $\cos \theta = \dfrac{\sqrt{21}}{5}$; $\tan \theta = \dfrac{\sin \theta}{\cos \theta} = -\dfrac{2}{\sqrt{21}} = -\dfrac{2\sqrt{21}}{21}$; $\csc \theta = \dfrac{1}{\sin \theta} = -\dfrac{5}{2}$;

    $\sec \theta = \dfrac{1}{\cos \theta} = \dfrac{5}{\sqrt{21}} = \dfrac{5\sqrt{21}}{21}$; $\cot \theta = \dfrac{1}{\tan \theta} = -\dfrac{\sqrt{21}}{2}$

43. a. $\sin \theta$ is negative and $\tan \theta$ positive in Quadrant III.   **b.** $\cos^2\theta = 1 - \left(-\dfrac{3}{4}\right)^2 =$

    $1 - \dfrac{9}{16} = \dfrac{7}{16}$; $\cos \theta < 0$ for θ in Quadrant III, so $\cos \theta = -\dfrac{\sqrt 7}{4}$; $\tan \theta = \dfrac{3}{\sqrt 7} = \dfrac{3\sqrt 7}{7}$;

    $\csc \theta = \dfrac{1}{\sin \theta} = -\dfrac{4}{3}$; $\sec \theta = \dfrac{1}{\cos \theta} = -\dfrac{4}{\sqrt 7} = -\dfrac{4\sqrt 7}{7}$; $\cot \theta = \dfrac{1}{\tan \theta} = \dfrac{\sqrt 7}{3}$

44. a. $\cos \theta$ and $\tan \theta$ are both positive in Quadrant I.   **b.** $\sin^2\theta = 1 - \left(\dfrac{1}{3}\right)^2 =$

    $1 - \dfrac{1}{9} = \dfrac{8}{9}$; $\sin \theta > 0$ for θ in Quadrant I, so $\sin \theta = \dfrac{2\sqrt 2}{3}$; $\tan \theta = \dfrac{\sin \theta}{\cos \theta} = 2\sqrt 2$;

    $\csc \theta = \dfrac{1}{\sin \theta} = \dfrac{3}{2\sqrt 2} = \dfrac{3\sqrt 2}{4}$; $\sec \theta = \dfrac{1}{\cos \theta} = 3$; $\cot \theta = \dfrac{1}{\tan \theta} = \dfrac{1}{2\sqrt 2} = \dfrac{\sqrt 2}{4}$

45. $0°, 180°$ **46.** $90°, 270°$ **47.** $0°, 180°$ **48.** $90°$ **49.** $0°$ **50.** $180°$

51. $270°$ **52.** $40°, 140°$ **53.** $70°, 290°$ **54.** $100°, 260°$ **55.** $310°, 230°$

56. $20°, 200°$

C **57.** $\neq$ **58.** $=$ **59.** $\neq$

Pages 536-537 · WRITTEN EXERCISES

A   **1.** $\tan 17.3° = 0.3115$

2. $\cos 41.6° = 0.7478$

3. $\left.\begin{array}{l}\sin 61.7° = 0.8805 \\ \sin 61.75° = x\end{array}\right\} d$

$\sin 61.8° = 0.8813$

$\dfrac{0.05}{0.1} = \dfrac{d}{0.0008}; \ d = 0.0004$

$x = 0.8805 + 0.0004 = 0.8809$

4. $\left.\begin{array}{l}\cot 78.1° = 0.2107 \\ \cot 78.15° = x\end{array}\right\} d$

$\cot 78.2° = 0.2089$

$\dfrac{0.05}{0.1} = \dfrac{d}{-0.0018}; \ d = -0.0009$

$x = 0.2107 - 0.0009 = 0.2098$

5. $\left.\begin{array}{l}\csc 3.3° = 17.37 \\ \csc 3.33° = x\end{array}\right\} d$

$\csc 3.4° = 16.86$

$\dfrac{0.03}{0.1} = \dfrac{d}{-0.51}; \ d = -0.153$

$x = 17.37 - 0.15 = 17.22$

6. sec 2.2° and sec 2.3° are both equal to 1.001 to three decimal places; therefore sec 2.22° = 1.001.

7. $\cos 143.6° = -\cos 36.4° = -0.8049$

8. $\sin 247.8° = -\sin 67.8° = -0.9259$

9. $\cot(-126.5°) = \cot 53.5° = 0.7400$

10. $\tan(-62.7°) = -\tan 62.7° = -1.937$

11. sec 375.57° = sec 15.57°; since sec 15.5° and sec 15.6° are both equal to 1.038 to three decimal places, sec 375.57° = 1.038.

12. $\csc 472.15° = \csc 67.85°$

$\left.\begin{array}{l}\csc 67.8° = 1.080 \\ \csc 67.85° = x\end{array}\right\} d$

$\csc 67.9° = 1.079$

$\dfrac{0.05}{0.1} = \dfrac{d}{-0.001}; \ d = -0.0005$

$x = 1.080 - 0.0005 = 1.0795; \ 1.080$

13. $\cos 57°30' = 0.5373$

14. $\tan 31°40' = 0.6168$

15. $\left.\begin{array}{l}\cot 72°40' = 0.3121 \\ \cot 72°45' = x\end{array}\right\} d$

$\cot 72°50' = 0.3089$

$\dfrac{5}{10} = \dfrac{d}{-0.0032}; \ d = -0.0016$

$x = 0.3121 - 0.0016 = 0.3105$

16. $\left.\begin{array}{l}\sin 81°10' = 0.9881 \\ \sin 81°15' = x\end{array}\right\} d$

$\sin 81°20' = 0.9886$

$\dfrac{5}{10} = \dfrac{d}{0.0005}; \ d = 0.00025$

$x = 0.9881 + 0.0003 = 0.9884$

17. $\left.\begin{array}{l}\sec 16°10' = 1.041 \\ \sec 16°17' = x\end{array}\right\} d$

$\sec 16°20' = 1.042$

$\dfrac{7}{10} = \dfrac{d}{0.001}; \ d = 0.0007$

$x = 1.041 + 0.0007 = 1.0417; \ 1.042$

18. $\left.\begin{array}{l}\csc 61°50' = 1.134 \\ \csc 61°52' = x\end{array}\right\} d$

$\csc 62° = 1.133$

$\dfrac{2}{10} = \dfrac{d}{-0.001}; \ d = -0.0002$

$x = 1.134 - 0.0002 = 1.1338; \ 1.134$

19. $\sin 173°40' = \sin 6°20' = 0.1103$

20. $\cos(-62°10') = \cos 62°10' = 0.4669$

21. $\cot(-142°25') = \cot 37°35'$

$\left.\begin{array}{l}\cot 37°30' = 1.303 \\ \cot 37°35' = x\end{array}\right\}d$

$\cot 37°40' = 1.295$

$\dfrac{5}{10} = \dfrac{d}{-0.008}; d = -0.004$

$x = 1.303 - 0.004 = 1.299$

22. $\tan 173°35' = -\tan 6°25'$

$\left.\begin{array}{l}\tan 6°20' = 0.1110 \\ \tan 6°25' = x\end{array}\right\}d$

$\tan 6°30' = 0.1139$

$\dfrac{5}{10} = \dfrac{d}{0.0029}; d = 0.00145$

$x = 0.1110 + 0.0015 = 0.1125$

$\tan 173°35' = -0.1125$

23. $\left.\begin{array}{l}\cos 31°10' = 0.8557 \\ \cos 31°16'30'' = x\end{array}\right\}d$

$\cos 31°20' = 0.8542$

$\dfrac{6.5}{10} = \dfrac{d}{-0.0015}; d = -0.000975$

$x = 0.8557 - 0.0010 = 0.8547$

24. $\left.\begin{array}{l}\sin 72°10' = 0.9520 \\ \sin 72°18'15'' = x\end{array}\right\}d$

$\sin 72°20' = 0.9528$

$\dfrac{8.25}{10} = \dfrac{d}{0.0008}; d = 0.00066$

$x = 0.9520 + 0.0007 = 0.9527$

25. $d\left\{\begin{array}{l}\sin 20.4° = 0.3486 \\ \sin \theta = 0.3500\end{array}\right.$

$\sin 20.5° = 0.3502$

$\dfrac{d}{0.1} = \dfrac{0.0014}{0.0016}; d = 0.09$

$\theta = 20.4° + 0.09° = 20.49°$

26. $d\left\{\begin{array}{l}\cos 34.9° = 0.8202 \\ \cos \theta = 0.8200\end{array}\right.$

$\cos 35.0° = 0.8192$

$\dfrac{d}{0.1} = \dfrac{0.0002}{0.001}; d = 0.02$

$\theta = 34.9° + 0.02° = 34.92°$

27. $d\left\{\begin{array}{l}\cot 33.6° = 1.5051 \\ \cot \theta = 1.5000\end{array}\right.$

$\cot 33.7° = 1.4994$

$\dfrac{d}{0.1} = \dfrac{0.0051}{0.0057}; d = 0.089$

$\theta = 33.6° + 0.089° = 33.69°$

28. $d\left\{\begin{array}{l}\tan 50.9° = 1.230 \\ \tan \theta = 1.234\end{array}\right.$

$\tan 51.0° = 1.235$

$\dfrac{d}{0.1} = \dfrac{0.004}{0.005}; d = 0.08$

$\theta = 50.9° + 0.08° = 50.98°$

29. $d\left\{\begin{array}{l}\sec 76.6° = 4.315 \\ \sec \theta = 4.321\end{array}\right.$

$\sec 76.7° = 4.347$

$\dfrac{d}{0.1} = \dfrac{0.006}{0.032}; d = 0.01875$

$\theta = 76.6° + 0.02° = 76.62°$

30. $d\left\{\begin{array}{l}\csc 14.4° = 4.021 \\ \csc \theta = 4.000\end{array}\right.$

$\csc 14.5° = 3.994$

$\dfrac{d}{0.1} = \dfrac{0.021}{0.027}; d = 0.08$

$\theta = 14.4° + 0.08° = 14.48°$

31. $d\left\{\begin{array}{l}\cos 35°30' = 0.8141 \\ \cos \theta = 0.8131\end{array}\right.$

$\cos 35°40' = 0.8124$

$\dfrac{d}{10} = \dfrac{0.0010}{0.0017}; d = 6$

$\theta = 35°30' + 6' = 35°36'$

32. $d\left\{\begin{array}{l}\sin 12°10' = 0.2108 \\ \sin \theta = 0.2115\end{array}\right.$

$\sin 12°20' = 0.2136$

$\dfrac{d}{10} = \dfrac{0.0007}{0.0028}; d = 2.5$

$\theta = 12°10' + 3' = 12°13'$

33. $d\begin{cases}\tan 6°30' = 0.1139 \\ \tan \theta \ \ = 0.1156\end{cases}$

$\qquad \tan 6°40' = 0.1169$

$\qquad \dfrac{d}{10} = \dfrac{0.0017}{0.003}; d = 5.7$

$\qquad \theta = 6°30' + 6' = 6°36'$

34. $d\begin{cases}\cos 76°10' = 0.2391 \\ \cos \theta \ \ = 0.2372\end{cases}$

$\qquad \cos 76°20' = 0.2363$

$\qquad \dfrac{d}{10} = \dfrac{0.0019}{0.0028}; d = 6.8$

$\qquad \theta = 76°10' + 7' = 76°17'$

35. $d\begin{cases}\sin 52°0' \ \ = 0.7880 \\ \sin \theta \ \ \ \ = 0.7891\end{cases}$

$\qquad \sin 52°10' = 0.7898$

$\qquad \dfrac{d}{10} = \dfrac{0.0011}{0.0018}; d = 6$

$\qquad \theta = 52°0' + 6' = 52°6'$

36. $d\begin{cases}\tan 65°10' = 2.161 \\ \tan \theta \ \ = 2.176\end{cases}$

$\qquad \tan 65°20' = 2.177$

$\qquad \dfrac{d}{10} = \dfrac{0.015}{0.016}; d = 9$

$\qquad \theta = 65°10' + 9' = 65°19'$

37. From Table 4, $\theta = 28.2°$; $\sin(180° - 28.2°) = \sin 28.2°$; $\theta = 28.2°$ or $\theta = 151.8°$.

38. From Table 4, $\theta = 40.4°$; $\cos(360° - 40.4°) = \cos 40.4°$; $\theta = 40.4°$ or $319.6°$.

39. θ is in Quadrant II or Quadrant IV. Let α be the reference angle for θ; $\tan \theta = -\tan \alpha$; $\tan \alpha = 1.582$; from Table 4, $\alpha = 57.7°$; $\theta = 180° - 57.7° = 122.3°$ or $\theta = 360° - 57.7° = 302.3°$.

40. θ is in Quadrant III or Quadrant IV. Let α be the reference angle for θ; $\sin \theta = -\sin \alpha$; $\sin \alpha = 0.8100$; from Table 4, $\alpha = 54.1°$; $\theta = 180° + 54.1° = 234.1°$ or $\theta = 360° - 54.1° = 305.9°$.

41. From Table 4, $\theta = 78.4°$; $\cos(360° - 78.4°) = \cos 78.4°$; $\theta = 78.4°$ or $\theta = 281.6°$.

42. From Table 4, $\theta = 30.6°$; $\tan(180° + 30.6°) = \tan 30.6°$; $\theta = 30.6°$ or $\theta = 210.6°$.

43. From Table 4, $\cos 64.7° \approx 0.4275$; let $\alpha = 64.7°$ be the reference angle for θ; since $180° < \theta < 360°$ and $\cos \theta > 0$, θ is in Quadrant IV and $\theta = 360° - \alpha = 295.3°$.

44. Since $90° < \theta < 270°$ and $\sin \theta < 0$, θ is in Quadrant III. Let α be the reference angle for θ; $\sin \theta = -\sin \alpha$; $\sin \alpha = 0.5212$. From Table 4, $\alpha \approx 31.4°$; $\theta = 180° + 31.4° = 211.4°$.

45. Since $\sin \theta < 0$ and $\cos \theta > 0$, θ is in Quadrant IV. Let α be the reference angle for θ; $\sin \theta = -\sin \alpha$; $\sin \alpha = 0.6118$. From Table 4, $\alpha \approx 37.7°$; $\theta = 360° - 37.7° = 322.3°$.

46. Since $\cos \theta > 0$ and $\tan \theta < 0$, θ is in Quadrant IV. Let α be the reference angle for θ; $\cos \theta = \cos \alpha$; $\cos \alpha = 0.7815$. From Table 4, $\alpha = 38.6°$; $\theta = 360° - 38.6° = 321.4°$.

Pages 537–538 · CALCULATOR KEY-IN

   1. a. 0.9605   **b.** 0.5254   **c.** 154.9   **2. a.** 25.96°   **b.** 32.33°   **c.** 75°28'59"

   3. a. −30°   **b.** 135°   **c.** −45°

Pages 542-543 · WRITTEN EXERCISES

A   1. $\sin 28.6° = \dfrac{a}{145}$; $a = 145(0.4787) = 69.4$; $\cos 28.6° = \dfrac{b}{145}$; $b = 145(0.8780) = 127$;

$\angle B = 90.0° - 28.6° = 61.4°$

2. $\cos 42.8° = \dfrac{a}{16.3}$; $a = 16.3(0.7337) = 12.0$; $\sin 42.8° = \dfrac{b}{16.3}$; $b = 16.3(0.6794) = 11.1$;

$\angle A = 90.0° - 42.8° = 47.2°$

3. $\tan 71.5° = \dfrac{b}{1.82}$; $b = 1.82(2.989) = 5.44$; $\sec 71.5° = \dfrac{c}{1.82}$; $c = 1.82(3.152) = 5.74$;

$\angle A = 90.0° - 71.5° = 18.5°$

4. $\tan 57.5° = \dfrac{a}{355}$; $a = 355(1.570) = 557$; $\sec 57.5° = \dfrac{c}{355}$; $c = 355(1.861) = 661$;

$\angle B = 90.0° - 57.5° = 32.5°$

5. $\cot 47.7° = \dfrac{a}{83.6}$; $a = 83.6(0.9099) = 76.1$; $\csc 47.7° = \dfrac{c}{83.6}$; $c = 83.6(1.352) = 113$;

$\angle A = 90.0° - 47.7° = 42.3°$

6. $\cot 31.0° = \dfrac{b}{3.21}$; $b = 3.21(1.664) = 5.34$; $\csc 31.0° = \dfrac{c}{3.21}$; $c = 3.21(1.942) = 6.23$;

$\angle B = 90.0° - 31.0° = 59.0°$

7. $\sin A = \dfrac{460}{640} = 0.7188$; $\angle A = 46.0°$; $\angle B = 90.0° - 46.0° = 44.0°$; $b = \sqrt{c^2 - a^2} =$

$\sqrt{198000} = 445$

8. $\tan A = \dfrac{52.5}{37.0} = 1.419$; $\angle A = 54.8°$; $\angle B = 90.0° - 54.8° = 35.2°$; $c = \sqrt{a^2 + b^2} =$

$\sqrt{4125.25} = 64.2$

9. $\tan A = \dfrac{0.145}{0.325} = 0.4462$; $\angle A = 24.0°$; $\angle B = 90.0° - 24.0° = 66.0°$; $c = \sqrt{a^2 + b^2} =$

$\sqrt{0.12665} = 0.356$

10. $\cos A = \dfrac{2.60}{6.20} = 0.4194$; $\angle A = 65.2°$; $\angle B = 90.0° - 65.2° = 24.8°$; $a = \sqrt{c^2 - b^2} =$

$\sqrt{31.68} = 5.63$

11. $\cos 63°20' = \dfrac{a}{392}$; $a = 392(0.4488) = 176$; $\sin 63°20' = \dfrac{b}{392}$; $b = 392(0.8936) = 350$;

$\angle A = 90°0' - 63°20' = 26°40'$

12. $\sin 38°40' = \dfrac{a}{42.5}$; $a = 42.5(0.6248) = 26.6$; $\cos 38°40' = \dfrac{b}{42.5}$; $b = 42.5(0.7808) =$

33.2; $\angle B = 90°0' - 38°40' = 51°20'$

13. $\cot 12°30' = \dfrac{b}{1.34}$; $b = 1.34(4.511) = 6.04$; $\csc 12°30' = \dfrac{c}{1.34}$; $c = 1.34(4.620) = 6.19$;

$\angle B = 90°0' - 12°30' = 77°30'$

14. $\sec 67°30' = \dfrac{c}{420}$; $c = 420(2.613) = 1100$; $\tan 67°30' = \dfrac{b}{420}$; $b = 420(2.414) = 1010$;

$\angle A = 90°0' - 67°30' = 22°30'$

15. $\tan 40°50' = \dfrac{a}{52.5}$; $a = 52.5(0.8642) = 45.4$; $\sec 40°50' = \dfrac{c}{52.5}$; $c = 52.5(1.322) = 69.4$;

$\angle B = 90°0' - 40°50' = 49°10'$

16. $\cot 75°10' = \dfrac{a}{0.620}$; $a = 0.620(0.2648) = 0.164$; $\csc 75°10' = \dfrac{c}{0.620}$; $c = 0.620(1.034) =$

0.641; $\angle A = 90°0' - 75°10' = 14°50'$

B   **17.** Let A and B be the base angles and V the vertex angle. $\tan A = \dfrac{10}{8} = 1.25$;

$\angle A = 51.3°$; $\angle B = 51.3°$ and $\angle V = 180° - 2(51.3°) = 77.4°$

18. Let A, B, C, and D be the vertices of the trapezoid in clockwise order beginning at the

lower left and E the right angle shown; $AE = \dfrac{1}{2}(25 - 15) = 5$; $\tan A = \dfrac{12}{5} = 2.4$;

$\angle A = 67.4°$; $\angle D = \angle A = 67.4°$; $\angle B = \angle C = \dfrac{1}{2}[360° - 2(67.4°)] = 112.6°$

19-23. Let O be the center of the circle, $\overline{OL}$ and $\overline{OR}$, the radii (left to right), and S the

right angle.

19. a. $\angle LOR = \dfrac{1}{5}(360°) = 72°$; $\angle SOR = \dfrac{1}{2}\angle LOR = 36°$; $\sin 36° = \dfrac{SR}{1}$; $SR = 0.588$;

perimeter $= 10 \cdot SR = 5.88$

  b. $\angle LOR = \dfrac{1}{5}(360°) = 72°$; $\angle SOR = \dfrac{1}{2}\angle LOR = 36°$; $\tan 36° = \dfrac{SR}{1}$; $SR = 0.727$;

perimeter $= 10 \cdot SR = 7.27$

20. a. $\angle LOR = \dfrac{1}{10}(360°) = 36°$; $\angle SOR = \dfrac{1}{2}\angle LOR = 18°$; $\sin 18° = \dfrac{SR}{1}$; $SR = 0.309$;

perimeter $= 20 \cdot SR = 6.18$

  b. $\angle LOR = \dfrac{1}{10}(360°) = 36°$; $\angle SOR = \dfrac{1}{2}\angle LOR = 18°$; $\tan 18° = \dfrac{SR}{1}$; $SR = 0.325$;

perimeter $= 20 \cdot SR = 6.50$

21. a. $\angle LOR = \dfrac{1}{20}(360°) = 18°$; $\angle SOR = \dfrac{1}{2}\angle LOR = 9°$; $\sin 9° = \dfrac{SR}{1}$; $SR = 0.1564$;

perimeter $= 40 \cdot SR = 6.26$

  b. $\angle LOR = \dfrac{1}{20}(360°) = 18°$; $\angle SOR = \dfrac{1}{2}\angle LOR = 9°$; $\tan 9° = \dfrac{SR}{1}$; $SR = 0.1584$;

perimeter $= 40 \cdot SR = 6.34$

22. 2π = circumference of a unit circle, which is greater than the perimeter of the inscribed polygon and less than the perimeter of the circumscribed polygon.

C **23. a.** $\angle LOR = \dfrac{1}{n}(360°) = \left(\dfrac{360}{n}\right)°$; $\angle SOR = \dfrac{1}{2}\angle LOR = \left(\dfrac{180}{n}\right)°$; $\sin\left(\dfrac{180}{n}\right)° = \dfrac{SR}{1}$;

$SR = \sin\left(\dfrac{180}{n}\right)°$; perimeter $= 2n \cdot SR = 2n\,\sin\left(\dfrac{180}{n}\right)°$

b. $\angle LOR = \dfrac{1}{n}(360°) = \left(\dfrac{360}{n}\right)°$; $\angle SOR = \dfrac{1}{2}\angle LOR = \left(\dfrac{180}{n}\right)°$; $\tan\left(\dfrac{180}{n}\right)° = \dfrac{SR}{1}$;

$SR = \tan\left(\dfrac{180}{n}\right)°$; perimeter $= 2n \cdot SR = 2n\,\tan\left(\dfrac{180}{n}\right)°$

24. As n gets larger and larger, the perimeter of both polygons approach the circumference of the circle; $2n\,\sin\left(\dfrac{180}{n}\right)°$ and $2n\,\tan\left(\dfrac{180}{n}\right)°$ both approach 2π, that is, $n\,\sin\left(\dfrac{180}{n}\right)°$ and $n\,\tan\left(\dfrac{180}{n}\right)°$ both approach π.

Pages 543-544 · PROBLEMS

A **1.** $\tan A = \dfrac{22.5}{32.4} = 0.6944$; $\angle A = 34.8°$

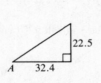

Ex. 1

Ex. 2

2. $\tan 66.8° = \dfrac{h}{1200}$; $h = 1200(2.333) = 2800$; 2800 m

3. $\sin 11.5° = \dfrac{a}{1500}$; $a = 1500(0.1994) = 299$; 299 m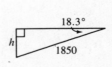

4. $\cos A = \dfrac{2.75}{12.5} = 0.22$; $\angle A = 77.3°$; $\angle ABC = 180° - 2(77.3)° = 25.4°$

Ex. 4

Ex. 5

5. $\sin 18.3° = \dfrac{h}{1850}$; $h = 1850(0.3140) = 581$; 581 m

6. $\cos A = \dfrac{1.75}{4} = 0.4375$; $\angle A = 64.1°$; $d = \sqrt{4^2 - (1.75)^2} = \sqrt{16 - 3.0625} =$
3.60; 3.60 m

7. $\angle AED = 36°$; $\angle ADB = \dfrac{1}{2}(180° - 36°) = 72°$; $\cos 72° = \dfrac{AD}{240}$;
$AD = 240(0.3090) = 74.2$; $\sin 72° = \dfrac{AB}{240}$; $AB = 240(0.9511) = 228$; 228 m by 74.2 m

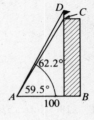

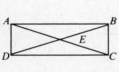

Ex. 7

Ex. 8

Ex. 9

8. $\cot 52° = \dfrac{\frac{1}{2}x}{190}$; $x = 380(0.7813) = 297$; 2.97 m

B **9.** Note: Figure not drawn to scale. $\angle BAD = 62.2°$; $\tan 62.2° = \dfrac{BD}{100}$; $BD = 100(1.897) =$
189.7; $\angle CAB = 59.5°$; $\tan 59.5° = \dfrac{BC}{100}$; $BC = 100(1.698) = 169.8$; $CD = BD - BC =$
$189.7 - 169.8 = 19.9$; 19.9 m

10. Note: Figure not drawn to scale. $\cos 26° = \dfrac{40 - x}{40}$; $40 - x = 40(0.8988)$;
$x = 40 - 35.952 = 4.05$; 4.05 cm

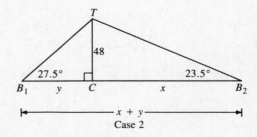

11. $\angle B_2 TC = 90° - 23.5° = 66.5°$; $\tan 66.5° = \dfrac{x}{48}$, $x = 48(2.2998) = 110.4$; $\angle B_1 TC =$
$90° - 27.5° = 62.5°$, $\tan 62.5° = \dfrac{y}{48}$, $y = 48(1.9210) = 92.2$. Case 1: Distance between
boats B_1 and $B_2 = x - y = 110.4 - 92.2 = 18.2$; 18.2 m. (Case 2: Boats on opposite
sides of tower. The distance between them $= x + y = 110.4 + 92.2 = 202.6$; 203 m.)

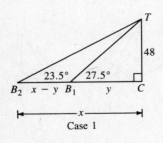

Case 1   Case 2

12. In a 30°-60°-90°△ with longer leg y and hypotenuse h, sec 30° $= \dfrac{2\sqrt{3}}{3}$; $h = \dfrac{2y\sqrt{3}}{3}$;

$$FD = \frac{2x\sqrt{3}}{3}; FC = \frac{2\sqrt{3}}{3}\left(\frac{2x\sqrt{3}}{3}\right) = \frac{4x}{3}; FB = \frac{2\sqrt{3}}{3}\left(\frac{4x}{3}\right) = \frac{8x\sqrt{3}}{9};$$

$$AF = \frac{2\sqrt{3}}{3}\left(\frac{8x\sqrt{3}}{9}\right) = \frac{16x}{9}; \frac{16x}{9} = 2; FE = x = 1.13$$

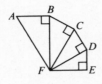

Ex. 12

Ex. 13

C   **13.** Note: Figure not drawn to scale. Let $BC = x$; tan 32° $= \dfrac{h}{1600 - x}$;

$h = (1600 - x)(0.6249)$; tan 50.5° $= \dfrac{h}{x}$; $h = x(1.213)$; $(1600 - x)(0.6249) = x(1.213)$;

$999.84 - 0.6249x = 1.213x$; $1.8379x = 999.84$; $x = 544$; $h = 544(1.213) = 660$; 660 m

14. Note: Figure not drawn to scale. ∠DAB = 12.3°; tan 12.3° $= \dfrac{DC}{AC} = \dfrac{DC}{8000 + x}$;

$DC = (8000 + x)(0.2180)$; ∠DBC = 16.4°; tan 16.4° $= \dfrac{DC}{x}$; $DC = x(0.2943)$;

$(8000 + x)(0.2180) = x(0.2943)$; $1744 + 0.2180x = 0.2943x$; $0.0763x = 1744$;

$x = 22{,}900$; $DC = x(0.2943) = 22{,}900(0.2943) = 6740$; the plane is at a height of 6,740 ft

at a distance of 22,900 ft from the nearer end of the runway.

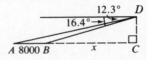

15. cot $\theta = \dfrac{x}{18}$; $x = 18$ cot θ; ∠ACB = 90 − θ; cot(90° − θ) $= \dfrac{x}{8}$;

$x = 8$ cot(90° − θ) $= 8$ tan θ; 8 tan θ = 18 cot θ; cot $\theta \neq 0$; 8 tan$^2\theta$ = 18;

tan$^2\theta = \dfrac{18}{8} = 2.25$; tan $\theta > 0$ so tan $\theta = \sqrt{2.25} = 1.500$; $x = 8$ tan $\theta = 12.0$; 12.0 ft

Ex. 15

Ex. 16

16. The set of all points in space equidistant from A, D, and C is a line perpendicular to the plane of $\triangle ADC$, intersecting the plane at P, the intersection of the perpendicular bisectors of the sides of $\triangle ADC$, which are also the medians of $\triangle ADC$. B and E are on that line. Draw $\triangle BPD$. Let x be the length of an edge of the tetrahedron. Since P is the point where the medians of equilateral $\triangle ADC$ intersect, $DP = \dfrac{2}{3}$ (length of median) $= \dfrac{2}{3} \cdot \dfrac{x\sqrt{3}}{2} = \dfrac{x\sqrt{3}}{3}$; $\sin \angle DBP = \dfrac{\frac{x\sqrt{3}}{3}}{x} = \dfrac{\sqrt{3}}{3} = 0.5774$; $\angle DBP = 35.3°$. Since E is the center of the tetrahedron, $DE = BE$ and $\triangle DEB$ is isosceles; $\angle DEB = 180° - 2(\angle DBP) = 180° - 70.6° = 109.4°$.

Page 545 · READING ALGEBRA

1.

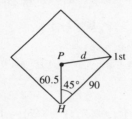

2.

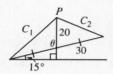

3.

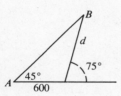

4.

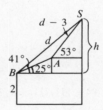

Pages 548-549 · WRITTEN EXERCISES

A

1. $c^2 = 5^2 + 7^2 - 2(5)(7) \cos 40° = 25 + 49 - 70(0.7660) = 20.38$; $c = 4.51$

2. $a^2 = 15^2 + 10^2 - 2(15)(10) \cos 74° = 225 + 100 - 300(0.2756) = 242.32$; $a = 15.6$

3. $b^2 = 12^2 + 11^2 - 2(12)(11) \cos 81° = 144 + 121 - 264(0.1564) = 223.7104$; $b = 15.0$

4. $c^2 = 4^2 + 2^2 - 2(4)(2) \cos 20° = 16 + 4 - 16(0.9397) = 4.9648$; $c = 2.23$

5. $a^2 = 30^2 + 20^2 - 2(30)(20) \cos 140° = 900 + 400 - 1200(-0.7660) = 2219.2$; $a = 47.1$

6. $b^2 = 100^2 + 300^2 - 2(100)(300) \cos 150° = 10{,}000 + 90{,}000 - 60{,}000(-0.8660) = 151{,}960$; $b = 390$

7. $\cos B = \dfrac{7^2 + 12^2 - 9^2}{2(7)(12)} = \dfrac{112}{168} = 0.6667$; $\angle B = 48.2°$

8. $\cos C = \dfrac{8^2 + 9^2 - 15^2}{2(8)(9)} = \dfrac{-80}{144} = -0.5556$; $\angle C = 123.8°$

9. $\angle C$ is the largest angle; $\cos C = \dfrac{12^2 + 10^2 - 18^2}{2(12)(10)} = \dfrac{-80}{240} = -0.3333$; $\angle C = 109.5°$

10. $\angle B$ is the smallest angle; $\cos B = \dfrac{30^2 + 40^2 - 20^2}{2(30)(40)} = \dfrac{2100}{2400} = 0.8750;\ \angle B = 29.0°$

11. $\angle A$ is the smallest angle; $\cos A = \dfrac{(0.8)^2 + (1.2)^2 - (0.6)^2}{2(0.8)(1.2)} = \dfrac{1.72}{1.92} = 0.8958;\ \angle A = 26.4°$

12. $\angle B$ is the largest angle; $\cos B = \dfrac{(1.5)^2 + (2.0)^2 - (3.0)^2}{2(1.5)(2.0)} = \dfrac{-2.75}{6} = -0.4583;$
$\angle B = 117.3°$

B **13.** $x^2 = 3^2 + 5^2 - 2(3)(5)\cos 35° = 9 + 25 - 30(0.8192) = 9.424;\ x = 3.07;$
$y^2 = 3^2 + 5^2 - 2(3)(5)\cos 145° = 9 + 25 - 30(-0.8192) = 58.576;\ y = 7.65$

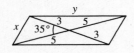

Ex. 13   Ex. 14

14. $d_1{}^2 = a^2 + b^2 - 2ab \cos\theta;\ d_2{}^2 = a^2 + b^2 - 2ab \cos(180° - \theta) =$
$a^2 + b^2 + 2ab \cos\theta;\ d_1{}^2 + d_2{}^2 = a^2 + b^2 - 2ab \cos\theta + a^2 + b^2 + 2ab \cos\theta =$
$2a^2 + 2b^2 = 2(a^2 + b^2)$

C **15.** $\cos B = \dfrac{2^2 + 3^2 - 4^2}{2(2)(3)} = -\dfrac{3}{12} = -0.25;\ (AM)^2 = 3^2 + 1^2 - 2(3)(1)(-0.25) = 11.5;$

$AM = 3.39$

16. (1) $b^2 = 1^2 + 1^2 - 2(1)(1)\cos 2\theta = 2 - 2\cos 2\theta;$ (2) $\sin\theta = \dfrac{\frac{b}{2}}{1} = \dfrac{b}{2};\ b = 2\sin\theta;$

$b^2 = 4\sin^2\theta;\ 2 - 2\cos 2\theta = 4\sin^2\theta;\ -2\cos 2\theta = -2 + 4\sin^2\theta;\ \cos 2\theta = 1 - 2\sin^2\theta$

Page 549 · PROBLEMS

A **1.** $d^2 = 8^2 + 12^2 - 2(8)(12)\cos 135° = 64 + 144 - 192(-0.7071) = 343.7632;\ d = 18.5;$
1850 km

2. $d^2 = 4^2 + 7^2 - 2(4)(7)\cos 52° = 16 + 49 - 56(0.6157) = 30.5208;\ d = 5.52;\ 552$ m

3. $\cos\theta = \dfrac{20^2 + 60^2 - 50^2}{2(20)(60)} = \dfrac{1500}{2400} = 0.6250;\ \theta = 51.3°$

4. See sketch for Exercise 1, page 545. $d^2 = 60.5^2 + 90^2 - 2(60.5)(90)\cos 45° =$
$3660.25 + 8100 - 10890(0.7071) = 4059.931;\ d = 63.7;\ 63.7$ ft

5. $d^2 = 2(9.58 \times 10^{-9})^2 - 2(9.58 \times 10^{-9})^2 \cos 104.8° = 2(9.58 \times 10^{-9})^2[1 - \cos 104.8°] =$
$(1.84 \times 10^{-16})[1 - (-0.2554)] = 2.31 \times 10^{-16};\ d = 1.52 \times 10^{-8};\ 1.52 \times 10^{-8}$ cm

B **6.** $\cos(90° - \theta) = \sin\theta = \dfrac{4^2 + 6^2 - 5^2}{2(4)(6)} = \dfrac{27}{48} = 0.5625;\ \theta = 34.2°$

7. See sketch for Exercise 2, page 545. $\theta = 90° + 15° = 105°$;

$c_1{}^2 = 30^2 + 20^2 - 2(30)(20) \cos 105° = 900 + 400 - 1200(-0.2588) = 1610.56$;

$c_1 = 40.1$; $c_2{}^2 = 30^2 + 20^2 - 2(30)(20) \cos 75° = 900 + 400 - 1200(0.2588) = 989.44$;

$c_2 = 31.5$; 40.1 m and 31.5 m

C 8. $\cos \theta = \dfrac{50^2 + 80^2 - 90^2}{2(50)(80)} = \dfrac{800}{8000} = 0.1000$; $\theta = 84.3°$; since θ is acute, the given diagonal

is the shorter one; let d = length of longer diagonal;

$d^2 = 50^2 + 80^2 - 2(50)(80)(\cos(180° - 84.3°)) = 2500 + 6400 + 8000 \cos 84.3° = 9694.4$;

$d = 98.5$; 98.5 cm

Pages 552-553 · WRITTEN EXERCISES

A 1. $\dfrac{\sin 65°}{b} = \dfrac{\sin 35°}{16}$; $b = \dfrac{16 \sin 65°}{\sin 35°} = \dfrac{16(0.9063)}{0.5736} = 25.3$

2. $\dfrac{\sin 48°}{a} = \dfrac{\sin 63°}{10}$; $a = \dfrac{10 \sin 48°}{\sin 63°} = \dfrac{10(0.7431)}{0.8910} = 8.34$

3. $\angle B = 180° - (110° + 40°) = 30°$; $\dfrac{\sin 110°}{a} = \dfrac{\sin 30°}{2.10}$; $a = \dfrac{2.10 \sin 110°}{\sin 30°} =$
$\dfrac{2.10(0.9397)}{0.5} = 3.95$

4. $\angle A = 180° - (100° + 50°) = 30°$; $\dfrac{\sin 100°}{c} = \dfrac{\sin 30°}{2.50}$; $c = \dfrac{2.50 \sin 100°}{\sin 30°} =$
$\dfrac{2.50(0.9848)}{0.5} = 4.92$

5. $\angle B = 180° - (42° + 98°) = 40°$; $\dfrac{\sin 40°}{b} = \dfrac{\sin 98°}{30}$; $b = \dfrac{30 \sin 40°}{\sin 98°} = \dfrac{30(0.6428)}{0.9903} = 19.5$

6. $\angle A = 180° - (105° + 25°) = 50°$; $\dfrac{\sin 50°}{a} = \dfrac{\sin 105°}{120}$; $a = \dfrac{120 \sin 50°}{\sin 105°} =$
$\dfrac{120(0.7660)}{0.9659} = 95.2$

7. $\dfrac{\sin B}{15} = \dfrac{\sin 40°}{20}$; $\sin B = \dfrac{15 \sin 40°}{20} = 0.75(0.6428) = 0.4821$; $\angle B = 28.8°$ or $151.2°$;

$151.2°$ is not a solution since $151.2° + 40° > 180°$; $\angle B = 28.8°$

8. $\dfrac{\sin A}{1.5} = \dfrac{\sin 35°}{2.0}$; $\sin A = \dfrac{1.5 \sin 35°}{2.0} = 0.75(0.5736) = 0.4302$; $\angle A = 25.5°$ or $154.5°$;

$154.5°$ is not a solution since $154.5° + 35° > 180°$; $\angle A = 25.5°$

9. $\dfrac{\sin A}{2.0} = \dfrac{\sin 125°}{3.2}$; $\sin A = \dfrac{2.0 \sin 125°}{3.2} = 0.625(0.8192) = 0.5120$; since $\angle C$ is obtuse,

$\angle A$ and $\angle B$ are both acute; $\angle A = 30.8°$ and $\angle B = 180° - (30.8° + 125°) = 24.2°$

10. $\dfrac{\sin B}{50} = \dfrac{\sin 37°}{40}$; $\sin B = \dfrac{50 \sin 37°}{40} = 1.25(0.6018) = 0.7523$; $\angle B = 48.8°$ or $131.2°$

11. $\dfrac{\sin C}{15} = \dfrac{\sin 40°}{11}$; $\sin C = \dfrac{15 \sin 40°}{11} = \dfrac{5(0.6428)}{11} = 0.8765$; $\angle C = 61.2°$ or $118.8°$

12. $\dfrac{\sin B}{12} = \dfrac{\sin 110°}{18}$; $\sin B = \dfrac{12 \sin 110°}{18} = \dfrac{0.9397}{1.5} = 0.6265$; since $\angle C$ is obtuse, $\angle B$ is acute; $\angle B = 38.8°$

13-18. Since $0° < \theta < 180°$, $\sin \theta = \sqrt{1 - \cos^2\theta}$.

13. $\sin B = \sqrt{1 - \cos^2 B} = \sqrt{1 - \dfrac{9}{25}} = \sqrt{\dfrac{16}{25}} = \dfrac{4}{5}$; $\dfrac{a}{b} = \dfrac{\sin A}{\sin B} = \dfrac{\frac{2}{3}}{\frac{4}{5}} = \dfrac{2}{3} \cdot \dfrac{5}{4} = \dfrac{5}{6}$

14. $\sin A = \sqrt{1 - \cos^2 A} = \sqrt{1 - \dfrac{16}{25}} = \sqrt{\dfrac{9}{25}} = \dfrac{3}{5}$; $\dfrac{a}{b} = \dfrac{\sin A}{\sin B} = \dfrac{\frac{3}{5}}{\frac{4}{5}} = \dfrac{3}{5} \cdot \dfrac{5}{4} = \dfrac{3}{4}$

15. $\sin A = \sqrt{1 - \cos^2 A} = \sqrt{1 - \dfrac{144}{169}} = \sqrt{\dfrac{25}{169}} = \dfrac{5}{13}$; $\sin B = \sqrt{1 - \dfrac{16}{25}} = \sqrt{\dfrac{9}{25}} = \dfrac{3}{5}$;

$\dfrac{a}{b} = \dfrac{\sin A}{\sin B} = \dfrac{\frac{5}{13}}{\frac{3}{5}} = \dfrac{5}{13} \cdot \dfrac{5}{3} = \dfrac{25}{39}$

16. $\sin A = \sqrt{1 - \cos^2 A} = \sqrt{1 - \dfrac{225}{289}} = \sqrt{\dfrac{64}{289}} = \dfrac{8}{17}$; $\sin B = \sqrt{1 - \dfrac{64}{289}} = $

$\sqrt{\dfrac{225}{289}} = \dfrac{15}{17}$; $\dfrac{a}{b} = \dfrac{\sin A}{\sin B} = \dfrac{\frac{8}{17}}{\frac{15}{17}} = \dfrac{8}{15}$

17. $\sin A = \sqrt{1 - \cos^2 A} = \sqrt{1 - \dfrac{1}{4}} = \sqrt{\dfrac{3}{4}} = \dfrac{\sqrt{3}}{2}$; $\sin B = \sqrt{1 - \dfrac{2}{4}} = \sqrt{\dfrac{2}{4}} = \dfrac{\sqrt{2}}{2}$;

$\dfrac{a}{b} = \dfrac{\sin A}{\sin B} = \dfrac{\frac{\sqrt{3}}{2}}{\frac{\sqrt{2}}{2}} = \dfrac{\sqrt{3}}{\sqrt{2}} = \dfrac{\sqrt{6}}{2}$

18. $\sin A = \sqrt{1 - \cos^2 A} = \sqrt{1 - \dfrac{3}{4}} = \sqrt{\dfrac{1}{4}} = \dfrac{1}{2}$; since $\tan B = 1$ and $0° < \theta < 180°$,

$\angle B = 45°$ and $\sin B = \dfrac{\sqrt{2}}{2}$; $\dfrac{a}{b} = \dfrac{\sin A}{\sin B} = \dfrac{\frac{1}{2}}{\frac{\sqrt{2}}{2}} = \dfrac{\sqrt{2}}{2}$

19-20. Note: $0° < \theta < 180°$ so $\sin \theta \neq 0$; also $b \neq 0$.

B **19.** $\dfrac{\sin A}{a} = \dfrac{\sin B}{b}$; $\dfrac{\sin A}{\sin B} = \dfrac{a}{b}$; $\dfrac{\sin A}{\sin B} + 1 = \dfrac{a}{b} + 1$; $\dfrac{\sin A}{\sin B} + \dfrac{\sin B}{\sin B} = \dfrac{a}{b} + \dfrac{b}{b}$;

$\dfrac{\sin A + \sin B}{\sin B} = \dfrac{a + b}{b}$

20. $\dfrac{\sin A}{a} = \dfrac{\sin B}{b}$; $\dfrac{\sin A}{\sin B} = \dfrac{a}{b}$; $\dfrac{\sin A}{\sin B} - 1 = \dfrac{a}{b} - 1$; $\dfrac{\sin A}{\sin B} - \dfrac{\sin B}{\sin B} = \dfrac{a}{b} - \dfrac{b}{b}$;

$\dfrac{\sin A - \sin B}{\sin B} = \dfrac{a - b}{b}$

21. Using the given right triangles, $\sin \theta = \dfrac{\frac{b}{2}}{1} = \dfrac{b}{2}$; $b = 2 \sin \theta$; by the law of

sines, $\dfrac{\sin 2\theta}{b} = \dfrac{\sin(90° - \theta)}{1}$; $\sin 2\theta = b \cos \theta$; $b = \dfrac{\sin 2\theta}{\cos \theta}$; $\dfrac{\sin 2\theta}{\cos \theta} = 2 \sin \theta$; $\sin 2\theta = 2 \sin \theta \cos \theta$

Pages 553-554 · PROBLEMS

1. Let $\angle A = 25°$, $\angle B = 60°$, and $\angle C = 180° - (25° + 60°) = 95°$; the shortest side is a, the longest, c. $\dfrac{\sin 95°}{45} = \dfrac{\sin 25°}{a}$; $a = \dfrac{45 \sin 25°}{\sin 95°} = \dfrac{45(0.4226)}{0.9962} = 19.1$; 19.1 m

2. Let B and A be the base angles and C the vertex angle; $\angle C = 180° - 2 \cdot 18° = 144°$; $\dfrac{\sin 144°}{c} = \dfrac{\sin 18°}{35}$; $c = \dfrac{35 \sin 144°}{\sin 18°} = \dfrac{35(0.5878)}{0.3090} = 66.6$; 66.6 cm

3. Let $\angle A = 72°$, $\angle B = 61°$, and $\angle C = 180° - (72° + 61°) = 47°$; the shortest side is c; $\dfrac{\sin 47°}{c} = \dfrac{\sin 72°}{30}$; $c = \dfrac{30 \sin 47°}{\sin 72°} = \dfrac{30(0.7314)}{0.9511} = 23.1$; 23.1 cm

4. Let x = length of each leg; $\dfrac{\sin 29°}{641} = \dfrac{\sin \left[\frac{1}{2}(180 - 29)\right]°}{x}$; $x = \dfrac{641 \sin 75.5°}{\sin 29°} = \dfrac{641(0.9681)}{0.4848} = 1280$; 1280 ft

5. Let $GT = p$; $\dfrac{\sin P}{p} = \dfrac{\sin T}{2000}$; $\angle T = 180° - (84° + 65°) = 31°$; $\dfrac{\sin 84°}{p} = \dfrac{\sin 31°}{2000}$; $p = \dfrac{2000 \sin 84°}{\sin 31°} = \dfrac{2000(0.9945)}{0.5150} = 3860$; 3860 yd

6. Let $PR = t$; $\dfrac{\sin T}{t} = \dfrac{\sin R}{180}$; $\angle R = 180° - (74° + 59°) = 47°$; $\dfrac{\sin 59°}{t} = \dfrac{\sin 47°}{180}$; $t = \dfrac{180 \sin 59°}{\sin 47°} = \dfrac{180(0.8572)}{0.7314} = 211$; 211 m

7. Let $AB = c$; $\dfrac{\sin 69°}{c} = \dfrac{\sin B}{25}$; $\angle B = 180° - (82° + 69°) = 29°$; $\dfrac{\sin 69°}{c} = \dfrac{\sin 29°}{25}$; $c = \dfrac{25 \sin 69°}{\sin 29°} = \dfrac{25(0.9336)}{0.4848} = 48.1$; 48.1 m

8. Note: Figure not drawn to scale. Since the angle of depression at the far end of the runway ($\angle HPA$) is 12°, the angle of elevation of the airplane at A ($\angle PAB$) is also 12°. $\angle APB = \angle HPB - HPA = 3°$; $\angle APB = 180° - \angle PAB - \angle APB = 165°$

$$\frac{\sin 3°}{10,000} = \frac{\sin 12°}{d}; \quad d = \frac{10,000(\sin 12°)}{\sin 3°} = \frac{10,000(0.2079)}{0.0523} = 39,721; \ 39,700 \text{ ft}$$

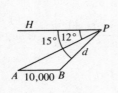

Ex. 8

Ex. 9

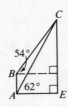

Ex. 10

B   9. $\angle BAC = \angle BAD - \angle CAD = 14°$; $\angle ABD = 90° - \angle BAD = 58°$; $\dfrac{\sin 14°}{h} = \dfrac{\sin 58°}{20}$

$h = \dfrac{20(\sin 14°)}{\sin 58°} = \dfrac{20(0.2419)}{0.8480} = 5.71; \ 5.71 \text{ m}$

10. $AB = 24$; $\angle ABC = 144°$; $\angle BAC = 28°$; $\therefore \angle BCA = 180° - (144° + 28°) = 8°$;

$\dfrac{AC}{\sin 144°} = \dfrac{24}{\sin 8°}; \ AC = \dfrac{24 \sin 144°}{\sin 8°} = \dfrac{24(0.5878)}{0.1392} = 101.34;$

$CE = AC \sin 62° = (101.34)(0.8829) = 89.47; \ 89.5 \text{ m}$

11. $\dfrac{\sin 35°}{10} = \dfrac{\sin F}{6}; \ \sin F = \dfrac{6 \sin 35°}{10} = \dfrac{3(0.5736)}{5} = 0.3442; \ \angle F = 20.1° \text{ or } 159.9°;$

147.1° is not a solution since $159.9° + 35° > 180°$; $\angle F = 20.1°$;

$\angle N = 180° - (35° + 20.1°) = 124.9°; \ \dfrac{\sin 35°}{10} = \dfrac{\sin 124.9°}{n};$

$n = \dfrac{10 \sin 124.9°}{\sin 35°} = \dfrac{10(0.8202)}{0.5736} \approx 14.3; \ 14.3 \text{ km}$

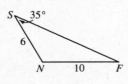

Ex. 11

Ex. 12

12. $\angle ACD = 90° - 53° = 37°$; $\angle ACB = 180° - 37° = 143°$; $\dfrac{\sin 143°}{30} = \dfrac{\sin \angle BAC}{10};$

$\sin \angle BAC = \dfrac{10}{30}(0.6018) = 0.2006; \ \angle BAC = 11.6°; \ \angle BAD = 11.6° + 53° = 64.6°$

C   13. Let h = height of building and d = distance from building to point A;

$\dfrac{\sin 51°}{d} = \dfrac{\sin[180° - (82° + 51°)]}{50}; \ \dfrac{\sin 51°}{d} = \dfrac{\sin 47°}{50};$

$d = \dfrac{50 \sin 51°}{\sin 47°} = \dfrac{50(0.7771)}{0.7314} = 53.1; \ \tan 20° = \dfrac{h}{d} = \dfrac{h}{53.1};$

$h = 53.1 \tan 20° = 53.1(0.3640) = 19.3; \ 19.3 \text{ m}$

Page 554 · COMPUTER EXERCISES

1. Answers may vary. A sample program is given.
   ```
   10  PRINT "ENTER ANGLE X, ANGLE Y, SIDE X"
   20  INPUT X, Y, SX
   30  LET Z = 180 − X − Y
   40  LET A = X * 3.14159/180
   50  LET B = Y * 3.14159/180
   60  LET C = Z * 3.14159/180
   70  LET F = SX/SIN(A)
   80  LET SZ = F * SIN(C)
   90  LET SY = F * SIN(B)
   100 PRINT X, SX
   110 PRINT Y, SY
   120 PRINT Z, SZ
   130 END
   ```

2. **a.** $b \approx 9.719$; $c \approx 9.151$; $\angle C = 68°$ **b.** $b \approx 10.475$; $c \approx 35.735$; $\angle C = 118°$
   c. $b \approx 0.241$; $c \approx 0.420$; $\angle C = 36.2°$

3. Answers may vary. For example, change lines 10, 20, 70, and 80 as follows:
   ```
   10 PRINT "ENTER ANGLE X, ANGLE Y, SIDE Z"
   20 INPUT X, Y, SZ
   70 LET F = SZ/SIN(C)
   80 LET SX = F * SIN(A)
   ```

4. **a.** $a \approx 20.064$; $b \approx 20.581$; $\angle C = 40°$ **b.** $a \approx 48.330$; $b \approx 60.388$; $\angle C = 25.9°$
   c. $b \approx 8.452$; $c \approx 2.012$; $\angle A = 52°$

5. Answers may vary. A sample program is given.
   ```
   10  PRINT "ENTER ANGLE X, ANGLE Y, SIDE"
   20  INPUT X, Y, S
   30  LET Z = 180 − X − Y
   40  LET A = X * 3.14159/180
   50  LET B = Y * 3.14159/180
   60  LET C = Z * 3.14159/180
   62  PRINT "ENTER NAME OF SIDE (X, Y, OR Z)"
   63  INPUT S$
   64  IF S$ = "X" THEN LET F = S/SIN(A)
   65  IF S$ = "Z" THEN LET F = S/SIN(C)
   70  LET SX = F * SIN(A)
   80  LET SZ = F * SIN(C)
   90  LET SY = F * SIN(B)
   ```

(continued)

```
100 PRINT X, SX
110 PRINT Y, SY
120 PRINT Z, SZ
130 END
```

Pages 558-559 · WRITTEN EXERCISES

A **1.** $\angle A = 180° - 50° - 30° = 100°$; $\dfrac{\sin 100°}{15} = \dfrac{\sin 50°}{c}$; $c = \dfrac{15 \sin 50°}{\sin 100°} =$

$\dfrac{15(0.7660)}{0.9848} = 11.7$; $\dfrac{\sin 100°}{15} = \dfrac{\sin 30°}{b}$; $b = \dfrac{15 \sin 30°}{\sin 100°} = \dfrac{15(0.5)}{0.9848} = 7.62$

2. $b^2 = 30^2 + 20^2 - 2(30)(20) \cos 40° = 900 + 400 - 1200(0.7660) = 380.8$; $b = 19.5$;

$\dfrac{\sin A}{20} = \dfrac{\sin 40°}{19.5}$; $\sin A = \dfrac{20 \sin 40°}{19.5} = \dfrac{20(0.6428)}{19.5} = 0.6593$; since $\angle A$ is not the larges$t$

angle, $\angle A$ is acute; $\angle A = 41.2°$; $\angle C = 180° - 40° - 41.2° = 98.8°$

3. $\cos A = \dfrac{7^2 + 9^2 - 4^2}{2(7)(9)} = \dfrac{114}{126} = 0.9048$; $\angle A = 25.2°$; $\dfrac{\sin B}{7} = \dfrac{\sin 25.2°}{4}$;

$\sin B = \dfrac{7 \sin 25.2°}{4} = 1.75(0.4258) = 0.7452$; since $\angle B$ is not the largest angle,

$\angle B$ is acute; $\angle B = 48.2°$; $\angle C = 180° - 25.2° - 48.2° = 106.6°$

4. $\dfrac{\sin 110°}{c} = \dfrac{\sin 25°}{12}$; $c = \dfrac{12 \sin 110°}{\sin 25°} = \dfrac{12(0.9397)}{0.4226} = 26.7$;

$\angle A = 180° - 110° - 25° = 45°$; $\dfrac{\sin 45°}{a} = \dfrac{\sin 25°}{12}$; $a = \dfrac{12 \sin 45°}{\sin 25°} = \dfrac{12(0.7071)}{0.4226} = 20.$

5. $a^2 = 12^2 + 15^2 - 2(12)(15) \cos 100° = 431.51$; $a = 20.77$; $\dfrac{\sin B}{12} = \dfrac{\sin 100°}{20.77}$; $\sin B =$

$\dfrac{12 \sin 100°}{20.77} = \dfrac{12(0.9848)}{20.77} = 0.5690$; since $\angle A$ is obtuse, $\angle B$ is acute; $\angle B = 34.7°$

$\angle C = 180° - 100° - 34.7° = 45.3°$

6. $\cos A = \dfrac{30^2 + 40^2 - 20^2}{2(30)(40)} = \dfrac{2100}{2400} = 0.8750$; $\angle A = 29.0°$; $\dfrac{\sin B}{30} = \dfrac{\sin 29°}{20}$;

$\sin B = \dfrac{30 \sin 29°}{20} = 1.5(0.4848) = 0.7272$; since $\angle B$ is not the largest angle, $\angle B$ $\mathrm{i}s$

acute; $\angle B = 46.7°$; $\angle C = 180° - 29° - 46.7° = 104.3°$

7. $\dfrac{\sin B}{20} = \dfrac{\sin 130°}{30}$; $\sin B = \dfrac{20 \sin 130°}{30} = \dfrac{2(0.7660)}{3} = 0.5107$; since $\angle A$ is obtuse, $\angle B$ $\mathrm{i}s$

acute; $\angle B = 30.7°$; $\angle C = 180° - 130° - 30.7° = 19.3°$; $\dfrac{\sin 19.3°}{c} = \dfrac{\sin 130°}{30}$;

$c = \dfrac{30 \sin 19.3°}{\sin 130°} = \dfrac{30(0.3305)}{0.7660} = 12.9$

8. $\dfrac{\sin C}{15} = \dfrac{\sin 115°}{20}$; $\sin C = \dfrac{15 \sin 115°}{20} = \dfrac{15(0.9063)}{20} = 0.6797$; since $\angle B$ is obtuse, $\angle C$ is acute; $\angle C = 42.8°$; $\angle A = 180° - 115° - 42.8° = 22.2°$; $\dfrac{\sin 22.2°}{a} = \dfrac{\sin 115°}{20}$;

$a = \dfrac{20 \sin 22.2°}{\sin 115°} = \dfrac{20(0.3778)}{0.9063} = 8.34$

9. $\dfrac{\sin A}{12} = \dfrac{\sin 35°}{7}$; $\sin A = \dfrac{12 \sin 35°}{7} = \dfrac{2(0.5736)}{7} = 0.9833$; $\angle A = 79.5°$ or $100.5°$; if $\angle A = 79.5°$, $\angle C = 180° - 35° - 79.5° = 65.5°$ and $\dfrac{\sin 65.5°}{c} = \dfrac{\sin 35°}{7}$;

$c = \dfrac{7 \sin 65.5°}{\sin 35°} = \dfrac{7(0.9100)}{0.5736} = 11.1$; if $\angle A = 100.5°$, $\angle C = 180° - 35° - 100.5° = 44.5°$ and $\dfrac{\sin 44.5°}{c} = \dfrac{\sin 35°}{7}$; $c = \dfrac{7 \sin 44.5°}{\sin 35°} = \dfrac{7(0.7009)}{0.5736} = 8.55$

10. $\dfrac{\sin B}{15} = \dfrac{\sin 55°}{12}$; $\sin B = \dfrac{15 \sin 55°}{12} = 1.25(0.8192) = 1.024$; no solution

11. $\dfrac{\sin C}{18} = \dfrac{\sin 40°}{11}$; $\sin C = \dfrac{18 \sin 40°}{11} = \dfrac{18(0.6428)}{11} = 1.052$; no solution

12. $\dfrac{\sin B}{15} = \dfrac{\sin 50°}{13}$; $\sin B = \dfrac{15 \sin 50°}{13} = \dfrac{15(0.7660)}{13} = 0.8839$; $\angle B = 62.1°$ or $117.9°$; if $\angle B = 62.1°$, $\angle A = 180° - 50° - 62.1° = 67.9°$ and $\dfrac{\sin 67.9°}{a} = \dfrac{\sin 50°}{13}$;

$a = \dfrac{13 \sin 67.9°}{\sin 50°} = \dfrac{13(0.9265)}{0.7660} = 15.7$; if $\angle B = 117.9°$, $\angle A = 180° - 50° - 117.9° = 12.1°$ and $\dfrac{\sin 12.1°}{a} = \dfrac{\sin 50°}{13}$; $a = \dfrac{13 \sin 12.1°}{\sin 50°} = \dfrac{13(0.2096)}{0.7660} = 3.56$

13. Since $\angle C$ is obtuse, $\overline{AB}$ (with length c) is the longest side of $\triangle ABC$; $c^2 = 5^2 + 3^2 - 2(5)(3) \cos 120° = 25 + 9 - 30(-0.5) = 49$; $c = 7$; $\dfrac{\sin A}{3} = \dfrac{\sin 120°}{7}$; $\sin A = \dfrac{3 \sin 120°}{7} = \dfrac{3(0.8660)}{7} = 0.3712$; since $\angle C$ is obtuse, $\angle A$ is acute; $\angle A = 21.8°$; let M be the midpoint of $\overline{AB}$; $AM = \dfrac{1}{2}c = 3.5$; using the law of cosines for $\triangle AMC$, $(CM)^2 = 5^2 + (3.5)^2 - 2(5)(3.5) \cos 21.8° = 25 + 12.25 - 35(0.9285) = 4.75$; $CM = 2.18$

14. $\angle C = 180° - 2.50° = 180° - 100° = 80°$; $\dfrac{\sin 80°}{10} = \dfrac{\sin 50°}{b}$; $b = \dfrac{10 \sin 50°}{\sin 80°} = \dfrac{10(0.7660)}{0.9848} = 7.78$; let M be the midpoint of $\overline{AC}$; $AM = \dfrac{1}{2}AC = \dfrac{1}{2}b = 3.89$; using the law of cosines for $\triangle ABM$, $(BM)^2 = 10^2 + (3.89)^2 - 2(10)(3.89) \cos 50° = 100 + 15.1 - 50.0 = 65.1$; $BM = 8.07$

15. Draw $\overline{BE} \parallel \overline{CD}$; $ED = BC = 2$; $AE = 3$; $\angle BEA = 60°$ and $\angle ABE =$
$180° - (50° + 60°) = 70°$; $\dfrac{\sin 60°}{BA} = \dfrac{\sin 70°}{3}$; $BA = \dfrac{3 \sin 60°}{\sin 70°} = \dfrac{3(0.8660)}{0.9397} = 2.76$;
$(BD)^2 = (2.76)^2 + 5^2 - 2(2.76)(5) \cos 50° = 7.6176 + 25 - 27.6(0.6428) = 14.8767$;
$BD = 3.86$; $\dfrac{\sin 50°}{BE} = \dfrac{\sin 70°}{3}$; $BE = \dfrac{3 \sin 50°}{\sin 70°} = \dfrac{3(0.7660)}{0.9397} = 2.45$; $CD = BE = 2.45$
$(AC)^2 = (2.45)^2 + 5^2 - 2(2.45)(5) \cos 60° = 6.0025 + 25 - 24.5(0.5) = 18.7525$;
$AC = 4.33$

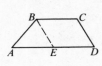

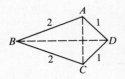

Ex. 15   **Ex. 16**

16. $(BD)^2 = 1^2 + 2^2 - 2(1)(2) \cos 118° = 1 + 4 - 4(-0.4695) = 6.878$; $BD = 2.62$;
$\dfrac{\sin \angle ABD}{1} = \dfrac{\sin 118°}{2.62}$; $\sin \angle ABD = \dfrac{0.8829}{2.62} = 0.3370$; since $\angle BAD$ is obtuse, $\angle ABD$ is
acute; $\angle ABD = 19.7°$; $\angle DBC = \angle ABD$; $\angle ABC = 2 \cdot \angle ABD = 39.4°$; $(AC)^2 =$
$2^2 + 2^2 - 2(2)(2) \cos 39.4° = 4 + 4 - 8(0.7727) = 1.82$; $AC = 1.35$

C   17. Let $\angle A = 57°$, $\angle B = 60°$, and $\angle C = 63°$; the shortest side has length a, the longest
has length $c = a + 5$. $\dfrac{\sin 57°}{a} = \dfrac{\sin 63°}{a + 5}$; $a \sin 63° = a \sin 57° + 5 \sin 57°$;
$a(\sin 63° - \sin 57°) = 5 \sin 57°$; $a = \dfrac{5 \sin 57°}{\sin 63° - \sin 57°} = \dfrac{5(0.8387)}{0.8910 - 0.8387} =$
$\dfrac{4.1935}{0.0523} = 80.2$; $c = a + 5 = 85.2$; $\dfrac{\sin 60°}{b} = \dfrac{\sin 57°}{80.2}$; $b = \dfrac{80.2 \sin 60°}{\sin 57°} =$
$\dfrac{80.2(0.8660)}{0.8387} = 82.8$. (If a calculator is used and only the final result is rounded, then the
answers will be $a = 80.1$, $b = 82.7$, and $c = 85.1$.)

18. Note: Sketch not drawn to scale. $100 = a^2 + b^2 - 2ab \cos 65°$; $\dfrac{1}{2} ab \sin 65° = $ area $=$
20, so $ab = \dfrac{40}{\sin 65°} = 44.14$; $a^2 + 2ab + b^2 = 100 + (2)(\cos 65°)(44.14) + (2)(44.14)$
$(a + b)^2 = 225.57$; $a + b = \sqrt{225.57} = 15.02$; perimeter $= a + b + 10 = 25.02$; 25.0

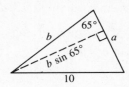

Pages 559-560 · PROBLEMS

A

1. See sketch for Exercise 3, page 545. Let 100 km be the unit measure; $\dfrac{\sin\theta}{6} = \dfrac{\sin 45°}{d}$;

$d = \dfrac{6\sin 45°}{\sin\theta}$; $75° = 45° + \theta$; $\theta = 30°$; $d = \dfrac{6\sin 45°}{\sin 30°} = \dfrac{6(0.7071)}{0.5} = 8.49$; $\dfrac{849\text{ km}}{300\text{ km/h}} =$

2.83; 2.83 h

2. Note: Figure not drawn to scale. $\theta = 90° - 62° = 28°$; $\varphi = 62° - \dfrac{1}{2}(180° - 140°) = 42°$;

$\dfrac{\sin 28°}{d} = \dfrac{\sin 42°}{15}$; $d = \dfrac{15\sin 28°}{\sin 42°} = \dfrac{15(0.4695)}{0.6691} = 10.5$; 10.5 m

Ex. 2

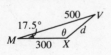

Ex. 3

3. $\dfrac{\sin\theta}{300} = \dfrac{\sin 48°}{270}$; $\sin\theta = \dfrac{300\sin 48°}{270} = \dfrac{10(0.7431)}{9} = 0.8257$; θ must be acute, so

$\theta = 55.7°$; then $\angle A = 180° - (48° + 55.7°) = 180° - 103.7° = 76.3°$ and $\dfrac{\sin 76.3°}{a} =$

$\dfrac{\sin 48°}{270}$; $a = \dfrac{270\sin 76.3°}{\sin 48°} = \dfrac{270(0.9715)}{0.7431} = 353$; the second cable makes an angle of 55.7°

with the ground and the distance between the cables at the ground is 353 m.

4. Let 100 km be the unit measure; $d = 5^2 + 3^2 - 2(5)(3)\cos 17.5° =$

$25 + 9 - 30(0.9537) = 5.39$; $d = 2.32$; $\dfrac{\sin\theta}{5} = \dfrac{\sin 17.5°}{2.32}$; $\sin\theta = \dfrac{5\sin 17.5°}{2.32} =$

$\dfrac{5(0.3007)}{2.32} = 0.6481$; $\theta = 40.4°$ or $139.6°$; since θ is the largest angle, $\theta = 139.6°$; Jim is

232 km from Vista and should turn through an angle of 139.6°.

Ex. 4

Ex. 5

5. $(0.340)10 = 3.4$; $(0.340)18 = 6.12$; $d^2 = (3.4)^2 + (6.12)^2 - 2(3.4)(6.12)\cos 52° =$

11.56 + 37.4544 − 41.616(0.6157) = 23.4; $d = 4.84$; 4.84 km. (Arithmetic may be simplified by solving for the time it takes sound to travel between the plants ≈ 14 s; $(0.340)14 = 4.76$; answer differs because of rounding.)

B **6.** Note: Figure not drawn to scale. H is Houston, S is satellite, C is center of Earth; let 1000 km be the unit measure; $(SH)^2 = (6.4)^2 + (42.2)^2 - 2(6.4)(42.2) \cos 29.7° =$

$40.96 + 1780.84 - 540.16(0.8686) = 1352.60$; $SH = 36.8$; $\dfrac{\sin H}{42.2} = \dfrac{\sin 29.7°}{36.8}$; $\sin H =$

$\dfrac{42.2 \sin 29.7°}{36.8} = \dfrac{42.2(0.4955)}{36.8} = 0.5682$; $\angle H = 34.6°$ or $145.4°$; since $\angle H$ is the largest

angle, $\angle H = 145.4°$; $\theta = 145.4° - 90° = 55.4°$

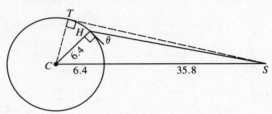

Exs. 6, 7

7. Draw a tangent from S intersecting the circle in the figure at T; the latitude of T is the greatest latitude from which a signal can travel in a straight line; latitude of $T = \angle TCS$;

$\cos \angle TCS = \dfrac{6.4}{42.2} = 0.1517$; $\angle TCS = 81.3°$; 81.3°N or 81.3°S.

8. $\cos \theta = \dfrac{1^2 + 2^2 - (2.5)^2}{2(1)(2)} = \dfrac{-1.25}{4} = -0.3125$; $\theta = 108.2°$; $\dfrac{\sin \varphi}{2} = \dfrac{\sin 108.2°}{2.5}$; $\sin \varphi =$

$\dfrac{2 \sin 108.2°}{2.5} = 0.8(0.9500) = 0.7600$; since θ is obtuse, φ is acute; $\varphi = 49.5°$; let

d = length of shorter diagonal; $\sin 49.5° = \dfrac{\frac{d}{2}}{1} = \dfrac{d}{2}$; $d = 2 \sin 49.5° = 2(0.7604) =$

1.52; 1.52 m

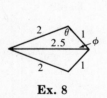

Ex. 8

Ex. 9

Ex. 10

9. $\angle DAC = 12°$; $\angle DBC = 9°$; $\csc 12° = \dfrac{AD}{80}$; $AD = 80 \csc 12° = 80(4.810) = 385$;

$\csc 9° = \dfrac{BD}{80}$; $BD = 80 \csc 9° = 80(6.392) = 511$; $(AB)^2 =$

$(385)^2 + (511)^2 - 2(385)(511) \cos 36° = 148,225 + 261,121 - 393,470(0.8090) =$

$91,000$; $AB = 302$; 302 m

10. $\dfrac{\sin \theta}{120} = \dfrac{\sin 45°}{100}$; $\sin \theta = \dfrac{120 \sin 45°}{100} = 1.2(0.7071) = 0.8485$; $\theta = 58°$ or $122°$; since θ is

the largest angle, $\theta = 122°$; $\varphi = 180° - 122° = 58°$; $\cos 58° = \dfrac{\frac{BC}{2}}{100} = \dfrac{BC}{200}$; $BC =$

$200 \cos 58° = 200(0.5299) = 106$; 106 km

C 11. Note: Figure not drawn to scale. Consider $\triangle AXY$;

$$\angle XAY = 180° - (25° + 96° + 19°) = 40°; \frac{\sin 25°}{AX} = \frac{\sin 40°}{1}; AX = \frac{\sin 25°}{\sin 40°} =$$

$$\frac{0.4226}{0.6428} = 0.657.\text{ Consider }\triangle BYX; \angle XBY = 180° - (25° + 113° + 19°) = 23°;$$

$$\frac{\sin 19°}{BY} = \frac{\sin 23°}{1}; BY = \frac{0.3256}{0.3907} = 0.833.\text{ Now consider }\triangle AXW\text{ and }\triangle BYZ;$$

$$\sin 65° = \frac{AW}{0.657}\text{ and }\sin 42° = \frac{BZ}{0.833}; AW = 0.657 \sin 65° = 0.657(0.9063) = 0.595\text{ km};$$

$BZ = 0.833 \sin 42° = 0.833(0.6691) = 557$ km. The balloon at A is 595 m high; the balloon at B is 557 m high; A is thus 38 m higher than B. Likewise, $\cos 65° = \dfrac{WX}{0.657}$ and

$$\cos 42° = \frac{YZ}{0.833}; WX = 0.657 \cos 65° = 0.657(0.4226) = 0.278\text{ km};$$

$YZ = 0.833 \cos 42° = 0.833(0.7431) = 0.619$ km. $AC = WZ = WX + XY + YZ =$ $0.278 + 1 + 0.619 = 1.897$ km; $BC = 38$ m; $AB = \sqrt{1897^2 + 38^2} = \sqrt{3,600,053} =$ 1897 m; the distance between the balloons is 1.90 km.

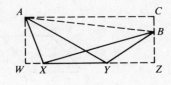

Ex. 11

Ex. 13

12. See figure for Exercise 4, page 545. Let 1 km be the unit measure; $\angle BAS =$

$$360° - (65° + 53° + 90°) = 152°; \angle SBA = 41° - 25° = 16°; \frac{d}{\sin 152°} = \frac{d - 3}{\sin 16°};$$

$$\frac{d}{0.4695} = \frac{d - 3}{0.2756}; (0.4695 - 0.2756)d = 3(0.4695); d = 7.2641; h = d \sin 41° =$$

$(7.264)(0.6561) = 4.77; 4.77 + 2 = 6.77$; the summit is about 6.77 km above sea level.

13. $\cos \angle CBD = \dfrac{4^2 + 7^2 - 5^2}{2(4)(7)} = \dfrac{40}{56} = 0.7143; \angle CBD = 44.4°; \cos \angle ABD =$

$$\frac{3^2 + 7^2 - 6^2}{2(3)(7)} = \frac{22}{42} = 0.5238; \angle ABD = 58.4°; \angle ABC = 58.4° + 44.4° = 102.8°; (AC)^2 =$$

$3^2 + 4^2 - 2(3)(4) \cos 102.8° = 9 + 16 - 24(-0.2215) = 30.316; AC = 5.51; 5.51$ cm

Pages 563-564 · WRITTEN EXERCISES

A 1. $\angle C = 180° - (30° + 45°) = 180° - 75° = 105°;$

$$K = \frac{1}{2}b^2 \frac{\sin A \sin C}{\sin B} = \frac{1}{2}(20)^2 \frac{\sin 30° \sin 105°}{\sin 45°} = \frac{1}{2}(400)\frac{0.5(0.9659)}{0.7071} = 137$$

2. $K = \dfrac{1}{2}ab \sin C = \dfrac{1}{2}(10)(8) \sin 40° = 40(0.6428) = 25.7$

3. $K = \dfrac{1}{2}bc \sin A = \dfrac{1}{2}(4)(18) \sin 32° = 36(0.5299) = 19.1$

4. $K = \dfrac{1}{2}ab \sin C = \dfrac{1}{2}(20)(25) \sin 60° = 250(0.8660) = 217$

5. $s = \dfrac{1}{2}(a + b + c) = \dfrac{1}{2}(5 + 12 + 10) = \dfrac{1}{2}(27) = 13.5;$

$K = \sqrt{13.5(13.5 - 5)(13.5 - 12)(13.5 - 10)} = \sqrt{602.4375} = 24.5$

6. $\angle A = 180° - (135° + 30°) = 15°;$

$K = \dfrac{1}{2}b^2 \dfrac{\sin A \sin C}{\sin B} = \dfrac{1}{2}(10)^2 \dfrac{\sin 15° \sin 135°}{\sin 30°} = \dfrac{1}{2}(100)\dfrac{(0.2588)(0.7071)}{0.5} = 18.3$

7. $K = \dfrac{1}{2}ab \sin C = \dfrac{1}{2}(12)(15) \sin 120° = 90(0.8660) = 77.9$

8. $s = \dfrac{1}{2}(a + b + c) = \dfrac{1}{2}(5 + 7 + 8) = \dfrac{1}{2}(20) = 10;$

$K = \sqrt{10(10 - 5)(10 - 7)(10 - 8)} = \sqrt{300} = 17.3$

9. Area of $\square\,ABCD = 2 \cdot$ Area of $\triangle ABD = 2\left(\dfrac{1}{2}db \sin A\right) = db \sin A =$
$8(12) \sin 65° = 96(0.9063) = 87.0$

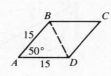

Ex. 9   **Ex. 10**

10. Area of $\square\,ABCD = 2 \cdot$ Area of $\triangle ABD = 2\left(\dfrac{1}{2}db \sin A\right) = db \sin A =$
$15(15) \sin 50° = 225(0.7660) = 172$

B   **11.** Let C be the largest angle and A and B the smaller angles, with $a = 9$ and $b = 12;$

$K = \dfrac{1}{2}ab \sin C;\ 48 = \dfrac{1}{2}(9)(12) \sin C;\ \sin C = \dfrac{48}{54} = 0.8889;\ \angle C = 62.7°$ or $117.3°;$ if

$\angle C = 62.7°,\ c^2 = 9^2 + 12^2 - 2(9)(12) \cos 62.7° = 125.94$ and $c = 11.2 < b;$

$\angle C = 117.3°$

12. Let $\angle A = 45°,\ \angle B = 25°,$ and $\angle C = 110°;\ \overline{AB},$ with length $c,$ is the longest side.

$K = \dfrac{1}{2}c^2 \dfrac{\sin A \sin B}{\sin C};\ 75 = \dfrac{1}{2}c^2 \dfrac{\sin 45° \sin 25°}{\sin 110°};\ c^2 = \dfrac{150 \sin 110°}{\sin 45° \sin 25°} =$

$\dfrac{150(0.9397)}{(0.7071)(0.4226)} = 471.70;\ c = 21.7$

13. Let C be the center of the pentagon. Drawing segments from C to each vertex

produces five congruent isosceles triangles with vertex angle $\left(\dfrac{360}{5}\right)° = 72°,$ base

angles $\dfrac{1}{2}(180° - 72°) = \dfrac{1}{2}(108°) = 54°,$ and base 10 cm long; area of pentagon $=$

$5\left[\dfrac{1}{2}(10)^2 \dfrac{\sin 54° \sin 54°}{\sin 72°}\right] = 250\dfrac{(\sin 54°)^2}{\sin 72°} = 250\dfrac{(0.8090)^2}{0.9511} = 172;\ 172$ cm^2

14. Proceed as in Ex. 13. Resulting triangles have same angles measures, but legs of length 1; area of pentagon $= 5\left[\dfrac{1}{2}(1)(1)\sin 72°\right] = 2.5(0.9511) = 2.38$

15. $K = \dfrac{1}{2}ab\,\sin C;\; K^2 = \left(\dfrac{1}{2}ab\,\sin C\right)^2 = \dfrac{1}{4}a^2b^2\sin^2 C$

16. $2(s - b) = 2s - 2b = a + b + c - 2b = a - b + c;\; 2(s - c) = 2s - 2c = a + b + c - 2c = a + b - c$

C **17. a.** By the law of cosines $c^2 = a^2 + b^2 - 2ab\,\cos C;\; a^2 + b^2 - c^2 = 2ab\,\cos C$

  b. $\sin^2 C + \cos^2 C = 1;\; \cos^2 C = 1 - \sin^2 C$

  c. By Ex. 15, $\dfrac{1}{4}a^2b^2\sin^2 C = K^2;\; 16\left(\dfrac{1}{4}a^2b^2\sin^2 C\right) = 4a^2b^2\sin^2 C = 16K^2$

  d. Add. prop. of equality   **e.** $x^2 - y^2 = (x + y)(x - y)$

  f. Assoc. prop. for add.; $x^2 + 2xy + y^2 = (x + y)^2;\; x^2 - 2xy + y^2 = (x - y)^2$

  g. $x^2 - y^2 = (x + y)(x - y)$ **h.** Ex. 16

  i. Div. prop. of equality; prop. of square roots

Pages 565-566 · CHAPTER REVIEW

1. b   **2.** d; $\dfrac{8}{15}(-360) = -192$ **3.** b; the 6 functions are 3 pairs of reciprocals.

4. d; $a = \dfrac{18}{\sqrt{3}} = 6\sqrt{3};\; c = 2a = 12\sqrt{3}$

5. d; vertical segment is $\dfrac{1}{2}(12) = 6;\; x = 6\sqrt{2}$

6. a; $r = \sqrt{(-3)^2 + 5^2} = \sqrt{34};\; \sec\theta = \dfrac{r}{x} = \dfrac{\sqrt{34}}{-3} = -\dfrac{\sqrt{34}}{3}$

7. c; let $y = -12$ and $x = 5;\; r = 13;\; \cos\theta = \dfrac{x}{r} = \dfrac{5}{13}$

8. a; $\cos 240° = -\cos 60° = -\dfrac{1}{2}$ **9.** d; $\cos 132.6° = -\cos 47.4° = -0.6769$

10. b; θ is in Quadrant II. Let α be the reference angle for θ; $\tan\theta = -\tan\alpha$; $\tan\alpha = 1.580;\; \alpha = 57°40'$ (Table 5); $\theta = 180° - 57°40' = 122°20'$

11. b; $\cos B = \dfrac{7}{10} = 0.7000;\; B = 45.6°$ **12.** b; $\sin 55° = \dfrac{12}{c};\; c = \dfrac{12}{\sin 55°} = \dfrac{12}{0.8192} = 14.6$

13. b; let $x =$ the height of the triangle that forms two right triangles with base $= 15$ cm and angles opposite the bases $= 40°;\; x = 15\tan 50° = 15(1.1918) = 17.9$

14. b; $b^2 = a^2 + c^2 - 2ac\,\cos B;\; \cos B = \dfrac{a^2 + c^2 - b^2}{2ac}$

15. c; $d =$ distance apart; one has walked 12 km, the other 14 km;
$d^2 = 12^2 + 14^2 - 2 \cdot 12 \cdot 14 \cos 135° = 144 + 196 - 336(-0.7071) = 577.6;\quad d = 24.0$

16. c; largest angle is opposite the 9 cm side; $\cos \theta = \dfrac{4^2 + 6^2 - 9^2}{2 \cdot 4 \cdot 6} = -\dfrac{29}{48} = -0.6042$

$\theta = 127.2°$

17. c; $\dfrac{\sin A}{12.3} = \dfrac{\sin 103°}{15.0}$; $\sin A = \dfrac{12.3 \sin 103°}{15.0} = \dfrac{12.3(0.9744)}{15.0} = 0.7990$; $\angle A = 53°$

18. b; let x = the height of the tower; then $\sin 42° = \dfrac{x}{40}$; $x = 40 \sin 42° = 40(0.6691) =$

26.765; $\sin \theta = \dfrac{x}{30} = \dfrac{26.765}{30} = 0.89217$; $\theta = 63.1°$; vertex angle =

$180° - (42° + 63.1°) = 74.9°$

19. b; $c \sin B < b < c$; $10 < b < 20$

20. d; $s = \dfrac{1}{2}(3 + 6 + 7) = 8$; $K = \sqrt{8 \cdot 5 \cdot 2 \cdot 1} = \sqrt{80} = 4\sqrt{5}$

Page 567 · CHAPTER TEST

1. a. $6.46° = 6° + (0.46 \times 60)' = 6° + 27.6' = 6° + 27' + (0.6 \times 60)'' = 6°27'36''$

b. $7°15'90'' = 7° + \left(\dfrac{15}{60}\right)° + \left(\dfrac{90}{3600}\right)° = 7° + 0.25° + 0.025° = 7.275°$

2. Let x = length of hypotenuse and y = longer leg of $30° - 60°$ right triangle; $x = 12\sqrt{2}$

$y = \dfrac{x}{2}\sqrt{3} = \dfrac{12\sqrt{2}}{2}\sqrt{3} = 6\sqrt{6}$; $6\sqrt{6}$ cm

3. $\cos \theta = -\sqrt{1 - \sin^2\theta} = -\sqrt{1 - \dfrac{9}{16}} = -\sqrt{\dfrac{7}{16}} = -\dfrac{\sqrt{7}}{4}$; $\tan \theta = \dfrac{\sin \theta}{\cos \theta} = \dfrac{\dfrac{3}{4}}{-\dfrac{\sqrt{7}}{4}} =$

$-\dfrac{3}{\sqrt{7}} = -\dfrac{3\sqrt{7}}{7}$

4. Reference angle for $\theta = -210°$ is $\alpha = 30°$; $\sin \theta = \sin \alpha = \dfrac{1}{2}$; $\cos \theta = -\cos \alpha = -\dfrac{\sqrt{3}}{2}$

$\tan \theta = -\tan \alpha = -\dfrac{\sqrt{3}}{3}$; $\csc \theta = \dfrac{1}{\sin \theta} = 2$; $\sec \theta = \dfrac{1}{\cos \theta} = -\dfrac{2}{\sqrt{3}} = -\dfrac{2\sqrt{3}}{3}$;

$\cot \theta = \dfrac{1}{\tan \theta} = -\sqrt{3}$

5. a. $\cos 113.4° = -\cos(180° - 113.4°) = -\cos 66.6° = -0.3971$

b. θ is in Quadrant II; the reference angle for θ is $\alpha = 180° - \theta$; $\tan \alpha = -\tan \theta =$ 2.097; $\alpha = 64.5°$; $\theta = 115.5°$

6. $\angle B = 46.5°$; $\sin 46.5° = \dfrac{750}{d}$; $d = \dfrac{750}{\sin 46.5°} = \dfrac{750}{0.7254} = 1034$; 1030 m

7. $\cos \theta = \dfrac{5^2 + 3^2 - 7^2}{2(5)(3)} = \dfrac{-15}{30} = -0.5$; $\theta = 120°$

Ex. 6   Ex. 7

8. $\angle C = 180° - (102° + 38°) = 40°; \dfrac{\sin 102°}{a} = \dfrac{\sin 40°}{16}; a = \dfrac{16 \sin 102°}{\sin 40°} =$

$\dfrac{16(0.9781)}{0.6428} = 24.3; \dfrac{\sin 38°}{b} = \dfrac{\sin 40°}{16}; b = \dfrac{16 \sin 38°}{\sin 40°} = \dfrac{16(0.6157)}{0.6428} = 15.3$

9. $\dfrac{\sin C}{34} = \dfrac{\sin 27°}{28}; \sin C = \dfrac{34 \sin 27°}{28} = \dfrac{34(0.4540)}{28} = 0.5513; \angle C = 33.5°$ or $146.5°$; since

$\angle C$ is the largest angle, $\angle C = 146.5°; \angle A = 180° - (27° + 146.5°) = 6.5°; \dfrac{\sin 6.5°}{a} =$

$\dfrac{\sin 27°}{28}; a = \dfrac{28 \sin 6.5°}{\sin 27°} = \dfrac{28(0.1132)}{0.4540} = 6.98$

10. Let $\angle A = 55°$ and $\angle B = 75°; \angle C = 180° - (55° + 75°) = 50°$; since $\angle C$ is the smallest

angle, $c = 10; K = \dfrac{1}{2}c^2 \dfrac{\sin A \sin B}{\sin C} = \dfrac{1}{2}(10^2) \dfrac{\sin 55° \sin 75°}{\sin 50°} =$

$\dfrac{1}{2}(100) \dfrac{(0.8192)(0.9659)}{0.7660} = 51.6$

Page 568 · MIXED REVIEW

1. Center at $\left(\dfrac{-2 + -2}{2}, \dfrac{-7 + 1}{2}\right) = (-2, -3); r = \dfrac{1}{2}\sqrt{[-2 - (-2)]^2 + (-7 - 1)^2} =$

$\dfrac{1}{2}\sqrt{0 + 64} = \dfrac{1}{2}\sqrt{64} = \dfrac{1}{2} \cdot 8 = 4; (x + 2)^2 + (y + 3)^2 = 16$

2. $\dfrac{1}{5}(3d - 7) = \dfrac{3}{4}(d - 1) - 2; 4(3d - 7) = 15(d - 1) - 40;$

$12d - 28 = 15d - 15 - 40; 12d - 28 = 15d - 55; -3d = -27; d = 9$

3. $|2 - m| < 1; -1 < 2 - m < 1; -3 < -m < -1; 1 < m < 3; \{m: 1 < m < 3\}$

4. $q^3 + 2q^2 - 3q > 0; q(q^2 + 2q - 3) > 0; q(q + 3)(q - 1) > 0$; true if one factor is positive or all are positive; drawing a sign graph yields the solution set $\{q: -3 < q < 0$ or
   $q > 1\}$

5. $21x - 6y = 15$

   $\underline{8x + 6y = 72}$

   $29x = 87; \quad x = 3; 21 - 2y = 5; -2y = -16; y = 8; (3, 8)$

6. $6x + y = -6$; $y = -6x - 6$; $4x^2 + y^2 = 4$; $4x^2 + (-6x - 6)^2 = 4$;

$4x^2 + 36x^2 + 72x + 36 = 4$; $40x^2 + 72x + 32 = 0$; $5x^2 + 9x + 4 = 0$;

$(5x + 4)(x + 1) = 0$; $5x + 4 = 0$ or $x + 1 = 0$; $x = -\dfrac{4}{5}$ or $x = -1$; if $x = -\dfrac{4}{5}$,

$y = -6\left(-\dfrac{4}{5}\right) - 6 = -\dfrac{6}{5}$; if $x = -1$; $y = -6(-1) - 6 = 0$; $\left\{\left(-\dfrac{4}{5}, -\dfrac{6}{5}\right), (-1, 0)\right\}$

7.
$$\begin{array}{r} x - y + z = 0 \\ -x + y + z = -10 \\ \hline 2z = -10; \quad z = -5 \end{array} \qquad \begin{array}{r} x + y - z = 6 \\ x - y + z = 0 \\ \hline 2x = 6; \quad x = 3 \end{array}$$

$3 + y - (-5) = 6$; $y + 8 = 6$; $y = -2$; $(3, -2, -5)$

8. $2 - i$ and $2 + i$ are roots; $x - (2 - i)$ and $x - (2 + i)$ are factors of $P(x)$

$x^4 - 3x^3 - 11x^2 + 53x - 60$ as is their product $[(x - 2) + i][(x - 2) - i] =$

$x^2 - 4x + 5$; $\dfrac{x^4 - 3x^3 - 11x^2 + 53x - 60}{x^2 - 4x + 5} = x^2 + x - 12$; $x^2 + x - 12 = 0$;

$x = \dfrac{-1 \pm \sqrt{1 + 48}}{2} = \dfrac{-1 \pm 7}{2} = -4$ or 3; $\{2 - i, 2 + i, -4, 3\}$

9. $a^2 = 5^2 + 4^2 - 2(5)(4) \cos 120° = 25 + 16 - 40(-0.5) = 61$; $a = 7.8$;

$\dfrac{\sin B}{4} = \dfrac{\sin 120°}{7.8}$; $\sin B = \dfrac{4 \sin 120°}{7.8} = \dfrac{4(0.8660)}{7.8} = 0.4441$; $\angle B$ is acute since $\angle A$ is

obtuse; $\angle B = 26.4°$ (If a calculator is used and only the final result is rounded, then
the answer for $\angle B$ will be $26.3°$.)

10. a. $\displaystyle\sum_{k=1}^{200} 5(k + 1) = 5 \sum_{k=1}^{200} (k + 1)$; $a = 2$; $t_{200} = 2 + (199)(1) = 201$;

$5 \cdot S_{200} = 5\left(\dfrac{200}{2}\right)(2 + 201) = 101{,}500$

b. $\displaystyle\sum_{i=1}^{10} 3 \cdot 2^i = 3 \sum_{i=1}^{10} 2^i$; $a = 2$; $3 \cdot S_{10} = 3\left(\dfrac{2 - 2 \cdot 2^{10}}{1 - 2}\right) = 3(2046) = 6138$

11. $f^{-1}(27) = \log_3 27 = 3$

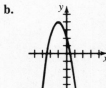

$f(x) = 3^x$

$f^{-1}(x) = \log_3 x$

12. $b^2 - 4ac < 0$; $3^2 - 4(-2)k < 0$; $9 + 8k < 0$; $8k < -9$; $k < -\dfrac{9}{8}$

13. a.

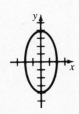

b.

14. Let x = amount invested at 5½%; $x + 2000$ = amount invested at 9½%;
$0.055x + 0.095(x + 2000) = 265$; $55x + 95(x + 2000) = 265,000$;
$55x + 95x + 190,000 = 265,000$; $150x = 75,000$; $x = 500$; $x + 2000 = 2500$;
$500 + 2500 = 3000$; \$3000

15. $f(2 - \sqrt{3}) = \dfrac{(2 - \sqrt{3}) - 1}{(2 - \sqrt{3}) + 1} = \dfrac{1 - \sqrt{3}}{3 - \sqrt{3}} = \dfrac{(1 - \sqrt{3})(3 + \sqrt{3})}{(3 - \sqrt{3})(3 + \sqrt{3})} = \dfrac{3 - 2\sqrt{3} - 3}{9 - 3} =$
$\dfrac{-2\sqrt{3}}{6} = -\dfrac{\sqrt{3}}{3}$

16. $a = 9$, $d = 7$; $t_{50} = 9 + 49(7) = 352$

17. $k = 2$, $n = 5$; the third term is $10(2x)^{5-(3-1)}y^{3-1} = 10(2x)^3 y^2 = 10(8x^3)y^2 = 80x^3 y^2$

18. a. $\sqrt[3]{\dfrac{3}{8}} - \sqrt[3]{81} = \dfrac{\sqrt[3]{3}}{\sqrt[3]{8}} - \sqrt[3]{27 \cdot 3} = \dfrac{\sqrt[3]{3}}{2} - 3\sqrt[3]{3} = -\dfrac{5\sqrt[3]{3}}{2}$

    b. $(2\sqrt{7} - \sqrt{14})^2 = (2\sqrt{7})^2 - 2(2\sqrt{7})\sqrt{14} + (\sqrt{14})^2 = 28 - 4\sqrt{7}(\sqrt{7})(\sqrt{2}) + 14 =$
    $42 - 28\sqrt{2}$

19. $(\sqrt{6})^{3x-1} = 216^x$; $(6^{1/2})^{3x-1} = (6^3)^x$; $6^{1/2(3x-1)} = 6^{3x}$; $\dfrac{1}{2}(3x - 1) = 3x$; $3x - 1 = 6x$;
$3x = -1$; $x = -\dfrac{1}{3}$

20. $\log_x 27 = -\dfrac{3}{4}$; $x^{-3/4} = 27$; $x = 27^{-4/3} = \dfrac{1}{27^{4/3}} = \dfrac{1}{81}$

21. $x = 2\log_3 6 - \log_3 4$; $x = \log_3\left(\dfrac{6^2}{4}\right) = \log_3 9 = 2$

22. Since $180° < \theta < 360°$ and $\cos \theta < 0$, θ is in Quadrant III and $\sin \theta < 0$;
$\sin \theta = -\sqrt{1 - \cos^2\theta} = -\sqrt{1 - \dfrac{225}{289}} = -\sqrt{\dfrac{64}{289}} = -\dfrac{8}{17}$; $\tan \theta = \dfrac{\sin \theta}{\cos \theta} = \dfrac{-\dfrac{8}{17}}{-\dfrac{15}{17}} = \dfrac{8}{15}$;
$\csc \theta = \dfrac{1}{\sin \theta} = -\dfrac{17}{8}$; $\sec \theta = \dfrac{1}{\cos \theta} = -\dfrac{17}{15}$; $\cot \theta = \dfrac{1}{\tan \theta} = \dfrac{15}{8}$

23. $\angle Z = 180° - (10° + 134.7°) = 180° - 144.7° = 35.3°$; $\dfrac{\sin 134.7°}{y} = \dfrac{\sin 10°}{12}$;
$y = \dfrac{12 \sin 134.7°}{\sin 10°} = \dfrac{12(0.7108)}{0.1736} = 49.1$; $\dfrac{\sin 35.3°}{z} = \dfrac{\sin 10°}{12}$;
$z = \dfrac{12 \sin 35.3°}{\sin 10°} = \dfrac{12(0.5779)}{0.1736} = 39.9$

Page 569 · PREPARING FOR COLLEGE ENTRANCE EXAMS

1. C	**2.** C	**3.** C
4. C	**5.** A	**6.** B
7. D	**8.** E	

Pages 574-575 · WRITTEN EXERCISES

A **1.** $30° = 30 \cdot \dfrac{\pi}{180} = \dfrac{\pi}{6}$ **2.** $60° = 60 \cdot \dfrac{\pi}{180} = \dfrac{\pi}{3}$ **3.** $45° = 45 \cdot \dfrac{\pi}{180} = \dfrac{\pi}{4}$

4. $-90° = -90 \cdot \dfrac{\pi}{180} = -\dfrac{\pi}{2}$ **5.** $-150° = -150 \cdot \dfrac{\pi}{180} = -\dfrac{5\pi}{6}$

6. $120° = 120 \cdot \dfrac{\pi}{180} = \dfrac{2\pi}{3}$ **7.** $180° = 180 \cdot \dfrac{\pi}{180} = \pi$

8. $-135° = -135 \cdot \dfrac{\pi}{180} = -\dfrac{3\pi}{4}$ **9.** $-300° = -300 \cdot \dfrac{\pi}{180} = -\dfrac{5\pi}{3}$

10. $240° = 240 \cdot \dfrac{\pi}{180} = \dfrac{4\pi}{3}$ **11.** $720° = 720 \cdot \dfrac{\pi}{180} = 4\pi$ **12.** $405° = 405 \cdot \dfrac{\pi}{180} = \dfrac{9\pi}{4}$

13. $\dfrac{\pi}{3} = \left(\dfrac{\pi}{3} \cdot \dfrac{180}{\pi}\right)° = 60°$ **14.** $-\dfrac{\pi}{6} = \left(-\dfrac{\pi}{6} \cdot \dfrac{180}{\pi}\right)° = -30°$

15. $\dfrac{\pi}{2} = \left(\dfrac{\pi}{2} \cdot \dfrac{180}{\pi}\right)° = 90°$ **16.** $\dfrac{\pi}{4} = \left(\dfrac{\pi}{4} \cdot \dfrac{180}{\pi}\right)° = 45°$ **17.** $\dfrac{2\pi}{3} = \left(\dfrac{2\pi}{3} \cdot \dfrac{180}{\pi}\right)° = 120$

18. $-\dfrac{5\pi}{3} = \left(-\dfrac{5\pi}{3} \cdot \dfrac{180}{\pi}\right)° = -300°$ **19.** $-\dfrac{5\pi}{6} = \left(-\dfrac{5\pi}{6} \cdot \dfrac{180}{\pi}\right)° = -150°$

20. $\dfrac{5\pi}{4} = \left(\dfrac{5\pi}{4} \cdot \dfrac{180}{\pi}\right)° = 225°$ **21.** $-\pi = \left(-\pi \cdot \dfrac{180}{\pi}\right)° = -180°$

22. $\dfrac{7\pi}{4} = \left(\dfrac{7\pi}{4} \cdot \dfrac{180}{\pi}\right)° = 315°$ **23.** $\dfrac{13\pi}{6} = \left(\dfrac{13\pi}{6} \cdot \dfrac{180}{\pi}\right)° = 390°$

24. $\dfrac{5\pi}{2} = \left(\dfrac{5\pi}{2} \cdot \dfrac{180}{\pi}\right)° = 450°$ **25.** $20° = 20 \cdot \dfrac{\pi}{180} = \dfrac{\pi}{9} \approx 0.35$

26. $-80° = -80 \cdot \dfrac{\pi}{180} = -\dfrac{4\pi}{9} \approx -1.40$ **27.** $100° = 100 \cdot \dfrac{\pi}{180} = \dfrac{5\pi}{9} \approx 1.75$

28. $200° = 200 \cdot \dfrac{\pi}{180} = \dfrac{10\pi}{9} \approx 3.49$ **29.** $63° = 63 \cdot \dfrac{\pi}{180} = \dfrac{7\pi}{20} \approx 1.10$

30. $72° = 72 \cdot \dfrac{\pi}{180} = \dfrac{2\pi}{5} \approx 1.26$ **31.** $-186° = -186 \cdot \dfrac{\pi}{180} = -\dfrac{31\pi}{30} \approx -3.25$

32. $126° = 126 \cdot \dfrac{\pi}{180} = \dfrac{7\pi}{10} \approx 2.20$ **33.** $2 = \left(2 \cdot \dfrac{180}{\pi}\right)° = \left(\dfrac{360}{\pi}\right)° \approx 114.6°$

34. $-3 = \left(-3 \cdot \dfrac{180}{\pi}\right)° = \left(-\dfrac{540}{\pi}\right)° \approx -171.9°$

35. $0.6 = \left[(0.6)\left(\dfrac{180}{\pi}\right)\right]° = \left(\dfrac{108}{\pi}\right)° \approx 34.4°$

36. $-1.2 = \left[(-1.2)\left(\dfrac{180}{\pi}\right)\right]^\circ = \left(-\dfrac{216}{\pi}\right)^\circ \approx -68.8^\circ$

37. $-2.5 = \left[(-2.5)\left(\dfrac{180}{\pi}\right)\right]^\circ = \left(-\dfrac{450}{\pi}\right)^\circ \approx -143.2^\circ$

38. $1.5 = \left[(1.5)\left(\dfrac{180}{\pi}\right)\right]^\circ = \left(\dfrac{270}{\pi}\right)^\circ \approx 85.9^\circ$ **39.** $10 = \left(10 \cdot \dfrac{180}{\pi}\right)^\circ = \left(\dfrac{1800}{\pi}\right)^\circ \approx 573.0^\circ$

40. $12 = \left(12 \cdot \dfrac{180}{\pi}\right)^\circ = \left(\dfrac{2160}{\pi}\right)^\circ \approx 687.5^\circ$

41. $\theta = \dfrac{s}{r} = \dfrac{8}{2} = 4;\ A = \dfrac{1}{2}rs = \dfrac{1}{2}(2 \cdot 8) = 8$

42. $\theta = \dfrac{s}{r} = \dfrac{6}{3} = 2;\ A = \dfrac{1}{2}rs = \dfrac{1}{2}(3 \cdot 6) = 9$

43. $s = r\theta = 2(1.5) = 3;\ A = \dfrac{1}{2}r^2\theta = \dfrac{1}{2}(4)(1.5) = 3$

44. $s = r\theta = 3 \cdot 1 = 3;\ A = \dfrac{1}{2}r^2\theta = \dfrac{1}{2} \cdot 9 \cdot 1 = 4.5$

45. $s = \dfrac{2A}{r} = \dfrac{2 \cdot 9}{3} = 6;\ \theta = \dfrac{s}{r} = \dfrac{6}{3} = 2$ **46.** $s = \dfrac{2A}{r} = \dfrac{2 \cdot 6}{2} = 6;\ \theta = \dfrac{s}{r} = \dfrac{6}{2} = 3$

47. $r = \dfrac{s}{\theta} = \dfrac{6}{1.5} = 4;\ A = \dfrac{1}{2}rs = \dfrac{1}{2} \cdot 4 \cdot 6 = 12$

48. $r = \dfrac{s}{\theta} = \dfrac{1.5}{0.5} = 3;\ A = \dfrac{1}{2}rs = \dfrac{1}{2} \cdot 3(1.5) = 2.25$

49. $s = \dfrac{2A}{r} = \dfrac{2 \cdot 6}{4} = 3;\ \theta = \dfrac{s}{r} = \dfrac{3}{4} = 0.75$

50. $s = \dfrac{2A}{r} = \dfrac{2 \cdot 3}{4} = 1.5;\ \theta = \dfrac{s}{r} = \dfrac{1.5}{4} = 0.375$

B   **51.** $A = \dfrac{1}{2}r^2\theta;\ r = \sqrt{\dfrac{2A}{\theta}} = \sqrt{\dfrac{2 \cdot 6}{3}} = \sqrt{4} = 2;\ s = r\theta = 2 \cdot 3 = 6$

52. $A = \dfrac{1}{2}r^2\theta;\ r = \sqrt{\dfrac{2A}{\theta}} = \sqrt{\dfrac{2 \cdot 9}{0.3}} = \sqrt{60} = 2\sqrt{15};\ s = r\theta = \dfrac{3}{10}(2\sqrt{15}) = \dfrac{3\sqrt{15}}{5}$

53. Any angle with measure $6.65 + 2\pi n$ for n an integer is coterminal with α; if $n = -1$, $6.65 - 2\pi \approx 0.37;\ 0.37$

54. Any angle with measure $13 + 2\pi n$ for n an integer is coterminal with α; if $n = -2$, $13 - 4\pi \approx 0.43;\ 0.43$

55. Any angle with measure $-3 + 2\pi n$ for n an integer is coterminal with α; if $n = 1$, $-3 + 2\pi \approx 3.28;\ 3.28$

56. Any angle with measure $-20 + 2\pi n$ for n an integer is coterminal with α; if $n = 4$, $-20 + 8\pi \approx 5.13;\ 5.13$

Pages 575-576 · PROBLEMS

A   1. $\theta = 40° = \dfrac{40 \cdot \pi}{180} \approx 0.70$; $s \approx 4000(0.7) = 2800$; 2800 mi

2. $\theta = 90° - 25.8° = 64.2°$; $\theta = 64.2\left(\dfrac{\pi}{180}\right) \approx 1.12$; $s \approx 4500$; 4500 mi

3. $\omega = \dfrac{1}{2}$ rpm $= \dfrac{1}{2} \cdot 2\pi = \pi$ radians/min; $r = \dfrac{1}{2} \cdot 40 = 20$; $v = r\omega = 20\pi$;

20π ft/min ≈ 63 ft/min

4. rim speed of smaller wheel = rim speed of larger wheel = $\omega r = 50 \cdot 2\pi \cdot 15 =$

1500π cm/min ≈ 4700 cm/min; angular speed of smaller wheel $= \dfrac{v}{r} = \dfrac{1500\pi}{6} =$

250π radians/min

5. $\theta = 24° = 24 \cdot \dfrac{\pi}{180} \approx 0.42$; distance traveled in one roundtrip $= 2s =$

$2r\theta \approx 2(1)(0.42) = 0.84$ m; number of trips in one day $= \dfrac{24 \cdot 60 \cdot 60}{2} = 43,200$; tota$\rceil$

distance traveled in one day $= 43,200(0.84) = 36,288$ m ≈ 36 km

B   6. $\omega = 10$ rev/s $= 10 \cdot 2\pi = 20\pi$ radians/s; $v = r\omega = 1 \cdot 20\pi$; 20π ft/s ≈ 63 ft/s;

63 ft/s $= 226,800$ ft/hr ≈ 43 mph;

7. $\theta = 0.518° = 0.518\left(\dfrac{\pi}{180}\right) \approx 0.009$; $s = r\theta \approx 240,000(0.009) = 2160$; ≈ 2200 mi

C   8. $\overline{OA}$, $\overline{OB}$ and $\overline{OC}$ are radii, each with length 2;

$\angle ODC = 90°$; $OD = OB - DB = 2 - 1 = 1$.

Therefore $\angle DOC = 60° = \angle DOA$ and $DC = \sqrt{3} = DA$;

area of $\triangle AOC = \dfrac{1}{2} \cdot 2\sqrt{3} \cdot 1 = \sqrt{3}$; area of the

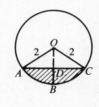

sector determined by $\angle AOC = \pi \cdot 2^2 \cdot \dfrac{120}{360} = \dfrac{4\pi}{3}$.

Area of the shaded region $= \dfrac{4\pi}{3} - \sqrt{3} = \dfrac{4\pi - 3\sqrt{3}}{3}$; volume of water $= \dfrac{4\pi - 3\sqrt{3}}{3}h$,

where h is the height of the cylinder. Area of circle $O = 4\pi$; capacity volume $= 4\pi h$

Ratio of water to capacity $= \dfrac{\dfrac{4\pi h - 3\sqrt{3}\,h}{3}}{4\pi h} = \dfrac{1}{3} - \dfrac{\sqrt{3}}{4\pi} \approx 0.333 - \dfrac{1.73}{4 \cdot 30.14} =$

$0.333 - 0.138 = 0.195$; about 20%

9. $\omega = \dfrac{\dfrac{2\pi}{12} \text{ rad/h}}{3600 \text{ s/h}} = \dfrac{2\pi}{12 \cdot 3600}$ rad/s $= 0.000145$ rad/s; 0.00015 rad/s;

$v = (50)(0.000145) = 0.00725$; 0.0073 mm/s

10. $\omega = 1$ rev/day $= \dfrac{1}{24 \cdot 60 \cdot 60} \cdot 2\pi$ rad/s $\approx 7.3 \times 10^{-5}$ rad/s

Page 576 · CHALLENGE

Between 1:00 and 1:30, the hour hand moves through an angle of $\frac{\pi}{12}$; $\omega =$

$\frac{\pi}{12} \div 30 = \frac{\pi}{360}$ rad/min; the minute hand moves through an angle of π; $\omega = \frac{\pi}{30}$; let

$\alpha =$ angle between 12 and the hour hand, $\beta =$ angle between 12 and minute hand, and

$\theta =$ angle between hands; at x minutes after 1, $\alpha = \frac{\pi}{6} + x \cdot \frac{\pi}{360}$ and $\beta = x \cdot \frac{\pi}{30}$; be-

tween 1:00 and 1:05, $\theta = \alpha - \beta$; at 1:05, $\theta = \alpha$; between 1:05 and 1:30, $\theta = \beta - \alpha$; when

$0 < x \leq 5$, $0 < \theta \leq \frac{\pi}{6}$ so $5 < x < 30$, that is $\theta = \beta - \alpha$; $\frac{\pi}{5} = x \cdot \frac{\pi}{30} - \left(\frac{\pi}{6} + x \cdot \frac{\pi}{360}\right)$;

$72\pi = 12\pi x - 60\pi - \pi x$; $132 = 11x$; $x = 12$; 1:12

Pages 580-581 · WRITTEN EXERCISES

A 1. $\sin \frac{\pi}{6} = \frac{1}{2}$; $\cos \frac{\pi}{6} = \frac{\sqrt{3}}{2}$; $\tan \frac{\pi}{6} = \frac{\sqrt{3}}{3}$; $\csc \frac{\pi}{6} = 2$; $\sec \frac{\pi}{6} = \frac{2\sqrt{3}}{3}$; $\cot \frac{\pi}{6} = \sqrt{3}$

2. $\sin \frac{\pi}{4} = \frac{\sqrt{2}}{2}$; $\cos \frac{\pi}{4} = \frac{\sqrt{2}}{2}$; $\tan \frac{\pi}{4} = 1$; $\csc \frac{\pi}{4} = \sqrt{2}$; $\sec \frac{\pi}{4} = \sqrt{2}$; $\cot \frac{\pi}{4} = 1$

3. $\sin \pi = 0$; $\cos \pi = -1$; $\tan \pi = 0$; $\csc \pi$ is undefined; $\sec \pi = -1$; $\cot \pi$ is undefined

4. $\sin \frac{2\pi}{3} = \frac{\sqrt{3}}{2}$; $\cos \frac{2\pi}{3} = -\frac{1}{2}$; $\tan \frac{2\pi}{3} = -\sqrt{3}$; $\csc \frac{2\pi}{3} = \frac{2\sqrt{3}}{3}$; $\sec \frac{2\pi}{3} = -2$;

$\cot \frac{2\pi}{3} = -\frac{\sqrt{3}}{3}$

5. $\sin \frac{3\pi}{4} = \frac{\sqrt{2}}{2}$; $\cos \frac{3\pi}{4} = -\frac{\sqrt{2}}{2}$; $\tan \frac{3\pi}{4} = -1$; $\csc \frac{3\pi}{4} = \sqrt{2}$; $\sec \frac{3\pi}{4} = -\sqrt{2}$;

$\cot \frac{3\pi}{4} = -1$

6. $\sin \frac{3\pi}{2} = -1$; $\cos \frac{3\pi}{2} = 0$; $\tan \frac{3\pi}{2}$ is undefined; $\csc \frac{3\pi}{2} = -1$; $\sec \frac{3\pi}{2}$ is undefined;

$\cot \frac{3\pi}{2} = 0$

7. $\sin \frac{11\pi}{6} = -\frac{1}{2}$; $\cos \frac{11\pi}{6} = \frac{\sqrt{3}}{2}$; $\tan \frac{11\pi}{6} = -\frac{\sqrt{3}}{3}$; $\csc \frac{11\pi}{6} = -2$; $\sec \frac{11\pi}{6} = \frac{2\sqrt{3}}{3}$;

$\cot \frac{11\pi}{6} = -\sqrt{3}$

8. $\sin \frac{7\pi}{6} = -\frac{1}{2}$; $\cos \frac{7\pi}{6} = -\frac{\sqrt{3}}{2}$; $\tan \frac{7\pi}{6} = \frac{\sqrt{3}}{3}$; $\csc \frac{7\pi}{6} = -2$; $\sec \frac{7\pi}{6} = -\frac{2\sqrt{3}}{3}$;

$\cot \frac{7\pi}{6} = \sqrt{3}$

9. $\sin \dfrac{13\pi}{3} = \dfrac{\sqrt{3}}{2}$; $\cos \dfrac{13\pi}{3} = \dfrac{1}{2}$; $\tan \dfrac{13\pi}{3} = \sqrt{3}$; $\csc \dfrac{13\pi}{3} = \dfrac{2\sqrt{3}}{3}$; $\sec \dfrac{13\pi}{3} = 2$;

   $\cot \dfrac{13\pi}{3} = \dfrac{\sqrt{3}}{3}$

10. $\sin \dfrac{14\pi}{3} = \dfrac{\sqrt{3}}{2}$; $\cos \dfrac{14\pi}{3} = -\dfrac{1}{2}$; $\tan \dfrac{14\pi}{3} = -\sqrt{3}$; $\csc \dfrac{14\pi}{3} = \dfrac{2\sqrt{3}}{3}$; $\sec \dfrac{14\pi}{3} = -2$;

   $\cot \dfrac{14\pi}{3} = -\dfrac{\sqrt{3}}{3}$

11. $\sin\left(-\dfrac{5\pi}{4}\right) = \dfrac{\sqrt{2}}{2}$; $\cos\left(-\dfrac{5\pi}{4}\right) = -\dfrac{\sqrt{2}}{2}$; $\tan\left(-\dfrac{5\pi}{4}\right) = -1$; $\csc\left(-\dfrac{5\pi}{4}\right) = \sqrt{2}$;

    $\sec\left(-\dfrac{5\pi}{4}\right) = -\sqrt{2}$; $\cot\left(-\dfrac{5\pi}{4}\right) = -1$

12. $\sin\left(-\dfrac{7\pi}{4}\right) = \dfrac{\sqrt{2}}{2}$; $\cos\left(-\dfrac{7\pi}{4}\right) = \dfrac{\sqrt{2}}{2}$; $\tan\left(-\dfrac{7\pi}{4}\right) = 1$; $\csc\left(-\dfrac{7\pi}{4}\right) = \sqrt{2}$;

    $\sec\left(-\dfrac{7\pi}{4}\right) = \sqrt{2}$; $\cot\left(-\dfrac{7\pi}{4}\right) = 1$

13. $\sin 1.2 = 0.9320$; $\cos 1.2 = 0.3624$; $\tan 1.2 = 2.572$

14. $\sin 0.5 = 0.4794$; $\cos 0.5 = 0.8776$; $\tan 0.5 = 0.5463$

15. $\sin 1.35 = 0.9757$; $\cos 1.35 = 0.2190$; $\tan 1.35 = 4.455$

16. $\sin 0.64 = 0.5972$; $\cos 0.64 = 0.8021$; $\tan 0.64 = 0.7445$

17. $x = 0.42$ 18. $x = \dfrac{\pi}{3}$ or $x = 1.05$ 19. $x = \dfrac{\pi}{4}$ or $x = 0.79$

20. $x = 0.61$ 21. $\cos^2 \dfrac{5\pi}{3} + \sin^2 \dfrac{5\pi}{3} = \left(\dfrac{1}{2}\right)^2 + \left(-\dfrac{\sqrt{3}}{2}\right)^2 = \dfrac{1}{4} + \dfrac{3}{4} = 1$

22. $\cos^2 \dfrac{5\pi}{6} + \sin^2 \dfrac{5\pi}{6} = \left(-\dfrac{\sqrt{3}}{2}\right)^2 + \left(\dfrac{1}{2}\right)^2 = \dfrac{3}{4} + \dfrac{1}{4} = 1$

23. $\cos^2 1 + \sin^2 1 = (0.5403)^2 + (0.8415)^2 = 0.2919 + 0.7081 = 1$

24. $\cos^2 0.6 + \sin^2 0.6 = (0.8253)^2 + (0.5646)^2 = 0.6811 + 0.3188 = 0.9999 \approx 1$

25. $\sin 7 = \sin(7 + 2\pi n)$ for every integer n; let $n = -1$; $\sin 7 = \sin(7 - 2\pi) \approx$
    $\sin 0.72 = 0.6594$

26. Since $0 < s < \dfrac{\pi}{2}$, $\sin s$, $\cos s$, and $\tan s$ are all positive; $\Delta OAQ \sim \Delta OMP$ so

    $\dfrac{OA}{\cos s} = \dfrac{AQ}{\sin s}$; $\dfrac{1}{\cos s} = \dfrac{AQ}{\sin s}$; $\dfrac{\sin s}{\cos s} = AQ$; $\tan s = AQ$.

27. Since $0 < s < \dfrac{\pi}{2}$, $\sin s$, $\cos s$, and $\tan s$ are all positive; $\Delta OAQ \sim \Delta OMP$ so

    $\dfrac{OA}{\cos s} = \dfrac{OQ}{OP}$; $\dfrac{1}{\cos s} = \dfrac{OQ}{1}$; $\dfrac{1}{\cos s} = OQ$; $\sec s = OQ$.

28. Since $0 < s < \dfrac{\pi}{2}$, s and $\sin s$ are both positive. The shortest distance from P to $\overrightarrow{OA}$ is the length of the perpendicular, $\sin s$; then $\sin s < s$.

C   29. Since $0 < s < \dfrac{\pi}{2}$, s and $\tan s$ are both positive; area of sector $OAP = \dfrac{1}{2}rs = \dfrac{1}{2}s$; area of $\triangle OAQ = \dfrac{1}{2} \cdot OA \cdot AQ = \dfrac{1}{2}\tan s$ (see Ex. 26); $\dfrac{1}{2}s < \dfrac{1}{2}\tan s$; $s < \tan s$.

30. From Ex. 28 and 29, above, $\sin s < s < \tan s$ for $0 < s < \dfrac{\pi}{2}$; since $\sin s > 0$ for $0 < s < \dfrac{\pi}{2}$, $\dfrac{\sin s}{\sin s} < \dfrac{s}{\sin s} < \dfrac{\tan s}{\sin s}$; $1 < \dfrac{s}{\sin s} < \dfrac{\sin s}{\cos s \cdot \sin s}$; $1 < \dfrac{s}{\sin s} < \dfrac{1}{\cos s}$.

Page 581 · CALCULATOR KEY-IN

1. 0.5	2. 0	3. 0
4. 1	5. −0.9848	6. 0.5774
7. −0.5440	8. 0.1736	9. 0.5624
10. 0.1736	11. −0.6175	12. 0.1559

13. For x close to 0, $\sin x$ is approximately equal to x.

Pages 584-586 · WRITTEN EXERCISES

A   1. odd

2. even

3. neither

4. neither

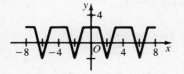

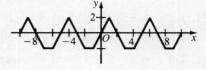

5. even

6. odd

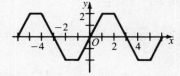

7. a. 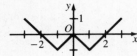   **b.**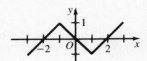

8. a. 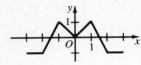   **b.**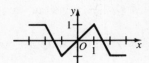

9. a. 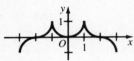   **b.**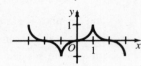

10. a. 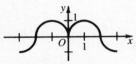   **b.**

11. $f(-x) = (-x)^4 - 3(-x)^2 + 5 = x^4 - 3x^2 + 5 = f(x)$; even

12. $f(-x) = (-x)^2 - 4(-x) = x^2 + 4x$; neither

13. $f(-x) = (-x)^3 + (-x)^2 = -x^3 + x^2$; neither

14. $f(-x) = (-x)^3 + 3(-x) + 3 = -x^3 - 3x + 3$; neither

15. $f(-x) = \dfrac{-x}{(-x)^2 - 4} = -\dfrac{x}{x^2 - 4} = -f(x)$; odd

16. $f(-x) = -x\sqrt{(-x)^2 - 1} = -x\sqrt{x^2 - 1} = -f(x)$; odd

B   **17.** $f(-x) = -x\sin(-x) = -x(-\sin x) = x\sin x = f(x)$; even

18. $f(-x) = -x\cos(-x) = -x\cos x = -f(x)$; odd

19. $f(-x) = \sin(-x)\cos(-x) = -\sin x\cos x = -f(x)$; odd

20. $f(-x) = \sin(-x) + \cos(-x) = -\sin x + \cos x$; neither

21. Let $p = \pi$; $\sin 2(x + \pi) = \sin(2x + 2\pi) = \sin 2x$; if $0 < p < \pi$,
$2x < 2(x + p) < 2x + 2\pi$ and $\sin 2(x + p) \neq \sin 2x$.

22. Let $p = \pi$; $\cos 2(x + \pi) = \cos(2x + 2\pi) = \cos 2x$; if $0 < p < \pi$,
$2x < 2(x + p) < 2x + 2\pi$ and $\cos 2(x + p) \neq \cos 2x$.

23. Let $p = 4\pi$; $\cos \dfrac{1}{2}(x + 4\pi) = \cos\left(\dfrac{1}{2}x + 2\pi\right) = \cos \dfrac{1}{2}x$; if $0 < p < 4\pi$,
$\dfrac{1}{2}x < \dfrac{1}{2}(x + p) < \dfrac{1}{2}x + 2\pi$ and $\cos \dfrac{1}{2}(x + p) \neq \cos \dfrac{1}{2}x$.

24. Let $p = 4\pi$; $\sin \dfrac{1}{2}(x + 4\pi) = \sin\left(\dfrac{1}{2}x + 2\pi\right) = \sin \dfrac{1}{2}x$; if $0 < p < 4\pi$,
$\dfrac{1}{2}x < \dfrac{1}{2}(x + p) < \dfrac{1}{2}x + 2\pi$ and $\sin \dfrac{1}{2}(x + p) \neq \sin \dfrac{1}{2}x$.

25. Let f and g be odd functions with the same domain; that is, for every x in the common domain, $f(-x) = -f(x)$ and $g(-x) = -g(x)$; then $f(-x) \cdot g(-x) = -f(x)[-g(x)] = f(x) \cdot g(x)$ and the product of the two functions is even.

26. Let f and g be functions with the same domain, f even and g odd; that is, for every x in the common domain, $f(-x) = f(x)$ and $g(-x) = -g(x)$; then $f(-x) \cdot g(-x) = f(x)[-g(x)] = -f(x) \cdot g(x)$ and the product of the two functions is odd.

C   **27.** Since $f(x)$ has period p, $f\left[k\left(x + \dfrac{p}{k}\right)\right] = f(kx + p) = f(kx)$; since p and $\dfrac{p}{k}$ are

both positive, k is positive; then if $0 < n < \dfrac{p}{k}$, $kx < k(x + n) < k\left(x + \dfrac{p}{k}\right)$ and $f[k(x + n)] \neq f(kx)$.

28. a. $O(-x) = \dfrac{f(-x) - f[-(-x)]}{2} = \dfrac{f(-x) - f(x)}{2} = -\dfrac{f(x) - f(-x)}{2} = -O(x);$

$E(-x) = \dfrac{f(-x) + f[-(-x)]}{2} = \dfrac{f(-x) + f(x)}{2} = \dfrac{f(x) + f(-x)}{2} = E(x)$

b. $O(x) + E(x) = \dfrac{f(x) - f(-x)}{2} + \dfrac{f(x) + f(-x)}{2} = \dfrac{f(x) - f(-x) + f(x) + f(-x)}{2} =$

$\dfrac{2f(x)}{2} = f(x)$

c. $O(x) = \dfrac{x^3 - 3x^2 + 2x + 1 - (-x^3 - 3x^2 - 2x + 1)}{2} = \dfrac{2x^3 + 4x}{2} = x^3 + 2x;$

$E(x) = \dfrac{x^3 - 3x^2 + 2x + 1 + (-x^3) - 3x^2 - 2x + 1}{2} = \dfrac{-6x^2 + 2}{2} = -3x^2 + 1$

d. $O(x) = \dfrac{e^x - e^{-x}}{2}; \; E(x) = \dfrac{e^x + e^{-x}}{2}$

Page 591 · WRITTEN EXERCISES

A   **1. a.** $\dfrac{1}{2}$ **b.** $\dfrac{1}{2}; -\dfrac{1}{2}$ **c.** 2π **2. a.** 3   **b.** $3; -3$ **c.** 2π

3. a. 1   **b.** $1, -1$ **c.** $\dfrac{2\pi}{3}$ **4. a.** 1   **b.** $1, -1$ **c.** π

5. a. 4   **b.** $4, -4$ **c.** $\dfrac{\pi}{2}$ **6. a.** 1   **b.** $1, -1$ **c.** 1

7. a. 2   **b.** $2, -2$ **c.** 4π **8. a.** $\dfrac{1}{2}$ **b.** $\dfrac{1}{2}, -\dfrac{1}{2}$ **c.** π

9. a. $\dfrac{1}{3}$ **b.** $\dfrac{1}{3}, -\dfrac{1}{3}$ **c.** 2   **10. a.** 2   **b.** $2, -2$ **c.** 4

11. a. 1   **b.** $2, 0$ **c.** 1   **12. a.** 2   **b.** $5, 1$ **c.** 2

13. The curve is a sine curve; $a = 2$; period $= 2\pi$ so $\dfrac{2\pi}{b} = 2\pi$, $b = 1$; $y = 2 \sin x$.

14. The curve is a sine curve; $a = 1$; period $= \pi$ so $\dfrac{2\pi}{b} = \pi$, $b = 2$; $y = \sin 2x$.

15. The curve is a cosine curve; $a = \dfrac{1}{2}$; period $= 4\pi$ so $\dfrac{2\pi}{b} = 4\pi$, $b = \dfrac{1}{2}$; $y = \dfrac{1}{2} \cos \dfrac{1}{2}x$.

16. The curve is a cosine curve; $a = 2$; period $= \pi$ so $\dfrac{2\pi}{b} = \pi$, $b = 2$; $y = 2 \cos 2x$.

17. The curve is a sine curve; $a = 1$; period $= 2$ so $\dfrac{2\pi}{b} = 2$, $b = \pi$; $y = \sin \pi x$.

18. The curve is a cosine curve; $a = 3$; period $= 8$ so $\dfrac{2\pi}{b} = 8$, $b = \dfrac{\pi}{4}$; $y = 3 \cos \dfrac{\pi}{4}x$.

19. The curve is a cosine curve; $a = 3$; period $= 8$ so $\dfrac{2\pi}{b} = 8$, $b = \dfrac{\pi}{4}$;

$c = \dfrac{M + m}{2} = \dfrac{6 + 0}{2} = 3$; $y = 3 + 3 \cos \dfrac{\pi}{4}x$.

20. The curve is a cosine curve; $a = 1$; period $= 5$ so $\dfrac{2\pi}{b} = 5$, $b = \dfrac{2\pi}{5}$;

$c = \dfrac{M + m}{2} = \dfrac{0 - 2}{2} = -1$; $y = -1 + \cos \dfrac{2\pi}{5}x$.

21. $a = \dfrac{M - m}{2} = \dfrac{2 + 2}{2} = 2$; $\dfrac{2\pi}{b} = \pi$; $b = 2$; $c = \dfrac{M + m}{2} = \dfrac{2 - 2}{2} = 0$; $y = 2 \sin 2x$

22. $a = \dfrac{M - m}{2} = \dfrac{1 + 1}{2} = 1$; $\dfrac{2\pi}{b} = 6\pi$; $b = \dfrac{1}{3}$; $c = \dfrac{M + m}{2} = \dfrac{1 - 1}{2} = 0$; $y = \sin \dfrac{1}{3}x$

23. $a = \dfrac{M - m}{2} = \dfrac{1 + 1}{2} = 1$; $\dfrac{2\pi}{b} = 1$; $b = 2\pi$; $c = \dfrac{M + m}{2} = \dfrac{1 - 1}{2} = 0$; $y = \sin 2\pi x$

24. $a = \dfrac{M - m}{2} = \dfrac{3 + 3}{2} = 3$; $\dfrac{2\pi}{b} = 4$; $b = \dfrac{\pi}{2}$; $c = \dfrac{M + m}{2} = \dfrac{3 - 3}{2} = 0$; $y = 3 \sin \dfrac{\pi}{2}x$

25. $a = \dfrac{M - m}{2} = \dfrac{5 - 1}{2} = 2$; $\dfrac{2\pi}{b} = 2\pi$; $b = 1$; $c = \dfrac{M + m}{2} = \dfrac{5 + 1}{2} = 3$; $y = 3 + 2 \sin x$

26. $a = \dfrac{M - m}{2} = \dfrac{6 - 0}{2} = 3$; $\dfrac{2\pi}{b} = 2$; $b = \pi$; $c = \dfrac{M + m}{2} = \dfrac{6 + 0}{2} = 3$; $y = 3 + 3 \sin \pi x$

27.

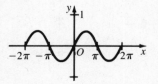

28.

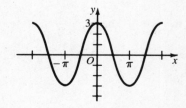

29.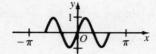

30.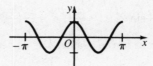

31.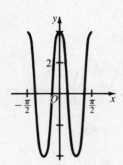

32.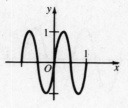

B **33.**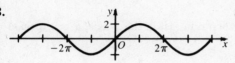

34.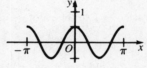

35.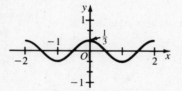

36.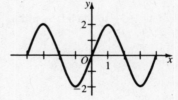

37.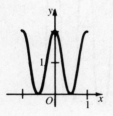

38.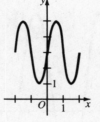

39. $d = \dfrac{\pi}{4}$; shift graph of $y = \sin x + 1$

to the right $\dfrac{\pi}{4}$ units; $a = 1$;

period $= \dfrac{2\pi}{1} = 2\pi$; $c = 1$.

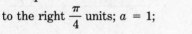

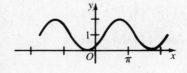

40. Reflect graph of $y = 3 \cos 2x$ in the

x-axis; $a = 3$; period $= \dfrac{2\pi}{2} = \pi$; $c = 0$.

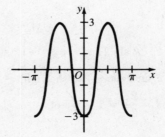

41. $y = -\sin 2\left(x + \dfrac{\pi}{3}\right)$; $d = -\dfrac{\pi}{3}$; shift graph of $y = \sin 2x$ to the left $\dfrac{\pi}{3}$ units, then reflect it in the x-axis; $a = 1$; period $= \dfrac{2\pi}{2} = \pi$; $c = 0$.

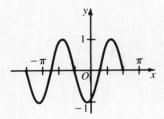

Ex. 41

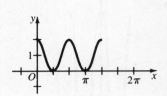

Ex. 42

C   **42.** $y = -\cos(3x - \pi) + 1 = -\left[\cos\left(3\left(x - \dfrac{\pi}{3}\right)\right) - 1\right]$; $d = \pi$; shift graph of

$y = \cos 3x - 1$ to the right $\dfrac{\pi}{3}$ units, then reflect it in the x-axis; $a = 1$; period $= \dfrac{2\pi}{3}$; $c = -1$.

43. $y = \dfrac{1}{2} - 2\sin(4x + \pi) = -\left[2\sin\left(4\left(x + \dfrac{\pi}{4}\right)\right) - \dfrac{1}{2}\right]$; $d = -\pi$; shift the graph of $2\sin 4x - \dfrac{1}{2}$ to the left $\dfrac{\pi}{4}$ units, then reflect it in the x-axis; $a = 2$; period $= \dfrac{2\pi}{4} = \dfrac{\pi}{2}$; $c = -\dfrac{1}{2}$.

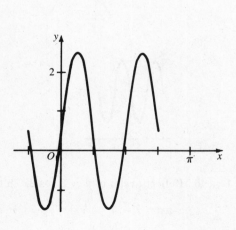

Ex. 43

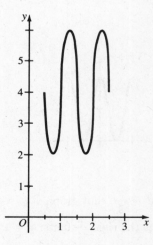

Ex. 44

44. $y = 4 - 2\sin(2\pi x - \pi) = -\left[2\sin\left(2\pi\left(x - \dfrac{1}{2}\right)\right) - 4\right]$; shift graph of

$y = 2\sin 2\pi x - 4$ to the right $\dfrac{1}{2}$ unit, then reflect it in the x-axis; $a = 2$;

period $= \dfrac{2\pi}{2\pi} = 1$; $c = -4$.

45. $y = \sin x \cos x = \dfrac{1}{2}(2 \sin x \cos x) = \dfrac{1}{2} \sin 2x;\ a = \dfrac{1}{2};$ period $= \dfrac{2\pi}{2} = \pi;\ c = 0.$

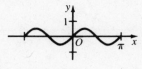

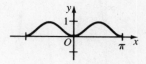

Ex. 45   Ex. 46

46. $y = \sin^2 x = \dfrac{1}{2} - \dfrac{1}{2}[1 - 2\sin^2 x] = \dfrac{1}{2} - \dfrac{1}{2}\cos 2x = -\left[\dfrac{1}{2}\cos 2x - \dfrac{1}{2}\right];$ reflect

graph of $y = \dfrac{1}{2}\cos 2x - \dfrac{1}{2}$ in the x-axis; $a = \dfrac{1}{2};$ period $= \dfrac{2\pi}{2} = \pi;\ c = -\dfrac{1}{2}$

Page 592 · COMPUTER EXERCISES

1. 10 FOR X = 0 TO 1.6 STEP 0.1
20 LET F = SIN(X)
30 LET Y = INT(100 ∗ F + .5)/100
40 PRINT X, Y
50 NEXT X
60 END

2. Change the program in Exercise 1 as follows:
10 FOR X = 0 TO 6.4 STEP 0.3

3. Change the program in Exercise 2 as follows:
5 INPUT A, B
20 LET F = A ∗ SIN(B ∗ X)

4. a.

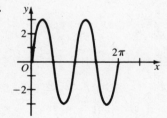

b.

c.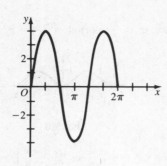

d.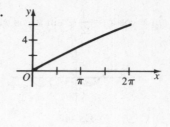

Pages 592-593 · APPLICATION

1. frequency $= 352$; period $= \dfrac{1}{352}$; $\dfrac{2\pi}{b} = \dfrac{1}{352}$; $b = 2\pi \cdot 352 = 704\pi$; $a = \dfrac{1}{2}$;

   $y = \dfrac{1}{2} \cos 704\pi t$

2. **a.** Frequency $= \dfrac{4}{3}(396) = 528$; C'

   b. Let x = length of vibrating part of string; $\dfrac{30}{x} \cdot 330 = 396$; $x = \dfrac{30 \cdot 330}{396} = 25$; 25 cm

Pages 596-597 · WRITTEN EXERCISES

A 1. $\cot(-x) = \dfrac{\cos(-x)}{\sin(-x)} = \dfrac{\cos x}{-\sin x} = -\dfrac{\cos x}{\sin x} = -\cot x$

2. $\sec(-x) = \dfrac{1}{\cos(-x)} = \dfrac{1}{\cos x} = \sec x$

3. $\csc(-x) = \dfrac{1}{\sin(-x)} = \dfrac{1}{-\sin x} = -\dfrac{1}{\sin x} = -\csc x$

4. $\tan(-x) + \sec(-x) = \dfrac{\sin(-x)}{\cos(-x)} + \dfrac{1}{\cos(-x)} = \dfrac{1 - \sin x}{\cos x}$; $\tan x + \sec x =$

   $\dfrac{\sin x}{\cos x} + \dfrac{1}{\cos x} = \dfrac{1 + \sin x}{\cos x}$; $\tan(-x) + \sec(-x)$ is never equal to $-(\tan x + \sec x)$;

   $\tan(-x) + \sec(-x) = \tan x + \sec x$ only when $x = n\pi$ for n an integer.

5.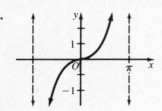

6.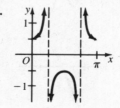

7.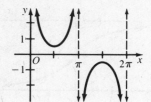

8.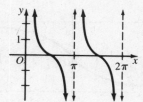

9.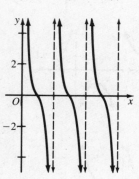

10.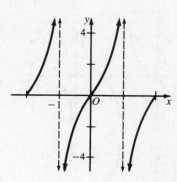

11.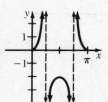

12.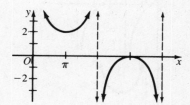

13.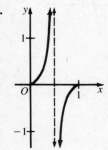

14.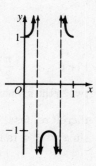

15.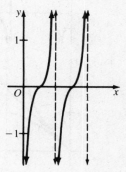

16. No; the tangent function has no maximum value or minimum value.

17. No; the secant function has no maximum value or minimum value.

18.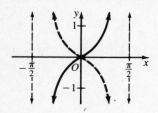

19.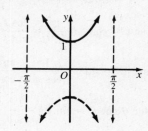

20.

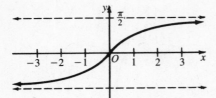

21.

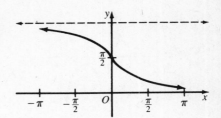

22.

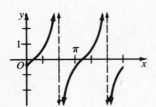

23.

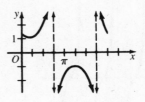

24.

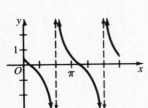

25.

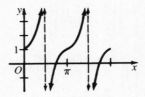

26.

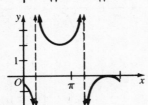

27.

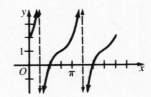

C 28.

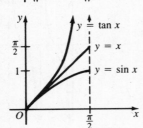

For $0 < x < \dfrac{\pi}{2}$, the graph of $y = x$ lies between the graphs of $y = \sin x$ and $y = \tan x$;

therefore, for $0 < x < \dfrac{\pi}{2}$,

$\sin x < x < \tan x$.

Pages 601-602 · WRITTEN EXERCISES

A **1.** $\sec^2\alpha - 1 = \tan^2\alpha$ **2.** $\csc^2 t - \cot^2 t = 1$

3. $\cos t \csc t = \cos t \cdot \dfrac{1}{\sin t} = \dfrac{\cos t}{\sin t} = \cot t$

4. $\sin \varphi \sec \varphi = \sin \varphi \cdot \dfrac{1}{\cos \varphi} = \dfrac{\sin \varphi}{\cos \varphi} = \tan \varphi$

5. $\sin \theta \sec \theta \cot \theta = \sin \theta \cdot \dfrac{1}{\cos \theta} \cdot \dfrac{\cos \theta}{\sin \theta} = 1$

6. $\dfrac{\cos x}{\sec x} + \dfrac{\sin x}{\csc x} = \cos x \cos x + \sin x \sin x = \cos^2 x + \sin^2 x = 1$

7. $\dfrac{\csc x}{\sin x} - \dfrac{\cot x}{\tan x} = \csc x \csc x - \cot x \cot x = \csc^2 x - \cot^2 x = 1$

8. $\dfrac{1}{\sin^2\theta} - \dfrac{1}{\tan^2\theta} = \csc^2\theta - \cot^2\theta = 1$

9. $\dfrac{\sec t}{\cos t} - \sec t \cos t = \sec t \sec t - \sec t \cdot \dfrac{1}{\sec t} = \sec^2 t - 1 = \tan^2 t$

10. $1 - \dfrac{\cos^2\alpha}{\cot^2\alpha} = 1 - \cos^2\alpha \tan^2\alpha = 1 - \cos^2\alpha \cdot \dfrac{\sin^2\alpha}{\cos^2\alpha} = 1 - \sin^2\alpha = \cos^2\alpha$

11. $\dfrac{1 + \tan^2\alpha}{\tan^2\alpha} = \sec^2\alpha \cot^2\alpha = \dfrac{1}{\cos^2\alpha} \cdot \dfrac{\cos^2\alpha}{\sin^2\alpha} = \dfrac{1}{\sin^2\alpha} = \csc^2\alpha$

12. $\dfrac{\sec^2 t - 1}{\sec^2 t} = \tan^2 t \cos^2 t = \dfrac{\sin^2 t}{\cos^2 t} \cdot \cos^2 t = \sin^2 t$

13. $\dfrac{\csc^2 x - \cot^2 x}{\sec x} = 1 \cdot \cos x = \cos x$ 14. $\cos^2 x^2 + \sin^2 x^2 = 1$

15. $\sec^2(\ln x) - \tan^2(\ln x) = 1$

16. $\dfrac{\sin x}{\csc x} - \sin x \csc x = \sin x \sin x - \sin x \cdot \dfrac{1}{\sin x} = \sin^2 x - 1 = -\cos^2 x$

17. $\dfrac{\sin\theta \cos\theta}{1 - \sin^2\theta} = \dfrac{\sin\theta \cos\theta}{\cos^2\theta} = \dfrac{\sin\theta}{\cos\theta} = \tan\theta$

18. $\tan^2\alpha - \cot^2\alpha + \csc^2\alpha = \tan^2\alpha - (\cot^2\alpha - \csc^2\alpha) = \tan^2\alpha - (-1) = \tan^2\alpha + 1 = \sec^2\alpha$

19. $\dfrac{1 - \sin^2\alpha}{1 - \sin\alpha} - 1 = \dfrac{(1 - \sin\alpha)(1 + \sin\alpha)}{1 - \sin\alpha} - 1 = 1 + \sin\alpha - 1 = \sin\alpha$

20. $\cos^2 t(\cot^2 t + 1) = \cos^2 t \csc^2 t = \dfrac{\cos^2 t}{\sin^2 t} = \cot^2 t$

21. $\sec x - \sin x \tan x = \dfrac{1}{\cos x} - \sin x \cdot \dfrac{\sin x}{\cos x} = \dfrac{1 - \sin^2 x}{\cos x} = \dfrac{\cos^2 x}{\cos x} = \cos x$

22. $\sin x(\csc x - \sin x) = \sin x \cdot \dfrac{1}{\sin x} - \sin x \sin x = 1 - \sin^2 x = \cos^2 x$

23. $\sin^2\alpha + \cos^2\alpha = 1;\ \dfrac{\sin^2\alpha}{\cos^2\alpha} + \dfrac{\cos^2\alpha}{\cos^2\alpha} = \dfrac{1}{\cos^2\alpha};\ \tan^2\alpha + 1 = \sec^2\alpha$

24. $\sin^2\alpha + \cos^2\alpha = 1;\ \dfrac{\sin^2\alpha}{\sin^2\alpha} + \dfrac{\cos^2\alpha}{\sin^2\alpha} = \dfrac{1}{\sin^2\alpha};\ 1 + \cot^2\alpha = \csc^2\alpha$

25. $\sec x = \dfrac{1}{\cos x} = \pm\dfrac{1}{\sqrt{1 - \sin^2 x}}$ 26. $\csc x = \dfrac{1}{\sin x} = \pm\dfrac{1}{\sqrt{1 - \cos^2 x}}$

27. $\tan t = \dfrac{\sin t}{\cos t} = \pm \dfrac{\sin t}{\sqrt{1 - \sin^2 t}}$

28. $\tan t = \dfrac{\sin t}{\cos t} = \pm \dfrac{\sqrt{1 - \cos^2 t}}{\cos t}$

29. $\tan \alpha \sec \alpha = \dfrac{\sin \alpha}{\cos \alpha} \cdot \dfrac{1}{\cos \alpha} = \dfrac{\sin \alpha}{\cos^2 \alpha} = \dfrac{\sin \alpha}{1 - \sin^2 \alpha}$

30. $\tan \alpha \sec \alpha = \dfrac{\sin \alpha}{\cos \alpha} \cdot \dfrac{1}{\cos \alpha} = \dfrac{\sin \alpha}{\cos^2 \alpha} = \pm \dfrac{\sqrt{1 - \cos^2 \alpha}}{\cos^2 \alpha}$

31. $\sin^2 x(1 + \tan^2 x) = \sin^2 x \sec^2 x = \dfrac{\sin^2 x}{\cos^2 x} = \tan^2 x$

32. $\tan \alpha(\tan \alpha + \cot \alpha) = \tan^2 \alpha + \tan \alpha \cdot \dfrac{1}{\tan \alpha} = \tan^2 \alpha + 1 = \sec^2 \alpha$

33. $\cos^2 \theta - \sin^2 \theta = \cos^2 \theta - 1 + 1 - \sin^2 \theta = \cos^2 \theta - 1 + \cos^2 \theta = 2 \cos^2 \theta - 1$

34. $\cos^2 x - \sin^2 x = \cos^2 x - 1 + 1 - \sin^2 x = -\sin^2 x + 1 - \sin^2 x = 1 - 2 \sin^2 x$

35. $\sec^2 x + \csc^2 x = \dfrac{1}{\cos^2 x} + \dfrac{1}{\sin^2 x} = \dfrac{\sin^2 x + \cos^2 x}{\cos^2 x \sin^2 x} = \dfrac{1}{\cos^2 x \sin^2 x} = \sec^2 x \csc^2 x$

36. $\tan^2 t - \sin^2 t = \dfrac{\sin^2 t}{\cos^2 t} - \dfrac{\sin^2 t \cos^2 t}{\cos^2 t} = \dfrac{\sin^2 t - \sin^2 t \cos^2 t}{\cos^2 t} = \dfrac{\sin^2 t(1 - \cos^2 t)}{\cos^2 t} =$
$\dfrac{\sin^2 t \sin^2 t}{\cos^2 t} = \tan^2 t \sin^2 t$

37. $\sec \alpha - \cos \alpha = \dfrac{1}{\cos \alpha} - \dfrac{\cos^2 \alpha}{\cos \alpha} = \dfrac{1 - \cos^2 \alpha}{\cos \alpha} = \dfrac{\sin^2 \alpha}{\cos \alpha} = \dfrac{\sin \alpha \sin \alpha}{\cos \alpha} = \sin \alpha \tan \alpha$

38. $\csc \theta - \sin \theta = \dfrac{1}{\sin \theta} - \dfrac{\sin^2 \theta}{\sin \theta} = \dfrac{1 - \sin^2 \theta}{\sin \theta} = \dfrac{\cos^2 \theta}{\sin \theta} = \dfrac{\cos \theta \cos \theta}{\sin \theta} = \cos \theta \cot \theta$

39. $\sin^4 t - \cos^4 t = (\sin^2 t + \cos^2 t)(\sin^2 t - \cos^2 t) = 1(\sin^2 t - \cos^2 t) = \sin^2 t - \cos^2 t$

40. $\sin^4 x + \cos^4 x + 2 \sin^2 x \cos^2 x = \sin^4 x + 2 \sin^2 x \cos^2 x + \cos^4 x =$
$(\sin^2 x + \cos^2 x)^2 = 1^2 = 1$

B 41. $\dfrac{\tan x + \cot x}{\csc^2 x} = \sin^2 x\left(\tan x + \dfrac{1}{\tan x}\right) = \sin^2 x\left(\dfrac{\tan^2 x + 1}{\tan x}\right) = \sin^2 x\left(\dfrac{\sec^2 x}{\tan x}\right) =$
$\sin^2 x \cdot \dfrac{\cos x}{\sin x} \cdot \dfrac{1}{\cos^2 x} = \dfrac{\sin x}{\cos x} = \tan x$

42. $\dfrac{\csc \alpha - \sin \alpha}{\cot^2 \alpha} = \dfrac{\sin^2 \alpha}{\cos^2 \alpha}\left(\dfrac{1}{\sin \alpha} - \sin \alpha\right) = \dfrac{\sin^2 \alpha}{\cos^2 \alpha}\left(\dfrac{1 - \sin^2 \alpha}{\sin \alpha}\right) = \dfrac{\sin^2 \alpha}{\cos^2 \alpha}\left(\dfrac{\cos^2 \alpha}{\sin \alpha}\right) = \sin \alpha$

43. $\cot \theta(\cos \theta \tan \theta + \sin \theta) = \cot \theta \cos \theta \cdot \dfrac{1}{\cot \theta} + \cot \theta \sin \theta =$
$\cos \theta + \dfrac{\cos \theta}{\sin \theta} \cdot \sin \theta = \cos \theta + \cos \theta = 2 \cos \theta$

44. $\cos t + \sin t \tan t = \cos t + \sin t \cdot \dfrac{\sin t}{\cos t} = \cos t + \dfrac{\sin^2 t}{\cos t} = \dfrac{\cos^2 t + \sin^2 t}{\cos t} =$
$\dfrac{1}{\cos t} = \sec t$

45. $\dfrac{1 + \sin \alpha}{\cos \alpha} + \dfrac{\cos \alpha}{1 + \sin \alpha} = \dfrac{1 + 2 \sin \alpha + \sin^2\alpha + \cos^2\alpha}{\cos \alpha(1 + \sin \alpha)} = \dfrac{1 + 2 \sin \alpha + 1}{\cos \alpha(1 + \sin \alpha)} =$

$\dfrac{2 + 2 \sin \alpha}{\cos \alpha(1 + \sin \alpha)} = \dfrac{2(1 + \sin \alpha)}{\cos \alpha(1 + \sin \alpha)} = \dfrac{2}{\cos \alpha} = 2 \sec \alpha$

46. $\dfrac{\sec x + \csc x}{1 + \tan x} = \left(\dfrac{1}{\cos x} + \dfrac{1}{\sin x}\right) \div \left(1 + \dfrac{\sin x}{\cos x}\right) =$

$\left(\dfrac{\sin x + \cos x}{\cos x \sin x}\right)\left(\dfrac{\cos x}{\cos x + \sin x}\right) = \dfrac{1}{\sin x} = \csc x$

47. $(1 - \sin x)(\sec x + \tan x) = \sec x - \sin x \sec x - \sin x \tan x + \tan x =$

$\dfrac{1}{\cos x} - \sin x \cdot \dfrac{1}{\cos x} - \sin x \cdot \dfrac{\sin x}{\cos x} + \tan x = \dfrac{1}{\cos x} - \tan x - \dfrac{\sin^2x}{\cos x} + \tan x =$

$\dfrac{1 - \sin^2x}{\cos x} = \dfrac{\cos^2x}{\cos x} = \cos x$

48. $(\sec \theta - \tan \theta)(\csc \theta + 1) = \sec \theta \csc \theta - \tan \theta \csc \theta + \sec \theta - \tan \theta =$

$\dfrac{1}{\cos \theta} \cdot \dfrac{1}{\sin \theta} - \dfrac{\sin \theta}{\cos \theta} \cdot \dfrac{1}{\sin \theta} + \dfrac{1}{\cos \theta} - \dfrac{\sin \theta}{\cos \theta} = \dfrac{1}{\cos \theta \sin \theta} - \dfrac{\sin^2\theta}{\cos \theta \sin \theta} =$

$\dfrac{1 - \sin^2\theta}{\cos \theta \sin \theta} = \dfrac{\cos^2\theta}{\cos \theta \sin \theta} = \dfrac{\cos \theta}{\sin \theta} = \cot \theta$

49. $(\sin t + \cos t)^2 + (\sin t - \cos t)^2 = \sin^2t + 2 \sin t \cos t + \cos^2t + \sin^2t - 2 \sin t \cos t + \cos^2t = 2(\sin^2t + \cos^2t) = 2 \cdot 1 = 2$

50. $(1 + \tan x)^2 + (1 - \tan x)^2 = 1 + 2 \tan x + \tan^2x + 1 - 2 \tan x + \tan^2x = 2(1 + \tan^2x) = 2 \sec^2x$

51. $(\cos x + 3 \sin x)^2 + (3 \cos x - \sin x)^2 = \cos^2x + 6 \sin x \cos x + 9 \sin^2x + 9 \cos^2x - 6 \sin x \cos x + \sin^2x = 10 \cos^2x + 10 \sin^2x = 10(\cos^2x + \sin^2x) = 10 \cdot 1 = 10$

52. $[(3 \cos x + 4 \sin x)^2 + (4 \cos x - 3 \sin x)^2]^{1/2} =$
$[9 \cos^2x + 24 \sin x \cos x + 16 \sin^2x + 16 \cos^2x - 24 \sin x \cos x + 9 \sin^2x]^{1/2} =$
$[25 \cos^2x + 25 \sin^2x]^{1/2} = [25(\cos^2x + \sin^2x)]^{1/2} = (25 \cdot 1)^{1/2} = 5$

53. $\dfrac{1}{1 - \sin x} - \dfrac{1}{1 + \sin x} = \dfrac{1 + \sin x - 1 + \sin x}{1 - \sin^2x} = \dfrac{2 \sin x}{\cos^2x} = \dfrac{2 \sin x}{\cos x \cdot \cos x} =$
$2 \tan x \sec x$

54. $\dfrac{1 - \tan \alpha}{1 + \tan \alpha} = \dfrac{1 - \dfrac{\sin \alpha}{\cos \alpha}}{1 + \dfrac{\sin \alpha}{\cos \alpha}} = \dfrac{\cos \alpha - \sin \alpha}{\cos \alpha} \cdot \dfrac{\cos \alpha}{\cos \alpha + \sin \alpha} = \dfrac{\cos \alpha - \sin \alpha}{\cos \alpha + \sin \alpha};$

$\dfrac{\cot \alpha - 1}{\cot \alpha + 1} = \dfrac{\dfrac{\cos \alpha}{\sin \alpha} - 1}{\dfrac{\cos \alpha}{\sin \alpha} + 1} = \dfrac{\cos \alpha - \sin \alpha}{\sin \alpha} \cdot \dfrac{\sin \alpha}{\cos \alpha + \sin \alpha} = \dfrac{\cos \alpha - \sin \alpha}{\cos \alpha + \sin \alpha}$

55. $(\tan t + \cot t)(\cos t + \sin t) = \tan t \cos t + \cot t \cos t + \tan t \sin t +$

$\cot t \sin t = \dfrac{\sin t}{\cos t} \cdot \cos t + \dfrac{\cos t}{\sin t} \cdot \cos t + \dfrac{\sin t}{\cos t} \cdot \sin t + \dfrac{\cos t}{\sin t} \cdot \sin t =$

$\sin t + \dfrac{\cos^2 t}{\sin t} + \dfrac{\sin^2 t}{\cos t} + \cos t = \dfrac{\sin^2 t + \cos^2 t}{\sin t} + \dfrac{\sin^2 t + \cos^2 t}{\cos t} = \dfrac{1}{\sin t} + \dfrac{1}{\cos t} =$

$\csc t + \sec t = \sec t + \csc t$

56. $\dfrac{\cos \theta}{\sec \theta + \tan \theta} = \dfrac{\cos \theta(\sec \theta - \tan \theta)}{\sec^2 \theta - \tan^2 \theta} = \cos \theta(\sec \theta - \tan \theta) =$

$\cos \theta \cdot \dfrac{1}{\cos \theta} - \cos \theta \cdot \dfrac{\sin \theta}{\cos \theta} = 1 - \sin \theta$

57. $\dfrac{1}{1 + \sin s} + \dfrac{1}{1 - \sin s} = \dfrac{1 - \sin s + 1 + \sin s}{1 - \sin^2 s} = \dfrac{2}{\cos^2 s} = 2 \sec^2 s$

58. $\dfrac{\sec x - 1}{\sin^2 x} = \dfrac{\sec x - 1}{1 - \cos^2 x} = \dfrac{1}{(1 - \cos x)(1 + \cos x)}\left(\dfrac{1}{\cos x} - 1\right) =$

$\dfrac{1}{(1 - \cos x)(1 + \cos x)} \cdot \dfrac{1 - \cos x}{\cos x} = \dfrac{1}{\cos x(1 + \cos x)} = \dfrac{\sec x}{\cos x + 1} =$

$\dfrac{\sec^2 x}{\sec x(\cos x + 1)} = \dfrac{\sec^2 x}{\sec x \cdot \dfrac{1}{\sec x} + \sec x} = \dfrac{\sec^2 x}{1 + \sec x}$

59. $\dfrac{\sec \theta - 1}{\tan \theta} = \dfrac{\tan \theta(\sec \theta - 1)}{\tan^2 \theta} = \dfrac{\tan \theta(\sec \theta - 1)}{\sec^2 \theta - 1} = \dfrac{\tan \theta(\sec \theta - 1)}{(\sec \theta - 1)(\sec \theta + 1)} =$

$\dfrac{\tan \theta}{\sec \theta + 1}$

60. $(a \cos \theta + b \sin \theta)^2 + (b \cos \theta - a \sin \theta)^2 =$
$a^2 \cos^2 \theta + 2ab \sin \theta \cos \theta + b^2 \sin^2 \theta + b^2 \cos^2 \theta - 2ab \sin \theta \cos \theta + a^2 \sin^2 \theta =$
$(a^2 + b^2) \cos^2 \theta + (a^2 + b^2) \sin^2 \theta = (a^2 + b^2)(\cos^2 \theta + \sin^2 \theta) = (a^2 + b^2)(1) =$
$a^2 + b^2$

C 61. $\dfrac{\sin^2 x + 2 \cos x - 1}{\sin^2 x + 3 \cos x - 3} = \dfrac{\sin^2 x + 2 \cos x - \sin^2 x - \cos^2 x}{\sin^2 x + 3 \cos x - 2 - \sin^2 x - \cos^2 x} = \dfrac{2 \cos x - \cos^2 x}{3 \cos x - 2 - \cos^2 x} =$

$\dfrac{\cos^2 x - 2 \cos x}{\cos^2 x - 3 \cos x + 2} = \dfrac{\cos x(\cos x - 2)}{(\cos x - 2)(\cos x - 1)} = \dfrac{\cos x}{\cos x - 1};$

$\dfrac{1}{1 - \sec x} = \dfrac{1}{1 - \dfrac{1}{\cos x}} = \dfrac{1}{\dfrac{\cos x - 1}{\cos x}} = \dfrac{\cos x}{\cos x - 1}$

62. $\sqrt{\dfrac{1 - \cos x}{1 + \cos x}} = \sqrt{\dfrac{1 - \cos x}{1 + \cos x} \cdot \dfrac{1 - \cos x}{1 - \cos x}} = \sqrt{\dfrac{1 - 2 \cos x + \cos^2 x}{1 - \cos^2 x}} =$

$\sqrt{\dfrac{1 - 2 \cos x + \cos^2 x}{\sin^2 x}} = \sqrt{\dfrac{1}{\sin^2 x} - \dfrac{2 \cos x}{\sin x \cdot \sin x} + \dfrac{\cos^2 x}{\sin^2 x}} =$

$\sqrt{\csc^2 x - 2 \csc x \cot x + \cot^2 x} = \sqrt{(\csc x - \cot x)^2} = |\csc x - \cot x|$

Pages 605-606 · WRITTEN EXERCISES

A 1. $\cos 15° = \cos(60° - 45°) = \cos 60° \cos 45° + \sin 60° \sin 45° = \dfrac{1}{2} \cdot \dfrac{\sqrt{2}}{2} + \dfrac{\sqrt{3}}{2} \cdot \dfrac{\sqrt{2}}{2} = $
$\dfrac{\sqrt{2} + \sqrt{6}}{4}$

2. $\sin 75° = \sin(45° + 30°) = \sin 45° \cos 30° + \cos 45° \sin 30° = \dfrac{\sqrt{2}}{2} \cdot \dfrac{\sqrt{3}}{2} + \dfrac{\sqrt{2}}{2} \cdot \dfrac{1}{2} = $
$\dfrac{\sqrt{6} + \sqrt{2}}{4}$

3. $\sin 105° = \sin(60° + 45°) = \sin 60° \cos 45° + \cos 60° \sin 45° = \dfrac{\sqrt{3}}{2} \cdot \dfrac{\sqrt{2}}{2} + \dfrac{1}{2} \cdot \dfrac{\sqrt{2}}{2} = $
$\dfrac{\sqrt{6} + \sqrt{2}}{4}$

4. $\cos 105° = \cos(60° + 45°) = \cos 60° \cos 45° - \sin 60° \sin 45° = \dfrac{1}{2} \cdot \dfrac{\sqrt{2}}{2} - \dfrac{\sqrt{3}}{2} \cdot \dfrac{\sqrt{2}}{2} = $
$\dfrac{\sqrt{2} - \sqrt{6}}{4}$

5. $\cos 195° = \cos(225° - 30°) = \cos 225° \cos 30° + \sin 225° \sin 30° = $
$-\dfrac{\sqrt{2}}{2} \cdot \dfrac{\sqrt{3}}{2} + \left(-\dfrac{\sqrt{2}}{2} \cdot \dfrac{1}{2}\right) = \dfrac{-\sqrt{6} - \sqrt{2}}{4}$

6. $\sin 255° = \sin(300° - 45°) = \sin 300° \cos 45° - \cos 300° \sin 45° = $
$-\dfrac{\sqrt{3}}{2} \cdot \dfrac{\sqrt{2}}{2} - \dfrac{1}{2} \cdot \dfrac{\sqrt{2}}{2} = \dfrac{-\sqrt{6} - \sqrt{2}}{4}$

7. $\cos 25° \cos 35° - \sin 25° \sin 35° = \cos(25° + 35°) = \cos 60° = \dfrac{1}{2}$

8. $\sin 35° \cos 5° - \cos 35° \sin 5° - \sin(35° - 5°) = \sin 30° = \dfrac{1}{2}$

9. $\sin 100° \cos 50° + \cos 100° \sin 50° = \sin(100° + 50°) = \sin 150° = \dfrac{1}{2}$

10. $\cos 50° \cos 80° + \sin 50° \sin 80° = \cos(50° - 80°) = \cos(-30°) = \cos 30° = \dfrac{\sqrt{3}}{2}$

11. $\cos \dfrac{\pi}{3} \cos \dfrac{\pi}{12} + \sin \dfrac{\pi}{3} \sin \dfrac{\pi}{12} = \cos\left(\dfrac{\pi}{3} - \dfrac{\pi}{12}\right) = \cos \dfrac{\pi}{4} = \dfrac{\sqrt{2}}{2}$

12. $\sin \dfrac{\pi}{4} \cos \dfrac{\pi}{12} + \cos \dfrac{\pi}{4} \sin \dfrac{\pi}{12} = \sin\left(\dfrac{\pi}{4} + \dfrac{\pi}{12}\right) = \sin \dfrac{\pi}{3} = \dfrac{\sqrt{3}}{2}$

13. $\sin 2\theta \cos \theta - \cos 2\theta \sin \theta = \sin(2\theta - \theta) = \sin \theta$

14. $\cos 2\varphi \cos \varphi + \sin 2\varphi \sin \varphi = \cos(2\varphi - \varphi) = \cos \varphi$

15. $\sin(\pi - \theta) = \sin \pi \cos \theta - \cos \pi \sin \theta = 0 \cdot \cos \theta - (-1) \sin \theta = \sin \theta$

16. $\cos(\pi + x) = \cos \pi \cos x - \sin \pi \sin x = -1 \cdot \cos x - 0 \cdot \sin x = -\cos x$

17. $\cos\left(\dfrac{\pi}{2} + x\right) = \cos \dfrac{\pi}{2} \cos x - \sin \dfrac{\pi}{2} \sin x = 0 \cdot \cos x - 1 \cdot \sin x = -\sin x$

18. $\sin\left(\dfrac{\pi}{2} + x\right) = \sin \dfrac{\pi}{2} \cos x + \cos \dfrac{\pi}{2} \sin x = 1 \cdot \cos x + 0 \cdot \sin x = \cos x$

19. $\sin(270° - x) = \sin 270° \cos x - \cos 270° \sin x = -1 \cdot \cos x - 0 \cdot \sin x = -\cos x$

20. $\cos(270° + x) = \cos 270° \cos x - \sin 270° \sin x = 0 \cdot \cos x - (-1) \sin x = \sin x$

B   21. $\sin\left(\dfrac{\pi}{6} + \theta\right) + \sin\left(\dfrac{\pi}{6} - \theta\right) = \sin \dfrac{\pi}{6} \cos \theta + \cos \dfrac{\pi}{6} \sin \theta + \sin \dfrac{\pi}{6} \cos \theta -$

$\cos \dfrac{\pi}{6} \sin \theta = 2 \sin \dfrac{\pi}{6} \cos \theta = 2 \cdot \dfrac{1}{2} \cdot \cos \theta = \cos \theta$

22. $\cos\left(\dfrac{\pi}{3} + \theta\right) + \cos\left(\dfrac{\pi}{3} - \theta\right) = \cos \dfrac{\pi}{3} \cos \theta - \sin \dfrac{\pi}{3} \sin \theta + \cos \dfrac{\pi}{3} \cos \theta +$

$\sin \dfrac{\pi}{3} \sin \theta = 2 \cos \dfrac{\pi}{3} \cos \theta = 2 \cdot \dfrac{1}{2} \cdot \cos \theta = \cos \theta$

23. $\dfrac{\sin(\alpha + \beta)}{\cos \alpha \cos \beta} = \dfrac{\sin \alpha \cos \beta + \cos \alpha \sin \beta}{\cos \alpha \cos \beta} = \dfrac{\sin \alpha \cos \beta}{\cos \alpha \cos \beta} + \dfrac{\cos \alpha \sin \beta}{\cos \alpha \cos \beta} =$

$\dfrac{\sin \alpha}{\cos \alpha} + \dfrac{\sin \beta}{\cos \beta} = \tan \alpha + \tan \beta$

24. $\dfrac{\sin(\alpha + \beta)}{\sin \alpha \sin \beta} = \dfrac{\sin \alpha \cos \beta + \cos \alpha \sin \beta}{\sin \alpha \sin \beta} = \dfrac{\sin \alpha \cos \beta}{\sin \alpha \sin \beta} + \dfrac{\cos \alpha \sin \beta}{\sin \alpha \sin \beta} =$

$\dfrac{\cos \beta}{\sin \beta} + \dfrac{\cos \alpha}{\sin \alpha} = \cot \beta + \cot \alpha = \cot \alpha + \cot \beta$

25. $\dfrac{\cos(\alpha + \beta)}{\cos \alpha \cos \beta} = \dfrac{\cos \alpha \cos \beta - \sin \alpha \sin \beta}{\cos \alpha \cos \beta} = \dfrac{\cos \alpha \cos \beta}{\cos \alpha \cos \beta} - \dfrac{\sin \alpha \sin \beta}{\cos \alpha \cos \beta} =$

$1 - \tan \alpha \tan \beta$

26. $\dfrac{\cos(\alpha - \beta)}{\sin \alpha \cos \beta} = \dfrac{\cos \alpha \cos \beta + \sin \alpha \sin \beta}{\sin \alpha \cos \beta} = \dfrac{\cos \alpha \cos \beta}{\sin \alpha \cos \beta} + \dfrac{\sin \alpha \sin \beta}{\sin \alpha \cos \beta} =$

$\dfrac{\cos \alpha}{\sin \alpha} + \dfrac{\sin \beta}{\cos \beta} = \cot \alpha + \tan \beta$

27. $\cos(\alpha - \beta) - \cos(\alpha + \beta) = \cos \alpha \cos \beta + \sin \alpha \sin \beta - [\cos \alpha \cos \beta - \sin \alpha \sin \beta]$
$= \cos \alpha \cos \beta + \sin \alpha \sin \beta - \cos \alpha \cos \beta + \sin \alpha \sin \beta = 2 \sin \alpha \sin \beta$

28. $\sin(\alpha - \beta) + \sin(\alpha + \beta) = \sin \alpha \cos \beta - \cos \alpha \sin \beta + \sin \alpha \cos \beta + \cos \alpha \sin \beta$
$= 2 \sin \alpha \cos \beta$

29. $\cos(\alpha - \beta) + \cos(\alpha + \beta) = \cos \alpha \cos \beta + \sin \alpha \sin \beta + \cos \alpha \cos \beta - \sin \alpha \sin \beta =$
$2 \cos \alpha \cos \beta$

30-31. Since α is in Quadrant II, $\cos \alpha < 0$; $\cos \alpha = -\sqrt{1 - \sin^2\alpha} = -\sqrt{1 - \dfrac{16}{25}} =$

$-\sqrt{\dfrac{9}{25}} = -\dfrac{3}{5}$; since β is in Quadrant III, $\sin \beta < 0$; $\sin \beta = -\sqrt{1 - \cos^2\beta} =$

$-\sqrt{1 - \dfrac{25}{169}} = -\sqrt{\dfrac{144}{169}} = -\dfrac{12}{13}$.

30. **a.** $\sin(\alpha + \beta) = \sin \alpha \cos \beta + \cos \alpha \sin \beta = \dfrac{4}{5}\left(-\dfrac{5}{13}\right) + \left(-\dfrac{3}{5}\right)\left(-\dfrac{12}{13}\right) =$

$-\dfrac{20}{65} + \dfrac{36}{65} = \dfrac{16}{65}$

b. $\cos(\alpha + \beta) = \cos \alpha \cos \beta - \sin \alpha \sin \beta = -\dfrac{3}{5}\left(-\dfrac{5}{13}\right) - \dfrac{4}{5}\left(-\dfrac{12}{13}\right) =$

$\dfrac{15}{65} + \dfrac{48}{65} = \dfrac{63}{65}$

c. Since $\sin(\alpha + \beta)$ and $\cos(\alpha + \beta)$ are both positive, $\alpha + \beta$ is in Quadrant I.

31. a. $\sin(\alpha - \beta) = \sin \alpha \cos \beta - \cos \alpha \sin \beta = \dfrac{4}{5}\left(-\dfrac{5}{13}\right) - \left(-\dfrac{3}{5}\right)\left(-\dfrac{12}{13}\right) =$

$-\dfrac{20}{65} - \dfrac{36}{65} = -\dfrac{56}{65}$

b. $\cos(\alpha - \beta) = \cos \alpha \cos \beta + \sin \alpha \sin \beta = -\dfrac{3}{5}\left(-\dfrac{5}{13}\right) + \dfrac{4}{5}\left(-\dfrac{12}{13}\right) =$

$\dfrac{15}{65} - \dfrac{48}{65} = -\dfrac{33}{65}$

c. Since $\sin(\alpha - \beta)$ and $\cos(\alpha - \beta)$ are both negative, $\alpha - \beta$ is in Quadrant III.

32. $\sin(\alpha - \beta) = \sin[\alpha + (-\beta)] = \sin \alpha \cos(-\beta) + \cos \alpha \sin(-\beta) =$
$\sin \alpha \cos \beta + \cos \alpha[-\sin \beta] = \sin \alpha \cos \beta - \cos \alpha \sin \beta$

33. Answers may vary. Example: let $\alpha = \beta = \dfrac{\pi}{2}$; $\sin\left(\dfrac{\pi}{2} + \dfrac{\pi}{2}\right) = \sin \pi = 0$;

$\sin \dfrac{\pi}{2} + \sin \dfrac{\pi}{2} = 1 + 1 = 2$

34. Using the Law of Sines, $\dfrac{\sin \alpha}{h} = \dfrac{\sin(90 - \alpha)}{x}$, or $\dfrac{\sin \alpha}{h} = \dfrac{\cos \alpha}{x}$; $x = \dfrac{h \cos \alpha}{\sin \alpha}$;

$\dfrac{\sin \beta}{h} = \dfrac{\sin(90 - \beta)}{d - x}$; $d - x = \dfrac{h \cos \beta}{\sin \beta}$; $d = d - x + x = \dfrac{h \cos \beta}{\sin \beta} + \dfrac{h \cos \alpha}{\sin \alpha} =$

$\dfrac{h \cos \beta \sin \alpha + h \cos \alpha \sin \beta}{\sin \beta \sin \alpha} = \dfrac{h \sin(\alpha + \beta)}{\sin \alpha \sin \beta}$; $h = \dfrac{d \sin \alpha \sin \beta}{\sin(\alpha + \beta)}$. h can also be found

using area formulas: $\dfrac{1}{2}dh = \dfrac{1}{2}d^2 \dfrac{\sin \alpha \sin \beta}{\sin[180° - (\alpha + \beta)]} = \dfrac{1}{2}d^2 \dfrac{\sin \alpha \sin \beta}{\sin(\alpha + \beta)}$;

$h = \dfrac{d \sin \alpha \sin \beta}{\sin(\alpha + \beta)}$

35. Using the Law of Sines, $\dfrac{\sin(180° - \alpha)}{h} = \dfrac{\sin[90° - (180° - \alpha)]}{x}$; $\dfrac{\sin \alpha}{h} = \dfrac{-\cos \alpha}{x}$;

$x = \dfrac{-h \cos \alpha}{\sin \alpha}$; $\dfrac{\sin \beta}{h} = \dfrac{\sin(90° - \beta)}{d + x}$; $\dfrac{\sin \beta}{h} = \dfrac{\cos \beta}{d + x}$; $d + x = \dfrac{h \cos \beta}{\sin \beta}$;

$d = d + x - x = \dfrac{h \cos \beta}{\sin \beta} + \dfrac{h \cos \alpha}{\sin \alpha} = \dfrac{h \cos \beta \sin \alpha + h \cos \alpha \sin \beta}{\sin \beta \sin \alpha} =$

$\dfrac{h \sin(\alpha + \beta)}{\sin \alpha \sin \beta}$; $h = \dfrac{d \sin \alpha \sin \beta}{\sin(\alpha + \beta)}$. h can also be found using area formulas; see Ex. 34.

36. $\dfrac{\sec \alpha \sec \beta}{1 - \tan \alpha \tan \beta} = \dfrac{\dfrac{1}{\cos \alpha} \cdot \dfrac{1}{\cos \beta}}{1 - \dfrac{\sin \alpha}{\cos \alpha} \cdot \dfrac{\sin \beta}{\cos \beta}} = \dfrac{\dfrac{1}{\cos \alpha \cos \beta}}{\dfrac{\cos \alpha \cos \beta - \sin \alpha \sin \beta}{\cos \alpha \cos \beta}} =$

$\dfrac{1}{\cos \alpha \cos \beta - \sin \alpha \sin \beta} = \dfrac{1}{\cos(\alpha + \beta)} = \sec(\alpha + \beta)$

Page 607 · COMPUTER EXERCISES

1. 10 LET S5 = .087155743
   20 LET C5 = SQR(1 − S5 ↑ 2)
   30 LET A = 5
   40 PRINT A; S5
   50 LET SO = S5
   60 LET CO = C5
   70 FOR A = 10 TO 90 STEP 5
   80 LET SN = SO * C5 + S5 * CO
   90 LET CN = SQR(1 − SN ↑ 2)
   100 PRINT A; SN
   110 LET SO = SN
   120 LET CO = CN
   130 NEXT A
   140 END

2. Add lines 25 and 95; change lines 40, 70, and 100 as follows:
   25 LET T5 = S5/C5
   95 LET TN = SN/CN
   40 PRINT A; S5; C5; T5
   70 FOR A = 10 TO 85 STEP 5
   100 PRINT A; SN; CN; TN

x	$\sin(x)$	$\cos(x)$	$\tan(x)$
5	.087155743	.996194698	.0874886638
10	.173648178	.984807753	.176326981
15	.258819046	.965925826	.267949193
20	.342020144	.93969262	.363970235
25	.422618263	.906307786	.46630766
30	.500000001	.866025403	.577350271
35	.573576438	.819152043	.700207541
40	.642787611	.766044442	.839099635
45	.707106783	.70710678	1
50	.766044445	.642787608	1.1917536
55	.819152046	.573576434	1.42814802
60	.866025405	.499999998	1.73205082
65	.906307789	.422618259	2.14450694
70	.939692622	.342020139	2.74747746
75	.965925827	.258819041	3.73205087
80	.984807754	.173648171	5.67128205
85	.996194698	.0871557371	11.4300531

3. 5   PRINT "ENTER N, SIN(X)"
   10 INPUT N, SX
   20 LET CX = SQR(1 − SX ↑ 2)
   50 LET SO = SX
   60 LET CO = CX
   70 FOR A = 2 TO N
   80 LET SN = SO * CX + SX * CO
   90 LET CN = SQR(1 − SN ↑ 2)
  110 LET SO = SN
  120 LET CO = CN
  130 NEXT A
  140 PRINT "SIN("; N; "X) = "; SN
  150 END

4. a. SIN(7X) = 0.890966414   **b.** SIN(15X) = 1

Pages 610-611 · WRITTEN EXERCISES

A   **1.** $1 - 2\sin^2\dfrac{\theta}{2} = \cos\left(2\cdot\dfrac{\theta}{2}\right) = \cos\theta$ **2.** $2\cos 2\alpha\sin 2\alpha = \sin(2\cdot 2\alpha) = \sin 4\alpha$

3. $\cos^2 2t - \sin^2 2t = \cos(2\cdot 2t) = \cos 4t$ **4.** $2\cos^2\dfrac{x}{2} - 1 = \cos\left(2\cdot\dfrac{x}{2}\right) = \cos x$

5. $\sqrt{\dfrac{1 - \cos 2\alpha}{2}} = \sin\alpha,\ 0 < \alpha < \pi$ **6.** $\sqrt{\dfrac{1 + \cos 2\alpha}{2}} = \cos\alpha,\ -\dfrac{\pi}{2} < \alpha < \dfrac{\pi}{2}$

7. $2\cos^2 15° - 1 = \cos(2\cdot 15°) = \cos 30° = \dfrac{\sqrt{3}}{2}$

8. $2\sin 15°\cos 15° = \sin(2\cdot 15°) = \sin 30° = \dfrac{1}{2}$

9. $\cos^2\dfrac{\pi}{3} + \sin^2\dfrac{\pi}{3} = 1$ **10.** $\cos^2\dfrac{\pi}{4} - \sin^2\dfrac{\pi}{4} = \cos\left(2\cdot\dfrac{\pi}{4}\right) = \cos\dfrac{\pi}{2} = 0$

11. $2\sin 105°\cos 105° = \sin(2\cdot 105°) = \sin 210° = -\dfrac{1}{2}$

12. $1 - 2\sin^2 165° = \cos(2\cdot 165°) = \cos 330° = \dfrac{\sqrt{3}}{2}$

13. $\sin 22.5° = \sqrt{\dfrac{1 - \cos 45°}{2}} = \sqrt{\dfrac{1 - \dfrac{\sqrt{2}}{2}}{2}} = \sqrt{\dfrac{2 - \sqrt{2}}{4}} = \dfrac{\sqrt{2 - \sqrt{2}}}{2}$

14. $\cos 67.5° = \sqrt{\dfrac{1 + \cos 135°}{2}} = \sqrt{\dfrac{1 - \dfrac{\sqrt{2}}{2}}{2}} = \sqrt{\dfrac{2 - \sqrt{2}}{4}} = \dfrac{\sqrt{2 - \sqrt{2}}}{2}$

15. $\cos\dfrac{5\pi}{8} = -\sqrt{\dfrac{1 + \cos\dfrac{5\pi}{4}}{2}} = -\sqrt{\dfrac{1 - \dfrac{\sqrt{2}}{2}}{2}} = -\sqrt{\dfrac{2 - \sqrt{2}}{4}} = -\dfrac{\sqrt{2 - \sqrt{2}}}{2}$

16. $\sin \dfrac{5\pi}{8} = \sqrt{\dfrac{1 - \cos \dfrac{5\pi}{4}}{2}} = \sqrt{\dfrac{1 + \dfrac{\sqrt{2}}{2}}{2}} = \sqrt{\dfrac{2 + \sqrt{2}}{4}} = \dfrac{\sqrt{2 + \sqrt{2}}}{2}$

17. $\cos 157.5° = -\sqrt{\dfrac{1 + \cos 315°}{2}} = -\sqrt{\dfrac{1 + \dfrac{\sqrt{2}}{2}}{2}} = -\sqrt{\dfrac{2 + \sqrt{2}}{4}} = -\dfrac{\sqrt{2 + \sqrt{2}}}{2}$

18. $\sin 202.5° = -\sqrt{\dfrac{1 - \cos 405°}{2}} = -\sqrt{\dfrac{1 - \dfrac{\sqrt{2}}{2}}{2}} = -\sqrt{\dfrac{2 - \sqrt{2}}{4}} = -\dfrac{\sqrt{2 - \sqrt{2}}}{2}$

19-20. Since $0 < \alpha < 180°$ and $\cos \alpha$ is negative, $\sin \alpha$ is positive and α is in Quadrant II;

$\sin \alpha = \sqrt{1 - \cos^2\alpha} = \sqrt{1 - \dfrac{9}{25}} = \sqrt{\dfrac{16}{25}} = \dfrac{4}{5}$.

19. $\sin 2\alpha = 2 \sin \alpha \cos \alpha = 2 \cdot \dfrac{4}{5}\left(-\dfrac{3}{5}\right) = -\dfrac{24}{25}$

20. $\cos 2\alpha = 2 \cos^2\alpha - 1 = 2\left(-\dfrac{3}{5}\right)^2 - 1 = 2 \cdot \dfrac{9}{25} - 1 = -\dfrac{7}{25}$

21. Since $90° < \alpha < 180°$, $45° < \dfrac{\alpha}{2} < 90°$ and $\cos \dfrac{\alpha}{2} > 0$; $\cos \dfrac{\alpha}{2} = \sqrt{\dfrac{1 + \cos \alpha}{2}} =$

$\sqrt{\dfrac{1 - \dfrac{3}{5}}{2}} = \sqrt{\dfrac{1}{5}} = \dfrac{\sqrt{5}}{5}$.

22. Since $90° < \alpha < 180°$, $45° < \dfrac{\alpha}{2} < 90°$ and $\sin \dfrac{\alpha}{2} > 0$; $\sin \dfrac{\alpha}{2} = \sqrt{\dfrac{1 - \cos \alpha}{2}} =$

$\sqrt{\dfrac{1 + \dfrac{3}{5}}{2}} = \sqrt{\dfrac{4}{5}} = \dfrac{2\sqrt{5}}{5}$.

23-24. Since $180° < \beta < 360°$ and $\cos \beta$ is positive, $\sin \beta$ is negative and β is in

Quadrant IV; $\sin \beta = -\sqrt{1 - \cos^2\beta} = -\sqrt{1 - \dfrac{25}{169}} = -\sqrt{\dfrac{144}{169}} = -\dfrac{12}{13}$.

23. $\cos 2\beta = 2 \cos^2\beta - 1 = 2\left(\dfrac{5}{13}\right)^2 - 1 = 2 \cdot \dfrac{25}{169} - 1 = -\dfrac{119}{169}$

24. $\sin 2\beta = 2 \sin \beta \cos \beta = 2\left(-\dfrac{12}{13}\right)\left(\dfrac{5}{13}\right) = -\dfrac{120}{169}$

25. Since $270° < \beta < 360°$, $135° < \dfrac{\beta}{2} < 180°$ and $\sin \dfrac{\beta}{2} > 0$; $\sin \dfrac{\beta}{2} = \sqrt{\dfrac{1 - \cos \beta}{2}} =$

$\sqrt{\dfrac{1 - \dfrac{5}{13}}{2}} = \sqrt{\dfrac{4}{13}} = \dfrac{2\sqrt{13}}{13}$.

26. Since $270° < \beta < 360°$, $135° < \dfrac{\beta}{2} < 180°$ and $\cos \dfrac{\beta}{2} < 0$; $\cos \dfrac{\beta}{2} = -\sqrt{\dfrac{1 + \cos \beta}{2}} =$

$-\sqrt{\dfrac{1 + \dfrac{5}{13}}{2}} = -\sqrt{\dfrac{9}{13}} = -\dfrac{3\sqrt{13}}{13}$.

27. $(\sin x + \cos x)^2 = \sin^2 x + \cos^2 x + 2 \sin x \cos x = 1 + \sin 2x$

28. $\cos^4\theta - \sin^4\theta = (\cos^2\theta + \sin^2\theta)(\cos^2\theta - \sin^2\theta) = 1 \cdot \cos 2\theta = \cos 2\theta$

B **29.** $\cot \alpha + \tan \alpha = \dfrac{\cos \alpha}{\sin \alpha} + \dfrac{\sin \alpha}{\cos \alpha} = \dfrac{\cos^2\alpha + \sin^2\alpha}{\sin \alpha \cos \alpha} = \dfrac{1}{\sin \alpha \cos \alpha} = \dfrac{2}{2 \sin \alpha \cos \alpha} = \dfrac{2}{\sin 2\alpha} = 2 \csc 2\alpha$

30. $\sin 4t = 2 \sin 2t \cos 2t = 2 \cdot 2 \sin t \cos t(\cos^2 t - \sin^2 t) = $
$4 \sin t \cos^3 t - 4 \sin^3 t \cos t = 4(\sin t \cos^3 t - \sin^3 t \cos t)$

31. $\csc 2\alpha = \dfrac{1}{2 \sin \alpha \cos \alpha} = \dfrac{1}{2} \cdot \dfrac{1}{\cos \alpha} \cdot \dfrac{1}{\sin \alpha} = \dfrac{1}{2} \sec \alpha \csc \alpha$

32. $\sec 2\alpha = \dfrac{1}{\cos 2\alpha} = \dfrac{1}{2 \cos^2\alpha - 1}$; $\dfrac{\sec^2\alpha}{2 - \sec^2\alpha} = \dfrac{1}{\cos^2\alpha}\left(\dfrac{1}{2 - \dfrac{1}{\cos^2\alpha}}\right) = $
$\dfrac{1}{\cos^2\alpha} \cdot \dfrac{\cos^2\alpha}{2 \cos^2\alpha - 1} = \dfrac{1}{2 \cos^2\alpha - 1}$

33. a.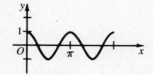

b. $a = 1$; period $= \pi$

34. a.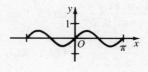

b. $a = \dfrac{1}{2}$; period $= \pi$

C **35.** $\cos 3\alpha = \cos(2\alpha + \alpha) = \cos 2\alpha \cos \alpha - \sin 2\alpha \sin \alpha = $
$(2 \cos^2\alpha - 1) \cos \alpha - 2 \sin \alpha \cos \alpha \sin \alpha = \cos \alpha(2 \cos^2\alpha - 1 - 2 \sin^2\alpha) = $
$\cos \alpha[2 \cos^2\alpha - 1 - 2(1 - \cos^2\alpha)] = \cos \alpha[2 \cos^2\alpha - 1 - 2 + 2 \cos^2\alpha] = $
$\cos \alpha(4 \cos^2\alpha - 3) = 4 \cos^3\alpha - 3 \cos \alpha$

36. $\sin 3\alpha = \sin(2\alpha + \alpha) = \sin 2\alpha \cos \alpha + \cos 2\alpha \sin \alpha = $
(1) $2 \sin \alpha \cos^2\alpha + (\cos^2\alpha - \sin^2\alpha) \sin \alpha = 2 \sin \alpha \cos^2\alpha + \cos^2\alpha \sin \alpha - \sin^3\alpha = $
   $3 \sin \alpha \cos^2\alpha - \sin^3\alpha$ or
(2) $2 \sin \alpha \cos^2\alpha + (1 - 2 \sin^2\alpha) \sin \alpha = 2 \sin \alpha \cos^2\alpha + \sin \alpha - 2 \sin^3\alpha$ or
(3) $2 \sin \alpha \cos^2\alpha + (2 \cos^2\alpha - 1) \sin \alpha = 2 \sin \alpha \cos^2\alpha + 2 \cos^2 \sin \alpha - \sin \alpha = $
   $4 \sin \alpha \cos^2\alpha - \sin \alpha$

Page 611 · CHALLENGE

The visitor pointed to one of the paths and asked, "Is that the path to your village?" If the visitor was pointing to the road to the truth-tellers' village, a person from either village would answer "Yes." If the visitor was pointing to the road to the liars' village, a person from either village would answer "No."

Pages 614-615 · WRITTEN EXERCISES

A **1.** $\dfrac{\tan 20° + \tan 40°}{1 - \tan 20° \tan 40°} = \tan(20° + 40°) = \tan 60° = \sqrt{3}$

2. $\dfrac{\tan 60° - \tan 15°}{1 + \tan 60° \tan 15°} = \tan(60° - 15°) = \tan 45° = 1$

3. $\dfrac{\tan 210° - \tan 30°}{1 + \tan 210° \tan 30°} = \tan(210° - 30°) = \tan 180° = 0$

4. $\dfrac{\tan 25° + \tan 200°}{1 - \tan 25° \tan 200°} = \tan(25° + 200°) = \tan 225° = 1$

5. $\dfrac{\tan \dfrac{2\pi}{3} + \tan \dfrac{7\pi}{6}}{1 - \tan \dfrac{2\pi}{3} \tan \dfrac{7\pi}{6}} = \tan\left(\dfrac{2\pi}{3} + \dfrac{7\pi}{6}\right) = \tan \dfrac{11\pi}{6} = -\dfrac{\sqrt{3}}{3}$

6. $\dfrac{\tan \dfrac{7\pi}{6} - \tan \dfrac{\pi}{3}}{1 + \tan \dfrac{7\pi}{6} \tan \dfrac{\pi}{3}} = \tan\left(\dfrac{7\pi}{6} - \dfrac{\pi}{3}\right) = \tan \dfrac{5\pi}{6} = -\dfrac{\sqrt{3}}{3}$

7. $\dfrac{2 \tan 67.5°}{1 - \tan^2 67.5°} = \tan(2 \cdot 67.5°) = \tan 135° = -1$

8. $\dfrac{2 \tan 22.5°}{1 - \tan^2 22.5°} = \tan(2 \cdot 22.5°) = \tan 45° = 1$

9. $\tan 15° = \tan(45° - 30°) = \dfrac{\tan 45° - \tan 30°}{1 + \tan 45° \tan 30°} = \dfrac{1 - \dfrac{\sqrt{3}}{3}}{1 + \dfrac{\sqrt{3}}{3}} = \dfrac{3 - \sqrt{3}}{3} \cdot \dfrac{3}{3 + \sqrt{3}} =$

$\dfrac{3 - \sqrt{3}}{3 + \sqrt{3}} = \dfrac{(3 - \sqrt{3})(3 - \sqrt{3})}{(3 + \sqrt{3})(3 - \sqrt{3})} = \dfrac{12 - 6\sqrt{3}}{6} = 2 - \sqrt{3}$

10. $\tan 75° = \tan(45° + 30°) = \dfrac{\tan 45° + \tan 30°}{1 - \tan 45° \tan 30°} = \dfrac{1 + \dfrac{\sqrt{3}}{3}}{1 - \dfrac{\sqrt{3}}{3}} = \dfrac{3 + \sqrt{3}}{3} \cdot \dfrac{3}{3 - \sqrt{3}} =$

$\dfrac{3 + \sqrt{3}}{3 - \sqrt{3}} = \dfrac{(3 + \sqrt{3})(3 + \sqrt{3})}{(3 - 3\sqrt{3})(3 + \sqrt{3})} = \dfrac{12 + 6\sqrt{3}}{6} = 2 + \sqrt{3}$

11. $\tan 105° = \tan(60° + 45°) = \dfrac{\tan 60° + \tan 45°}{1 - \tan 60° \tan 45°} = \dfrac{\sqrt{3} + 1}{1 - \sqrt{3}} = \dfrac{(\sqrt{3} + 1)(1 + \sqrt{3})}{(1 - \sqrt{3})(1 + \sqrt{3})} =$
$\dfrac{4 + 2\sqrt{3}}{-2} = -2 - \sqrt{3}$

12. $\tan 195° = \tan(150° + 45°) = \dfrac{\tan 150° + \tan 45°}{1 - \tan 150° \tan 45°} = \dfrac{\dfrac{-\sqrt{3}}{3} + 1}{1 + \dfrac{\sqrt{3}}{3}} =$

$\dfrac{3 - \sqrt{3}}{3} \cdot \dfrac{3}{3 + \sqrt{3}} = \dfrac{3 - \sqrt{3}}{3 + \sqrt{3}} = \dfrac{(3 - \sqrt{3})(3 - \sqrt{3})}{(3 + \sqrt{3})(3 - \sqrt{3})} = \dfrac{12 - 6\sqrt{3}}{6} = 2 - \sqrt{3}$

13. $\tan \dfrac{11\pi}{12} = \tan\left(\dfrac{2\pi}{3} + \dfrac{\pi}{4}\right) = \dfrac{\tan \dfrac{2\pi}{3} + \tan \dfrac{\pi}{4}}{1 - \tan \dfrac{2\pi}{3} \tan \dfrac{\pi}{4}} = \dfrac{1 - \sqrt{3}}{1 + \sqrt{3}} = \dfrac{(1 - \sqrt{3})(1 - \sqrt{3})}{(1 + \sqrt{3})(1 - \sqrt{3})} =$
$\dfrac{4 - 2\sqrt{3}}{-2} = -2 + \sqrt{3}$

14. $\tan\dfrac{5\pi}{12} = \tan\left(\dfrac{\pi}{4} + \dfrac{\pi}{6}\right) = \dfrac{\tan\dfrac{\pi}{4} + \tan\dfrac{\pi}{6}}{1 - \tan\dfrac{\pi}{4}\tan\dfrac{\pi}{6}} = \dfrac{1 + \dfrac{\sqrt{3}}{3}}{1 - \dfrac{\sqrt{3}}{3}} = \dfrac{3 + \sqrt{3}}{3} \cdot \dfrac{3}{3 - \sqrt{3}} =$

$\dfrac{3 + \sqrt{3}}{3 - \sqrt{3}} = \dfrac{(3 + \sqrt{3})(3 + \sqrt{3})}{(3 - \sqrt{3})(3 + \sqrt{3})} = \dfrac{12 + 6\sqrt{3}}{6} = 2 + \sqrt{3}$

15. $\tan 22.5° = \tan\dfrac{45°}{2} = \dfrac{\sin 45°}{1 + \cos 45°} = \dfrac{\dfrac{\sqrt{2}}{2}}{1 + \dfrac{\sqrt{2}}{2}} = \dfrac{\sqrt{2}}{2} \cdot \dfrac{2}{2 + \sqrt{2}} = \dfrac{\sqrt{2}}{2 + \sqrt{2}} =$

$\dfrac{2\sqrt{2} - 2}{2} = \sqrt{2} - 1$

16. $\tan 67.5° = \tan\dfrac{135°}{2} = \dfrac{\sin 135°}{1 + \cos 135°} = \dfrac{\dfrac{\sqrt{2}}{2}}{1 - \dfrac{\sqrt{2}}{2}} = \dfrac{\sqrt{2}}{2} \cdot \dfrac{2}{2 - \sqrt{2}} = \dfrac{\sqrt{2}}{2 - \sqrt{2}} =$

$\dfrac{2\sqrt{2} + 2}{2} = \sqrt{2} + 1$

17. $\tan\dfrac{5\pi}{8} = \tan\dfrac{\dfrac{5\pi}{4}}{2} = \dfrac{\sin\dfrac{5\pi}{4}}{1 + \cos\dfrac{5\pi}{4}} = \dfrac{-\dfrac{\sqrt{2}}{2}}{1 - \dfrac{\sqrt{2}}{2}} = -\dfrac{\sqrt{2}}{2} \cdot \dfrac{2}{2 - \sqrt{2}} = \dfrac{-\sqrt{2}}{2 - \sqrt{2}} =$

$\dfrac{-2\sqrt{2} - 2}{2} = -\sqrt{2} - 1$

18. $\tan\dfrac{11\pi}{8} = \tan\left(\pi + \dfrac{3\pi}{8}\right) = \tan\dfrac{3\pi}{8} = \tan\dfrac{\dfrac{3\pi}{4}}{2} = \dfrac{\sin\dfrac{3\pi}{4}}{1 + \cos\dfrac{3\pi}{4}} = \dfrac{\dfrac{\sqrt{2}}{2}}{1 - \dfrac{\sqrt{2}}{2}} =$

$\dfrac{\sqrt{2}}{2} \cdot \dfrac{2}{2 - \sqrt{2}} = \dfrac{\sqrt{2}}{2 - \sqrt{2}} = \dfrac{2\sqrt{2} + 2}{2} = \sqrt{2} + 1$

19. $\cot 165° = \dfrac{1}{\tan 165°} = \dfrac{1}{\tan(45° + 120°)} = \dfrac{1 - \tan 45°\tan 120°}{\tan 45° + \tan 120°} = \dfrac{1 + \sqrt{3}}{1 - \sqrt{3}} =$

$\dfrac{(1 + \sqrt{3})(1 + \sqrt{3})}{(1 - \sqrt{3})(1 + \sqrt{3})} = \dfrac{4 + 2\sqrt{3}}{-2} = -2 - \sqrt{3}$

20. $\cot 285° = \dfrac{1}{\tan 285°} = \dfrac{1}{\tan(45° + 240°)} = \dfrac{1 - \tan 45°\tan 240°}{\tan 45° + \tan 240°} = \dfrac{1 - \sqrt{3}}{1 + \sqrt{3}} =$

$\dfrac{(1 - \sqrt{3})(1 - \sqrt{3})}{(1 + \sqrt{3})(1 - \sqrt{3})} = \dfrac{4 - 2\sqrt{3}}{-2} = -2 + \sqrt{3}$

B **21.** $\tan(\alpha + \beta) = \dfrac{\tan\alpha + \tan\beta}{1 - \tan\alpha\tan\beta} = \dfrac{-\dfrac{3}{4} + \dfrac{12}{5}}{1 - \left(-\dfrac{3}{4}\right)\left(\dfrac{12}{5}\right)} = \dfrac{33}{20} \cdot \dfrac{20}{56} = \dfrac{33}{56}$

22. $\tan(\alpha - \beta) = \dfrac{\tan\alpha - \tan\beta}{1 + \tan\alpha\tan\beta} = \dfrac{-\dfrac{3}{4} - \dfrac{12}{5}}{1 + \left(-\dfrac{3}{4}\right)\left(\dfrac{12}{5}\right)} = -\dfrac{63}{20}\left(-\dfrac{20}{16}\right) = \dfrac{63}{16}$

23. $\tan 2\alpha = \dfrac{2 \tan \alpha}{1 - \tan^2\alpha} = \dfrac{2\left(-\dfrac{3}{4}\right)}{1 - \dfrac{9}{16}} = -\dfrac{3}{2} \cdot \dfrac{16}{7} = -\dfrac{24}{7}$

24. Since α is in Quadrant II, $\sin \alpha > 0$ and $\cos \alpha < 0$; $\dfrac{\sin \alpha}{\cos \alpha} = -\dfrac{3}{4}$; $\sin \alpha = -\dfrac{3}{4} \cos \alpha$

$-\dfrac{3}{4} \cos \alpha = \sqrt{1 - \cos^2\alpha}$; $\dfrac{9}{16} \cos^2\alpha = 1 - \cos^2\alpha$; $\dfrac{25}{16} \cos^2\alpha = 1$; $\cos^2\alpha = \dfrac{16}{25}$;

$\cos \alpha = -\dfrac{4}{5}$; $\sin \alpha = -\dfrac{3}{4}\left(-\dfrac{4}{5}\right) = \dfrac{3}{5}$; $\tan \dfrac{\alpha}{2} = \dfrac{\sin \alpha}{1 + \cos \alpha} = \dfrac{\dfrac{3}{5}}{1 - \dfrac{4}{5}} = \dfrac{3}{5} \cdot \dfrac{5}{1} = 3.$

25. $\tan\left(\dfrac{\pi}{4} - \alpha\right) = \dfrac{\tan \dfrac{\pi}{4} - \tan \alpha}{1 + \tan \dfrac{\pi}{4} \tan \alpha} = \dfrac{1 - \tan \alpha}{1 + 1 \cdot \tan \alpha} = \dfrac{1 - \tan \alpha}{1 + \tan \alpha}$

26. $\tan\left(\dfrac{\pi}{4} + \alpha\right) = \dfrac{\tan \dfrac{\pi}{4} + \tan \alpha}{1 - \tan \dfrac{\pi}{4} \tan \alpha} = \dfrac{1 + \tan \alpha}{1 - 1 \cdot \tan \alpha} = \dfrac{1 + \tan \alpha}{1 - \tan \alpha}$

27. $\cot(\alpha + \beta) = \dfrac{1}{\tan(\alpha + \beta)} = \dfrac{1 - \tan \alpha \tan \beta}{\tan \alpha + \tan \beta} = \dfrac{1 - \dfrac{1}{\cot \alpha} \cdot \dfrac{1}{\cot \beta}}{\dfrac{1}{\cot \alpha} + \dfrac{1}{\cot \beta}} =$

$\dfrac{\dfrac{\cot \alpha \cot \beta - 1}{\cot \alpha \cot \beta}}{\dfrac{\cot \beta + \cot \alpha}{\cot \alpha \cot \beta}} = \dfrac{\cot \alpha \cot \beta - 1}{\cot \alpha + \cot \beta}$

28. $\cot(\alpha - \beta) = \dfrac{1}{\tan(\alpha - \beta)} = \dfrac{1 + \tan \alpha \tan \beta}{\tan \alpha - \tan \beta} = \dfrac{1 + \dfrac{1}{\cot \alpha} \cdot \dfrac{1}{\cot \beta}}{\dfrac{1}{\cot \alpha} - \dfrac{1}{\cot \beta}} =$

$\dfrac{\dfrac{\cot \alpha \cot \beta + 1}{\cot \alpha \cot \beta}}{\dfrac{\cot \beta - \cot \alpha}{\cot \alpha \cot \beta}} = \dfrac{\cot \alpha \cot \beta + 1}{\cot \beta - \cot \alpha}$

29. $\cot 2\alpha = \cot(\alpha + \alpha) = \dfrac{\cot \alpha \cot \alpha - 1}{\cot \alpha + \cot \alpha} = \dfrac{\cot^2\alpha - 1}{2 \cot \alpha}$

30. $\tan \dfrac{\theta}{2} = \dfrac{\sin \dfrac{\theta}{2}}{\cos \dfrac{\theta}{2}} = \dfrac{2 \sin^2 \dfrac{\theta}{2}}{2 \sin \dfrac{\theta}{2} \cos \dfrac{\theta}{2}} = \dfrac{1 - \cos \theta}{\sin \theta}$

C **31.** $\tan \dfrac{7\pi}{8} = \dfrac{\sin \dfrac{7\pi}{8}}{\cos \dfrac{7\pi}{8}} = \dfrac{\dfrac{1}{2}\sqrt{2 - \sqrt{2}}}{-\dfrac{1}{2}\sqrt{2 + \sqrt{2}}} = -\sqrt{\dfrac{2 - \sqrt{2}}{2 + \sqrt{2}}} = -\sqrt{\dfrac{(2 - \sqrt{2})(2 - \sqrt{2})}{(2 + \sqrt{2})(2 - \sqrt{2})}} =$

$-\sqrt{\dfrac{6 - 4\sqrt{2}}{2}} = -\sqrt{3 - 2\sqrt{2}}$

32. $3 - 2\sqrt{2} = 1 - 2\sqrt{2} + 2 = (-1 + \sqrt{2})^2; -\sqrt{3 - 2\sqrt{2}} = -\sqrt{(-1 + \sqrt{2})^2} = -(-1 + \sqrt{2}) = 1 - \sqrt{2}$

33. $\tan 3\alpha = \tan(2\alpha + \alpha) = \dfrac{\tan 2\alpha + \tan \alpha}{1 - \tan 2\alpha \tan \alpha} = \dfrac{\dfrac{2\tan \alpha}{1 - \tan^2\alpha} + \tan \alpha}{1 - \dfrac{2\tan \alpha}{1 - \tan^2\alpha} \cdot \tan \alpha} =$

$\dfrac{\dfrac{2\tan \alpha + \tan \alpha - \tan^3\alpha}{1 - \tan^2\alpha}}{\dfrac{1 - \tan^2\alpha - 2\tan^2\alpha}{1 - \tan^2\alpha}} = \dfrac{3\tan \alpha - \tan^3\alpha}{1 - 3\tan^2\alpha}$

Pages 618-619 · CHAPTER REVIEW

1. c; $210\left(\dfrac{\pi}{180}\right) = \dfrac{7\pi}{6}$ **2.** d; $\dfrac{11\pi}{3} \cdot \dfrac{180}{\pi} = 660$ **3.** c; $\sec\left(-\dfrac{5\pi}{3}\right) = \sec\dfrac{\pi}{3} = \dfrac{1}{\cos\dfrac{\pi}{3}} = 2$

4. a; $\tan s = \sqrt{3}$; $\tan\dfrac{\pi}{3} = \sqrt{3}$; $s = -\pi + \dfrac{\pi}{3} = -\dfrac{2\pi}{3}$

5. b; $f(-x) = -x\sqrt{(-x)^2 + 1} = -x\sqrt{x^2 + 1} = -f(x)$ **6.** b

7. c; amplitude is 2, period is 3 **8.** d

9. a; $y = 2\tan\pi x = 2\tan\pi(x + p) = 2\tan(\pi x + \pi p) = 2\tan\pi x$ if $\pi p = \pi$, or $p = 1$

10. c **11.** d; $\cos x + \sin^2 x \sec x = \cos x + \dfrac{\sin^2 x}{\cos x} = \dfrac{\cos^2 x + \sin^2 x}{\cos x} = \dfrac{1}{\cos x} = \sec x$

12. a; $\sec^2 x = \dfrac{1}{\cos^2 x} = \dfrac{1}{1 - \sin^2 x} = \dfrac{1}{1 - u^2}$

13. c; $\cos 255° = \cos(225° + 30°) = \cos 225° \cos 30° - \sin 225° \sin 30° =$

$\left(-\dfrac{\sqrt{2}}{2}\right) \cdot \dfrac{\sqrt{3}}{2} - \left(-\dfrac{\sqrt{2}}{2}\right) \cdot \dfrac{1}{2} = -\dfrac{\sqrt{6}}{4} + \dfrac{\sqrt{2}}{4} = \dfrac{\sqrt{2} - \sqrt{6}}{4}$

14. d; $\sin 2\pi \cos\dfrac{\pi}{6} - \cos 2\pi \sin\dfrac{\pi}{6} = \sin\left(2\pi - \dfrac{\pi}{6}\right) = \sin\dfrac{11\pi}{6} = -\dfrac{1}{2}$

15. b; $\cos 2\theta = 1 - 2\sin^2\theta = 1 - 2\left(\dfrac{3}{4}\right)^2 = 1 - \dfrac{9}{8} = -\dfrac{1}{8}$

16. d; $\sin 75° \cos 75° = \dfrac{1}{2}\sin(2 \cdot 75°) = \dfrac{1}{2}\sin 150°$; $\sin^2 75° - \cos^2 75° =$

$-(\cos^2 75° - \sin^2 75°) = -\cos 150°$; $\dfrac{\sin 75° \cos 75°}{\sin^2 75° - \cos^2 75°} = \dfrac{\dfrac{1}{2}\sin 150°}{-\cos 150°} = -\dfrac{1}{2}\tan 150° =$

$-\dfrac{1}{2}\left(-\dfrac{\sqrt{3}}{3}\right) = \dfrac{\sqrt{3}}{6}$

17. a; $\dfrac{\theta}{2}$ is in Quadrant II; $\tan\dfrac{\theta}{2} = -\sqrt{\dfrac{1 - \dfrac{5}{13}}{1 + \dfrac{5}{13}}} = -\sqrt{\dfrac{\dfrac{8}{13}}{\dfrac{18}{13}}} = -\sqrt{\dfrac{4}{9}} = -\dfrac{2}{3}$

18. b; $\tan\left(\alpha - \dfrac{\pi}{4}\right) \tan\left(\alpha + \dfrac{\pi}{4}\right) = \dfrac{\tan\alpha - \tan\dfrac{\pi}{4}}{1 + \tan\alpha\tan\dfrac{\pi}{4}} \cdot \dfrac{\tan\alpha + \tan\dfrac{\pi}{4}}{1 - \tan\alpha\tan\dfrac{\pi}{4}} =$

$\dfrac{\tan\alpha - 1}{1 + \tan\alpha} \cdot \dfrac{\tan\alpha + 1}{1 - \tan\alpha} = -1.$

Page 619 · CHAPTER TEST

1. a. $120° = 120 \cdot \dfrac{\pi}{180} = -\dfrac{2\pi}{3}$ **b.** $\dfrac{5\pi}{9} = \left(\dfrac{5\pi}{9} \cdot \dfrac{180}{\pi}\right)° = 100°$

2. $A = \dfrac{75}{360} \cdot \pi \cdot 3^2 = \dfrac{75\pi}{40} = \dfrac{15\pi}{8}$

3. $\sin\dfrac{2\pi}{3} = \dfrac{\sqrt{3}}{2}$; $\cos\dfrac{2\pi}{3} = -\dfrac{1}{2}$; $\tan\dfrac{2\pi}{3} = -\sqrt{3}$; $\csc\dfrac{2\pi}{3} = \dfrac{2\sqrt{3}}{3}$; $\sec\dfrac{2\pi}{3} = -2$;

$\cot\dfrac{2\pi}{3} = -\dfrac{\sqrt{3}}{3}$

4. $f(-x) = \cos(-x) - (-x)\tan(-x) = \cos x - x\tan x = f(x)$; even

5. $a = 2$; maximum value $= 2$, minimum value $= -2$; period $= \dfrac{2\pi}{3}$

6. $a = 3$; period $= 8$; $\dfrac{2\pi}{b} = 8$; $b = \dfrac{\pi}{4}$; $c = 0$; $y = 3\sin\dfrac{\pi}{4}x$

7.

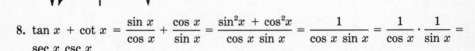

8. $\tan x + \cot x = \dfrac{\sin x}{\cos x} + \dfrac{\cos x}{\sin x} = \dfrac{\sin^2 x + \cos^2 x}{\cos x \sin x} = \dfrac{1}{\cos x \sin x} = \dfrac{1}{\cos x} \cdot \dfrac{1}{\sin x} =$
$\sec x \csc x$

9. $\cos(\alpha + 45°) + \sin(\alpha - 45°) = \cos\alpha\cos 45° - \sin\alpha\sin 45° + \sin\alpha\cos 45° -$
$\cos\alpha\sin 45° = \dfrac{\sqrt{2}}{2}\cos\alpha - \dfrac{\sqrt{2}}{2}\sin\alpha + \dfrac{\sqrt{2}}{2}\sin\alpha - \dfrac{\sqrt{2}}{2}\cos\alpha = 0$

10. $\cos\alpha = -\sqrt{1 - \sin^2\alpha} = -\sqrt{1 - \dfrac{144}{169}} = -\sqrt{\dfrac{25}{169}} = -\dfrac{5}{13}$

   a. $\sin 2\alpha = 2\sin\alpha\cos\alpha = 2\left(\dfrac{12}{13}\right)\left(-\dfrac{5}{13}\right) = -\dfrac{120}{169}$

   b. $\cos 2\alpha = 1 - 2\sin^2\alpha = 1 - 2\left(\dfrac{12}{13}\right)^2 = 1 - 2\left(\dfrac{144}{169}\right) = -\dfrac{119}{169}$

11. $\cos \theta = \sqrt{1 - \sin^2\theta} = \sqrt{1 - \dfrac{9}{25}} = \sqrt{\dfrac{16}{25}} = \dfrac{4}{5}$; $\tan \theta = \dfrac{\sin \theta}{\cos \theta} = \dfrac{-\dfrac{3}{5}}{\dfrac{4}{5}} = -\dfrac{3}{4}$

a. $\tan 2\theta = \dfrac{2 \tan \theta}{1 - \tan^2\theta} = \dfrac{2\left(-\dfrac{3}{4}\right)}{1 - \left(-\dfrac{3}{4}\right)^2} = -\dfrac{3}{2} \cdot \dfrac{16}{7} = -\dfrac{24}{7}$

b. $\tan \dfrac{\theta}{2} = \dfrac{\sin \theta}{1 + \cos \theta} = \dfrac{-\dfrac{3}{5}}{1 + \dfrac{4}{5}} = -\dfrac{3}{5} \cdot \dfrac{5}{9} = -\dfrac{3}{9} = -\dfrac{1}{3}$

Page 625 · WRITTEN EXERCISES

A 1.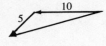

2.

3.

4.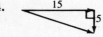

5.

6.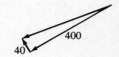

7.

8.

9.

10.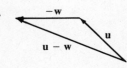

11.

12.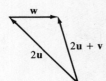

13.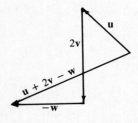

14.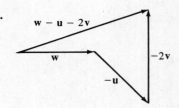

15. $\alpha = 180° - (45° + 45°) = 90°$; $\|\mathbf{w}\|^2 = 125^2 + 96^2 = 24{,}841$; $\|\mathbf{w}\| = 158$;

$\tan \theta = \dfrac{96}{125} = 0.768$; $\theta = 37.5°$; bearing $= 135° + 37.5° = 172.5°$

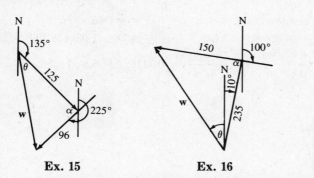

Ex. 15 **Ex. 16** **Ex. 17**

16. $\alpha = 180° - (10° + 80°) = 90°$; $\|\mathbf{w}\|^2 = 150^2 + 235^2 = 77{,}725$; $\|\mathbf{w}\| = 279$; $\tan(\theta + 10°) =$

$\dfrac{150}{235} = 0.6383$; $\theta + 10° = 32.6°$; $\theta = 22.6°$; bearing $= 360° - 22.6° = 337.4°$

B **17.** $\alpha = 180° - (20° + 70°) = 90°$; $\|\mathbf{w}\|^2 = 272^2 + 204^2 = 115{,}600$; $\|\mathbf{w}\| = 340$;

$\tan \theta = \dfrac{204}{272} = 0.75$; $\theta = 36.9°$; bearing $= 200° - 36.9° = 163.1°$

18. $\alpha = 25° + 55° = 80°$; $\|\mathbf{w}\|^2 = 2160^2 + 6420^2 - 2(2160)(6420) \cos 80° = 41{,}065{,}972$;

$\|\mathbf{w}\| = 6410$; $\dfrac{\sin \theta}{6420} = \dfrac{\sin 80°}{6410}$; $\sin \theta = \dfrac{6420(0.9848)}{6410} = 0.9863$; $\theta = 80.5°$;

bearing $= 125° - 80.5° = 44.5°$

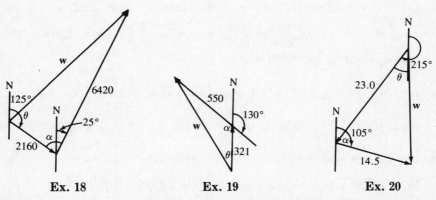

Ex. 18 **Ex. 19** **Ex. 20**

19. $\alpha = 180° - 50° = 130°$; $\|\mathbf{w}\|^2 = 550^2 + 321^2 - 2(550)(321) \cos 130° = 632{,}509$;

$\|\mathbf{w}\| = 795$; $\dfrac{\sin \theta}{550} = \dfrac{\sin \alpha}{795}$; $\sin \theta = \dfrac{550(0.7660)}{795} = 0.5299$; $\theta = 32.0°$;

bearing $= 360° - 32.0° = 328°$

20. $\alpha = 180° - (35° + 75°) = 70°$; $\|\mathbf{w}\|^2 = 23.0^2 + 14.5^2 - 2(23.0)(14.5) \cos 70° = 511.12$;

$\|\mathbf{w}\| = 22.6$; $\dfrac{\sin \theta}{14.5} = \dfrac{\sin \alpha}{22.6}$; $\sin \theta = \dfrac{14.5(0.9397)}{22.6} = 0.6029$; $\theta = 37.1°$;

bearing $= 215° - 37.1° = 177.9°$

21. Note: Figure not drawn to scale; $\mathbf{w} + \mathbf{u} + \mathbf{v} = 0$; $\mathbf{w} = -(\mathbf{u} + \mathbf{v})$; $\alpha = 180° - (15° + 15°) = 150°$; $\|\mathbf{w}\|^2 = 3.62^2 + 1.08^2 - 2(3.62)(1.08) \cos 150° = 21.0424$; $\|\mathbf{w}\| = 4.59$; $\dfrac{\sin \theta}{1.08} = \dfrac{\sin \alpha}{4.59}$; $\sin \theta = \dfrac{1.08(0.5)}{4.59} = 0.1176$; $\theta = 6.8°$; bearing $= 195° - 6.8° = 188.2°$

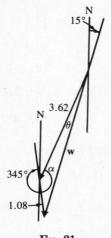

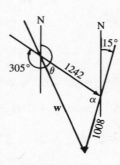

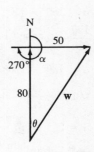

Ex. 21   Ex. 22   Ex. 23

22. $2(\mathbf{w} - \mathbf{u}) = 3(\mathbf{w} + \mathbf{v})$; $2\mathbf{w} - 2\mathbf{u} = 3\mathbf{w} + 3\mathbf{v}$; $\mathbf{w} = -2\mathbf{u} - 3\mathbf{v} = -(2\mathbf{u} + 3\mathbf{v})$; $\alpha = 180° - (15° + 55°) = 110°$; $\|\mathbf{w}\|^2 = 1008^2 + 1242^2 - 2(1008)(1242) \cos 110° = 3,415,002$; $\|\mathbf{w}\| = 1850$; $\dfrac{\sin \theta}{1008} = \dfrac{\sin \alpha}{1850}$; $\sin \theta = \dfrac{1008(0.9397)}{1850} = 0.5120$; $\theta = 30.8°$; bearing $= 305° - 180° + 30.8° = 155.8°$

23. $4\mathbf{w} + \mathbf{u} = 7\mathbf{w} + \mathbf{v}$; $3\mathbf{w} = \mathbf{u} - \mathbf{v}$; $\mathbf{w} = \dfrac{1}{3}(\mathbf{u} - \mathbf{v})$; $\mathbf{w} = \dfrac{1}{3}\mathbf{u} - \dfrac{1}{3}\mathbf{v}$;

$\|\mathbf{w}\| = \sqrt{80^2 + 50^2} = 94.3$; $\tan \theta = \dfrac{50}{80} = 0.625$; $\theta = 32.0°$; bearing $= 32.0°$

24. $\mathbf{w} + 2\mathbf{u} + 3\mathbf{v} = 0$; $\mathbf{w} = -(2\mathbf{u} + 3\mathbf{v})$; $\alpha = 180° - (80° + 10°) = 90°$;

$\|\mathbf{w}\| = \sqrt{2.5^2 + 10.5^2} = 10.8$; $\tan \theta = \dfrac{10.5}{2.5} = 4.2000$; $\theta = 76.6°$; bearing $= 280° + 76.6° = 356.6°$

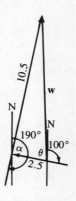

Page 626 · PROBLEMS

A   1. $\|\mathbf{d}\| = \sqrt{240^2 + 100^2} = 260$; $\tan \theta = \dfrac{240}{100} = 2.4$; $\theta = 67.4°$;

the port is 260 km from the ship, with bearing
$360° - 67.4° = 292.6°$.

2. $\|\mathbf{d}\| = \sqrt{320^2 + 480^2} = 577$; $\tan \theta = \dfrac{480}{320} = 1.5$; $\theta = 56.3°$;

bearing $= 360° - (\theta - 45°) = 405° - 56.3° = 348.7°$; the
plane is 577 km from its starting point, with bearing 348.7°.

3.   Note: Figure not drawn to scale; $\|\mathbf{v}\| = \sqrt{600^2 + 50^2} = 602$;

$\tan \theta = \dfrac{50}{600} = 0.0833$; $\theta = 4.8°$; the plane should fly at a speed

of 602 km/h with heading 4.8°.

4. $\alpha = 180° - (30° + 60°) = 90°$; $\|\mathbf{s}\| = \sqrt{320^2 + 40^2} = 320$; $\tan \theta = $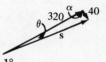

$\dfrac{40}{320} = 0.125$; $\theta = 7.1°$; bearing $= 60° + 7.1° = 67.1°$; the plane's

ground speed is 322 km/h and the bearing of its true course is 67.1°.

5.   Note: Figure not drawn to scale; $\alpha = 90° - 30° = 60°$;

$\|\mathbf{v}\|^2 = 600^2 + 50^2 - 2(600)(50) \cos 60° = 332,500$; $\|\mathbf{v}\| = 577$;

$\dfrac{\sin \theta}{50} = \dfrac{\sin \alpha}{577}$; $\sin \theta = \dfrac{50(0.8660)}{577} = 0.0750$; $\theta = 4.3°$; the plane

should fly at a speed of 577 km/h with a heading of 4.3°.

6. $\alpha = 180° - (60° + 60°) = 60°$;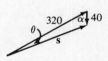

$\|\mathbf{s}\|^2 = 320^2 + 40^2 - 2(320)(40) \cos 60° = 91,200$;

$\|\mathbf{s}\| = 302$; $\dfrac{\sin \theta}{40} = \dfrac{\sin \alpha}{302}$; $\sin \theta = \dfrac{40(0.8660)}{302} = 0.1147$; $\theta = 6.6°$;

bearing $= 60° + 6.6° = 66.6°$; the plane's ground speed is 302 km/h and the bearing of
its true course is 66.6°.

B   7.   Let A represent the position of the first ship and B that of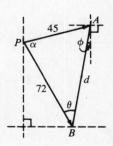

the second; $\alpha = 180° - (75° + 25°) = 80°$;

$d^2 = 72^2 + 45^2 - 2(72)(45) \cos 80° = 6084$; $d = 78.0$;

$\dfrac{\sin \theta}{45} = \dfrac{\sin \alpha}{78.0}$; $\sin \theta = \dfrac{45(0.9848)}{78.0} = 0.5682$; $\theta = 34.6°$; bearing

of A from $B = \theta - (90° - 65°) = 34.6° - 25° = 9.6°$; $\phi = 9.6°$;

bearing of B from $A = 180° + 9.6° = 189.6°$.

8. $\alpha = 180° - (55° + 65°) = 60°$; $\|\mathbf{v}\|^2 =$
$600^2 + 140^2 - 2(600)(140)\cos 60° = 295{,}600$; $\|\mathbf{v}\| = 544$; $\dfrac{\sin\theta}{600} = \dfrac{\sin\alpha}{544}$;
$\sin\theta = \dfrac{600(0.8660)}{544} = 0.9551$; $\theta = 72.8°$; bearing $= 180° - (\theta + 35°) =$
$145° - 72.8° = 72.2°$; the plane should use a heading of 72.2°; it will
have to fly 544 km.

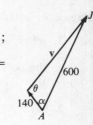

9. Note: Figure not drawn to scale; $\phi = 50° - 20° = 30°$;
$\dfrac{\sin\theta}{60} = \dfrac{\sin\phi}{640}$; $\sin\theta = \dfrac{60(0.5)}{640} = 0.0469$; $\theta = 2.7°$;
$\alpha = 180° - (2.7° + 30°) = 147.3°$; $\dfrac{\sin\alpha}{s} = \dfrac{\sin\phi}{640}$;
$s = \dfrac{(0.5402)(640)}{0.5} = 691$; since the plane's ground speed
will be 691 km/h, the trip will take $\dfrac{540}{691} \approx 0.78$ h ≈ 47 min
and the ETA is 2:47 P.M. The compass heading will be
$140° + \theta = 142.7°$.

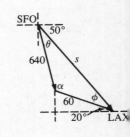

10. Note: Figure not drawn to scale; $\alpha = 360° - (70° + 140°) =$
$150°$; $\dfrac{\sin\theta}{60} = \dfrac{\sin\alpha}{640}$; $\sin\theta = \dfrac{60(0.5)}{640} = 0.0469$; $\theta = 2.7°$;
$\phi = 180° - (150° + 2.7°) = 27.3°$; $\dfrac{\sin\phi}{s} = \dfrac{\sin\alpha}{640}$;
$s = \dfrac{640(0.4586)}{0.5} = 587$; since the plane's ground speed is
587 km/h, the trip will take $\dfrac{540}{587} \approx 0.92$ h ≈ 55 min and the
ETA is 5:55 P.M. The heading is $360° - (\theta + 40°) =$
$320° - 2.7° = 317.3°$.

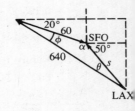

Pages 630-631 · WRITTEN EXERCISES

A　1. Let $B = (x,y)$; $\overrightarrow{OA} + \overrightarrow{AB} = \overrightarrow{OB}$; $(3\mathbf{i} - \mathbf{j}) + (-\mathbf{i} + 2\mathbf{j}) = x\mathbf{i} + y\mathbf{j}$; $2\mathbf{i} + \mathbf{j} = x\mathbf{i} + y\mathbf{j}$
$x = 2$; $y = 1$; $B = (2,1)$.

2. Let $B = (x,y)$; $\overrightarrow{OA} + \overrightarrow{AB} = \overrightarrow{OB}$; $(-2\mathbf{i} + \mathbf{j}) + (3\mathbf{i} + \mathbf{j}) = x\mathbf{i} + y\mathbf{j}$; $\mathbf{i} + 2\mathbf{j} = x\mathbf{i} + y\mathbf{j}$
$x = 1$; $y = 2$; $B = (1,2)$.

3. Let $A = (x,y)$; $\overrightarrow{OA} + \overrightarrow{AB} = \overrightarrow{OB}$; $(x\mathbf{i} + y\mathbf{j}) + (3\mathbf{i} + \mathbf{j}) = 3\mathbf{i} + 4\mathbf{j}$;
$(x + 3)\mathbf{i} + (y + 1)\mathbf{j} = 3\mathbf{i} + 4\mathbf{j}$; $x + 3 = 3$ and $y + 1 = 4$; $x = 0$, $y = 3$; $A = (0,3)$.

4. Let $A = (x,y)$; $\overrightarrow{OA} + \overrightarrow{AB} = \overrightarrow{OB}$; $(x\mathbf{i} + y\mathbf{j}) + (\mathbf{i} - 3\mathbf{j}) = -2\mathbf{i} + 0\mathbf{j}$;
$(x + 1)\mathbf{i} + (y - 3)\mathbf{j} = -2\mathbf{i} + 0\mathbf{j}$; $x + 1 = -2$ and $y - 3 = 0$; $x = -3$, $y = 3$;
$A = (-3,3)$.

5. $s + 1 = 4$; $s = 3$; $t - 2 = 3$; $t = 5$

6. $2s - 3 = s$; $s = 3$; $3t - 2 = t$; $t = 1$

7. $s + t = 5$ and $s - t = -1$; solving simultaneously, $2s = 4$; $s = 2$; $2 + t = 5$; $t = 3$

8. $s + 2t = 1$ and $s - t = 0$; $t = s$; $s + 2s = 1$; $3s = 1$; $s = t = \dfrac{1}{3}$

9. a. $\mathbf{w} = \mathbf{u} + \mathbf{v} = (2\mathbf{i} + \mathbf{j}) + (\mathbf{i} - 5\mathbf{j}) =$
$(2 + 1)\mathbf{i} + (1 - 5)\mathbf{j} = 3\mathbf{i} - 4\mathbf{j}$

b.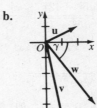

   c. $\|\mathbf{w}\| = \sqrt{3^2 + (-4)^2} = 5$

   d. $\tan \gamma = \dfrac{4}{3} = 1.333$; $\gamma = 306.9°$

10. a. $\mathbf{w} = \mathbf{u} - \mathbf{v} = (\mathbf{i} - \mathbf{j}) - (5\mathbf{i} + 2\mathbf{j}) =$
$(1 - 5)\mathbf{i} + (-1 - 2)\mathbf{j} = -4\mathbf{i} - 3\mathbf{j}$

b.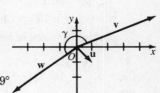

   c. $\|\mathbf{w}\| = \sqrt{(-4)^2 + (-3)^2} = 5$

   d. $\tan(\gamma - 180°) = \dfrac{3}{4} = 0.75$; $\gamma - 180° = 36.9°$; $\gamma = 216.9°$

11. a. $\mathbf{w} = 2\mathbf{u} - \mathbf{v} = 2(4\mathbf{i} + 3\mathbf{j}) - (-4\mathbf{i} + \mathbf{j}) =$
$(8\mathbf{i} + 6\mathbf{j}) - (-4\mathbf{i} + \mathbf{j}) = (8 + 4)\mathbf{i} + (6 - 1)\mathbf{j} =$
$12\mathbf{i} + 5\mathbf{j}$ **c.** $\|\mathbf{w}\| = \sqrt{12^2 + 5^2} = 13$

b.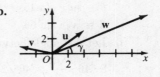

   d. $\tan \gamma = \dfrac{5}{12} = 0.4167$; $\gamma = 22.6°$

12. a. $\mathbf{w} = 2\mathbf{u} + 3\mathbf{v} = 2(-4\mathbf{i} + 3\mathbf{j}) + 3(\mathbf{i} + 2\mathbf{j}) =$
$(-8\mathbf{i} + 6\mathbf{j}) + (3\mathbf{i} + 6\mathbf{j}) = -5\mathbf{i} + 12\mathbf{j}$ **c.** $\|\mathbf{w}\| =$
$\sqrt{(-5)^2 + 12^2} = 13$ **d.** $\tan(180° - \gamma) = \dfrac{12}{5} = 2.4$;
$180° - \gamma = 67.4°$; $\gamma = 112.6°$

b.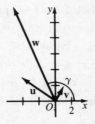

13. $\cos \theta = \dfrac{\mathbf{u} \cdot \mathbf{v}}{\|\mathbf{u}\|\,\|\mathbf{v}\|} = \dfrac{-2 \cdot 4 + 1 \cdot 3}{\sqrt{(-2)^2 + 1^2}\,\sqrt{4^2 + 3^2}} = \dfrac{-5}{\sqrt{5}\,(5)} = -\dfrac{\sqrt{5}}{5} = -0.4472$; $\theta = 116.6°$

14. $\cos \theta = \dfrac{\mathbf{u} \cdot \mathbf{v}}{\|\mathbf{u}\|\,\|\mathbf{v}\|} = \dfrac{3 \cdot 3 + (-4)(2)}{\sqrt{3^2 + (-4)^2}\,\sqrt{3^2 + 2^2}} = \dfrac{1}{5\sqrt{13}} = \dfrac{\sqrt{13}}{65} = 0.0555$; $\theta = 86.8°$

15. $\cos \theta = \dfrac{\mathbf{u} \cdot \mathbf{v}}{\|\mathbf{u}\|\,\|\mathbf{v}\|} = \dfrac{3 \cdot 1 + (-1)(2)}{\sqrt{3^2 + (-1)^2}\,\sqrt{1^2 + 2^2}} = \dfrac{1}{\sqrt{10}\,\sqrt{5}} = \dfrac{1}{5\sqrt{2}} = \dfrac{\sqrt{2}}{10} = 0.1414$; $\theta = 81.9°$

16. $\cos \theta = \dfrac{\mathbf{u} \cdot \mathbf{v}}{\|\mathbf{u}\|\,\|\mathbf{v}\|} = \dfrac{2 \cdot 6 + 3(-4)}{\sqrt{2^2 + 3^2}\,\sqrt{6^2 + (-4)^2}} = 0$; $\theta = 90°$

17. Let $\mathbf{u} = x\mathbf{i} + y\mathbf{j}$; $\mathbf{u}$ and $\mathbf{v}$ are orthogonal if and only if $x + y = 0$; one solution to the
equation is $x = 1$, $y = -1$; $\mathbf{u} = \mathbf{i} - \mathbf{j}$; $\dfrac{\mathbf{u}}{\|\mathbf{u}\|} = \dfrac{\mathbf{i} - \mathbf{j}}{\sqrt{1^2 + (-1)^2}} = \dfrac{\mathbf{i} - \mathbf{j}}{\sqrt{2}} = \dfrac{\sqrt{2}}{2}\mathbf{i} - \dfrac{\sqrt{2}}{2}\mathbf{j}$

18. Let $\mathbf{u} = x\mathbf{i} + y\mathbf{j}$; $4x - 3y = 0$; let $x = 3$, $y = 4$; $\mathbf{u} = 3\mathbf{i} + 4\mathbf{j}$;

$$\frac{\mathbf{u}}{\|\mathbf{u}\|} = \frac{3\mathbf{i} + 4\mathbf{j}}{\sqrt{3^2 + 4^2}} = \frac{3\mathbf{i} + 4\mathbf{j}}{\sqrt{25}} = \frac{3}{5}\mathbf{i} + \frac{4}{5}\mathbf{j}$$

19. Let $\mathbf{u} = x\mathbf{i} + y\mathbf{j}$; $12x - 5y = 0$; let $x = 5$, $y = 12$; $\mathbf{u} = 5\mathbf{i} + 12\mathbf{j}$;

$$\frac{\mathbf{u}}{\|\mathbf{u}\|} = \frac{5\mathbf{i} + 12\mathbf{j}}{\sqrt{5^2 + 12^2}} = \frac{5\mathbf{i} + 12\mathbf{j}}{\sqrt{169}} = \frac{5}{13}\mathbf{i} + \frac{12}{13}\mathbf{j}$$

20. Let $\mathbf{u} = x\mathbf{i} + y\mathbf{j}$; $2x + 4y = 0$; let $x = -2$, $y = 1$; $\mathbf{u} = -2\mathbf{i} + \mathbf{j}$;

$$\frac{\mathbf{u}}{\|\mathbf{u}\|} = \frac{-2\mathbf{i} + \mathbf{j}}{\sqrt{(-2)^2 + 1^2}} = \frac{-2\mathbf{i} + \mathbf{j}}{\sqrt{5}} = \frac{-2\sqrt{5}}{5}\mathbf{i} + \frac{\sqrt{5}}{5}\mathbf{j}$$

B 21. **a.** Let $\mathbf{u} = a\mathbf{i} + b\mathbf{j}$ and $\mathbf{v} = c\mathbf{i} + d\mathbf{j}$; $a = \|\mathbf{u}\| \cdot \cos 10° = 10(0.9848) = 9.85$; $b = \|\mathbf{u}\| \cdot \sin 10° = 10(0.1736) = 1.74$; $c = \|\mathbf{v}\| \cdot \cos 70° = 15(0.3420) = 5.13$; $d = \|\mathbf{v}\| \cdot \sin 70° = 15(0.9397) = 14.1$; $\mathbf{u} = 9.85\mathbf{i} + 1.74\mathbf{j}$ and $\mathbf{v} = 5.13\mathbf{i} + 14.1\mathbf{j}$

   b. Let θ = angle between $\mathbf{u}$ and $\mathbf{v}$; $\theta = 70° - 10° = 60°$; $\mathbf{u} \cdot \mathbf{v} = \|\mathbf{u}\| \|\mathbf{v}\| \cos \theta =$

   $$10 \cdot 15 \cdot \frac{1}{2} = 75 \qquad \textbf{c. } \mathbf{u} \cdot \mathbf{v} = ac + bd = (9.85)(5.13) + (1.74)(14.1) = 75.1$$

22. **a.** Let $\mathbf{u} = a\mathbf{i} + b\mathbf{j}$ and $\mathbf{v} = c\mathbf{i} + d\mathbf{j}$; $a = \|\mathbf{u}\| \cdot \cos 15° = 8(0.9659) = 7.73$;

   $b = \|\mathbf{u}\| \cdot \sin 15° = 8(0.2588) = 2.07$; $c = \|\mathbf{v}\| \cdot \cos 60° = 10(0.5) = 5$;

   $d = \|\mathbf{v}\| \cdot \sin 60° = 10(0.8660) = 8.66$; $\mathbf{u} = 7.73\mathbf{i} + 2.07\mathbf{j}$ and $\mathbf{v} = 5\mathbf{i} + 8.66\mathbf{j}$

   b. Let θ = angle between $\mathbf{u}$ and $\mathbf{v}$; $\theta = 60° - 15° = 45°$; $\mathbf{u} \cdot \mathbf{v} = \|\mathbf{u}\| \|\mathbf{v}\| \cos \theta =$

   $$8 \cdot 10 \cdot \frac{\sqrt{2}}{2} = 40\sqrt{2} = 56.6 \quad \textbf{c. } \mathbf{u} \cdot \mathbf{v} = ac + bd = (7.73)(5) + (2.07)(8.66) = 56.6$$

23. **a.** Let $\mathbf{u} = a\mathbf{i} + b\mathbf{j}$ and $\mathbf{v} = c\mathbf{i} + d\mathbf{j}$; $a = \|\mathbf{u}\| \cos 68° = 12.5(0.3746) = 4.68$;

   $b = \|\mathbf{u}\| \sin 68° = 12.5(0.9272) = 11.6$; $c = \|\mathbf{v}\| \cos 116° = 18.0(-0.4384) = -7.89$;

   $d = \|\mathbf{v}\| \sin 116° = 18.0(0.8988) = 16.2$; $\mathbf{u} = 4.68\mathbf{i} + 11.6\mathbf{j}$ and $\mathbf{v} = -7.89\mathbf{i} + 16.2\mathbf{j}$

   b. Let θ = angle between $\mathbf{u}$ and $\mathbf{v}$; $\theta = 116° - 68° = 48°$;

   $\mathbf{u} \cdot \mathbf{v} = \|\mathbf{u}\| \|\mathbf{v}\| \cos \theta = 12.5(18.0)(0.6691) = 151$

   c. $\mathbf{u} \cdot \mathbf{v} = ac + bd = 4.68(-7.89) + 11.6(16.2) = 151$

24. **a.** Let $u = a\mathbf{i} + b\mathbf{j}$ and $\mathbf{v} = c\mathbf{i} + d\mathbf{j}$; $a = \|\mathbf{u}\| \cos 57° = 8.70(0.5446) = 4.74$; $b = \|\mathbf{u}\| \cdot \sin 57° = 8.70(0.8387) = 7.30$; $c = \|\mathbf{v}\| \cdot \cos(-28°) = 6.60(0.8829) = 5.83$; $d = \|\mathbf{v}\| \cdot \sin(-28°) = 6.60(-0.4695) = -3.10$; $\mathbf{u} = 4.74\mathbf{i} + 7.30\mathbf{j}$ and $\mathbf{v} = 5.83\mathbf{i} - 3.10\mathbf{j}$

   b. Let θ = angle between $\mathbf{u}$ and $\mathbf{v}$; $\theta = 57° - (-28°) = 85°$; $\mathbf{u} \cdot \mathbf{v} = \|\mathbf{u}\| \|\mathbf{v}\| \cos 85° = (8.70)(6.60)(0.0872) = 5.01$ **c.** $\mathbf{u} \cdot \mathbf{v} = ac + bd = 4.74(5.83) + 7.30(-3.10) = 5.00$

C 25. By the law of cosines, $\|\mathbf{u} - \mathbf{v}\|^2 = \|\mathbf{u}\|^2 + \|\mathbf{v}\|^2 - 2\|\mathbf{u}\| \|\mathbf{v}\| \cos \theta = \|\mathbf{u}\|^2 + \|\mathbf{v}\|^2 - 2\mathbf{u} \cdot \mathbf{v}$;

   $\mathbf{u} \cdot \mathbf{v} = \dfrac{1}{2}[\|\mathbf{u}\|^2 + \|\mathbf{v}\|^2 - \|\mathbf{u} - \mathbf{v}\|^2] = \dfrac{1}{2}[a^2 + b^2 + c^2 + d^2 - (a - c)^2 - (b - d)^2] =$

   $\dfrac{1}{2}[a^2 + b^2 + c^2 + d^2 - a^2 + 2ac - c^2 - b^2 + 2bd - d^2] = \dfrac{1}{2}(2ac + 2bd) =$

   $ac + bd$

26. Let $\mathbf{u} = a\mathbf{i} + b\mathbf{j}$; $\mathbf{u} \cdot \mathbf{i} = a \cdot 1 + b \cdot 0 = a$ and $\mathbf{u} \cdot \mathbf{j} = a \cdot 0 + b \cdot 1 = b$;

   $(\mathbf{u} \cdot \mathbf{i})\mathbf{i} + (\mathbf{u} \cdot \mathbf{j})\mathbf{j} = a\mathbf{i} + b\mathbf{j} = \mathbf{u}$.

Pages 631-632 · COMPUTER EXERCISES

1. 10 PRINT "ENTER X AND Y COMPONENTS"
   20 INPUT X, Y
   30 LET M = SQR(X ↑ 2 + Y ↑ 2)
   40 LET A = ATN(Y/X) * 180/3.14159265
   50 IF X < 0 THEN LET A = A + 180
   60 IF A < 0 THEN LET A = A + 360
   70 PRINT "MAGNITUDE = "; M
   80 PRINT "ANGLE = "; A
   90 END

2. **a.** MAGNITUDE = 9.21954447   **b.** MAGNITUDE = 17
      ANGLE = 319.398705   ANGLE = 151.927513
   c. MAGNITUDE = 64.1755406
      ANGLE = 206.764687

3. 10 PRINT "ENTER MAGNITUDE 1, ANGLE 1"
   20 INPUT M1, A1
   30 PRINT "ENTER MAGNITUDE 2, ANGLE 2"
   40 INPUT M2, A2
   50 LET Y1 = M1 * SIN(A1 * 3.14159265/180)
   60 LET X1 = M1 * COS(A1 * 3.14159265/180)
   70 LET Y2 = M2 * SIN(A2 * 3.14159265/180)
   80 LET X2 = M2 * COS(A2 * 3.14159265/180)
   90 LET X = X1 + X2
   100 LET Y = Y1 + Y2
   110 LET M = SQR(X ↑ 2 + Y ↑ 2)
   120 LET A = ATN(Y/X) * 180/3.14159265
   130 IF X < 0 THEN LET A = A + 180
   140 IF A < 0 THEN LET A = A + 360
   150 PRINT "MAGNITUDE = "; M
   160 PRINT "ANGLE = "; A
   170 END

4. **a.** MAGNITUDE = 21.6009675   **b.** MAGNITUDE = 11.2980008
      ANGLE = 79.6485928   ANGLE = 39.5829305
   c. MAGNITUDE = 70.0145352   **d.** MAGNITUDE = 353.163902
      ANGLE = 167.140754   ANGLE = 101.425964
   e. MAGNITUDE = 50.0000001
      ANGLE = 263.130102

Pages 632-636 · EXTRA

A   1. $\mathbf{F}_3 = -(\mathbf{F}_1 + \mathbf{F}_2) = -[(3 - 1)\mathbf{i} + (-2 + 3)\mathbf{j}] = -2\mathbf{i} - \mathbf{j}$

2. $\mathbf{F}_3 = -(\mathbf{F}_1 + \mathbf{F}_2) = -[(5 - 2)\mathbf{i} + (-1 + 1)\mathbf{j}] = -3\mathbf{i}$

3. $\mathbf{d} = \overrightarrow{AB} = (2 + 2)\mathbf{i} + (3 - 0)\mathbf{j} = 4\mathbf{i} + 3\mathbf{j};$
   $W = \mathbf{F} \cdot \mathbf{d} = (3\mathbf{i} - \mathbf{j}) \cdot (4\mathbf{i} + 3\mathbf{j}) = 12 - 3 = 9; \ 9 \ \text{J}$

4. $\mathbf{d} = \overrightarrow{AB} = (5 + 3)\mathbf{i} + (-1 - 2)\mathbf{j} = 8\mathbf{i} - 3\mathbf{j};$
   $W = \mathbf{F} \cdot \mathbf{d} = 5\mathbf{i} \cdot (8\mathbf{i} - 3\mathbf{j}) = 5 \cdot 8 + 0(-3) = 40; \ 40 \ \text{J}$

5. **a.** $\mathbf{d}_1 = \overrightarrow{AB} = (3 + 2)\mathbf{i} + (3 - 1)\mathbf{j} = 5\mathbf{i} + 2\mathbf{j};$
   $\mathbf{d}_2 = \overrightarrow{BC} = (5 - 3)\mathbf{i} + (0 - 3)\mathbf{j} = 2\mathbf{i} - 3\mathbf{j};$
   $W = \mathbf{F} \cdot \mathbf{d}_1 + \mathbf{F} \cdot \mathbf{d}_2 = (3\mathbf{i} - \mathbf{j}) \cdot (5\mathbf{i} + 2\mathbf{j}) + (3\mathbf{i} - \mathbf{j}) \cdot (2\mathbf{i} - 3\mathbf{j}) =$
   $3 \cdot 5 + (-1)2 + 3 \cdot 2 + (-1)(-3) = 22; \ 22 \ \text{J}$
   b. $\mathbf{d} = \overrightarrow{AC} = (5 + 2)\mathbf{i} + (0 - 1)\mathbf{j} = 7\mathbf{i} - \mathbf{j};$
   $W = \mathbf{F} \cdot \mathbf{d} = (3\mathbf{i} - \mathbf{j}) \cdot (7\mathbf{i} - \mathbf{j}) = 3 \cdot 7 + (-1)(-1) = 22; \ 22 \ \text{J}$

6. $\mathbf{d} = \overrightarrow{AB} = (4 + 1)\mathbf{i} + (1 - 0)\mathbf{j} = 5\mathbf{i} + \mathbf{j}; \ W = \mathbf{F} \cdot \mathbf{d} + \mathbf{G} \cdot \mathbf{d} =$
   $(2\mathbf{i} + 5\mathbf{j}) \cdot (5\mathbf{i} + \mathbf{j}) + (4\mathbf{i} - 2\mathbf{j}) \cdot (5\mathbf{i} + \mathbf{j}) = 2 \cdot 5 + 5 \cdot 1 + 4 \cdot 5 + (-2)(1) = 33;$
   $33 \ \text{J}; \ \mathbf{F} + \mathbf{G} = (2\mathbf{i} + 5\mathbf{j}) + (4\mathbf{i} - 2\mathbf{j}) = (2 + 4)\mathbf{i} + (5 - 2)\mathbf{j} = 6\mathbf{i} + 3\mathbf{j};$
   $W = (\mathbf{F} + \mathbf{G}) \cdot \mathbf{d} = (6\mathbf{i} + 3\mathbf{j}) \cdot (5\mathbf{i} + \mathbf{j}) = 6 \cdot 5 + 3 \cdot 1 = 33; \ 33 \ \text{J}$

7. $\mathbf{F} = -(\mathbf{F}_1 + \mathbf{F}_2); \ \alpha = 180° - 60° = 120°; \ \|\mathbf{F}\|^2 =$
   $10^2 + 5^2 - 2(10)(5) \cos 120° = 175; \ \|\mathbf{F}\| = 13.2; \ \dfrac{\sin \theta}{10} = \dfrac{\sin 120°}{13.2};$
   $\sin \theta = \dfrac{10(0.8660)}{13.2} = 0.6561; \ \theta = 41°; \ \text{bearing} = 360° - 41° = 319°;$
   $\mathbf{F} : 13.2 \ \text{N, bearing } 319°$

8. $\mathbf{F} = -(\mathbf{F}_1 + \mathbf{F}_2); \ \alpha = 180° - (60° + 30°) = 90°; \ \|\mathbf{F}\| = \sqrt{15^2 + 6^2} = 16.2;$
   $\tan \theta = \dfrac{6}{15} = 0.4; \ \theta = 21.8°; \ \text{bearing} = 270° - (\theta + 60°) = 210° - 21.8° = 188.2°;$
   $\mathbf{F} : 16.2 \ \text{N, bearing } 188.2°$

9. The engine must overcome the force of gravity by exerting an upward force of $1500(9.8) = 1.47 \times 10^4 \ \text{N}$; the displacement $\mathbf{d}$ is also upward and $\|\mathbf{d}\| = 100; \ W = \|\mathbf{F}\|\|\mathbf{d}\| = 1.47 \times 10^4 \times 100 = 1.47 \times 10^6 \ \text{J}$

10. See the figure for Example 1, page 633 in the text with α = angle between $\mathbf{H}$ and $\mathbf{G}$;
    $\|\mathbf{G}\| = 50 \times 9.8 = 490 \ \text{N}; \ \alpha = 20°; \ \sin \alpha = \dfrac{\|\mathbf{F}\|}{\|\mathbf{G}\|}; \ \|\mathbf{F}\| = 490(0.3420) = 168; \ 168 \ \text{N}$

11. The man must overcome the force of gravity by exerting an upward force of $9.8 \times 75 = 735 \ \text{N}$; the displacement $\mathbf{d}$ has norm 12; the angle between $\mathbf{F}$ and $\mathbf{d}$ is $90° - 78° = 12°; \ W = \mathbf{F} \cdot \mathbf{d} = \|\mathbf{F}\|\|\mathbf{d}\| \cos 12° = 735 \cdot 12(0.9781) = 8627; \ 8.63 \times 10^3 \ \text{J}$

B   **12.** The force **F** needed to overcome the force of gravity is $120{,}000 \times 9.8 = 1.18 \times 10^6$ N; the displacement **d** has norm 5000 and the angle between **F** and **d** is $90° - 22° = 68°$; $W = \mathbf{F} \cdot \mathbf{d} = \|\mathbf{F}\|\|\mathbf{d}\| \cos \theta = (1.18 \times 10^6)(5000)(0.3746) = 2.21 \times 10^9$ J; $(2.21 \times 10^9) \div (3.6 \times 10^6) = 614$; 614 kW·h.

13. Let **F** = the force of 120 N at an angle of 40° with the horizontal and **d** = displacement; $\|\mathbf{d}\| = 200$; angle between **F** and **d** = $40° - 23° = 17°$; $W = \mathbf{F} \cdot \mathbf{d} = \|\mathbf{F}\|\|\mathbf{d}\| \cos 17° = 120(200)(0.9563) = 2.30 \times 10^4$ J.

14. The force exerted by gravity = $20 \times 9.8 = 196$ N; $\beta = 60°$; $\alpha = 180° - 120° = 60°$; $\|\mathbf{t}\| = 196$; tension in wire = 196 N.

15. $200(9.8) = 1960$; angle between $\mathbf{F}_1$ and $\mathbf{F}_2 = 40° + 60° = 100°$; $\beta = 90° - 40° = 50°$; $\alpha = 90° - 60° = 30°$; $\dfrac{\sin \alpha}{\|\mathbf{F}_1\|} = \dfrac{\sin 100°}{1960}$; $\|\mathbf{F}_1\| = \dfrac{1960(0.5)}{0.9848} = 995$; $\dfrac{\sin \beta}{\|\mathbf{F}_2\|} = \dfrac{\sin 100°}{1960} = 1525$; 995 N and 1525 N

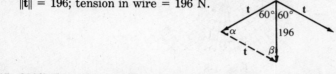

C   **16.** $9.8(100) = 980$; $\alpha = \theta$; $\theta + \phi = 90° - 15° = 75°$; $\beta = 180° - (\phi + \alpha) = 180° - (\phi + \theta) = 105°$; $\|\mathbf{t}\|^2 = 980^2 + 400^2 - 2(980)(400) \cos 105° = 1{,}323{,}314$; $\|\mathbf{t}\| = 1150$; tension = 1.15×10^3 N; $\dfrac{\sin \alpha}{400} = \dfrac{\sin 105°}{1150}$; $\sin \alpha = \dfrac{400(0.9659)}{1150} = 0.3360$; $\alpha = 19.6°$; $\theta = \alpha = 19.6°$

17. Note: Figure not drawn to scale; $\phi = 90° - (15° + 70°) = 5°$; $\alpha = 70°$; $\dfrac{\sin 70°}{\|\mathbf{t}\|} = \dfrac{\sin 5°}{980}$; $\|\mathbf{t}\| = \dfrac{980(0.9397)}{0.0872} = 10{,}561$; tension = 1.06×10^4 N; $\dfrac{1.06 \times 10^4}{4.5} \approx 2400$ lb

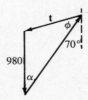

Pages 640-641 · WRITTEN EXERCISES

A   1. $x = 3 \cos 60° = 3\left(\dfrac{1}{2}\right) = \dfrac{3}{2}$; $y = 3 \sin 60° = 3\left(\dfrac{\sqrt{3}}{2}\right) = \dfrac{3\sqrt{3}}{2}$; $\left(\dfrac{3}{2}, \dfrac{3\sqrt{3}}{2}\right)$

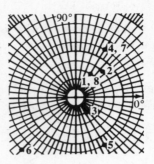

Exs. 1-8

2. $x = 4 \cos 45° = 4\left(\dfrac{\sqrt{2}}{2}\right) = 2\sqrt{2}$; $y = 4 \sin 45° = 4\left(\dfrac{\sqrt{2}}{2}\right) = 2\sqrt{2}$; $(2\sqrt{2}, 2\sqrt{2})$

3. $x = -2 \cos 135° = -2\left(-\dfrac{\sqrt{2}}{2}\right) = \sqrt{2}$; $y = -2 \sin 135° = -2\left(\dfrac{\sqrt{2}}{2}\right) = -\sqrt{2}$; $(\sqrt{2}, -\sqrt{2})$

4. $x = -6 \cos 240° = -6\left(-\dfrac{1}{2}\right) = 3$; $y = -6 \sin 240° = -6\left(-\dfrac{\sqrt{3}}{2}\right) = 3\sqrt{3}$; $(3, 3\sqrt{3}$

5. $x = 6 \cos(-60°) = 6\left(\dfrac{1}{2}\right) = 3$; $y = 6 \sin(-60°) = 6\left(-\dfrac{\sqrt{3}}{2}\right) = -3\sqrt{3}$; $(3, -3\sqrt{3})$

6. $x = 8 \cos(-135°) = 8\left(-\dfrac{\sqrt{2}}{2}\right) = -4\sqrt{2}$; $y = 8 \sin(-135°) = 8\left(-\dfrac{\sqrt{2}}{2}\right) = -4\sqrt{2}$; $(-4\sqrt{2}, -4\sqrt{2})$

7. $x = -6 \cos(-120°) = -6\left(-\dfrac{1}{2}\right) = 3$; $y = -6 \sin(-120°) = -6\left(-\dfrac{\sqrt{3}}{2}\right) = 3\sqrt{3}$; $(3, 3\sqrt{3})$

8. $x = -3 \cos(-120°) = -3\left(-\dfrac{1}{2}\right) = \dfrac{3}{2}$; $y = -3 \sin(-120°) = -3\left(-\dfrac{\sqrt{3}}{2}\right) = \dfrac{3\sqrt{3}}{2} = \left(\dfrac{3}{2}, \dfrac{3\sqrt{3}}{2}\right)$

9-16. Answers may vary.

9. Let $r = \sqrt{(-3)^2 + 0^2} = 3$; $\cos \theta = \dfrac{-3}{3} = -1$ and $\sin \theta = \dfrac{0}{3} = 0$; let $\theta = 180°$; $(3, 180°$

10. Let $r = \sqrt{0^2 + 2^2} = 2$; $\cos \theta = \dfrac{0}{2} = 0$ and $\sin \theta = \dfrac{2}{2} = 1$; let $\theta = 90°$; $(2, 90°)$

11. Let $r = \sqrt{(-2)^2 + (-2)^2} = \sqrt{8} = 2\sqrt{2}$; $\cos \theta = \dfrac{-2}{2\sqrt{2}} = -\dfrac{\sqrt{2}}{2}$ and $\sin \theta = -\dfrac{\sqrt{2}}{2}$; le $\theta = 225°$; $(2\sqrt{2}, 225°)$

12. Let $r = \sqrt{(\sqrt{3})^2 + (-1)^2} = 2$; $\cos \theta = \dfrac{\sqrt{3}}{2}$ and $\sin \theta = -\dfrac{1}{2}$; let $\theta = -30°$; $(2, -30°$

13. Let $r = \sqrt{(-1)^2 + (\sqrt{3})^2} = 2$; $\cos \theta = -\dfrac{1}{2}$ and $\sin \theta = \dfrac{\sqrt{3}}{2}$; let $\theta = 120°$; $(2, 120°)$

14. Let $r = -\sqrt{(-\sqrt{2})^2 + (-\sqrt{2})^2} = -2$; $\cos \theta = \dfrac{-\sqrt{2}}{-2} = \dfrac{\sqrt{2}}{2}$ and $\sin \theta = \dfrac{\sqrt{2}}{2}$; let $\theta = 45°$; $(-2, 45°)$

15. Let $r = -\sqrt{(-3)^2 + (-\sqrt{3})^2} = -\sqrt{12} = -2\sqrt{3}$; $\cos \theta = \dfrac{-3}{-2\sqrt{3}} = \dfrac{\sqrt{3}}{2}$ and $\sin \theta = \dfrac{-\sqrt{3}}{-2\sqrt{3}} = \dfrac{1}{2}$; let $\theta = 30°$, $(-2\sqrt{3}, 30°)$

16. Let $r = \sqrt{(-\sqrt{2})^2 + (\sqrt{6})^2} = \sqrt{8} = 2\sqrt{2}$; $\cos \theta = \dfrac{-\sqrt{2}}{2\sqrt{2}} = -\dfrac{1}{2}$ and $\sin \theta = \dfrac{\sqrt{6}}{2\sqrt{2}} = \dfrac{\sqrt{3}}{2}$; let $\theta = 120°$; $(2\sqrt{2}, 120°)$

17. $x = 2$; $r \cos \theta = 2$ **18.** $y = -1$; $r \sin \theta = -1$

19. $y = x$; $r \sin \theta = r \cos \theta$; $\sin \theta = \cos \theta$; $\sin \theta - \cos \theta = 0$

20. $x^2 + y^2 = 4$; $r^2 = 4$ **21.** $x^2 + y^2 = 4y$; $r^2 = 4r \sin \theta$; $r = 4 \sin \theta$

22. $x^2 + y^2 + 6x = 0$; $r^2 + 6r \cos \theta = 0$; $r + 6 \cos \theta = 0$; $r = -6 \cos \theta$

23. $r = 3$; $\pm\sqrt{x^2 + y^2} = 3$; $x^2 + y^2 = 9$

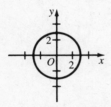

Ex. 23

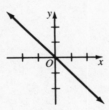

Ex. 24

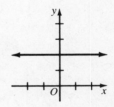

Ex. 25

24. $\theta = 135°$; $\dfrac{x}{y} = \dfrac{r \cos \theta}{r \sin \theta} = \dfrac{-\dfrac{\sqrt{2}}{2}}{\dfrac{\sqrt{2}}{2}} = -1$; $y = -x$ **25.** $r \sin \theta = 2$; $y = 2$

26. $r \cos \theta = -1$; $x = -1$

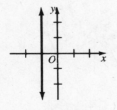

Ex. 26

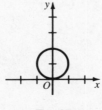

Ex. 27

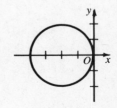

Ex. 28

B   **27.** $r = 2 \sin \theta$; $r^2 = 2r \sin \theta$; $x^2 + y^2 = 2y$; $x^2 + y^2 - 2y = 0$; $x^2 + y^2 - 2y + 1 = 1$; $x^2 + (y - 1)^2 = 1$

28. $r + 4 \cos \theta = 0$; $r^2 + 4r \cos \theta = 0$; $x^2 + y^2 + 4x = 0$; $x^2 + 4x + 4 + y^2 = 4$; $(x + 2)^2 + y^2 = 4$

29. $r(1 - \cos\theta) = 2$; $r - r\cos\theta = 2$; $r = r\cos\theta + 2$; $r^2 = (r\cos\theta)^2 + 4r\cos\theta + 4$; $x^2 + y^2 = x^2 + 4x + 4$; $y^2 = 4x + 4$

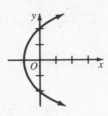

Ex. 29

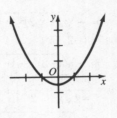

Ex. 30

30. $r(1 - \sin\theta) = 1$; $r - r\sin\theta = 1$; $r = r\sin\theta + 1$; $r^2 = (r\sin\theta)^2 + 2r\sin\theta + 1$; $x^2 + y^2 = y^2 + 2y + 1$; $x^2 = 2y + 1$

31.

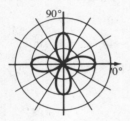

32.

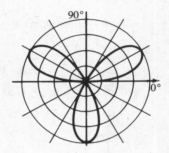

33.

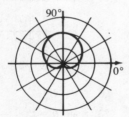

34.

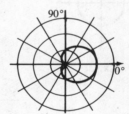

C   35.

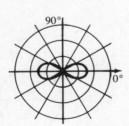

36.

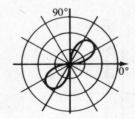

Page 641 · EXTRA

1.

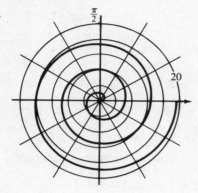

2.

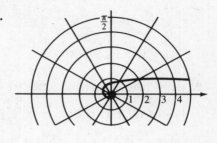

3.

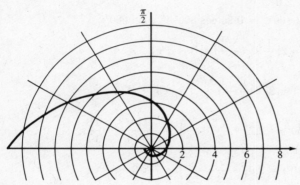

Pages 645-646 · WRITTEN EXERCISES

A 1.

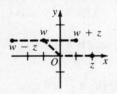

2.

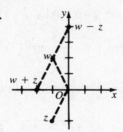

3.

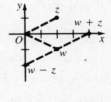

4.

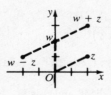

5.

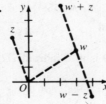

6.

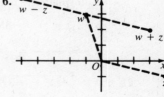

7. $wz = 2 \cdot 3[\cos(60° + 20°) + i \sin(60° + 20°)] = 6(\cos 80° + i \sin 80°);$

$\dfrac{w}{z} = \dfrac{2}{3}[\cos(60° - 20°) + i \sin(60° - 20°)] = \dfrac{2}{3}(\cos 40° + i \sin 40°)$

8. $wz = 3 \cdot 2[\cos(0° + 120°) + i \sin(0° + 120°)] = 6(\cos 120° + i \sin 120°);$

$\dfrac{w}{z} = \dfrac{3}{2}[\cos(0° - 120°) + i \sin(0° - 120°) = \dfrac{3}{2}[\cos(-120°) + i \sin(-120°)] =$

$\dfrac{3}{2}(\cos 240° + i \sin 240°)$

9. $wz = 2.2(0.5)[\cos(150° + 220°) + i \sin(150° + 220°)] = 1.1(\cos 370° + i \sin 370°) =$

$1.1(\cos 10° + i \sin 10°); \dfrac{w}{z} = \dfrac{2.2}{0.5}[\cos(150° - 220°) + i \sin(150° - 220°)] =$

$4.4[\cos(-70°) + i \sin(-70°)] = 4.4(\cos 290° + i \sin 290°)$

10. $wz = 0.5(2.0)[\cos(150° + 210°) + i \sin(150° + 210°)] = \cos 360° + i \sin 360° =$

$\cos 0° + i \sin 0°; \dfrac{w}{z} = \dfrac{0.5}{2.0}[\cos(150° - 210°) + i \sin(150° - 210°)] =$

$0.25[\cos(-60°) + i \sin(-60°)] = 0.25(\cos 300° + i \sin 300°)$

11. $2(\cos 60° + i \sin 60°) = 2\left(\dfrac{1}{2} + i\dfrac{\sqrt{3}}{2}\right) = 1 + i\sqrt{3}$

12. $2(\cos 120° + i \sin 120°) = 2\left(-\dfrac{1}{2} + i\dfrac{\sqrt{3}}{2}\right) = -1 + i\sqrt{3}$

13. $2.2(\cos 150° + i \sin 150°) = 2.2\left(-\dfrac{\sqrt{3}}{2} + \dfrac{i}{2}\right) = -\dfrac{11\sqrt{3}}{10} + \dfrac{11}{10}i$

14. $2.0(\cos 210° + i \sin 210°) = 2.0\left(-\dfrac{\sqrt{3}}{2} - \dfrac{i}{2}\right) = -\sqrt{3} - i$

15. $3(\cos 20° + i \sin 20°) = 3[0.9397 + i(0.3420)] = 2.819 + 1.026i$

16. $0.5(\cos 220° + i \sin 220°) = 0.5[-0.7660 + i(-0.6428)] = -0.3830 - 0.3214i$

17. $r = \sqrt{(-\sqrt{3})^2 + 1^2} = 2; \cos \theta = \dfrac{-\sqrt{3}}{2}$ and θ is in Quadrant II; $\theta = 150°$;
$2(\cos 150° + i \sin 150°)$

18. $r = \sqrt{1^2 + (-\sqrt{3})^2} = 2; \cos \theta = \dfrac{1}{2}$ and θ is in Quadrant IV; $\theta = 300°$;
$2(\cos 300° + i \sin 300°)$

19. $2\sqrt{2}(1 - i) = 2\sqrt{2} - 2\sqrt{2}i; r = \sqrt{(-2\sqrt{2})^2 + (-2\sqrt{2})^2} = 4; \cos \theta = \dfrac{2\sqrt{2}}{4} = \dfrac{\sqrt{2}}{2}$ and
θ is in Quadrant IV; $\theta = 315°; 4(\cos 315° + i \sin 315°)$

20. $-3\sqrt{2}(1 + i) = -3\sqrt{2} - 3\sqrt{2}i; r = \sqrt{(-3\sqrt{2})^2 + (-3\sqrt{2})^2} = 6;$
$\cos \theta = \dfrac{-3\sqrt{2}}{6} = -\dfrac{\sqrt{2}}{2}$ and θ is in Quadrant III; $\theta = 225°; 6(\cos 225° + i \sin 225°)$

21. $r = \sqrt{(-2)^2 + (-3)^2} = \sqrt{13} = 3.606; \cos \theta = \dfrac{-2}{3.606} = -0.5546$ and θ is in
Quadrant III; $\theta = 236.3°; 3.61(\cos 236.3° + i \sin 236.3°)$

22. $r = \sqrt{3^2 + (-1)^2} = \sqrt{10} = 3.162; \cos \theta = \dfrac{3}{3.162} = 0.9488$ and θ is in Quadrant IV
$\theta = 341.6°; 3.16(\cos 341.6° + i \sin 341.6°)$

23. $r = \sqrt{12^2 + 5^2} = 13$; $\cos\theta = \dfrac{12}{13} = 0.9231$ and θ is in Quadrant I; $\theta = 22.6°$;
$13(\cos 22.6° + i\sin 22.6°)$

24. $r = \sqrt{(-3)^2 + (-4)^2} = 5$; $\cos\theta = -\dfrac{3}{5} = -0.6$ and θ is in Quadrant III; $\theta = 233.1°$;
$5(\cos 233.1° + i\sin 233.1°)$

25. **a.** $wz = 2 \cdot 4[\cos(150° + 120°) + i\sin(150° + 120°)] = 8(\cos 270° + i\sin 270°)$

    b. $8(\cos 270° + i\sin 270°) = 8(0 + i(-1)) = -8i$

    c. $w = 2(\cos 150° + i\sin 150°) = 2\left(-\dfrac{\sqrt{3}}{2} + \dfrac{i}{2}\right) = -\sqrt{3} + i$;

       $z = 4(\cos 120° + i\sin 120°) = 4\left(-\dfrac{1}{2} + \dfrac{i\sqrt{3}}{2}\right) = -2 + 2i\sqrt{3}$

    d. $wz = (-\sqrt{3} + i)(-2 + 2i\sqrt{3}) = 2\sqrt{3} - 2i - 6i - 2\sqrt{3} = -8i$

26. **a.** $wz = 4 \cdot 2[\cos(30° + 60°) + i\sin(30° + 60°)] = 8(\cos 90° + i\sin 90°)$

    b. $8(\cos 90° + i\sin 90°) = 8(0 + i) = 8i$

    c. $w = 4(\cos 30° + i\sin 30°) = 4\left(\dfrac{\sqrt{3}}{2} + \dfrac{i}{2}\right) = 2\sqrt{3} + 2i$;

       $z = 2(\cos 60° + i\sin 60°) = 2\left(\dfrac{1}{2} + \dfrac{i\sqrt{3}}{2}\right) = 1 + i\sqrt{3}$

    d. $wz = (2\sqrt{3} + 2i)(1 + i\sqrt{3}) = 2\sqrt{3} + 2i + 6i - 2\sqrt{3} = 8i$

27. **a.** $wz = 6 \cdot 2[\cos(60° + 150°) + i\sin(60° + 150°)] = 12(\cos 210° + i\sin 210°)$

    b. $12(\cos 210° + i\sin 210°) = 12\left(-\dfrac{\sqrt{3}}{2} + i\left(-\dfrac{1}{2}\right)\right) = -6\sqrt{3} - 6i$

    c. $w = 6(\cos 60° + i\sin 60°) = 6\left(\dfrac{1}{2} + \dfrac{i\sqrt{3}}{2}\right) = 3 + 3i\sqrt{3}$;

       $z = 2(\cos 150° + i\sin 150°) = 2\left(-\dfrac{\sqrt{3}}{2} + \dfrac{i}{2}\right) = -\sqrt{3} + i$

    d. $wz = (3 + 3i\sqrt{3})(-\sqrt{3} + i) = -3\sqrt{3} - 9i + 3i - 3\sqrt{3} = -6\sqrt{3} - 6i$

28. **a.** $wz = 4 \cdot 2[\cos(120° + 30°) + i\sin(120° + 30°)] = 8(\cos 150° + i\sin 150°)$

    b. $8(\cos 150° + i\sin 150°) = 8\left(-\dfrac{\sqrt{3}}{2} + \dfrac{i}{2}\right) = -4\sqrt{3} + 4i$

    c. $w = 4(\cos 120° + i\sin 120°) = 4\left(-\dfrac{1}{2} + \dfrac{i\sqrt{3}}{2}\right) = -2 + 2i\sqrt{3}$;

       $z = 2(\cos 30° + i\sin 30°) = 2\left(\dfrac{\sqrt{3}}{2} + \dfrac{i}{2}\right) = \sqrt{3} + i$

    d. $wz = (-2 + 2i\sqrt{3})(\sqrt{3} + i) = -2\sqrt{3} + 6i - 2i - 2\sqrt{3} = -4\sqrt{3} + 4i$

29. Let $w = r_1(\cos\theta + i\sin\theta)$ and $z = r_2(\cos\varphi + i\sin\varphi)$;
$|wz| = |r_1 r_2[\cos(\theta + \varphi) + i\sin(\theta + \varphi)]| = r_1 r_2 = |w||z|$

30. If $w \neq z$ and $w \neq -z$, $|w + z|$ is the length of the diagonal of a parallelogram with sides of length $|w|$ and $|z|$; the sum of the lengths of any two sides of a triangle is greater than the length of the third side; that is, the shortest distance between two points is the length of the segment between them. If $w = z$, then $|w + z| = 2|w| = |w| + |z|$; if $w = -z$, $|w + z| = 0 < |w| + |z|$; in any case, $|w + z| \leq |w| + |z|$.

31. Let z be a complex number, $z = x + yi$; $z\bar{z} = (x + yi)(x - yi) = x^2 + xyi - xyi - y^2i^2 = x^2 + y^2 = (\sqrt{x^2 + y^2})^2 = |z|^2$

32. Let z be a complex number; $\dfrac{1}{z} = \dfrac{1 \cdot \bar{z}}{z \cdot \bar{z}} = \dfrac{\bar{z}}{|z|^2}$

C   **33.** Let z be a complex number, $z = b(\cos \beta + i \sin \beta) = b \cos \beta + bi \sin \beta$;

$$\frac{1}{z} = \frac{\bar{z}}{|z|^2} = \frac{b \cos \beta - bi \sin \beta}{b^2} = \frac{1}{b}(\cos \beta - i \sin \beta)$$

34. Let $w = a(\cos \alpha + i \sin \alpha)$ and $z = b(\cos \beta + i \sin \beta)$;

$$\frac{w}{z} = w \cdot \frac{1}{z} = a(\cos \alpha + i \sin \alpha)\left[\frac{1}{b}(\cos \beta - i \sin \beta)\right] =$$

$$\frac{a}{b}[\cos \alpha \cos \beta + i \sin \alpha \cos \beta - i \sin \beta \cos \alpha + \sin \alpha \sin \beta] =$$

$$\frac{a}{b}[\cos \alpha \cos \beta + \sin \alpha \sin \beta + i(\sin \alpha \cos \beta - \sin \beta \cos \alpha)] =$$

$$\frac{a}{b}[\cos(\alpha - \beta) + i \sin(\alpha - \beta)]$$

35. Let $w = r_1(\cos \theta + i \sin \theta)$ and $z = r_2(\cos \varphi + i \sin \varphi)$;
$wz = r_1r_2[\cos(\theta + \varphi) + i \sin(\theta + \varphi)]$; the angle between $\overrightarrow{Oz}$ and
$\overrightarrow{Owz} = (\theta + \varphi) - \varphi = \theta$; also, $\dfrac{|w|}{|wz|} = \dfrac{|w|}{|w||z|}$ (Ex. 29) $= \dfrac{1}{|z|}$; by
the Side-Angle-Side Similarity Theorem, the two triangles are similar.

Page 649 · WRITTEN EXERCISES

A   **1.** $1 + i = \sqrt{2}(\cos 45° + i \sin 45°)$; $(1 + i)^{10} = (\sqrt{2})^{10}(\cos 450° + i \sin 450°) = 32(\cos 90° + i \sin 90°) = 32(0 + i) = 32i$

     2. $-1 - i = \sqrt{2}(\cos 225° + i \sin 225°)$; $(-1 - i)^8 = (\sqrt{2})^8(\cos 1800° + i \sin 1800°) = 16(\cos 0° + i \sin 0°) = 16(1 + i \cdot 0) = 16$

     3. $-1 + i = \sqrt{2}(\cos 135° + i \sin 135°)$; $(-1 + i)^9 = (\sqrt{2})^9(\cos 1215° + i \sin 1215°) = 16\sqrt{2}(\cos 135° + i \sin 135°) = 16\sqrt{2}\left(-\dfrac{\sqrt{2}}{2} + \dfrac{i\sqrt{2}}{2}\right) = -16 + 16i$

     4. $1 - i = \sqrt{2}(\cos 315° + i \sin 315°)$; $(1 - i)^7 = (\sqrt{2})^7(\cos 2205° + i \sin 2205°) = 8\sqrt{2}(\cos 45° + i \sin 45°) = 8\sqrt{2}\left(\dfrac{\sqrt{2}}{2} + \dfrac{i\sqrt{2}}{2}\right) = 8 + 8i$

5. $\sqrt{3} + i = 2(\cos 30° + i \sin 30°)$; $(\sqrt{3} + i)^8 = 2^8(\cos 240° + i \sin 240°) =$

$256\left(-\dfrac{1}{2} - \dfrac{i\sqrt{3}}{2}\right) = 128 - 128i\sqrt{3}$

6. $1 + i\sqrt{3} = 2(\cos 60° + i \sin 60°)$; $(1 + i\sqrt{3})^{10} = 2^{10}(\cos 600° + i \sin 600°) =$

$1024(\cos 240° + i \sin 240°) = 1024\left(-\dfrac{1}{2} - \dfrac{i\sqrt{3}}{2}\right) = -512 - 512i\sqrt{3}$

7. $-1 + i\sqrt{3} = 2(\cos 120° + i \sin 120°)$; $(-1 + i\sqrt{3})^7 = 2^7(\cos 840° + i \sin 840°) =$

$128(\cos 120° + i \sin 120°) = 128\left(-\dfrac{1}{2} + \dfrac{i\sqrt{3}}{2}\right) = -64 + 64i\sqrt{3}$

8. $-\sqrt{3} + i = 2(\cos 150° + i \sin 150°)$; $(-\sqrt{3} + i)^9 = 2^9(\cos 1350° + i \sin 1350°) =$

$512(\cos 270° + i \sin 270°) = 512(0 - i) = -512i$

9. $\cos \dfrac{k \cdot 360°}{3} + i \sin \dfrac{k \cdot 360°}{3} = \cos(k \cdot 120°) + i \sin(k \cdot 120°)$ for $k = 0, 1, 2$; roots are

$\cos 0° + i \sin 0° = 1 + 0 = 1$; $\cos 120° + i \sin 120° = -\dfrac{1}{2} + \dfrac{i\sqrt{3}}{2}$;

$\cos 240° + i \sin 240° = -\dfrac{1}{2} - \dfrac{i\sqrt{3}}{2}$

10. $\cos \dfrac{k \cdot 360°}{4} + i \sin \dfrac{k \cdot 360°}{4} = \cos(k \cdot 90°) + i \sin(k \cdot 90°)$, $k = 0, 1, 2, 3$; roots are

$\cos 0° + i \sin 0° = 1 + 0 = 1$; $\cos 90° + i \sin 90° = 0 + i = i$;

$\cos 180° + i \sin 180° = -1 + 0 = -1$; $\cos 270° + i \sin 270° = 0 - i = -i$

11. $\cos \dfrac{k \cdot 360°}{6} + i \sin \dfrac{k \cdot 360°}{6} = \cos(k \cdot 60°) + i \sin(k \cdot 60°)$; $k = 0, 1, 2, 3, 4, 5$; roots are

$\cos 0° + i \sin 0° = 1 + 0 = 1$; $\cos 60° + i \sin 60° = \dfrac{1}{2} + \dfrac{i\sqrt{3}}{2}$;

$\cos 120° + i \sin 120° = -\dfrac{1}{2} + \dfrac{i\sqrt{3}}{2}$; $\cos 180° + i \sin 180° = -1 + 0 = -1$;

$\cos 240° + i \sin 240° = -\dfrac{1}{2} - \dfrac{i\sqrt{3}}{2}$; $\cos 300° + i \sin 300° = \dfrac{1}{2} - \dfrac{i\sqrt{3}}{2}$

12. $\cos \dfrac{k \cdot 360°}{8} + i \sin \dfrac{k \cdot 360°}{8} = \cos(k \cdot 45°) + i \sin(k \cdot 45°)$, $k = 0, 1, 2, 3, 4, 5, 6, 7$;

roots are $\cos 0° + i \sin 0° = 1 + 0 = 1$; $\cos 45° + i \sin 45° = \dfrac{\sqrt{2}}{2} + \dfrac{i\sqrt{2}}{2}$;

$\cos 90° + i \sin 90° = 0 + i = i$; $\cos 135° + i \sin 135° = -\dfrac{\sqrt{2}}{2} + \dfrac{i\sqrt{2}}{2}$;

$\cos 180° + i \sin 180° = -1 + 0 = -1$; $\cos 225° + i \sin 225° = -\dfrac{\sqrt{2}}{2} - \dfrac{i\sqrt{2}}{2}$;

$\cos 270° + i \sin 270° = 0 - i = -i$; $\cos 315° + i \sin 315° = \dfrac{\sqrt{2}}{2} - \dfrac{i\sqrt{2}}{2}$

13. $\cos \dfrac{k \cdot 360°}{9} + i \sin \dfrac{k \cdot 360°}{9} = \cos(k \cdot 40°) + i \sin(k \cdot 40°)$, $k = 0, 1, 2, 3, 4, 5, 6, 7, 8$;

roots are $\cos 0° + i \sin 0°$; $\cos 40° + i \sin 40°$; $\cos 80° + i \sin 80°$;
$\cos 120° + i \sin 120°$; $\cos 160° + i \sin 160°$; $\cos 200° + i \sin 200°$;
$\cos 240° + i \sin 240°$; $\cos 280° + i \sin 280°$; $\cos 320° + i \sin 320°$

14. $\cos \dfrac{k \cdot 360°}{10} + i \sin \dfrac{k \cdot 360°}{10} = \cos k \cdot 36° + i \sin k \cdot 36°$, $\quad k = 0, 1, 2, 3, 4, 5, 6, 7, 8, 9$

roots are $\cos 0° + i \sin 0°$; $\cos 36° + i \sin 36°$; $\cos 72° + i \sin 72°$;
$\cos 108° + i \sin 108°$; $\cos 144° + i \sin 144°$; $\cos 180° + i \sin 180°$; $\cos 216° + i \sin 216°$
$\cos 252° + i \sin 252°$; $\cos 288° + i \sin 288°$; $\cos 324° + i \sin 324°$

15. $-1 = \cos 180° + i \sin 180°$; $\quad r^3(\cos 3\theta + i \sin 3\theta) = 1(\cos 180° + i \sin 180°)$; $\quad r = 1$;
$3\theta = 180° + k \cdot 360°$; $\theta = 60° + k \cdot 120°$; $\theta = 60°, 180°, 300°$; $r_1 = \cos 60° + i \sin 60° =$
$\dfrac{1}{2} + \dfrac{i\sqrt{3}}{2}$; $\quad r_2 = \cos 180° + i \sin 180° = -1 + 0 = -1$; $\quad r_3 = \cos 300° + i \sin 300° =$
$\dfrac{1}{2} - \dfrac{i\sqrt{3}}{2}$

16. $i = \cos 90° + i \sin 90°$; $\quad r^3(\cos 3\theta + i \sin 3\theta) = 1(\cos 90° + i \sin 90°)$; $\quad r = 1$; $\quad 3\theta =$
$90° + k \cdot 360°$; $\quad \theta = 30° + k \cdot 120°$; $\quad \theta = 30°$, $150°$, $270°$; $\quad r_1 = \cos 30° + i \sin 30° =$
$\dfrac{\sqrt{3}}{2} + \dfrac{i}{2}$; $r_2 = \cos 150° + i \sin 150° = -\dfrac{\sqrt{3}}{2} + \dfrac{i}{2}$;
$r_3 = \cos 270° + i \sin 270° = 0 - i = -i$

B **17.** $-8 + 8i\sqrt{3} = 16(\cos 120° + i \sin 120°)$; $r^4(\cos 4\theta + i \sin 4\theta) =$
$16(\cos 120° + i \sin 120°)$; $\quad r^4 = 16$; $\quad r = 2$; $\quad 4\theta = 120° + k \cdot 360°$; $\quad \theta = 30° + k \cdot 90°$
$\theta = 30°, 120°, 210°, 300°$; $r_1 = 2(\cos 30° + i \sin 30°) = 2\left(\dfrac{\sqrt{3}}{2} + \dfrac{i}{2}\right) = \sqrt{3} + i$;
$r_2 = 2(\cos 120° + i \sin 120°) = 2\left(-\dfrac{1}{2} + \dfrac{i\sqrt{3}}{2}\right) = -1 + i\sqrt{3}$;
$r_3 = 2(\cos 210° + i \sin 210°) = 2\left(-\dfrac{\sqrt{3}}{2} - \dfrac{i}{2}\right) = -\sqrt{3} - i$;
$r_4 = 2(\cos 300° + i \sin 300°) = 2\left(\dfrac{1}{2} - \dfrac{i\sqrt{3}}{2}\right) = 1 - i\sqrt{3}$

18. $-8 - 8i\sqrt{3} = 16(\cos 240° + i \sin 240°)$; $r^4(\cos 4\theta + i \sin 4\theta) =$
$16(\cos 240° + i \sin 240°)$; $r^4 = 16$; $r = 2$; $4\theta = 240° + k \cdot 360°$; $\theta = 60° + k \cdot 90°$;
$\theta = 60°, 150°, 240°, 330°$; $r_1 = 2(\cos 60° + i \sin 60°) = 2\left(\dfrac{1}{2} + \dfrac{i\sqrt{3}}{2}\right) = 1 + i\sqrt{3}$;
$r_2 = 2(\cos 150° + i \sin 150°) = 2\left(-\dfrac{\sqrt{3}}{2} - \dfrac{i}{2}\right) = -\sqrt{3} + i$;
$r_3 = 2(\cos 240° + i \sin 240°) = 2\left(-\dfrac{1}{2} - \dfrac{i\sqrt{3}}{2}\right) = -1 - i\sqrt{3}$;
$r_4 = 2(\cos 330° + i \sin 330°) = 2\left(\dfrac{\sqrt{3}}{2} - \dfrac{i}{2}\right) = \sqrt{3} - i$

19. $4\sqrt{3} - 4i = 8(\cos 330° + i \sin 330°)$; $r^3(\cos 3\theta + i \sin 3\theta) = 8(\cos 330° + i \sin 330°)$;
    $r^3 = 8$; $r = 2$; $3\theta = 330° + k \cdot 360°$; $\theta = 110° + k \cdot 120°$; $\theta = 110°, 230°, 350°$; $r_1 = 2(\cos 110° + i \sin 110°)$; $r_2 = 2(\cos 230° + i \sin 230°)$; $r_3 = 2(\cos 350° + i \sin 350°)$

20. $-4 + 4i\sqrt{3} = 8(\cos 120° + i \sin 120°)$; $r^3 = 8$; $r = 2$; $3\theta = 120° + k \cdot 360°$;
    $\theta = 40° + k \cdot 120$; $\theta = 40°, 160°, 280°$; $r_1 = 2(\cos 40° + i \sin 40°)$;
    $r_2 = 2(\cos 160° + i \sin 160°)$; $r_3 = 2(\cos 280° + i \sin 280°)$

21. **a.** $\omega^6 = \cos(6 \cdot 60°) + i \sin(6 \cdot 60°) = \cos 360° + i \sin 360° = 1 + 0 = 1$
    b. From Ex. 11, the 6th roots of unity are $r_1 = \cos 0° + i \sin 0°$, $r_2 = \omega$,
    $r_3 = \cos 120° + i \sin 120°$, $r_4 = \cos 180° + i \sin 180°$, $r_5 = \cos 240° + i \sin 240°$, and
    $r_6 = \cos 300° + i \sin 300°$;
    $\omega^2 = \cos 2 \cdot 60° + i \sin 2 \cdot 60° = \cos 120° + i \sin 120° = r_3$;
    $\omega^3 = \cos 3 \cdot 60° + i \sin 3 \cdot 60° = \cos 180° + i \sin 180° = r_4$;
    $\omega^4 = \cos 4 \cdot 60° + i \sin 4 \cdot 60° = \cos 240° + i \sin 240° = r_5$;
    $\omega^5 = \cos 5 \cdot 60° + i \sin 5 \cdot 60° = \cos 300° + i \sin 300° = r_6$;
    $\omega^6 = \cos 6 \cdot 60° + i \sin 6 \cdot 60° = \cos 360° + i \sin 360° = \cos 0° + i \sin 0° = r_1$

22. **a.** $(\omega^5)^1 = \omega^5 = r_6$; $(\omega^5)^2 = \omega^{10} = \omega^6 \cdot \omega^4 = (\cos 0° + i \sin 0°)\omega^4 = (1 + 0)\omega^4 = \omega^4 = r_5$; $(\omega^5)^3 = \omega^{15} = \omega^6 \cdot \omega^6 \cdot \omega^3 = 1 \cdot 1 \cdot \omega^3 = \omega^3 = r_4$; $(\omega^5)^4 = \omega^{20} = (\omega^6)^3 \cdot \omega^2 = 1^3 \cdot \omega^2 = \omega^2 = r_3$; $(\omega^5)^5 = \omega^{25} = (\omega^6)^4\omega = 1^4 \cdot \omega = \omega = r_2$; $(\omega^5)^6 = \omega^{30} = (\omega^6)^5 = 1^5 = 1 = \omega^6 = r_1$

    b. $(\omega^2)^1 = \omega^2 = r_3$; $(\omega^2)^2 = \omega^4 = r_5$; $(\omega^2)^3 = \omega^6 = 1 = r_1$; $(\omega^2)^4 = \omega^8 = \omega^6 \cdot \omega^2 = 1 \cdot \omega^2 = \omega^2 = r_3$; $(\omega^2)^5 = \omega^{10} = \omega^6 \cdot \omega^4 = 1 \cdot \omega^4 = \omega^4 = r_5$; $(\omega^2)^6 = (\omega^6)^2 = 1^2 = 1 = r_1$; none of the powers of ω^2 are equal to r_2, r_4, or r_6; ω_2 is not a primitive 6th root of unity.

Page 650 · COMPUTER EXERCISES

1. 10 PRINT "ENTER X AND Y"
    20 INPUT X, Y
    30 LET A = ATN(Y/X) * 180/3.14159265
    40 IF X < 0 THEN LET A = A + 180
    50 IF A < 0 THEN LET A = A + 360
    60 LET R = SQR(X ↑ 2 + Y ↑ 2)
    70 PRINT "R = "; R, "ANGLE = "; A
    80 GOTO 10

2. **a.** R = 7.61577312   ANGLE = 66.8014096
    b. R = 14.2126704   ANGLE = 129.289407
    c. R = 5.38516481   ANGLE = 338.198591
    d. R = 18.7882942   ANGLE = 244.798877

3.
```
10   PRINT "ENTER X, Y, AND N"
20   INPUT X, Y, N
30   LET A = ATN(Y/X)
40   IF X < 0 THEN LET A = A + 3.14159265
50   LET A = A * N
60   LET R = SQR(X ↑ 2 + Y ↑ 2) ↑ N
70   LET XN = R * COS(A)
80   LET YN = R * SIN(A)
90   PRINT "("; X; " + "; Y; "I) ↑ "; N; " = "; XN; " + "; YN; "I"
100  END
```

4. a. 16   **b.** -64 **c.** $32i$

    d. $38 + 41i$ **e.** $-352 + 936i$ **f.** $122 + 597i$

Page 654 · WRITTEN EXERCISES

A   **1.** $\dfrac{\pi}{4}$ **2.** $\dfrac{\pi}{6}$ **3.** $-\dfrac{\pi}{3}$ **4.** $\mathrm{Cos}^{-1}\dfrac{\sqrt{3}}{2} = \dfrac{\pi}{6}$ **5.** $\mathrm{Sin}^{-1}\dfrac{\sqrt{2}}{2} = \dfrac{\pi}{4}$

6. $\mathrm{Sin}^{-1}(-1) = -\dfrac{\pi}{2}$ **7.** $\mathrm{Cos}^{-1}\dfrac{1}{2} = \dfrac{\pi}{3}$ **8.** $\mathrm{Sin}^{-1}\left(-\dfrac{1}{2}\right) = -\dfrac{\pi}{6}$

9. $\mathrm{Cos}^{-1}\left(-\dfrac{1}{2}\right) = \dfrac{2\pi}{3}$ **10.** $\mathrm{Cos}\left(-\dfrac{\pi}{6}\right) = \dfrac{\sqrt{3}}{2}$ **11.** $\mathrm{Sin}\,\dfrac{\pi}{6} = \dfrac{1}{2}$

12. Let $v = \mathrm{Cos}^{-1}\left(-\dfrac{4}{5}\right)$; $0 \le v \le \pi$ so $\sin v > 0$;

$\sin v = \sqrt{1 - \cos^2 v} = \sqrt{1 + \left(-\dfrac{4}{5}\right)^2} = \sqrt{\dfrac{9}{25}} = \dfrac{3}{5}$; $\sin\left[\mathrm{Cos}^{-1}\left(-\dfrac{4}{5}\right)\right] = \dfrac{3}{5}$

13. Let $v = \mathrm{Sin}^{-1}\left(-\dfrac{5}{13}\right)$; $-\dfrac{\pi}{2} \le v \le \dfrac{\pi}{2}$ so $\cos v > 0$;

$\cos v = \sqrt{1 - \sin^2 v} = \sqrt{1 - \left(-\dfrac{5}{13}\right)^2} = \sqrt{\dfrac{144}{169}} = \dfrac{12}{13}$; $\cos\left[\mathrm{Sin}^{-1}\left(-\dfrac{5}{13}\right)\right] = \dfrac{12}{13}$

14. Let $v = \mathrm{Sin}^{-1}\dfrac{2}{3}$; $-\dfrac{\pi}{2} \le v \le \dfrac{\pi}{2}$ so $\cos v > 0$;

$\cos v = \sqrt{1 - \sin^2 v} = \sqrt{1 - \left(\dfrac{2}{3}\right)^2} = \sqrt{\dfrac{5}{9}} = \dfrac{\sqrt{5}}{3}$; $\cos\left[\mathrm{Sin}^{-1}\dfrac{2}{3}\right] = \dfrac{\sqrt{5}}{3}$

15. Let $v = \mathrm{Cos}^{-1}\left(-\dfrac{2}{5}\right)$; $0 \le v \le \pi$ so $\sin v > 0$;

$\sin v = \sqrt{1 - \cos^2 v} = \sqrt{1 - \left(-\dfrac{2}{5}\right)^2} = \sqrt{\dfrac{21}{25}} = \dfrac{\sqrt{21}}{5}$; $\sin\left[\mathrm{Cos}^{-1}\left(-\dfrac{2}{5}\right)\right] = \dfrac{\sqrt{21}}{5}$

B   **16.** $\cos\left(\dfrac{\pi}{6} + \dfrac{\pi}{3}\right) = \cos\dfrac{\pi}{2} = 0$ **17.** $\sin\left(\dfrac{2\pi}{3} - \dfrac{\pi}{6}\right) = \sin\dfrac{\pi}{2} = 1$

18. Let $y = \mathrm{Cos}^{-1}x$; $0 \le y \le \pi$ so $\sin y \ge 0$; $\sin y = \sqrt{1 - \cos^2 y} = \sqrt{1 - x^2}$;

$\sin(\mathrm{Cos}^{-1}x) = \sin y = \sqrt{1 - x^2}$

19. Let $y = \text{Sin}^{-1}x;\ -\dfrac{\pi}{2} \le y \le \dfrac{\pi}{2}$ so $\cos y \ge 0;$ $\cos y = \sqrt{1 - \sin^2 y} = \sqrt{1 - x^2}\,;$

$\cos(\text{Sin}^{-1}x) = \cos y = \sqrt{1 - x^2}$

20. Let $y = \text{Cos}^{-1}x;\ 0 \le y \le \pi$ so $\sin y \ge 0;$ $\sin y = \sqrt{1 - \cos^2 y} = \sqrt{1 - x^2}\,;$

$\cos(2\,\text{Cos}^{-1}x) = \cos 2y = 1 - 2\sin^2 y = 1 - 2(\sqrt{1 - x^2})^2 = 1 - 2(1 - x^2) =$

$1 - 2 + 2x^2 = 2x^2 - 1$

21. Let $y = \text{Sin}^{-1}x;\ -\dfrac{\pi}{2} \le y \le \dfrac{\pi}{2}$ so $\cos y \ge 0;$ $\cos y = \sqrt{1 - \sin^2 y} = \sqrt{1 - x^2}\,;$

$\sin(2\,\text{Sin}^{-1}x) = \sin 2y = 2 \sin y \cos y = 2x\sqrt{1 - x^2}$

22. Let $a = \text{Sin}^{-1}u$ and $b = \text{Sin}^{-1}v;\ -\dfrac{\pi}{2} \le a \le \dfrac{\pi}{2}$ and $-\dfrac{\pi}{2} \le b \le \dfrac{\pi}{2}$, so $\cos a$ and $\cos b$

are each $\ge 0;$ $\cos a = \sqrt{1 - \sin^2 a} = \sqrt{1 - u^2}\,;$ similarly, $\cos b = \sqrt{1 - v^2}\,;$

$\sin(\text{Sin}^{-1}u + \text{Sin}^{-1}v) = \sin(a + b) = \sin a \cos b + \cos a \sin b =$

$u\sqrt{1 - v^2} + v\sqrt{1 - u^2}$

23. Let $a = \text{Cos}^{-1}u$ and $b = \text{Cos}^{-1}v;\ 0 \le a \le \pi$ and $0 \le b \le \pi$, so $\sin a$ and $\sin b$ are

each $\ge 0;$ $\sin a = \sqrt{1 - \cos^2 a} = \sqrt{1 - u^2}\,;$ similarly, $\sin b = \sqrt{1 - v^2}\,;$

$\cos(\text{Cos}^{-1}u - \text{Cos}^{-1}v) = \cos(a - b) = \cos a \cos b + \sin a \sin b =$

$uv + \sqrt{1 - u^2}(\sqrt{1 - v^2});\ u^2 \le 1$ and $v^2 \le 1,$ so $uv + \sqrt{1 - u^2}(\sqrt{1 - v^2}) =$

$uv + \sqrt{(1 - u^2)(1 - v^2)} = uv + \sqrt{1 - u^2 - v^2 + u^2 v^2}$

24. Let $a = \text{Cos}^{-1}\dfrac{3}{5}$ and $b = \text{Cos}^{-1}\dfrac{4}{5};\ 0 \le a \le \dfrac{\pi}{2}$ and $0 \le b \le \dfrac{\pi}{2}$ so

$-\dfrac{\pi}{2} \le a - b \le \dfrac{\pi}{2};\ 0 \le \text{Sin}^{-1}\dfrac{7}{25} \le \dfrac{\pi}{2};$ $\sin a = \sqrt{1 - \cos^2 a} = \sqrt{1 - \left(\dfrac{3}{5}\right)^2} = \dfrac{4}{5}\,;$

similarly, $\sin b = \dfrac{3}{5};$ $\sin\left(\text{Cos}^{-1}\dfrac{3}{5} - \text{Cos}^{-1}\dfrac{4}{5}\right) = \sin(a - b) =$

$\sin a \cos b - \cos a \sin b = \dfrac{4}{5} \cdot \dfrac{4}{5} - \dfrac{3}{5} \cdot \dfrac{3}{5} = \dfrac{7}{25};$ since $\sin(a - b) > 0,$

$0 \le a - b \le \dfrac{\pi}{2};$ thus $\text{Sin}^{-1}\dfrac{7}{25} = \text{Cos}^{-1}\dfrac{3}{5} - \text{Cos}^{-1}\dfrac{4}{5}$

25. Let $a = \text{Cos}^{-1}\dfrac{5}{13}$ and $b = \text{Sin}^{-1}\dfrac{4}{5};\ 0 \le a \le \dfrac{\pi}{2}$ and $0 \le b \le \dfrac{\pi}{2}$ so

$-\dfrac{\pi}{2} \le a - b \le \dfrac{\pi}{2};$ $\sin\left(\text{Cos}^{-1}\dfrac{5}{13}\right) = \dfrac{12}{13};$ since $\dfrac{12}{13} > \dfrac{4}{5},$ $a > b$ and $a - b > 0;$

thus $0 \le a - b \le \dfrac{\pi}{2};\ 0 \le \text{Cos}^{-1}\dfrac{63}{65} \le \dfrac{\pi}{2};$ $\sin a = \sqrt{1 - \cos^2 a} = \sqrt{1 - \left(\dfrac{5}{13}\right)^2} = \dfrac{12}{13};$

similarly, $\cos b = \dfrac{3}{5};$ $\cos\left(\text{Cos}^{-1}\dfrac{5}{13} - \text{Sin}^{-1}\dfrac{4}{5}\right) = \cos(a - b) =$

$\cos a \cos b + \sin a \sin b = \dfrac{5}{13} \cdot \dfrac{3}{5} + \dfrac{12}{13} \cdot \dfrac{4}{5} = \dfrac{63}{65};$ $\text{Cos}^{-1}\dfrac{63}{65} = \text{Cos}^{-1}\dfrac{5}{13} - \text{Sin}^{-1}\dfrac{4}{5}.$

Page 658 · WRITTEN EXERCISES

A 1. $\dfrac{2\pi}{3}$ 2. $-\dfrac{\pi}{2}$ 3. $\text{Tan}^{-1}(-\sqrt{3}) = -\dfrac{\pi}{3}$

4. $\text{Cot}^{-1}(-1) = \dfrac{3\pi}{4}$ 5. $\text{Cot}^{-1}0 = \dfrac{\pi}{2}$ 6. $\text{Tan}^{-1}\left(-\dfrac{\sqrt{3}}{3}\right) = -\dfrac{\pi}{6}$

7. $\text{Tan}^{-1}(-1) = -\dfrac{\pi}{4}$ 8. $\text{Cot}^{-1}\left[\tan\left(-\dfrac{\pi}{6}\right)\right] = \text{Cot}^{-1}\left(-\dfrac{\sqrt{3}}{3}\right) = -\dfrac{\pi}{3}$

9. $\tan(\text{Cot}^{-1}2) = \tan\left(\text{Tan}^{-1}\dfrac{1}{2}\right) = \dfrac{1}{2}$ 10. $\cos(\text{Sec}^{-1}3) = \cos\left[\text{Cos}^{-1}\dfrac{1}{3}\right] = \dfrac{1}{3}$

11. Let $y = \text{Sin}^{-1}\left(-\dfrac{4}{5}\right)$; $\sin y = -\dfrac{4}{5}$ and $-\dfrac{\pi}{2} \le y \le \dfrac{\pi}{2}$; $\cos y \ge 0$ and

$\cos y = \sqrt{1 - \sin^2 y} = \sqrt{1 - \left(\dfrac{4}{5}\right)^2} = \dfrac{3}{5}$; $\cot\left[\text{Sin}^{-1}\left(-\dfrac{4}{5}\right)\right] = \cot y = \dfrac{\cos y}{\sin y} = -\dfrac{3}{4}$

12. Let $y = \text{Sin}^{-1}\dfrac{5}{13}$; $\sin y = \dfrac{5}{13}$ and $-\dfrac{\pi}{2} \le y \le \dfrac{\pi}{2}$; $\cos y \ge 0$ and

$\cos y = \sqrt{1 - \sin^2 y} = \sqrt{1 - \left(\dfrac{5}{13}\right)^2} = \dfrac{12}{13}$; $\tan\left(\text{Sin}^{-1}\dfrac{5}{13}\right) = \tan y = \dfrac{\sin y}{\cos y} = \dfrac{5}{12}$.

13. Let $y = \text{Tan}^{-1}2$; draw a first-quadrant angle with $\tan y = 2$, say the legs of the right
triangle have lengths 1 and 2; $r = \sqrt{5}$; $\cos(\text{Tan}^{-1}2) = \cos y = \dfrac{1}{\sqrt{5}} = \dfrac{\sqrt{5}}{5}$.

14. $\text{Cot}^{-1}\dfrac{1}{2} = \text{Tan}^{-1}2$; let $y = \text{Tan}^{-1}2$ and use the same triangle as in Ex. 13, above

$\sin\left(\text{Cot}^{-1}\dfrac{1}{2}\right) = \sin(\text{Tan}^{-1}2) = \sin y = \dfrac{2}{\sqrt{5}} = \dfrac{2\sqrt{5}}{5}$.

15. Let $a = \text{Sin}^{-1}\dfrac{3}{5}$ and $b = \text{Tan}^{-1}\dfrac{8}{15}$; find $\tan a = \dfrac{3}{4}$; $\tan\left(\text{Sin}^{-1}\dfrac{3}{5} + \text{Tan}^{-1}\dfrac{8}{15}\right) =$

$\tan(a + b) = \dfrac{\tan a + \tan b}{1 - \tan a \tan b} = \dfrac{\dfrac{3}{4} + \dfrac{8}{15}}{1 - \left(\dfrac{3}{4}\right)\left(\dfrac{8}{15}\right)} = \dfrac{77}{36}$.

16. Let $a = \text{Tan}^{-1}\dfrac{5}{12}$ and find $\sin a = \dfrac{5}{13}$; since $0 \le a \le \dfrac{\pi}{2}$, $a = \text{Sin}^{-1}\dfrac{5}{13}$;

$\cos\left(\text{Tan}^{-1}\dfrac{5}{12} - \text{Sin}^{-1}\dfrac{5}{13}\right) = \cos 0 = 1$.

17. Let $a = \text{Cot}^{-1}2$ and find $\sin a = \dfrac{\sqrt{5}}{5}$ and $\cos a = \dfrac{2\sqrt{5}}{5}$;

$\sin(2 \text{ Cot}^{-1}2) = \sin 2a = 2 \sin a \cos a = 2\left(\dfrac{\sqrt{5}}{5}\right)\left(\dfrac{2\sqrt{5}}{5}\right) = \dfrac{4}{5}$.

18. Let $a = \text{Cos}^{-1}\left(-\dfrac{4}{5}\right)$ and find $\tan a = -\dfrac{3}{4}$; $\tan\left[2\ \text{Cos}^{-1}\left(-\dfrac{4}{5}\right)\right] =$

$\tan 2a = \dfrac{2\tan a}{1 - \tan^2 a} = \dfrac{2\left(-\dfrac{3}{4}\right)}{1 - \left(-\dfrac{3}{4}\right)^2} = -\dfrac{24}{7}.$

B **19.** Let $a = \text{Cos}^{-1}x$; $\sec(\text{Cos}^{-1}x) = \sec a = \dfrac{1}{\cos a}\ (\cos a \neq 0) = \dfrac{1}{x}$; for $x \neq 0$,

$\sec(\text{Cos}^{-1}x) = \dfrac{1}{x}.$

20. Let $a = \text{Cot}^{-1}x$; $\tan(\text{Cot}^{-1}x) = \tan a = \dfrac{1}{\cot a}\ (\cot a \neq 0) = \dfrac{1}{x}$; for $x \neq 0$,

$\tan(\text{Cot}^{-1}x) = \dfrac{1}{x}.$

21. Let $a = \text{Tan}^{-1}x$; $-\dfrac{\pi}{2} < a < \dfrac{\pi}{2}$; if a is in Quadrant I or II with $\tan a = x$,

$\sin a = \dfrac{x}{\sqrt{x^2 + 1}}$; $\sin(\text{Tan}^{-1}x) = \dfrac{x}{\sqrt{x^2 + 1}} = \dfrac{x\sqrt{x^2 + 1}}{x^2 + 1}.$

22. Let $a = \text{Cot}^{-1}x$; $0 < a < \pi$; if a is in Quadrant I or II with $\cot a = x$,

$\cos a = \dfrac{x}{\sqrt{x^2 + 1}}$; $\cos(\text{Cot}^{-1}x) = \dfrac{x}{\sqrt{x^2 + 1}} = \dfrac{x\sqrt{x^2 + 1}}{x^2 + 1}.$

23. Let $a = \text{Tan}^{-1}x$; from Ex. 21, above, $\sin a = \dfrac{x}{\sqrt{x^2 + 1}}$; $\cos a = \dfrac{1}{\sqrt{x^2 + 1}}$;

$\sin(2\ \text{Tan}^{-1}x) = \sin 2a = 2\sin a\cos a = 2\left(\dfrac{x}{\sqrt{x^2 + 1}}\right)\left(\dfrac{1}{\sqrt{x^2 + 1}}\right) = \dfrac{2x}{x^2 + 1}.$

24. Let $a = \text{Cot}^{-1}x$; from Ex. 22, above, $\cos a = \dfrac{x}{\sqrt{x^2 + 1}}$;

$\cos(2\ \text{Cot}^{-1}x) = \cos 2a = 2\cos^2 a - 1 = 2\left(\dfrac{x}{\sqrt{x^2 + 1}}\right)^2 - 1 = \dfrac{2x^2}{x^2 + 1} - 1 = \dfrac{x^2 - 1}{x^2 + 1}.$

25. Let $a = \text{Cot}^{-1}x$ and $b = \text{Cot}^{-1}y$; $\tan a = \dfrac{1}{\cot a}\ (\cot a \neq 0) = \dfrac{1}{x}$ and

$\tan b = \dfrac{1}{\cot b}\ (\cot b \neq 0) = \dfrac{1}{y}$; for $xy \neq 1$, $\tan(\text{Cot}^{-1}x + \text{Cot}^{-1}y) =$

$\tan(a + b) = \dfrac{\tan a + \tan b}{1 - \tan a\tan b} = \dfrac{\dfrac{1}{x} + \dfrac{1}{y}}{1 - \dfrac{1}{x}\cdot\dfrac{1}{y}} = \dfrac{x + y}{xy - 1}.$

26. Let $a = \text{Tan}^{-1}x$ and $b = \text{Tan}^{-1}y$; $-\dfrac{\pi}{2} < a < \dfrac{\pi}{2}$ and $-\dfrac{\pi}{2} < b < \dfrac{\pi}{2}$;

$\cot\left[\text{Tan}^{-1}x - \text{Tan}^{-1}y\right] = \cot(a - b) = \dfrac{1}{\tan(a - b)}\quad(\tan(a - b) \neq 0)$

$= \dfrac{1 + \tan a\tan b}{\tan a - \tan b} = \dfrac{1 + xy}{x - y}$; since $-\pi < a - b < \pi$, $\tan(a - b) \neq 0$ if $a \neq b$;

for $-\dfrac{\pi}{2} < a < \dfrac{\pi}{2}$ and $-\dfrac{\pi}{2} < b < \dfrac{\pi}{2}$, $a \neq b$ if $\tan a \neq \tan b$, that is, if $x \neq y$; for

$x \neq y$, $\cot\left[\text{Tan}^{-1}x - \text{Tan}^{-1}y\right] = \dfrac{1 + xy}{x - y}.$

C   27. 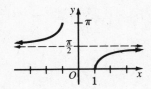   28.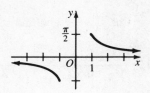

29. Since $\cot(z + \pi) = \cot z$, $\cot z = x$; $x < 0$, so $\tan z = \dfrac{1}{\cot z} = \dfrac{1}{x}$ and $-\dfrac{\pi}{2} < z < 0$, so

$z = \text{Tan}^{-1}\dfrac{1}{x}$; $\pi + \text{Tan}^{-1}\dfrac{1}{x} = \pi + z = y = \text{Cot}^{-1}x$.

Pages 661-662 · WRITTEN EXERCISES

A   **1.** $3 \cos \theta = 2$; $\cos \theta = \dfrac{2}{3}$; $\{48.2°, 311.8°\}$; $\{\theta: \theta = 48.2° + k \cdot 360°$ or $\theta = 311.8° + k \cdot 360°,$
     k an integer$\}$

2. $5 \sin \theta = 4$; $\sin \theta = \dfrac{4}{5}$; $\{53.1°, 126.9°\}$;

$\{\theta: \theta = 53.1° + k \cdot 360°$ or $\theta = 126.9° + k \cdot 360°$, k an integer$\}$

3. $2 \sin^2 x = 1$; $\sin^2 x = \dfrac{1}{2}$; $\sin x = \pm\dfrac{\sqrt{2}}{2}$; $\left\{\dfrac{\pi}{4}, \dfrac{3\pi}{4}, \dfrac{5\pi}{4}, \dfrac{7\pi}{4}\right\}$;
$\left\{x: x = \dfrac{(2k + 1)\pi}{4}, k \text{ an integer}\right\}$

4. $4 \cos^2 x = 3$; $\cos^2 x = \dfrac{3}{4}$; $\cos x = \pm\dfrac{\sqrt{3}}{2}$; $\left\{\dfrac{\pi}{6}, \dfrac{5\pi}{6}, \dfrac{7\pi}{6}, \dfrac{11\pi}{6}\right\}$;
$\left\{x: x = \dfrac{\pi}{6} + k\pi \text{ or } x = \dfrac{5\pi}{6} + k\pi, k \text{ an integer}\right\}$

5. $\sin \theta + \cos \theta = 0$; $\sin \theta = -\cos \theta$; $\tan \theta = -1$; $\{135°, 315°\}$;
$\{\theta: \theta = 135° + k \cdot 180°, k \text{ an integer}\}$

6. $\sec \theta = \csc \theta$; $\dfrac{\sec \theta}{\csc \theta} = 1$; $\tan \theta = 1$; $\{45°, 225°\}$; $\{\theta: \theta = 45° + k \cdot 180°, k \text{ an integer}\}$

7. $\sec x = 9 \cos x$; $\dfrac{\sec x}{\cos x} = 9$; $\cos^2 x = \dfrac{1}{9}$; $\cos x = \pm\dfrac{1}{3}$; $\{1.23, 1.91, 4.37, 5.05\}$;
$\{x: x = 1.23 + k\pi, \text{ or } x = 1.91 + k\pi, k \text{ an integer}\}$

8. $5 \sin x + 2 \cos x = 0$; $5 \sin x = -2 \cos x$; $\tan x = -\dfrac{2}{5}$; $\{2.76, 5.90\}$,
$\{x: x = 2.76 + k\pi, k \text{ an integer}\}$

9. $\tan\left(x - \dfrac{\pi}{8}\right) = 1$; $x - \dfrac{\pi}{8} = \dfrac{\pi}{4}$ or $x - \dfrac{\pi}{8} = \dfrac{5\pi}{4}$; $\left\{\dfrac{3\pi}{8}, \dfrac{11\pi}{8}\right\}$;
$\left\{x: x = \dfrac{3\pi}{8} + k\pi, k \text{ an integer}\right\}$

10. $2\sin\left(x + \dfrac{\pi}{4}\right) = 1$; $\sin\left(x + \dfrac{\pi}{4}\right) = \dfrac{1}{2}$; $x + \dfrac{\pi}{4} = \dfrac{\pi}{6}$ or $x + \dfrac{\pi}{4} = \dfrac{5\pi}{6}$; $x = -\dfrac{\pi}{12}$ or

$x = \dfrac{7\pi}{12}$; $\left\{\dfrac{7\pi}{12}, \dfrac{23\pi}{12}\right\}$; $\left\{x: x = -\dfrac{\pi}{12} + 2k\pi \text{ or } x = \dfrac{7\pi}{12} + 2k\pi, k \text{ an integer}\right\}$

11. $\cos(\theta + 15°) = 0$; $\theta + 15° = 90°$ or $\theta + 15° = 270°$; $\{75°, 255°\}$;
$\{\theta: \theta = 75° + k \cdot 180°, k \text{ an integer}\}$

12. $\cot(\theta - 10°) = \sqrt{3}$; $\theta - 10° = 30°$ or $\theta - 10° = 210°$; $\{40°, 220°\}$;
$\{\theta: 40° + k\pi, k \text{ an integer}\}$

13. $\cos^2\theta = 3\sin^2\theta$; $\tan^2\theta = \dfrac{1}{3}$; $\tan\theta = \pm\dfrac{\sqrt{3}}{3}$; $\{30°, 150°, 210°, 330°\}$

14. $4\sin\theta = 3\csc\theta$; $\sin^2\theta = \dfrac{3}{4}$; $\sin\theta = \pm\dfrac{\sqrt{3}}{2}$; $\{60°, 120°, 240°, 300°\}$

15. $3\sec x = \csc x$; $\dfrac{\sec x}{\csc x} = \dfrac{1}{3}$; $\tan x = \dfrac{1}{3}$; $\{0.32, 3.46\}$

16. $2\cos 2\theta = 1$; $\cos 2\theta = \dfrac{1}{2}$; $1 - 2\sin^2\theta = \dfrac{1}{2}$, $2\sin^2\theta = \dfrac{1}{2}$; $\sin^2\theta = \dfrac{1}{4}$;
$\sin\theta = \pm\sqrt{\dfrac{1}{4}} = \pm\dfrac{1}{2}$; $\{30°, 150°, 210°, 330°\}$

17. $\csc^2\theta - 2 = 0$; $\csc^2\theta = 2$; $\sin^2\theta = \dfrac{1}{2}$; $\sin\theta = \pm\dfrac{\sqrt{2}}{2}$; $\{45°, 135°, 225°, 315°\}$

18. $2\cot^2\theta = 1$; $\cot^2\theta = \dfrac{1}{2}$; $\tan^2\theta = 2$; $\tan\theta = \pm\sqrt{2}$; $\{54.7°, 125.3°, 234.7°, 305.3°\}$

19. $\sin 2x - \cos x = 0$; $2\sin x\cos x - \cos x = 0$; $\cos x(2\sin x - 1) = 0$; $\cos x = 0$ or
$\sin x = \dfrac{1}{2}$; $\left\{\dfrac{\pi}{6}, \dfrac{\pi}{2}, \dfrac{5\pi}{6}, \dfrac{3\pi}{2}\right\}$

20. $\sin 2\theta + \sin\theta = 0$; $2\sin\theta\cos\theta + \sin\theta = 0$; $\sin\theta(2\cos\theta + 1) = 0$;
$\sin\theta = 0$ or $\cos\theta = -\dfrac{1}{2}$; $\{0°, 120°, 180°, 240°\}$

21. $\cos 2\theta = \sin\theta$; $1 - 2\sin^2\theta = \sin\theta$; $2\sin^2\theta + \sin\theta - 1 = 0$;
$(2\sin\theta - 1)(\sin\theta + 1) = 0$; $\sin\theta = \dfrac{1}{2}$ or $\sin\theta = -1$; $\{30°, 150°, 270°\}$

22. $\cos 2x - \cos x = 0$; $2\cos^2 x - 1 - \cos x = 0$; $(2\cos x + 1)(\cos x - 1) = 0$;
$\cos x = -\dfrac{1}{2}$ or $\cos x = 1$; $\left\{0, \dfrac{2\pi}{3}, \dfrac{4\pi}{3}\right\}$

23. $2\sin 2\theta = \sqrt{3}$; $\sin 2\theta = \dfrac{\sqrt{3}}{2}$; $2\theta = 60°, 120°, 420°, \text{ or } 480°$; $\{30°, 60°, 210°, 240°\}$

24. $2\sin x = \sec x$; $2\sin x\cos x = 1$; $\sin 2x = 1$; $2x = \dfrac{\pi}{2}$ or $2x = \dfrac{5\pi}{2}$; $\left\{\dfrac{\pi}{4}, \dfrac{5\pi}{4}\right\}$

25. $6 \cos^2\theta - 5 \cos\theta + 1 = 0$; $(3 \cos\theta - 1)(2 \cos\theta - 1) = 0$; $\cos\theta = \dfrac{1}{3}$ or $\cos\theta = \dfrac{1}{2}$; $\{60°, 70.5°, 289.5°, 300°\}$

26. $2 \tan^2\theta = 1 - \tan\theta$; $2 \tan^2\theta + \tan\theta - 1 = 0$; $(2 \tan\theta - 1)(\tan\theta + 1) = 0$; $\tan\theta = \dfrac{1}{2}$ or $\tan\theta = -1$; $\{26.6°, 135°, 206.6°, 315°\}$

B 27. $\cos 2x = 2 - 5 \cos x$; $2 \cos^2x - 1 = 2 - 5 \cos x$; $2 \cos^2x + 5 \cos x - 3 = 0$;

$(2 \cos x - 1)(\cos x + 3) = 0$; $\cos x = -3$ (reject) or $\cos x = \dfrac{1}{2}$; $\left\{\dfrac{\pi}{3}, \dfrac{5\pi}{3}\right\}$

28. $\cos 2x + 7 \sin x + 3 = 0$; $1 - 2 \sin^2x + 7 \sin x + 3 = 0$; $2 \sin^2x - 7 \sin x - 4 = 0$;

$(2 \sin x + 1)(\sin x - 4) = 0$; $\sin x = 4$ (reject) or $\sin x = -\dfrac{1}{2}$; $\left\{\dfrac{7\pi}{6}, \dfrac{11\pi}{6}\right\}$

29. $2 \sin^2\left(x - \dfrac{\pi}{6}\right) = 1$; $\sin^2\left(x - \dfrac{\pi}{6}\right) = \dfrac{1}{2}$; $\sin\left(x - \dfrac{\pi}{6}\right) = \pm\dfrac{\sqrt{2}}{2}$; $x - \dfrac{\pi}{6} = \dfrac{\pi}{4}, \dfrac{3\pi}{4}, \dfrac{5\pi}{4}$

or $\dfrac{7\pi}{4}$; $\left\{\dfrac{5\pi}{12}, \dfrac{11\pi}{12}, \dfrac{17\pi}{12}, \dfrac{23\pi}{12}\right\}$

30. $\tan^2\left(x + \dfrac{\pi}{3}\right) = 1$; $\tan\left(x + \dfrac{\pi}{3}\right) = \pm 1$; $x + \dfrac{\pi}{3} = \dfrac{3\pi}{4}, \dfrac{5\pi}{4}, \dfrac{7\pi}{4}$, or $\dfrac{9\pi}{4}$;

$\left\{\dfrac{5\pi}{12}, \dfrac{11\pi}{12}, \dfrac{17\pi}{12}, \dfrac{23\pi}{12}\right\}$

31. $\sin 3x + \cos 3x = 0$; $\sin 3x = -\cos 3x$; $\tan 3x = -1$; $3x = \dfrac{3\pi}{4}, \dfrac{7\pi}{4}, \dfrac{11\pi}{4}, \dfrac{15\pi}{4}, \dfrac{19\pi}{4}$, or

$\dfrac{23\pi}{4}$; $\left\{\dfrac{\pi}{4}, \dfrac{7\pi}{12}, \dfrac{11\pi}{12}, \dfrac{5\pi}{4}, \dfrac{19\pi}{12}, \dfrac{23\pi}{12}\right\}$

32. $\tan^2 3x = 3$; $\tan 3x = \pm\sqrt{3}$; $3x = \dfrac{\pi}{3}, \dfrac{2\pi}{3}, \dfrac{4\pi}{3}, \dfrac{5\pi}{3}, \dfrac{7\pi}{3}, \dfrac{8\pi}{3}, \dfrac{10\pi}{3}, \dfrac{11\pi}{3}, \dfrac{13\pi}{3}, \dfrac{14\pi}{3}, \dfrac{16\pi}{3}$

or $\dfrac{17\pi}{3}$; $\left\{\dfrac{\pi}{9}, \dfrac{2\pi}{9}, \dfrac{4\pi}{9}, \dfrac{5\pi}{9}, \dfrac{7\pi}{9}, \dfrac{8\pi}{9}, \dfrac{10\pi}{9}, \dfrac{11\pi}{9}, \dfrac{13\pi}{9}, \dfrac{14\pi}{9}, \dfrac{16\pi}{9}, \dfrac{17\pi}{9}\right\}$

33. $\cos 4\theta = \cos 2\theta$; $2 \cos^2 2\theta - 1 = \cos 2\theta$; $2 \cos^2 2\theta - \cos 2\theta - 1 = 0$;

$(2 \cos 2\theta + 1)(\cos 2\theta - 1) = 0$; $\cos 2\theta = -\dfrac{1}{2}$ or $\cos 2\theta = 1$;

$2\theta = 0°, 120°, 240°, 360°, 480°$, or $600°$; $\{0°, 60°, 120°, 180°, 240°, 300°\}$

34. $\sin 4x = \cos 2x$; $2 \sin 2x \cos 2x - \cos 2x = 0$; $\cos 2x(2 \sin 2x - 1) = 0$;

$\cos 2x = 0$ or $\sin 2x = \dfrac{1}{2}$; $2x = \dfrac{\pi}{6}, \dfrac{\pi}{2}, \dfrac{5\pi}{6}, \dfrac{3\pi}{2}, \dfrac{13\pi}{6}, \dfrac{5\pi}{2}, \dfrac{17\pi}{6}$, or $\dfrac{7\pi}{2}$;

$\left\{\dfrac{\pi}{12}, \dfrac{\pi}{4}, \dfrac{5\pi}{12}, \dfrac{3\pi}{4}, \dfrac{13\pi}{12}, \dfrac{5\pi}{4}, \dfrac{17\pi}{12}, \dfrac{7\pi}{4}\right\}$

35. $\sin 2x = \cot x$; $2 \sin x \cos x = \dfrac{\cos x}{\sin x}$; $2 \sin^2x \cos x - \cos x = 0$;

$\cos x(2 \sin^2x - 1) = 0$; $\cos x = 0$ or $\sin x = \pm\dfrac{\sqrt{2}}{2}$; $\left\{\dfrac{\pi}{4}, \dfrac{\pi}{2}, \dfrac{3\pi}{4}, \dfrac{5\pi}{4}, \dfrac{3\pi}{2}, \dfrac{7\pi}{4}\right\}$

36. $2 \sin 2\theta = \tan \theta$; $4 \sin \theta \cos \theta = \dfrac{\sin \theta}{\cos \theta}$; $4 \sin \theta \cos^2\theta - \sin \theta = 0$;

$\sin \theta(4 \cos^2\theta - 1) = 0$; $\sin \theta = 0$ or $\cos \theta = \pm\dfrac{1}{2}$; $\{0°, 60°, 120°, 180°, 240°, 300°\}$

37. $\cos 2\theta = 2 \sin^2\theta$; $1 - 2 \sin^2\theta = 2 \sin^2\theta$; $\sin^2\theta = \dfrac{1}{4}$; $\sin \theta = \pm\dfrac{1}{2}$; $\{30°, 150°, 210°, 330°\}$

38. $\cos 2\theta + 2 \cos^2\theta = 0$; $2 \cos^2\theta - 1 + 2 \cos^2\theta = 0$; $4 \cos^2\theta = 1$; $\cos^2\theta = \dfrac{1}{4}$; $\cos \theta = \pm\dfrac{1}{2}$;
$\{60°, 120°, 240°, 300°\}$

39. $\sin(2\theta - 20°) = \dfrac{1}{2}$; $2\theta - 20° = 30°, 150°, 390°$, or $510°$; $\{25°, 85°, 205°, 265°\}$

40. $\cos(3\theta - 15°) = \dfrac{\sqrt{3}}{2}$; $3\theta - 15° = 30°, 330°, 390°, 690°, 750°, 1050°$;

$\{15°, 115°, 135°, 235°, 255°, 355°\}$

41. $\cos(3x + \pi) = \dfrac{\sqrt{2}}{2}$; $3x + \pi = \dfrac{7\pi}{4}, \dfrac{9\pi}{4}, \dfrac{15\pi}{4}, \dfrac{17\pi}{4}, \dfrac{23\pi}{4}$, or $\dfrac{25\pi}{4}$;

$\left\{\dfrac{\pi}{4}, \dfrac{5\pi}{12}, \dfrac{11\pi}{12}, \dfrac{13\pi}{12}, \dfrac{19\pi}{12}, \dfrac{7\pi}{4}\right\}$

42. $\tan\left(2x - \dfrac{\pi}{3}\right) = 1$; $2x - \dfrac{\pi}{3} = \dfrac{\pi}{4}, \dfrac{5\pi}{4}, \dfrac{9\pi}{4}$, or $\dfrac{13\pi}{4}$; $\left\{\dfrac{7\pi}{24}, \dfrac{19\pi}{24}, \dfrac{31\pi}{24}, \dfrac{43\pi}{24}\right\}$

43. $\tan(\theta + 32°) = \cot(\theta - 20°)$; let $\alpha = \theta + 32°$ and $\beta = \theta - 20°$; $\tan \alpha = \cot \beta$;

$\dfrac{\sin \alpha}{\cos \alpha} = \dfrac{\cos \beta}{\sin \beta}$; $\cos \alpha \cos \beta - \sin \alpha \sin \beta = 0$; $\cos(\alpha + \beta) = 0$; $12° = \alpha + \beta < 732°$;

$\alpha + \beta = 90°, 270°, 450°$, or $630°$; $\alpha + \beta = 2\theta + 12$; $\{39°, 129°, 219°, 309°\}$

44. $\sin(\theta - 10°) = \cos \theta$; $\sin(\theta - 10°) = \sin(90° - \theta)$; $\theta - 10° = 90° - \theta + k \cdot 360°$, k an
integer; $2\theta = 100° + k \cdot 360°$; $\theta = 50° + k \cdot 180°$; $\{50°, 230°\}$

45. $\cos 2\theta = \cos \theta + 1$; $2 \cos^2\theta - 1 - \cos \theta - 1 = 0$; $2 \cos^2\theta - \cos \theta - 2 = 0$;

$\cos \theta = \dfrac{1 \pm \sqrt{17}}{4}$; reject $\dfrac{1 + \sqrt{17}}{4}$ since $\cos \theta \le 1$; $\cos \theta = \dfrac{1 - \sqrt{17}}{4}$; $\{141.3°, 218.7°\}$

46. $\cot^2 x - \cos^2 x = \dfrac{\cos^2 x}{\sin^2 x} - \cos^2 x (\sin^2 x \ne 0) = \dfrac{\cos^2 x - \cos^2 x \sin^2 x}{\sin^2 x} =$

$\dfrac{\cos^2 x(1 - \sin^2 x)}{\sin^2 x} = \dfrac{\cos^2 x \cdot \cos^2 x}{\sin^2 x} = \cot^2 x \cos^2 x$; $\{x: 0 < x < \pi \text{ or } \pi < x < 2\pi\}$

47. $\cos^2 x + 2 \sin x + 1 = 0$; $1 - \sin^2 x + 2 \sin x + 1 = 0$; $\sin^2 x - 2 \sin x - 2 = 0$;
$\sin x = 1 \pm \sqrt{3}$; reject $1 + \sqrt{3}$ since $\sin x \le 1$; $\sin x = 1 - \sqrt{3}$; $\{3.96, 5.46\}$

48. $\sin^2\theta + 4 \cos \theta - 3 = 0$; $1 - \cos^2\theta + 4 \cos \theta - 3 = 0$; $\cos^2\theta - 4 \cos \theta + 2 = 0$;
$\cos \theta = 2 \pm \sqrt{2}$; reject $2 + \sqrt{2}$ since $\cos \theta \le 1$; $\cos \theta = 2 - \sqrt{2}$; $\{54.1°, 305.9°\}$

Pages 663-666 · EXTRA

Answers may vary slightly if a calculator is used and only final answers are rounded.

A 1. $c = \sqrt{1^2 + (\sqrt{3})^2} = 2$; $\cos \gamma = \dfrac{1}{2}$ and $\sin \gamma = \dfrac{\sqrt{3}}{2}$; $\gamma = 60°$;

$\cos \theta + \sqrt{3} \sin \theta = 2 \cos(\theta - 60°)$

2. $c = \sqrt{1^2 + 1^2} = \sqrt{2}$; $\cos \gamma = \dfrac{1}{\sqrt{2}} = \dfrac{\sqrt{2}}{2}$ and $\sin \gamma = \dfrac{\sqrt{2}}{2}$; $\gamma = 45°$;

$\cos \theta + \sin \theta = \sqrt{2} \cos(\theta - 45°)$

3. $c = \sqrt{3^2 + (-4)^2} = 5$; $\cos \gamma = \dfrac{3}{5}$ and $\sin \gamma = -\dfrac{4}{5}$; $\gamma = -53.1°$;

$3 \cos \theta - 4 \sin \theta = 5 \cos(\theta + 53.1°)$

4. $c = \sqrt{4^2 + (-3)^2} = 5$; $\cos \gamma = \dfrac{4}{5}$ and $\sin \gamma = -\dfrac{3}{5}$; $\gamma = -36.9°$;

$4 \cos \theta - 3 \sin \theta = 5 \cos(\theta + 36.9°)$

5. $c = \sqrt{1^2 + (-1)^2} = \sqrt{2}$; $\cos \gamma = \dfrac{1}{\sqrt{2}} = \dfrac{\sqrt{2}}{2}$ and $\sin \gamma = -\dfrac{\sqrt{2}}{2}$; $\gamma = -\dfrac{\pi}{4}$;

$\cos x - \sin x = \sqrt{2} \cos\left(x + \dfrac{\pi}{4}\right)$

6. $c = \sqrt{(-\sqrt{3})^2 + 1^2} = 2$; $\cos \gamma = -\dfrac{\sqrt{3}}{2}$ and $\sin \gamma = \dfrac{1}{2}$; $\gamma = \dfrac{5\pi}{6}$;

$\sin x - \sqrt{3} \cos x = 2 \cos\left(x - \dfrac{5\pi}{6}\right)$

7. $c = \sqrt{2^2 + 1^2} = \sqrt{5}$; $\cos \gamma = \dfrac{2}{\sqrt{5}} = \dfrac{2\sqrt{5}}{5}$ and $\sin \gamma = \dfrac{\sqrt{5}}{5}$; $\gamma = 0.46$;

$\sin x + 2 \cos x = \sqrt{5} \cos(x - 0.46)$

8. $c = \sqrt{3^2 + 2^2} = \sqrt{13}$; $\cos \gamma = \dfrac{3}{\sqrt{13}} = \dfrac{3\sqrt{13}}{13}$ and $\sin \gamma = \dfrac{2\sqrt{13}}{13}$; $\gamma = 0.59$;

$3 \cos x + 2 \sin x = \sqrt{13} \cos(x - 0.59)$

9. $c = \sqrt{1^2 + (\sqrt{3})^2} = 2$; $\cos \gamma = \dfrac{1}{2}$ and $\sin \gamma = \dfrac{\sqrt{3}}{2}$; $\gamma = 60°$;

$\cos \theta + \sqrt{3} \sin \theta = 2 \cos(\theta - 60°)$; $2 \cos(\theta - 60°) = 1$; $\cos(\theta - 60°) = \dfrac{1}{2}$;

$\theta - 60° = 60°$ or $-60°$; $\{0°, 120°\}$

10. $c = \sqrt{1^2 + (-1)^2} = \sqrt{2}$; $\cos \gamma = \dfrac{1}{\sqrt{2}} = \dfrac{\sqrt{2}}{2}$ and $\sin \gamma = -\dfrac{\sqrt{2}}{2}$; $\gamma = -45°$;

$\cos \theta - \sin \theta = \sqrt{2} \cos(\theta + 45°)$; $\sqrt{2}[\sqrt{2} \cos(\theta + 45°)] = 1$; $\cos(\theta + 45°) = \dfrac{1}{2}$;

$\theta + 45° = 60°$ or $300°$; $\{15°, 255°\}$

11. $c = \sqrt{(-1)^2 + 1^2} = \sqrt{2}$; $\cos \gamma = -\dfrac{1}{\sqrt{2}} = -\dfrac{\sqrt{2}}{2}$ and $\sin \gamma = \dfrac{\sqrt{2}}{2}$; $\gamma = \dfrac{3\pi}{4}$;

$\sin x - \cos x = \sqrt{2} \cos\left(x - \dfrac{3\pi}{4}\right)$; $2\sqrt{2} \cos\left(x - \dfrac{3\pi}{4}\right) = \sqrt{6}$; $\cos\left(x - \dfrac{3\pi}{4}\right) = \dfrac{\sqrt{3}}{2}$;

$x - \dfrac{3\pi}{4} = -\dfrac{\pi}{6}$ or $\dfrac{\pi}{6}$; $\left\{\dfrac{7\pi}{12}, \dfrac{11\pi}{12}\right\}$

12. $c = \sqrt{(\sqrt{3})^2 + 1^2} = 2$; $\cos \gamma = \dfrac{\sqrt{3}}{2}$ and $\sin \gamma = \dfrac{1}{2}$; $\gamma = \dfrac{\pi}{6}$;

$\sqrt{3} \cos x + \sin x = 2 \cos\left(x - \dfrac{\pi}{6}\right)$; $2 \cos\left(x - \dfrac{\pi}{6}\right) = \sqrt{2}$; $\cos\left(x - \dfrac{\pi}{6}\right) = \dfrac{\sqrt{2}}{2}$;

$x - \dfrac{\pi}{6} = \dfrac{\pi}{4}$ or $\dfrac{7\pi}{4}$; $\left\{\dfrac{5\pi}{12}, \dfrac{23\pi}{12}\right\}$

B 13. $c = \sqrt{3^2 + 1^2} = \sqrt{10}$; $\cos \gamma = \dfrac{3}{\sqrt{10}} = 0.9487$ and $\sin \gamma = \dfrac{1}{\sqrt{10}} = 0.3162$; $\gamma = 18.4°$;

$3 \cos \theta + \sin \theta = \sqrt{10} \cos(\theta - 18.4°)$; $\sqrt{10} \cos(\theta - 18.4°) = 2$;

$\cos(\theta - 18.4°) = \dfrac{2}{\sqrt{10}} = 0.6325$; $\theta - 18.4° = 50.8°$ or $309.2°$; $\{69.2°, 327.6°\}$

14. $c = \sqrt{1 + (-2)^2} = \sqrt{5}$; $\cos \gamma = \dfrac{1}{\sqrt{5}} = 0.4472$ and $\sin \gamma = -\dfrac{2}{\sqrt{5}} = -0.8944$;

$\gamma = -63.4°$; $\cos \theta - 2 \sin \theta = \sqrt{5} \cos(\theta + 63.4°)$; $\sqrt{5} \cos(\theta + 63.4°) = 2$;

$\cos(\theta + 63.4°) = \dfrac{2}{\sqrt{5}} = 0.8944$; $\theta + 63.4° = 333.4°$ or $386.6°$; $\{270°, 323.2°\}$

15. $c = \sqrt{(-4)^2 + 2^2} = 2\sqrt{5}$; $\cos \gamma = \dfrac{-4}{2\sqrt{5}} = -0.8944$ and $\sin \gamma = \dfrac{2}{2\sqrt{5}} = 0.4472$;

$\gamma = 3.14 - 0.46 = 2.68$; $2 \sin x - 4 \cos x = 2\sqrt{5} \cos(x - 2.68)$;

$2\sqrt{5} \cos(x - 2.68) = 3$; $\cos(x - 2.68) = \dfrac{3}{2\sqrt{5}} = 0.6708$; $x - 2.68 = -0.84$ or 0.84; $\{1.84, 3.52\}$

16. $c = \sqrt{3^2 + 4^2} = 5$; $\cos \gamma = \dfrac{3}{5}$ and $\sin \gamma = \dfrac{4}{5}$; $\gamma = 0.93$;

$3 \cos x + 4 \sin x = 5 \cos(x - 0.93)$; $5 \cos(x - 0.93) = 2$; $\cos(x - 0.93) = 0.4$;

$x - 0.93 = 1.16$ or 5.12; $\{2.09, 6.05\}$

17. $c = \sqrt{5^2 + (-2)^2} = \sqrt{29}$; $\cos \gamma = \dfrac{5}{\sqrt{29}} = 0.9285$; $\sin \gamma = -\dfrac{2}{\sqrt{29}} = -0.3714$;

$\gamma = -21.8°$; $5 \cos 2\theta - 2 \sin 2\theta = \sqrt{29} \cos(2\theta + 21.8°)$; $\sqrt{29} \cos(2\theta + 21.8°) = 3$;

$\cos(2\theta + 21.8°) = \dfrac{3}{\sqrt{29}} = 0.5571$; $2\theta + 21.8° = 56.1°, 303.9°, 416.1°,$ or $663.9°$;

$\{17.2°, 141.1°, 197.2°, 321.1°\}$

18. $c = \sqrt{(-3)^2 + 1^2} = \sqrt{10}$; $\cos \gamma = \dfrac{-3}{\sqrt{10}} = -0.9487$; $\sin \gamma = \dfrac{1}{\sqrt{10}} = 0.3162$; $\gamma = 161.6$

$\sin 2\theta - 3 \cos 2\theta = \sqrt{10} \cos(2\theta - 161.6°)$; $\sqrt{10} \cos(2\theta - 161.6°) = 1$;

$\cos(2\theta - 161.6°) = \dfrac{1}{\sqrt{10}} = 0.3162$; $2\theta - 161.6° = -71.6°, 71.6°, 288.4°,$ or $431.6°$;

$\{45°, 116.6°, 225°, 296.6°\}$

19.

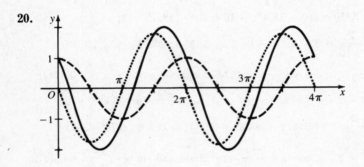

20.

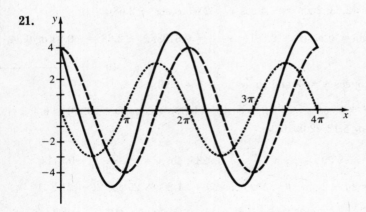

21.

22.

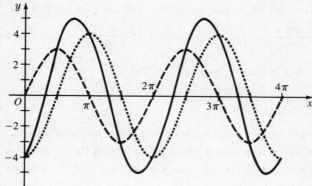

23. Let $c = \sqrt{a^2 + b^2}$ and w be the angle such that $\cos w = \dfrac{a}{c}$ and $\sin w = \dfrac{b}{c}$; let

$\gamma = 90 - w$; then $\sin \gamma = \sin(90 - w) = \cos w = \dfrac{a}{c}$ and $\cos \gamma = \cos(90 - w) =$

$\sin w = \dfrac{b}{c}$; then $a \cos \theta + b \sin \theta = c\left(\dfrac{a}{c} \cos \theta + \dfrac{b}{c} \sin \theta\right) =$

$c(\sin \gamma \cos \theta + \cos \gamma \sin \theta) = c \sin(\theta + \gamma)$

24. $750 = 9.8(100)\,[0.4 \cos \theta + \sin \theta] = 392 \cos \theta + 980 \sin \theta$; $375 =$
$196 \cos \theta + 490 \sin \theta$; convert $196 \cos \theta + 490 \sin \theta$ to the form $c \cos(\theta - \gamma)$; $c =$

$\sqrt{196^2 + 490^2} = 527.7$; $\cos \gamma = \dfrac{196}{527.7} = 0.3714$ and $\sin \gamma = \dfrac{490}{527.7} = 0.9286$; $\gamma = 68.2°$;

$527.7 \cos(\theta - 68.2°) = 375$; $\quad \cos(\theta - 68.2°) = \dfrac{375}{527.7} = 0.7106$; $\quad \theta - 68.2° = -44.7°$;

$\theta = 23.5°$

25. a. $60 = \dfrac{9.8(20)\,(0.3)}{\cos \theta + 0.3 \sin \theta}$; $\cos \theta + 0.3 \sin \theta = \dfrac{58.8}{60} = 0.98$; convert $\cos \theta + 0.3 \sin \theta$

to the form $c \cos(\theta - \gamma)$; $c = \sqrt{1^2 + (0.3)^2} = 1.044$; $\cos \gamma = \dfrac{1}{1.044} = 0.9579$ and

$\sin \gamma = \dfrac{3}{1.044} = 0.2874$; $\gamma = 16.7°$; $1.044 \cos(\theta - 16.7°) = 0.98$;

$\cos(\theta - 16.7°) = 0.9387$; $\theta - 16.7° = 20.2°$; $\theta = 36.9°$

b. The force is minimum when $\cos(\theta - 16.7°)$ is maximum, that is, when $\theta - 16.7° = 0°$,

or $\theta = 16.7°$; $\dfrac{9.8(20)\,(0.3)}{1.044 \cos 0°} = 56.3$; minimum force is 56.3 N.

Pages 666-668 · COMPUTER KEY-IN

1. Answers may vary. Sample results are given.
   a. 3.14260537, 3.14158951, 3.14159267   **b.** 3.14196328, 3.14159257, 3.14159302
   c. 3.17253103, 3.13905576, 3.14186692   **d.** 3.14163420, 3.14159255, 3.14159256
   e. $N = 5$, d; $N = 10$, b; $N = 15$, a

2. a. Answers may vary. For example, $a = \dfrac{1}{5}$, $b = \dfrac{2}{3}$
   b. Answers may vary. Example: 3.14159298

3. Let $x = \text{Tan}^{-1}a$ and $y = \text{Tan}^{-1}b$, so that $\tan x = a$ and $\tan y = b$. Then

$$\tan(x + y) = \frac{\tan x + \tan y}{1 - \tan x \tan y} = \frac{a + b}{1 - ab} \text{ (page 612). If } -\frac{\pi}{2} < x + y < \frac{\pi}{2}, \text{ then}$$

$$\text{Tan}^{-1}(\tan(x + y)) = x + y = \text{Tan}^{-1}a + \text{Tan}^{-1}b = \text{Tan}^{-1}\left(\frac{a + b}{1 - ab}\right).$$

Pages 669-670 · CHAPTER REVIEW

1. b; let θ be the angle formed by the air speed and resultant vectors, α be the angle formed by the wind and air speed vectors, and β be the angle formed by the air speed vector and due north; $135° - \theta + \beta = 180° = 45° + \alpha + \beta$; $90° = \alpha + \theta$; the triangle formed by the air speed, wind, and resultant vectors is a right triangle; $\sin \theta = \frac{40}{240}$; $\theta = 9.6°$; heading is $135° - 9.6° = 125.4°$.

2. c; $\|v - u\| = c$; $c^2 = 6^2 + 10^2 - 2 \cdot 6 \cdot 10 \cos 120° = 196$; $c = 14$

3. c; $A(x, y)$; $1 - x = -3$, $-2 - y = 2$; $x = 4$, $y = -4$

4. d; $u = 9i - 12j$; $v = xi + yj$; $u \cdot v = 9x - 12y = 0$; let $x = 4$, $y = 3$; $v = 4i + 3j$

$$\frac{v}{\|v\|} = \frac{4i + 3j}{5} = \frac{4}{5}i + \frac{3}{5}j$$

5. c; $r \cos \theta + r \sin \theta - 2 = 0$; $r(\cos \theta + \sin \theta) = 2$; $r = \dfrac{2}{\cos \theta + \sin \theta}$

6. a; $x = 3 \cos(-30°)$, $y = 3 \sin(-30°)$; $x = \dfrac{3\sqrt{3}}{2}$, $y = -\dfrac{3}{2}$

7. d; $r = \sqrt{(\sqrt{3})^2 + (-1)^2} = 2$; $\tan \theta = \dfrac{-1}{\sqrt{3}}$; $\theta = 330°$; $2(\cos 330° + i \sin 330°)$

8. d; $\dfrac{w}{z} = \dfrac{6}{3}(\cos(-180°) + i \sin(-180°)) = 2(-1) + 2i(0) = -2$

9. d; $\theta = 135°$; $r = \sqrt{\left(-\dfrac{\sqrt{2}}{2}\right)^2 + \left(\dfrac{\sqrt{2}}{2}\right)^2} = 1$; $\left(-\dfrac{\sqrt{2}}{2} + \dfrac{\sqrt{2}}{2}i\right)^{10} = $

$1^{10}(\cos 1350° + i \sin 1350°) = 0 + i(-1) = -i$

10. b; $(-i)^3 = -i^3 = -(-i) = i$ 11. a; $\text{Cos}^{-1}\left[\cos\left(-\dfrac{\pi}{3}\right)\right] = \text{Cos}^{-1}\dfrac{1}{2} = \dfrac{\pi}{3}$

12. b; $\text{Sin}^{-1}x = \theta$; $\sin \theta = x$; $\cos(2 \text{ Sin}^{-1}x) = \cos 2\theta = 1 - 2\sin^2\theta = 1 - 2x^2$

13. a; $\text{Sec}^{-1}(-2) = x$; $\sec x = -2 = \dfrac{1}{\cos x}$; $\cos x = -\dfrac{1}{2}$; $x = \dfrac{2\pi}{3}$

14. b; $\text{Tan}^{-1}(-2) = \theta$; $\tan \theta = -2$; $\sec^2\theta = 1 + \tan^2\theta = 5$; $\dfrac{1}{\cos^2\theta} = \sec^2\theta = 5$;

$\cos^2\theta = \dfrac{1}{5}$; $\cos 2\theta = 2 \cos^2\theta - 1 = \dfrac{2}{5} - 1 = -\dfrac{3}{5}$

15. d; $2 \sin 2\theta = 1$; $\sin 2\theta = \dfrac{1}{2}$; $2\theta = 30°, 150°, 390°, 510°$; $\theta = 15°, 75°, 195°, 255°$

16. c; $2 \sin^2(2x + \pi) = 1$; $\sin(2x + \pi) = \pm \dfrac{\sqrt{2}}{2}$; $2x + \pi = \dfrac{5\pi}{4}, \dfrac{7\pi}{4}, \dfrac{9\pi}{4}, \dfrac{11\pi}{4}, \dfrac{13\pi}{4}, \dfrac{15\pi}{4},$

$\dfrac{17\pi}{4}, \dfrac{19\pi}{4}$; $2x = \dfrac{\pi}{4}, \dfrac{3\pi}{4}, \dfrac{5\pi}{4}, \dfrac{7\pi}{4}, \dfrac{9\pi}{4}, \dfrac{11\pi}{4}, \dfrac{13\pi}{4}, \dfrac{15\pi}{4}$; $x = \dfrac{\pi}{8}, \dfrac{3\pi}{8}, \dfrac{5\pi}{8}, \dfrac{7\pi}{8}, \dfrac{9\pi}{8},$

$\dfrac{11\pi}{8}, \dfrac{13\pi}{8}, \dfrac{15\pi}{8}$

Pages 670-671 · CHAPTER TEST

1. $\alpha = 230° - 175° = 55°$; $d^2 = 40^2 + 40^2 - 2(40)(40) \cos 55° = 1364.48$; $d = 37$;

$\dfrac{\sin \beta}{40} = \dfrac{\sin 55°}{37}$; $\sin \beta = \dfrac{40(0.8192)}{37} = 0.8856$; $\beta = 62.3°$; bearing of second ship from

first $= 360° - (\beta + 5°) = 355° - 62.3° = 292.7°$; $\theta = \beta = 62.3°$; bearing of first ship

from second $= \theta + 55° = 62.3° + 55° = 117.3°$

2. a. $3\mathbf{u} + \mathbf{v} = 3(4\mathbf{i} + 3\mathbf{j}) + (-12\mathbf{i} + 5\mathbf{j}) = (12\mathbf{i} + 9\mathbf{j}) + (-12\mathbf{i} + 5\mathbf{j}) = 14\mathbf{j}$;

$\|3\mathbf{u} + \mathbf{v}\| = \sqrt{0^2 + 14^2} = 14$ **b.** Let θ be the angle between $\mathbf{u}$ and $\mathbf{v}$; $\cos \theta =$

$\dfrac{\mathbf{u} \cdot \mathbf{v}}{\|\mathbf{u}\| \|\mathbf{v}\|} = \dfrac{4(-12) + 3(5)}{\sqrt{4^2 + 3^2} \sqrt{(-12)^2 + 5^2}} = \dfrac{-48 + 15}{5(13)} = -\dfrac{33}{65} = -0.5077$; $\theta = 120.6°$

For example:

3.

Polar coordinates	$(2, 90°)$	$(3, 270°)$	$(4, 120°)$	$(\sqrt{6}, -45°)$
Rectangular coordinates	$(0, 2)$	$(0, -3)$	$(-2, 2\sqrt{3})$	$(\sqrt{3}, -\sqrt{3})$

4.

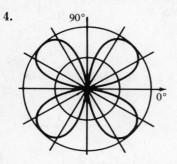

5. $wz = 6 \cdot 2[\cos(150° + 210°) + i \sin(150° + 210°)] =$

$12(\cos 360° + i \sin 360°) = 12(1 + 0i) = 12$;

$\dfrac{w}{z} = \dfrac{6}{2}[\cos(150° - 210°) + i \sin(150° - 210°)] =$

$3[\cos(-60°) + i \sin(-60°)] = 3\left(\dfrac{1}{2} - \dfrac{i\sqrt{3}}{2}\right) =$

$\dfrac{3}{2} - \dfrac{3i\sqrt{3}}{2}$

6. $-i = \cos 270° + i \sin 270°$; $r^5(\cos 5\theta + i \sin 5\theta) = 1(\cos 270° + i \sin 270°)$; $r = 1$;

$5\theta = 270° + k \cdot 360°$; $\theta = 54° + k \cdot 72°$, $k = 0, 1, 2, 3, 4$; $r_1 = \cos 54° + i \sin 54°$;

$r_2 = \cos(54° + 72°) + i \sin(54° + 72°) = \cos 126° + i \sin 126°$;

$r_3 = \cos(54° + 144°) + i \sin(54° + 144°) = \cos 198° + i \sin 198°$;

$r_4 = \cos(54° + 216°) + i \sin(54° + 216°) = \cos 270° + i \sin 270°$

$r_5 = \cos(54° + 288°) + i \sin(54° + 288°) = \cos 342° + i \sin 342°$

7. Let y be a second-quadrant angle with $\cos y = -\dfrac{3}{5}$; $\sin y = \dfrac{4}{5}$; $\sin\left[2\,\mathrm{Cos}^{-1}\left(-\dfrac{3}{5}\right)\right] =$

$\sin 2y = 2\sin y \cos y = 2\left(\dfrac{4}{5}\right)\left(-\dfrac{3}{5}\right) = -\dfrac{24}{25}$

8. Let y be a second-quadrant angle with $\cot y = -4 = \dfrac{-4}{1}$; $\cos y = \dfrac{-4}{\sqrt{1^2 + (-4)^2}} =$

$-\dfrac{4}{\sqrt{17}} = -\dfrac{4\sqrt{17}}{17}$

9. $\sin 2x = \sin x$; $2\sin x \cos x - \sin x = 0$; $\sin x(2\cos x - 1) = 0$; $\sin x = 0$ or

$\cos x = \dfrac{1}{2}$; $\left\{x: x = k\pi,\ x = \dfrac{\pi}{3} + 2k\pi,\ \text{or } x = \dfrac{5\pi}{3} + 2k\pi,\ k \text{ an integer}\right\}$

10. $\cos 2\theta + 2\cos^2\left(\dfrac{\theta}{2}\right) = 1$; $2\cos^2\theta - 1 + 2\left(\dfrac{1 + \cos\theta}{2}\right) = 1$; $2\cos^2\theta + \cos\theta = 1$;

$2\cos^2\theta + \cos\theta - 1 = 0$; $(2\cos\theta - 1)(\cos\theta + 1) = 0$; $\cos\theta = \dfrac{1}{2}$ or $\cos\theta = -1$;

$\{60°, 180°, 300°\}$

Page 671 · MIXED REVIEW

1. $6t^2 + 5t = 21$; $6t^2 + 5t - 21 = 0$; $(2t - 3)(3t + 7) = 0$; $t = \dfrac{3}{2}$ or $t = -\dfrac{7}{3}$

2. $\dfrac{x}{x - 1} + \dfrac{x + 2}{x} = 2$; $x^2 + (x - 1)(x + 2) = 2x(x - 1)$; $x^2 + x^2 + x - 2 = 2x^2 - 2x$

$3x = 2$; $x = \dfrac{2}{3}$

3. $\sqrt{r + 8} = r + 6$; $r + 8 = r^2 + 12r + 36$; $r^2 + 11r + 28 = 0$; $(r + 4)(r + 7) =$

$r = -4$ or $r = -7$ (reject); $r = -4$

4. $\left|2j - \dfrac{1}{2}\right| \geq \dfrac{3}{2}$; $2j - \dfrac{1}{2} \geq \dfrac{3}{2}$ or $2j - \dfrac{1}{2} \leq -\dfrac{3}{2}$; $2j \geq 2$ or $2j \leq -1$; $j \geq 1$ or $j \leq -\dfrac{1}{2}$

$\left\{j: j \leq -\dfrac{1}{2} \text{ or } j \geq 1\right\}$

5. $4x^2 - 4x - 8 \leq 0$; $x^2 - x - 2 \leq 0$; $(x - 2)(x + 1) \leq 0$; $x \leq 2$ and $x \geq -1$, or $x \geq$

and $x \leq -1$; $\{x: -1 \leq x \leq 2\}$

6. $\dfrac{m - 1}{5} + \dfrac{m + 2}{2} = -2$; $2m - 2 + 5m + 10 = -20$; $7m = -28$; $m = -4$

7. $3 - \dfrac{2y - 7}{4} > 5$; $-\dfrac{2y - 7}{4} > 2$; $2y - 7 < -8$; $2y < -1$; $y < -\dfrac{1}{2}$; $\left\{y: y < -\dfrac{1}{2}\right\}$

8. $125^{2z-1} = \sqrt[3]{5}$; $(5^3)^{2z-1} = 5^{1/3}$; $5^{6z-3} = 5^{1/3}$; $6z - 3 = \dfrac{1}{3}$; $6z = \dfrac{10}{3}$; $z = \dfrac{5}{9}$

9. $(2a - 1)^{-1/2} = 5\sqrt{2}$; $(2a - 1)^{1/2} = \dfrac{1}{5\sqrt{2}}$; $2a - 1 = \dfrac{1}{50}$; $100a - 50 = 1$; $100a = 51$;

$a = \dfrac{51}{100} = 0.51$

10. Let $x = \log_8 32$; $8^x = 32$; $(2^3)^x = 32$; $2^{3x} = 2^5$; $3x = 5$; $x = \dfrac{5}{3}$

11. $\dfrac{2^2 + 2^{-1}}{4^0 - 2^{-2}} = \dfrac{4 + \dfrac{1}{2}}{1 - \dfrac{1}{4}} = \dfrac{\dfrac{9}{2}}{\dfrac{3}{4}} = \dfrac{9}{2} \cdot \dfrac{4}{3} = 6$

12. $(-27^{2/3})^{-2} = \dfrac{1}{(-27^{2/3})^2} = \dfrac{1}{27^{4/3}} = \dfrac{1}{3^4} = \dfrac{1}{81}$

13. $\displaystyle\sum_{k=1}^{500} (7 - 2k) = \dfrac{500}{2}[2(5) + 499(-2)] = 250(-988) = -247{,}000$

14. slope of $5x - 2y$ is $10 = -\dfrac{5}{-2} = \dfrac{5}{2}$; $m = -\dfrac{2}{5}$; $\dfrac{y + 2}{x - 4} = -\dfrac{2}{5}$; $5y + 10 = -2x + 8$;

$5y = -2x - 2$; $y = -\dfrac{2}{5}x - \dfrac{2}{5}$

15. $\underline{-1\,\lfloor}\ 4\quad 0\ -3\ -2$

$\qquad\ \ -4\quad 4\ -1 \quad 4m^2 - 4m + 1 - \dfrac{3}{m + 1}$

$\qquad \overline{4\ -4\quad 1\ -3}$

16. $[x - (-2 + 3i)][x - (-2 - 3i)] = 0$; $(x + 2 - 3i)(x + 2 + 3i) = 0$;

$x^2 + 2x + 3ix + 2x + 4 + 6i - 3ix - 6i + 9 = 0$; $x^2 + 4x + 13 = 0$

17. $f(g(-1)) = f(\sqrt{-1 + 5}) = f(2) = |2 - 10| = |-8| = 8$;

$g(f(-1)) = g(|-1 - 10|) = g(|-11|) = g(11) = \sqrt{11 + 5} = 4$

18. $y \log_{10} 7.18 = \log_{10} 157$; $y = \dfrac{\log_{10} 157}{\log_{10} 7.18} = \dfrac{2.1959}{0.8561} = 2.57$

19. $\sin\left(-\dfrac{2\pi}{3}\right) = -\dfrac{\sqrt{3}}{2}$; $\cos\left(-\dfrac{2\pi}{3}\right) = -\dfrac{1}{2}$; $\tan\left(-\dfrac{2\pi}{3}\right) = \sqrt{3}$; $\csc\left(-\dfrac{2\pi}{3}\right) = -\dfrac{2\sqrt{3}}{3}$;

$\sec\left(-\dfrac{2\pi}{3}\right) = -2$; $\cot\left(-\dfrac{2\pi}{3}\right) = \dfrac{\sqrt{3}}{3}$

20. $s^2 = 24^2 + 20^2 - 2(24)(20)\cos 78.4° = 783$; $s = 28.0$; $\dfrac{\sin R}{20} = \dfrac{\sin 78.4°}{28.0}$;

$\sin R = \dfrac{20(0.9796)}{28.0} = 0.6997$; $\angle R = 44.4°$; $\angle T = 180° - (78.4° + 44.4°) = 57.2°$

21. Let θ be the angle between $\mathbf{u}$ and $\mathbf{v}$;

$\cos\theta = \dfrac{\mathbf{u}\cdot\mathbf{v}}{\|\mathbf{u}\|\,\|\mathbf{v}\|} = \dfrac{6\cdot 12 + (-8)(9)}{\sqrt{6^2 + (-8)^2}\,\sqrt{12^2 + 9^2}} = \dfrac{72 - 72}{10\cdot 15} = 0$; $\theta = 90°$

22. $r = \sqrt{(2\sqrt{3})^2 + 2^2} = 4$; $\cos\theta = \dfrac{2\sqrt{3}}{4} = \dfrac{\sqrt{3}}{2}$ and $\sin\theta = \dfrac{1}{2}$; let $\theta = 30°$;

$(2\sqrt{3} + 2i)^4 = [4(\cos 30° + i\sin 30°)]^4 = 256(\cos 120° + i\sin 120°)$

23. a.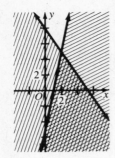

b.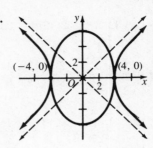

24. a. $\dfrac{\sqrt{3} + 2}{\sqrt{3} - 2} = \dfrac{(\sqrt{3} + 2)(\sqrt{3} + 2)}{(\sqrt{3} - 2)(\sqrt{3} + 2)} = \dfrac{3 + 4\sqrt{3} + 4}{3 - 4} = \dfrac{7 + 4\sqrt{3}}{-1} = -7 - 4\sqrt{3}$

    b. $\dfrac{4}{-1 + i} = \dfrac{4(-1 - i)}{(-1 + i)(-1 - i)} = \dfrac{-4 - 4i}{1 - (-1)} = \dfrac{-4 - 4i}{2} = -2 - 2i$

    c. $\dfrac{\sqrt[3]{-24}}{\sqrt[3]{15}} = \dfrac{\sqrt[3]{3(-8)}}{\sqrt[3]{(5)(3)}} = \dfrac{-2}{\sqrt[3]{5}} = -\dfrac{2\sqrt[3]{25}}{5}$

25. a. $7x - 9y = 29$ $35x - 45y = 145$

       $5x - 7y = 19$, $\underline{35x - 49y = 133}$

                                 $4y = 12;$ $y = 3;\ 7x - 27 = 29;\ 7x = 56;\ x = 8;\ (8, 3)$

    b. $x = -2y + 6;\ x^2 + y^2 = 4y^2 - 24y + 36 + y^2 = 9;\ 5y^2 - 24y + 27 = 0;$

       $(5y - 9)(y - 3) = 0;\ y = \dfrac{9}{5}$ or $y = 3;$ if $y = \dfrac{9}{5},\ x = -2\left(\dfrac{9}{5}\right) + 6 = \dfrac{12}{5};$

       if $y = 3;\ x = -2(3) + 6 = 0;\ \left\{\left(\dfrac{12}{5}, \dfrac{9}{5}\right), (0, 3)\right\}$

    c. $x + y - z = 0$ $3x + 3y - 3z = 0$ $48x + 8z = 24$

       $\underline{5x - y + 2z = 3}$, $\underline{2x - 3y - 5z = 29}$, $\underline{5x - 8z = 29}$

       $6x + z = 3$ $5x - 8z = 29$ $53x = 53;$ $x = 1;$

       $6 + z = 3;\ z = -3;\ 1 + y + 3 = 0;\ y = -4;\ (1, -4, -3)$

26. $\sin[\mathrm{Cos}^{-1}(-1) + \mathrm{Sin}^{-1}(-1)] = \sin\left(\pi - \dfrac{\pi}{2}\right) = \sin\dfrac{\pi}{2} = 1$

Page 672 · PREPARING FOR COLLEGE ENTRANCE EXAMS

1. A   **2.** C   **3.** A   **4.** C   **5.** D   **6.** E   **7.** C   **8.** C

Page 673 · CUMULATIVE REVIEW

  1. Examples: $-225°,\ 465°$

  2. $\sin \theta = \dfrac{5}{\sqrt{29}} = \dfrac{5\sqrt{29}}{29};\ \cos \theta = -\dfrac{2\sqrt{29}}{29};\ \tan \theta = -\dfrac{5}{2};\ \csc \theta = \dfrac{\sqrt{29}}{5};\ \sec \theta = -\dfrac{\sqrt{29}}{2};$

       $\cot \theta = -\dfrac{2}{5}$

3. Let d = distance from ground to top of ramp; $\sin 20° = \dfrac{d}{8}$; $d = 8(0.3420) = 2.74$;

2.74 ft

4. $\cos A = \dfrac{9^2 + 6^2 - 5^2}{2 \cdot 9 \cdot 6} = \dfrac{92}{108} = 0.8519$; $\angle A = 31.6°$; $\dfrac{\sin B}{9} = \dfrac{\sin 31.6°}{5}$;

$\sin B = \dfrac{9(0.5240)}{5} = 0.9432$; $\angle B = 70.6°$ or $109.4°$; since b is the longest side of $\triangle ABC$,

$\angle B = 109.4°$; $\angle C = 180° - (109.4° + 31.6°) = 39.0°$

5. $K = \dfrac{1}{2} bc \sin A = \dfrac{1}{2}(9)(6)(0.5240) = 14.1$

6. $-200° = \left(-200 \cdot \dfrac{\pi}{180}\right)^R = -\dfrac{10\pi}{9}{}^R$

7. $\sin\left(-\dfrac{13\pi}{6}\right) = -\dfrac{1}{2}$; $\cos\left(-\dfrac{13\pi}{6}\right) = \dfrac{\sqrt{3}}{2}$; $\tan\left(-\dfrac{13\pi}{6}\right) = -\dfrac{\sqrt{3}}{3}$; $\csc\left(-\dfrac{13\pi}{6}\right) = -2$;

$\sec\left(-\dfrac{13\pi}{6}\right) = \dfrac{2\sqrt{3}}{3}$; $\cot\left(-\dfrac{13\pi}{6}\right) = -\sqrt{3}$

8. amplitude = 5; period = $\dfrac{2\pi}{\dfrac{\pi}{3}} = 6$; maximum value = 3; minimum value = -7

9. $\dfrac{\cos\theta}{\sin^3\theta} = \dfrac{\cos\theta}{\sin\theta\sin^2\theta} = \cot\theta \cdot \dfrac{1}{\sin^2\theta} = \cot\theta\csc^2\theta = \cot\theta(1 + \cot^2\theta)$

10. **a.** $\dfrac{\sec x}{\cot x + \tan x} = \dfrac{\sec x}{\dfrac{\cos x}{\sin x} + \dfrac{\sin x}{\cos x}} = \dfrac{\sec x}{\dfrac{\cos^2 x + \sin^2 x}{\sin x \cos x}} = \sec x \cdot \dfrac{\sin x \cos x}{\cos^2 x + \sin^2 x} =$

$\dfrac{1}{\cos x} \cdot \dfrac{\sin x \cos x}{1} = \sin x$

b. $\cot(\alpha + \beta) = \dfrac{1}{\tan(\alpha + \beta)} = \dfrac{1 - \tan\alpha\tan\beta}{\tan\alpha + \tan\beta} = \dfrac{1 - \dfrac{1}{\cot\alpha} \cdot \dfrac{1}{\cot\beta}}{\dfrac{1}{\cot\alpha} + \dfrac{1}{\cot\beta}} =$

$\dfrac{\dfrac{\cot\alpha\cot\beta - 1}{\cot\alpha\cot\beta}}{\dfrac{\cot\beta + \cot\alpha}{\cot\alpha\cot\beta}} = \dfrac{\cot\alpha\cot\beta - 1}{\cot\alpha + \cot\beta}$

11. Since $90° < \phi < 270°$ and $\sin\phi < 0$, $180° < \phi < 270°$;

$\cos\phi = -\sqrt{1 - \sin^2\phi} = -\sqrt{1 - \dfrac{9}{25}} = -\dfrac{4}{5}$

a. Since $180° < \phi < 270°$, $90° < \dfrac{\phi}{2} < 135°$, and $\cos\dfrac{\phi}{2} < 0$;

$\cos\dfrac{\phi}{2} = -\sqrt{\dfrac{1 - \dfrac{4}{5}}{2}} = -\sqrt{\dfrac{1}{10}} = -\dfrac{\sqrt{10}}{10}$

b. $\cos 2\phi = 1 - 2\sin^2\phi = 1 - 2\left(-\dfrac{3}{5}\right)^2 = \dfrac{7}{25}$

c. $\tan(180° - \phi) = \tan(-\phi) = -\tan\phi = -\dfrac{\sin\phi}{\cos\phi} = -\left(\dfrac{-\dfrac{3}{5}}{-\dfrac{4}{5}}\right) = -\dfrac{3}{4}$

d. $\sin(90° + \phi) = \sin[90° - (-\phi)] = \cos(-\phi) = \cos\phi = -\dfrac{4}{5}$

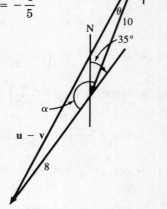

12. $\alpha = 165°$; $|\mathbf{u} - \mathbf{v}|^2 = 8^2 + 10^2 - 2(8)(10)\cos 165° = 318.54$; $|\mathbf{u} - \mathbf{v}| = 17.8$;

$\dfrac{\sin\theta}{8} = \dfrac{\sin 16°}{17.8}$; $\sin\theta = \dfrac{8(0.2588)}{17.8} = 0.1163$; $\theta = 6.7°$, bearing $= 200° + \theta = 206.7°$

13. Let $\mathbf{u} = a\mathbf{i} + b\mathbf{j}$; $(a\mathbf{i} + b\mathbf{j}) \cdot (2\mathbf{i} - \mathbf{j}) = 0$; $2a - b = 0$; let $a = 1$ and $b = 2$; $\mathbf{u} = \mathbf{i} + 2\mathbf{j}$;

$\dfrac{\mathbf{u}}{\|\mathbf{u}\|} = \dfrac{\mathbf{i} + 2\mathbf{j}}{\sqrt{1^2 + 2^2}} = \dfrac{\mathbf{i} + 2\mathbf{j}}{\sqrt{5}} = \dfrac{\sqrt{5}}{5}\mathbf{i} + \dfrac{2\sqrt{5}}{5}\mathbf{j}$

14. $r = \sqrt{2^2 + (-2\sqrt{3})^2} = 4$; $\cos\theta = \dfrac{1}{2}$ and $\sin\theta = -\dfrac{\sqrt{3}}{2}$; let $\theta = 300°$;

$(2 - 2i\sqrt{3})^5 = [4(\cos 300° + i\sin 300°)]^5 = 1024(\cos 1500° + i\sin 1500°) =$

$1024(\cos 60° + i\sin 60°) = 1024\left(\dfrac{1}{2} + \dfrac{i\sqrt{3}}{2}\right) = 512 + 512i\sqrt{3}$

15. $-8i = 8(\cos 270° + i\sin 270°)$; $r^3(\cos 3\theta + i\sin 3\theta) = 8(\cos 270° + i\sin 270°)$;

$r^3 = 8$; $r = 2$; $\cos 3\theta = \cos 270°$; $3\theta = 270° + k \cdot 360°$; $\theta = 90° + k \cdot 120°$, $k = 0, 1, 2$;

$r_1 = 2(\cos 90° + i\sin 90°) = 2(0 + i) = 2i$;

$r_2 = 2[\cos(90° + 120°) + i\sin(90° + 120°)] = 2(\cos 210° + i\sin 210°) =$

$2\left(-\dfrac{\sqrt{3}}{2} - \dfrac{i}{2}\right) = -\sqrt{3} - i$; $r_3 = 2[\cos(90° + 240°) + i\sin(90° + 240°)] =$

$2(\cos 330° + i\sin 330°) = 2\left(\dfrac{\sqrt{3}}{2} - \dfrac{i}{2}\right) = \sqrt{3} - i$

16. π

17. Let y be a first-quadrant angle with $\cot y = \dfrac{4}{3}$; $\sin y = \dfrac{3}{5}$ and $\cos y = \dfrac{4}{5}$;

$$\sin\left(\text{Cos}^{-1}\frac{1}{2} - \text{Cot}^{-1}\frac{4}{3}\right) = \sin\left(\frac{\pi}{3} - y\right) = \sin\frac{\pi}{3}\cos y - \cos\frac{\pi}{3}\sin y =$$

$$\frac{\sqrt{3}}{2}\left(\frac{4}{5}\right) - \frac{1}{2}\left(\frac{3}{5}\right) = \frac{4\sqrt{3} - 3}{10}$$

18. Let y be a fourth-quadrant angle with $\sin y = -\dfrac{5}{13}$; $\tan y = -\dfrac{5}{12}$;

$$\tan\left[2\,\text{Sin}^{-1}\left(-\frac{5}{13}\right)\right] = \tan 2y = \frac{2\tan y}{1 - \tan^2 y} = \frac{2\left(-\dfrac{5}{12}\right)}{1 - \left(-\dfrac{5}{12}\right)^2} = \frac{-\dfrac{5}{6}}{\dfrac{119}{144}} = -\frac{120}{119}$$

19. $2\csc^2 x + 3\csc x - 2 = 0$; $(2\csc x - 1)(\csc x + 2) = 0$; $\csc x = \dfrac{1}{2}$ (reject) or

$\csc x = -2;\ \left\{\dfrac{7\pi}{6}, \dfrac{11\pi}{6}\right\}$

20. $x + \dfrac{\pi}{3} = \dfrac{7\pi}{6}$ or $x + \dfrac{\pi}{3} = \dfrac{11\pi}{6}$; $\left\{\dfrac{5\pi}{6}, \dfrac{3\pi}{2}\right\}$

21. $\cos 2\theta - 3\cos\theta - 1 = 0$; $2\cos^2\theta - 1 - 3\cos\theta - 1 = 0$; $2\cos^2\theta - 3\cos\theta - 2 = 0$;

$(\cos\theta - 2)(2\cos\theta + 1) = 0$; $\cos\theta = 2$ (reject) or $\cos\theta = -\dfrac{1}{2}$; $\{120°, 240°\}$

22. $3\tan^2\theta = 1$; $\tan^2\theta = \dfrac{1}{3}$; $\tan\theta = \pm\dfrac{\sqrt{3}}{3}$; $\{30°, 150°, 210°, 330°\}$

Page 676 · WRITTEN EXERCISES

A 1. $\begin{bmatrix} 0 \\ 0 \end{bmatrix}$ 2. $\begin{bmatrix} 0 & 0 \\ 0 & 0 \\ 0 & 0 \end{bmatrix}$ 3. $\begin{bmatrix} 0 & 0 & 0 \end{bmatrix}$ 4. $\begin{bmatrix} 0 & 0 \\ 0 & 0 \\ 0 & 0 \\ 0 & 0 \\ 0 & 0 \end{bmatrix}$

5. $x = y = z = 0$ 6. $x - 4 = 0$; $x = 4$; $6y = 0$; $y = 0$; $10 - z = 0$; $z = 10$

7. $5 - x = 0$; $x = 5$; $2y + 6 = 0$; $y = -3$; $z - 3 = 0$; $z = 3$

8. $x = -4$ 9. $x = 8$; $y = -5$

B 10. $\begin{matrix} x + y = 2 \\ x - y = 8 \end{matrix}$; $2x = 10$; $x = 5$; $5 + y = 2$; $y = -3$

11. $8 - y = -3y$; $2y = -8$; $y = -4$; $x + 2z = -5$; $x = -2z - 5$; $x + z = -1$;
    $-2z - 5 + z = -1$; $-z = 4$; $z = -4$; $x = -2(-4) - 5 = 3$

12. $x - y = 4$; $x = y + 4$; $2x + 3y = 3$; $2y + 8 + 3y = 3$; $5y = -5$; $y = -1$;
    $x = -1 + 4 = 3$

13. $\begin{matrix} 2x - y = 6 \\ 3x + 5y = 22 \end{matrix}$; $\begin{matrix} 10x - 5y = 30 \\ 3x + 5y = 22 \end{matrix}$; $13x = 52$; $x = 4$; $8 - y = 6$; $y = 2$

14. $ax = 1$; $x = \dfrac{1}{a}$; $by = 0$; $y = 0$

15. $ax + b = 1$; $ax = 1 - b$; $x = \dfrac{1 - b}{a}$; $cy + d = 0$; $cy = -d$; $y = -\dfrac{d}{c}$

16. $\begin{matrix} ax + y = 1 \\ bx + y = 0 \end{matrix}$; $ax - bx = 1$; $x(a - b) = 1$; $x = \dfrac{1}{a - b}$, $a \neq b$; $\dfrac{b}{a - b} + y = 0$;

    $y = -\dfrac{b}{a - b}$

17. $\begin{matrix} ax + by = 1 \\ cx + dy = 1 \end{matrix}$; $\begin{matrix} acx + bcy = c \\ acx + ady = a \end{matrix}$; $ady - bcy = a - c$; $y = \dfrac{a - c}{ad - bc}$;

    $ax + \dfrac{ba - bc}{ad - bc} = 1$; $ax = \dfrac{ad - bc - ba + bc}{ad - bc}$; $x = \dfrac{d - b}{ad - bc}$

Page 680 · WRITTEN EXERCISES

A 1. $\begin{bmatrix} 4 & 2 \\ -1 & 0 \end{bmatrix} + \begin{bmatrix} 1 & 2 \\ 0 & 3 \end{bmatrix} = \begin{bmatrix} 4+1 & 2+2 \\ -1+0 & 0+3 \end{bmatrix} = \begin{bmatrix} 5 & 4 \\ -1 & 3 \end{bmatrix}$

2. $\begin{bmatrix} 2 & -6 \\ 2 & 10 \end{bmatrix} + \begin{bmatrix} -2 & 2 \\ 2 & -7 \end{bmatrix} = \begin{bmatrix} 2+(-2) & -6+2 \\ 2+2 & 10+(-7) \end{bmatrix} = \begin{bmatrix} 0 & -4 \\ 4 & 3 \end{bmatrix}$

3. $\begin{bmatrix} 8 & 0 \\ 4 & 10 \end{bmatrix} - \begin{bmatrix} 3 & 4 \\ -1 & 9 \end{bmatrix} = \begin{bmatrix} 8 & 0 \\ 4 & 10 \end{bmatrix} + \begin{bmatrix} -3 & -4 \\ 1 & -9 \end{bmatrix} = \begin{bmatrix} 8 + (-3) & 0 + (-4) \\ 4 + 1 & 10 + (-9) \end{bmatrix} = \begin{bmatrix} 5 & -4 \\ 5 & 1 \end{bmatrix}$

4. $\begin{bmatrix} 10 & 3 \\ -4 & 6 \end{bmatrix} - \begin{bmatrix} 4 & -2 \\ 9 & -2 \end{bmatrix} = \begin{bmatrix} 10 & 3 \\ -4 & 6 \end{bmatrix} + \begin{bmatrix} -4 & 2 \\ -9 & 2 \end{bmatrix} = \begin{bmatrix} 10 + (-4) & 3 + 2 \\ -4 + (-9) & 6 + 2 \end{bmatrix} = \begin{bmatrix} 6 & 5 \\ -13 & 8 \end{bmatrix}$

5. $\begin{bmatrix} 4 & 7 \\ 2 & -1 \\ 0 & 5 \end{bmatrix} + \begin{bmatrix} 0 & 5 \\ 2 & 4 \\ 3 & -2 \end{bmatrix} = \begin{bmatrix} 4 + 0 & 7 + 5 \\ 2 + 2 & -1 + 4 \\ 0 + 3 & 5 + (-2) \end{bmatrix} = \begin{bmatrix} 4 & 12 \\ 4 & 3 \\ 3 & 3 \end{bmatrix}$

6. $\begin{bmatrix} 5 & 8 \\ -2 & 14 \\ 0 & -6 \end{bmatrix} - \begin{bmatrix} 4 & 4 \\ 4 & -2 \\ -5 & -5 \end{bmatrix} = \begin{bmatrix} 5 & 8 \\ -2 & 14 \\ 0 & -6 \end{bmatrix} + \begin{bmatrix} -4 & -4 \\ -4 & 2 \\ 5 & 5 \end{bmatrix} = \begin{bmatrix} 5 + (-4) & 8 + (-4) \\ -2 + (-4) & 14 + 2 \\ 0 + 5 & -6 + 5 \end{bmatrix} =$
$\begin{bmatrix} 1 & 4 \\ -6 & 16 \\ 5 & -1 \end{bmatrix}$

7. $\begin{bmatrix} 0 & -2 & 5 \\ 3 & -6 & 2 \end{bmatrix} + \begin{bmatrix} 14 & 7 & 0 \\ 4 & 5 & -7 \end{bmatrix} = \begin{bmatrix} 0 + 14 & -2 + 7 & 5 + 0 \\ 3 + 4 & -6 + 5 & 2 + (-7) \end{bmatrix} = \begin{bmatrix} 14 & 5 & 5 \\ 7 & -1 & -5 \end{bmatrix}$

8. $12 \begin{bmatrix} 3 & 0 \\ -5 & 2 \end{bmatrix} = \begin{bmatrix} 12 \cdot 3 & 12 \cdot 0 \\ 12(-5) & 12 \cdot 2 \end{bmatrix} = \begin{bmatrix} 36 & 0 \\ -60 & 24 \end{bmatrix}$

9. $2 \begin{bmatrix} 5 & -2 \\ -3 & 4 \\ 0 & 6 \end{bmatrix} + \begin{bmatrix} 1 & 7 \\ 0 & -4 \\ 6 & 5 \end{bmatrix} = \begin{bmatrix} 10 & -4 \\ -6 & 8 \\ 0 & 12 \end{bmatrix} + \begin{bmatrix} 1 & 7 \\ 0 & -4 \\ 6 & 5 \end{bmatrix} = \begin{bmatrix} 11 & 3 \\ -6 & 4 \\ 6 & 17 \end{bmatrix}$

10. $\begin{bmatrix} 3 & 0 \\ 5 & -4 \\ 0 & -3 \end{bmatrix} - 4 \begin{bmatrix} 10 & -2 \\ 2 & 4 \\ -7 & 0 \end{bmatrix} = \begin{bmatrix} 3 & 0 \\ 5 & -4 \\ 0 & -3 \end{bmatrix} - \begin{bmatrix} 40 & -8 \\ 8 & 16 \\ -28 & 0 \end{bmatrix} = \begin{bmatrix} -37 & 8 \\ -3 & -20 \\ 28 & -3 \end{bmatrix}$

11. $\begin{bmatrix} 3 & -4 & 2 \\ 5 & 8 & 0 \end{bmatrix} + (-3) \begin{bmatrix} 2 & 0 & 1 \\ -1 & -1 & 2 \end{bmatrix} = \begin{bmatrix} 3 & -4 & 2 \\ 5 & 8 & 0 \end{bmatrix} + \begin{bmatrix} -6 & 0 & -3 \\ 3 & 3 & -6 \end{bmatrix} = \begin{bmatrix} -3 & -4 & -1 \\ 8 & 11 & -6 \end{bmatrix}$

12. $\begin{bmatrix} 15 & -6 \\ -2 & 10 \end{bmatrix} - \begin{bmatrix} 15 & -6 \\ -2 & 10 \end{bmatrix} = \begin{bmatrix} 0 & 0 \\ 0 & 0 \end{bmatrix}$ 13. $\begin{bmatrix} 7 & -5 \\ 4 & -1 \end{bmatrix} + \begin{bmatrix} -7 & 5 \\ -4 & 1 \end{bmatrix} = \begin{bmatrix} 0 & 0 \\ 0 & 0 \end{bmatrix}$

14. $O_{2 \times 3} + \begin{bmatrix} 3 & 5 & 2 \\ -2 & 8 & 0 \end{bmatrix} = \begin{bmatrix} 3 & 5 & 2 \\ -2 & 8 & 0 \end{bmatrix}$

15. $O_{2 \times 3} - 5 \begin{bmatrix} 2 & 0 & 3 \\ 2 & 4 & -1 \end{bmatrix} = O_{2 \times 3} + \begin{bmatrix} -10 & 0 & -15 \\ -10 & -20 & 5 \end{bmatrix} = \begin{bmatrix} -10 & 0 & -15 \\ -10 & -20 & 5 \end{bmatrix}$

16. $3 \begin{bmatrix} 2 \\ 2 \\ 5 \end{bmatrix} + 5 \begin{bmatrix} 0 \\ 6 \\ 3 \end{bmatrix} = \begin{bmatrix} 6 \\ 6 \\ 15 \end{bmatrix} + \begin{bmatrix} 0 \\ 30 \\ 15 \end{bmatrix} = \begin{bmatrix} 6 \\ 36 \\ 30 \end{bmatrix}$

B 17. $X + \begin{bmatrix} 2 & 0 \\ 1 & 3 \end{bmatrix} = \begin{bmatrix} 5 & -3 \\ -1 & 0 \end{bmatrix}; X + \begin{bmatrix} 2 & 0 \\ 1 & 3 \end{bmatrix} + \begin{bmatrix} -2 & 0 \\ -1 & -3 \end{bmatrix} = \begin{bmatrix} 5 & -3 \\ -1 & 0 \end{bmatrix} + \begin{bmatrix} -2 & 0 \\ -1 & -3 \end{bmatrix};$
$X = \begin{bmatrix} 3 & -3 \\ -2 & -3 \end{bmatrix}$

18. $X + \begin{bmatrix} 0 & 2 \\ 5 & 0 \end{bmatrix} = \begin{bmatrix} 2 & -4 \\ 3 & 0 \end{bmatrix}$; $X + \begin{bmatrix} 0 & 2 \\ 5 & 0 \end{bmatrix} + \begin{bmatrix} 0 & -2 \\ -5 & 0 \end{bmatrix} = \begin{bmatrix} 2 & -4 \\ 3 & 0 \end{bmatrix} + \begin{bmatrix} 0 & -2 \\ -5 & 0 \end{bmatrix}$;

$X = \begin{bmatrix} 2 & -6 \\ -2 & 0 \end{bmatrix}$

19. $2X + \begin{bmatrix} 0 & -4 \\ 1 & 6 \end{bmatrix} = 2\begin{bmatrix} 1 & 1 \\ \frac{1}{2} & 1 \end{bmatrix}$; $2X + \begin{bmatrix} 0 & -4 \\ 1 & 6 \end{bmatrix} + \begin{bmatrix} 0 & 4 \\ -1 & -6 \end{bmatrix} = \begin{bmatrix} 2 & 2 \\ 1 & 2 \end{bmatrix} + \begin{bmatrix} 0 & 4 \\ -1 & -6 \end{bmatrix}$;

$2X = \begin{bmatrix} 2 & 6 \\ 0 & -4 \end{bmatrix}$; $X = \begin{bmatrix} 1 & 3 \\ 0 & -2 \end{bmatrix}$

20. $3X + \begin{bmatrix} -9 & 2 \\ 1 & -5 \end{bmatrix} = \frac{1}{3}\begin{bmatrix} 9 & -3 \\ -6 & 12 \end{bmatrix}$; $3X + \begin{bmatrix} -9 & 2 \\ 1 & -5 \end{bmatrix} + \begin{bmatrix} 9 & -2 \\ -1 & 5 \end{bmatrix} =$

$\begin{bmatrix} 3 & -1 \\ -2 & 4 \end{bmatrix} + \begin{bmatrix} 9 & -2 \\ -1 & 5 \end{bmatrix}$; $3X\begin{bmatrix} 12 & -3 \\ -3 & 9 \end{bmatrix}$; $X = \begin{bmatrix} 4 & -1 \\ -1 & 3 \end{bmatrix}$

C   **21-23.** Let $A = \begin{bmatrix} a & b \\ c & d \end{bmatrix}$ and $B = \begin{bmatrix} e & f \\ g & h \end{bmatrix}$.

21. $A + B = \begin{bmatrix} a+e & b+f \\ c+g & d+h \end{bmatrix} = \begin{bmatrix} e+a & f+b \\ g+c & h+d \end{bmatrix} = B + A$

22. $(-1)A = (-1)\begin{bmatrix} a & b \\ c & d \end{bmatrix} = \begin{bmatrix} -1(a) & -1(b) \\ -1(c) & -1(d) \end{bmatrix} = \begin{bmatrix} -a & -b \\ -c & -d \end{bmatrix} = -A$

23. $(pq)B = (pq)\begin{bmatrix} e & f \\ g & h \end{bmatrix} = \begin{bmatrix} (pq)e & (pq)f \\ (pq)g & (pq)h \end{bmatrix} = \begin{bmatrix} p(qe) & p(qf) \\ p(qg) & p(qh) \end{bmatrix} = p\begin{bmatrix} qe & qf \\ qg & qh \end{bmatrix} = p(qB)$

Page 685 · WRITTEN EXERCISES

A   **1.** $[2 \quad 6]\begin{bmatrix} 1 \\ 5 \end{bmatrix} = [2 + 30] = [32]$ **2.** $[-4 \quad 0 \quad 2]\begin{bmatrix} 1 \\ -2 \\ 0 \end{bmatrix} = [-4 + 0 + 0] = [-4]$

3. $\begin{bmatrix} 6 \\ -1 \end{bmatrix}[3 \quad 0 \quad 4 \quad 2] = \begin{bmatrix} 18 & 0 & 24 & 12 \\ -3 & 0 & -4 & -2 \end{bmatrix}$ **4.** $\begin{bmatrix} -1 & 2 \\ 1 & 0 \end{bmatrix}\begin{bmatrix} 3 \\ 2 \end{bmatrix} = \begin{bmatrix} 1 \\ 3 \end{bmatrix}$

5. $\begin{bmatrix} 3 & -1 \\ 2 & 0 \end{bmatrix}\begin{bmatrix} 2 & 4 \\ 0 & -2 \end{bmatrix} = \begin{bmatrix} 6 & 14 \\ 4 & 8 \end{bmatrix}$ **6.** $\begin{bmatrix} 4 & 0 \\ 2 & -2 \\ 5 & 2 \end{bmatrix}\begin{bmatrix} 2 & 3 & 0 \\ -1 & 0 & -1 \end{bmatrix} = \begin{bmatrix} 8 & 12 & 0 \\ 6 & 6 & 2 \\ 8 & 15 & -2 \end{bmatrix}$

7. $\begin{bmatrix} 2 & 1 & 0 \\ 0 & -4 & 1 \\ 4 & -2 & 0 \end{bmatrix}\begin{bmatrix} -1 & 0 & 0 \\ 0 & 1 & -2 \\ 0 & 1 & -1 \end{bmatrix} = \begin{bmatrix} -2 & 1 & -2 \\ 0 & -3 & 7 \\ -4 & -2 & 4 \end{bmatrix}$

8. $\begin{bmatrix} 0 & 1 & 0 \\ 2 & -1 & 0 \\ 0 & 0 & 1 \end{bmatrix}\begin{bmatrix} 2 & -3 & 1 \\ -1 & 0 & -2 \\ 0 & 1 & 0 \end{bmatrix} = \begin{bmatrix} -1 & 0 & -2 \\ 5 & -6 & 4 \\ 0 & 1 & 0 \end{bmatrix}$

9. $\begin{bmatrix} 3 & 0 \\ 0 & -1 \\ 1 & 2 \end{bmatrix} \begin{bmatrix} 1 & 0 & -1 & 1 \\ 0 & 1 & 1 & -1 \end{bmatrix} = \begin{bmatrix} 3 & 0 & -3 & 3 \\ 0 & -1 & -1 & 1 \\ 1 & 2 & 1 & -1 \end{bmatrix}$

10. $\begin{bmatrix} 1 & 0 & 2 \\ -2 & 1 & 0 \\ 1 & 0 & 0 \end{bmatrix} \begin{bmatrix} a & b & c \\ d & e & f \\ g & h & i \end{bmatrix} = \begin{bmatrix} a+2g & b+2h & c+2i \\ -2a+d & -2b+e & -2c+f \\ a & b & c \end{bmatrix}$

11. $\begin{bmatrix} 1 & 0 & 2 \\ 5 & -1 & 0 \\ 0 & -2 & 4 \end{bmatrix} \begin{bmatrix} r & s & t \\ u & v & w \\ x & y & z \end{bmatrix} = \begin{bmatrix} r+2x & s+2y & t+2z \\ 5r-u & 5s-v & 5t-w \\ -2u+4x & -2v+4y & -2w+4z \end{bmatrix}$

12. $\begin{bmatrix} a & b & c \\ d & e & f \\ g & h & i \end{bmatrix} \begin{bmatrix} 2 & 1 & 4 \\ -2 & 10 & -2 \\ -4 & 2 & -1 \end{bmatrix} = \begin{bmatrix} 2a-2b-4c & a+10b+2c & 4a-2b-c \\ 2d-2e-4f & d+10e+2f & 4d-2e-f \\ 2g-2h-4i & g+10h+2i & 4g-2h-i \end{bmatrix}$

B 13. $AB = \begin{bmatrix} 2 & 1 \\ -1 & 0 \end{bmatrix} \begin{bmatrix} 0 & 1 \\ 1 & 1 \end{bmatrix} = \begin{bmatrix} 1 & 3 \\ 0 & -1 \end{bmatrix}$; $BA = \begin{bmatrix} 0 & 1 \\ 1 & 1 \end{bmatrix} \begin{bmatrix} 2 & 1 \\ -1 & 0 \end{bmatrix} = \begin{bmatrix} -1 & 0 \\ 1 & 1 \end{bmatrix}$

14. $BC = \begin{bmatrix} 0 & 1 \\ 1 & 1 \end{bmatrix} \begin{bmatrix} 0 & -3 \\ 1 & 0 \end{bmatrix} = \begin{bmatrix} 1 & 0 \\ 1 & -3 \end{bmatrix}$; $CB = \begin{bmatrix} 0 & -3 \\ 1 & 0 \end{bmatrix} \begin{bmatrix} 0 & 1 \\ 1 & 1 \end{bmatrix} = \begin{bmatrix} -3 & -3 \\ 0 & 1 \end{bmatrix}$

15. $(AB)C = \begin{bmatrix} 1 & 3 \\ 0 & -1 \end{bmatrix} \begin{bmatrix} 0 & -3 \\ 1 & 0 \end{bmatrix}$ (from Ex. 13) $= \begin{bmatrix} 3 & -3 \\ -1 & 0 \end{bmatrix}$;

$A(BC) = \begin{bmatrix} 2 & 1 \\ -1 & 0 \end{bmatrix} \begin{bmatrix} 1 & 0 \\ 1 & -3 \end{bmatrix}$ (from Ex. 14) $= \begin{bmatrix} 3 & -3 \\ -1 & 0 \end{bmatrix}$

16. From Ex. 14, $BC = \begin{bmatrix} 1 & 0 \\ 1 & -3 \end{bmatrix}$; $AC = \begin{bmatrix} 2 & 1 \\ -1 & 0 \end{bmatrix} \begin{bmatrix} 0 & -3 \\ 1 & 0 \end{bmatrix} = \begin{bmatrix} 1 & -6 \\ 0 & 3 \end{bmatrix}$;

$AC + BC = \begin{bmatrix} 1 & -6 \\ 0 & 3 \end{bmatrix} + \begin{bmatrix} 1 & 0 \\ 1 & -3 \end{bmatrix} = \begin{bmatrix} 2 & -6 \\ 1 & 0 \end{bmatrix}$;

$(A+B)C = \left(\begin{bmatrix} 2 & 1 \\ -1 & 0 \end{bmatrix} + \begin{bmatrix} 0 & 1 \\ 1 & 1 \end{bmatrix} \right) \begin{bmatrix} 0 & -3 \\ 1 & 0 \end{bmatrix} = \begin{bmatrix} 2 & 2 \\ 0 & 1 \end{bmatrix} \begin{bmatrix} 0 & -3 \\ 1 & 0 \end{bmatrix} = \begin{bmatrix} 2 & -6 \\ 1 & 0 \end{bmatrix}$

17. From Ex. 16, $A + B = \begin{bmatrix} 2 & 2 \\ 0 & 1 \end{bmatrix}$; $A - B = \begin{bmatrix} 2 & 1 \\ -1 & 0 \end{bmatrix} - \begin{bmatrix} 0 & 1 \\ 1 & 1 \end{bmatrix} = \begin{bmatrix} 2 & 0 \\ -2 & -1 \end{bmatrix}$;

$(A+B)(A-B) = \begin{bmatrix} 2 & 2 \\ 0 & 1 \end{bmatrix} \begin{bmatrix} 2 & 0 \\ -2 & -1 \end{bmatrix} = \begin{bmatrix} 0 & -2 \\ -2 & -1 \end{bmatrix}$;

$A^2 - B^2 = \begin{bmatrix} 2 & 1 \\ -1 & 0 \end{bmatrix} \begin{bmatrix} 2 & 1 \\ -1 & 0 \end{bmatrix} - \begin{bmatrix} 0 & 1 \\ 1 & 1 \end{bmatrix} \begin{bmatrix} 0 & 1 \\ 1 & 1 \end{bmatrix} = \begin{bmatrix} 3 & 2 \\ -2 & -1 \end{bmatrix} - \begin{bmatrix} 1 & 1 \\ 1 & 2 \end{bmatrix} = \begin{bmatrix} 2 & 1 \\ -3 & -3 \end{bmatrix}$

18. From Ex. 16, $(A+B)^2 = \begin{bmatrix} 2 & 2 \\ 0 & 1 \end{bmatrix} \begin{bmatrix} 2 & 2 \\ 0 & 1 \end{bmatrix} = \begin{bmatrix} 4 & 6 \\ 0 & 1 \end{bmatrix}$; from Ex. 17, $A^2 = \begin{bmatrix} 3 & 2 \\ -2 & -1 \end{bmatrix}$

and $B^2 = \begin{bmatrix} 1 & 1 \\ 1 & 2 \end{bmatrix}$; from Ex. 13, $AB = \begin{bmatrix} 1 & 3 \\ 0 & -1 \end{bmatrix}$; $A^2 + 2AB + B^2 =$

$\begin{bmatrix} 3 & 2 \\ -2 & -1 \end{bmatrix} + 2 \begin{bmatrix} 1 & 3 \\ 0 & -1 \end{bmatrix} + \begin{bmatrix} 1 & 1 \\ 1 & 2 \end{bmatrix} = \begin{bmatrix} 4 & 3 \\ -1 & 1 \end{bmatrix} + \begin{bmatrix} 2 & 6 \\ 0 & -2 \end{bmatrix} = \begin{bmatrix} 6 & 9 \\ -1 & -1 \end{bmatrix}$

19. $O_{2\times2} \cdot A = \begin{bmatrix} 0 & 0 \\ 0 & 0 \end{bmatrix}\begin{bmatrix} 2 & 1 \\ -1 & 0 \end{bmatrix} = \begin{bmatrix} 0 & 0 \\ 0 & 0 \end{bmatrix}$; $A \cdot O_{2\times2} = \begin{bmatrix} 2 & 1 \\ -1 & 0 \end{bmatrix}\begin{bmatrix} 0 & 0 \\ 0 & 0 \end{bmatrix} = \begin{bmatrix} 0 & 0 \\ 0 & 0 \end{bmatrix}$

20. $I_{2\times2} \cdot C = \begin{bmatrix} 1 & 0 \\ 0 & 1 \end{bmatrix}\begin{bmatrix} 0 & -3 \\ 1 & 0 \end{bmatrix} = \begin{bmatrix} 0 & -3 \\ 1 & 0 \end{bmatrix}$; $C \cdot I_{2\times2} = \begin{bmatrix} 0 & -3 \\ 1 & 0 \end{bmatrix}\begin{bmatrix} 1 & 0 \\ 0 & 1 \end{bmatrix} = \begin{bmatrix} 0 & -3 \\ 1 & 0 \end{bmatrix}$

21. $AB = \begin{bmatrix} 2 & -3 \\ 2 & 1 \end{bmatrix}\begin{bmatrix} \dfrac{1}{8} & \dfrac{3}{8} \\ -\dfrac{1}{4} & \dfrac{1}{4} \end{bmatrix} = \begin{bmatrix} 1 & 0 \\ 0 & 1 \end{bmatrix}$ **22.** $BA = \begin{bmatrix} \dfrac{1}{8} & \dfrac{3}{8} \\ -\dfrac{1}{4} & \dfrac{1}{4} \end{bmatrix}\begin{bmatrix} 2 & -3 \\ 2 & 1 \end{bmatrix} = \begin{bmatrix} 1 & 0 \\ 0 & 1 \end{bmatrix}$

23. a. $D^2 = \begin{bmatrix} -1 & 0 & 2 \\ 0 & 1 & -1 \\ 1 & -1 & 0 \end{bmatrix}\begin{bmatrix} -1 & 0 & 2 \\ 0 & 1 & -1 \\ 1 & -1 & 0 \end{bmatrix} = \begin{bmatrix} 3 & -2 & -2 \\ -1 & 2 & -1 \\ -1 & -1 & 3 \end{bmatrix}$

b. $D^3 = D \times D \times D = D \times D^2$ or $D^2 \times D$; $D^3 = \begin{bmatrix} 3 & -2 & -2 \\ -1 & 2 & -1 \\ -1 & -1 & 3 \end{bmatrix}\begin{bmatrix} -1 & 0 & 2 \\ 0 & 1 & -1 \\ 1 & -1 & 0 \end{bmatrix} =$

$\begin{bmatrix} -5 & 0 & 8 \\ 0 & 3 & -4 \\ 4 & -4 & -1 \end{bmatrix}$

c. $(-D)^2 = \begin{bmatrix} 1 & 0 & -2 \\ 0 & -1 & 1 \\ -1 & 1 & 0 \end{bmatrix}\begin{bmatrix} 1 & 0 & -2 \\ 0 & -1 & 1 \\ -1 & 1 & 0 \end{bmatrix} = \begin{bmatrix} 3 & -2 & -2 \\ -1 & 2 & -1 \\ -1 & -1 & 3 \end{bmatrix}$

C   **24-27.** Let $A = \begin{bmatrix} a & b \\ c & d \end{bmatrix}$, $B = \begin{bmatrix} e & f \\ g & h \end{bmatrix}$, and $C = \begin{bmatrix} i & j \\ k & l \end{bmatrix}$

24. $AI = \begin{bmatrix} a & b \\ c & d \end{bmatrix}\begin{bmatrix} 1 & 0 \\ 0 & 1 \end{bmatrix} = \begin{bmatrix} a & b \\ c & d \end{bmatrix} = A$; $IA = \begin{bmatrix} 1 & 0 \\ 0 & 1 \end{bmatrix}\begin{bmatrix} a & b \\ c & d \end{bmatrix} = \begin{bmatrix} a & b \\ c & d \end{bmatrix} = A$

25. $AO = \begin{bmatrix} a & b \\ c & d \end{bmatrix}\begin{bmatrix} 0 & 0 \\ 0 & 0 \end{bmatrix} = \begin{bmatrix} 0 & 0 \\ 0 & 0 \end{bmatrix} = 0$; $OA = \begin{bmatrix} 0 & 0 \\ 0 & 0 \end{bmatrix}\begin{bmatrix} a & b \\ c & d \end{bmatrix} = \begin{bmatrix} 0 & 0 \\ 0 & 0 \end{bmatrix} = 0$

26. $(AB)C = \left(\begin{bmatrix} a & b \\ c & d \end{bmatrix}\begin{bmatrix} e & f \\ g & h \end{bmatrix}\right)\begin{bmatrix} i & j \\ k & l \end{bmatrix} = \begin{bmatrix} ae + bg & af + bh \\ ce + dg & cf + dh \end{bmatrix}\begin{bmatrix} i & j \\ k & l \end{bmatrix} =$

$\begin{bmatrix} aei + bgi + afk + bhk & aej + bgi + afl + bhl \\ cei + dgi + cfk + dhk & cej + dgi + cfl + dhl \end{bmatrix} =$

$\begin{bmatrix} a(ei + fk) + b(gi + hk) & a(ej + fl) + b(gj + hl) \\ c(ei + fk) + d(gi + hk) & c(ej + fl) + d(gj + hl) \end{bmatrix}$;

$A(BC) = \begin{bmatrix} a & b \\ c & d \end{bmatrix}\left(\begin{bmatrix} e & f \\ g & h \end{bmatrix}\begin{bmatrix} i & j \\ k & l \end{bmatrix}\right) = \begin{bmatrix} a & b \\ c & d \end{bmatrix}\begin{bmatrix} ei + fk & ej + fl \\ gi + hk & gj + hl \end{bmatrix} =$

$\begin{bmatrix} a(ei + fk) + b(gi + hk) & a(ej + fl) + b(gj + hl) \\ c(ei + fk) + d(gi + hk) & c(ej + fl) + d(gj + hl) \end{bmatrix}$

27. $A(B + C) = \begin{bmatrix} a & b \\ c & d \end{bmatrix} \left(\begin{bmatrix} e & f \\ g & h \end{bmatrix} + \begin{bmatrix} i & j \\ k & l \end{bmatrix} \right) = \begin{bmatrix} a & b \\ c & d \end{bmatrix} \begin{bmatrix} e + i & f + j \\ g + k & h + l \end{bmatrix} =$

$\begin{bmatrix} a(e + i) + b(g + k) & a(f + j) + b(h + l) \\ c(e + i) + d(g + k) & c(f + j) + d(h + l) \end{bmatrix};$

$AB + AC = \begin{bmatrix} a & b \\ c & d \end{bmatrix} \begin{bmatrix} e & f \\ g & h \end{bmatrix} + \begin{bmatrix} a & b \\ c & d \end{bmatrix} \begin{bmatrix} i & j \\ k & l \end{bmatrix} =$

$\begin{bmatrix} ae + dg & af + bh \\ ce + dg & cf + dh \end{bmatrix} + \begin{bmatrix} ai + bk & aj + bl \\ ci + dk & cj + dl \end{bmatrix} =$

$\begin{bmatrix} ae + bg + ai + bk & af + bh + aj + bl \\ ce + dg + ci + dk & cf + dh + cj + dl \end{bmatrix} =$

$\begin{bmatrix} a(e + i) + b(g + k) & a(f + j) + b(h + l) \\ c(e + i) + d(g + k) & c(f + j) + d(h + l) \end{bmatrix}$

Pages 690-691 · WRITTEN EXERCISES

A　**1.**

2.

To Station

$\begin{array}{c} & \begin{array}{ccccc} 1 & 2 & 3 & 4 & 5 \end{array} \\ \text{From Station} \begin{array}{c} 1 \\ 2 \\ 3 \\ 4 \\ 5 \end{array} & \begin{bmatrix} 0 & 1 & 0 & 0 & 0 \\ 1 & 0 & 1 & 1 & 0 \\ 0 & 1 & 0 & 0 & 1 \\ 0 & 1 & 0 & 0 & 1 \\ 0 & 0 & 0 & 0 & 0 \end{bmatrix} = A \end{array}$

3. $A^2 = \begin{bmatrix} 0 & 1 & 0 & 0 & 0 \\ 1 & 0 & 1 & 1 & 0 \\ 0 & 1 & 0 & 0 & 1 \\ 0 & 1 & 0 & 0 & 1 \\ 0 & 0 & 0 & 0 & 0 \end{bmatrix} \begin{bmatrix} 0 & 1 & 0 & 0 & 0 \\ 1 & 0 & 1 & 1 & 0 \\ 0 & 1 & 0 & 0 & 1 \\ 0 & 1 & 0 & 0 & 1 \\ 0 & 0 & 0 & 0 & 0 \end{bmatrix} = \begin{bmatrix} 1 & 0 & 1 & 1 & 0 \\ 0 & 3 & 0 & 0 & 2 \\ 1 & 0 & 1 & 1 & 0 \\ 1 & 0 & 1 & 1 & 0 \\ 0 & 0 & 0 & 0 & 0 \end{bmatrix}$

4. $\begin{array}{c} \\ \text{old members} \\ \text{new members} \end{array} \begin{array}{c} \text{fitness} \\ \begin{array}{cc} \text{room} & \text{pool} \end{array} \\ \begin{bmatrix} 1.00 & 0.60 \\ 0.56 & 0.86 \end{bmatrix} = T \end{array}$

5. $\begin{array}{c} \begin{array}{cc} \text{old} & \text{new} \\ \text{members} & \text{members} \end{array} \\ P = \begin{bmatrix} 450 & 250 \end{bmatrix} \end{array}$

6. $P \times T = \begin{bmatrix} 450 & 250 \end{bmatrix} \begin{bmatrix} 1.00 & 0.60 \\ 0.56 & 0.86 \end{bmatrix} = \begin{bmatrix} 450 + 140 & 270 + 215 \end{bmatrix} = \begin{bmatrix} 590 & 485 \end{bmatrix}$; 590 members will use the fitness room; 485 will use the pool.

B　**7.** $\begin{array}{c} & \begin{array}{c} \text{To} \\ \begin{array}{cccc} 1 & 2 & 3 & 4 \end{array} \end{array} \\ \text{From} \begin{array}{c} 1 \\ 2 \\ 3 \\ 4 \end{array} & \begin{bmatrix} 0 & 1 & 1 & 1 \\ 1 & 0 & 0 & 0 \\ 1 & 1 & 0 & 1 \\ 1 & 0 & 0 & 0 \end{bmatrix} = A; \end{array}$　$A^2 = \begin{bmatrix} 3 & 1 & 0 & 1 \\ 0 & 1 & 1 & 1 \\ 2 & 1 & 1 & 1 \\ 0 & 1 & 1 & 1 \end{bmatrix}$

8. $A + A^2 = \begin{bmatrix} 0 & 1 & 1 & 1 \\ 1 & 0 & 0 & 0 \\ 1 & 1 & 0 & 1 \\ 1 & 0 & 0 & 0 \end{bmatrix} + \begin{bmatrix} 3 & 1 & 0 & 1 \\ 0 & 1 & 1 & 1 \\ 2 & 1 & 1 & 1 \\ 0 & 1 & 1 & 1 \end{bmatrix} = \begin{bmatrix} 3 & 2 & 1 & 2 \\ 1 & 1 & 1 & 1 \\ 3 & 2 & 1 & 2 \\ 1 & 1 & 1 & 1 \end{bmatrix}$

9. $A^3 = A \cdot A^2 = \begin{bmatrix} 0 & 1 & 1 & 1 \\ 1 & 0 & 0 & 0 \\ 1 & 1 & 0 & 1 \\ 1 & 0 & 0 & 0 \end{bmatrix}\begin{bmatrix} 3 & 1 & 0 & 1 \\ 0 & 1 & 1 & 1 \\ 2 & 1 & 1 & 1 \\ 0 & 1 & 1 & 1 \end{bmatrix} = \begin{bmatrix} 2 & 3 & 3 & 3 \\ 3 & 1 & 0 & 1 \\ 3 & 3 & 2 & 3 \\ 3 & 1 & 0 & 1 \end{bmatrix}$

10. $A + A^2 + A^3 = \begin{bmatrix} 0 & 1 & 1 & 1 \\ 1 & 0 & 0 & 0 \\ 1 & 1 & 0 & 1 \\ 1 & 0 & 0 & 0 \end{bmatrix} + \begin{bmatrix} 3 & 1 & 0 & 1 \\ 0 & 1 & 1 & 1 \\ 2 & 1 & 1 & 1 \\ 0 & 1 & 1 & 1 \end{bmatrix} + \begin{bmatrix} 2 & 3 & 3 & 3 \\ 3 & 1 & 0 & 1 \\ 3 & 3 & 2 & 3 \\ 3 & 1 & 0 & 1 \end{bmatrix} = \begin{bmatrix} 5 & 5 & 4 & 5 \\ 4 & 2 & 1 & 2 \\ 6 & 5 & 3 & 5 \\ 4 & 2 & 1 & 2 \end{bmatrix}$

$\begin{array}{cc} & \text{taking} \quad \text{not taking} \\ & \text{2nd} \qquad \text{2nd} \\ & \text{semester} \quad \text{semester} \end{array}$

$\begin{array}{r} \text{taking 1st semester} \\ \text{not taking 1st semester} \end{array}\begin{bmatrix} 0.75 & 0.25 \\ 0.20 & 0.80 \end{bmatrix} = T; P = [500 \quad 220];$

$P \times T = [500 \quad 220]\begin{bmatrix} 0.75 & 0.25 \\ 0.20 & 0.80 \end{bmatrix} = [419 \quad 301];$ 419 students will study programming and 301 will not.

$\begin{array}{cc} & \text{To} \\ & 1 \ 2 \ 3 \ 4 \ 5 \end{array}$

11. From $\begin{array}{c} 1 \\ 2 \\ 3 \\ 4 \\ 5 \end{array}\begin{bmatrix} 0 & 1 & 0 & 0 & 0 \\ 1 & 0 & 1 & 0 & 0 \\ 1 & 0 & 0 & 1 & 0 \\ 1 & 0 & 0 & 0 & 1 \\ 1 & 1 & 1 & 1 & 0 \end{bmatrix} = A;$

$A + A^2 + A^3 = \begin{bmatrix} 0 & 1 & 0 & 0 & 0 \\ 1 & 0 & 1 & 0 & 0 \\ 1 & 0 & 0 & 1 & 0 \\ 1 & 0 & 0 & 0 & 1 \\ 1 & 1 & 1 & 1 & 0 \end{bmatrix} + \begin{bmatrix} 1 & 0 & 1 & 0 & 0 \\ 1 & 1 & 0 & 1 & 0 \\ 1 & 1 & 0 & 0 & 1 \\ 1 & 2 & 1 & 1 & 0 \\ 3 & 1 & 1 & 1 & 1 \end{bmatrix} + \begin{bmatrix} 1 & 1 & 0 & 1 & 0 \\ 2 & 1 & 1 & 0 & 1 \\ 2 & 2 & 2 & 1 & 0 \\ 4 & 1 & 2 & 1 & 1 \\ 4 & 4 & 2 & 2 & 1 \end{bmatrix} =$

$\begin{bmatrix} 2 & 2 & 1 & 1 & 0 \\ 4 & 2 & 2 & 1 & 1 \\ 4 & 3 & 2 & 2 & 1 \\ 6 & 3 & 3 & 2 & 2 \\ 8 & 6 & 4 & 4 & 2 \end{bmatrix}$ Each point can send a message back to itself in two ways (using no more than 2 relays).

city   suburb

12. $\begin{array}{l}\text{city}\\\text{suburb}\end{array}\begin{bmatrix}0.80 & 0.20\\0.30 & 0.70\end{bmatrix} = T;\ T^2 = \begin{bmatrix}0.70 & 0.30\\0.45 & 0.55\end{bmatrix};\ P = [0.40x \quad 0.60x];$

$P \times T^2 = [0.40x \quad 0.60x]\begin{bmatrix}0.70 & 0.30\\0.45 & 0.55\end{bmatrix} = [0.55 \quad 0.45];$ 55% of the population living in

either cities or suburbs will live in a city and 45% will live in the suburbs.

To

13. From $\begin{array}{c}\\1\\2\\3\\4\\5\\6\end{array}\begin{array}{cccccc}1 & 2 & 3 & 4 & 5 & 6\\\end{array}$
$\begin{array}{c}1\\2\\3\\4\\5\\6\end{array}\begin{bmatrix}0 & 1 & 0 & 1 & 0 & 0\\0 & 0 & 1 & 0 & 0 & 0\\0 & 1 & 0 & 0 & 1 & 1\\1 & 0 & 0 & 0 & 1 & 0\\0 & 0 & 1 & 1 & 0 & 0\\1 & 0 & 0 & 0 & 0 & 0\end{bmatrix} = A;\ A + A^2 + A^3 =$

$\begin{bmatrix}0 & 1 & 0 & 1 & 0 & 0\\0 & 0 & 1 & 0 & 0 & 0\\0 & 1 & 0 & 0 & 1 & 1\\1 & 0 & 0 & 0 & 1 & 0\\0 & 0 & 1 & 1 & 0 & 0\\1 & 0 & 0 & 0 & 0 & 0\end{bmatrix} + \begin{bmatrix}1 & 0 & 1 & 0 & 1 & 0\\0 & 1 & 0 & 0 & 1 & 1\\1 & 0 & 2 & 1 & 0 & 0\\0 & 1 & 1 & 2 & 0 & 0\\1 & 1 & 0 & 0 & 2 & 1\\0 & 1 & 0 & 1 & 0 & 0\end{bmatrix} + \begin{bmatrix}0 & 2 & 1 & 2 & 1 & 1\\1 & 0 & 2 & 1 & 0 & 0\\1 & 3 & 0 & 1 & 3 & 2\\2 & 1 & 1 & 0 & 3 & 1\\1 & 1 & 3 & 3 & 0 & 0\\1 & 0 & 1 & 0 & 1 & 0\end{bmatrix} =$

$\begin{bmatrix}1 & 3 & 2 & 3 & 2 & 1\\1 & 1 & 3 & 1 & 1 & 1\\2 & 4 & 2 & 2 & 4 & 3\\3 & 2 & 2 & 2 & 4 & 1\\2 & 2 & 4 & 4 & 2 & 1\\2 & 1 & 1 & 1 & 1 & 0\end{bmatrix}$ Adding the columns shows that points 3 and 5 have the greatest number of incoming message routes.
$\overline{11}\ \overline{13}\ \overline{14}\ \overline{13}\ \overline{14}\ \overline{7}$

Pages 694-695 · WRITTEN EXERCISES

1. $\begin{vmatrix}3 & 5\\1 & 4\end{vmatrix} = 3 \cdot 4 - 1 \cdot 5 = 7$

2. $\begin{vmatrix}4 & 5\\0 & 2\end{vmatrix} = 4 \cdot 2 - 5 \cdot 0 = 8$

3. $\begin{vmatrix}5 & -3\\3 & 1\end{vmatrix} = 5 \cdot 1 - (-3)(3) = 14$

4. $\begin{vmatrix}0 & 8\\1 & 10\end{vmatrix} = 0 \cdot 10 - 1 \cdot 8 = -8$

5. $\begin{vmatrix}2 & 0\\0 & -2\end{vmatrix} = 2(-2) - 0 \cdot 0 = -4$

6. $\begin{vmatrix}6 & 2\\9 & 3\end{vmatrix} = 6 \cdot 3 - 2 \cdot 9 = 0$

7. $\begin{vmatrix}2 & -5 & 3\\0 & 8 & 1\\-5 & 4 & 0\end{vmatrix} = 0 + 25 + 0 - (-120) - 8 - 0 = 137$

8. $\begin{vmatrix} 3 & 0 & -5 \\ 5 & 1 & 8 \\ -4 & 0 & 1 \end{vmatrix} = 3 + 0 + 0 - 20 - 0 - 0 = -17$

9. $\begin{vmatrix} 12 & -9 & 13 \\ 0 & 0 & 8 \\ -9 & 2 & 1 \end{vmatrix} = 0 + 648 + 0 - 0 - 192 - 0 = 456$

10. $\begin{vmatrix} 2 & 3 & -1 \\ -3 & 0 & -8 \\ 11 & -4 & 6 \end{vmatrix} = 0 + (-264) + (-12) - 0 - 64 - (-54) = -286$

11. $\begin{vmatrix} 2 & 0 & 0 \\ 0 & 3 & 0 \\ 0 & 0 & -1 \end{vmatrix} = -6 + 0 + 0 - 0 - 0 - 0 = -6$

12. $\begin{vmatrix} 0 & 2 & -3 \\ 3 & 5 & -3 \\ 1 & 2 & 0 \end{vmatrix} = 0 + (-6) + (-18) - (-15) - 0 - 0 = -9$

B 13. If $A = \begin{bmatrix} a & b \\ 0 & 0 \end{bmatrix}$, $\det A = a \cdot 0 - b \cdot 0 = 0$; if $A = \begin{bmatrix} 0 & 0 \\ a & b \end{bmatrix}$, $\det A = 0 \cdot b - 0 \cdot a = 0$

if $A = \begin{bmatrix} a & 0 \\ b & 0 \end{bmatrix}$, $\det A = a \cdot 0 - 0 \cdot b = 0$; if $A = \begin{bmatrix} 0 & a \\ 0 & b \end{bmatrix}$, $\det A = 0 \cdot b - a \cdot 0 = 0$

14. If $B = \begin{bmatrix} 0 & 0 & 0 \\ a & b & c \\ d & e & f \end{bmatrix}$, $\det B = 0 \cdot bf + 0 \cdot cd + 0 \cdot ae - 0 \cdot bd - 0 \cdot ce - 0 \cdot af = 0$;

if $B = \begin{bmatrix} a & b & c \\ 0 & 0 & 0 \\ d & e & f \end{bmatrix}$, $\det B = 0 \cdot af + 0 \cdot bd + 0 \cdot ce - 0 \cdot cd - 0 \cdot ae - 0 \cdot bf = 0$;

if $B = \begin{bmatrix} a & b & c \\ d & e & f \\ 0 & 0 & 0 \end{bmatrix}$, $\det B = 0 \cdot ae + 0 \cdot bf + 0 \cdot cd - 0 \cdot ec - 0 \cdot af - 0 \cdot bd = 0$;

if $B = \begin{bmatrix} 0 & a & d \\ 0 & b & e \\ 0 & c & f \end{bmatrix}$, $\det B = 0 \cdot bf + 0 \cdot ae + 0 \cdot cd - 0 \cdot bd - 0 \cdot ce - 0 \cdot af = 0$;

if $B = \begin{bmatrix} a & 0 & d \\ b & 0 & e \\ c & 0 & f \end{bmatrix}$, $\det B = 0 \cdot af + 0 \cdot ec + 0 \cdot db - 0 \cdot cd - 0 \cdot ae - 0 \cdot bf = 0$;

if $B = \begin{bmatrix} a & d & 0 \\ b & e & 0 \\ c & f & 0 \end{bmatrix}$, $\det B = 0 \cdot ae + 0 \cdot cd + 0 \cdot bf - 0 \cdot ec - 0 \cdot af - 0 \cdot bd = 0$.

C **15.** Let $A = \begin{bmatrix} a & b \\ c & d \end{bmatrix}$; $\begin{vmatrix} a & b \\ c & d \end{vmatrix} = ad - bc$; $\begin{vmatrix} ra & rb \\ c & d \end{vmatrix} = ra \cdot d - rb \cdot c = r(ad - bc)$;

$\begin{vmatrix} a & b \\ rc & rd \end{vmatrix} = a \cdot rd - b \cdot rc = r(ad - bc)$; $\begin{vmatrix} ra & b \\ rc & d \end{vmatrix} = ra \cdot d - b \cdot rc = r(ad - bc)$;

$\begin{vmatrix} a & rb \\ c & rd \end{vmatrix} = a \cdot rd - rb \cdot c = r(ad - bc)$

16. Let $A = \begin{bmatrix} a & b \\ c & d \end{bmatrix}$; $\det A = ad - bc$; $\det(rA) = \begin{vmatrix} ra & rb \\ rc & rd \end{vmatrix} = ra \cdot rd - rb \cdot rc =$

$r^2(ad - bc) = r^2 \det A$

Pages 698-699 · WRITTEN EXERCISES

A **1.** $A = \begin{bmatrix} 3 & 1 \\ -4 & 1 \end{bmatrix}$; $\det A = 3 - (-4) = 7$; $A^{-1} = \dfrac{1}{7}\begin{bmatrix} 1 & -1 \\ 4 & 3 \end{bmatrix} = \begin{bmatrix} \dfrac{1}{7} & -\dfrac{1}{7} \\ \dfrac{4}{7} & \dfrac{3}{7} \end{bmatrix}$

2. $A = \begin{bmatrix} 2 & 0 \\ 3 & 5 \end{bmatrix}$; $\det A = 10 - 0 = 10$; $A^{-1} = \dfrac{1}{10}\begin{bmatrix} 5 & 0 \\ -3 & 2 \end{bmatrix} = \begin{bmatrix} \dfrac{1}{2} & 0 \\ -\dfrac{3}{10} & \dfrac{1}{5} \end{bmatrix}$

3. $A = \begin{bmatrix} 2 & -1 \\ 5 & 2 \end{bmatrix}$; $\det A = 4 - (-5) = 9$; $A^{-1} = \dfrac{1}{9}\begin{bmatrix} 2 & 1 \\ -5 & 2 \end{bmatrix} = \begin{bmatrix} \dfrac{2}{9} & \dfrac{1}{9} \\ -\dfrac{5}{9} & \dfrac{2}{9} \end{bmatrix}$

4. $A = \begin{bmatrix} 1 & 0 \\ 0 & 1 \end{bmatrix}$; $\det A = 1 - 0 = 1$; $A^{-1} = \begin{bmatrix} 1 & 0 \\ 0 & 1 \end{bmatrix} = A$

5. $A = \begin{bmatrix} -1 & 2 \\ -2 & 3 \end{bmatrix}$; $\det A = -3 - (-4) = 1$; $A^{-1} = \begin{bmatrix} 3 & -2 \\ 2 & -1 \end{bmatrix}$

6. $A = \begin{bmatrix} 6 & 10 \\ -3 & -5 \end{bmatrix}$; $\det A = -30 - (-30) = 0$; A has no inverse.

7. $A = \begin{bmatrix} 1 & -2 \\ 1 & 6 \end{bmatrix}$; $\det A = 6 - (-2) = 8$; $A^{-1} = \dfrac{1}{8}\begin{bmatrix} 6 & 2 \\ -1 & 1 \end{bmatrix} = \begin{bmatrix} \dfrac{3}{4} & \dfrac{1}{4} \\ -\dfrac{1}{8} & \dfrac{1}{8} \end{bmatrix}$

8. $A = \begin{bmatrix} 2 & -3 \\ -1 & 8 \end{bmatrix}$; $\det A = 16 - 3 = 13$; $A^{-1} = \dfrac{1}{13}\begin{bmatrix} 8 & 3 \\ 1 & 2 \end{bmatrix} = \begin{bmatrix} \dfrac{8}{13} & \dfrac{3}{13} \\ \dfrac{1}{13} & \dfrac{2}{13} \end{bmatrix}$

9. $\begin{array}{r} x + y = 8 \\ x - 3y = -4 \end{array}$; $\begin{bmatrix} 1 & 1 \\ 1 & -3 \end{bmatrix}\begin{bmatrix} x \\ y \end{bmatrix} = \begin{bmatrix} 8 \\ -4 \end{bmatrix}$; $\begin{vmatrix} 1 & 1 \\ 1 & -3 \end{vmatrix} = -3 - 1 = -4$;

$$\begin{bmatrix} x \\ y \end{bmatrix} = -\frac{1}{4}\begin{bmatrix} -3 & -1 \\ -1 & 1 \end{bmatrix}\begin{bmatrix} 8 \\ -4 \end{bmatrix} = \begin{bmatrix} \frac{3}{4} & \frac{1}{4} \\ \frac{1}{4} & -\frac{1}{4} \end{bmatrix}\begin{bmatrix} 8 \\ -4 \end{bmatrix} = \begin{bmatrix} 5 \\ 3 \end{bmatrix}; \ (5, 3)$$

10. $\begin{array}{r} 3x - 5y = 1 \\ 2x - y = 3 \end{array}$; $\begin{bmatrix} 3 & -5 \\ 2 & -1 \end{bmatrix}\begin{bmatrix} x \\ y \end{bmatrix} = \begin{bmatrix} 1 \\ 3 \end{bmatrix}$; $\begin{vmatrix} 3 & -5 \\ 2 & -1 \end{vmatrix} = -3 - (-10) = 7$;

$$\begin{bmatrix} x \\ y \end{bmatrix} = \frac{1}{7}\begin{bmatrix} -1 & 5 \\ -2 & 3 \end{bmatrix}\begin{bmatrix} 1 \\ 3 \end{bmatrix} = \begin{bmatrix} -\frac{1}{7} & \frac{5}{7} \\ -\frac{2}{7} & \frac{3}{7} \end{bmatrix}\begin{bmatrix} 1 \\ 3 \end{bmatrix} = \begin{bmatrix} 2 \\ 1 \end{bmatrix}; \ (2, 1)$$

11. $\begin{bmatrix} 4 & 3 \\ 4 & 1 \end{bmatrix}\begin{bmatrix} x \\ y \end{bmatrix} = \begin{bmatrix} 1 \\ -5 \end{bmatrix}$; $\begin{vmatrix} 4 & 3 \\ 4 & 1 \end{vmatrix} = 4 - 12 = -8$;

$$\begin{bmatrix} x \\ y \end{bmatrix} = -\frac{1}{8}\begin{bmatrix} 1 & -3 \\ -4 & 4 \end{bmatrix}\begin{bmatrix} 1 \\ -5 \end{bmatrix} = \begin{bmatrix} -\frac{1}{8} & \frac{3}{8} \\ \frac{1}{2} & -\frac{1}{2} \end{bmatrix}\begin{bmatrix} 1 \\ -5 \end{bmatrix} = \begin{bmatrix} -2 \\ 3 \end{bmatrix}; \ (-2, 3)$$

12. $\begin{bmatrix} 5 & -3 \\ 2 & 7 \end{bmatrix}\begin{bmatrix} x \\ y \end{bmatrix} = \begin{bmatrix} 21 \\ -8 \end{bmatrix}$; $\begin{vmatrix} 5 & -3 \\ 2 & 7 \end{vmatrix} = 35 - (-6) = 41$;

$$\begin{bmatrix} x \\ y \end{bmatrix} = \frac{1}{41}\begin{bmatrix} 7 & 3 \\ -2 & 5 \end{bmatrix}\begin{bmatrix} 21 \\ -8 \end{bmatrix} = \begin{bmatrix} \frac{7}{41} & \frac{3}{41} \\ -\frac{2}{41} & \frac{5}{41} \end{bmatrix}\begin{bmatrix} 21 \\ -8 \end{bmatrix} = \begin{bmatrix} 3 \\ -2 \end{bmatrix}; \ (3, -2)$$

13. $\begin{bmatrix} 4 & 1 \\ 3 & 7 \end{bmatrix}\begin{bmatrix} x \\ y \end{bmatrix} = \begin{bmatrix} 1 \\ 3 \end{bmatrix}$; $\begin{vmatrix} 4 & 1 \\ 3 & 7 \end{vmatrix} = 28 - 3 = 25$;

$$\begin{bmatrix} x \\ y \end{bmatrix} = \frac{1}{25}\begin{bmatrix} 7 & -1 \\ -3 & 4 \end{bmatrix}\begin{bmatrix} 1 \\ 3 \end{bmatrix} = \begin{bmatrix} \frac{7}{25} & -\frac{1}{25} \\ -\frac{3}{25} & \frac{4}{25} \end{bmatrix}\begin{bmatrix} 1 \\ 3 \end{bmatrix} = \begin{bmatrix} \frac{4}{25} \\ \frac{9}{25} \end{bmatrix}; \ \left(\frac{4}{25}, \frac{9}{25}\right)$$

14. $\begin{bmatrix} 6 & 2 \\ 3 & -5 \end{bmatrix}\begin{bmatrix} x \\ y \end{bmatrix} = \begin{bmatrix} 17 \\ -4 \end{bmatrix}$; $\begin{vmatrix} 6 & 2 \\ 3 & -5 \end{vmatrix} = -30 - 6 = -36$;

$$\begin{bmatrix} x \\ y \end{bmatrix} = -\frac{1}{36}\begin{bmatrix} -5 & -2 \\ -3 & 6 \end{bmatrix}\begin{bmatrix} 17 \\ -4 \end{bmatrix} = \begin{bmatrix} \frac{5}{36} & \frac{1}{18} \\ \frac{1}{12} & -\frac{1}{6} \end{bmatrix}\begin{bmatrix} 17 \\ -4 \end{bmatrix} = \begin{bmatrix} \frac{77}{36} \\ \frac{25}{12} \end{bmatrix}; \ \left(\frac{77}{36}, \frac{25}{12}\right)$$

15. $\begin{bmatrix} 1 & 1 \\ 2 & 2 \end{bmatrix}\begin{bmatrix} x \\ y \end{bmatrix} = \begin{bmatrix} 1 \\ 5 \end{bmatrix}$; $\begin{vmatrix} 1 & 1 \\ 2 & 2 \end{vmatrix} = 2 - 2 = 0$; no unique solution

16. $\begin{bmatrix} 1 & 0 \\ -1 & 1 \end{bmatrix}\begin{bmatrix} x \\ y \end{bmatrix} = \begin{bmatrix} 3 \\ 2 \end{bmatrix}$; $\begin{vmatrix} 1 & 0 \\ -1 & 1 \end{vmatrix} = 1 - 0 = 1$; $\begin{bmatrix} x \\ y \end{bmatrix} = \begin{bmatrix} 1 & 0 \\ 1 & 1 \end{bmatrix}\begin{bmatrix} 3 \\ 2 \end{bmatrix} = \begin{bmatrix} 3 \\ 5 \end{bmatrix}; \ (3, 5)$

B 17. $\begin{vmatrix} 1 & 3 \\ 2 & 7 \end{vmatrix} = 7 - 6 = 1$; $A = \begin{bmatrix} 7 & -3 \\ -2 & 1 \end{bmatrix}\begin{bmatrix} 4 & 1 \\ -2 & 3 \end{bmatrix} = \begin{bmatrix} 34 & -2 \\ -10 & 1 \end{bmatrix}$

18. $\begin{vmatrix} 3 & 2 \\ 2 & 2 \end{vmatrix} = 6 - 4 = 2; A = \dfrac{1}{2} \begin{bmatrix} 2 & -2 \\ -2 & 3 \end{bmatrix} \begin{bmatrix} 5 & 0 \\ -1 & -1 \end{bmatrix} = \begin{bmatrix} 1 & -1 \\ -1 & \dfrac{3}{2} \end{bmatrix} \begin{bmatrix} 5 & 0 \\ -1 & -1 \end{bmatrix} =$

$\begin{bmatrix} 6 & 1 \\ -\dfrac{13}{2} & -\dfrac{3}{2} \end{bmatrix}$

19. $\begin{vmatrix} 4 & 2 \\ 1 & 1 \end{vmatrix} = 4 - 2 = 2; A = \dfrac{1}{2} \begin{bmatrix} 1 & -2 \\ -1 & 4 \end{bmatrix} \begin{bmatrix} 2 & 3 \\ 0 & 1 \end{bmatrix} = \begin{bmatrix} \dfrac{1}{2} & -1 \\ -\dfrac{1}{2} & 2 \end{bmatrix} \begin{bmatrix} 2 & 3 \\ 0 & 1 \end{bmatrix} = \begin{bmatrix} 1 & \dfrac{1}{2} \\ -1 & \dfrac{1}{2} \end{bmatrix}$

20. $\begin{bmatrix} 5 & 3 \\ 3 & 2 \end{bmatrix} A = \begin{bmatrix} 1 & 2 \\ -1 & 3 \end{bmatrix} + \begin{bmatrix} 1 & 3 \\ 2 & 1 \end{bmatrix} = \begin{bmatrix} 2 & 5 \\ 1 & 4 \end{bmatrix}; \begin{vmatrix} 5 & 3 \\ 3 & 2 \end{vmatrix} = 10 - 9 = 1;$

$A = \begin{bmatrix} 2 & -3 \\ -3 & 5 \end{bmatrix} \begin{bmatrix} 2 & 5 \\ 1 & 4 \end{bmatrix} = \begin{bmatrix} 1 & -2 \\ -1 & 5 \end{bmatrix}$

Page 699 · CHALLENGE

$X = 53$

Page 703 · WRITTEN EXERCISES

A 1. $\begin{vmatrix} 1 & 2 & 3 \\ 2 & -3 & 1 \\ 1 & 2 & 4 \end{vmatrix} = 1 \begin{vmatrix} -3 & 1 \\ 2 & 4 \end{vmatrix} - 2 \begin{vmatrix} 2 & 1 \\ 1 & 4 \end{vmatrix} + 3 \begin{vmatrix} 2 & -3 \\ 1 & 2 \end{vmatrix} = -14 - 14 + 21 = -7$

2. $\begin{vmatrix} 5 & 0 & -1 \\ 2 & 2 & 3 \\ -4 & 0 & -3 \end{vmatrix} = 0 + 2 \begin{vmatrix} 5 & -1 \\ -4 & -3 \end{vmatrix} - 0 = 0 - 38 - 0 = -38$

3. $\begin{vmatrix} -2 & -2 & 0 \\ 0 & 2 & 3 \\ 1 & -1 & 1 \end{vmatrix} = -2 \begin{vmatrix} 2 & 3 \\ -1 & 1 \end{vmatrix} - 0 + 1 \begin{vmatrix} -2 & 0 \\ 2 & 3 \end{vmatrix} = -10 - 0 + (-6) = -16$

4. $\begin{vmatrix} 2 & 3 & -1 \\ 8 & 0 & -3 \\ 1 & 1 & 5 \end{vmatrix} = 1 \begin{vmatrix} 3 & -1 \\ 0 & -3 \end{vmatrix} - 1 \begin{vmatrix} 2 & -1 \\ 8 & -3 \end{vmatrix} + 5 \begin{vmatrix} 2 & 3 \\ 8 & 0 \end{vmatrix} = -9 - 2 - 120 = -131$

5. $\begin{vmatrix} 10 & -1 & -2 \\ 12 & 8 & 1 \\ 0 & 1 & 0 \end{vmatrix} = 0 - 1 \begin{vmatrix} 10 & -2 \\ 12 & 1 \end{vmatrix} + 0 = 0 - 34 + 0 = -34$

6. $\begin{vmatrix} -1 & 3 & -4 \\ 0 & -1 & 0 \\ 1 & 2 & 10 \end{vmatrix} = -4 \begin{vmatrix} 0 & -1 \\ 1 & 2 \end{vmatrix} - 0 + 10 \begin{vmatrix} -1 & 3 \\ 0 & -1 \end{vmatrix} = -4 - 0 + 10 = 6$

7. $\begin{vmatrix} 4 & 0 & -5 \\ 9 & 1 & 11 \\ -4 & 0 & 3 \end{vmatrix} = 0 + 1 \begin{vmatrix} 4 & -5 \\ -4 & 3 \end{vmatrix} - 0 = 0 - 8 - 0 = -8$

8. $\begin{vmatrix} 4 & 0 & -2 \\ 3 & 1 & 6 \\ -1 & 0 & 3 \end{vmatrix} = -3\begin{vmatrix} 0 & -2 \\ 0 & 3 \end{vmatrix} + 1\begin{vmatrix} 4 & -2 \\ -1 & 3 \end{vmatrix} - 6\begin{vmatrix} 4 & 0 \\ -1 & 0 \end{vmatrix} = 0 + 10 - 0 = 10$

9-11. Choice of row or column may vary.

9. $\begin{vmatrix} 1 & 2 & 3 \\ 3 & 2 & 10 \\ -1 & -1 & 2 \end{vmatrix} = -1\begin{vmatrix} 2 & 3 \\ 2 & 10 \end{vmatrix} - (-1)\begin{vmatrix} 1 & 3 \\ 3 & 10 \end{vmatrix} + 2\begin{vmatrix} 1 & 2 \\ 3 & 2 \end{vmatrix} = -14 + 1 - 8 = -21$

10. $\begin{vmatrix} 0 & 2 & -5 \\ -2 & 1 & 3 \\ 1 & 0 & 8 \end{vmatrix} = 0 - (-2)\begin{vmatrix} 2 & -5 \\ 0 & 8 \end{vmatrix} + 1\begin{vmatrix} 2 & -5 \\ 1 & 3 \end{vmatrix} = 0 + 32 + 11 = 43$

11. $\begin{vmatrix} 0 & -7 & -14 \\ 5 & 6 & -5 \\ 1 & 3 & 4 \end{vmatrix} = 0 - 5\begin{vmatrix} -7 & -14 \\ 3 & 4 \end{vmatrix} + 1\begin{vmatrix} -7 & -14 \\ 6 & -5 \end{vmatrix} = 0 - 70 + 119 = 49$

B **12.** $\begin{vmatrix} 0 & -35 & 63 \\ 3 & 95 & x \\ 1 & -35 & 63 \end{vmatrix} = 63\begin{vmatrix} 3 & 95 \\ 1 & -35 \end{vmatrix} - x\begin{vmatrix} 0 & -35 \\ 1 & -35 \end{vmatrix} + 63\begin{vmatrix} 0 & -35 \\ 3 & 95 \end{vmatrix} = -12{,}600 - 35x + 6615;$

$-12{,}600 - 35x + 6615 = 0; 35x = -5985; x = -171$

13. $\begin{vmatrix} 1 & 3 & 4 \\ 5 & 15 & 10 \\ -1 & x & 2 \end{vmatrix} = -1\begin{vmatrix} 3 & 4 \\ 15 & 10 \end{vmatrix} - x\begin{vmatrix} 1 & 4 \\ 5 & 10 \end{vmatrix} + 2\begin{vmatrix} 1 & 3 \\ 5 & 15 \end{vmatrix} = 30 + 10x + 0;$

$30 + 10x = 80; 10x = 50; x = 5$

14. $\begin{vmatrix} 12 & -7 & 19 \\ 0 & x & 5 \\ -9 & 3 & 43 \end{vmatrix} = 0 + x\begin{vmatrix} 12 & 19 \\ -9 & 43 \end{vmatrix} - 5\begin{vmatrix} 12 & -7 \\ -9 & 3 \end{vmatrix} = 0 + 687x + 135; \ 687x + 135 = 135$

$687x = 0; x = 0$

15. $\begin{vmatrix} x & 2 & 3 \\ 1 & x & 3 \\ 1 & -1 & 1 \end{vmatrix} = x\begin{vmatrix} x & 3 \\ -1 & 1 \end{vmatrix} - 1\begin{vmatrix} 2 & 3 \\ -1 & 1 \end{vmatrix} + 1\begin{vmatrix} 2 & 3 \\ x & 3 \end{vmatrix} = x(x + 3) - 5 + 6 - 3x = x^2 + 1$

$x^2 + 1 = 5; x^2 = 4; x = 2 \text{ or } x = -2$

16. $\begin{vmatrix} 4 & 0 & 3 & 7 \\ 3 & 2 & 0 & 0 \\ -5 & -1 & 5 & 8 \\ 2 & 0 & 4 & 2 \end{vmatrix} = -3\begin{vmatrix} 0 & 3 & 7 \\ -1 & 5 & 8 \\ 0 & 4 & 2 \end{vmatrix} + 2\begin{vmatrix} 4 & 3 & 7 \\ -5 & 5 & 8 \\ 2 & 4 & 2 \end{vmatrix} - 0 + 0 =$

$-3\left(0 - (-1)\begin{vmatrix} 3 & 7 \\ 4 & 2 \end{vmatrix} + 0\right) + 2\left(4\begin{vmatrix} 5 & 8 \\ 4 & 2 \end{vmatrix} - (-5)\begin{vmatrix} 3 & 7 \\ 4 & 2 \end{vmatrix} + 2\begin{vmatrix} 3 & 7 \\ 5 & 8 \end{vmatrix}\right) =$

$-3(-22) + 2(-88 - 110 - 22) = 66 + (-440) = -374$

17. $\begin{vmatrix} 5 & 0 & 0 & 0 \\ 3 & -3 & 0 & 0 \\ 8 & 2 & 2 & 0 \\ -4 & 10 & 3 & 2 \end{vmatrix} = 5\begin{vmatrix} -3 & 0 & 0 \\ 2 & 2 & 0 \\ 10 & 3 & 2 \end{vmatrix} - 0 + 0 - 0 = 5\left(-3\begin{vmatrix} 2 & 0 \\ 3 & 2 \end{vmatrix} - 0 + 0\right)$

$$= 5(-12) = -60$$

C 18. $\begin{vmatrix} a & b & c \\ a & b & c \\ d & e & f \end{vmatrix} = a\begin{vmatrix} b & c \\ e & f \end{vmatrix} - a\begin{vmatrix} b & c \\ e & f \end{vmatrix} + d\begin{vmatrix} b & c \\ b & c \end{vmatrix} =$

$a(bf - ec) - a(bf - ec) + d(bc - bc) = 0;$

$\begin{vmatrix} a & b & c \\ d & e & f \\ a & b & c \end{vmatrix} = a\begin{vmatrix} e & f \\ b & c \end{vmatrix} - d\begin{vmatrix} b & c \\ b & c \end{vmatrix} + a\begin{vmatrix} b & c \\ e & f \end{vmatrix} =$

$a(ec - bf) - d(bc - bc) + a(bf - ec) = aec - abf + abf - aec = 0;$

$\begin{vmatrix} a & b & c \\ d & e & f \\ d & e & f \end{vmatrix} = a\begin{vmatrix} e & f \\ e & f \end{vmatrix} - d\begin{vmatrix} b & c \\ e & f \end{vmatrix} + d\begin{vmatrix} b & c \\ e & f \end{vmatrix} =$

$a(ef - ef) - d(bf - ec) + d(bf - ec) = 0$

19. $\begin{vmatrix} 0 & 0 & 0 \\ a & b & c \\ d & e & f \end{vmatrix} = 0\begin{vmatrix} b & c \\ e & f \end{vmatrix} - 0\begin{vmatrix} a & c \\ d & f \end{vmatrix} + 0\begin{vmatrix} a & b \\ d & e \end{vmatrix} = 0 - 0 + 0 = 0;$

$\begin{vmatrix} a & b & c \\ 0 & 0 & 0 \\ d & e & f \end{vmatrix} = 0\begin{vmatrix} b & c \\ e & f \end{vmatrix} + 0\begin{vmatrix} a & c \\ d & f \end{vmatrix} - 0\begin{vmatrix} a & b \\ d & e \end{vmatrix} = 0 + 0 - 0 = 0;$

$\begin{vmatrix} a & b & c \\ d & e & f \\ 0 & 0 & 0 \end{vmatrix} = 0\begin{vmatrix} b & c \\ e & f \end{vmatrix} - 0\begin{vmatrix} a & c \\ d & f \end{vmatrix} + 0\begin{vmatrix} a & b \\ d & e \end{vmatrix} = 0 - 0 + 0 = 0$

Page 706 · WRITTEN EXERCISES

A 1. $\begin{vmatrix} 6 & 9 & 3 \\ 4 & 2 & 6 \\ -15 & 20 & 10 \end{vmatrix} = \begin{vmatrix} 3\cdot 2 & 3\cdot 3 & 3\cdot 1 \\ 2\cdot 2 & 2\cdot 1 & 2\cdot 3 \\ 5(-3) & 5\cdot 4 & 5\cdot 2 \end{vmatrix} = 3\cdot 2\cdot 5\begin{vmatrix} 2 & 3 & 1 \\ 2 & 1 & 3 \\ -3 & 4 & 2 \end{vmatrix} =$

$30\begin{vmatrix} 2-2\cdot 1 & 3-3\cdot 1 & 1 \\ 2-2\cdot 3 & 1-3\cdot 3 & 3 \\ -3-2\cdot 2 & 4-3\cdot 2 & 2 \end{vmatrix} = 30\begin{vmatrix} 0 & 0 & 1 \\ -4 & -8 & 3 \\ -7 & -2 & 2 \end{vmatrix} = 30\begin{vmatrix} -4 & -8 \\ -7 & -2 \end{vmatrix} = 30(-4)\begin{vmatrix} 1 & 2 \\ -7 & -2 \end{vmatrix} =$

$-120(12) = -1440$

2. $\begin{vmatrix} -1 & 4 & 12 \\ 1 & -2 & -12 \\ 8 & 16 & 6 \end{vmatrix} = \begin{vmatrix} -1+1 & 4+(-2) & 12+(-12) \\ 1 & -2 & -12 \\ 8 & 16 & 6 \end{vmatrix} = \begin{vmatrix} 0 & 2 & 0 \\ 1 & -2 & -12 \\ 8 & 16 & 6 \end{vmatrix} =$

$2\cdot 2\begin{vmatrix} 0 & 1 & 0 \\ 1 & -2 & -12 \\ 4 & 8 & 3 \end{vmatrix} = -4\begin{vmatrix} 1 & -12 \\ 4 & 3 \end{vmatrix} = -4(51) = -204$

3.
$$\begin{vmatrix} 3 & 0 & 0 \\ 0 & 3 & 0 \\ 0 & 0 & 3 \end{vmatrix} = 3 \cdot 3 \cdot 3 \begin{vmatrix} 1 & 0 & 0 \\ 0 & 1 & 0 \\ 0 & 0 & 1 \end{vmatrix} = 27 \begin{vmatrix} 1 & 0 \\ 0 & 1 \end{vmatrix} = 27$$

4.
$$\begin{vmatrix} 4 & 12 & 18 \\ 3 & 9 & 13 \\ 2 & 6 & 28 \end{vmatrix} = \begin{vmatrix} 4 & 3 \cdot 4 & 18 \\ 3 & 3 \cdot 3 & 13 \\ 2 & 3 \cdot 2 & 28 \end{vmatrix} = 3 \begin{vmatrix} 4 & 4 & 18 \\ 3 & 3 & 13 \\ 2 & 2 & 28 \end{vmatrix} = 3 \cdot 0 \text{ (Prop. 3)} = 0$$

5.
$$\begin{vmatrix} 16 & -2 & -4 \\ 8 & 9 & -7 \\ 16 & -2 & -4 \end{vmatrix} = 0 \text{ (Prop. 3)}$$

6.
$$\begin{vmatrix} 1 & 5 & 10 \\ 0 & -5 & -8 \\ 1 & 5 & -2 \end{vmatrix} = \begin{vmatrix} 1-1 & 5-5 & 10-(-2) \\ 0 & -5 & -8 \\ 1 & 5 & -2 \end{vmatrix} = \begin{vmatrix} 0 & 0 & 12 \\ 0 & -5 & -8 \\ 1 & 5 & -2 \end{vmatrix} = 12 \begin{vmatrix} 0 & -5 \\ 1 & 5 \end{vmatrix} = 60$$

7.
$$\begin{vmatrix} 50 & 5 & 3 \\ 25 & 0 & 1 \\ 75 & 2 & 3 \end{vmatrix} = 25 \begin{vmatrix} 2 & 5 & 3 \\ 1 & 0 & 1 \\ 3 & 2 & 3 \end{vmatrix} = 25 \begin{vmatrix} 2 & 5 & 3-2 \\ 1 & 0 & 1-1 \\ 3 & 2 & 3-3 \end{vmatrix} = 25 \begin{vmatrix} 2 & 5 & 1 \\ 1 & 0 & 0 \\ 3 & 2 & 0 \end{vmatrix} = 25 \begin{vmatrix} 1 & 0 \\ 3 & 2 \end{vmatrix} = 50$$

8.
$$\begin{vmatrix} 26 & 29 & 29 \\ 25 & 28 & 26 \\ 25 & 30 & 27 \end{vmatrix} = \begin{vmatrix} 26 - \dfrac{26}{29} \cdot 29 & 29-29 & 29 \\ 25 - \dfrac{26}{29} \cdot 26 & 28-26 & 26 \\ 25 - \dfrac{26}{29} \cdot 27 & 30-27 & 27 \end{vmatrix} = \begin{vmatrix} 0 & 0 & 29 \\ \dfrac{49}{29} & 2 & 26 \\ \dfrac{23}{29} & 3 & 27 \end{vmatrix} = 29 \begin{vmatrix} \dfrac{49}{29} & 2 \\ \dfrac{23}{29} & 3 \end{vmatrix} =$$

$$29\left(\frac{101}{29}\right) = 101$$

9.
$$\begin{vmatrix} 5 & 1 & 1 \\ 1 & 5 & 1 \\ 1 & 1 & 5 \end{vmatrix} = \begin{vmatrix} 5-5 \cdot 1 & 1-1 & 1 \\ 1-5 \cdot 1 & 5-1 & 1 \\ 1-5 \cdot 5 & 1-5 & 5 \end{vmatrix} = \begin{vmatrix} 0 & 0 & 1 \\ -4 & 4 & 1 \\ -24 & -4 & 5 \end{vmatrix} = 1 \begin{vmatrix} -4 & 4 \\ -24 & -4 \end{vmatrix} =$$

$$1(-4)(-4) \begin{vmatrix} 1 & -1 \\ 6 & 1 \end{vmatrix} = 16(7) = 112$$

B 10.
$$\begin{vmatrix} 12 & 2 & 0 \\ 14 & 1 & -1 \\ 13 & 1 & 3 \end{vmatrix} = \begin{vmatrix} 12-6 \cdot 2 & 2 & 0 \\ 14-6 \cdot 1 & 1 & -1 \\ 13-6 \cdot 1 & 1 & 3 \end{vmatrix} = \begin{vmatrix} 0 & 2 & 0 \\ 8 & 1 & -1 \\ 7 & 1 & 3 \end{vmatrix} = -2 \begin{vmatrix} 8 & -1 \\ 7 & 3 \end{vmatrix} = -2(31) = -62$$

11.
$$\begin{vmatrix} 6 & 0 & 0 & 0 \\ 0 & 6 & 0 & 0 \\ 0 & 0 & 6 & 0 \\ 0 & 0 & 0 & 6 \end{vmatrix} = 6 \cdot 6 \cdot 6 \cdot 6 \begin{vmatrix} 1 & 0 & 0 & 0 \\ 0 & 1 & 0 & 0 \\ 0 & 0 & 1 & 0 \\ 0 & 0 & 0 & 1 \end{vmatrix} = 1296 \begin{vmatrix} 1 & 0 & 0 \\ 0 & 1 & 0 \\ 0 & 0 & 1 \end{vmatrix} = 1296 \begin{vmatrix} 1 & 0 \\ 0 & 1 \end{vmatrix} = 1296$$

12. $\begin{vmatrix} 1 & 1 & 1 & -1 \\ 2 & 2 & -2 & 2 \\ -3 & -3 & 3 & 3 \\ -4 & 4 & 4 & 4 \end{vmatrix} = \begin{vmatrix} 1+(-1) & 1 & 1 & -1 \\ 2+2 & 2 & -2 & 2 \\ -3+3 & -3 & 3 & 3 \\ -4+4 & 4 & 4 & 4 \end{vmatrix} = \begin{vmatrix} 0 & 1 & 1 & -1 \\ 4 & 2 & -2 & 2 \\ 0 & -3 & 3 & 3 \\ 0 & 4 & 4 & 4 \end{vmatrix} = -4 \begin{vmatrix} 1 & 1 & -1 \\ -3 & 3 & 3 \\ 4 & 4 & 4 \end{vmatrix} =$

$\begin{vmatrix} 1 & 1 & -1 \\ -3 & 3 & 3 \\ 4-4\cdot1 & 4-4\cdot1 & 4-4(-1) \end{vmatrix} = -4\begin{vmatrix} 1 & 1 & -1 \\ -3 & 3 & 3 \\ 0 & 0 & 8 \end{vmatrix} = -4\cdot3\cdot8 \begin{vmatrix} 1 & 1 & -1 \\ -1 & 1 & 1 \\ 0 & 0 & 1 \end{vmatrix} =$

$-96 \begin{vmatrix} 1 & 1 \\ -1 & 1 \end{vmatrix} = -96(2) = -192$

13. Let $A = \begin{vmatrix} a & b & c \\ d & e & f \\ g & h & i \end{vmatrix}$; det $A = a(ei - fh) - b(di - fg) + c(dh - eg) =$

$aei + bfg + cdh - afh - bdi - ceg$; $\begin{vmatrix} b & a & c \\ e & d & f \\ h & g & i \end{vmatrix} =$

$b(di - fg) - a(ei - fh) + c(eg - dh) = -aei - bfg - cdh + afh + bdi + ceg =$

$-\det A$; similarly, $\begin{vmatrix} a & c & b \\ d & f & e \\ g & i & h \end{vmatrix} = -\det A$ and $\begin{vmatrix} c & b & a \\ f & e & d \\ i & h & g \end{vmatrix} = -\det A$; $\begin{vmatrix} d & e & f \\ a & b & c \\ g & h & i \end{vmatrix} =$

$d(bi - ch) - e(ai - cg) + f(ah - bg) = -aei - bfg - cdh + afh + bdi + ceg =$

$-\det A$; similarly $\begin{vmatrix} a & b & c \\ g & h & i \\ d & e & f \end{vmatrix} = -\det A$ and $\begin{vmatrix} g & h & i \\ d & e & f \\ a & b & c \end{vmatrix} = -\det A$

14. Let $A = \begin{bmatrix} a & b \\ c & d \end{bmatrix}$; det $A = ad - bc$; $\begin{vmatrix} a & b+ka \\ c & d+kc \end{vmatrix} = a(d+kc) - (b+ka)c =$

$ad + akc - bc - akc = ad - bc = \det A$; $\begin{vmatrix} a+kb & b \\ c+kd & d \end{vmatrix} =$

$(a+kb)d - b(c+kd) = ad + kbd - bc - bkd = ad - bc = \det A$;

$\begin{vmatrix} a+kc & b+kd \\ c & d \end{vmatrix} = (a+kc)d - (b+kd)c = ad + kcd - bc - ckd =$

$ad - bc = \det A$; $\begin{vmatrix} a & b \\ c+ka & d+kb \end{vmatrix} = a(d+kb) - b(c+ka) =$

$ad + akb - bc - bka = ad - bc = \det A.$

Pages 710-711 · WRITTEN EXERCISES

1. $D = \begin{vmatrix} 2 & 1 & -1 \\ 1 & 1 & 1 \\ 1 & 2 & 1 \end{vmatrix} = 2(-1) - 3 + 2 = -3$; $D_x = \begin{vmatrix} 2 & 1 & -1 \\ 7 & 1 & 1 \\ 4 & 2 & 1 \end{vmatrix} = 2(-1) - 7(3) + 4(2) =$

-15; $D_y = \begin{vmatrix} 2 & 2 & -1 \\ 1 & 7 & 1 \\ 1 & 4 & 1 \end{vmatrix} = 2(3) - 6 + 9 = 9$; $D_z = \begin{vmatrix} 2 & 1 & 2 \\ 1 & 1 & 7 \\ 1 & 2 & 4 \end{vmatrix} = 2(-10) - 0 + 5 = 15$;

$x = \dfrac{D_x}{D} = \dfrac{-15}{-3} = 5$; $y = \dfrac{D_y}{D} = \dfrac{9}{-3} = -3$; $z = \dfrac{D_z}{D} = \dfrac{-15}{-3} = 5$; $(5, -3, 5)$

2. $D = \begin{vmatrix} 1 & -1 & 1 \\ 3 & 2 & 1 \\ 1 & 5 & 2 \end{vmatrix} = -1 - 3(-7) + (-3) = 17; \; D_x = \begin{vmatrix} 4 & -1 & 1 \\ 3 & 2 & 1 \\ 0 & 5 & 2 \end{vmatrix} =$

$4(-1) - 3(-7) = 17; \; D_y = \begin{vmatrix} 1 & 4 & 1 \\ 3 & 3 & 1 \\ 1 & 0 & 2 \end{vmatrix} = 6 - 3(8) + 1 = -17; \; D_z = \begin{vmatrix} 1 & -1 & 4 \\ 3 & 2 & 3 \\ 1 & 5 & 0 \end{vmatrix} =$

$-15 - 3(-20) + (-11) = 34; \; x = \dfrac{17}{17} = 1; \; y = \dfrac{-17}{17} = -1; \; z = \dfrac{34}{17} = 2; \; (1, -1, 2)$

3. $D = \begin{vmatrix} 2 & 1 & 1 \\ 3 & 2 & 3 \\ 1 & 3 & 2 \end{vmatrix} = 2(-5) - 3(-1) + 1 = -6; \; D_x = \begin{vmatrix} 4 & 1 & 1 \\ 16 & 2 & 3 \\ 12 & 3 & 2 \end{vmatrix} =$

$4(-5) - 16(-1) + 12 = 8; \; D_y = \begin{vmatrix} 2 & 4 & 1 \\ 3 & 16 & 3 \\ 1 & 12 & 2 \end{vmatrix} = 2(-4) - 3(-4) + (-4) = 0;$

$D_z = \begin{vmatrix} 2 & 1 & 4 \\ 3 & 2 & 16 \\ 1 & 3 & 12 \end{vmatrix} = 2(-24) - 3(0) + 8 = -40; \; x = \dfrac{8}{-6} = -\dfrac{4}{3}; \; y = \dfrac{0}{-6} = 0;$

$z = \dfrac{-40}{-6} = \dfrac{20}{3}; \; \left(-\dfrac{4}{3}, 0, \dfrac{20}{3} \right)$

4. $D = \begin{vmatrix} 1 & 1 & -1 \\ 2 & 1 & -2 \\ 3 & 0 & -4 \end{vmatrix} = -(-2) + (-1) = 1; \; D_x = \begin{vmatrix} 0 & 1 & -1 \\ 1 & 1 & -2 \\ 1 & 0 & -4 \end{vmatrix} = -(-4) + (-1) = 3;$

$D_y = \begin{vmatrix} 1 & 0 & -1 \\ 2 & 1 & -2 \\ 3 & 1 & -4 \end{vmatrix} = -1 - 0 = -1; \; D_z = \begin{vmatrix} 1 & 1 & 0 \\ 2 & 1 & 1 \\ 3 & 0 & 1 \end{vmatrix} = 1 - (-1) = 2;$

$x = \dfrac{3}{1} = 3; \; y = \dfrac{-1}{1} = -1; \; z = \dfrac{2}{1} = 2; \; (3, -1, 2)$

5. $D = \begin{vmatrix} 2 & 1 & -1 \\ 4 & -1 & 4 \\ 0 & -3 & 2 \end{vmatrix} = 2(10) - 4(-1) = 24; \; D_x = \begin{vmatrix} 3 & 1 & -1 \\ 0 & -1 & 4 \\ 6 & -3 & 2 \end{vmatrix} = 3(10) + 6(3) = 48;$

$D_y = \begin{vmatrix} 2 & 3 & -1 \\ 4 & 0 & 4 \\ 0 & 6 & 2 \end{vmatrix} = 2(-24) - 4(12) = -96; \; D_z = \begin{vmatrix} 2 & 1 & 3 \\ 4 & -1 & 0 \\ 0 & -3 & 6 \end{vmatrix} = 2(-6) - 4(15) = -72;$

$x = \dfrac{48}{24} = 2; \; y = \dfrac{-96}{24} = -4; \; z = \dfrac{-72}{24} = -3; \; (2, -4, -3)$

6. $D = \begin{vmatrix} 1 & 3 & 1 \\ 1 & 0 & 4 \\ 0 & -6 & 1 \end{vmatrix} = 24 - 9 = 15; \; D_x = \begin{vmatrix} 0 & 3 & 1 \\ -2 & 0 & 4 \\ 1 & -6 & 1 \end{vmatrix} = -(-2)(9) + 12 = 30;$

$D_y = \begin{vmatrix} 1 & 0 & 1 \\ 1 & -2 & 4 \\ 0 & 1 & 1 \end{vmatrix} = -6 - (-1) = -5; \; D_z = \begin{vmatrix} 1 & 3 & 0 \\ 1 & 0 & -2 \\ 0 & -6 & 1 \end{vmatrix} = -12 - 3 = -15;$

$x = \dfrac{30}{15} = 2; \; y = \dfrac{-5}{15} = -\dfrac{1}{3}; \; z = \dfrac{-15}{15} = -1; \; \left(2, -\dfrac{1}{3}, -1 \right)$

7. $D = \begin{vmatrix} 1 & 2 & -1 \\ 1 & 1 & 1 \\ 2 & -1 & 1 \end{vmatrix} = 2 - 1 + 2(3) = 7; D_x = \begin{vmatrix} 4 & 2 & -1 \\ 2 & 1 & 1 \\ 0 & -1 & 1 \end{vmatrix} = 4(2) - 2(1) = 6;$

$D_y = \begin{vmatrix} 1 & 4 & -1 \\ 1 & 2 & 1 \\ 2 & 0 & 1 \end{vmatrix} = -4(-1) + 2(3) = 10; D_z = \begin{vmatrix} 1 & 2 & 4 \\ 1 & 1 & 2 \\ 2 & -1 & 0 \end{vmatrix} = 4(-3) - 2(-5) = -2;$

$x = \dfrac{6}{7}; y = \dfrac{10}{7}; z = -\dfrac{2}{7}; \left(\dfrac{6}{7}, \dfrac{10}{7}, -\dfrac{2}{7}\right)$

8. $D = \begin{vmatrix} 1 & -2 & 0 \\ 1 & 0 & 2 \\ 0 & -1 & -2 \end{vmatrix} = 2 - 4 = -2; D_x = \begin{vmatrix} 8 & -2 & 0 \\ 3 & 0 & 2 \\ 2 & -1 & -2 \end{vmatrix} = -2(-4) - 2(6) = -4;$

$D_y = \begin{vmatrix} 1 & 8 & 0 \\ 1 & 3 & 2 \\ 0 & 2 & -2 \end{vmatrix} = -10 - (-16) = 6; D_z = \begin{vmatrix} 1 & -2 & 8 \\ 1 & 0 & 3 \\ 0 & -1 & 2 \end{vmatrix} = 3 - 4 = -1;$

$x = \dfrac{-4}{-2} = 2; y = \dfrac{6}{-2} = -3; z = \dfrac{-1}{-2} = \dfrac{1}{2}; \left(2, -3, \dfrac{1}{2}\right)$

9. $D = \begin{vmatrix} 4 & 8 \\ 8 & 16 \end{vmatrix} = 64 - 64 = 0; D_y = \begin{vmatrix} 4 & 1 \\ 8 & 2 \end{vmatrix} = 8 - 8 = 0;$ more than one solution

10. $D = \begin{vmatrix} -3 & -1 \\ 9 & 3 \end{vmatrix} = -9 + 9 = 0; D_y = \begin{vmatrix} -3 & 4 \\ 9 & 7 \end{vmatrix} = -21 - 36 \neq 0;$ no solution

11. $D = \begin{vmatrix} 10 & -3 \\ 11 & 3 \end{vmatrix} = 30 + 33 \neq 0;$ one solution

12. $D = \begin{vmatrix} 3 & -8 \\ 2 & -5 \end{vmatrix} = -15 + 16 \neq 0;$ one solution

B 13. $D = \begin{vmatrix} 2 & -3 & 1 & -3 \\ 1 & 2 & 3 & -1 \\ 3 & 5 & 6 & 0 \\ 3 & -1 & 0 & -2 \end{vmatrix} = \begin{vmatrix} -1 & -9 & -8 & 0 \\ 1 & 2 & 3 & -1 \\ 3 & 5 & 6 & 0 \\ 1 & -5 & -6 & 0 \end{vmatrix} = \begin{vmatrix} -1 & -9 & -8 & 0 \\ 1 & 2 & 3 & -1 \\ 3 & 5 & 6 & 0 \\ 4 & 0 & 0 & 0 \end{vmatrix} = -1 \begin{vmatrix} -1 & -9 & -8 \\ 3 & 5 & 6 \\ 4 & 0 & 0 \end{vmatrix} =$

$4 \begin{vmatrix} 1 & 9 & 8 \\ 3 & 5 & 6 \\ 1 & 0 & 0 \end{vmatrix} = 4(54 - 40) = 56; D_p = \begin{vmatrix} -1 & -3 & 1 & -3 \\ 1 & 2 & 3 & -1 \\ 4 & 5 & 6 & 0 \\ 6 & -1 & 0 & -2 \end{vmatrix} = \begin{vmatrix} -4 & -9 & -8 & 0 \\ 1 & 2 & 3 & -1 \\ 4 & 5 & 6 & 0 \\ 4 & -5 & -6 & 0 \end{vmatrix} =$

$\begin{vmatrix} -4 & -9 & -8 & 0 \\ 1 & 2 & 3 & -1 \\ 4 & 5 & 6 & 0 \\ 8 & 0 & 0 & 0 \end{vmatrix} = -1 \begin{vmatrix} -4 & -9 & -8 \\ 4 & 5 & 6 \\ 8 & 0 & 0 \end{vmatrix} = 8 \begin{vmatrix} 4 & 9 & 8 \\ 4 & 5 & 6 \\ 1 & 0 & 0 \end{vmatrix} = 8(14) = 112;$

$D_q = \begin{vmatrix} 2 & -1 & 1 & -3 \\ 1 & 1 & 3 & -1 \\ 3 & 4 & 6 & 0 \\ 3 & 6 & 0 & -2 \end{vmatrix} = \begin{vmatrix} -1 & -4 & -8 & 0 \\ 1 & 1 & 3 & -1 \\ 3 & 4 & 6 & 0 \\ 1 & 4 & -6 & 0 \end{vmatrix} = -1 \begin{vmatrix} -1 & -4 & -8 \\ 3 & 4 & 6 \\ 1 & 4 & -6 \end{vmatrix} = -1 \begin{vmatrix} 0 & 0 & -14 \\ 3 & 4 & 6 \\ 1 & 4 & -6 \end{vmatrix} =$

$$14\begin{vmatrix} 0 & 0 & 1 \\ 3 & 4 & 6 \\ 1 & 4 & -6 \end{vmatrix} = 14(12-4) = 112; \quad D_r = \begin{vmatrix} 2 & -3 & -1 & -3 \\ 1 & 2 & 1 & -1 \\ 3 & 5 & 4 & 0 \\ 3 & -1 & 6 & -2 \end{vmatrix} = \begin{vmatrix} -1 & -9 & -4 & 0 \\ 1 & 2 & 1 & -1 \\ 3 & 5 & 4 & 0 \\ 1 & -5 & 4 & 0 \end{vmatrix} =$$

$$-1\begin{vmatrix} -1 & -9 & -4 \\ 3 & 5 & 4 \\ 1 & -5 & 4 \end{vmatrix} = -1\begin{vmatrix} 0 & -14 & 0 \\ 3 & 5 & 4 \\ 1 & -5 & 4 \end{vmatrix} = 14\begin{vmatrix} 3 & 4 \\ 1 & 4 \end{vmatrix} = -14(12-4) = -112;$$

$$D_s = \begin{vmatrix} 2 & -3 & 1 & -1 \\ 1 & 2 & 3 & 1 \\ 3 & 5 & 6 & 4 \\ 3 & -1 & 0 & 6 \end{vmatrix} = \begin{vmatrix} -7 & -3 & 1 & -19 \\ 7 & 2 & 3 & 13 \\ 18 & 5 & 6 & 34 \\ 0 & -1 & 0 & 0 \end{vmatrix} = -1\begin{vmatrix} -7 & 1 & -19 \\ 7 & 3 & 13 \\ 18 & 6 & 34 \end{vmatrix} = -1\begin{vmatrix} 0 & 1 & 0 \\ 28 & 3 & 70 \\ 60 & 6 & 148 \end{vmatrix} =$$

$$\begin{vmatrix} 28 & 70 \\ 60 & 148 \end{vmatrix} = -56; \quad p = \frac{112}{56} = 2; \quad q = \frac{112}{56} = 2; \quad r = -\frac{112}{56} = -2; \quad s = -\frac{56}{56} = -1;$$

$$(2, 2, -2, -1)$$

14. $D = \begin{vmatrix} 1 & -2 & 1 & 0 \\ 2 & 0 & -1 & 1 \\ 0 & 1 & 2 & -3 \\ 3 & -3 & 2 & 0 \end{vmatrix} = \begin{vmatrix} 1 & -2 & 1 & 0 \\ 2 & 0 & -1 & 1 \\ 6 & 1 & -1 & 0 \\ 3 & -3 & 2 & 0 \end{vmatrix} = \begin{vmatrix} 1 & -2 & 1 \\ 6 & 1 & -1 \\ 3 & -3 & 2 \end{vmatrix} = \begin{vmatrix} 1 & -2 & 1 \\ 7 & -1 & 0 \\ 1 & 1 & 0 \end{vmatrix} = \begin{vmatrix} 7 & -1 \\ 1 & 1 \end{vmatrix} = 8;$

$$D_w = \begin{vmatrix} -4 & -2 & 1 & 0 \\ -3 & 0 & -1 & 1 \\ -14 & 1 & 2 & -3 \\ -13 & -3 & 2 & 0 \end{vmatrix} = \begin{vmatrix} -4 & -2 & 1 & 0 \\ -3 & 0 & -1 & 1 \\ -23 & 1 & -1 & 0 \\ -13 & -3 & 2 & 0 \end{vmatrix} = \begin{vmatrix} -4 & -2 & 1 \\ -23 & 1 & -1 \\ -13 & -3 & 2 \end{vmatrix} = \begin{vmatrix} -4 & -2 & 1 \\ -27 & -1 & 0 \\ -5 & 1 & 0 \end{vmatrix} =$$

$$\begin{vmatrix} -27 & -1 \\ -5 & 1 \end{vmatrix} = -32; \quad D_x = \begin{vmatrix} 1 & -4 & 1 & 0 \\ 2 & -3 & -1 & 1 \\ 0 & -14 & 2 & -3 \\ 3 & -13 & 2 & 0 \end{vmatrix} = \begin{vmatrix} 1 & -4 & 1 & 0 \\ 2 & -3 & -1 & 1 \\ 6 & -23 & -1 & 0 \\ 3 & -13 & 2 & 0 \end{vmatrix} = \begin{vmatrix} 1 & -4 & 1 \\ 6 & -23 & -1 \\ 3 & -13 & 2 \end{vmatrix} =$$

$$\begin{vmatrix} 1 & -4 & 1 \\ 7 & -27 & 0 \\ 1 & -5 & 0 \end{vmatrix} = \begin{vmatrix} 7 & -27 \\ 1 & -5 \end{vmatrix} = -8; \quad D_y = \begin{vmatrix} 1 & -2 & -4 & 0 \\ 2 & 0 & -3 & 1 \\ 0 & 1 & -14 & -3 \\ 3 & -3 & -13 & 0 \end{vmatrix} = \begin{vmatrix} 1 & -2 & -4 & 0 \\ 2 & 0 & -3 & 1 \\ 6 & 1 & -23 & 0 \\ 3 & -3 & -13 & 0 \end{vmatrix} =$$

$$\begin{vmatrix} 1 & -2 & -4 \\ 6 & 1 & -23 \\ 3 & -3 & -13 \end{vmatrix} = \begin{vmatrix} 1 & -2 & -4 \\ 0 & 13 & 1 \\ 0 & 3 & -1 \end{vmatrix} = \begin{vmatrix} 13 & 1 \\ 3 & -1 \end{vmatrix} = -16; \quad D_z = \begin{vmatrix} 1 & -2 & 1 & -4 \\ 2 & 0 & -1 & -3 \\ 0 & 1 & 2 & -14 \\ 3 & -3 & 2 & -13 \end{vmatrix} =$$

$$\begin{vmatrix} 1 & -2 & 1 & -4 \\ 0 & 4 & -3 & 5 \\ 0 & 1 & 2 & -14 \\ 0 & 3 & -1 & -1 \end{vmatrix} = \begin{vmatrix} 4 & -3 & 5 \\ 1 & 2 & -14 \\ 3 & -1 & -1 \end{vmatrix} = \begin{vmatrix} -5 & -3 & 8 \\ 7 & 2 & -16 \\ 0 & -1 & 0 \end{vmatrix} = \begin{vmatrix} -5 & 8 \\ 7 & -16 \end{vmatrix} = 24;$$

$$w = \frac{-32}{8} = -4; \quad x = \frac{-8}{8} = -1; \quad y = \frac{-16}{8} = -2; \quad z = \frac{24}{8} = 3; \quad (-4, -1, -2, 3)$$

1. 10 PRINT "ENTER A, B, C, D"
   20 INPUT A, B, C, D
   30 LET DT = A * D − B * C
   40 IF DT <> 0 THEN 70
   50 PRINT "NO INVERSE EXISTS"
   60 GOTO 140
   70 LET A1 = D/DT
   80 LET B1 = −B/DT
   90 LET C1 = −C/DT
   100 LET D1 = A/DT
   110 PRINT "INVERSE MATRIX IS"
   120 PRINT A1; "   "; B1
   130 PRINT C1; "   "; D1
   140 END

2. **a.** INVERSE MATRIX IS   **b.** INVERSE MATRIX IS

$$\begin{bmatrix} .75 & -1.25 \\ -1.75 & 3.25 \end{bmatrix} \qquad \begin{bmatrix} -8.5 & -2.5 \\ 1.5 & .5 \end{bmatrix}$$

   c. NO INVERSE EXISTS

3. 10 PRINT "ENTER ELEMENTS OF ROW 1"
   20 INPUT A1, A2, A3
   30 PRINT "ENTER ELEMENTS OF ROW 2"
   40 INPUT B1, B2, B3
   50 PRINT "ENTER ELEMENTS OF ROW 3"
   60 INPUT C1, C2, C3
   70 LET D = A1 * (B2 * C3 − B3 * C2) − A2 * (B1 * C3 − B3 * C1) +
      A3 * (B1 * C2 − B2 * C1)
   80 PRINT "DETERMINANT = "; D
   90 END

4. **a.** −74   **b.** −14,475

5. 10 PRINT "ENTER ELEMENTS OF EQUATION 1 AND CONSTANT TERM"
   20 INPUT A1, A2, A3, AC
   30 PRINT "ENTER ELEMENTS OF EQUATION 2 AND CONSTANT TERM"
   40 INPUT B1, B2, B3, BC
   50 PRINT "ENTER ELEMENTS OF EQUATION 3 AND CONSTANT TERM"
   60 INPUT C1, C2, C3, CC
   70 LET D = A1 * (B2 * C3 − B3 * C2) − A2 * (B1 * C3 − B3 * C1) +
      A3 * (B1 * C2 − B2 * C1)
   80 IF D = 0 THEN 170

(continued)

90 LET DX = AC * (B2 * C3 − B3 * C2) − A2 * (BC * C3 − B3 * CC) +
    A3 * (BC * C2 − B2 * CC)

100 LET DY = A1 * (BC * C3 − B3 * CC) − AC * (B1 * C3 − B3 * C1) +
    A3 * (B1 * CC − BC * C1)

110 LET DZ = A1 * (B2 * CC − BC * C2) − A2 * (B1 * CC − BC * C1) +
    AC * (B1 * C2 − B2 * C1)

120 LET X = DX/D

130 LET Y = DY/D

140 LET Z = DZ/D

150 PRINT "X = "; X; " Y = "; Y; " Z = "; Z

160 END

170 PRINT "DETERMINANT IS ZERO"

180 END

6. a. $X = 3$; $Y = 2.5$; $Z = -1$ **b.** $X = 4$; $Y = -5$; $Z = 0$

Pages 713-714 · CHAPTER REVIEW

1. c; $-2 + x = 0$; $x = 2$ **2.** d; $B - 2A = \begin{bmatrix} 3 & -2 \\ -1 & 4 \end{bmatrix} - \begin{bmatrix} -4 & 6 \\ -2 & 12 \end{bmatrix} = \begin{bmatrix} 7 & -8 \\ 1 & -8 \end{bmatrix}$

3. d; $\begin{bmatrix} 3 & -2 \\ -1 & 4 \end{bmatrix}\begin{bmatrix} -2 & 3 \\ -1 & 6 \end{bmatrix} = \begin{bmatrix} -6+2 & 9-12 \\ 2-4 & -3+24 \end{bmatrix} = \begin{bmatrix} -4 & -3 \\ -2 & 21 \end{bmatrix}$

4. c; $\begin{bmatrix} 0 & 1 & 1 \\ 0 & 0 & 1 \\ 1 & 1 & 0 \end{bmatrix}^2 = \begin{bmatrix} 0 & 1 & 1 \\ 0 & 0 & 1 \\ 1 & 1 & 0 \end{bmatrix}\begin{bmatrix} 0 & 1 & 1 \\ 0 & 0 & 1 \\ 1 & 1 & 0 \end{bmatrix} = \begin{bmatrix} 1 & 1 & 1 \\ 1 & 1 & 0 \\ 0 & 1 & 2 \end{bmatrix}$ **5.** b; $3 \cdot (-1) - 4 \cdot 1 = -7$

6. a; $((-1) \cdot 4 \cdot (-1) + 1 \cdot 2 \cdot 1 + 0 \cdot (-2) \cdot 1) -$
$(0 \cdot 4 \cdot 1 + 2 \cdot (-2) \cdot (-1) + (-1) \cdot 1 \cdot 1) = 6 - 3 = 3$

7. a; $A^{-1} = \dfrac{1}{\det A}\begin{bmatrix} 6 & -1 \\ 0 & -2 \end{bmatrix} = -\dfrac{1}{12}\begin{bmatrix} 6 & -1 \\ 0 & -2 \end{bmatrix} = \begin{bmatrix} -\dfrac{1}{2} & \dfrac{1}{12} \\[2mm] 0 & \dfrac{1}{6} \end{bmatrix}$

8. b; $-(-1)\begin{vmatrix} 2 & 5 \\ 1 & 2 \end{vmatrix} + 0 + -(-3)\begin{vmatrix} 4 & 2 \\ 2 & 1 \end{vmatrix} = -1 + 3 \cdot 0 = -1$

9. c; $-1\begin{vmatrix} 2 & -2 \\ 3 & 8 \end{vmatrix} + 0 + (-2)\begin{vmatrix} 3 & 2 \\ -12 & 3 \end{vmatrix} = (-1) \cdot 22 - 2 \cdot 33 = -88$

10. c; $D = \begin{vmatrix} 2 & 1 & 3 \\ 5 & 2 & 0 \\ 0 & 2 & 3 \end{vmatrix} = 27$; $D_x = \begin{vmatrix} -2 & 1 & 3 \\ 5 & 2 & 0 \\ -13 & 2 & 3 \end{vmatrix} = 81$; $D_y = \begin{vmatrix} 2 & -2 & 3 \\ 5 & 5 & 0 \\ 0 & -13 & 3 \end{vmatrix} = -135$;

$D_z = \begin{vmatrix} 2 & 1 & -2 \\ 5 & 2 & 5 \\ 0 & 2 & -13 \end{vmatrix} = -27$; $x = \dfrac{D_x}{D} = \dfrac{81}{27} = 3$; $y = \dfrac{D_y}{D} = \dfrac{-135}{27} = -5$;

$z = \dfrac{D_z}{D} = \dfrac{-27}{27} = -1$; $(3, -5, -1)$

Pages 714-715 · CHAPTER TEST

1. $\begin{bmatrix} 3x & -12 \\ 2 & -y \end{bmatrix} = \begin{bmatrix} 0 \\ 0 \end{bmatrix}$; $3x - 12 = 0$; $3x = 12$; $x = 4$; $2 - y = 0$; $y = 2$

2. $A + B = \begin{bmatrix} 3 + (-2) & -1 + 1 & 0 + 5 \\ -5 + 5 & 1 + (-5) & 4 + 1 \\ -2 + 0 & 1 + 3 & -1 + (-1) \end{bmatrix} = \begin{bmatrix} 1 & 0 & 5 \\ 0 & -4 & 5 \\ -2 & 4 & -2 \end{bmatrix}$

3. $A - B = \begin{bmatrix} 3 - (-2) & -1 - 1 & 0 - 5 \\ -5 - 5 & 1 - (-5) & 4 - 1 \\ -2 - 0 & 1 - 3 & -1 - (-1) \end{bmatrix} = \begin{bmatrix} 5 & -2 & -5 \\ -10 & 6 & 3 \\ -2 & -2 & 0 \end{bmatrix}$

4. $3B = \begin{bmatrix} 3(-2) & 3 \cdot 1 & 3 \cdot 5 \\ 3 \cdot 5 & 3(-5) & 3 \cdot 1 \\ 3 \cdot 0 & 3 \cdot 3 & 3(-1) \end{bmatrix} = \begin{bmatrix} -6 & 3 & 15 \\ 15 & -15 & 3 \\ 0 & 9 & -3 \end{bmatrix}$

5. $2A - B = \begin{bmatrix} 2 \cdot 3 - (-2) & 2(-1) - 1 & 2 \cdot 0 - 5 \\ 2(-5) - 5 & 2 \cdot 1 - (-5) & 2 \cdot 4 - 1 \\ 2(-2) - 0 & 2 \cdot 1 - 3 & 2(-1) - (-1) \end{bmatrix} = \begin{bmatrix} 8 & -3 & -5 \\ -15 & 7 & 7 \\ -4 & -1 & -1 \end{bmatrix}$

6. $A \times B = \begin{bmatrix} 3 & -1 & 0 \\ -5 & 1 & 4 \\ -2 & 1 & -1 \end{bmatrix} \begin{bmatrix} -2 & 1 & 5 \\ 5 & -5 & 1 \\ 0 & 3 & -1 \end{bmatrix} = \begin{bmatrix} -11 & 8 & 14 \\ 15 & 2 & -28 \\ 9 & -10 & -8 \end{bmatrix}$

7. $B^2 = B \times B = \begin{bmatrix} -2 & 1 & 5 \\ 5 & -5 & 1 \\ 0 & 3 & -1 \end{bmatrix} \begin{bmatrix} -2 & 1 & 5 \\ 5 & -5 & 1 \\ 0 & 3 & -1 \end{bmatrix} = \begin{bmatrix} 9 & 8 & -14 \\ -35 & 33 & 19 \\ 15 & -18 & 4 \end{bmatrix}$

8. From: $\begin{array}{c} \\ \text{plane} \\ \text{train} \end{array} \overset{\displaystyle \begin{array}{cc} \text{plane} & \text{train} \end{array}}{\begin{bmatrix} 0.85 & 0.15 \\ 0.18 & 0.82 \end{bmatrix}} = T$; $P = [40{,}000 \quad 10{,}000]$;

$P \times T = [40{,}000 \quad 10{,}000] \begin{bmatrix} 0.85 & 0.15 \\ 0.18 & 0.82 \end{bmatrix} = [35{,}800 \quad 14{,}200]$; there will be 35,800 airline passengers and 14,200 train riders.

9. $\begin{vmatrix} -2 & 1 \\ 18 & 6 \end{vmatrix} = -12 - 18 = -30$

10. $\begin{vmatrix} 1 & -2 & 2 \\ 0 & -5 & 1 \\ 1 & 0 & 3 \end{vmatrix} = 1 \begin{vmatrix} -5 & 1 \\ 0 & 3 \end{vmatrix} - 0 + 1 \begin{vmatrix} -2 & 2 \\ -5 & 1 \end{vmatrix} = -15 - 0 + 8 = -7$

11. $\begin{vmatrix} 2 & 3 \\ -1 & 0 \end{vmatrix} = 3$; $A = \dfrac{1}{3} \begin{bmatrix} 0 & -3 \\ 1 & 2 \end{bmatrix} \begin{bmatrix} 7 & 3 \\ 4 & 0 \end{bmatrix} = \dfrac{1}{3} \begin{bmatrix} -12 & 0 \\ 15 & 3 \end{bmatrix} = \begin{bmatrix} -4 & 0 \\ 5 & 1 \end{bmatrix}$

12. $\begin{vmatrix} 2 & -1 & 0 \\ 1 & 0 & 3 \\ 3 & 1 & 5 \end{vmatrix} = -1 \begin{vmatrix} -1 & 0 \\ 1 & 5 \end{vmatrix} + 0 - 3 \begin{vmatrix} 2 & -1 \\ 3 & 1 \end{vmatrix} = 5 + 0 - 15 = -10$

13. $\begin{vmatrix} 2 & 1 & -1 \\ 16 & 8 & -8 \\ 3 & 0 & -4 \end{vmatrix} = 8 \begin{vmatrix} 2 & 1 & -1 \\ 2 & 1 & -1 \\ 3 & 0 & -4 \end{vmatrix} = 8 \cdot 0 \text{ (by Prop. 3)} = 0$

14. $\begin{vmatrix} 4 & 3 & -1 \\ -3 & -3 & 5 \\ 5 & 5 & 3 \end{vmatrix} = \begin{vmatrix} 0 & 0 & -1 \\ 17 & 12 & 5 \\ 17 & 14 & 3 \end{vmatrix} = -1 \begin{vmatrix} 17 & 12 \\ 17 & 14 \end{vmatrix} = -34$

15. $D = \begin{vmatrix} 4 & -3 & 0 \\ 6 & 0 & -8 \\ 0 & 2 & -4 \end{vmatrix} = \begin{vmatrix} 4 & -3 & 0 \\ 6 & -4 & 0 \\ 0 & 2 & -4 \end{vmatrix} = -4 \begin{vmatrix} 4 & -3 \\ 6 & -4 \end{vmatrix} = -8 \begin{vmatrix} 4 & -3 \\ 3 & -2 \end{vmatrix} = -8(-8 + 9) = -8;$

$D_x = \begin{vmatrix} 1 & -3 & 0 \\ 1 & 0 & -8 \\ 0 & 2 & -4 \end{vmatrix} = \begin{vmatrix} 1 & -3 & 0 \\ 1 & -4 & 0 \\ 0 & 2 & -4 \end{vmatrix} = -4 \begin{vmatrix} 1 & -3 \\ 1 & -4 \end{vmatrix} = -4(-4 + 3) = 4;$

$D_y = \begin{vmatrix} 4 & 1 & 0 \\ 6 & 1 & -8 \\ 0 & 0 & -4 \end{vmatrix} = -4 \begin{vmatrix} 4 & 1 \\ 6 & 1 \end{vmatrix} = -4(4 - 6) = 8; \quad D_z = \begin{vmatrix} 4 & -3 & 1 \\ 6 & 0 & 1 \\ 0 & 2 & 0 \end{vmatrix} = -2 \begin{vmatrix} 4 & 1 \\ 6 & 1 \end{vmatrix} =$

$-2(4 - 6) = 4; \quad x = \dfrac{4}{-8} = -\dfrac{1}{2}; \quad y = \dfrac{8}{-8} = -1; \quad z = \dfrac{4}{-8} = -\dfrac{1}{2}; \quad \left(-\dfrac{1}{2}, -1, -\dfrac{1}{2}\right)$

CHAPTER 16 · Probability and Statistics

1. $10 \cdot 6 \cdot 4 = 240$ **2.** $2^{10} = 1024$ **3.** $3^{10} = 59,049$

4. $26 \cdot 25 \cdot 24 = 15,600$ **5.** $6 \cdot 5 \cdot 1 = 30$ **6.** $26 \cdot 10^4 = 260,000$

7. $7^4 = 2401$ **8.** $5 \cdot 4 = 20$

9. $5 \cdot 5 \cdot 3 = 75$ **10.** 1-digit: 3; 2-digit: $5 \cdot 3 = 15$; 3-digit: $5 \cdot 5 \cdot 3 = 75$; total: 93

11. 1-digit: 2; 2-digit: $4 \cdot 2 = 8$; total: 10

12. 1-digit: 1; 2-digit: 4; 3-digit: $4 \cdot 5 \cdot 1 = 20$; 4-digit: $4 \cdot 5 \cdot 5 \cdot 1 = 100$; total: 125

13. 3-digit: $5 \cdot 5 \cdot 2 = 50$; 4-digit: $5 \cdot 5 \cdot 5 \cdot 2 = 250$; total: 300

14. 2 letters: $3(26 \cdot 26 \cdot 10) = 20,280$; 3 letters: $26^3 = 17,576$; total: 37,856

15. 15, 18, 45, 48, 51, 54, 57, 75, 78, 81, 84, and 87; 12 multiples

16. 9, 99, 222, 225, 252, 255, 522, 525, 552, 555, and 999; 11 multiples

17. $(36)^3 = 46,656$ combinations; $(46,656) \div 4 = 11,644$ min ≈ 8 days

18. $4^8 = 65,536$ **19.** $20^4 = 160,000$

20. 1 vowel: $3 \cdot 5 \cdot 21^2 = 6615$; 2 vowels: $3 \cdot 5^2 \cdot 21 = 1575$; 3 vowels: $5^3 = 125$; total: 8315

All blocks same color: 2 ways; 1 block of one color and 5 blocks of other color: 2 ways; 2 blocks of one color and 4 blocks of other color: 4 ways (the 2 blocks can either be adjacent or opposite each other); 3 blocks of each color: 2 ways; total = 10 ways.

1. $\dfrac{6 \cdot 5}{2} = 15$ **2.** $24 \cdot 6 = 144$ **3.** $4 \cdot 6 = 24$ **4.** $20 \cdot 19 \cdot 18 = 6840$

5. $\dfrac{5!}{3!} = 5 \cdot 4 = 20$ **6.** $10! = 3,628,800$ **7.** $\dfrac{6!}{3!} = 6 \cdot 5 \cdot 4 = 120$

8. $\dfrac{6!}{4!} = 6 \cdot 5 = 30$ **9.** $5! = 120$ **10.** $4! = 24$

11. $6! = 720$ **12.** $\dfrac{5!}{1!} = 5! = 120$

13. $3 \cdot 5 \cdot 4 \cdot 3 = 180$ **14.** 1-digit: 5; 2-digit: $5 \cdot 4 = 20$; 3-digit: $5 \cdot 4 \cdot 3 = 60$; total: 85

15. $7(_6P_3) = 7\left(\dfrac{6!}{3!}\right) = \dfrac{7 \cdot 6!}{3!} = \dfrac{7!}{(7-4)!} = {_7P_4}$

16. $6(_5P_{r-1}) = 6\left(\dfrac{5!}{(6-r)!}\right) = \dfrac{6 \cdot 5!}{(6-r)!} = \dfrac{6!}{(6-r)!} = {_6P_r}$

439

17. $n(_{n-1}P_4) = n\left(\dfrac{(n-1)!}{(n-5)!}\right) = \dfrac{n(n-1)!}{(n-5)!} = \dfrac{n!}{(n-5)!} = {}_nP_5$

18. ${}_5P_3 - {}_5P_2 = \dfrac{5!}{2!} - \dfrac{5!}{3!} = \dfrac{5!}{2!} \cdot \dfrac{3}{3} - \dfrac{5!}{3!} = \dfrac{3 \cdot 5!}{3!} - \dfrac{5!}{3!} = \dfrac{2 \cdot 5!}{3!} = 2\left(\dfrac{5!}{3!}\right) =$

$2\left(\dfrac{5!}{(5-2)!}\right) = 2(_5P_2)$

19. ${}_nP_5 - {}_nP_4 = \dfrac{n!}{(n-5)!} - \dfrac{n!}{(n-4)!} = \dfrac{n!}{(n-5)!} \cdot \dfrac{n-4}{n-4} - \dfrac{n!}{(n-4)!} = \dfrac{n![(n-4)-1]}{(n-4)!} =$

$\dfrac{(n-5)n!}{(n-4)!} = (n-5)_nP_4$

20. ${}_nP_r - {}_nP_{r-1} = \dfrac{n!}{(n-r)!} - \dfrac{n!}{(n-(r-1))!} =$

$\dfrac{n!}{(n-r)!} \cdot \dfrac{(n-(r-1))}{(n-(r-1))} - \dfrac{n!}{(n-(r-1))!} = \dfrac{n!(n-(r-1)-1)}{(n-(r-1))!} =$

$\dfrac{n!(n-r)}{(n-(r-1))!} = (n-r)_nP_{r-1}$

C   21. ${}_nP_5 = 14(_nP_4); \dfrac{n!}{(n-5)!} = 14 \cdot \dfrac{n!}{(n-4)!}; 14(n-5)! = (n-4)!;$

$14(n-5)! \cdot \dfrac{n-4}{n-4} = (n-4)!; \dfrac{14(n-4)!}{n-4} = (n-4)!; 14 = n-4; n = 18$

22. $\dfrac{n!}{(n-3)!} = 17\left(\dfrac{n!}{(n-2)!}\right); \dfrac{(n-2)!}{(n-3)!} = 17; n-2 = 17; n = 19$

Page 726 · WRITTEN EXERCISES

A   1. $\dfrac{7!}{2!2!} = 1260$ **2.** $\dfrac{5!}{2!2!} = 30$ **3.** $\dfrac{11!}{4!4!2!} = 34{,}650$

4. $\dfrac{6!}{3!3!} = 20$ **5.** $\dfrac{7!}{2!2!2!} = 630$ **6.** $\dfrac{10!}{2!3!3!} = 50{,}400$

7. $\dfrac{5!}{2!2!} = 30$ **8.** $\dfrac{5!}{3!} = 20$

B   9. $\dfrac{7!}{3!2!2!} = 210$ **10.** $\dfrac{9!}{3!4!2!} = 1260$ **11.** $\dfrac{5!}{2!} = 60$

12. $\dfrac{5!}{2!2!} = 30$ **13.** $\dfrac{5!}{3!2!} = 10$

C   14. There are 6!, or 720, permutations with one P; there are 5 ways to drop a letter leav-

ing 6 letters (including 2 P's), so there are $5 \cdot \dfrac{6!}{2!}$, or 1800, permutations with 2 P's

total = 2520.

Pages 729-730 · WRITTEN EXERCISES

A

1. **a.** $\emptyset$, $\{K\}$, $\{L\}$, $\{M\}$, $\{K, L\}$, $\{K, M\}$, $\{L, M\}$, $\{K, L, M\}$
   b. $\{K, L\}$, $\{K, M\}$, $\{L, M\}$, $\{K, L, M\}$

2. **a.** $\{2, 4\}$, $\{2, 6\}$, $\{2, 8\}$, $\{4, 6\}$, $\{4, 8\}$, $\{6, 8\}$ **b.** $\{6\}$, $\{8\}$, $\{2, 4\}$, $\{2, 6\}$, $\{2, 8\}$, $\{4, 6\}$, $\{4, 8\}$, $\{6, 8\}$, $\{2, 4, 6\}$, $\{2, 4, 8\}$, $\{2, 6, 8\}$, $\{4, 6, 8\}$, $\{2, 4, 6, 8\}$

3. $\dfrac{6!}{4!2!} = \dfrac{6 \cdot 5}{2} = 15$ 4. $\dfrac{4!}{1!3!} = 4$ 5. $\dfrac{7!}{4!3!} = \dfrac{7 \cdot 6 \cdot 5}{3 \cdot 2} = 35$

6. $\dfrac{8!}{3!5!} = \dfrac{8 \cdot 7 \cdot 6}{3 \cdot 2} = 56$ 7. $\dfrac{14!}{12!2!} = \dfrac{14 \cdot 13}{2} = 91$ 8. $\dfrac{10!}{7!3!} = \dfrac{10 \cdot 9 \cdot 8}{3 \cdot 2} = 120$

9. $\dfrac{9!}{3!6!} = \dfrac{9 \cdot 8 \cdot 7}{3 \cdot 2} = 84$ 10. $\dfrac{100!}{2!98!} = \dfrac{100 \cdot 99}{2} = 4950$

11. **a.** $_5C_4 = 5$ **b.** $_5C_3 = \dfrac{5 \cdot 4 \cdot 3}{1 \cdot 2 \cdot 3} = 10$ **c.** $_5C_2 = {_5C_3} = 10$

12. **a.** $_8C_7 = {_8C_1} = 8$ **b.** $_8C_5 = {_8C_3} = \dfrac{8 \cdot 7 \cdot 6}{1 \cdot 2 \cdot 3} = 56$ **c.** $_8C_2 = \dfrac{8 \cdot 7}{1 \cdot 2} = 28$

13. $_{15}C_5 = \dfrac{15 \cdot 14 \cdot 13 \cdot 12 \cdot 11}{1 \cdot 2 \cdot 3 \cdot 4 \cdot 5} = 3003$ 14. $_{40}C_4 = \dfrac{40 \cdot 39 \cdot 38 \cdot 37}{1 \cdot 2 \cdot 3 \cdot 4} = 91{,}390$

15. $_6C_2 = 15$ 16. $_7C_3 = \dfrac{7 \cdot 6 \cdot 5}{1 \cdot 2 \cdot 3} = 35$

B

17. $_7C_3 = \dfrac{7 \cdot 6 \cdot 5}{1 \cdot 2 \cdot 3} = 35$ 18. $_{10}C_8 = {_{10}C_2} = \dfrac{10 \cdot 9}{1 \cdot 2} = 45$

19. $_{10}C_4 = \dfrac{10 \cdot 9 \cdot 8 \cdot 7}{1 \cdot 2 \cdot 3 \cdot 4} = 210$ 20. $_{52}C_5 = \dfrac{52 \cdot 51 \cdot 50 \cdot 49 \cdot 48}{1 \cdot 2 \cdot 3 \cdot 4 \cdot 5} = 2{,}598{,}960$

21. $_{13}C_{10} \cdot {_{39}C_3} = \dfrac{13 \cdot 12 \cdot 11}{1 \cdot 2 \cdot 3} \cdot \dfrac{39 \cdot 38 \cdot 37}{1 \cdot 2 \cdot 3} = 2{,}613{,}754$

22. $4(_{13}C_{11})(_{39}C_2) = 4 \cdot \dfrac{13 \cdot 12}{1 \cdot 2} \cdot \dfrac{39 \cdot 38}{1 \cdot 2} = 231{,}192$

23. $13(_{13}C_2)(_{26}C_2) = 13 \cdot \dfrac{13 \cdot 12}{1 \cdot 2} \cdot \dfrac{26 \cdot 25}{1 \cdot 2} = 329{,}550$

24. $(_{13}C_4)(_{13}C_3)(_{13}C_3) = 58{,}484{,}140$

C

25. $_8C_4 + {_8C_5} + {_8C_6} + {_8C_7} + {_8C_8} = 70 + 56 + 28 + 8 + 1 = 163$

26. **a.** $_4C_2 \cdot {_5C_1} = 6 \cdot 5 = 30$ **b.** $_4C_3 + {_5C_3} = 4 + 10 = 14$

27. $_nC_r = \dfrac{n!}{r!(n - r)!}$; $_nC_{n-r} = \dfrac{n!}{(n - r)![n - (n - r)]!} = \dfrac{n!}{(n - r)!r!} = {_nC_r}$

28. Each of the n members is or is not selected in forming a subset. There are 2 choices for each of n members of the set. By the fundamental counting principle, there are 2^n subsets.

Page 731 · COMPUTER EXERCISES

1. 10 PRINT "ENTER N"
   20 INPUT N
   30 LET F = 1
   40 FOR L = 1 TO N
   50 LET F = F * L
   60 NEXT L
   70 PRINT N; "! = "; F
   80 GOTO 10
   110 PRINT "ENTER N"
   120 INPUT N
   130 LET F = 1
   140 FOR L = 1 TO N
   150 LET F = F * L
   160 NEXT L
   170 PRINT N; "! = "; F
   180 GOTO 10

2. **a.** 3628800   **b.** 6.2270208E + 09   **c.** 2.09227899E + 13   **d.** 2.43290201E + 1

3. 10   PRINT "ENTER INTEGERS N, R (N > R > 0)"
   20   INPUT N, R
   30   IF R <= 0 THEN 10
   40   IF N < R THEN 10
   50   IF N * R <> INT(N * R) THEN 10
   60   LET X = N
   70   GOSUB 200
   80   LET A = F
   90   LET X = R
   100 GOSUB 200
   110 LET B = F
   120 LET X = N − R
   130 GOSUB 200
   140 LET C = A/(B * F)
   150 PRINT N; "C"; R; " = "; C
   160 GOTO 10
   200 LET F = 1
   210 FOR L = 1 TO X
   220 LET F = F * L
   230 NEXT L
   240 RETURN
   250 END

4. a. 220   **b.** 48620

5. 10   PRINT "ENTER INTEGERS N, R (N > R > 0)"
   20   INPUT N, R
   30   IF R <= 0 THEN 10
   40   IF N < R THEN 10
   50   IF R * N <> INT(R * N) THEN 10
   60   LET P = N
   70   LET C = N
   80   FOR L = 2 TO R
   90   LET P = P − 1
   100 LET C = C * P
   110 NEXT L
   120 GOSUB 200
   130 LET C = C/F
   140 PRINT N; "C"; R;" = "; C
   150 GOTO 10
   200 LET F = 1
   210 FOR L = 1 TO R
   220 LET F = F * L
   230 NEXT L
   240 RETURN
   250 END

   a. 52 C 5 = 2598960
   b. 52 C 13 = 6.3501356E + 11
   c. It is likely.

Page 733 · WRITTEN EXERCISES

A

1. 36

2. $\{(1, 1), (2, 2), (3, 3), (4, 4), (5, 5), (6, 6)\}$

3. $\{(4, 6), (5, 5), (6, 4)\}$

4. $\{(2, 1), (3, 2), (4, 3), (5, 4), (6, 5)\}$

5. $\{(2, 6), (3, 5), (3, 6), (4, 4), (4, 5), (4, 6), (5, 3), (5, 4), (5, 5), (5, 6), (6, 2), (6, 3), (6, 4),$
   $(6, 5), (6, 6)\}$

6. $\{(H, H, H), (H, H, T), (H, T, H), (T, H, H), (H, T, T), (T, H, T), (T, T, H), (T, T, T)\};$
   $\{(H, T, T), (T, H, T), (T, T, H), (T, T, T)\}$

B

7. $\{(H, 1), (H, 2), (H, 3), (H, 4), (H, 5), (H, 6), (T, 1), (T, 2), (T, 3), (T, 4), (T, 5), (T, 6)\};$
   $\{(H, 1), (H, 2), (H, 3), (H, 4), (T, 1), (T, 2), (T, 3), (T, 4)\}$

8. $\{(R, R), (R, W), (R, B), (W, R), (W, W), (W, B)\}; \{(W, W), (W, B)\}$

9. $\{(3,6),(4,5),(5,4),(6,3)\}$

10. $\{(2,1),(3,1),(3,2),(4,1),(4,2),(4,3),(5,1),(5,2),(5,3),(5,4),(6,1),(6,2),(6,3),$
$(6,4),(6,5)\}$

11. $\{(1,1),(1,2),(1,3),(1,4),(1,5),(1,6),(2,2),(2,4),(2,6),(3,3),(3,6),(4,4),(5,5),(6,6)\}$

C 12. $\{(1,1),(1,2),(1,3),(1,4),(1,5),(1,6),(2,1),(2,2),(2,3),(2,4),(2,5),(2,6),(3,1),(3,2),$
$(3,3),(3,4),(3,5),(3,6),(4,5),(5,5),(6,5),(4,6),(5,6),(6,6)\}$

13. $\{(1,2),(2,1),(3,2),(4,3),(5,4),(6,5)\}$ **14.** $\{(1,1),(2,1),(4,1),(6,1),(1,4),(3,4)\}$

15. $\{(3,1),(3,3),(3,5),(6,2),(6,4),(6,6)\}$

Pages 736-737 · WRITTEN EXERCISES

A   1. a. $\dfrac{1}{13}$ **b.** $\dfrac{1}{4}$ **c.** $\dfrac{1}{52}$ **d.** $\dfrac{1}{26}$ **e.** $\dfrac{2}{3}$ **f.** 0

2. a. $\dfrac{1}{2}$ **b.** $\dfrac{1}{2}$ **c.** $\dfrac{1}{3}$ **3. a.** $\dfrac{1}{2}$ **b.** 0   **c.** $\dfrac{5}{6}$ **d.** $\dfrac{1}{2}$

4. a. $\dfrac{1}{20}$ **b.** $\dfrac{1}{2}$ **c.** $\dfrac{6}{20}=\dfrac{3}{10}$ **d.** $\dfrac{5}{20}=\dfrac{1}{4}$ **e.** 0   **f.** 1

5. a. $\dfrac{1}{8}$ **b.** $\dfrac{1}{8}$ **c.** $\dfrac{3}{8}$ **d.** $\dfrac{7}{8}$

6. a. $\dfrac{1}{190}$ **b.** $\dfrac{99}{190}$ **c.** $\dfrac{19}{190}=\dfrac{1}{10}$

7. a. 1   **b.** $\dfrac{9000}{1,000,000}=\dfrac{9}{1000}$ **c.** $\dfrac{991,000}{1,000,000}=\dfrac{991}{1000}$

B   8. If a = number of Cortland, then a = number of Red Delicious, $2a$ = number of Bald-
win, and $4a$ = number of MacIntosh.

a. $\dfrac{4a}{8a}=\dfrac{1}{2}$ **b.** $\dfrac{2a}{8a}=\dfrac{1}{4}$ **c.** $\dfrac{a}{8a}+\dfrac{a}{8a}=\dfrac{1}{4}$

9. $_{12}C_2=\dfrac{12\cdot 11}{1\cdot 2}=66$ ways to draw 2 marbles

a. $\dfrac{_2C_2}{66}=\dfrac{1}{66}$ **b.** $\dfrac{_4C_2}{66}=\dfrac{\frac{4\cdot 3}{1\cdot 2}}{66}=\dfrac{1}{11}$ **c.** $\dfrac{_6C_2}{66}=\dfrac{\frac{6\cdot 5}{1\cdot 2}}{66}=\dfrac{5}{22}$

d. $\dfrac{_6C_2}{66}=\dfrac{\frac{6\cdot 5}{1\cdot 2}}{66}=\dfrac{5}{22}$ **e.** $\dfrac{_2C_1\cdot _4C_1}{_{12}C_2}=\dfrac{2\cdot 4}{66}=\dfrac{4}{33}$

10. a. $\dfrac{_{13}C_2}{_{52}C_2}=\dfrac{13\cdot 12}{52\cdot 51}=\dfrac{1}{17}$ **b.** $\dfrac{_{26}C_2}{_{52}C_2}=\dfrac{26\cdot 25}{52\cdot 51}=\dfrac{25}{102}$ **c.** $\dfrac{_{39}C_2}{_{52}C_2}=\dfrac{39\cdot 38}{52\cdot 51}=\dfrac{19}{34}$

d. $\dfrac{_4C_2}{_{52}C_2}=\dfrac{4\cdot 3}{52\cdot 51}=\dfrac{1}{221}$

C   11. a. $\dfrac{{}_4C_4 \cdot {}_{48}C_9}{{}_{52}C_{13}} = \dfrac{\dfrac{48 \cdot 47 \cdot 46 \cdot 45 \cdot 44 \cdot 43 \cdot 42 \cdot 41 \cdot 40}{1 \cdot 2 \cdot 3 \cdot 4 \cdot 5 \cdot 6 \cdot 7 \cdot 8 \cdot 9}}{\dfrac{52 \cdot 51 \cdot 50 \cdot 49 \cdot 48 \cdot 47 \cdot 46 \cdot 45 \cdot 44 \cdot 43 \cdot 42 \cdot 41 \cdot 40}{1 \cdot 2 \cdot 3 \cdot 4 \cdot 5 \cdot 6 \cdot 7 \cdot 8 \cdot 9 \cdot 10 \cdot 11 \cdot 12 \cdot 13}}$

$= \dfrac{10 \cdot 11 \cdot 12 \cdot 13}{52 \cdot 51 \cdot 50 \cdot 49} = \dfrac{11}{4165}$

b. $\dfrac{{}_{48}C_{13}}{{}_{52}C_{13}} = \dfrac{48 \cdot 47 \cdot \ldots \cdot 36}{52 \cdot 51 \cdot \ldots \cdot 40} = \dfrac{39 \cdot 38 \cdot 37 \cdot 36}{52 \cdot 51 \cdot 50 \cdot 49} = \dfrac{6327}{20{,}825}$

c. $\dfrac{{}_{40}C_{13}}{{}_{52}C_{13}} = \dfrac{40 \cdot 39 \cdot \ldots \cdot 28}{52 \cdot 51 \cdot \ldots \cdot 40} = \dfrac{1{,}263{,}994}{66{,}703{,}105}$

d. $\dfrac{{}_{26}C_{13}}{{}_{52}C_{13}} = \dfrac{26 \cdot 25 \cdot \ldots \cdot 14}{52 \cdot 51 \cdot \ldots \cdot 40} = \dfrac{19}{1{,}160{,}054}$

Page 738 · COMPUTER EXERCISES

1. 10 PRINT "ENTER NUMBER OF TOSSES"
   20 INPUT NT
   30 LET S = 0
   40 FOR N = 1 TO NT
   50 LET X = INT(RND(1) * 2)
   60 IF X = 1 THEN LET S = S + 1
   70 NEXT N
   80 PRINT "TOTAL NUMBER OF HEADS IN"; NT; "TOSSES = "; S
   90 GOTO 10

2. Answers will vary. Sample output is given.
   a. TOTAL NUMBER OF HEADS IN 100 TOSSES = 46
   b. TOTAL NUMBER OF HEADS IN 200 TOSSES = 101
   c. TOTAL NUMBER OF HEADS IN 300 TOSSES = 132
   d. TOTAL NUMBER OF HEADS IN 500 TOSSES = 263

3. 10 PRINT "ENTER NUMBER OF DICE ROLLS"
   20 INPUT NR
   30 LET S = 0
   40 FOR N = 1 TO NR
   50 LET X = INT(RND(0) * 6) + 1
   55 LET Y = INT(RND(0) * 6) + 1
   56 LET D = X + Y
   60 IF D = 7 THEN LET S = S + 1
   70 NEXT N
   80 PRINT "TOTAL NUMBER OF SEVENS IN"; NR; "ROLLS = "; S
   90 GOTO 10

4. Answers will vary. Sample output is given.

   a. TOTAL NUMBER OF SEVENS IN 50 ROLLS = 10

   b. TOTAL NUMBER OF SEVENS IN 180 ROLLS = 23

   c. TOTAL NUMBER OF SEVENS IN 250 ROLLS = 29

   d. TOTAL NUMBER OF SEVENS IN 360 ROLLS = 54

5. 10 PRINT "ENTER NUMBER OF DICE ROLLS"

   20 INPUT NR

   30 LET S = 0

   40 FOR N = 1 to NR

   50 LET X = INT(RND(0) ∗ 6) + 1

   55 LET Y = INT(RND(0) ∗ 6) + 1

   60 IF X = Y THEN LET S = S + 1

   70 NEXT N

   80 PRINT "FRACTION OF ROLLS THAT WERE DOUBLES = "; S; "/"; NR;
     " = "; S/NR

   90 GOTO 10

6. Answers will vary. Sample output is given.

   a. FRACTION OF ROLLS THAT WERE DOUBLES = 7/50 = .14

   b. FRACTION OF ROLLS THAT WERE DOUBLES = 25/180 = .138888889

   c. FRACTION OF ROLLS THAT WERE DOUBLES = 43/250 = .172

   d. FRACTION OF ROLLS THAT WERE DOUBLES = 59/360 = .163888889

7. Answers will vary. Probability of rolling a double = $\dfrac{1}{6} \approx 0.16667$.

Pages 744-746 · WRITTEN EXERCISES

A   **1.** $\dfrac{1}{36}$ **2. a.** $\dfrac{6}{11}$ **b.** $\dfrac{9}{11}$ **3. a.** $\dfrac{1}{2} \cdot \dfrac{4}{9} = \dfrac{2}{9} \neq \dfrac{1}{2} \cdot \dfrac{1}{2}$; no

     b. $\dfrac{1}{5} \cdot \dfrac{1}{3} = \dfrac{1}{15}$; yes   **4. a.** $\dfrac{1}{4} \cdot \dfrac{1}{4} = \dfrac{1}{16}$; yes   **b.** $\dfrac{3}{8} \cdot \dfrac{3}{8} = \dfrac{9}{64}$; yes

5. **a.** $\{(1,H),(2,H),(3,H),(4,H),(5,H),(6,H),(1,T),(2,T),(3,T),(4,T),(5,T),(6,T)\}$

   b. $A = \{(1,H),(3,H),(5,H),(1,T),(3,T),(5,T)\}$; $B = \{(1,H),(2,H),(3,H),(4,H),$
    $(5,H),(6,H)\}$; $A \cup B = \{(1,H),(2,H),(3,H),(4,H),(5,H),(6,H),(1,T),(3,T),$
    $(5,T)\}$; $A \cap B = \{(1,H),\ (3,H),\ (5,H)\}$

   c. $P(A) = \dfrac{6}{12} = \dfrac{1}{2}$; $P(B) = \dfrac{6}{12} = \dfrac{1}{2}$; $P(A \cup B) = \dfrac{9}{12} = \dfrac{3}{4}$; $P(A \cap B) = \dfrac{3}{12} = \dfrac{1}{4}$

   d. $P(A \cap B) \neq 0$; A and B are not mutually exclusive. $P(A \cap B) = P(A) \cdot P(B)$;
    A and B are independent.

6. **a.** $P(A) = \dfrac{1}{6}$, $P(B) = \dfrac{5}{36}$, $P(A \cup B) = \dfrac{10}{36} = \dfrac{5}{18}$, $P(A \cap B) = \dfrac{1}{36}$

   b. $P(A \cap B) = \dfrac{1}{36} \neq P(A) \cdot P(B)$; no

7. **a.** $P(\text{Sum is } 9.) = \dfrac{4}{36} = \dfrac{1}{9}$

   b. Event $E = \{(1,5),(2,4),(3,3),(4,2),(5,1),(4,4)\}$; $P(E) = \dfrac{6}{36} = \dfrac{1}{6}$

8. **a.** $\dfrac{_4C_2}{_{52}C_2} = \dfrac{4 \cdot 3}{52 \cdot 51} = \dfrac{1}{221}$ **b.** $\dfrac{1}{221}$ **c.** $\dfrac{1}{221} + \dfrac{1}{221} = \dfrac{2}{221}$

9. Let A be the event that at least two tosses come up tails. Let B be the event that at least one toss comes up heads.

   a. $P(3 \text{ tails}) = \dfrac{1}{8}$; $P(2 \text{ tails}) = \dfrac{3}{8}$; $P(A) = \dfrac{4}{8} = \dfrac{1}{2}$

   b. $P(\text{no heads}) = \dfrac{1}{8}$; $P(B) = 1 - \dfrac{1}{8} = \dfrac{7}{8}$; the events are not independent, since

      $P(A \cap B) = \dfrac{3}{8} \neq \dfrac{1}{2} \cdot \dfrac{7}{8}$.

10. **a.** $\dfrac{1}{13} \cdot \dfrac{1}{13} = \dfrac{1}{169}$ **b.** $\dfrac{1}{2} \cdot \dfrac{1}{2} = \dfrac{1}{4}$

B   11. $\dfrac{2}{_6P_6} = \dfrac{2}{6!} = \dfrac{1}{360}$

12. Let A be the event that the telegram is for an executive. Let B be the event that the telegram is for a woman.

   a. $P(A) = \dfrac{4}{11}$

   b. $P(B) = \dfrac{6}{11}$; the events are not independent, since $P(A \cap B) = \dfrac{3}{11} \neq \dfrac{4}{11} \cdot \dfrac{6}{11}$.

13. **a.** yes; $P(A \cap B) = \dfrac{1}{26} = P(A) \cdot P(B)$ **b.** yes; $P(A \cap C) = \dfrac{1}{13} = P(A) \cdot P(C)$

   c. no; $P(B \cap C) = 0 \neq P(B) \cdot P(C)$

14. $0.4 + 0.6 - (0.4)(0.6) = 1.0 - 0.24 = 0.76$

15. **a.** $\dfrac{1}{3} \cdot \dfrac{1}{4} = \dfrac{1}{12}$ **b.** $\dfrac{3}{4} \cdot \dfrac{1}{3} \cdot \left(1 - \dfrac{1}{4}\right) = \dfrac{3}{4} \cdot \dfrac{1}{3} \cdot \dfrac{3}{4} = \dfrac{3}{16}$

   c. $\dfrac{1}{4} \cdot \dfrac{1}{3} \cdot \left(1 - \dfrac{3}{4}\right) + \dfrac{1}{4} \cdot \dfrac{3}{4} \cdot \left(1 - \dfrac{1}{3}\right) + \dfrac{1}{3} \cdot \dfrac{3}{4} \cdot \left(1 - \dfrac{1}{4}\right) + \dfrac{1}{4} \cdot \dfrac{1}{3} \cdot \dfrac{3}{4} =$

      $\dfrac{1}{48} + \dfrac{1}{8} + \dfrac{3}{16} + \dfrac{1}{16} = \dfrac{19}{48}$

   d. $P(\text{at least one asks}) = 1 - P(\text{none ask}) = 1 - \dfrac{3}{4} \cdot \dfrac{2}{3} \cdot \dfrac{1}{4} = 1 - \dfrac{1}{8} = \dfrac{7}{8}$

16. **a.** $(0.7)(0.5) = 0.35$; 35%   **b.** $(0.7)(0.5) = 0.35$; 35%   **c.** $(0.3)(0.5) = 0.15$; 15%

   d. $1 - P(\text{rains in neither}) = 1 - 0.15 = 0.85$; 85%

C   **17. a.** $\dfrac{26}{52} \cdot \dfrac{25}{51} = \dfrac{25}{102}$ **b.** $\dfrac{4 \cdot 3}{52 \cdot 51} = \dfrac{1}{221}$

     c. P(at least one black or not a queen) $= 1 - P$(both are red and both are queens) $=$

         $1 - P$(two red queens); P(two red queens) $= \dfrac{{}_2C_2}{{}_{52}C_2} = \dfrac{1}{1326}$; $1 - \dfrac{1}{1326} = \dfrac{1325}{1326}$

Page 747 · READING ALGEBRA

1. $0 \cdot \dfrac{1}{16} + 1 \cdot \dfrac{1}{4} + 2 \cdot \dfrac{3}{8} + 3 \cdot \dfrac{1}{4} + 4 \cdot \dfrac{1}{16} = 2$

2. $\dfrac{{}_4C_2}{2^4} = \dfrac{6}{16} = \dfrac{3}{8}$ **3.** less than $\dfrac{1}{2}$

4. $1 \cdot \dfrac{1}{6} + 2 \cdot \dfrac{1}{6} + 3 \cdot \dfrac{1}{6} + 4 \cdot \dfrac{1}{6} + 5 \cdot \dfrac{1}{6} + 6 \cdot \dfrac{1}{6} = 21 \cdot \dfrac{1}{6} = 3\dfrac{1}{2}$; no

5. $3\dfrac{1}{2}$ **6.** Expectation is an average score.

Page 747 · CHALLENGE

Three sides are green. Two of these belong to the card that is green on both sides, and one to the card that is red on one side and green on the other. Therefore if the top side of the top card is green, the probability is $\dfrac{1}{3}$ that the other side is red.

Page 751 · WRITTEN EXERCISES

A   **1.** mean $= \dfrac{34 + 42 + 44 + 70 + 73 + 79}{6} = 57$;

      variance $= \dfrac{(-23)^2 + (-15)^2 + (-13)^2 + (13)^2 + (16)^2 + (22)^2}{6} = 305$;

      $\sigma = \sqrt{305} = 17$; range $= 79 - 34 = 45$

   2. mean $= \dfrac{8 + 15 + 38 + 64 + 85 + 102}{6} = 52$;

      variance $= \dfrac{(-44)^2 + (-37)^2 + (-14)^2 + (12)^2 + (33)^2 + (50)^2}{6} = \dfrac{7234}{6} \approx 1206$;

      $\sigma = \sqrt{1206} \approx 35$; range $= 102 - 8 = 94$

   3. mean $= \dfrac{42 + 46 + 50 + 50 + 52 + 54 + 56}{7} = 50$; variance $=$

      $\dfrac{(-8)^2 + (-4)^2 + 0 + 0 + 2^2 + 4^2 + 6^2}{7} = 19$; $\sigma = \sqrt{19} = 4$; range $= 56 - 42 = 14$

   4. mean $= \dfrac{47 + 48 + 45 + 45 + 41 + 38 + 37}{7} = 43$;

      variance $= \dfrac{4^2 + 5^2 + 2^2 + 2^2 + (-2)^2 + (-5)^2 + (-6)^2}{7} = 16$;

      $\sigma = \sqrt{16} = 4$; range $= 48 - 37 = 11$

5. mean $= \dfrac{166.72}{12} \approx 13.89$; 13.89°C; $\sigma = \sqrt{\dfrac{1097.7}{12}} \approx 9.56$; 9.56°C

6. mean $= \dfrac{639}{9} = 71.0$; variance $= \dfrac{40}{9} = 4.4$; $\sigma = \sqrt{4.4} = 2.1$; range $= 74 - 67 = 7$

B 7. $x = $ 5th score; $\dfrac{85 + 75 + 80 + 95 + x}{5} = 85$; $x + 335 = 425$; $x = 90$;

she must score 90.

8. $\dfrac{\text{sum}}{8} = 15$; sum $= 120$ 　　　　　 9. Mean increases by 6; range is unchanged;
　　　　　　　　　　　　　　　　　　　　　　　　　σ is unchanged (dispersion is not affected).

10. Let $s = $ sum of entries, $m = $ least value, $M = $ greatest value. After doubling, sum $=$

$2s$, minimum $= 2m$, maximum $= 2M$. New mean $= \dfrac{2s}{n} = 2 \cdot \dfrac{s}{n}$; mean is doubled. New

range $= 2M - 2m = 2(M - m)$; range is doubled. For any entry e, new entry is $2e$ and

squared deviation from new mean $= (2e - 2 \cdot (\text{old mean}))^2 = (2 \cdot (\text{original deviation}))^2 =$

$4 \cdot (\text{original deviation})^2$. New $\sigma = \sqrt{\dfrac{4(\text{sum of original squared deviations})}{n}} = 2\sigma$.

11. Answers will vary; examples are given.
　　a. 79, 80, 80, 81 　　　　　**b.** 42, 82, 98, 98 　　　　　**c.** 70, 70, 90, 90

C 12. **a.** sum $= 50 \cdot 75 = 3750$ 　　　　　　　**b.** sum $= 40 \cdot 80 = 3200$

　　c. mean $= \dfrac{\text{sum of } x_i\text{'s} + \text{sum of } y_i\text{'s}}{90} = \dfrac{3750 + 3200}{90} \approx 77.2$

13. **a.** $\dfrac{nM_1 + mM_2}{n + m}$ 　　　　　**b.** $\dfrac{nM_1 + mM_2}{n + m} = \dfrac{M_1 + M_2}{2}$; $2nM_1 + 2mM_2 =$

　　$nM_1 + mM_2 + nM_2 + mM_1$; $n(M_1 - M_2) = m(M_1 - M_2)$; either $M_1 = M_2$ or $n = m$

Pages 756-757 · WRITTEN EXERCISES

A 1. 0.2257 　　　　　　　　　　　　　　　　　2. $2(0.0793) = 0.1586$

3. $P(-4 < X < -3) = P(3 < X < 4) = 0.5000 - 0.4987 = 0.0013$

4. **a.** $P(X < M - \sigma) = 0.5000 - A(1) = 0.1587$
　　b. $P(X > M - 2\sigma) = 0.5000 + A(2) = 0.9772$
　　c. $P(X > M + 3\sigma) = 0.5000 - A(3) = 0.0013$

5. $P(-3 < X < 3) = 2 \cdot A(3) = 0.9974$

6. **a.** $P(X > M + \sigma) = 0.5000 - A(1) = 0.1587 = 15.87\%$
　　b. $P(X < M - 2\sigma) = 0.5000 - A(2) = 0.0228 = 2.28\%$
　　c. $P(-1 < X < 1) = 2 \cdot A(1) = 0.6826 = 68.26\%$

7. **a.** $P(X > 3) = 0.5000 - A(3) = 0.0013$ 　　　**b.** $P(X < -1) = 0.5000 - A(1) = 0.1587$

8. **a.** $P(X < 0) = 0.5000$ 　　**b.** $P\left(X > \dfrac{72}{30}\right) = P(X > 2.4) = 0.5000 - A(2.4) = 0.0082$

B **9.** P(at least one lasts more than 990 h) $= 1 - P$(all last less than 990 h) $=$
$1 - [P(\text{one lasts less than 990 h})]^3 = 1 - [P(X < 3)]^3 = 1 - (0.9987)^3 \approx 0.0039$

10. a. $k = 0$ **b.** $k \approx 4.0$

11. Total area under standard normal curve is 1.

12. $P(|X| > k) = P(X < -k \text{ or } X > k) = 2P(X > k) = 2[1 - P(X < k)]$
(See Exercise 11.)

C **13. a.** $y = \dfrac{1}{\sqrt{2\pi}} e^0 = \dfrac{1}{\sqrt{2\pi}} \approx 0.3989$ **b.** $y = \dfrac{1}{\sqrt{2\pi}} e^{-1/2} = \dfrac{1}{\sqrt{2e\pi}} \approx 0.2420$

c. $y = \dfrac{1}{\sqrt{2\pi}} e^{-2} = \dfrac{1}{e^2\sqrt{2\pi}} \approx 0.05399$

Pages 757-758 · COMPUTER KEY-IN

Sample runs are shown.

1. a.

0	0	
2	1	*
3	1	*
4	6	******
5	5	*****
6	5	*****
7	2	**
8	0	
9	0	
10	0	

THE AVERAGE SCORE WAS 4.9

Fraction of experiments giving score of 5 heads = 0.25.

b.

0	0	
1	0	
2	1	*
3	5	*****
4	14	**************
5	11	***********
6	18	******************
7	11	***********
8	0	
9	0	
10	0	

THE AVERAGE SCORE WAS 5.21666667

Fraction of experiments giving score of 5 heads $\approx$ 0.18333.

c. 0   0
    1   0
    2   5   *****
    3   14   **************
    4   20   ********************
    5   26   **************************
    6   18   ******************
    7   11   ***********
    8   2   **
    9   2   **
    10   2   **

THE AVERAGE SCORE WAS 5.01

Fraction of experiments giving score of 5 heads = 0.26.

2. a. 0   0
       1   0
       2   0
       3   1   *
       4   2   **
       5   2   **
       6   6   ******
       7   5   *****
       8   3   ***
       9   1   *
       10   0

THE AVERAGE SCORE WAS 6.25

b. 0   0
    1   0
    2   2   **
    3   3   ***
    4   7   *******
    5   6   ******
    6   11   ***********
    7   17   *****************
    8   12   ************
    9   0
    10   2   **

THE AVERAGE SCORE WAS 6.2

c. 0   0

     1   0

     2   1   *

     3   4   * * * *

     4   16   * * * * * * * * * * * * * * * *

     5   22   *

     6   21   *

     7   17   * * * * * * * * * * * * * * * * *

     8   14   * * * * * * * * * * * * * *

     9   5   * * * * *

   10   0

THE AVERAGE SCORE WAS 5.9

Page 760 · CHAPTER REVIEW

1. c; 1-digit: 3; 2-digit: $3 \cdot 3 = 9$

2. a; $10 \cdot 9 \cdot 8 \cdot 7 = 5040$

3. b; $_6P_3 = \dfrac{6!}{3!} = 120$

4. b; $\dfrac{7!}{2!2!} = 1260$

5. d; $_9C_4 = \dfrac{9!}{4!5!} = 126$

6. c

7. b; at least two heads: $\{(H, H, T), (H, T, H), (T, H, H), (H, H, H)\}$;

$P(\text{at least two heads}) = \dfrac{4}{8} = \dfrac{1}{2}$

8. a; $P(A \cap B) = \dfrac{1}{2} \cdot \dfrac{1}{2} = \dfrac{1}{4}$

9. c; $P(A \cap B) = 0$; $P(A \cup B) = P(A) + P(B) - P(A \cap B) = P(A) + P(B)$

10. b; $M = \dfrac{100 + 79 + 86 + 91}{4} = 89$;

variance $= \dfrac{(100 - 89)^2 + (79 - 89)^2 + (86 - 89)^2 + (91 - 89)^2}{4}$

$= \dfrac{121 + 100 + 9 + 4}{4} = \dfrac{234}{4} = 58.5$

11. b; $P(-3 < X < +3) = 2 \cdot P(0 < X < 3) = 2(0.4987) = 0.9974$

Page 761 · CHAPTER TEST

1. 1-digit: 2; 2-digit: $4 \cdot 2 = 8$; 3-digit: $4 \cdot 4 \cdot 2 = 32$; total: 42

2. $_5P_2 = 20$

3. $\dfrac{4!}{3!} = 4$

4. $_4C_3 = \dfrac{4 \cdot 3 \cdot 2}{1 \cdot 2 \cdot 3} = 4$; $\{P, Q, R\}$, $\{P, Q, S\}$, $\{P, R, S\}$, $\{Q, R, S\}$

5. With 1 S: $_6C_6 = 1$; with 2 S's: $_5C_4 = 5$; total: 6

6. a. $\{(H, 1), (H, 2), (H, 3), (T, 1), (T, 2), (T, 3)\}$

b. $\{(T, 1), (T, 3), (T, 5)\}$

7. a. $\dfrac{1}{4}$ **b.** $\dfrac{1}{13}$ **c.** $\dfrac{2}{13}$

8. a. $P(A) = 1 - P(\text{neither is red}) = 1 - \dfrac{{}_6C_2}{{}_9C_2} = 1 - \dfrac{5}{12} = \dfrac{7}{12}; P(B) = 3 \cdot P(\text{both red}) =$

$3 \cdot \left(\dfrac{1}{3} \cdot \dfrac{1}{4}\right) = \dfrac{1}{4}; P(A \cap B) = P(\text{both red}) = \dfrac{{}_3C_2}{{}_9C_2} = \dfrac{3}{36} = \dfrac{1}{12};$

$P(A \cup B) = P(A) + P(B) - P(A \cap B) = \dfrac{7}{12} + \dfrac{1}{4} - \dfrac{1}{12} = \dfrac{3}{4}$

b. No, $P(A \cap B) \ne 0$; no, $P(A \cap B) \ne P(A) \cdot P(B)$.

9. $P(\text{snow in Anchorage or in Tokyo}) = 0.8 + 0.3 - (0.8)(0.3) = 0.86 = 86\%$

10. mean $= \dfrac{72}{12} = 6$; range $= 9 - 3 = 6$; variation $= \dfrac{44}{12} \approx 3.7$; $\sigma = \sqrt{\dfrac{44}{12}} \approx 1.9$

11. $P(X > M + 1\sigma) = 0.5000 - A(1) = 0.1587$

Page 762 · MIXED REVIEW

1. Let $x =$ number bought; $\dfrac{6250}{x} = \dfrac{7130}{x - 40} - 3; \dfrac{6250 + 3x}{x} = \dfrac{7130}{x - 40};$

$7130x = (x - 40)(3x + 6250); 7130x = 3x^2 + 6130x - 250,000;$

$3x^2 - 1000x - 250,000 = 0; (3x + 500)(x - 500) = 0; x = -\dfrac{500}{3}$ (reject) or $x = 500;$
$x = 500$; number sold $= x - 40 = 460$

2. The given segment has midpoint $(-5, -1)$ and slope $\dfrac{3}{4}$; its perpendicular bisector contains $(-5, -1)$ and has slope $-\dfrac{4}{3}$; $y + 1 = -\dfrac{4}{3}(x + 5)$; $4x + 3y = -23$

3. a. $\left[\left(\dfrac{2}{3}\right)^5 + \left(\dfrac{1}{3}\right)^5\right]^{1/2} = \sqrt{\dfrac{33}{3^5}} = \dfrac{1}{9}\sqrt{\dfrac{33}{3}} = \dfrac{1}{9}\sqrt{11} = \dfrac{\sqrt{11}}{9}$

b. $\log 32 + \log 25 - \log 8 = \log\left(\dfrac{32 \cdot 25}{8}\right) = \log 100 = 2$

4. a. $\dfrac{m(2 + m)(2 - m)}{m(m + 2)(m^2 - 2m + 4)} \cdot \dfrac{1}{(m - 2)^2} = \dfrac{-1}{(m - 2)(m^2 - 2m + 4)}$

b. $\dfrac{y^{-1} + x^{-1}y^{-2}}{(xy)^{-2} - 1} \cdot \dfrac{x^2y^2}{x^2y^2} = \dfrac{x^2y + x}{1 - x^2y^2} = \dfrac{x(xy + 1)}{(1 + xy)(1 - xy)} = \dfrac{x}{1 - xy}$

5. Let $t =$ number of hours working together; $\dfrac{t + 1}{5} + \dfrac{t}{7} = 1$; $7(t + 1) + 5t = 35$;
$12t = 28$; $t = \dfrac{28}{12} = \dfrac{7}{3}$; $2\dfrac{1}{3}$ h

6. $5 + x = 25 - 10\sqrt{x} + x$; $10\sqrt{x} = 20$; $\sqrt{x} = 2$; $x = 4$

7. $y^3 = -\dfrac{125}{3}$; $y = \dfrac{-5}{\sqrt[3]{3}} \cdot \dfrac{\sqrt[3]{9}}{\sqrt[3]{9}} = -\dfrac{5\sqrt[3]{9}}{3}$

8. $3z^2 + 4z - 2 = 0$; $z = \dfrac{-4 \pm \sqrt{16 + 24}}{6} = \dfrac{-4 \pm 2\sqrt{10}}{6} = \dfrac{-2 \pm \sqrt{10}}{3}$

9. 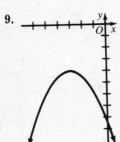 **10.** 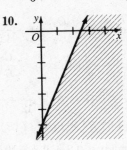 **11.**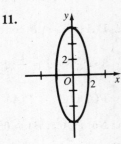

12. $r = \sqrt{2}$, $\theta = -45°$; roots: $\sqrt[10]{2}(\cos 351° + i \sin 351°)$, $\sqrt[10]{2}(\cos 279° + i \sin 279°)$, $\sqrt[10]{2}(\cos 207° + i \sin 207°)$, $\sqrt[10]{2}(\cos 135° + i \sin 135°)$, and $\sqrt[10]{2}(\cos 63° + i \sin 63°)$

13. $c^2 = 36 + 100 - 120 \cos 139.4°$; $c = 15.07 \approx 15.1$; $\dfrac{\sin A}{10} = \dfrac{\sin B}{6} = \dfrac{\sin 139.4°}{15.07}$;

$\sin A = \dfrac{10(\sin 139.4°)}{15.07} = \dfrac{10(0.6508)}{15.07} = 0.4319$; $\angle A = 25.6°$;

$\sin B = \dfrac{6(\sin 139.4°)}{15.07} = \dfrac{6(0.6508)}{15.07} = 0.2591$; $\angle B = 15.0°$ **14.** $S = \dfrac{t_1}{1 - r} = \dfrac{16}{\frac{5}{4}} = \dfrac{64}{5}$

15. $t_1 = -1$; $d = 2$; $t_{100} = -1 + 99.2 = 197$; $S_{100} = \dfrac{100(-1 + 197)}{2} = 9800$

16. $t_1 = -\dfrac{3}{2}$; $r = 2$; $S_8 = \dfrac{-\dfrac{3}{2}(1 - 2^8)}{1 - 2} = \dfrac{3}{2}(-255) = -382.5$

17. $\tan^2\theta + \csc^2\theta - \cot^2\theta = \tan^2\theta + (1 + \cot^2\theta) - \cot^2\theta = 1 + \tan^2\theta = \sec^2\theta$

18. 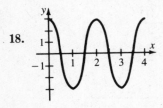 **19.** $\dfrac{1}{14}\begin{bmatrix} 1 & 2 \\ -3 & 8 \end{bmatrix} = \begin{bmatrix} \dfrac{1}{14} & \dfrac{1}{7} \\ -\dfrac{3}{14} & \dfrac{4}{7} \end{bmatrix}$

20. 3 ways to choose the hundreds' place $(2, 3, \text{or } 4)$, 6 ways to choose the tens' place $(0, 1, 2, 3, 4, \text{or } 5)$, and 3 ways to choose the ones' place $(1, 3, \text{or } 5)$; $3 \cdot 6 \cdot 3 = 54$

21. $\dfrac{{}_{13}C_2 \cdot {}_{26}C_1}{{}_{52}C_3} = \dfrac{\dfrac{13 \cdot 12}{2} \cdot 26}{\dfrac{53 \cdot 51 \cdot 50}{3 \cdot 2}} = \dfrac{39}{425}$

22. mean $= \dfrac{720}{4} = 180$; range $= 200 - 150 = 50$; variation $= \dfrac{1550}{4} = 387.5$

Page 763 · PREPARING FOR COLLEGE ENTRANCE EXAMS

1. D   **2.** E   **3.** C   **4.** B   **5.** B   **6.** E

A

1. $d = \dfrac{5}{10} \times 0.0013 \approx 0.0007$; $\log 3.475 \approx 0.5403 + 0.0007 = 0.5410$

2. $d = \dfrac{2}{10} \times 0.0005 = 0.0001$; $\log 8.612 \approx 0.9350 + 0.0001 = 0.9351$

3. $d = \dfrac{8}{10} \times 0.0005 = 0.0004$; $\log 7.768 \approx 0.8899 + 0.0004 = 0.8903$; $\log 77.68 \approx 1.8903$

4. $d = \dfrac{6}{10} \times 0.0018 \approx 0.0011$; $\log 2.396 \approx 0.3784 + 0.0011 = 0.3795$; $\log 239.6 \approx 2.3795$

5. $d = \dfrac{4}{10} \times 0.0008 \approx 0.0003$; $\log 5.624 \approx 0.7497 + 0.0003 = 0.7500$;

   $\log 0.5624 \approx 9.7500 - 10$

6. $d = \dfrac{7}{10} \times 0.0011 \approx 0.0008$; $\log 3.857 \approx 0.5855 + 0.0008 = 0.5863$;

   $\log 0.03857 \approx 8.5863 - 10$

7. $d = \dfrac{44}{100} \times 0.0006 \approx 0.0003$; $\log 6.8244 \approx 0.8338 + 0.0003 = 0.8341$;

   $\log 68,244 \approx 4.8341$

8. $d = \dfrac{76}{100} \times 0.0031 \approx 0.0024$; $\log 1.38760 \approx 0.1399 + 0.0024 = 0.1423$;

   $\log 138,760 \approx 5.1423$

9. $d = \dfrac{2}{10} \times 0.0009 \approx 0.0002$; $\log 4.962 \approx 0.6955 + 0.0002 = 0.6957$;

   $\log 0.4962 \approx 9.6957 - 10$

10. $d = \dfrac{4}{10} \times 0.0026 \approx 0.0010$; $\log 1.634 \approx 0.2122 + 0.0010 = 0.2132$;

    $\log 0.001634 \approx 7.2132 - 10$

11. $d = \dfrac{6}{10} \times 0.0009 \approx 0.0005$; $\log 4.856 \approx 0.6857 + 0.0005 = 0.6862$; $\log 48,560 \approx 4.6862$

12. $d = \dfrac{2}{10} \times 0.0005 = 0.0001$; $\log 7.982 \approx 0.9020 + 0.0001 = 0.9021$; $\log 79,820 \approx 4.9021$

13. $\dfrac{c}{0.010} = \dfrac{0.0004}{0.0008}$; $c = 0.005$; antilog $0.6968 \approx 4.97 + 0.005 = 4.975$

14. $\dfrac{c}{0.010} = \dfrac{0.0005}{0.0008}$; $c \approx 0.006$; antilog $0.7728 \approx 5.92 + 0.006 = 5.926$

15. $\dfrac{c}{0.010} = \dfrac{0.0005}{0.0018}$; $c \approx 0.003$; antilog $0.3843 \approx 2.42 + 0.003 = 2.423$;

  antilog $1.3843 \approx 2.423 \times 10^1 = 24.23$

16. $\dfrac{c}{0.010} = \dfrac{0.0001}{0.0006}$; $c \approx 0.002$; antilog $0.8402 \approx 6.92 + 0.002 = 6.922$;

  antilog $3.8402 \approx 6.922 \times 10^3 = 6922$

17. $\dfrac{c}{0.010} = \dfrac{0.003}{0.005}$; $c = 0.006$; antilog $0.9531 \approx 8.97 + 0.006 = 8.976$;

  antilog $8.9531 - 10 \approx 8.976 \times 10^{-3} = 0.08976$

18. $\dfrac{c}{0.010} = \dfrac{0.0019}{0.0032}$; $c \approx 0.006$; antilog $0.1322 \approx 1.35 + 0.006 = 1.356$;

  antilog $(5.1322 - 10) \approx 1.356 \times 10^{-5} = 0.00001356$

19. $\dfrac{c}{0.010} = \dfrac{0.0002}{0.0005}$; $c = 0.004$; antilog $0.9296 \approx 8.50 + 0.004 = 8.504$;

  antilog $(9.9296 - 10) \approx 8.504 \times 10^{-1} = 0.8504$

20. $\dfrac{c}{0.010} = \dfrac{0.0008}{0.0025}$; $c \approx 0.003$; antilog $0.2388 \approx 1.73 + 0.003 = 1.733$;

  antilog $(7.2388 - 10) \approx 1.733 \times 10^{-3} = 0.001733$

21. antilog $0.8041 = 6.370$; antilog $(6.8041 - 10) = 6.370 \times 10^{-4} = 0.0006370$

Page 796 · WRITTEN EXERCISES

A 1. $\log AC = \log A + \log C = 3.6100 + 1.2000 = 4.8100$

  2. $\log BC = \log B + \log C = 8.1234 - 10 + 1.2000 = 9.3234 - 10$

  3. $\log \dfrac{A}{B} = \log A - \log B = 3.6100 - (8.1234 - 10) =$

   $(13.6100 - 10) - (8.1234 - 10) = 5.4866$

  4. $\log \dfrac{A}{C} = \log A - \log C = 3.6100 - 1.2000 = 2.4100$

  5. $\log 100B = \log 100 + \log B = 2 + (8.1234 - 10) = 0.1234$

  6. $\log 0.01A = \log 0.01 + \log A = -2 + 3.6100 = 1.6100$

  7. $\log \dfrac{1000}{C} = \log 1000 - \log C = 3 - (1.2000) = 1.8000$

  8. $\log \dfrac{0.001}{B} = \log 0.001 - \log B = -3 - (8.1234 - 10) = (17 - 20) - (8.1234 - 10) =$

   $8.8766 - 10$

  9. $\log B^2 = 2 \log B = 2(8.1310 - 10) = 16.2620 - 20 = 6.2620 - 10$

  10. $\log C^{10} = 10 \log C = 10(3.2148) = 32.148$

11. $\log \sqrt{C} = \log C^{1/2} = \dfrac{1}{2} \log C = \dfrac{1}{2}(3.2148) = 1.6074$

12. $\log \sqrt[3]{A} = \log A^{1/3} = \dfrac{1}{3} \log A = \dfrac{1}{3}(13.600) = 4.5333$

13. $\log C^{3/4} = \dfrac{3}{4} \log C = \dfrac{3}{4}(3.2148) = 2.4111$

14. $\log B^{3/2} = \dfrac{3}{2} \log B = \dfrac{3}{2}(8.1310 - 10) = 12.1965 - 15 = 7.1965 - 10$

15. $\log \sqrt{A^3} = \log A^{3/2} = \dfrac{3}{2} \log A = \dfrac{3}{2}(13.600) = 20.4000$

16. $\log \sqrt[3]{B^2} = \log B^{2/3} = \dfrac{2}{3} \log B = \dfrac{2}{3}(8.1310 - 10) = \dfrac{2}{3}(28.1310 - 30) =$
    $18.7540 - 20 = 8.7540 - 10$

17. $N = 281 \times 0.94$; $\log N = \log 281 + \log 0.94 =$
    $2.4487 + (9.9731 - 10) = 12.4218 - 10 = 2.4218$; $N = 264$

18. $N = 0.749 \times 0.562$; $\log N = \log 0.749 + \log 0.562 =$
    $(9.8745 - 10) + (9.7497 - 10) = 19.6242 - 20 = 9.6242 - 10$; $N = 0.421$

19. $N = 943 \times 804$; $\log N = \log 943 + \log 804 = 2.9745 + 2.9053 = 5.8798$; $N = 758,000$

20. $N = 0.321 \times 8.35$; $\log N = \log 0.321 + \log 8.35 = (9.5065 - 10) + 0.9217 = 0.4282$;
    $N = 2.68$

21. $N = \dfrac{117}{3.26}$; $\log N = \log 117 - \log 3.26 = 2.0682 - 0.5132 = 1.5550$; $N = 35.9$

22. $N = \dfrac{4960}{54,600}$; $\log N = \log 4960 - \log 54,600 = 3.6955 - 4.7372 =$
    $(13.6955 - 10) - 4.7372 = 8.9583 - 10$; $N = 0.0908$

23. $N = \dfrac{0.013}{427}$; $\log N = \log 0.013 - \log 427 = (8.1139 - 10) - 2.6304 = 5.4835 - 10$;
    $N = 0.0000304$

24. $N = \dfrac{0.526}{0.049}$; $\log N = \log 0.526 - \log 0.049 = (9.7210 - 10) - (8.6902 - 10) = 1.0308$;
    $N = 10.7$

25. $N = (2.81)^{10}$; $\log N = 10 \log 2.81 = 10(0.4487) = 4.4870$; $N = 30,700$

26. $N = (90.3)^5$; $\log N = 5 \log 90.3 = 5(1.9557) = 9.7785$; $N = 6,000,000,000$

27. $N = (0.395)^7$; $\log N = 7 \log 0.395 = 7(9.5966 - 10) = 67.1762 - 70 = 7.1762 - 10$;
    $N = 0.00150$

28. $N = (0.0431)^2$; $\log N = 2 \log 0.0431 = 2(8.6345 - 10) = 17.2690 - 20 = 7.2690 - 10$;
    $N = 0.00186$

29. $N = (21.4)^{1/3}$; $\log N = \dfrac{1}{3} \log 21.4 = \dfrac{1}{3}(1.3304) = 0.4435$; $N = 2.78$

30. $N = (8.26)^{2/3}$; $\log N = \dfrac{2}{3} \log 8.26 = \dfrac{2}{3}(0.9170) = 0.6113$; $N = 4.09$

31. $N = \sqrt{12.4}$; $\log N = \dfrac{1}{2} \log 12.4 = \dfrac{1}{2}(1.0934) = 0.5467$; $N = 3.52$

32. $N = \sqrt[3]{1.36}$; $\log N = \dfrac{1}{3} \log 1.36 = \dfrac{1}{3}(0.1335) = 0.0445$; $N = 1.11$

B   **33.** $N = 0.572 \times 6370$; $\log N = \log 0.572 + \log 6370 = (9.7574 - 10) + 3.8041 =$
13.5615 − 10 = 3.5615; $N = 3643$

34. $N = 23.64 \times 1.47$; $\log N = \log 23.64 + \log 1.47 = 1.3736 + 0.1673 = 1.5409$;
$N = 34.75$

35. $N = 0.8215 \times 0.051$; $\log N = \log 0.8215 + \log 0.051 =$
$(9.9146 - 10) + (8.7076 - 10) = 18.6222 - 20 = 8.6222 - 10$; $N = 0.04190$

36. $N = \dfrac{0.1496}{0.582}$; $\log N = \log 0.1496 - \log 0.582 = (9.1749 - 10) - (9.7649 - 10) =$
$(19.1749 - 20) - (9.7649 - 10) = 9.4100 - 10$; $N = 0.2570$

37. $N = \dfrac{137}{5242}$; $\log N = \log 137 - \log 5242 = 2.1367 - 3.7195 =$
$(12.1367 - 10) - 3.7195 = 8.4172 - 10$; $N = 0.02614$

38. $N = \dfrac{0.05274}{0.9412}$; $\log N = \log 0.05274 - \log 0.9412 = (8.7221 - 10) - (9.9737 - 10) =$
$(18.7221 - 20) - (9.9737 - 10) = 8.7484 - 10$; $N = 0.05603$

39. $N = 2.16 \times 46.73 \times 134.5$; $\log N = \log 2.16 + \log 46.73 + \log 134.5 =$
$0.3345 + 1.6696 + 2.1287 = 4.1328$; $N = 13{,}580$

40. $N = 94 \times 0.05 \times 1.728$; $\log N = \log 94 + \log 0.05 + \log 1.728 =$
$1.9731 + (8.6990 - 10) + 0.2375 = 0.9096$; $N = 8.120$

41. $N = 1.8 \times 32 \times 0.01347$; $\log N = \log 1.8 + \log 32 + \log 0.01347 =$
$0.2553 + 1.5051 + (8.1293 - 10) = 9.8897 - 10$; $N = 0.7757$

42. $N = (12.4)^3(3.86)^2$; $\log N = 3 \log 12.4 + 2 \log 3.86 = 3(1.0934) + 2(0.5866) =$
$3.2802 + 1.1732 = 4.4534$; $N = 28{,}410$

43. $N = (37.4)^5(812)^2$; $\log N = 5 \log 37.4 + 2 \log 812 = 5(1.5729) + 2(2.9096) =$
$7.8645 + 5.8192 = 13.6837$; $N = 48{,}270{,}000{,}000{,}000$

44. $N = (42.3)^4(0.0016)^2$; $\log N = 4 \log 42.3 + 2 \log 0.0016 =$
$4(1.6263) + 2(7.2041 - 10) = 6.5052 + (14.4082 - 20) = 0.9134$; $N = 8.192$

45. $N = \sqrt{\dfrac{427}{0.592}}$; $\log N = \dfrac{1}{2}(\log 427 - \log 0.592) = \dfrac{1}{2}(2.6304 - (9.7723 - 10)) =$

$\dfrac{1}{2}((12.6304 - 10) - (9.7723 - 10)) = \dfrac{1}{2}(2.8581) = 1.4291; N = 26.86$

46. $N = \sqrt[3]{\dfrac{(2.37)^2}{1.15}}$; $\log N = \dfrac{1}{3}(2 \log 2.37 - \log 1.15) = \dfrac{1}{3}(2(0.3747) - 0.0607) =$

$\dfrac{1}{3}(0.7494 - 0.0607) = \dfrac{1}{3}(0.6887) = 0.2296; N = 1.697$

47. $N = \sqrt{\dfrac{(2.03)^3}{97.5 \times 1.98}}$; $\log N = \dfrac{1}{2}(3 \log 2.03 - (\log 97.5 + \log 1.98)) = \dfrac{1}{2}(3(0.3075) -$

$(1.9890 + 0.2967)) = \dfrac{1}{2}(0.9225 - 2.2857) = \dfrac{1}{2}((10.9225 - 10) - 2.2857) =$

$\dfrac{1}{2}(8.6368 - 10) = 4.3184 - 5 = 9.3184 - 10; N = 0.2082$

C **48.** $N = \sqrt[5]{\dfrac{(527.4)^2}{1542 \times (0.2592)^2}}$; $\log N = \dfrac{1}{5}(2 \log 527.4 - (\log 1542 + 2 \log 0.2592)) =$

$\dfrac{1}{5}(2(2.7221) - (3.1881 + 2(9.4136 - 10))) = \dfrac{1}{5}(5.4442 - (3.1881 + (18.8272 - 20))) =$

$\dfrac{1}{5}(5.4442 - (3.1881 + (8.8272 - 10))) = \dfrac{1}{5}(5.4442 - 2.0153) = \dfrac{1}{5}(3.4289) = 0.6858;$

$N = 4.851$

49. $N = \sqrt{\dfrac{12{,}560^3}{79.21 \times 8004}}$; $\log N = \dfrac{1}{2}(3 \log 12{,}560 - (\log 79.21 + \log 8004)) =$

$\dfrac{1}{2}(3(4.0990) - (1.8988 + 3.9033)) = \dfrac{1}{2}(12.2970 - 5.8021) = \dfrac{1}{2}(6.4949) = 3.2475;$

$N = 1768$

50. $N = 92.37^{0.562}$; $\log N = 0.562 \log 92.37 = 0.562(1.9656) = 1.1047; N = 12.73$

51. $N = 0.3142^{1.273}$; $\log N = 1.273 \log 0.3142 = 1.273(9.4972 - 10) =$
$12.0899 - 12.7300 = 12.0899 - 2.7300 - 10 = 9.3599 - 10; N = 0.2291$

52. $V = \dfrac{4}{3}(3.142)(0.1526)^3$; $\log V = \log 1.333 + \log 3.142 + 3 \log 0.1526 =$
$0.1249 + 0.4972 + 3(9.1835 - 10) = 0.6221 + (27.5505 - 30) =$
$0.6221 + (7.5505 - 10) = 8.1726 - 10; V = 0.01488$

53. $N = 3^{51}$; $\log N = 51 \log 3 = 51(0.4771) = 24.3321$; since the characteristic of
$\log 3^{51}$ is 24, 3^{51} has 25 digits.